ALGEBRA

Arithmetic Operations

$$a(b + c) = ab + ac$$

$$\frac{a}{b} + \frac{c}{d} = \frac{ad + bc}{bd}$$

$$\frac{a + c}{b} = \frac{a}{b} + \frac{c}{b}$$

$$\frac{\frac{a}{b}}{\frac{c}{d}} = \frac{a}{b} \times \frac{d}{c} = \frac{ad}{bc}$$

Exponents and Radicals

$$x^m x^n = x^{m+n}$$

$$\frac{x^m}{x^n} = x^{m-n}$$

$$(x^m)^n = x^{mn}$$

$$x^{-n} = \frac{1}{x^n}$$

$$(xy)^n = x^n y^n$$

$$\left(\frac{x}{y}\right)^n = \frac{x^n}{y^n}$$

$$x^{1/n} = \sqrt[n]{x}$$

$$x^{m/n} = \sqrt[n]{x^m} = \left(\sqrt[n]{x}\right)^m$$

$$\sqrt[n]{xy} = \sqrt[n]{x}\sqrt[n]{y}$$

$$\sqrt[n]{\frac{x}{y}} = \frac{\sqrt[n]{x}}{\sqrt[n]{y}}$$

Factoring Special Polynomials

$$x^2 - y^2 = (x + y)(x - y)$$

$$x^3 + y^3 = (x + y)(x^2 - xy + y^2)$$

$$x^3 - y^3 = (x - y)(x^2 + xy + y^2)$$

Binomial Theorem

$$(x + y)^2 = x^2 + 2xy + y^2 \qquad (x - y)^2 = x^2 - 2xy + y^2$$

$$(x + y)^3 = x^3 + 3x^2y + 3xy^2 + y^3$$

$$(x - y)^3 = x^3 - 3x^2y + 3xy^2 - y^3$$

$$(x + y)^n = x^n + nx^{n-1}y + \frac{n(n-1)}{2}x^{n-2}y^2$$

$$+ \cdots + \binom{n}{k}x^{n-k}y^k + \cdots + nxy^{n-1} + y^n$$

where $\binom{n}{k} = \dfrac{n(n-1)\cdots(n-k+1)}{1 \cdot 2 \cdot 3 \cdot \cdots \cdot k}$

Quadratic Formula

If $ax^2 + bx + c = 0$, then $x = \dfrac{-b \pm \sqrt{b^2 - 4ac}}{2a}$.

Inequalities and Absolute Value

If $a < b$ and $b < c$, then $a < c$.

If $a < b$, then $a + c < b + c$.

If $a < b$ and $c > 0$, then $ca < cb$.

If $a < b$ and $c < 0$, then $ca > cb$.

If $a > 0$, then

$$|x| = a \quad \text{means} \quad x = a \quad \text{or} \quad x = -a$$

$$|x| < a \quad \text{means} \quad -a < x < a$$

$$|x| > a \quad \text{means} \quad x > a \quad \text{or} \quad x < -a$$

GEOMETRY

Geometric Formulas

Formulas for area A, circumference C, and volume V:

Triangle
$$A = \tfrac{1}{2}bh$$
$$= \tfrac{1}{2}ab \sin \theta$$

Circle
$$A = \pi r^2$$
$$C = 2\pi r$$

Sector of Circle
$$A = \tfrac{1}{2}r^2\theta$$
$$s = r\theta \quad (\theta \text{ in radians})$$

Sphere
$$V = \tfrac{4}{3}\pi r^3$$
$$A = 4\pi r^2$$

Cylinder
$$V = \pi r^2 h$$

Cone
$$V = \tfrac{1}{3}\pi r^2 h$$
$$A = \pi r\sqrt{r^2 + h^2}$$

Distance and Midpoint Formulas

Distance between $P_1(x_1, y_1)$ and $P_2(x_2, y_2)$:

$$d = \sqrt{(x_2 - x_1)^2 + (y_2 - y_1)^2}$$

Midpoint of $\overline{P_1P_2}$: $\left(\dfrac{x_1 + x_2}{2}, \dfrac{y_1 + y_2}{2}\right)$

Lines

Slope of line through $P_1(x_1, y_1)$ and $P_2(x_2, y_2)$:

$$m = \frac{y_2 - y_1}{x_2 - x_1}$$

Point-slope equation of line through $P_1(x_1, y_1)$ with slope m:

$$y - y_1 = m(x - x_1)$$

Slope-intercept equation of line with slope m and y-intercept b:

$$y = mx + b$$

Circles

Equation of the circle with center (h, k) and radius r:

$$(x - h)^2 + (y - k)^2 = r^2$$

TRIGONOMETRY

Angle Measurement

π radians $= 180°$

$$1° = \frac{\pi}{180} \text{ rad} \qquad 1 \text{ rad} = \frac{180°}{\pi}$$

$s = r\theta$

(θ in radians)

Right Angle Trigonometry

$$\sin \theta = \frac{\text{opp}}{\text{hyp}} \qquad \csc \theta = \frac{\text{hyp}}{\text{opp}}$$

$$\cos \theta = \frac{\text{adj}}{\text{hyp}} \qquad \sec \theta = \frac{\text{hyp}}{\text{adj}}$$

$$\tan \theta = \frac{\text{opp}}{\text{adj}} \qquad \cot \theta = \frac{\text{adj}}{\text{opp}}$$

Trigonometric Functions

$$\sin \theta = \frac{y}{r} \qquad \csc \theta = \frac{r}{y}$$

$$\cos \theta = \frac{x}{r} \qquad \sec \theta = \frac{r}{x}$$

$$\tan \theta = \frac{y}{x} \qquad \cot \theta = \frac{x}{y}$$

Graphs of Trigonometric Functions

Trigonometric Functions of Important Angles

θ	radians	$\sin \theta$	$\cos \theta$	$\tan \theta$
0°	0	0	1	0
30°	$\pi/6$	$1/2$	$\sqrt{3}/2$	$\sqrt{3}/3$
45°	$\pi/4$	$\sqrt{2}/2$	$\sqrt{2}/2$	1
60°	$\pi/3$	$\sqrt{3}/2$	$1/2$	$\sqrt{3}$
90°	$\pi/2$	1	0	—

Fundamental Identities

$$\csc \theta = \frac{1}{\sin \theta} \qquad \sec \theta = \frac{1}{\cos \theta}$$

$$\tan \theta = \frac{\sin \theta}{\cos \theta} \qquad \cot \theta = \frac{\cos \theta}{\sin \theta}$$

$$\cot \theta = \frac{1}{\tan \theta} \qquad \sin^2\theta + \cos^2\theta = 1$$

$$1 + \tan^2\theta = \sec^2\theta \qquad 1 + \cot^2\theta = \csc^2\theta$$

$$\sin(-\theta) = -\sin \theta \qquad \cos(-\theta) = \cos \theta$$

$$\tan(-\theta) = -\tan \theta \qquad \sin\left(\frac{\pi}{2} - \theta\right) = \cos \theta$$

$$\cos\left(\frac{\pi}{2} - \theta\right) = \sin \theta \qquad \tan\left(\frac{\pi}{2} - \theta\right) = \cot \theta$$

The Law of Sines

$$\frac{\sin A}{a} = \frac{\sin B}{b} = \frac{\sin C}{c}$$

The Law of Cosines

$$a^2 = b^2 + c^2 - 2bc \cos A$$

$$b^2 = a^2 + c^2 - 2ac \cos B$$

$$c^2 = a^2 + b^2 - 2ab \cos C$$

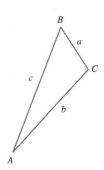

Addition and Subtraction Formulas

$$\sin(x + y) = \sin x \cos y + \cos x \sin y$$

$$\sin(x - y) = \sin x \cos y - \cos x \sin y$$

$$\cos(x + y) = \cos x \cos y - \sin x \sin y$$

$$\cos(x - y) = \cos x \cos y + \sin x \sin y$$

$$\tan(x + y) = \frac{\tan x + \tan y}{1 - \tan x \tan y}$$

$$\tan(x - y) = \frac{\tan x - \tan y}{1 + \tan x \tan y}$$

Double-Angle Formulas

$$\sin 2x = 2 \sin x \cos x$$

$$\cos 2x = \cos^2x - \sin^2x = 2 \cos^2x - 1 = 1 - 2 \sin^2x$$

$$\tan 2x = \frac{2 \tan x}{1 - \tan^2x}$$

Half-Angle Formulas

$$\sin^2x = \frac{1 - \cos 2x}{2} \qquad \cos^2x = \frac{1 + \cos 2x}{2}$$

海外优秀数学类教材系列丛书

影印版

Calculus

（Seventh Edition）

微积分 （第 7 版）（上册）

James Stewart

McMaster University

and

University of Toronto

高等教育出版社·北京
HIGHER EDUCATION PRESS   BEIJING

图字：01-2014-1752 号

Calculus: Early Transcendentals, International Metric Edition, 7th Edition
James Stewart

图书在版编目（C I P）数据

微积分 ＝ Calculus early transcendentals：第 7 版.
上册：英文／（加）史迪沃特（Stewart, J.）编著.
-- 影印本. -- 北京：高等教育出版社，2014.6（2017.7 重印）
（海外优秀数学类教材系列丛书）
ISBN 978 - 7 - 04 - 039620 - 1

Ⅰ. ①微… Ⅱ. ①史… Ⅲ. ①微积分 - 高等学校 - 教材 - 英文 Ⅳ. ①O172

中国版本图书馆 CIP 数据核字（2014）第 068171 号

策划编辑 于丽娜　　责任编辑 徐 可　　封面设计 王凌波　　责任印制 赵义民

出版发行	高等教育出版社	咨询电话	400 - 810 - 0598
社　　址	北京市西城区德外大街 4 号	网　　址	http://www.hep.edu.cn
邮政编码	100120		http://www.hep.com.cn
印　　刷	固安县铭成印刷有限公司	网上订购	http://www.landraco.com
开　　本	889mm×1194mm　1/16		http://www.landraco.com.cn
印　　张	45		
字　　数	1460 千字	版　　次	2014 年 6 月第 1 版
插　　页	5	印　　次	2017 年 7 月第 3 次印刷
购书热线	010 - 58581118	定　　价	66.70 元

本书如有缺页、倒页、脱页等质量问题，请到所购图书销售部门联系调换
版权所有　侵权必究
物 料 号　39620 - 00

出 版 说 明

本书是"海外优秀数学类教材系列丛书"之一。

该系列教材经国内高校一线教师、专家、学者推荐和评介，遴选 Pearson Education，John Wiley & Sons，McGraw-Hill，Cengage Learning 等国外出版公司近几年出版的优秀教材，由高等教育出版社影印出版，原汁原味呈献给读者。

遴选出来的原版教材具有以下特点：

1. 在国际上被广泛使用，在同类教材中具有一定的权威性；

2. 历经多年教学实践检验，取材广泛，内容翔实准确；

3. 教学资源配套完善，方便教师教学、学生学习；

4. 插图精美、丰富，图文并茂，可读性强；

5. 语言简练、流畅，注重可接受性，适合非英语国家的学生阅读。

希望该系列教材的出版能为国内教师吸收、借鉴国外优秀教学理念和教学成果，为高等教育提高教学质量、提升人才培养水平做出贡献。

高等教育出版社

2014 年 2 月

Contents

3 Differentiation Rules   173

4 Applications of Differentiation   273

8   **Further Applications of Integration**   **537**

9   **Differential Equations**   **579**

17   Second-Order Differential Equations   1141

Appendixes   A1

Index   A135

Preface

This *International Metric Version* differs from the regular version of *Calculus: Early Transcendentals,* Seventh Edition, in several ways:

The units used in almost all of the examples and exercises have been changed from US Customary units to metric units. There are a small number of exceptions: In some engineering applications (principally in Section 8.3) it may be useful for some engineers to be familiar with US units. And I wanted to retain a few exercises (for example, those involving baseball) where it would be inappropriate to use metric units.

I've changed the examples and exercises involving real-world data to be more international in nature, so that the vast majority of them now come from countries other than the United States. For example, there are now exercises and examples concerning Hong Kong postal rates; Canadian public debt; unemployment rates in Australia; hours of daylight in Ankara, Turkey; isothermals in China; percentage of the population in rural Argentina; populations of Malaysia, Indonesia, Mexico, and India; and power consumption in Ontario, among many others.

In addition to changing exercises so that the units are metric and the data have a more international flavor, a number of other exercises have been changed as well, the result being that about 10% of the exercises are different from those in the regular version.

 ## Philosophy of the Book

The art of teaching, Mark Van Doren said, is the art of assisting discovery. I have tried to write a book that assists students in discovering calculus—both for its practical power and its surprising beauty. In this edition, as in the first six editions, I aim to convey to the student a sense of the utility of calculus and develop technical competence, but I also strive to give some appreciation for the intrinsic beauty of the subject. Newton undoubtedly experienced a sense of triumph when he made his great discoveries. I want students to share some of that excitement.

The emphasis is on understanding concepts. I think that nearly everybody agrees that this should be the primary goal of calculus instruction. In fact, the impetus for the current calculus reform movement came from the Tulane Conference in 1986, which formulated as their first recommendation:

Focus on conceptual understanding.

I have tried to implement this goal through the *Rule of Three:* "Topics should be presented geometrically, numerically, and algebraically." Visualization, numerical and graphical experimentation, and other approaches have changed how we teach conceptual reasoning in fundamental ways. The Rule of Three has been expanded to become the *Rule of Four* by emphasizing the verbal, or descriptive, point of view as well.

In writing the seventh edition my premise has been that it is possible to achieve conceptual understanding and still retain the best traditions of traditional calculus. The book contains elements of reform, but within the context of a traditional curriculum.

Alternative Versions

I have written several other calculus textbooks that might be preferable for some instructors. Most of them also come in single variable and multivariable versions.

- *Calculus,* Seventh Edition, International Metric Version, is similar to the present textbook except that the exponential, logarithmic, and inverse trigonometric functions are covered in the second semester.

- *Essential Calculus*, International Edition, is a much briefer book (800 pages), though it contains almost all of the topics in *Calculus,* Seventh Edition, International Metric Version. The relative brevity is achieved through briefer exposition of some topics and putting some features on the website.

- *Essential Calculus: Early Transcendentals*, International Edition, resembles *Essential Calculus*, International Edition, but the exponential, logarithmic, and inverse trigonometric functions are covered in Chapter 3.

- *Calculus: Concepts and Contexts*, Fourth Edition, Metric International Version, emphasizes conceptual understanding even more strongly than this book. The coverage of topics is not encyclopedic and the material on transcendental functions and on parametric equations is woven throughout the book instead of being treated in separate chapters.

- *Calculus: Early Vectors* introduces vectors and vector functions in the first semester and integrates them throughout the book. It is suitable for students taking Engineering and Physics courses concurrently with calculus.

- *Brief Applied Calculus*, International Edition, is intended for students in business, the social sciences, and the life sciences.

What's New in the Seventh Edition?

The changes have resulted from talking with my colleagues and students at the University of Toronto and from reading journals, as well as suggestions from users and reviewers. Here are some of the many improvements that I've incorporated into this edition:

- Some material has been rewritten for greater clarity or for better motivation. See, for instance, the introduction to maximum and minimum values on page 274, the introduction to series on page 703, and the motivation for the cross product on page 808.

- New examples have been added (see Example 4 on page 1021 for instance). And the solutions to some of the existing examples have been amplified. A case in point: I added details to the solution of Example 2.3.11 because when I taught Section 2.3 from the sixth edition I realized that students need more guidance when setting up inequalities for the Squeeze Theorem.

- The art program has been revamped: New figures have been incorporated and a substantial percentage of the existing figures have been redrawn.

- The data in examples and exercises have been updated to be more timely.

- Three new projects have been added: *The Gini Index* (page 429) explores how to measure income distribution among inhabitants of a given country and is a nice application of areas between curves. (I thank Klaus Volpert for suggesting this project.)

Families of Implicit Curves (page 217) investigates the changing shapes of implicitly defined curves as parameters in a family are varied. *Families of Polar Curves* (page 664) exhibits the fascinating shapes of polar curves and how they evolve within a family.

- The section on the surface area of the graph of a function of two variables has been restored as Section 15.6 for the convenience of instructors who like to teach it after double integrals, though the full treatment of surface area remains in Chapter 16.

- I continue to seek out examples of how calculus applies to so many aspects of the real world. On page 909 you will see beautiful images of the earth's magnetic field strength and its second vertical derivative as calculated from Laplace's equation. I thank Roger Watson for bringing to my attention how this is used in geophysics and mineral exploration.

- More than 25% of the exercises in each chapter are new. Here are some of my favorites: 1.6.58, 2.6.51, 2.8.13–14, 3.3.56, 3.4.67, 3.5.69–72, 3.7.22, 4.3.86, 5.2.51–53, 6.4.30, 11.2.49–50, 11.10.71–72, 12.1.44, 12.4.43–44, and Problems 4, 5, and 8 on pages 837–38.

 ## Technology Enhancements

- The media and technology to support the text have been enhanced to give professors greater control over their course, to provide extra help to deal with the varying levels of student preparedness for the calculus course, and to improve support for conceptual understanding. New Enhanced WebAssign features including a customizable Cengage YouBook, *Just in Time* review, *Show Your Work,* Answer Evaluator, Personalized Study Plan, Master Its, solution videos, lecture video clips (with associated questions), and *Visualizing Calculus* (TEC animations with associated questions) have been developed to facilitate improved student learning and flexible classroom teaching.

- *Tools for Enriching Calculus* (TEC) has been completely redesigned and is accessible in Enhanced WebAssign and CourseMate. Selected Visuals and Modules are available at www.stewartcalculus.com.

 ## Features

CONCEPTUAL EXERCISES   The most important way to foster conceptual understanding is through the problems that we assign. To that end I have devised various types of problems. Some exercise sets begin with requests to explain the meanings of the basic concepts of the section. (See, for instance, the first few exercises in Sections 2.2, 2.5, 11.2, 14.2, and 14.3.) Similarly, all the review sections begin with a Concept Check and a True-False Quiz. Other exercises test conceptual understanding through graphs or tables (see Exercises 2.7.17, 2.8.35–40, 2.8.43–46, 9.1.11–13, 10.1.24–27, 11.10.2, 13.2.1–2, 13.3.33–39, 14.1.1–2, 14.1.32–42, 14.3.3–10, 14.6.1–2, 14.7.3–4, 15.1.5–10, 16.1.11–18, 16.2.17–18, and 16.3.1–2).

Another type of exercise uses verbal description to test conceptual understanding (see Exercises 2.5.10, 2.8.58, 4.3.63–64, and 7.8.67). I particularly value problems that combine and compare graphical, numerical, and algebraic approaches (see Exercises 2.6.39–40, 3.7.27, and 9.4.2).

GRADED EXERCISE SETS   Each exercise set is carefully graded, progressing from basic conceptual exercises and skill-development problems to more challenging problems involving applications and proofs.

REAL-WORLD DATA   My assistants and I spent a great deal of time looking in libraries, contacting companies and government agencies, and searching the Internet for interesting real-world data to introduce, motivate, and illustrate the concepts of calculus. As a result, many of the examples and exercises deal with functions defined by such numerical data or graphs. See, for instance, Figure 1 in Section 1.1 (seismograms from the Northridge earthquake), Exercise 2.8.36 (percentage of the population over age 60), Exercise 5.1.16 (velocity of the space shuttle *Endeavour*), and Figure 4 in Section 5.4 (San Francisco power consumption). Functions of two variables are illustrated by a table of values of the wind-chill index as a function of air temperature and wind speed (Example 2 in Section 14.1). Partial derivatives are introduced in Section 14.3 by examining a column in a table of values of the heat index (perceived air temperature) as a function of the actual temperature and the relative humidity. This example is pursued further in connection with linear approximations (Example 3 in Section 14.4). Directional derivatives are introduced in Section 14.6 by using a temperature contour map to estimate the rate of change of temperature traveling east from Chongqing. Double integrals are used to estimate the average snowfall in Colorado on December 20–21, 2006 (Example 4 in Section 15.1). Vector fields are introduced in Section 16.1 by depictions of actual velocity vector fields showing San Francisco Bay wind patterns.

PROJECTS   One way of involving students and making them active learners is to have them work (perhaps in groups) on extended projects that give a feeling of substantial accomplishment when completed. I have included four kinds of projects: *Applied Projects* involve applications that are designed to appeal to the imagination of students. The project after Section 9.3 asks whether a ball thrown upward takes longer to reach its maximum height or to fall back to its original height. (The answer might surprise you.) The project after Section 14.8 uses Lagrange multipliers to determine the masses of the three stages of a rocket so as to minimize the total mass while enabling the rocket to reach a desired velocity. *Laboratory Projects* involve technology; the one following Section 10.2 shows how to use Bézier curves to design shapes that represent letters for a laser printer. *Writing Projects* ask students to compare present-day methods with those of the founders of calculus—Fermat's method for finding tangents, for instance. Suggested references are supplied. *Discovery Projects* anticipate results to be discussed later or encourage discovery through pattern recognition (see the one following Section 7.6). Others explore aspects of geometry: tetrahedra (after Section 12.4), hyperspheres (after Section 15.7), and intersections of three cylinders (after Section 15.8). Additional projects can be found in the *Instructor's Guide* (see, for instance, Group Exercise 5.1: Position from Samples).

PROBLEM SOLVING   Students usually have difficulties with problems for which there is no single well-defined procedure for obtaining the answer. I think nobody has improved very much on George Polya's four-stage problem-solving strategy and, accordingly, I have included a version of his problem-solving principles following Chapter 1. They are applied, both explicitly and implicitly, throughout the book. After the other chapters I have placed sections called *Problems Plus*, which feature examples of how to tackle challenging calculus problems. In selecting the varied problems for these sections I kept in mind the following advice from David Hilbert: "A mathematical problem should be difficult in order to entice us, yet not inaccessible lest it mock our efforts." When I put these challenging problems on assignments and tests I grade them in a different way. Here I reward a student significantly for ideas toward a solution and for recognizing which problem-solving principles are relevant.

TECHNOLOGY   The availability of technology makes it not less important but more important to clearly understand the concepts that underlie the images on the screen. But, when properly used, graphing calculators and computers are powerful tools for discovering and understanding those concepts. This textbook can be used either with or without technology and I use two special symbols to indicate clearly when a particular type of machine is required. The icon ⊞ indicates an exercise that definitely requires the use of such technology, but that is not to say that it can't be used on the other exercises as well. The symbol [CAS] is reserved for problems in which the full resources of a computer algebra system (like Derive, Maple, Mathematica, or the TI-89/92) are required. But technology doesn't make pencil and paper obsolete. Hand calculation and sketches are often preferable to technology for illustrating and reinforcing some concepts. Both instructors and students need to develop the ability to decide where the hand or the machine is appropriate.

TOOLS FOR ENRICHING™ CALCULUS

TEC is a companion to the text and is intended to enrich and complement its contents. (It is now accessible in Enhanced WebAssign and CourseMate. Selected Visuals and Modules are available at www.stewartcalculus.com.) Developed by Harvey Keynes, Dan Clegg, Hubert Hohn, and myself, TEC uses a discovery and exploratory approach. In sections of the book where technology is particularly appropriate, marginal icons direct students to TEC modules that provide a laboratory environment in which they can explore the topic in different ways and at different levels. **Visuals are animations of figures in text; Modules are more elaborate activities and include exercises**. Instructors can choose to become involved at several different levels, ranging from simply encouraging students to use the Visuals and Modules for independent exploration, to assigning specific exercises from those included with each Module, or to creating additional exercises, labs, and projects that make use of the Visuals and Modules.

HOMEWORK HINTS

Homework Hints presented in the form of questions try to imitate an effective teaching assistant by functioning as a silent tutor. Hints for representative exercises (usually odd-numbered) are included in every section of the text, indicated by printing the exercise number in red. They are constructed so as not to reveal any more of the actual solution than is minimally necessary to make further progress, and are available to students at stewartcalculus.com and in CourseMate and Enhanced WebAssign.

ENHANCED WEBASSIGN

Technology is having an impact on the way homework is assigned to students, particularly in large classes. The use of online homework is growing and its appeal depends on ease of use, grading precision, and reliability. With the seventh edition we have been working with the calculus community and WebAssign to develop a more robust online homework system. Up to 70% of the exercises in each section are assignable as online homework, including free response, multiple choice, and multi-part formats.

The system also includes Active Examples, in which students are guided in step-by-step tutorials through text examples, with links to the textbook and to video solutions. New enhancements to the system include a customizable eBook, a *Show Your Work* feature, *Just in Time* review of precalculus prerequisites, an improved Assignment Editor, and an Answer Evaluator that accepts more mathematically equivalent answers and allows for homework grading in much the same way that an instructor grades.

www.stewartcalculus.com

This site includes the following.

- Homework Hints
- Algebra Review
- Lies My Calculator and Computer Told Me
- History of Mathematics, with links to the better historical websites
- Additional Topics (complete with exercise sets): Fourier Series, Formulas for the Remainder Term in Taylor Series, Rotation of Axes
- Archived Problems (Drill exercises that appeared in previous editions, together with their solutions)

- Challenge Problems (some from the Problems Plus sections from prior editions)
- Links, for particular topics, to outside web resources
- Selected Tools for Enriching Calculus (TEC) Modules and Visuals

 Content

Diagnostic Tests   The book begins with four diagnostic tests, in Basic Algebra, Analytic Geometry, Functions, and Trigonometry.

A Preview of Calculus   This is an overview of the subject and includes a list of questions to motivate the study of calculus.

1 Functions and Models   From the beginning, multiple representations of functions are stressed: verbal, numerical, visual, and algebraic. A discussion of mathematical models leads to a review of the standard functions, including exponential and logarithmic functions, from these four points of view.

2 Limits and Derivatives   The material on limits is motivated by a prior discussion of the tangent and velocity problems. Limits are treated from descriptive, graphical, numerical, and algebraic points of view. Section 2.4, on the precise ε-δ definition of a limit, is an optional section. Sections 2.7 and 2.8 deal with derivatives (especially with functions defined graphically and numerically) before the differentiation rules are covered in Chapter 3. Here the examples and exercises explore the meanings of derivatives in various contexts. Higher derivatives are introduced in Section 2.8.

3 Differentiation Rules   All the basic functions, including exponential, logarithmic, and inverse trigonometric functions, are differentiated here. When derivatives are computed in applied situations, students are asked to explain their meanings. Exponential growth and decay are covered in this chapter.

4 Applications of Differentiation   The basic facts concerning extreme values and shapes of curves are deduced from the Mean Value Theorem. Graphing with technology emphasizes the interaction between calculus and calculators and the analysis of families of curves. Some substantial optimization problems are provided, including an explanation of why you need to raise your head 42° to see the top of a rainbow.

5 Integrals   The area problem and the distance problem serve to motivate the definite integral, with sigma notation introduced as needed. (Full coverage of sigma notation is provided in Appendix E.) Emphasis is placed on explaining the meanings of integrals in various contexts and on estimating their values from graphs and tables.

6 Applications of Integration   Here I present the applications of integration—area, volume, work, average value—that can reasonably be done without specialized techniques of integration. General methods are emphasized. The goal is for students to be able to divide a quantity into small pieces, estimate with Riemann sums, and recognize the limit as an integral.

7 Techniques of Integration   All the standard methods are covered but, of course, the real challenge is to be able to recognize which technique is best used in a given situation. Accordingly, in Section 7.5, I present a strategy for integration. The use of computer algebra systems is discussed in Section 7.6.

8 Further Applications of Integration   Here are the applications of integration—arc length and surface area—for which it is useful to have available all the techniques of integration, as well as applications to biology, economics, and physics (hydrostatic force and centers of mass). I have also included a section on probability. There are more applications here than can realistically be covered in a given course. Instructors should select applications suitable for their students and for which they themselves have enthusiasm.

9 Differential Equations

Modeling is the theme that unifies this introductory treatment of differential equations. Direction fields and Euler's method are studied before separable and linear equations are solved explicitly, so that qualitative, numerical, and analytic approaches are given equal consideration. These methods are applied to the exponential, logistic, and other models for population growth. The first four or five sections of this chapter serve as a good introduction to first-order differential equations. An optional final section uses predator-prey models to illustrate systems of differential equations.

10 Parametric Equations and Polar Coordinates

This chapter introduces parametric and polar curves and applies the methods of calculus to them. Parametric curves are well suited to laboratory projects; the three presented here involve families of curves and Bézier curves. A brief treatment of conic sections in polar coordinates prepares the way for Kepler's Laws in Chapter 13.

11 Infinite Sequences and Series

The convergence tests have intuitive justifications (see page 714) as well as formal proofs. Numerical estimates of sums of series are based on which test was used to prove convergence. The emphasis is on Taylor series and polynomials and their applications to physics. Error estimates include those from graphing devices.

12 Vectors and The Geometry of Space

The material on three-dimensional analytic geometry and vectors is divided into two chapters. Chapter 12 deals with vectors, the dot and cross products, lines, planes, and surfaces.

13 Vector Functions

This chapter covers vector-valued functions, their derivatives and integrals, the length and curvature of space curves, and velocity and acceleration along space curves, culminating in Kepler's laws.

14 Partial Derivatives

Functions of two or more variables are studied from verbal, numerical, visual, and algebraic points of view. In particular, I introduce partial derivatives by looking at a specific column in a table of values of the heat index (perceived air temperature) as a function of the actual temperature and the relative humidity.

15 Multiple Integrals

Contour maps and the Midpoint Rule are used to estimate the average snowfall and average temperature in given regions. Double and triple integrals are used to compute probabilities, surface areas, and (in projects) volumes of hyperspheres and volumes of intersections of three cylinders. Cylindrical and spherical coordinates are introduced in the context of evaluating triple integrals.

16 Vector Calculus

Vector fields are introduced through pictures of velocity fields showing San Francisco Bay wind patterns. The similarities among the Fundamental Theorem for line integrals, Green's Theorem, Stokes' Theorem, and the Divergence Theorem are emphasized.

17 Second-Order Differential Equations

Since first-order differential equations are covered in Chapter 9, this final chapter deals with second-order linear differential equations, their application to vibrating springs and electric circuits, and series solutions.

 Ancillaries

Calculus, Early Transcendentals, Seventh Edition, International Metric Version, is supported by a complete set of ancillaries developed under my direction. Each piece has been designed to enhance student understanding and to facilitate creative instruction. With this edition, new media and technologies have been developed that help students to visualize calculus and instructors to customize content to better align with the way they teach their course. The tables on pages xxi–xxii describe each of these ancillaries.

Acknowledgments

The preparation of this and previous editions has involved much time spent reading the reasoned (but sometimes contradictory) advice from a large number of astute reviewers. I greatly appreciate the time they spent to understand my motivation for the approach taken. I have learned something from each of them.

SEVENTH EDITION REVIEWERS

Amy Austin, *Texas A&M University*

Anthony J. Bevelacqua, *University of North Dakota*

Zhen-Qing Chen, *University of Washington—Seattle*

Jenna Carpenter, *Louisiana Tech University*

Le Baron O. Ferguson, *University of California—Riverside*

Shari Harris, *John Wood Community College*

Amer Iqbal, *University of Washington—Seattle*

Akhtar Khan, *Rochester Institute of Technology*

Marianne Korten, *Kansas State University*

Joyce Longman, *Villanova University*

Richard Millspaugh, *University of North Dakota*

Lon H. Mitchell, *Virginia Commonwealth University*

Ho Kuen Ng, *San Jose State University*

Norma Ortiz-Robinson, *Virginia Commonwealth University*

Qin Sheng, *Baylor University*

Magdalena Toda, *Texas Tech University*

Ruth Trygstad, *Salt Lake Community College*

Klaus Volpert, *Villanova University*

Peiyong Wang, *Wayne State University*

TECHNOLOGY REVIEWERS

Maria Andersen, *Muskegon Community College*
Eric Aurand, *Eastfield College*
Joy Becker, *University of Wisconsin–Stout*
Przemyslaw Bogacki, *Old Dominion University*
Amy Elizabeth Bowman, *University of Alabama in Huntsville*
Monica Brown, *University of Missouri–St. Louis*
Roxanne Byrne, *University of Colorado at Denver and Health Sciences Center*
Teri Christiansen, *University of Missouri–Columbia*
Bobby Dale Daniel, *Lamar University*
Jennifer Daniel, *Lamar University*
Andras Domokos, *California State University, Sacramento*
Timothy Flaherty, *Carnegie Mellon University*
Lee Gibson, *University of Louisville*
Jane Golden, *Hillsborough Community College*
Semion Gutman, *University of Oklahoma*
Diane Hoffoss, *University of San Diego*
Lorraine Hughes, *Mississippi State University*
Jay Jahangiri, *Kent State University*
John Jernigan, *Community College of Philadelphia*

Brian Karasek, *South Mountain Community College*
Jason Kozinski, *University of Florida*
Carole Krueger, *The University of Texas at Arlington*
Ken Kubota, *University of Kentucky*
John Mitchell, *Clark College*
Donald Paul, *Tulsa Community College*
Chad Pierson, *University of Minnesota, Duluth*
Lanita Presson, *University of Alabama in Huntsville*
Karin Reinhold, *State University of New York at Albany*
Thomas Riedel, *University of Louisville*
Christopher Schroeder, *Morehead State University*
Angela Sharp, *University of Minnesota, Duluth*
Patricia Shaw, *Mississippi State University*
Carl Spitznagel, *John Carroll University*
Mohammad Tabanjeh, *Virginia State University*
Capt. Koichi Takagi, *United States Naval Academy*
Lorna TenEyck, *Chemeketa Community College*
Roger Werbylo, *Pima Community College*
David Williams, *Clayton State University*
Zhuan Ye, *Northern Illinois University*

PREVIOUS EDITION REVIEWERS

B. D. Aggarwala, *University of Calgary*

John Alberghini, *Manchester Community College*

Michael Albert, *Carnegie-Mellon University*

Daniel Anderson, *University of Iowa*

Donna J. Bailey, *Northeast Missouri State University*

Wayne Barber, *Chemeketa Community College*

Marilyn Belkin, *Villanova University*

Neil Berger, *University of Illinois, Chicago*

David Berman, *University of New Orleans*

Richard Biggs, *University of Western Ontario*

Robert Blumenthal, *Oglethorpe University*

Martina Bode, *Northwestern University*

Barbara Bohannon, *Hofstra University*

Philip L. Bowers, *Florida State University*

Amy Elizabeth Bowman, *University of Alabama in Huntsville*

Jay Bourland, *Colorado State University*

Stephen W. Brady, *Wichita State University*

Michael Breen, *Tennessee Technological University*

Robert N. Bryan, *University of Western Ontario*

David Buchthal, *University of Akron*

Jorge Cassio, *Miami-Dade Community College*

Jack Ceder, *University of California, Santa Barbara*

Scott Chapman, *Trinity University*

James Choike, *Oklahoma State University*

Barbara Cortzen, *DePaul University*

Carl Cowen, *Purdue University*

Philip S. Crooke, *Vanderbilt University*

Charles N. Curtis, *Missouri Southern State College*

Daniel Cyphert, *Armstrong State College*

Robert Dahlin

M. Hilary Davies, *University of Alaska Anchorage*

Gregory J. Davis, *University of Wisconsin–Green Bay*

Elias Deeba, *University of Houston–Downtown*

Daniel DiMaria, *Suffolk Community College*

Seymour Ditor, *University of Western Ontario*

Greg Dresden, *Washington and Lee University*

Daniel Drucker, *Wayne State University*

Kenn Dunn, *Dalhousie University*

Dennis Dunninger, *Michigan State University*

Bruce Edwards, *University of Florida*

David Ellis, *San Francisco State University*

John Ellison, *Grove City College*

Martin Erickson, *Truman State University*

Garret Etgen, *University of Houston*

Theodore G. Faticoni, *Fordham University*

Laurene V. Fausett, *Georgia Southern University*

Norman Feldman, *Sonoma State University*

Newman Fisher, *San Francisco State University*

José D. Flores, *The University of South Dakota*

William Francis, *Michigan Technological University*

James T. Franklin, *Valencia Community College, East*

Stanley Friedlander, *Bronx Community College*

Patrick Gallagher, *Columbia University–New York*

Paul Garrett, *University of Minnesota–Minneapolis*

Frederick Gass, *Miami University of Ohio*

Bruce Gilligan, *University of Regina*

Matthias K. Gobbert, *University of Maryland, Baltimore County*

Gerald Goff, *Oklahoma State University*

Stuart Goldenberg, *California Polytechnic State University*

John A. Graham, *Buckingham Browne & Nichols School*

Richard Grassl, *University of New Mexico*

Michael Gregory, *University of North Dakota*

Charles Groetsch, *University of Cincinnati*

Paul Triantafilos Hadavas, *Armstrong Atlantic State University*

Salim M. Haïdar, *Grand Valley State University*

D. W. Hall, *Michigan State University*

Robert L. Hall, *University of Wisconsin–Milwaukee*

Howard B. Hamilton, *California State University, Sacramento*

Darel Hardy, *Colorado State University*

Gary W. Harrison, *College of Charleston*

Melvin Hausner, *New York University/Courant Institute*

Curtis Herink, *Mercer University*

Russell Herman, *University of North Carolina at Wilmington*

Allen Hesse, *Rochester Community College*

Randall R. Holmes, *Auburn University*

James F. Hurley, *University of Connecticut*

Matthew A. Isom, *Arizona State University*

Gerald Janusz, *University of Illinois at Urbana-Champaign*

John H. Jenkins, *Embry-Riddle Aeronautical University, Prescott Campus*

Clement Jeske, *University of Wisconsin, Platteville*

Carl Jockusch, *University of Illinois at Urbana-Champaign*

Jan E. H. Johansson, *University of Vermont*

Jerry Johnson, *Oklahoma State University*

Zsuzsanna M. Kadas, *St. Michael's College*

Nets Katz, *Indiana University Bloomington*

Matt Kaufman

Matthias Kawski, *Arizona State University*

Frederick W. Keene, *Pasadena City College*

Robert L. Kelley, *University of Miami*

Virgil Kowalik, *Texas A&I University*

Kevin Kreider, *University of Akron*

Leonard Krop, *DePaul University*

Mark Krusemeyer, *Carleton College*

John C. Lawlor, *University of Vermont*

Christopher C. Leary, *State University of New York at Geneseo*

David Leeming, *University of Victoria*

Sam Lesseig, *Northeast Missouri State University*

Phil Locke, *University of Maine*

Joan McCarter, *Arizona State University*

Phil McCartney, *Northern Kentucky University*

James McKinney, *California State Polytechnic University, Pomona*

Igor Malyshev, *San Jose State University*

Larry Mansfield, *Queens College*

Mary Martin, *Colgate University*

Nathaniel F. G. Martin, *University of Virginia*

Gerald Y. Matsumoto, *American River College*

Tom Metzger, *University of Pittsburgh*

Michael Montaño, *Riverside Community College*

Teri Jo Murphy, *University of Oklahoma*

Martin Nakashima, *California State Polytechnic University, Pomona*

Richard Nowakowski, *Dalhousie University*

Hussain S. Nur, *California State University, Fresno*

Wayne N. Palmer, *Utica College*

Vincent Panico, *University of the Pacific*

F. J. Papp, *University of Michigan–Dearborn*

Mike Penna, *Indiana University–Purdue University Indianapolis*

Mark Pinsky, *Northwestern University*

Lothar Redlin, *The Pennsylvania State University*

Joel W. Robbin, *University of Wisconsin–Madison*

Lila Roberts, *Georgia College and State University*

E. Arthur Robinson, Jr., *The George Washington University*

Richard Rockwell, *Pacific Union College*

Rob Root, *Lafayette College*

Richard Ruedemann, *Arizona State University*

David Ryeburn, *Simon Fraser University*

Richard St. Andre, *Central Michigan University*

Ricardo Salinas, *San Antonio College*

Robert Schmidt, *South Dakota State University*

Eric Schreiner, *Western Michigan University*

Mihr J. Shah, *Kent State University–Trumbull*

Theodore Shifrin, *University of Georgia*

Wayne Skrapek, *University of Saskatchewan*

Larry Small, *Los Angeles Pierce College*

Teresa Morgan Smith, *Blinn College*

William Smith, *University of North Carolina*

Donald W. Solomon, *University of Wisconsin–Milwaukee*

Edward Spitznagel, *Washington University*

Joseph Stampfli, *Indiana University*

Kristin Stoley, *Blinn College*

M. B. Tavakoli, *Chaffey College*

Paul Xavier Uhlig, *St. Mary's University, San Antonio*

Stan Ver Nooy, *University of Oregon*

Andrei Verona, *California State University–Los Angeles*

Russell C. Walker, *Carnegie Mellon University*

William L. Walton, *McCallie School*

Jack Weiner, *University of Guelph*

Alan Weinstein, *University of California, Berkeley*

Theodore W. Wilcox, *Rochester Institute of Technology*

Steven Willard, *University of Alberta*

Robert Wilson, *University of Wisconsin–Madison*

Jerome Wolbert, *University of Michigan–Ann Arbor*

Dennis H. Wortman, *University of Massachusetts, Boston*

Mary Wright, *Southern Illinois University–Carbondale*

Paul M. Wright, *Austin Community College*

Xian Wu, *University of South Carolina*

In addition, I would like to thank Jordan Bell, George Bergman, Leon Gerber, Mary Pugh, Dusty Sabo, and Simon Smith for their suggestions; Al Shenk and Dennis Zill for permission to use exercises from their calculus texts; COMAP for permission to use project material; George Bergman, David Bleecker, Dan Clegg, Victor Kaftal, Anthony Lam, Jamie Lawson, Ira Rosenholtz, Paul Sally, Lowell Smylie, and Larry Wallen for ideas for exercises; Dan Drucker for the roller derby project; Thomas Banchoff, Tom Farmer, Fred Gass, John Ramsay, Larry Riddle, Philip Straffin, and Klaus Volpert for ideas for projects; Dan Anderson, Dan Clegg, Jeff Cole, Dan Drucker, and Barbara Frank for solving the new exercises and suggesting ways to improve them; Marv Riedesel, Mary Johnson, and John Manalo for accuracy in proofreading; and Jeff Cole and Dan Clegg for their careful preparation and proofreading of the answer manuscript.

In addition, I thank those who have contributed to past editions: Ed Barbeau, Fred Brauer, Andy Bulman-Fleming, Bob Burton, David Cusick, Tom DiCiccio, Garret Etgen, Chris Fisher, Stuart Goldenberg, Arnold Good, Gene Hecht, Harvey Keynes, E.L. Koh, Zdislav Kovarik, Kevin Kreider, Emile LeBlanc, David Leep, Gerald Leibowitz, Larry Peterson, Lothar Redlin, Carl Riehm, John Ringland, Peter Rosenthal, Doug Shaw, Dan Silver, Norton Starr, Saleem Watson, Alan Weinstein, and Gail Wolkowicz.

I also thank Kathi Townes and Stephanie Kuhns of TECHarts for their production services and the following Brooks/Cole staff: Cheryll Linthicum, content project manager; Liza Neustaetter, assistant editor; Maureen Ross, media editor; Sam Subity, managing media editor; Jennifer Jones, marketing manager; and Vernon Boes, art director. They have all done an outstanding job.

I have been very fortunate to have worked with some of the best mathematics editors in the business over the past three decades: Ron Munro, Harry Campbell, Craig Barth, Jeremy Hayhurst, Gary Ostedt, Bob Pirtle, Richard Stratton, and now Liz Covello. All of them have contributed greatly to the success of this book.

JAMES STEWART

■ Ancillaries for Instructors

Companion Website
www.cengage.com/international

This website contains a collection of book-specific instructor resources, including all art from the text in both jpeg and Power-Point formats, key equations and tables from the text, complete pre-built PowerPoint lectures, an electronic version of the Instructor's Guide, Solution Builder, ExamView testing software, and more!

Instructor's Guide
by Douglas Shaw

Each section of the text is discussed from several viewpoints. The Instructor's Guide contains suggested time to allot, points to stress, text discussion topics, core materials for lecture, work-shop/discussion suggestions, group work exercises in a form suitable for handout, and suggested homework assignments. An electronic version of the Instructor's Guide is available on the companion website.

Complete Solutions Manual
Single Variable Early Transcendentals
ISBN 0-8400-4937-4

Multivariable
ISBN 0-8400-4948-X

Includes worked-out solutions to all exercises in the text.

Solution Builder
www.cengage.com/international

This online instructor database offers complete worked out solutions to all exercises in the text. Solution Builder allows you to create customized, secure solutions printouts (in PDF format) matched exactly to the problems you assign in class.

ExamView Testing

Create, deliver, and customize tests in print and online formats with ExamView, an easy-to-use assessment and tutorial software. ExamView contains hundreds of multiple-choice and free response test items. ExamView testing is available on the companion website.

■ Ancillaries for Instructors and Students

Stewart Website
www.stewartcalculus.com

Contents: *Homework Hints* ■ *Algebra Review* ■ *Additional Topics* ■ *Drill exercises* ■ *Challenge Problems* ■ *Web Links* ■ *History of Mathematics* ■ *Tools for Enriching Calculus (TEC)*

TEC Tools for Enriching™ Calculus
By James Stewart, Harvey Keynes, Dan Clegg, and developer Hu Hohn

Tools for Enriching Calculus (TEC) functions as both a powerful tool for instructors, as well as a tutorial environment in which students can explore and review selected topics. The Flash simulation modules in TEC include instructions, written and audio explanations of the concepts, and exercises. TEC is accessible in CourseMate and WebAssign. Selected Visuals and Modules are available at www.stewartcalculus.com.

WebAssign Enhanced WebAssign
www.webassign.net

WebAssign's homework delivery system lets instructors deliver, collect, grade, and record assignments via the web. Enhanced WebAssign for Stewart's Calculus *now includes opportunities for students to review prerequisite skills and content both at the start of the course and at the beginning of each section. In addition, for selected problems, students can get extra help in the form of "enhanced feedback" (rejoinders) and video solutions.* **Other key features include:** *thousands of problems from Stewart's* Calculus, *a customizable Cengage YouBook, Personal Study Plans, Show Your Work, Just in Time Review, Answer Evaluator, Visualizing Calculus animations and modules, quizzes, lecture videos (with associated questions), and more!*

Cengage Customizable YouBook

YouBook is a Flash-based eBook that is interactive and customizable! Containing all the content from Stewart's Calculus, *YouBook features a text edit tool that allows instructors to modify the textbook narrative as needed. With YouBook, instructors can quickly re-order entire sections and chapters or hide any content they don't teach to create an eBook that perfectly matches their syllabus. Instructors can further customize the text by adding instructor-created or YouTube video links. Additional media assets include: animated figures, video clips, highlighting, notes, and more! YouBook is available in Enhanced WebAssign.*

■ Electronic items   ■ Printed items

(Table continues on page xxii.)

www.cengagebrain.com

CourseMate is a perfect self-study tool for students, and requires no set up from instructors. CourseMate brings course concepts to life with interactive learning, study, and exam preparation tools that support the printed textbook. CourseMate for Stewart's Calculus includes: an interactive eBook, Tools for Enriching Calculus, videos, quizzes, flashcards, and more! For instructors, CourseMate includes Engagement Tracker, a first-of-its-kind tool that monitors student engagement.

Maple CD-ROM

Maple provides an advanced, high performance mathematical computation engine with fully integrated numerics & symbolics, all accessible from a WYSIWYG technical document environment.

CengageBrain.com

To access additional course materials including CourseMate, please visit www.cengagebrain.com. At the CengageBrain.com home page, search for the ISBN of your title (from the back cover of your book) using the search box at the top of the page. This will take you to the product page where these resources can be found.

◼ Ancillaries for Students

Student Solutions Manual

Single Variable Early Transcendentals
ISBN 0-8400-4935-8

Multivariable
ISBN 0-8400-4946-3

Provides completely worked-out solutions to all odd-numbered exercises in the text, giving students a chance to check their answers and ensure they took the correct steps to arrive at an answer.

Study Guide

Single Variable Early Transcendentals
By Richard St. Andre
ISBN 1-1115-7553-3

Multivariable
By Richard St. Andre
ISBN 1-1115-7552-5

For each section of the text, the Study Guide provides students with a brief introduction, a short list of concepts to master, as well as summary and focus questions with explained answers. The Study Guide also contains "Technology Plus" questions, and multiple-choice "On Your Own" exam-style questions.

CalcLabs with Maple

Single Variable By Philip B. Yasskin and Robert Lopez
ISBN 0-8400-5811-X

Multivariable By Philip B. Yasskin and Robert Lopez
ISBN 0-8400-5812-8

CalcLabs with Mathematica

Single Variable By Selwyn Hollis
ISBN 0-8400-5814-4

Multivariable By Selwyn Hollis
ISBN 0-8400-5813-6

Each of these comprehensive lab manuals will help students learn to use the technology tools available to them. CalcLabs contain clearly explained exercises and a variety of labs and projects to accompany the text.

A Companion to Calculus

By Dennis Ebersole, Doris Schattschneider, Alicia Sevilla, and Kay Somers
ISBN 0-495-01124-X

Written to improve algebra and problem-solving skills of students taking a Calculus course, every chapter in this companion is keyed to a calculus topic, providing conceptual background and specific algebra techniques needed to understand and solve calculus problems related to that topic. It is designed for calculus courses that integrate the review of precalculus concepts or for individual use.

Linear Algebra for Calculus

by Konrad J. Heuvers, William P. Francis, John H. Kuisti, Deborah F. Lockhart, Daniel S. Moak, and Gene M. Ortner
ISBN 0-534-25248-6

This comprehensive book, designed to supplement the calculus course, provides an introduction to and review of the basic ideas of linear algebra.

◼ Electronic items ◼ Printed items

To the Student

Reading a calculus textbook is different from reading a newspaper or a novel, or even a physics book. Don't be discouraged if you have to read a passage more than once in order to understand it. You should have pencil and paper and calculator at hand to sketch a diagram or make a calculation.

Some students start by trying their homework problems and read the text only if they get stuck on an exercise. I suggest that a far better plan is to read and understand a section of the text before attempting the exercises. In particular, you should look at the definitions to see the exact meanings of the terms. And before you read each example, I suggest that you cover up the solution and try solving the problem yourself. You'll get a lot more from looking at the solution if you do so.

Part of the aim of this course is to train you to think logically. Learn to write the solutions of the exercises in a connected, step-by-step fashion with explanatory sentences—not just a string of disconnected equations or formulas.

The answers to the odd-numbered exercises appear at the back of the book, in Appendix I. Some exercises ask for a verbal explanation or interpretation or description. In such cases there is no single correct way of expressing the answer, so don't worry that you haven't found the definitive answer. In addition, there are often several different forms in which to express a numerical or algebraic answer, so if your answer differs from mine, don't immediately assume you're wrong. For example, if the answer given in the back of the book is $\sqrt{2} - 1$ and you obtain $1/(1 + \sqrt{2})$, then you're right and rationalizing the denominator will show that the answers are equivalent.

The icon ⌂ indicates an exercise that definitely requires the use of either a graphing calculator or a computer with graphing software. (Section 1.4 discusses the use of these graphing devices and some of the pitfalls that you may encounter.) But that doesn't mean that graphing devices can't be used to check your work on the other exercises as well. The symbol CAS is reserved for problems in which the full resources of a computer algebra system (like Derive, Maple, Mathematica, or the TI-89/92) are required.

You will also encounter the symbol ⊘, which warns you against committing an error. I have placed this symbol in the margin in situations where I have observed that a large proportion of my students tend to make the same mistake.

Tools for Enriching Calculus, which is a companion to this text, is referred to by means of the symbol TEC and can be accessed in Enhanced WebAssign and CourseMate (selected Visuals and Modules are available at www.stewartcalculus.com). It directs you to modules in which you can explore aspects of calculus for which the computer is particularly useful.

Homework Hints for representative exercises are indicated by printing the exercise number in red: **5**. These hints can be found on stewartcalculus.com as well as Enhanced WebAssign and CourseMate. The homework hints ask you questions that allow you to make progress toward a solution without actually giving you the answer. You need to pursue each hint in an active manner with pencil and paper to work out the details. If a particular hint doesn't enable you to solve the problem, you can click to reveal the next hint.

I recommend that you keep this book for reference purposes after you finish the course. Because you will likely forget some of the specific details of calculus, the book will serve as a useful reminder when you need to use calculus in subsequent courses. And, because this book contains more material than can be covered in any one course, it can also serve as a valuable resource for a working scientist or engineer.

Calculus is an exciting subject, justly considered to be one of the greatest achievements of the human intellect. I hope you will discover that it is not only useful but also intrinsically beautiful.

JAMES STEWART

Diagnostic Tests

Success in calculus depends to a large extent on knowledge of the mathematics that precedes calculus: algebra, analytic geometry, functions, and trigonometry. The following tests are intended to diagnose weaknesses that you might have in these areas. After taking each test you can check your answers against the given answers and, if necessary, refresh your skills by referring to the review materials that are provided.

A Diagnostic Test: Algebra

1. Evaluate each expression without using a calculator.

   (a) $(-3)^4$ (b) -3^4 (c) 3^{-4}

   (d) $\dfrac{5^{23}}{5^{21}}$ (e) $\left(\dfrac{2}{3}\right)^{-2}$ (f) $16^{-3/4}$

2. Simplify each expression. Write your answer without negative exponents.

   (a) $\sqrt{200} - \sqrt{32}$

   (b) $(3a^3b^3)(4ab^2)^2$

   (c) $\left(\dfrac{3x^{3/2}y^3}{x^2y^{-1/2}}\right)^{-2}$

3. Expand and simplify.

   (a) $3(x + 6) + 4(2x - 5)$ (b) $(x + 3)(4x - 5)$

   (c) $(\sqrt{a} + \sqrt{b})(\sqrt{a} - \sqrt{b})$ (d) $(2x + 3)^2$

   (e) $(x + 2)^3$

4. Factor each expression.

   (a) $4x^2 - 25$ (b) $2x^2 + 5x - 12$

   (c) $x^3 - 3x^2 - 4x + 12$ (d) $x^4 + 27x$

   (e) $3x^{3/2} - 9x^{1/2} + 6x^{-1/2}$ (f) $x^3y - 4xy$

5. Simplify the rational expression.

   (a) $\dfrac{x^2 + 3x + 2}{x^2 - x - 2}$ (b) $\dfrac{2x^2 - x - 1}{x^2 - 9} \cdot \dfrac{x + 3}{2x + 1}$

   (c) $\dfrac{x^2}{x^2 - 4} - \dfrac{x + 1}{x + 2}$ (d) $\dfrac{\dfrac{y}{x} - \dfrac{x}{y}}{\dfrac{1}{y} - \dfrac{1}{x}}$

6. Rationalize the expression and simplify.

(a) $\dfrac{\sqrt{10}}{\sqrt{5} - 2}$

(b) $\dfrac{\sqrt{4 + h} - 2}{h}$

7. Rewrite by completing the square.

(a) $x^2 + x + 1$

(b) $2x^2 - 12x + 11$

8. Solve the equation. (Find only the real solutions.)

(a) $x + 5 = 14 - \frac{1}{2}x$

(b) $\dfrac{2x}{x + 1} = \dfrac{2x - 1}{x}$

(c) $x^2 - x - 12 = 0$

(d) $2x^2 + 4x + 1 = 0$

(e) $x^4 - 3x^2 + 2 = 0$

(f) $3|x - 4| = 10$

(g) $2x(4 - x)^{-1/2} - 3\sqrt{4 - x} = 0$

9. Solve each inequality. Write your answer using interval notation.

(a) $-4 < 5 - 3x \leqslant 17$

(b) $x^2 < 2x + 8$

(c) $x(x - 1)(x + 2) > 0$

(d) $|x - 4| < 3$

(e) $\dfrac{2x - 3}{x + 1} \leqslant 1$

10. State whether each equation is true or false.

(a) $(p + q)^2 = p^2 + q^2$

(b) $\sqrt{ab} = \sqrt{a}\,\sqrt{b}$

(c) $\sqrt{a^2 + b^2} = a + b$

(d) $\dfrac{1 + TC}{C} = 1 + T$

(e) $\dfrac{1}{x - y} = \dfrac{1}{x} - \dfrac{1}{y}$

(f) $\dfrac{1/x}{a/x - b/x} = \dfrac{1}{a - b}$

Answers to Diagnostic Test A: Algebra

1. (a) 81
   (b) -81
   (c) $\frac{1}{81}$
   (d) 25
   (e) $\frac{9}{4}$
   (f) $\frac{1}{8}$

2. (a) $6\sqrt{2}$
   (b) $48a^5b^7$
   (c) $\dfrac{x}{9y^7}$

3. (a) $11x - 2$
   (b) $4x^2 + 7x - 15$
   (c) $a - b$
   (d) $4x^2 + 12x + 9$
   (e) $x^3 + 6x^2 + 12x + 8$

4. (a) $(2x - 5)(2x + 5)$
   (b) $(2x - 3)(x + 4)$
   (c) $(x - 3)(x - 2)(x + 2)$
   (d) $x(x + 3)(x^2 - 3x + 9)$
   (e) $3x^{-1/2}(x - 1)(x - 2)$
   (f) $xy(x - 2)(x + 2)$

5. (a) $\dfrac{x + 2}{x - 2}$
   (b) $\dfrac{x - 1}{x - 3}$
   (c) $\dfrac{1}{x - 2}$
   (d) $-(x + y)$

6. (a) $5\sqrt{2} + 2\sqrt{10}$
   (b) $\dfrac{1}{\sqrt{4 + h} + 2}$

7. (a) $\left(x + \frac{1}{2}\right)^2 + \frac{3}{4}$
   (b) $2(x - 3)^2 - 7$

8. (a) 6
   (b) 1
   (c) $-3, 4$
   (d) $-1 \pm \frac{1}{2}\sqrt{2}$
   (e) $\pm 1, \pm\sqrt{2}$
   (f) $\frac{2}{3}, \frac{22}{3}$
   (g) $\frac{12}{5}$

9. (a) $[-4, 3)$
   (b) $(-2, 4)$
   (c) $(-2, 0) \cup (1, \infty)$
   (d) $(1, 7)$
   (e) $(-1, 4]$

10. (a) False
    (b) True
    (c) False
    (d) False
    (e) False
    (f) True

> If you have had difficulty with these problems, you may wish to consult
> the Review of Algebra on the website www.stewartcalculus.com

B Diagnostic Test: Analytic Geometry

1. Find an equation for the line that passes through the point $(2, -5)$ and
   (a) has slope -3
   (b) is parallel to the x-axis
   (c) is parallel to the y-axis
   (d) is parallel to the line $2x - 4y = 3$

2. Find an equation for the circle that has center $(-1, 4)$ and passes through the point $(3, -2)$.

3. Find the center and radius of the circle with equation $x^2 + y^2 - 6x + 10y + 9 = 0$.

4. Let $A(-7, 4)$ and $B(5, -12)$ be points in the plane.
   (a) Find the slope of the line that contains A and B.
   (b) Find an equation of the line that passes through A and B. What are the intercepts?
   (c) Find the midpoint of the segment AB.
   (d) Find the length of the segment AB.
   (e) Find an equation of the perpendicular bisector of AB.
   (f) Find an equation of the circle for which AB is a diameter.

5. Sketch the region in the xy-plane defined by the equation or inequalities.
   (a) $-1 \leq y \leq 3$ (b) $|x| < 4$ and $|y| < 2$
   (c) $y < 1 - \frac{1}{2}x$ (d) $y \geq x^2 - 1$
   (e) $x^2 + y^2 < 4$ (f) $9x^2 + 16y^2 = 144$

Answers to Diagnostic Test B: Analytic Geometry

1. (a) $y = -3x + 1$ (b) $y = -5$
   (c) $x = 2$ (d) $y = \frac{1}{2}x - 6$

2. $(x + 1)^2 + (y - 4)^2 = 52$

3. Center $(3, -5)$, radius 5

4. (a) $-\frac{4}{3}$
   (b) $4x + 3y + 16 = 0$; x-intercept -4, y-intercept $-\frac{16}{3}$
   (c) $(-1, -4)$
   (d) 20
   (e) $3x - 4y = 13$
   (f) $(x + 1)^2 + (y + 4)^2 = 100$

5. (a)   (b)   (c)

   (d)   (e)   (f)

If you have had difficulty with these problems, you may wish to consult the review of analytic geometry in Appendixes B and C.

C Diagnostic Test: Functions

FIGURE FOR PROBLEM 1

1. The graph of a function f is given at the left.
(a) State the value of $f(-1)$.
(b) Estimate the value of $f(2)$.
(c) For what values of x is $f(x) = 2$?
(d) Estimate the values of x such that $f(x) = 0$.
(e) State the domain and range of f.

2. If $f(x) = x^3$, evaluate the difference quotient $\dfrac{f(2 + h) - f(2)}{h}$ and simplify your answer.

3. Find the domain of the function.

(a) $f(x) = \dfrac{2x + 1}{x^2 + x - 2}$ (b) $g(x) = \dfrac{\sqrt[3]{x}}{x^2 + 1}$ (c) $h(x) = \sqrt{4 - x} + \sqrt{x^2 - 1}$

4. How are graphs of the functions obtained from the graph of f?

(a) $y = -f(x)$ (b) $y = 2f(x) - 1$ (c) $y = f(x - 3) + 2$

5. Without using a calculator, make a rough sketch of the graph.

(a) $y = x^3$ (b) $y = (x + 1)^3$ (c) $y = (x - 2)^3 + 3$
(d) $y = 4 - x^2$ (e) $y = \sqrt{x}$ (f) $y = 2\sqrt{x}$
(g) $y = -2^x$ (h) $y = 1 + x^{-1}$

6. Let $f(x) = \begin{cases} 1 - x^2 & \text{if } x \leq 0 \\ 2x + 1 & \text{if } x > 0 \end{cases}$

(a) Evaluate $f(-2)$ and $f(1)$.   (b) Sketch the graph of f.

7. If $f(x) = x^2 + 2x - 1$ and $g(x) = 2x - 3$, find each of the following functions.
(a) $f \circ g$ (b) $g \circ f$ (c) $g \circ g \circ g$

Answers to Diagnostic Test C: Functions

1. (a) -2 (b) 2.8
(c) $-3, 1$ (d) $-2.5, 0.3$
(e) $[-3, 3], [-2, 3]$

2. $12 + 6h + h^2$

3. (a) $(-\infty, -2) \cup (-2, 1) \cup (1, \infty)$
(b) $(-\infty, \infty)$
(c) $(-\infty, -1] \cup [1, 4]$

4. (a) Reflect about the x-axis
(b) Stretch vertically by a factor of 2, then shift 1 unit downward
(c) Shift 3 units to the right and 2 units upward

5. (a)   (b) (c)

(d)   (e) (f)

(g)   (h)

6. (a) $-3, 3$
(b)

7. (a) $(f \circ g)(x) = 4x^2 - 8x + 2$
(b) $(g \circ f)(x) = 2x^2 + 4x - 5$
(c) $(g \circ g \circ g)(x) = 8x - 21$

If you have had difficulty with these problems, you should look at Sections 1.1–1.3 of this book.

D | Diagnostic Test: Trigonometry

1. Convert from degrees to radians.
   (a) 300°   (b) −18°

2. Convert from radians to degrees.
   (a) 5π/6   (b) 2

3. Find the length of an arc of a circle with radius 12 cm if the arc subtends a central angle of 30°.

4. Find the exact values.
   (a) $\tan(\pi/3)$ (b) $\sin(7\pi/6)$ (c) $\sec(5\pi/3)$

5. Express the lengths a and b in the figure in terms of θ.

6. If $\sin x = \frac{1}{3}$ and $\sec y = \frac{5}{4}$, where x and y lie between 0 and $\pi/2$, evaluate $\sin(x + y)$.

7. Prove the identities.
   (a) $\tan \theta \sin \theta + \cos \theta = \sec \theta$

   (b) $\dfrac{2 \tan x}{1 + \tan^2 x} = \sin 2x$

8. Find all values of x such that $\sin 2x = \sin x$ and $0 \le x \le 2\pi$.

9. Sketch the graph of the function $y = 1 + \sin 2x$ without using a calculator.

24 a θ b

FIGURE FOR PROBLEM 5

| Answers to Diagnostic Test D: Trigonometry

1. (a) $5\pi/3$ (b) $-\pi/10$

2. (a) $150°$ (b) $360°/\pi \approx 114.6°$

3. 2π cm

4. (a) $\sqrt{3}$ (b) $-\frac{1}{2}$ (c) 2

5. (a) $24 \sin \theta$ (b) $24 \cos \theta$

6. $\frac{1}{15}\left(4 + 6\sqrt{2}\right)$

8. $0, \pi/3, \pi, 5\pi/3, 2\pi$

9.

If you have had difficulty with these problems, you should look at Appendix D of this book.

A Preview of Calculus

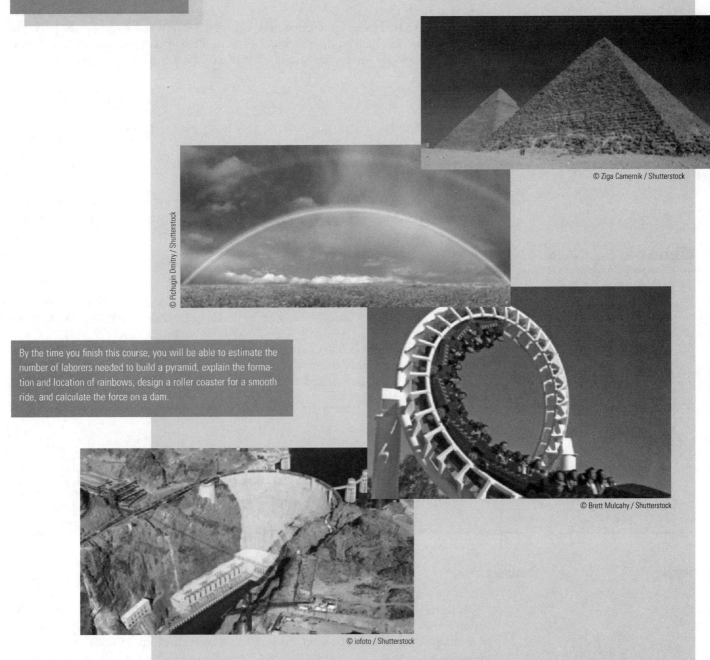

© Ziga Camernik / Shutterstock

© Pichugin Dmitry / Shutterstock

By the time you finish this course, you will be able to estimate the number of laborers needed to build a pyramid, explain the formation and location of rainbows, design a roller coaster for a smooth ride, and calculate the force on a dam.

© Brett Mulcahy / Shutterstock

© iofoto / Shutterstock

Calculus is fundamentally different from the mathematics that you have studied previously: calculus is less static and more dynamic. It is concerned with change and motion; it deals with quantities that approach other quantities. For that reason it may be useful to have an overview of the subject before beginning its intensive study. Here we give a glimpse of some of the main ideas of calculus by showing how the concept of a limit arises when we attempt to solve a variety of problems.

$$A = A_1 + A_2 + A_3 + A_4 + A_5$$

FIGURE 1

The Area Problem

The origins of calculus go back at least 2500 years to the ancient Greeks, who found areas using the "method of exhaustion." They knew how to find the area A of any polygon by dividing it into triangles as in Figure 1 and adding the areas of these triangles.

It is a much more difficult problem to find the area of a curved figure. The Greek method of exhaustion was to inscribe polygons in the figure and circumscribe polygons about the figure and then let the number of sides of the polygons increase. Figure 2 illustrates this process for the special case of a circle with inscribed regular polygons.

FIGURE 2

Let A_n be the area of the inscribed polygon with n sides. As n increases, it appears that A_n becomes closer and closer to the area of the circle. We say that the area of the circle is the *limit* of the areas of the inscribed polygons, and we write

$$A = \lim_{n \to \infty} A_n$$

The Greeks themselves did not use limits explicitly. However, by indirect reasoning, Eudoxus (fifth century BC) used exhaustion to prove the familiar formula for the area of a circle: $A = \pi r^2$.

We will use a similar idea in Chapter 5 to find areas of regions of the type shown in Figure 3. We will approximate the desired area A by areas of rectangles (as in Figure 4), let the width of the rectangles decrease, and then calculate A as the limit of these sums of areas of rectangles.

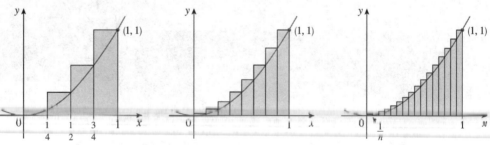

FIGURE 3   **FIGURE 4**

The area problem is the central problem in the branch of calculus called *integral calculus*. The techniques that we will develop in Chapter 5 for finding areas will also enable us to compute the volume of a solid, the length of a curve, the force of water against a dam, the mass and center of gravity of a rod, and the work done in pumping water out of a tank.

The Tangent Problem

Consider the problem of trying to find an equation of the tangent line t to a curve with equation $y = f(x)$ at a given point P. (We will give a precise definition of a tangent line in

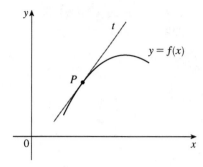

FIGURE 5

The tangent line at P

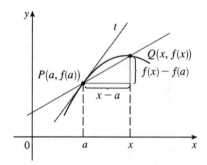

FIGURE 6

The secant line PQ

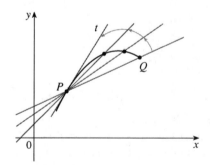

FIGURE 7

Secant lines approaching the tangent line

Chapter 2. For now you can think of it as a line that touches the curve at P as in Figure 5.) Since we know that the point P lies on the tangent line, we can find the equation of t if we know its slope m. The problem is that we need two points to compute the slope and we know only one point, P, on t. To get around the problem we first find an approximation to m by taking a nearby point Q on the curve and computing the slope m_{PQ} of the secant line PQ. From Figure 6 we see that

$$\boxed{1} \qquad m_{PQ} = \frac{f(x) - f(a)}{x - a}$$

Now imagine that Q moves along the curve toward P as in Figure 7. You can see that the secant line rotates and approaches the tangent line as its limiting position. This means that the slope m_{PQ} of the secant line becomes closer and closer to the slope m of the tangent line. We write

$$m = \lim_{Q \to P} m_{PQ}$$

and we say that m is the limit of m_{PQ} as Q approaches P along the curve. Since x approaches a as Q approaches P, we could also use Equation 1 to write

$$\boxed{2} \qquad m = \lim_{x \to a} \frac{f(x) - f(a)}{x - a}$$

Specific examples of this procedure will be given in Chapter 2.

The tangent problem has given rise to the branch of calculus called *differential calculus,* which was not invented until more than 2000 years after integral calculus. The main ideas behind differential calculus are due to the French mathematician Pierre Fermat (1601–1665) and were developed by the English mathematicians John Wallis (1616–1703), Isaac Barrow (1630–1677), and Isaac Newton (1642–1727) and the German mathematician Gottfried Leibniz (1646–1716).

The two branches of calculus and their chief problems, the area problem and the tangent problem, appear to be very different, but it turns out that there is a very close connection between them. The tangent problem and the area problem are inverse problems in a sense that will be described in Chapter 5.

■ Velocity

When we look at the speedometer of a car and read that the car is traveling at 48 km/h, what does that information indicate to us? We know that if the velocity remains constant, then after an hour we will have traveled 48 km. But if the velocity of the car varies, what does it mean to say that the velocity at a given instant is 48 km/h?

In order to analyze this question, let's examine the motion of a car that travels along a straight road and assume that we can measure the distance traveled by the car (in meters) at 1-second intervals as in the following chart:

t = Time elapsed (s)	0	2	4	6	8	10
d = Distance (m)	0	2	10	25	43	78

As a first step toward finding the velocity after 4 seconds have elapsed, we find the average velocity during the time interval $4 \leqslant t \leqslant 8$:

$$\text{average velocity} = \frac{\text{change in position}}{\text{time elapsed}}$$

$$= \frac{13 - 10}{8 - 4}$$

$$= 8.25 \text{ m/s}$$

Similarly, the average velocity in the time interval $4 \leqslant t \leqslant 6$ is

$$\text{average velocity} = \frac{25 - 10}{6 - 4} = 7.5 \text{ m/s}$$

We have the feeling that the velocity at the instant $t = 4$ can't be much different from the average velocity during a short time interval starting at $t = 4$. So let's imagine that the distance traveled has been measured at 0.2-second time intervals as in the following chart:

t	4.0	4.2	4.4	4.6	4.8	5.0
d	10.00	11.02	12.16	13.45	14.96	16.80

Then we can compute, for instance, the average velocity over the time interval $[4, 5]$:

$$\text{average velocity} = \frac{16.80 - 10.00}{5 - 4} = 6.8 \text{ m/s}$$

The results of such calculations are shown in the following chart:

Time interval	[4, 6]	[4, 5]	[4, 4.8]	[4, 4.6]	[4, 4.4]	[4, 4.2]
Average velocity (m/s)	7.5	6.8	6.2	5.75	5.4	5.1

The average velocities over successively smaller intervals appear to be getting closer to a number near 5, and so we expect that the velocity at exactly $t = 4$ is about **5 m/s**. In Chapter 2 we will define the instantaneous velocity of a moving object as the limiting value of the average velocities over smaller and smaller time intervals.

In Figure 8 we show a graphical representation of the motion of the car by plotting the distance traveled as a function of time. If we write $d = f(t)$, then $f(t)$ is the number of meters traveled after t seconds. The average velocity in the time interval $[4, t]$ is

$$\text{average velocity} = \frac{\text{change in position}}{\text{time elapsed}} = \frac{f(t) - f(4)}{t - 4}$$

which is the same as the slope of the secant line PQ in Figure 8. The velocity v when $t = 4$ is the limiting value of this average velocity as t approaches 4; that is,

$$v = \lim_{t \to 4} \frac{f(t) - f(4)}{t - 4}$$

and we recognize from Equation 2 that this is the same as the slope of the tangent line to the curve at P.

FIGURE 8

Thus, when we solve the tangent problem in differential calculus, we are also solving problems concerning velocities. The same techniques also enable us to solve problems involving rates of change in all of the natural and social sciences.

The Limit of a Sequence

In the fifth century BC the Greek philosopher Zeno of Elea posed four problems, now known as *Zeno's paradoxes,* that were intended to challenge some of the ideas concerning space and time that were held in his day. Zeno's second paradox concerns a race between the Greek hero Achilles and a tortoise that has been given a head start. Zeno argued, as follows, that Achilles could never pass the tortoise: Suppose that Achilles starts at position a_1 and the tortoise starts at position t_1. (See Figure 9.) When Achilles reaches the point $a_2 = t_1$, the tortoise is farther ahead at position t_2. When Achilles reaches $a_3 = t_2$, the tortoise is at t_3. This process continues indefinitely and so it appears that the tortoise will always be ahead! But this defies common sense.

FIGURE 9

Achilles a_1 a_2 a_3 a_4 a_5 $\cdots$

tortoise t_1 t_2 t_3 t_4 $\cdots$

One way of explaining this paradox is with the idea of a *sequence*. The successive positions of Achilles $(a_1, a_2, a_3, \ldots)$ or the successive positions of the tortoise $(t_1, t_2, t_3, \ldots)$ form what is known as a sequence.

In general, a sequence $\{a_n\}$ is a set of numbers written in a definite order. For instance, the sequence

$$\left\{1, \tfrac{1}{2}, \tfrac{1}{3}, \tfrac{1}{4}, \tfrac{1}{5}, \ldots\right\}$$

can be described by giving the following formula for the nth term:

$$a_n = \frac{1}{n}$$

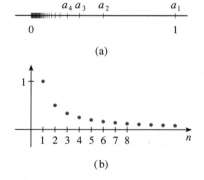

(a)

(b)

FIGURE 10

We can visualize this sequence by plotting its terms on a number line as in Figure 10(a) or by drawing its graph as in Figure 10(b). Observe from either picture that the terms of the sequence $a_n = 1/n$ are becoming closer and closer to 0 as n increases. In fact, we can find terms as small as we please by making n large enough. We say that the limit of the sequence is 0, and we indicate this by writing

$$\lim_{n \to \infty} \frac{1}{n} = 0$$

In general, the notation

$$\lim_{n \to \infty} a_n = L$$

is used if the terms a_n approach the number L as n becomes large. This means that the numbers a_n can be made as close as we like to the number L by taking n sufficiently large.

The concept of the limit of a sequence occurs whenever we use the decimal representation of a real number. For instance, if

$$a_1 = 3.1$$

$$a_2 = 3.14$$

$$a_3 = 3.141$$

$$a_4 = 3.1415$$

$$a_5 = 3.14159$$

$$a_6 = 3.141592$$

$$a_7 = 3.1415926$$

$$\vdots$$

then

$$\lim_{n \to \infty} a_n = \pi$$

The terms in this sequence are rational approximations to π.

Let's return to Zeno's paradox. The successive positions of Achilles and the tortoise form sequences $\{a_n\}$ and $\{t_n\}$, where $a_n < t_n$ for all n. It can be shown that both sequences have the same limit:

$$\lim_{n \to \infty} a_n = p = \lim_{n \to \infty} t_n$$

It is precisely at this point p that Achilles overtakes the tortoise.

The Sum of a Series

Another of Zeno's paradoxes, as passed on to us by Aristotle, is the following: "A man standing in a room cannot walk to the wall. In order to do so, he would first have to go half the distance, then half the remaining distance, and then again half of what still remains. This process can always be continued and can never be ended." (See Figure 11.)

FIGURE 11

Of course, we know that the man can actually reach the wall, so this suggests that perhaps the total distance can be expressed as the sum of infinitely many smaller distances as follows:

$$\boxed{3} \qquad 1 = \frac{1}{2} + \frac{1}{4} + \frac{1}{8} + \frac{1}{16} + \cdots + \frac{1}{2^n} + \cdots$$

Zeno was arguing that it doesn't make sense to add infinitely many numbers together. But there are other situations in which we implicitly use infinite sums. For instance, in decimal notation, the symbol $0.\overline{3} = 0.3333\ldots$ means

$$\frac{3}{10} + \frac{3}{100} + \frac{3}{1000} + \frac{3}{10,000} + \cdots$$

and so, in some sense, it must be true that

$$\frac{3}{10} + \frac{3}{100} + \frac{3}{1000} + \frac{3}{10,000} + \cdots = \frac{1}{3}$$

More generally, if d_n denotes the nth digit in the decimal representation of a number, then

$$0.d_1d_2d_3d_4\ldots = \frac{d_1}{10} + \frac{d_2}{10^2} + \frac{d_3}{10^3} + \cdots + \frac{d_n}{10^n} + \cdots$$

Therefore some infinite sums, or infinite series as they are called, have a meaning. But we must define carefully what the sum of an infinite series is.

Returning to the series in Equation 3, we denote by s_n the sum of the first n terms of the series. Thus

$$s_1 = \tfrac{1}{2} = 0.5$$

$$s_2 = \tfrac{1}{2} + \tfrac{1}{4} = 0.75$$

$$s_3 = \tfrac{1}{2} + \tfrac{1}{4} + \tfrac{1}{8} = 0.875$$

$$s_4 = \tfrac{1}{2} + \tfrac{1}{4} + \tfrac{1}{8} + \tfrac{1}{16} = 0.9375$$

$$s_5 = \tfrac{1}{2} + \tfrac{1}{4} + \tfrac{1}{8} + \tfrac{1}{16} + \tfrac{1}{32} = 0.96875$$

$$s_6 = \tfrac{1}{2} + \tfrac{1}{4} + \tfrac{1}{8} + \tfrac{1}{16} + \tfrac{1}{32} + \tfrac{1}{64} = 0.984375$$

$$s_7 = \tfrac{1}{2} + \tfrac{1}{4} + \tfrac{1}{8} + \tfrac{1}{16} + \tfrac{1}{32} + \tfrac{1}{64} + \tfrac{1}{128} = 0.9921875$$

$$\vdots$$

$$s_{10} = \tfrac{1}{2} + \tfrac{1}{4} + \cdots + \tfrac{1}{1024} \approx 0.99902344$$

$$\vdots$$

$$s_{16} = \frac{1}{2} + \frac{1}{4} + \cdots + \frac{1}{2^{16}} \approx 0.99998474$$

Observe that as we add more and more terms, the partial sums become closer and closer to 1. In fact, it can be shown that by taking n large enough (that is, by adding sufficiently many terms of the series), we can make the partial sum s_n as close as we please to the number 1. It therefore seems reasonable to say that the sum of the infinite series is 1 and to write

$$\frac{1}{2} + \frac{1}{4} + \frac{1}{8} + \cdots + \frac{1}{2^n} + \cdots = 1$$

In other words, the reason the sum of the series is 1 is that

$$\lim_{n \to \infty} s_n = 1$$

In Chapter 11 we will discuss these ideas further. We will then use Newton's idea of combining infinite series with differential and integral calculus.

Summary

We have seen that the concept of a limit arises in trying to find the area of a region, the slope of a tangent to a curve, the velocity of a car, or the sum of an infinite series. In each case the common theme is the calculation of a quantity as the limit of other, easily calculated quantities. It is this basic idea of a limit that sets calculus apart from other areas of mathematics. In fact, we could define calculus as the part of mathematics that deals with limits.

After Sir Isaac Newton invented his version of calculus, he used it to explain the motion of the planets around the sun. Today calculus is used in calculating the orbits of satellites and spacecraft, in predicting population sizes, in estimating how fast oil prices rise or fall, in forecasting weather, in measuring the cardiac output of the heart, in calculating life insurance premiums, and in a great variety of other areas. We will explore some of these uses of calculus in this book.

In order to convey a sense of the power of the subject, we end this preview with a list of some of the questions that you will be able to answer using calculus:

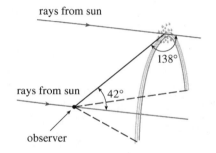

rays from sun

138°

rays from sun   42°

observer

FIGURE 12

1. How can we explain the fact, illustrated in Figure 12, that the angle of elevation from an observer up to the highest point in a rainbow is 42°? (See page 282.)

2. How can we explain the shapes of cans on supermarket shelves? (See page 337.)

3. Where is the best place to sit in a movie theater? (See page 456.)

4. How can we design a roller coaster for a smooth ride? (See page 184.)

5. How far away from an airport should a pilot start descent? (See page 208.)

6. How can we fit curves together to design shapes to represent letters on a laser printer? (See page 653.)

7. How can we estimate the number of workers that were needed to build the Great Pyramid of Khufu in ancient Egypt? (See page 451.)

8. Where should an infielder position himself to catch a baseball thrown by an outfielder and relay it to home plate? (See page 456.)

9. Does a ball thrown upward take longer to reach its maximum height or to fall back to its original height? (See page 604.)

10. How can we explain the fact that planets and satellites move in elliptical orbits? (See page 868.)

11. How can we distribute water flow among turbines at a hydroelectric station so as to maximize the total energy production? (See page 966.)

12. If a marble, a squash ball, a steel bar, and a lead pipe roll down a slope, which of them reaches the bottom first? (See page 1039.)

Functions and Models

Often a graph is the best way to represent a function because it conveys so much information at a glance. Shown is a graph of the ground acceleration created by the 2008 earthquake in Sichuan province in China. The hardest hit town was Beichuan, as pictured.

© Mark Ralston / AFP / Getty Images

Courtesy of the IRIS Consortium. www.iris.edu

The fundamental objects that we deal with in calculus are functions. This chapter prepares the way for calculus by discussing the basic ideas concerning functions, their graphs, and ways of transforming and combining them. We stress that a function can be represented in different ways: by an equation, in a table, by a graph, or in words. We look at the main types of functions that occur in calculus and describe the process of using these functions as mathematical models of real-world phenomena. We also discuss the use of graphing calculators and graphing software for computers.

1.1 Four Ways to Represent a Function

Functions arise whenever one quantity depends on another. Consider the following four situations.

A. The area A of a circle depends on the radius r of the circle. The rule that connects r and A is given by the equation $A = \pi r^2$. With each positive number r there is associated one value of A, and we say that A is a *function* of r.

B. The human population of the world P depends on the time t. The table gives estimates of the world population $P(t)$ at time t, for certain years. For instance,

$$P(1950) \approx 2{,}560{,}000{,}000$$

But for each value of the time t there is a corresponding value of P, and we say that P is a function of t.

C. The cost C of mailing a first-class letter depends on its weight w. Although there is no simple formula that connects w and C, the post office has a rule for determining C when w is known.

D. The vertical acceleration a of the ground as measured by a seismograph during an earthquake is a function of the elapsed time t. Figure 1 shows a graph generated by seismic activity during the Northridge earthquake that shook Los Angeles in 1994. For a given value of t, the graph provides a corresponding value of a.

Year	Population (millions)
1900	1650
1910	1750
1920	1860
1930	2070
1940	2300
1950	2560
1960	3040
1970	3710
1980	4450
1990	5280
2000	6080
2010	6870

Calif. Dept. of Mines and Geology

FIGURE 1
Vertical ground acceleration during the Northridge earthquake

Each of these examples describes a rule whereby, given a number (r, t, w, or t), another number (A, P, C, or a) is assigned. In each case we say that the second number is a function of the first number.

> A **function** f is a rule that assigns to each element x in a set D exactly one element, called $f(x)$, in a set E.

We usually consider functions for which the sets D and E are sets of real numbers. The set D is called the **domain** of the function. The number $f(x)$ is the **value of f at x** and is read "f of x." The **range** of f is the set of all possible values of $f(x)$ as x varies throughout the domain. A symbol that represents an arbitrary number in the *domain* of a function f is called an **independent variable**. A symbol that represents a number in the *range* of f is called a **dependent variable**. In Example A, for instance, r is the independent variable and A is the dependent variable.

FIGURE 2

Machine diagram for a function f

FIGURE 3

Arrow diagram for f

It's helpful to think of a function as a **machine** (see Figure 2). If x is in the domain of the function f, then when x enters the machine, it's accepted as an input and the machine produces an output $f(x)$ according to the rule of the function. Thus we can think of the domain as the set of all possible inputs and the range as the set of all possible outputs.

The preprogrammed functions in a calculator are good examples of a function as a machine. For example, the square root key on your calculator computes such a function. You press the key labeled $\sqrt{\ }$ (or $\sqrt{x}$) and enter the input x. If $x < 0$, then x is not in the domain of this function; that is, x is not an acceptable input, and the calculator will indicate an error. If $x \geqslant 0$, then an *approximation* to $\sqrt{x}$ will appear in the display. Thus the $\sqrt{x}$ key on your calculator is not quite the same as the exact mathematical function f defined by $f(x) = \sqrt{x}$.

Another way to picture a function is by an **arrow diagram** as in Figure 3. Each arrow connects an element of D to an element of E. The arrow indicates that $f(x)$ is associated with x, $f(a)$ is associated with a, and so on.

The most common method for visualizing a function is its graph. If f is a function with domain D, then its **graph** is the set of ordered pairs

$$\{(x, f(x)) \mid x \in D\}$$

(Notice that these are input-output pairs.) In other words, the graph of f consists of all points (x, y) in the coordinate plane such that $y = f(x)$ and x is in the domain of f.

The graph of a function f gives us a useful picture of the behavior or "life history" of a function. Since the y-coordinate of any point (x, y) on the graph is $y = f(x)$, we can read the value of $f(x)$ from the graph as being the height of the graph above the point x (see Figure 4). The graph of f also allows us to picture the domain of f on the x-axis and its range on the y-axis as in Figure 5.

FIGURE 4

FIGURE 5

FIGURE 6

The notation for intervals is given in Appendix A.

EXAMPLE 1 The graph of a function f is shown in Figure 6.
(a) Find the values of $f(1)$ and $f(5)$.
(b) What are the domain and range of f?

SOLUTION

(a) We see from Figure 6 that the point $(1, 3)$ lies on the graph of f, so the value of f at 1 is $f(1) = 3$. (In other words, the point on the graph that lies above $x = 1$ is 3 units above the x-axis.)

When $x = 5$, the graph lies about 0.7 unit below the x-axis, so we estimate that $f(5) \approx -0.7$.

(b) We see that $f(x)$ is defined when $0 \leqslant x \leqslant 7$, so the domain of f is the closed interval $[0, 7]$. Notice that f takes on all values from -2 to 4, so the range of f is

$$\{y \mid -2 \leqslant y \leqslant 4\} = [-2, 4]$$

FIGURE 7

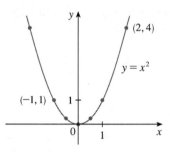

FIGURE 8

EXAMPLE 2 Sketch the graph and find the domain and range of each function.

(a) $f(x) = 2x - 1$ (b) $g(x) = x^2$

SOLUTION

(a) The equation of the graph is $y = 2x - 1$, and we recognize this as being the equation of a line with slope 2 and y-intercept -1. (Recall the slope-intercept form of the equation of a line: $y = mx + b$. See Appendix B.) This enables us to sketch a portion of the graph of f in Figure 7. The expression $2x - 1$ is defined for all real numbers, so the domain of f is the set of all real numbers, which we denote by $\mathbb{R}$. The graph shows that the range is also $\mathbb{R}$.

(b) Since $g(2) = 2^2 = 4$ and $g(-1) = (-1)^2 = 1$, we could plot the points $(2, 4)$ and $(-1, 1)$, together with a few other points on the graph, and join them to produce the graph (Figure 8). The equation of the graph is $y = x^2$, which represents a parabola (see Appendix C). The domain of g is $\mathbb{R}$. The range of g consists of all values of $g(x)$, that is, all numbers of the form x^2. But $x^2 \geqslant 0$ for all numbers x and any positive number y is a square. So the range of g is $\{y \mid y \geqslant 0\} = [0, \infty)$. This can also be seen from Figure 8.

EXAMPLE 3 If $f(x) = 2x^2 - 5x + 1$ and $h \neq 0$, evaluate $\dfrac{f(a + h) - f(a)}{h}$.

SOLUTION We first evaluate $f(a + h)$ by replacing x by $a + h$ in the expression for $f(x)$:

$$f(a + h) = 2(a + h)^2 - 5(a + h) + 1$$

$$= 2(a^2 + 2ah + h^2) - 5(a + h) + 1$$

$$= 2a^2 + 4ah + 2h^2 - 5a - 5h + 1$$

Then we substitute into the given expression and simplify:

$$\frac{f(a + h) - f(a)}{h} = \frac{(2a^2 + 4ah + 2h^2 - 5a - 5h + 1) - (2a^2 - 5a + 1)}{h}$$

$$= \frac{2a^2 + 4ah + 2h^2 - 5a - 5h + 1 - 2a^2 + 5a - 1}{h}$$

$$= \frac{4ah + 2h^2 - 5h}{h} = 4a + 2h - 5$$

The expression

$$\frac{f(a + h) - f(a)}{h}$$

in Example 3 is called a **difference quotient** and occurs frequently in calculus. As we will see in Chapter 2, it represents the average rate of change of $f(x)$ between $x = a$ and $x = a + h$.

Representations of Functions

There are four possible ways to represent a function:

- verbally   (by a description in words)
- numerically   (by a table of values)
- visually   (by a graph)
- algebraically   (by an explicit formula)

If a single function can be represented in all four ways, it's often useful to go from one representation to another to gain additional insight into the function. (In Example 2, for instance, we started with algebraic formulas and then obtained the graphs.) But certain functions are described more naturally by one method than by another. With this in mind, let's reexamine the four situations that we considered at the beginning of this section.

A. The most useful representation of the area of a circle as a function of its radius is probably the algebraic formula $A(r) = \pi r^2$, though it is possible to compile a table of values or to sketch a graph (half a parabola). Because a circle has to have a positive radius, the domain is $\{r \mid r > 0\} = (0, \infty)$, and the range is also $(0, \infty)$.

B. We are given a description of the function in words: $P(t)$ is the human population of the world at time t. Let's measure t so that $t = 0$ corresponds to the year 1900. The table of values of world population provides a convenient representation of this function. If we plot these values, we get the graph (called a *scatter plot*) in Figure 9. It too is a useful representation; the graph allows us to absorb all the data at once. What about a formula? Of course, it's impossible to devise an explicit formula that gives the exact human population $P(t)$ at any time t. But it is possible to find an expression for a function that *approximates* $P(t)$. In fact, using methods explained in Section 1.2, we obtain the approximation

$$P(t) \approx f(t) = (1.43653 \times 10^9) \cdot (1.01395)^t$$

Figure 10 shows that it is a reasonably good "fit." The function f is called a *mathematical model* for population growth. In other words, it is a function with an explicit formula that approximates the behavior of our given function. We will see, however, that the ideas of calculus can be applied to a table of values; an explicit formula is not necessary.

t	Population (millions)
0	1650
10	1750
20	1860
30	2070
40	2300
50	2560
60	3040
70	3710
80	4450
90	5280
100	6080
110	6870

FIGURE 9

A function defined by a table of values is called a *tabular* function.

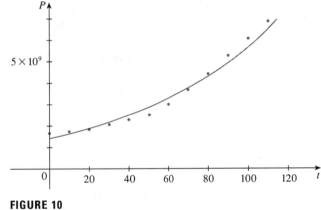

FIGURE 10

The function P is typical of the functions that arise whenever we attempt to apply calculus to the real world. We start with a verbal description of a function. Then we may be able to construct a table of values of the function, perhaps from instrument readings in a scientific experiment. Even though we don't have complete knowledge of the values of the function, we will see throughout the book that it is still possible to perform the operations of calculus on such a function.

C. Again the function is described in words: $C(w)$ is the cost of mailing a first-class letter with weight w. The rule that the Hong Kong Post Office used as of 2010 is as follows: The cost is $1.40 for up to 30 g, $2.20 for weights greater than 30 g and at most 50 g, and so on. The table of values shown in the margin is the most convenient representation for this function, though it is possible to sketch a graph (see Example 10).

D. The graph shown in Figure 1 is the most natural representation of the vertical acceleration function $a(t)$. It's true that a table of values could be compiled, and it is even possible to devise an approximate formula. But everything a geologist needs to know—amplitudes and patterns—can be seen easily from the graph. (The same is true for the patterns seen in electrocardiograms of heart patients and polygraphs for lie-detection.)

w (grams)	$C(w)$ (HK dollars)
$0 < w \le 30$	1.40
$30 < w \le 50$	2.20
$50 < w \le 100$	3.00
$100 < w \le 150$	3.70
$150 < w \le 200$	4.00
⋮	⋮

FIGURE 11

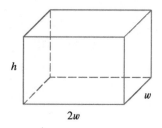

FIGURE 12

In setting up applied functions as in Example 5, it may be useful to review the principles of problem solving as discussed on page 75, particularly *Step 1: Understand the Problem.*

Domain Convention

If a function is given by a formula and the domain is not stated explicitly, the convention is that the domain is the set of all numbers for which the formula makes sense and defines a real number.

In the next example we sketch the graph of a function that is defined verbally.

EXAMPLE 4 When you turn on a hot-water faucet, the temperature T of the water depends on how long the water has been running. Draw a rough graph of T as a function of the time t that has elapsed since the faucet was turned on.

SOLUTION The initial temperature of the running water is close to room temperature because the water has been sitting in the pipes. When the water from the hot-water tank starts flowing from the faucet, T increases quickly. In the next phase, T is constant at the temperature of the heated water in the tank. When the tank is drained, T decreases to the temperature of the water supply. This enables us to make the rough sketch of T as a function of t in Figure 11.

In the following example we start with a verbal description of a function in a physical situation and obtain an explicit algebraic formula. The ability to do this is a useful skill in solving calculus problems that ask for the maximum or minimum values of quantities.

V EXAMPLE 5 A rectangular storage container with an open top has a volume of 10 m^3. The length of its base is twice its width. Material for the base costs \$10 per square meter; material for the sides costs \$6 per square meter. Express the cost of materials as a function of the width of the base.

SOLUTION We draw a diagram as in Figure 12 and introduce notation by letting w and $2w$ be the width and length of the base, respectively, and h be the height.

The area of the base is $(2w)w = 2w^2$, so the cost, in dollars, of the material for the base is $10(2w^2)$. Two of the sides have area wh and the other two have area $2wh$, so the cost of the material for the sides is $6[2(wh) + 2(2wh)]$. The total cost is therefore

$$C = 10(2w^2) + 6[2(wh) + 2(2wh)] = 20w^2 + 36wh$$

To express C as a function of w alone, we need to eliminate h and we do so by using the fact that the volume is 10 m^3. Thus

$$w(2w)h = 10$$

which gives

$$h = \frac{10}{2w^2} = \frac{5}{w^2}$$

Substituting this into the expression for C, we have

$$C = 20w^2 + 36w\left(\frac{5}{w^2}\right) = 20w^2 + \frac{180}{w}$$

Therefore the equation

$$C(w) = 20w^2 + \frac{180}{w} \qquad w > 0$$

expresses C as a function of w.

EXAMPLE 6 Find the domain of each function.

(a) $f(x) = \sqrt{x + 2}$
(b) $g(x) = \dfrac{1}{x^2 - x}$

SOLUTION

(a) Because the square root of a negative number is not defined (as a real number), the domain of f consists of all values of x such that $x + 2 \geq 0$. This is equivalent to $x \geq -2$, so the domain is the interval $[-2, \infty)$.

(b) Since

$$g(x) = \frac{1}{x^2 - x} = \frac{1}{x(x-1)}$$

and division by 0 is not allowed, we see that $g(x)$ is not defined when $x = 0$ or $x = 1$. Thus the domain of g is

$$\{x \mid x \neq 0, x \neq 1\}$$

which could also be written in interval notation as

$$(-\infty, 0) \cup (0, 1) \cup (1, \infty)$$

The graph of a function is a curve in the xy-plane. But the question arises: Which curves in the xy-plane are graphs of functions? This is answered by the following test.

> **The Vertical Line Test** A curve in the xy-plane is the graph of a function of x if and only if no vertical line intersects the curve more than once.

The reason for the truth of the Vertical Line Test can be seen in Figure 13. If each vertical line $x = a$ intersects a curve only once, at (a, b), then exactly one functional value is defined by $f(a) = b$. But if a line $x = a$ intersects the curve twice, at (a, b) and (a, c), then the curve can't represent a function because a function can't assign two different values to a.

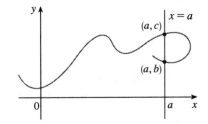

FIGURE 13

For example, the parabola $x = y^2 - 2$ shown in Figure 14(a) is not the graph of a function of x because, as you can see, there are vertical lines that intersect the parabola twice. The parabola, however, does contain the graphs of *two* functions of x. Notice that the equation $x = y^2 - 2$ implies $y^2 = x + 2$, so $y = \pm\sqrt{x + 2}$. Thus the upper and lower halves of the parabola are the graphs of the functions $f(x) = \sqrt{x + 2}$ [from Example 6(a)] and $g(x) = -\sqrt{x + 2}$. [See Figures 14(b) and (c).] We observe that if we reverse the roles of x and y, then the equation $x = h(y) = y^2 - 2$ *does* define x as a function of y (with y as the independent variable and x as the dependent variable) and the parabola now appears as the graph of the function h.

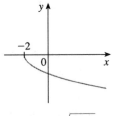

FIGURE 14   (a) $x = y^2 - 2$ (b) $y = \sqrt{x+2}$ (c) $y = -\sqrt{x+2}$

Piecewise Defined Functions

The functions in the following four examples are defined by different formulas in different parts of their domains. Such functions are called **piecewise defined functions**.

V   EXAMPLE 7 A function f is defined by

$$f(x) = \begin{cases} 1 - x & \text{if } x \leq -1 \\ x^2 & \text{if } x > -1 \end{cases}$$

Evaluate $f(-2), f(-1),$ and $f(0)$ and sketch the graph.

SOLUTION Remember that a function is a rule. For this particular function the rule is the following: First look at the value of the input x. If it happens that $x \leq -1$, then the value of $f(x)$ is $1 - x$. On the other hand, if $x > -1$, then the value of $f(x)$ is x^2.

$$\text{Since } -2 \leq -1, \text{ we have } f(-2) = 1 - (-2) = 3.$$

$$\text{Since } -1 \leq -1, \text{ we have } f(-1) = 1 - (-1) = 2.$$

$$\text{Since } 0 > -1, \text{ we have } f(0) = 0^2 = 0.$$

How do we draw the graph of f? We observe that if $x \leq -1$, then $f(x) = 1 - x$, so the part of the graph of f that lies to the left of the vertical line $x = -1$ must coincide with the line $y = 1 - x$, which has slope -1 and y-intercept 1. If $x > -1$, then $f(x) = x^2$, so the part of the graph of f that lies to the right of the line $x = -1$ must coincide with the graph of $y = x^2$, which is a parabola. This enables us to sketch the graph in Figure 15. The solid dot indicates that the point $(-1, 2)$ is included on the graph; the open dot indicates that the point $(-1, 1)$ is excluded from the graph. ▪

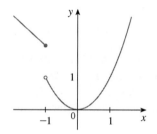

FIGURE 15

The next example of a piecewise defined function is the absolute value function. Recall that the **absolute value** of a number a, denoted by $|a|$, is the distance from a to 0 on the real number line. Distances are always positive or 0, so we have

$$|a| \geq 0 \qquad \text{for every number } a$$

For example,

$$|3| = 3 \qquad |-3| = 3 \qquad |0| = 0 \qquad |\sqrt{2} - 1| = \sqrt{2} - 1 \qquad |3 - \pi| = \pi - 3$$

In general, we have

$$\boxed{\begin{aligned} |a| &= a \qquad \text{if } a \geq 0 \\ |a| &= -a \quad \text{if } a < 0 \end{aligned}}$$

(Remember that if a is negative, then $-a$ is positive.)

For a more extensive review of absolute values, see Appendix A.

EXAMPLE 8 Sketch the graph of the absolute value function $f(x) = |x|$.

SOLUTION From the preceding discussion we know that

$$|x| = \begin{cases} x & \text{if } x \geq 0 \\ -x & \text{if } x < 0 \end{cases}$$

Using the same method as in Example 7, we see that the graph of f coincides with the line $y = x$ to the right of the y-axis and coincides with the line $y = -x$ to the left of the y-axis (see Figure 16). ▪

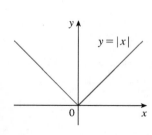

FIGURE 16

EXAMPLE 9 Find a formula for the function f graphed in Figure 17.

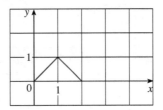

FIGURE 17

SOLUTION The line through $(0, 0)$ and $(1, 1)$ has slope $m = 1$ and y-intercept $b = 0$, so its equation is $y = x$. Thus, for the part of the graph of f that joins $(0, 0)$ to $(1, 1)$, we have

$$f(x) = x \qquad \text{if } 0 \leqslant x \leqslant 1$$

Point-slope form of the equation of a line:
$$y - y_1 = m(x - x_1)$$
See Appendix B.

The line through $(1, 1)$ and $(2, 0)$ has slope $m = -1$, so its point-slope form is

$$y - 0 = (-1)(x - 2) \qquad \text{or} \qquad y = 2 - x$$

So we have
$$f(x) = 2 - x \qquad \text{if } 1 < x \leqslant 2$$

We also see that the graph of f coincides with the x-axis for $x > 2$. Putting this information together, we have the following three-piece formula for f:

$$f(x) = \begin{cases} x & \text{if } 0 \leqslant x \leqslant 1 \\ 2 - x & \text{if } 1 < x \leqslant 2 \\ 0 & \text{if } x > 2 \end{cases}$$

EXAMPLE 10 In Example C at the beginning of this section we considered the cost $C(w)$ of mailing a first-class letter in Hong Kong with weight w. In effect, this is a piecewise defined function because, from the table of values on page 13, we have

$$C(w) = \begin{cases} 1.40 & \text{if } 0 < w \leqslant 30 \\ 2.20 & \text{if } 30 < w \leqslant 50 \\ 3.00 & \text{if } 50 < w \leqslant 100 \\ 3.70 & \text{if } 100 < w \leqslant 150 \\ 4.00 & \text{if } 150 < w \leqslant 200 \end{cases}$$

FIGURE 18

The graph is shown in Figure 18. You can see why functions similar to this one are called **step functions**—they jump from one value to the next. Such functions will be studied in Chapter 2.

■ **Symmetry**

If a function f satisfies $f(-x) = f(x)$ for every number x in its domain, then f is called an **even function**. For instance, the function $f(x) = x^2$ is even because

$$f(-x) = (-x)^2 = x^2 = f(x)$$

The geometric significance of an even function is that its graph is symmetric with respect to the y-axis (see Figure 19). This means that if we have plotted the graph of f for $x \geqslant 0$, we obtain the entire graph simply by reflecting this portion about the y-axis.

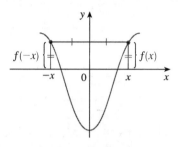

FIGURE 19 An even function   **FIGURE 20** An odd function

If f satisfies $f(-x) = -f(x)$ for every number x in its domain, then f is called an **odd function**. For example, the function $f(x) = x^3$ is odd because

$$f(-x) = (-x)^3 = -x^3 = -f(x)$$

The graph of an odd function is symmetric about the origin (see Figure 20). If we already have the graph of f for $x \geqslant 0$, we can obtain the entire graph by rotating this portion through $180°$ about the origin.

V **EXAMPLE 11** Determine whether each of the following functions is even, odd, or neither even nor odd.

(a) $f(x) = x^5 + x$ (b) $g(x) = 1 - x^4$ (c) $h(x) = 2x - x^2$

SOLUTION

(a)
$$f(-x) = (-x)^5 + (-x) = (-1)^5 x^5 + (-x)$$
$$= -x^5 - x = -(x^5 + x)$$
$$= -f(x)$$

Therefore f is an odd function.

(b)
$$g(-x) = 1 - (-x)^4 = 1 - x^4 = g(x)$$

So g is even.

(c)
$$h(-x) = 2(-x) - (-x)^2 = -2x - x^2$$

Since $h(-x) \neq h(x)$ and $h(-x) \neq -h(x)$, we conclude that h is neither even nor odd.

The graphs of the functions in Example 11 are shown in Figure 21. Notice that the graph of h is symmetric neither about the y-axis nor about the origin.

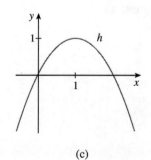

FIGURE 21   (a)   (b)   (c)

FIGURE 22

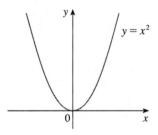

FIGURE 23

▨ Increasing and Decreasing Functions

The graph shown in Figure 22 rises from A to B, falls from B to C, and rises again from C to D. The function f is said to be increasing on the interval $[a, b]$, decreasing on $[b, c]$, and increasing again on $[c, d]$. Notice that if x_1 and x_2 are any two numbers between a and b with $x_1 < x_2$, then $f(x_1) < f(x_2)$. We use this as the defining property of an increasing function.

A function f is called **increasing** on an interval I if

$$f(x_1) < f(x_2) \qquad \text{whenever } x_1 < x_2 \text{ in } I$$

It is called **decreasing** on I if

$$f(x_1) > f(x_2) \qquad \text{whenever } x_1 < x_2 \text{ in } I$$

In the definition of an increasing function it is important to realize that the inequality $f(x_1) < f(x_2)$ must be satisfied for *every* pair of numbers x_1 and x_2 in I with $x_1 < x_2$.

You can see from Figure 23 that the function $f(x) = x^2$ is decreasing on the interval $(-\infty, 0]$ and increasing on the interval $[0, \infty)$.

1.1 Exercises

1. If $f(x) = x + \sqrt{2 - x}$ and $g(u) = u + \sqrt{2 - u}$, is it true that $f = g$?

2. If

$$f(x) = \frac{x^2 - x}{x - 1} \qquad \text{and} \qquad g(x) = x$$

is it true that $f = g$?

3. The graph of a function f is given.
(a) State the value of $f(1)$.
(b) Estimate the value of $f(-1)$.
(c) For what values of x is $f(x) = 1$?
(d) Estimate the value of x such that $f(x) = 0$.
(e) State the domain and range of f.
(f) On what interval is f increasing?

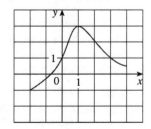

4. The graphs of f and g are given.
(a) State the values of $f(-4)$ and $g(3)$.
(b) For what values of x is $f(x) = g(x)$?

(c) Estimate the solution of the equation $f(x) = -1$.
(d) On what interval is f decreasing?
(e) State the domain and range of f.
(f) State the domain and range of g.

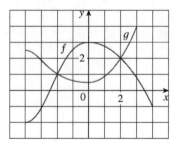

5. Figure 1 was recorded by an instrument operated by the California Department of Mines and Geology at the University Hospital of the University of Southern California in Los Angeles. Use it to estimate the range of the vertical ground acceleration function at USC during the Northridge earthquake.

6. In this section we discussed examples of ordinary, everyday functions: Population is a function of time, postage cost is a function of weight, water temperature is a function of time. Give three other examples of functions from everyday life that are described verbally. What can you say about the domain and range of each of your functions? If possible, sketch a rough graph of each function.

7–10 Determine whether the curve is the graph of a function of x. If it is, state the domain and range of the function.

7.

8.

9.

10.

11. The graph shown gives the weight of a certain person as a function of age. Describe in words how this person's weight varies over time. What do you think happened when this person was 30 years old?

12. The graph shows the height of the water in a bathtub as a function of time. Give a verbal description of what you think happened.

13. You put some ice cubes in a glass, fill the glass with cold water, and then let the glass sit on a table. Describe how the temperature of the water changes as time passes. Then sketch a rough graph of the temperature of the water as a function of the elapsed time.

14. Three runners compete in a 100-meter race. The graph depicts the distance run as a function of time for each runner. Describe

in words what the graph tells you about this race. Who won the race? Did each runner finish the race?

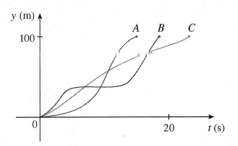

15. The graph shows the power consumption for a day in September in San Francisco. (P is measured in megawatts; t is measured in hours starting at midnight.)
(a) What was the power consumption at 6 AM? At 6 PM?
(b) When was the power consumption the lowest? When was it the highest? Do these times seem reasonable?

Pacific Gas & Electric

16. Sketch a rough graph of the number of hours of daylight as a function of the time of year.

17. Sketch a rough graph of the outdoor temperature as a function of time during a typical spring day.

18. Sketch a rough graph of the market value of a new car as a function of time for a period of 20 years. Assume the car is well maintained.

19. Sketch the graph of the amount of a particular brand of coffee sold by a store as a function of the price of the coffee.

20. You place a frozen pie in an oven and bake it for an hour. Then you take it out and let it cool before eating it. Describe how the temperature of the pie changes as time passes. Then sketch a rough graph of the temperature of the pie as a function of time.

21. A homeowner mows the lawn every Wednesday afternoon. Sketch a rough graph of the height of the grass as a function of time over the course of a four-week period.

22. An airplane takes off from an airport and lands an hour later at another airport, 400 km away. If t represents the time in minutes since the plane has left the terminal building, let $x(t)$ be

the horizontal distance traveled and $y(t)$ be the altitude of the plane.
(a) Sketch a possible graph of $x(t)$.
(b) Sketch a possible graph of $y(t)$.
(c) Sketch a possible graph of the ground speed.
(d) Sketch a possible graph of the vertical velocity.

23. The number N (in millions) of US cellular phone subscribers is shown in the table. (Midyear estimates are given.)

t	1996	1998	2000	2002	2004	2006
N	44	69	109	141	182	233

(a) Use the data to sketch a rough graph of N as a function of t.
(b) Use your graph to estimate the number of cell-phone subscribers at midyear in 2001 and 2005.

24. Temperature readings T (in °C) were recorded every three hours from midnight to 3:00 PM in Montréal on July 13, 2004. The time t was measured in hours from midnight.

t	0	3	6	9	12	15
T	21.5	19.8	20.0	22.2	24.8	25.8

(a) Use the readings to sketch a rough graph of T as a function of t.
(b) Use your graph to estimate the temperature at 11:00 AM.

25. If $f(x) = 3x^2 - x + 2$, find $f(2)$, $f(-2)$, $f(a)$, $f(-a)$, $f(a + 1)$, $2f(a)$, $f(2a)$, $f(a^2)$, $[f(a)]^2$, and $f(a + h)$.

26. A spherical balloon with radius r inches has volume $V(r) = \frac{4}{3}\pi r^3$. Find a function that represents the amount of air required to inflate the balloon from a radius of r inches to a radius of $r + 1$ inches.

27–30 Evaluate the difference quotient for the given function. Simplify your answer.

27. $f(x) = 4 + 3x - x^2$, $\quad \dfrac{f(3 + h) - f(3)}{h}$

28. $f(x) = x^3$, $\quad \dfrac{f(a + h) - f(a)}{h}$

29. $f(x) = \dfrac{1}{x}$, $\quad \dfrac{f(x) - f(a)}{x - a}$

30. $f(x) = \dfrac{x + 3}{x + 1}$, $\quad \dfrac{f(x) - f(1)}{x - 1}$

31–37 Find the domain of the function.

31. $f(x) = \dfrac{x + 4}{x^2 - 9}$

32. $f(x) = \dfrac{2x^3 - 5}{x^2 + x - 6}$

33. $f(t) = \sqrt[3]{2t - 1}$

34. $g(t) = \sqrt{3 - t} - \sqrt{2 + t}$

35. $h(x) = \dfrac{1}{\sqrt[4]{x^2 - 5x}}$

36. $f(u) = \dfrac{u + 1}{1 + \dfrac{1}{u + 1}}$

37. $F(p) = \sqrt{2 - \sqrt{p}}$

38. Find the domain and range and sketch the graph of the function $h(x) = \sqrt{4 - x^2}$.

39–50 Find the domain and sketch the graph of the function.

39. $f(x) = 2 - 0.4x$

40. $F(x) = x^2 - 2x + 1$

41. $f(t) = 2t + t^2$

42. $H(t) = \dfrac{4 - t^2}{2 - t}$

43. $g(x) = \sqrt{x - 5}$

44. $F(x) = |2x + 1|$

45. $G(x) = \dfrac{3x + |x|}{x}$

46. $g(x) = |x| - x$

47. $f(x) = \begin{cases} x + 2 & \text{if } x < 0 \\ 1 - x & \text{if } x \geq 0 \end{cases}$

48. $f(x) = \begin{cases} 3 - \frac{1}{2}x & \text{if } x \leq 2 \\ 2x - 5 & \text{if } x > 2 \end{cases}$

49. $f(x) = \begin{cases} x + 2 & \text{if } x \leq -1 \\ x^2 & \text{if } x > -1 \end{cases}$

50. $f(x) = \begin{cases} x + 9 & \text{if } x < -3 \\ -2x & \text{if } |x| \leq 3 \\ -6 & \text{if } x > 3 \end{cases}$

51–56 Find an expression for the function whose graph is the given curve.

51. The line segment joining the points $(1, -3)$ and $(5, 7)$

52. The line segment joining the points $(-5, 10)$ and $(7, -10)$

53. The bottom half of the parabola $x + (y - 1)^2 = 0$

54. The top half of the circle $x^2 + (y - 2)^2 = 4$

55.

56.
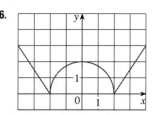

57–61 Find a formula for the described function and state its domain.

57. A rectangle has perimeter 20 m. Express the area of the rectangle as a function of the length of one of its sides.

58. A rectangle has area 16 m². Express the perimeter of the rectangle as a function of the length of one of its sides.

59. Express the area of an equilateral triangle as a function of the length of a side.

60. Express the surface area of a cube as a function of its volume.

61. An open rectangular box with volume 2 m³ has a square base. Express the surface area of the box as a function of the length of a side of the base.

62. A Norman window has the shape of a rectangle surmounted by a semicircle. If the perimeter of the window is 10 m, express the area A of the window as a function of the width x of the window.

63. A box with an open top is to be constructed from a rectangular piece of cardboard with dimensions 12 cm by 20 cm by cutting out equal squares of side x at each corner and then folding up the sides as in the figure. Express the volume V of the box as a function of x.

64. A cell phone plan has a basic charge of $35 a month. The plan includes 400 free minutes and charges 10 cents for each additional minute of usage. Write the monthly cost C as a function of the number x of minutes used and graph C as a function of x for $0 \le x \le 600$.

65. In a certain province the maximum speed permitted on freeways is 100 km/h and the minimum speed is 50 km/h. The fine for violating these limits is $10 for every kilometer per hour above the maximum speed or below the minimum speed. Express the amount of the fine F as a function of the driving speed x and graph $F(x)$ for $0 \le x \le 180$.

66. An electricity company charges its customers a base rate of $10 a month, plus 6 cents per kilowatt-hour (kWh) for the first 1200 kWh and 7 cents per kWh for all usage over 1200 kWh. Express the monthly cost E as a function of the amount x of electricity used. Then graph the function E for $0 \le x \le 2000$.

67. In a certain country, income tax is assessed as follows. There is no tax on income up to $10,000. Any income over $10,000 is taxed at a rate of 10%, up to an income of $20,000. Any income over $20,000 is taxed at 15%.
(a) Sketch the graph of the tax rate R as a function of the income I.
(b) How much tax is assessed on an income of $14,000? On $26,000?
(c) Sketch the graph of the total assessed tax T as a function of the income I.

68. The functions in Example 10 and Exercise 67 are called *step functions* because their graphs look like stairs. Give two other examples of step functions that arise in everyday life.

69–70 Graphs of f and g are shown. Decide whether each function is even, odd, or neither. Explain your reasoning.

69.

70.

71. (a) If the point $(5, 3)$ is on the graph of an even function, what other point must also be on the graph?
(b) If the point $(5, 3)$ is on the graph of an odd function, what other point must also be on the graph?

72. A function f has domain $[-5, 5]$ and a portion of its graph is shown.
(a) Complete the graph of f if it is known that f is even.
(b) Complete the graph of f if it is known that f is odd.

73–78 Determine whether f is even, odd, or neither. If you have a graphing calculator, use it to check your answer visually.

73. $f(x) = \dfrac{x}{x^2 + 1}$

74. $f(x) = \dfrac{x^2}{x^4 + 1}$

75. $f(x) = \dfrac{x}{x + 1}$

76. $f(x) = x|x|$

77. $f(x) = 1 + 3x^2 - x^4$

78. $f(x) = 1 + 3x^3 - x^5$

79. If f and g are both even functions, is $f + g$ even? If f and g are both odd functions, is $f + g$ odd? What if f is even and g is odd? Justify your answers.

80. If f and g are both even functions, is the product fg even? If f and g are both odd functions, is fg odd? What if f is even and g is odd? Justify your answers.

1.2 Mathematical Models: A Catalog of Essential Functions

A **mathematical model** is a mathematical description (often by means of a function or an equation) of a real-world phenomenon such as the size of a population, the demand for a product, the speed of a falling object, the concentration of a product in a chemical reaction, the life expectancy of a person at birth, or the cost of emission reductions. The purpose of the model is to understand the phenomenon and perhaps to make predictions about future behavior.

Figure 1 illustrates the process of mathematical modeling. Given a real-world problem, our first task is to formulate a mathematical model by identifying and naming the independent and dependent variables and making assumptions that simplify the phenomenon enough to make it mathematically tractable. We use our knowledge of the physical situation and our mathematical skills to obtain equations that relate the variables. In situations where there is no physical law to guide us, we may need to collect data (either from a library or the Internet or by conducting our own experiments) and examine the data in the form of a table in order to discern patterns. From this numerical representation of a function we may wish to obtain a graphical representation by plotting the data. The graph might even suggest a suitable algebraic formula in some cases.

FIGURE 1 The modeling process

The second stage is to apply the mathematics that we know (such as the calculus that will be developed throughout this book) to the mathematical model that we have formulated in order to derive mathematical conclusions. Then, in the third stage, we take those mathematical conclusions and interpret them as information about the original real-world phenomenon by way of offering explanations or making predictions. The final step is to test our predictions by checking against new real data. If the predictions don't compare well with reality, we need to refine our model or to formulate a new model and start the cycle again.

A mathematical model is never a completely accurate representation of a physical situation—it is an *idealization*. A good model simplifies reality enough to permit mathematical calculations but is accurate enough to provide valuable conclusions. It is important to realize the limitations of the model. In the end, Mother Nature has the final say.

There are many different types of functions that can be used to model relationships observed in the real world. In what follows, we discuss the behavior and graphs of these functions and give examples of situations appropriately modeled by such functions.

Linear Models

The coordinate geometry of lines is reviewed in Appendix B.

When we say that y is a **linear function** of x, we mean that the graph of the function is a line, so we can use the slope-intercept form of the equation of a line to write a formula for

the function as

$$y = f(x) = mx + b$$

where m is the slope of the line and b is the y-intercept.

A characteristic feature of linear functions is that they grow at a constant rate. For instance, Figure 2 shows a graph of the linear function $f(x) = 3x - 2$ and a table of sample values. Notice that whenever x increases by 0.1, the value of $f(x)$ increases by 0.3. So $f(x)$ increases three times as fast as x. Thus the slope of the graph $y = 3x - 2$, namely 3, can be interpreted as the rate of change of y with respect to x.

x	$f(x) = 3x - 2$
1.0	1.0
1.1	1.3
1.2	1.6
1.3	1.9
1.4	2.2
1.5	2.5

FIGURE 2

V EXAMPLE 1

(a) As dry air moves upward, it expands and cools. If the ground temperature is 20°C and the temperature at a height of 1 km is 10°C, express the temperature T (in °C) as a function of the height h (in kilometers), assuming that a linear model is appropriate.

(b) Draw the graph of the function in part (a). What does the slope represent?

(c) What is the temperature at a height of 2.5 km?

SOLUTION

(a) Because we are assuming that T is a linear function of h, we can write

$$T = mh + b$$

We are given that $T = 20$ when $h = 0$, so

$$20 = m \cdot 0 + b = b$$

In other words, the y-intercept is $b = 20$.

We are also given that $T = 10$ when $h = 1$, so

$$10 = m \cdot 1 + 20$$

The slope of the line is therefore $m = 10 - 20 = -10$ and the required linear function is

$$T = -10h + 20$$

(b) The graph is sketched in Figure 3. The slope is $m = -10°C/km$, and this represents the rate of change of temperature with respect to height.

(c) At a height of $h = 2.5$ km, the temperature is

$$T = -10(2.5) + 20 = -5°C$$

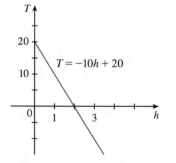

FIGURE 3

If there is no physical law or principle to help us formulate a model, we construct an **empirical model**, which is based entirely on collected data. We seek a curve that "fits" the data in the sense that it captures the basic trend of the data points.

V **EXAMPLE 2** Table 1 lists the average carbon dioxide level in the atmosphere, measured in parts per million at Mauna Loa Observatory from 1980 to 2008. Use the data in Table 1 to find a model for the carbon dioxide level.

SOLUTION We use the data in Table 1 to make the scatter plot in Figure 4, where t represents time (in years) and C represents the CO_2 level (in parts per million, ppm).

TABLE 1

Year	CO_2 level (in ppm)	Year	CO_2 level (in ppm)
1980	338.7	1996	362.4
1982	341.2	1998	366.5
1984	344.4	2000	369.4
1986	347.2	2002	373.2
1988	351.5	2004	377.5
1990	354.2	2006	381.9
1992	356.3	2008	385.6
1994	358.6		

FIGURE 4 Scatter plot for the average CO_2 level

Notice that the data points appear to lie close to a straight line, so it's natural to choose a linear model in this case. But there are many possible lines that approximate these data points, so which one should we use? One possibility is the line that passes through the first and last data points. The slope of this line is

$$\frac{385.6 - 338.7}{2008 - 1980} = \frac{46.9}{28} = 1.675$$

and its equation is

$$C - 338.7 = 1.675(t - 1980)$$

or

1 $$C = 1.675t - 2977.8$$

Equation 1 gives one possible linear model for the carbon dioxide level; it is graphed in Figure 5.

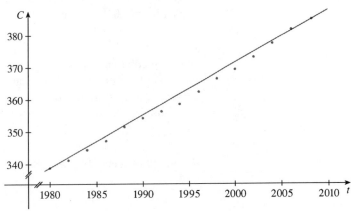

FIGURE 5
Linear model through
first and last data points

A computer or graphing calculator finds the regression line by the method of **least squares**, which is to minimize the sum of the squares of the vertical distances between the data points and the line. The details are explained in Section 14.7.

Notice that our model gives values higher than most of the actual CO_2 levels. A better linear model is obtained by a procedure from statistics called *linear regression*. If we use a graphing calculator, we enter the data from Table 1 into the data editor and choose the linear regression command. (With Maple we use the fit[leastsquare] command in the stats package; with Mathematica we use the Fit command.) The machine gives the slope and y-intercept of the regression line as

$$m = 1.65429 \qquad b = -2938.07$$

So our least squares model for the CO_2 level is

$$\boxed{2} \qquad\qquad C = 1.65429t - 2938.07$$

In Figure 6 we graph the regression line as well as the data points. Comparing with Figure 5, we see that it gives a better fit than our previous linear model.

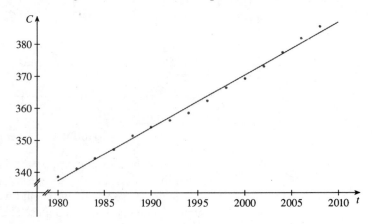

FIGURE 6
The regression line

V EXAMPLE 3   Use the linear model given by Equation 2 to estimate the average CO_2 level for 1987 and to predict the level for the year 2015. According to this model, when will the CO_2 level exceed 420 parts per million?

SOLUTION   Using Equation 2 with $t = 1987$, we estimate that the average CO_2 level in 1987 was

$$C(1987) = (1.65429)(1987) - 2938.07 \approx 349.00$$

This is an example of *interpolation* because we have estimated a value *between* observed values. (In fact, the Mauna Loa Observatory reported that the average CO_2 level in 1987 was 348.93 ppm, so our estimate is quite accurate.)

With $t = 2015$, we get

$$C(2015) = (1.65429)(2015) - 2938.07 \approx 395.32$$

So we predict that the average CO_2 level in the year 2015 will be 395.3 ppm. This is an example of *extrapolation* because we have predicted a value *outside* the region of observations. Consequently, we are far less certain about the accuracy of our prediction.

Using Equation 2, we see that the CO_2 level exceeds 420 ppm when

$$1.65429t - 2938.07 > 420$$

Solving this inequality, we get

$$t > \frac{3358.07}{1.65429} \approx 2029.92$$

We therefore predict that the CO_2 level will exceed 420 ppm by the year 2030. This prediction is risky because it involves a time quite remote from our observations. In fact, we see from Figure 6 that the trend has been for CO_2 levels to increase rather more rapidly in recent years, so the level might exceed 420 ppm well before 2030. ▬

▬ Polynomials

A function P is called a **polynomial** if

$$P(x) = a_n x^n + a_{n-1} x^{n-1} + \cdots + a_2 x^2 + a_1 x + a_0$$

where n is a nonnegative integer and the numbers $a_0, a_1, a_2, \ldots, a_n$ are constants called the **coefficients** of the polynomial. The domain of any polynomial is $\mathbb{R} = (-\infty, \infty)$. If the leading coefficient $a_n \neq 0$, then the **degree** of the polynomial is n. For example, the function

$$P(x) = 2x^6 - x^4 + \tfrac{2}{5} x^3 + \sqrt{2}$$

is a polynomial of degree 6.

A polynomial of degree 1 is of the form $P(x) = mx + b$ and so it is a linear function. A polynomial of degree 2 is of the form $P(x) = ax^2 + bx + c$ and is called a **quadratic function**. Its graph is always a parabola obtained by shifting the parabola $y = ax^2$, as we will see in the next section. The parabola opens upward if $a > 0$ and downward if $a < 0$. (See Figure 7.)

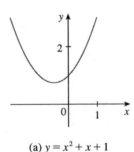

FIGURE 7
The graphs of quadratic functions are parabolas.

(a) $y = x^2 + x + 1$

(b) $y = -2x^2 + 3x + 1$

A polynomial of degree 3 is of the form

$$P(x) = ax^3 + bx^2 + cx + d \qquad a \neq 0$$

and is called a **cubic function**. Figure 8 shows the graph of a cubic function in part (a) and graphs of polynomials of degrees 4 and 5 in parts (b) and (c). We will see later why the graphs have these shapes.

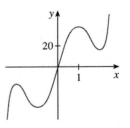

FIGURE 8   (a) $y = x^3 - x + 1$ (b) $y = x^4 - 3x^2 + x$ (c) $y = 3x^5 - 25x^3 + 60x$

Polynomials are commonly used to model various quantities that occur in the natural and social sciences. For instance, in Section 3.7 we will explain why economists often use a polynomial $P(x)$ to represent the cost of producing x units of a commodity. In the following example we use a quadratic function to model the fall of a ball.

TABLE 2

Time (seconds)	Height (meters)
0	450
1	445
2	431
3	408
4	375
5	332
6	279
7	216
8	143
9	61

EXAMPLE 4   A ball is dropped from the upper observation deck of the CN Tower, 450 m above the ground, and its height h above the ground is recorded at 1-second intervals in Table 2. Find a model to fit the data and use the model to predict the time at which the ball hits the ground.

SOLUTION   We draw a scatter plot of the data in Figure 9 and observe that a linear model is inappropriate. But it looks as if the data points might lie on a parabola, so we try a quadratic model instead. Using a graphing calculator or computer algebra system (which uses the least squares method), we obtain the following quadratic model:

3
$$h = 449.36 + 0.96t - 4.90t^2$$

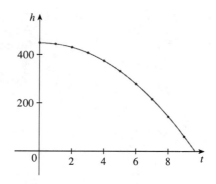

FIGURE 9
Scatter plot for a falling ball

FIGURE 10
Quadratic model for a falling ball

In Figure 10 we plot the graph of Equation 3 together with the data points and see that the quadratic model gives a very good fit.

The ball hits the ground when $h = 0$, so we solve the quadratic equation

$$-4.90t^2 + 0.96t + 449.36 = 0$$

The quadratic formula gives

$$t = \frac{-0.96 \pm \sqrt{(0.96)^2 - 4(-4.90)(449.36)}}{2(-4.90)}$$

The positive root is $t \approx 9.67$, so we predict that the ball will hit the ground after about 9.7 seconds.   ∎

Power Functions

A function of the form $f(x) = x^a$, where a is a constant, is called a **power function**. We consider several cases.

(i) $a = n$, where n is a positive integer

The graphs of $f(x) = x^n$ for $n = 1, 2, 3, 4,$ and 5 are shown in Figure 11. (These are polynomials with only one term.) We already know the shape of the graphs of $y = x$ (a line through the origin with slope 1) and $y = x^2$ [a parabola, see Example 2(b) in Section 1.1].

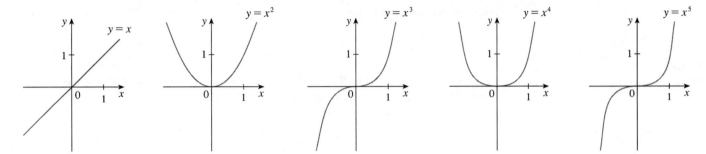

FIGURE 11   Graphs of $f(x) = x^n$ for $n = 1, 2, 3, 4, 5$

The general shape of the graph of $f(x) = x^n$ depends on whether n is even or odd. If n is even, then $f(x) = x^n$ is an even function and its graph is similar to the parabola $y = x^2$. If n is odd, then $f(x) = x^n$ is an odd function and its graph is similar to that of $y = x^3$. Notice from Figure 12, however, that as n increases, the graph of $y = x^n$ becomes flatter near 0 and steeper when $|x| \geqslant 1$. (If x is small, then x^2 is smaller, x^3 is even smaller, x^4 is smaller still, and so on.)

FIGURE 12
Families of power functions

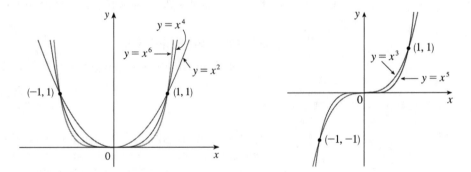

(ii) $a = 1/n$, where n is a positive integer

The function $f(x) = x^{1/n} = \sqrt[n]{x}$ is a **root function**. For $n = 2$ it is the square root function $f(x) = \sqrt{x}$, whose domain is $[0, \infty)$ and whose graph is the upper half of the parabola $x = y^2$. [See Figure 13(a).] For other even values of n, the graph of $y = \sqrt[n]{x}$ is similar to that of $y = \sqrt{x}$. For $n = 3$ we have the cube root function $f(x) = \sqrt[3]{x}$ whose domain is $\mathbb{R}$ (recall that every real number has a cube root) and whose graph is shown in Figure 13(b). The graph of $y = \sqrt[n]{x}$ for n odd ($n > 3$) is similar to that of $y = \sqrt[3]{x}$.

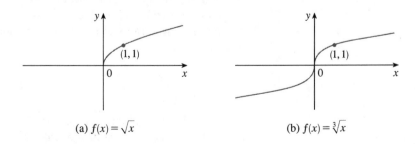

FIGURE 13
Graphs of root functions

(a) $f(x) = \sqrt{x}$

(b) $f(x) = \sqrt[3]{x}$

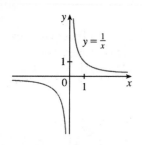

FIGURE 14
The reciprocal function

(iii) $a = -1$

The graph of the **reciprocal function** $f(x) = x^{-1} = 1/x$ is shown in Figure 14. Its graph has the equation $y = 1/x$, or $xy = 1$, and is a hyperbola with the coordinate axes as its asymptotes. This function arises in physics and chemistry in connection with Boyle's Law, which says that, when the temperature is constant, the volume V of a gas is inversely proportional to the pressure P:

$$V = \frac{C}{P}$$

where C is a constant. Thus the graph of V as a function of P (see Figure 15) has the same general shape as the right half of Figure 14.

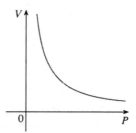

FIGURE 15
Volume as a function of pressure
at constant temperature

Power functions are also used to model species-area relationships (Exercises 26–27), illumination as a function of a distance from a light source (Exercise 25), and the period of revolution of a planet as a function of its distance from the sun (Exercise 28).

■ Rational Functions

A **rational function** f is a ratio of two polynomials:

$$f(x) = \frac{P(x)}{Q(x)}$$

where P and Q are polynomials. The domain consists of all values of x such that $Q(x) \neq 0$. A simple example of a rational function is the function $f(x) = 1/x$, whose domain is $\{x \mid x \neq 0\}$; this is the reciprocal function graphed in Figure 14. The function

$$f(x) = \frac{2x^4 - x^2 + 1}{x^2 - 4}$$

FIGURE 16
$f(x) = \dfrac{2x^4 - x^2 + 1}{x^2 - 4}$

is a rational function with domain $\{x \mid x \neq \pm 2\}$. Its graph is shown in Figure 16.

■ Algebraic Functions

A function f is called an **algebraic function** if it can be constructed using algebraic operations (such as addition, subtraction, multiplication, division, and taking roots) starting with polynomials. Any rational function is automatically an algebraic function. Here are two more examples:

$$f(x) = \sqrt{x^2 + 1} \qquad g(x) = \frac{x^4 - 16x^2}{x + \sqrt{x}} + (x - 2)\sqrt[3]{x + 1}$$

When we sketch algebraic functions in Chapter 4, we will see that their graphs can assume a variety of shapes. Figure 17 illustrates some of the possibilities.

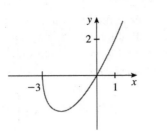

FIGURE 17   (a) $f(x) = x\sqrt{x+3}$ (b) $g(x) = \sqrt[4]{x^2 - 25}$ (c) $h(x) = x^{2/3}(x-2)^2$

An example of an algebraic function occurs in the theory of relativity. The mass of a particle with velocity v is

$$m = f(v) = \frac{m_0}{\sqrt{1 - v^2/c^2}}$$

where m_0 is the rest mass of the particle and $c = 3.0 \times 10^5$ km/s is the speed of light in a vacuum.

Trigonometric Functions

The Reference Pages are located at the front and back of the book.

Trigonometry and the trigonometric functions are reviewed on Reference Page 2 and also in Appendix D. In calculus the convention is that radian measure is always used (except when otherwise indicated). For example, when we use the function $f(x) = \sin x$, it is understood that $\sin x$ means the sine of the angle whose radian measure is x. Thus the graphs of the sine and cosine functions are as shown in Figure 18.

(a) $f(x) = \sin x$ (b) $g(x) = \cos x$

FIGURE 18

Notice that for both the sine and cosine functions the domain is $(-\infty, \infty)$ and the range is the closed interval $[-1, 1]$. Thus, for all values of x, we have

$$-1 \le \sin x \le 1 \qquad -1 \le \cos x \le 1$$

or, in terms of absolute values,

$$|\sin x| \le 1 \qquad |\cos x| \le 1$$

Also, the zeros of the sine function occur at the integer multiples of π; that is,

$$\sin x = 0 \quad \text{when} \quad x = n\pi \quad n \text{ an integer}$$

An important property of the sine and cosine functions is that they are periodic functions and have period 2π. This means that, for all values of x,

$$\sin(x + 2\pi) = \sin x \qquad \cos(x + 2\pi) = \cos x$$

The periodic nature of these functions makes them suitable for modeling repetitive phenomena such as tides, vibrating springs, and sound waves. For instance, in Example 4 in Section 1.3 we will see that a reasonable model for the number of hours of daylight in Philadelphia t days after January 1 is given by the function

$$L(t) = 12 + 2.8 \sin\left[\frac{2\pi}{365}(t - 80)\right]$$

The tangent function is related to the sine and cosine functions by the equation

$$\tan x = \frac{\sin x}{\cos x}$$

and its graph is shown in Figure 19. It is undefined whenever $\cos x = 0$, that is, when $x = \pm\pi/2, \pm 3\pi/2, \ldots$. Its range is $(-\infty, \infty)$. Notice that the tangent function has period π:

$$\tan(x + \pi) = \tan x \qquad \text{for all } x$$

The remaining three trigonometric functions (cosecant, secant, and cotangent) are the reciprocals of the sine, cosine, and tangent functions. Their graphs are shown in Appendix D.

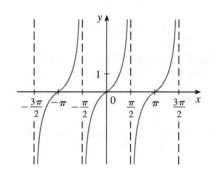

FIGURE 19

$y = \tan x$

◼ Exponential Functions

The **exponential functions** are the functions of the form $f(x) = a^x$, where the base a is a positive constant. The graphs of $y = 2^x$ and $y = (0.5)^x$ are shown in Figure 20. In both cases the domain is $(-\infty, \infty)$ and the range is $(0, \infty)$.

Exponential functions will be studied in detail in Section 1.5, and we will see that they are useful for modeling many natural phenomena, such as population growth (if $a > 1$) and radioactive decay (if $a < 1$).

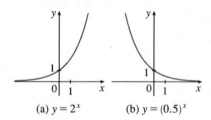

(a) $y = 2^x$ (b) $y = (0.5)^x$

FIGURE 20

◼ Logarithmic Functions

The **logarithmic functions** $f(x) = \log_a x$, where the base a is a positive constant, are the inverse functions of the exponential functions. They will be studied in Section 1.6. Figure 21 shows the graphs of four logarithmic functions with various bases. In each case the domain is $(0, \infty)$, the range is $(-\infty, \infty)$, and the function increases slowly when $x > 1$.

FIGURE 21

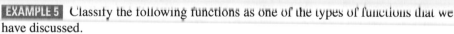

EXAMPLE 5   Classify the following functions as one of the types of functions that we have discussed.

(a) $f(x) = 5^x$ (b) $g(x) = x^5$

(c) $h(x) = \dfrac{1 + x}{1 - \sqrt{x}}$ (d) $u(t) = 1 - t + 5t^4$

SOLUTION

(a) $f(x) = 5^x$ is an exponential function. (The x is the exponent.)

(b) $g(x) = x^5$ is a power function. (The x is the base.) We could also consider it to be a polynomial of degree 5.

(c) $h(x) = \dfrac{1 + x}{1 - \sqrt{x}}$ is an algebraic function.

(d) $u(t) = 1 - t + 5t^4$ is a polynomial of degree 4.

1.2 Exercises

1–2 Classify each function as a power function, root function, polynomial (state its degree), rational function, algebraic function, trigonometric function, exponential function, or logarithmic function.

1. (a) $f(x) = \log_2 x$ (b) $g(x) = \sqrt[4]{x}$

(c) $h(x) = \dfrac{2x^3}{1 - x^2}$ (d) $u(t) = 1 - 1.1t + 2.54t^2$

(e) $v(t) = 5^t$ (f) $w(\theta) = \sin\theta\cos^2\theta$

2. (a) $y = \pi^x$ (b) $y = x^\pi$

(c) $y = x^2(2 - x^3)$ (d) $y = \tan t - \cos t$

(e) $y = \dfrac{s}{1 + s}$ (f) $y = \dfrac{\sqrt{x^3 - 1}}{1 + \sqrt[3]{x}}$

3–4 Match each equation with its graph. Explain your choices. (Don't use a computer or graphing calculator.)

3. (a) $y = x^2$ (b) $y = x^5$ (c) $y = x^8$

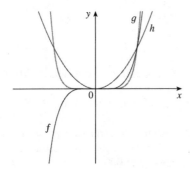

4. (a) $y = 3x$ (b) $y = 3^x$
(c) $y = x^3$ (d) $y = \sqrt[3]{x}$

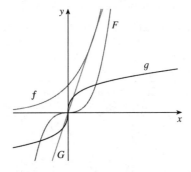

5. (a) Find an equation for the family of linear functions with slope 2 and sketch several members of the family.
(b) Find an equation for the family of linear functions such that $f(2) = 1$ and sketch several members of the family.
(c) Which function belongs to both families?

6. What do all members of the family of linear functions $f(x) = 1 + m(x + 3)$ have in common? Sketch several members of the family.

7. What do all members of the family of linear functions $f(x) = c - x$ have in common? Sketch several members of the family.

8. Find expressions for the quadratic functions whose graphs are shown.

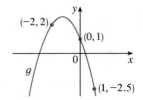

9. Find an expression for a cubic function f if $f(1) = 6$ and $f(-1) = f(0) = f(2) = 0$.

10. Recent studies indicate that the average surface temperature of the earth has been rising steadily. Some scientists have modeled the temperature by the linear function $T = 0.02t + 8.50$, where T is temperature in °C and t represents years since 1900.
(a) What do the slope and T-intercept represent?
(b) Use the equation to predict the average global surface temperature in 2100.

11. If the recommended adult dosage for a drug is D (in mg), then to determine the appropriate dosage c for a child of age a, pharmacists use the equation $c = 0.0417D(a + 1)$. Suppose the dosage for an adult is 200 mg.
(a) Find the slope of the graph of c. What does it represent?
(b) What is the dosage for a newborn?

12. The manager of a weekend flea market knows from past experience that if he charges x dollars for a rental space at the market, then the number y of spaces he can rent is given by the equation $y = 200 - 4x$.
(a) Sketch a graph of this linear function. (Remember that the rental charge per space and the number of spaces rented can't be negative quantities.)
(b) What do the slope, the y-intercept, and the x-intercept of the graph represent?

13. The relationship between the Fahrenheit (F) and Celsius (C) temperature scales is given by the linear function $F = \frac{9}{5}C + 32$.
(a) Sketch a graph of this function.
(b) What is the slope of the graph and what does it represent? What is the F-intercept and what does it represent?

14. Kelly leaves Winnipeg at 2:00 PM and drives at a constant speed west along the Trans-Canada highway. He passes Brandon, 210 km from Winnipeg, at 4:00 PM.
(a) Express the distance traveled in terms of the time elapsed.

⊞ Graphing calculator or computer required   **1.** Homework Hints available at stewartcalculus.com

(b) Draw the graph of the equation in part (a).

(c) What is the slope of this line? What does it represent?

15. Biologists have noticed that the chirping rate of crickets of a certain species is related to temperature, and the relationship appears to be very nearly linear. A cricket produces 112 chirps per minute at 20°C and 180 chirps per minute at 29°C.

(a) Find a linear equation that models the temperature T as a function of the number of chirps per minute N.

(b) What is the slope of the graph? What does it represent?

(c) If the crickets are chirping at 150 chirps per minute, estimate the temperature.

16. The manager of a furniture factory finds that it costs $2200 to manufacture 100 chairs in one day and $4800 to produce 300 chairs in one day.

(a) Express the cost as a function of the number of chairs produced, assuming that it is linear. Then sketch the graph.

(b) What is the slope of the graph and what does it represent?

(c) What is the y-intercept of the graph and what does it represent?

17. At the surface of the ocean, the water pressure is the same as the air pressure above the water, 1.05 kg/cm². Below the surface, the water pressure increases by 0.10 kg/cm² for every meter of descent.

(a) Express the water pressure as a function of the depth below the ocean surface.

(b) At what depth is the pressure 7 kg/cm²?

18. The monthly cost of driving a car depends on the number of kilometers driven. Lynn found that in May it cost her $380 to drive 768 km and in June it cost her $460 to drive 1280 km.

(a) Express the monthly cost C as a function of the distance driven d, assuming that a linear relationship gives a suitable model.

(b) Use part (a) to predict the cost of driving 2400 km per month.

(c) Draw the graph of the linear function. What does the slope represent?

(d) What does the y-intercept represent?

(e) Why does a linear function give a suitable model in this situation?

19–20 For each scatter plot, decide what type of function you might choose as a model for the data. Explain your choices.

19. (a)

(b)

20. (a)

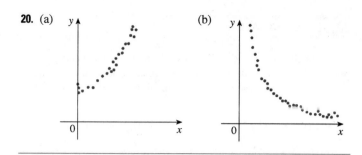

(b)

21. The table shows (lifetime) peptic ulcer rates (per 100 population) for various family incomes as reported by the National Health Interview Survey.

Income	Ulcer rate (per 100 population)
$4,000	14.1
$6,000	13.0
$8,000	13.4
$12,000	12.5
$16,000	12.0
$20,000	12.4
$30,000	10.5
$45,000	9.4
$60,000	8.2

(a) Make a scatter plot of these data and decide whether a linear model is appropriate.

(b) Find and graph a linear model using the first and last data points.

(c) Find and graph the least squares regression line.

(d) Use the linear model in part (c) to estimate the ulcer rate for an income of $25,000.

(e) According to the model, how likely is someone with an income of $80,000 to suffer from peptic ulcers?

(f) Do you think it would be reasonable to apply the model to someone with an income of $200,000?

22. Biologists have observed that the chirping rate of crickets of a certain species appears to be related to temperature. The table shows the chirping rates for various temperatures.

Temperature (°C)	Chirping rate (chirps/min)	Temperature (°C)	Chirping rate (chirps/min)
20	113	30	188
22	128	32	203
24	143	34	218
26	158	36	233
28	173		

(a) Make a scatter plot of the data.

(b) Find and graph the regression line.

(c) Use the linear model in part (b) to estimate the chirping rate at 40°C.

23. The table gives the winning heights for the men's Olympic pole vault competitions up to the year 2004.

Year	Height (m)	Year	Height (m)
1896	3.30	1960	4.70
1900	3.30	1964	5.10
1904	3.50	1968	5.40
1908	3.71	1972	5.64
1912	3.95	1976	5.64
1920	4.09	1980	5.78
1924	3.95	1984	5.75
1928	4.20	1988	5.90
1932	4.31	1992	5.87
1936	4.35	1996	5.92
1948	4.30	2000	5.90
1952	4.55	2004	5.95
1956	4.56		

(a) Make a scatter plot and decide whether a linear model is appropriate.
(b) Find and graph the regression line.
(c) Use the linear model to predict the height of the winning pole vault at the 2008 Olympics and compare with the actual winning height of 5.96 meters.
(d) Is it reasonable to use the model to predict the winning height at the 2100 Olympics?

24. The table shows the percentage of the population of Argentina that has lived in rural areas from 1955 to 2000. Find a model for the data and use it to estimate the rural percentage in 1988 and 2002.

Year	Percentage rural	Year	Percentage rural
1955	30.4	1980	17.1
1960	26.4	1985	15.0
1965	23.6	1990	13.0
1970	21.1	1995	11.7
1975	19.0	2000	10.5

25. Many physical quantities are connected by *inverse square laws*, that is, by power functions of the form $f(x) = kx^{-2}$. In particular, the illumination of an object by a light source is inversely proportional to the square of the distance from the source. Suppose that after dark you are in a room with just one lamp and you are trying to read a book. The light is too dim and so you move halfway to the lamp. How much brighter is the light?

26. It makes sense that the larger the area of a region, the larger the number of species that inhabit the region. Many

ecologists have modeled the species-area relation with a power function and, in particular, the number of species S of bats living in caves in central Mexico has been related to the surface area A of the caves by the equation $S = 0.7A^{0.3}$.
(a) The cave called *Misión Imposible* near Puebla, Mexico, has a surface area of $A = 60$ m^2. How many species of bats would you expect to find in that cave?
(b) If you discover that four species of bats live in a cave, estimate the area of the cave.

27. The table shows the number N of species of reptiles and amphibians inhabiting Caribbean islands and the area A of the island in square kilometers.

Island	A	N
Saba	10	5
Monserrat	104	9
Puerto Rico	8,958	40
Jamaica	11,423	39
Hispaniola	76,184	84
Cuba	114,511	76

(a) Use a power function to model N as a function of A.
(b) The Caribbean island of Dominica has area 754 km^2. How many species of reptiles and amphibians would you expect to find on Dominica?

28. The table shows the mean (average) distances d of the planets from the sun (taking the unit of measurement to be the distance from the earth to the sun) and their periods T (time of revolution in years).

Planet	d	T
Mercury	0.387	0.241
Venus	0.723	0.615
Earth	1.000	1.000
Mars	1.523	1.881
Jupiter	5.203	11.861
Saturn	9.541	29.457
Uranus	19.190	84.008
Neptune	30.086	164.784

(a) Fit a power model to the data.
(b) Kepler's Third Law of Planetary Motion states that

"The square of the period of revolution of a planet is proportional to the cube of its mean distance from the sun."

Does your model corroborate Kepler's Third Law?

1.3   New Functions from Old Functions

In this section we start with the basic functions we discussed in Section 1.2 and obtain new functions by shifting, stretching, and reflecting their graphs. We also show how to combine pairs of functions by the standard arithmetic operations and by composition.

■   Transformations of Functions

By applying certain transformations to the graph of a given function we can obtain the graphs of certain related functions. This will give us the ability to sketch the graphs of many functions quickly by hand. It will also enable us to write equations for given graphs. Let's first consider **translations**. If c is a positive number, then the graph of $y = f(x) + c$ is just the graph of $y = f(x)$ shifted upward a distance of c units (because each y-coordinate is increased by the same number c). Likewise, if $g(x) = f(x - c)$, where $c > 0$, then the value of g at x is the same as the value of f at $x - c$ (c units to the left of x). Therefore the graph of $y = f(x - c)$ is just the graph of $y = f(x)$ shifted c units to the right (see Figure 1).

> **Vertical and Horizontal Shifts**   Suppose $c > 0$. To obtain the graph of
>
> $y = f(x) + c$, shift the graph of $y = f(x)$ a distance c units upward
>
> $y = f(x) - c$, shift the graph of $y = f(x)$ a distance c units downward
>
> $y = f(x - c)$, shift the graph of $y = f(x)$ a distance c units to the right
>
> $y = f(x + c)$, shift the graph of $y = f(x)$ a distance c units to the left

FIGURE 1
Translating the graph of f

FIGURE 2
Stretching and reflecting the graph of f

Now let's consider the **stretching** and **reflecting** transformations. If $c > 1$, then the graph of $y = cf(x)$ is the graph of $y = f(x)$ stretched by a factor of c in the vertical direction (because each y-coordinate is multiplied by the same number c). The graph of $y = -f(x)$ is the graph of $y = f(x)$ reflected about the x-axis because the point (x, y) is replaced by the point $(x, -y)$. (See Figure 2 and the following chart, where the results of other stretching, shrinking, and reflecting transformations are also given.)

Vertical and Horizontal Stretching and Reflecting   Suppose $c > 1$. To obtain the graph of

$y = cf(x)$, stretch the graph of $y = f(x)$ vertically by a factor of c

$y = (1/c)f(x)$, shrink the graph of $y = f(x)$ vertically by a factor of c

$y = f(cx)$, shrink the graph of $y = f(x)$ horizontally by a factor of c

$y = f(x/c)$, stretch the graph of $y = f(x)$ horizontally by a factor of c

$y = -f(x)$, reflect the graph of $y = f(x)$ about the x-axis

$y = f(-x)$, reflect the graph of $y = f(x)$ about the y-axis

---

Figure 3 illustrates these stretching transformations when applied to the cosine function with $c = 2$. For instance, in order to get the graph of $y = 2\cos x$ we multiply the y-coordinate of each point on the graph of $y = \cos x$ by 2. This means that the graph of $y = \cos x$ gets stretched vertically by a factor of 2.

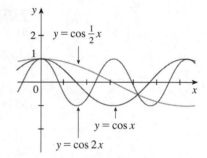

FIGURE 3

V **EXAMPLE 1**   Given the graph of $y = \sqrt{x}$, use transformations to graph $y = \sqrt{x} - 2$, $y = \sqrt{x - 2}$, $y = -\sqrt{x}$, $y = 2\sqrt{x}$, and $y = \sqrt{-x}$.

SOLUTION   The graph of the square root function $y = \sqrt{x}$, obtained from Figure 13(a) in Section 1.2, is shown in Figure 4(a). In the other parts of the figure we sketch $y = \sqrt{x} - 2$ by shifting 2 units downward, $y = \sqrt{x - 2}$ by shifting 2 units to the right, $y = -\sqrt{x}$ by reflecting about the x-axis, $y = 2\sqrt{x}$ by stretching vertically by a factor of 2, and $y = \sqrt{-x}$ by reflecting about the y-axis.

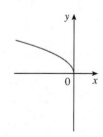

(a) $y = \sqrt{x}$ (b) $y = \sqrt{x} - 2$ (c) $y = \sqrt{x - 2}$ (d) $y = -\sqrt{x}$ (e) $y = 2\sqrt{x}$ (f) $y = \sqrt{-x}$

FIGURE 4

EXAMPLE 2   Sketch the graph of the function $f(x) = x^2 + 6x + 10$.

SOLUTION   Completing the square, we write the equation of the graph as

$$y = x^2 + 6x + 10 = (x + 3)^2 + 1$$

This means we obtain the desired graph by starting with the parabola $y = x^2$ and shifting 3 units to the left and then 1 unit upward (see Figure 5).

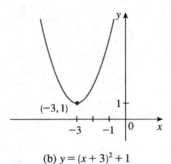

FIGURE 5   (a) $y = x^2$ (b) $y = (x + 3)^2 + 1$

EXAMPLE 3   Sketch the graphs of the following functions.
(a) $y = \sin 2x$ (b) $y = 1 - \sin x$

SOLUTION

(a) We obtain the graph of $y = \sin 2x$ from that of $y = \sin x$ by compressing horizontally by a factor of 2. (See Figures 6 and 7.) Thus, whereas the period of $y = \sin x$ is 2π, the period of $y = \sin 2x$ is $2\pi/2 = \pi$.

FIGURE 6   **FIGURE 7**

(b) To obtain the graph of $y = 1 - \sin x$, we again start with $y = \sin x$. We reflect about the x-axis to get the graph of $y = -\sin x$ and then we shift 1 unit upward to get $y = 1 - \sin x$. (See Figure 8.)

FIGURE 8

EXAMPLE 4   Figure 9 shows graphs of the number of hours of daylight as functions of the time of the year at several latitudes. Given that Ankara, Turkey is located at approximately 40°N latitude, find a function that models the length of daylight at Ankara.

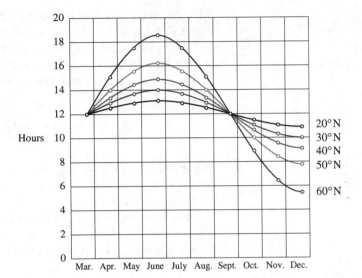

FIGURE 9

Graph of the length of daylight
from March 21 through December 21
at various latitudes

Lucia C. Harrison, *Daylight, Twilight, Darkness and Time*
(New York, 1935) page 40.

SOLUTION Notice that each curve resembles a shifted and stretched sine function. By looking at the blue curve we see that, at the latitude of Ankara, daylight lasts about 14.8 hours on June 21 and 9.2 hours on December 21, so the amplitude of the curve (the factor by which we have to stretch the sine curve vertically) is $\frac{1}{2}(14.8 - 9.2) = 2.8$.

By what factor do we need to stretch the sine curve horizontally if we measure the time t in days? Because there are about 365 days in a year, the period of our model should be 365. But the period of $y = \sin t$ is 2π, so the horizontal stretching factor is $c = 2\pi/365$.

We also notice that the curve begins its cycle on March 21, the 80th day of the year, so we have to shift the curve 80 units to the right. In addition, we shift it 12 units upward. Therefore we model the length of daylight in Ankara on the tth day of the year by the function

$$L(t) = 12 + 2.8 \sin\left[\frac{2\pi}{365}(t - 80)\right]$$

Another transformation of some interest is taking the *absolute value* of a function. If $y = |f(x)|$, then according to the definition of absolute value, $y = f(x)$ when $f(x) \geq 0$ and $y = -f(x)$ when $f(x) < 0$. This tells us how to get the graph of $y = |f(x)|$ from the graph of $y = f(x)$: The part of the graph that lies above the x-axis remains the same; the part that lies below the x-axis is reflected about the x-axis.

V EXAMPLE 5 Sketch the graph of the function $y = |x^2 - 1|$.

SOLUTION We first graph the parabola $y = x^2 - 1$ in Figure 10(a) by shifting the parabola $y = x^2$ downward 1 unit. We see that the graph lies below the x-axis when $-1 < x < 1$, so we reflect that part of the graph about the x-axis to obtain the graph of $y = |x^2 - 1|$ in Figure 10(b).

(a) $y = x^2 - 1$

(b) $y = |x^2 - 1|$

FIGURE 10

Combinations of Functions

Two functions f and g can be combined to form new functions $f + g$, $f - g$, fg, and f/g in a manner similar to the way we add, subtract, multiply, and divide real numbers. The sum and difference functions are defined by

$$(f + g)(x) = f(x) + g(x) \qquad (f - g)(x) = f(x) - g(x)$$

If the domain of f is A and the domain of g is B, then the domain of $f + g$ is the intersection $A \cap B$ because both $f(x)$ and $g(x)$ have to be defined. For example, the domain of $f(x) = \sqrt{x}$ is $A = [0, \infty)$ and the domain of $g(x) = \sqrt{2 - x}$ is $B = (-\infty, 2]$, so the domain of $(f + g)(x) = \sqrt{x} + \sqrt{2 - x}$ is $A \cap B = [0, 2]$.

Similarly, the product and quotient functions are defined by

$$(fg)(x) = f(x)g(x) \qquad \left(\frac{f}{g}\right)(x) = \frac{f(x)}{g(x)}$$

The domain of fg is $A \cap B$, but we can't divide by 0 and so the domain of f/g is $\{x \in A \cap B \mid g(x) \neq 0\}$. For instance, if $f(x) = x^2$ and $g(x) = x - 1$, then the domain of the rational function $(f/g)(x) = x^2/(x - 1)$ is $\{x \mid x \neq 1\}$, or $(-\infty, 1) \cup (1, \infty)$.

There is another way of combining two functions to obtain a new function. For example, suppose that $y = f(u) = \sqrt{u}$ and $u = g(x) = x^2 + 1$. Since y is a function of u and u is, in turn, a function of x, it follows that y is ultimately a function of x. We compute this by substitution:

$$y = f(u) = f(g(x)) = f(x^2 + 1) = \sqrt{x^2 + 1}$$

The procedure is called *composition* because the new function is *composed* of the two given functions f and g.

In general, given any two functions f and g, we start with a number x in the domain of g and find its image $g(x)$. If this number $g(x)$ is in the domain of f, then we can calculate the value of $f(g(x))$. Notice that the output of one function is used as the input to the next function. The result is a new function $h(x) = f(g(x))$ obtained by substituting g into f. It is called the *composition* (or *composite*) of f and g and is denoted by $f \circ g$ ("f circle g").

> **Definition** Given two functions f and g, the **composite function** $f \circ g$ (also called the **composition** of f and g) is defined by
>
> $$(f \circ g)(x) = f(g(x))$$

The domain of $f \circ g$ is the set of all x in the domain of g such that $g(x)$ is in the domain of f. In other words, $(f \circ g)(x)$ is defined whenever both $g(x)$ and $f(g(x))$ are defined. Figure 11 shows how to picture $f \circ g$ in terms of machines.

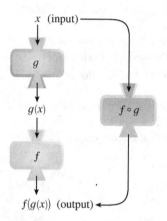

FIGURE 11
The $f \circ g$ machine is composed of the g machine (first) and then the f machine.

EXAMPLE 6 If $f(x) = x^2$ and $g(x) = x - 3$, find the composite functions $f \circ g$ and $g \circ f$.

SOLUTION We have

$$(f \circ g)(x) = f(g(x)) = f(x - 3) = (x - 3)^2$$

$$(g \circ f)(x) = g(f(x)) = g(x^2) = x^2 - 3$$

NOTE You can see from Example 6 that, in general, $f \circ g \neq g \circ f$. Remember, the notation $f \circ g$ means that the function g is applied first and then f is applied second. In Example 6, $f \circ g$ is the function that *first* subtracts 3 and *then* squares; $g \circ f$ is the function that *first* squares and *then* subtracts 3.

V **EXAMPLE 7** If $f(x) = \sqrt{x}$ and $g(x) = \sqrt{2 - x}$, find each function and its domain.

(a) $f \circ g$ (b) $g \circ f$ (c) $f \circ f$ (d) $g \circ g$

SOLUTION

(a) $$(f \circ g)(x) = f(g(x)) = f(\sqrt{2 - x}) = \sqrt{\sqrt{2 - x}} = \sqrt[4]{2 - x}$$

The domain of $f \circ g$ is $\{x \mid 2 - x \geq 0\} = \{x \mid x \leq 2\} = (-\infty, 2]$.

(b) $$(g \circ f)(x) = g(f(x)) = g(\sqrt{x}) = \sqrt{2 - \sqrt{x}}$$

For $\sqrt{x}$ to be defined we must have $x \geq 0$. For $\sqrt{2 - \sqrt{x}}$ to be defined we must have $2 - \sqrt{x} \geq 0$, that is, $\sqrt{x} \leq 2$, or $x \leq 4$. Thus we have $0 \leq x \leq 4$, so the domain of $g \circ f$ is the closed interval $[0, 4]$.

If $0 \leq a \leq b$, then $a^2 \leq b^2$.

(c) $$(f \circ f)(x) = f(f(x)) = f(\sqrt{x}) = \sqrt{\sqrt{x}} = \sqrt[4]{x}$$

The domain of $f \circ f$ is $[0, \infty)$.

(d) $$(g \circ g)(x) = g(g(x)) = g(\sqrt{2 - x}) = \sqrt{2 - \sqrt{2 - x}}$$

This expression is defined when both $2 - x \geq 0$ and $2 - \sqrt{2 - x} \geq 0$. The first inequality means $x \leq 2$, and the second is equivalent to $\sqrt{2 - x} \leq 2$, or $2 - x \leq 4$, or $x \geq -2$. Thus $-2 \leq x \leq 2$, so the domain of $g \circ g$ is the closed interval $[-2, 2]$. ▬

It is possible to take the composition of three or more functions. For instance, the composite function $f \circ g \circ h$ is found by first applying h, then g, and then f as follows:

$$(f \circ g \circ h)(x) = f(g(h(x)))$$

EXAMPLE 8 Find $f \circ g \circ h$ if $f(x) = x/(x + 1)$, $g(x) = x^{10}$, and $h(x) = x + 3$.

SOLUTION $$(f \circ g \circ h)(x) = f(g(h(x))) = f(g(x + 3))$$
$$= f((x + 3)^{10}) = \frac{(x + 3)^{10}}{(x + 3)^{10} + 1}$$ ▬

So far we have used composition to build complicated functions from simpler ones. But in calculus it is often useful to be able to *decompose* a complicated function into simpler ones, as in the following example.

EXAMPLE 9 Given $F(x) = \cos^2(x + 9)$, find functions f, g, and h such that $F = f \circ g \circ h$.

SOLUTION Since $F(x) = [\cos(x + 9)]^2$, the formula for F says: First add 9, then take the cosine of the result, and finally square. So we let

$$h(x) = x + 9 \qquad g(x) = \cos x \qquad f(x) = x^2$$

Then $$(f \circ g \circ h)(x) = f(g(h(x))) = f(g(x + 9)) = f(\cos(x + 9))$$
$$= [\cos(x + 9)]^2 = F(x)$$ ▬

1.3   Exercises

1. Suppose the graph of f is given. Write equations for the graphs that are obtained from the graph of f as follows.
   (a) Shift 3 units upward.   (b) Shift 3 units downward.
   (c) Shift 3 units to the right.   (d) Shift 3 units to the left.
   (e) Reflect about the x-axis.   (f) Reflect about the y-axis.
   (g) Stretch vertically by a factor of 3.
   (h) Shrink vertically by a factor of 3.

2. Explain how each graph is obtained from the graph of $y = f(x)$.
   (a) $y = f(x) + 8$ (b) $y = f(x + 8)$
   (c) $y = 8f(x)$ (d) $y = f(8x)$
   (e) $y = -f(x) - 1$ (f) $y = 8f\left(\frac{1}{8}x\right)$

3. The graph of $y = f(x)$ is given. Match each equation with its graph and give reasons for your choices.
   (a) $y = f(x - 4)$ (b) $y = f(x) + 3$
   (c) $y = \frac{1}{3}f(x)$ (d) $y = -f(x + 4)$
   (e) $y = 2f(x + 6)$

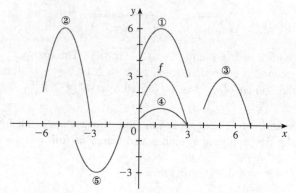

4. The graph of f is given. Draw the graphs of the following functions.
   (a) $y = f(x) - 2$ (b) $y = f(x - 2)$
   (c) $y = -2f(x)$ (d) $y = f\left(\frac{1}{3}x\right) + 1$

5. The graph of f is given. Use it to graph the following functions.
   (a) $y = f(2x)$ (b) $y = f\left(\frac{1}{2}x\right)$
   (c) $y = f(-x)$ (d) $y = -f(-x)$

6–7 The graph of $y = \sqrt{3x - x^2}$ is given. Use transformations to create a function whose graph is as shown.

6.

7.

8. (a) How is the graph of $y = 2 \sin x$ related to the graph of $y = \sin x$? Use your answer and Figure 6 to sketch the graph of $y = 2 \sin x$.
   (b) How is the graph of $y = 1 + \sqrt{x}$ related to the graph of $y = \sqrt{x}$? Use your answer and Figure 4(a) to sketch the graph of $y = 1 + \sqrt{x}$.

9–24 Graph the function by hand, not by plotting points, but by starting with the graph of one of the standard functions given in Section 1.2, and then applying the appropriate transformations.

9. $y = \dfrac{1}{x + 2}$ 10. $y = (x - 1)^3$

11. $y = -\sqrt[3]{x}$ 12. $y = x^2 + 6x + 4$

13. $y = \sqrt{x - 2} - 1$ 14. $y = 4 \sin 3x$

15. $y = \sin\left(\frac{1}{2}x\right)$ 16. $y = \dfrac{2}{x} - 2$

17. $y = \frac{1}{2}(1 - \cos x)$ 18. $y = 1 - 2\sqrt{x + 3}$

19. $y = 1 - 2x - x^2$ 20. $y = |x| - 2$

21. $y = |x - 2|$ 22. $y = \frac{1}{4}\tan\left(x - \frac{\pi}{4}\right)$

23. $y = |\sqrt{x} - 1|$ 24. $y = |\cos \pi x|$

25. The city of New Delhi, India, is located near latitude 30°N. Use Figure 9 to find a function that models the number of hours of daylight at New Delhi as a function of the time of year. To check the accuracy of your model, use the fact that on March 31 the sun rises at 6:13 AM and sets at 6:39 PM in New Delhi.

26. A variable star is one whose brightness alternately increases and decreases. For the most visible variable star, Delta Cephei, the time between periods of maximum brightness is 5.4 days, the average brightness (or magnitude) of the star is 4.0, and its brightness varies by ± 0.35 magnitude. Find a function that models the brightness of Delta Cephei as a function of time.

27. (a) How is the graph of $y = f(|x|)$ related to the graph of f?
(b) Sketch the graph of $y = \sin|x|$.
(c) Sketch the graph of $y = \sqrt{|x|}$.

28. Use the given graph of f to sketch the graph of $y = 1/f(x)$. Which features of f are the most important in sketching $y = 1/f(x)$? Explain how they are used.

29–30 Find (a) $f + g$, (b) $f - g$, (c) fg, and (d) f/g and state their domains.

29. $f(x) = x^3 + 2x^2$, $g(x) = 3x^2 - 1$

30. $f(x) = \sqrt{3 - x}$, $g(x) = \sqrt{x^2 - 1}$

31–36 Find the functions (a) $f \circ g$, (b) $g \circ f$, (c) $f \circ f$, and (d) $g \circ g$ and their domains.

31. $f(x) = x^2 - 1$, $g(x) = 2x + 1$

32. $f(x) = x - 2$, $g(x) = x^2 + 3x + 4$

33. $f(x) = 1 - 3x$, $g(x) = \cos x$

34. $f(x) = \sqrt{x}$, $g(x) = \sqrt[3]{1 - x}$

35. $f(x) = x + \dfrac{1}{x}$, $g(x) = \dfrac{x + 1}{x + 2}$

36. $f(x) = \dfrac{x}{1 + x}$, $g(x) = \sin 2x$

37–40 Find $f \circ g \circ h$.

37. $f(x) = 3x - 2$, $g(x) = \sin x$, $h(x) = x^2$

38. $f(x) = |x - 4|$, $g(x) = 2^x$, $h(x) = \sqrt{x}$

39. $f(x) = \sqrt{x - 3}$, $g(x) = x^2$, $h(x) = x^3 + 2$

40. $f(x) = \tan x$, $g(x) = \dfrac{x}{x - 1}$, $h(x) = \sqrt[3]{x}$

41–46 Express the function in the form $f \circ g$.

41. $F(x) = (2x + x^2)^4$

42. $F(x) = \cos^2 x$

43. $F(x) = \dfrac{\sqrt[3]{x}}{1 + \sqrt[3]{x}}$

44. $G(x) = \sqrt[3]{\dfrac{x}{1 + x}}$

45. $v(t) = \sec(t^2) \tan(t^2)$

46. $u(t) = \dfrac{\tan t}{1 + \tan t}$

47–49 Express the function in the form $f \circ g \circ h$.

47. $R(x) = \sqrt{\sqrt{x} - 1}$

48. $H(x) = \sqrt[8]{2 + |x|}$

49. $H(x) = \sec^4(\sqrt{x})$

50. Use the table to evaluate each expression.
(a) $f(g(1))$ (b) $g(f(1))$ (c) $f(f(1))$
(d) $g(g(1))$ (e) $(g \circ f)(3)$ (f) $(f \circ g)(6)$

x	1	2	3	4	5	6
$f(x)$	3	1	4	2	2	5
$g(x)$	6	3	2	1	2	3

51. Use the given graphs of f and g to evaluate each expression, or explain why it is undefined.
(a) $f(g(2))$ (b) $g(f(0))$ (c) $(f \circ g)(0)$
(d) $(g \circ f)(6)$ (e) $(g \circ g)(-2)$ (f) $(f \circ f)(4)$

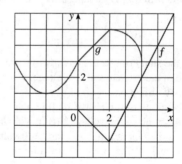

52. Use the given graphs of f and g to estimate the value of $f(g(x))$ for $x = -5, -4, -3, \ldots, 5$. Use these estimates to sketch a rough graph of $f \circ g$.

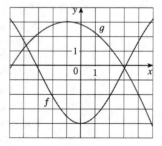

53. A stone is dropped into a lake, creating a circular ripple that travels outward at a speed of 60 cm/s.
(a) Express the radius r of this circle as a function of the time t (in seconds).
(b) If A is the area of this circle as a function of the radius, find $A \circ r$ and interpret it.

54. A spherical balloon is being inflated and the radius of the balloon is increasing at a rate of 2 cm/s.
(a) Express the radius r of the balloon as a function of the time t (in seconds).
(b) If V is the volume of the balloon as a function of the radius, find $V \circ r$ and interpret it.

55. A ship is moving at a speed of 30 km/h parallel to a straight shoreline. The ship is 6 km from shore and it passes a lighthouse at noon.
(a) Express the distance s between the lighthouse and the ship as a function of d, the distance the ship has traveled since noon; that is, find f so that $s = f(d)$.
(b) Express d as a function of t, the time elapsed since noon; that is, find g so that $d = g(t)$.
(c) Find $f \circ g$. What does this function represent?

56. An airplane is flying at a speed of 350 km/h at an altitude of 1 km and passes directly over a radar station at time $t = 0$.
(a) Express the horizontal distance d (in kilometers) that the plane has flown as a function of t.
(b) Express the distance s between the plane and the radar station as a function of d.
(c) Use composition to express s as a function of t.

57. The **Heaviside function** H is defined by

$$H(t) = \begin{cases} 0 & \text{if } t < 0 \\ 1 & \text{if } t \geq 0 \end{cases}$$

It is used in the study of electric circuits to represent the sudden surge of electric current, or voltage, when a switch is instantaneously turned on.
(a) Sketch the graph of the Heaviside function.
(b) Sketch the graph of the voltage $V(t)$ in a circuit if the switch is turned on at time $t = 0$ and 120 volts are applied instantaneously to the circuit. Write a formula for $V(t)$ in terms of $H(t)$.

(c) Sketch the graph of the voltage $V(t)$ in a circuit if the switch is turned on at time $t = 5$ seconds and 240 volts are applied instantaneously to the circuit. Write a formula for $V(t)$ in terms of $H(t)$. (Note that starting at $t = 5$ corresponds to a translation.)

58. The Heaviside function defined in Exercise 57 can also be used to define the **ramp function** $y = ctH(t)$, which represents a gradual increase in voltage or current in a circuit.
(a) Sketch the graph of the ramp function $y = tH(t)$.
(b) Sketch the graph of the voltage $V(t)$ in a circuit if the switch is turned on at time $t = 0$ and the voltage is gradually increased to 120 volts over a 60-second time interval. Write a formula for $V(t)$ in terms of $H(t)$ for $t \leq 60$.
(c) Sketch the graph of the voltage $V(t)$ in a circuit if the switch is turned on at time $t = 7$ seconds and the voltage is gradually increased to 100 volts over a period of 25 seconds. Write a formula for $V(t)$ in terms of $H(t)$ for $t \leq 32$.

59. Let f and g be linear functions with equations $f(x) = m_1x + b_1$ and $g(x) = m_2x + b_2$. Is $f \circ g$ also a linear function? If so, what is the slope of its graph?

60. If you invest x dollars at 4% interest compounded annually, then the amount $A(x)$ of the investment after one year is $A(x) = 1.04x$. Find $A \circ A$, $A \circ A \circ A$, and $A \circ A \circ A \circ A$. What do these compositions represent? Find a formula for the composition of n copies of A.

61. (a) If $g(x) = 2x + 1$ and $h(x) = 4x^2 + 4x + 7$, find a function f such that $f \circ g = h$. (Think about what operations you would have to perform on the formula for g to end up with the formula for h.)
(b) If $f(x) = 3x + 5$ and $h(x) = 3x^2 + 3x + 2$, find a function g such that $f \circ g = h$.

62. If $f(x) = x + 4$ and $h(x) = 4x - 1$, find a function g such that $g \circ f = h$.

63. Suppose g is an even function and let $h = f \circ g$. Is h always an even function?

64. Suppose g is an odd function and let $h = f \circ g$. Is h always an odd function? What if f is odd? What if f is even?

1.4 Graphing Calculators and Computers

In this section we assume that you have access to a graphing calculator or a computer with graphing software. We will see that the use of such a device enables us to graph more complicated functions and to solve more complex problems than would otherwise be possible. We also point out some of the pitfalls that can occur with these machines.

Graphing calculators and computers can give very accurate graphs of functions. But we will see in Chapter 4 that only through the use of calculus can we be sure that we have uncovered all the interesting aspects of a graph.

A graphing calculator or computer displays a rectangular portion of the graph of a function in a **display window** or **viewing screen**, which we refer to as a **viewing rectangle**. The default screen often gives an incomplete or misleading picture, so it is important to choose the viewing rectangle with care. If we choose the x-values to range from a minimum value of $Xmin = a$ to a maximum value of $Xmax = b$ and the y-values to range from a minimum of $Ymin = c$ to a maximum of $Ymax = d$, then the visible portion of the graph lies in the rectangle

$$[a, b] \times [c, d] = \{(x, y) \mid a \leqslant x \leqslant b, c \leqslant y \leqslant d\}$$

shown in Figure 1. We refer to this rectangle as the $[a, b]$ *by* $[c, d]$ *viewing rectangle.*

FIGURE 1
The viewing rectangle $[a, b]$ by $[c, d]$

The machine draws the graph of a function f much as you would. It plots points of the form $(x, f(x))$ for a certain number of equally spaced values of x between a and b. If an x-value is not in the domain of f, or if $f(x)$ lies outside the viewing rectangle, it moves on to the next x-value. The machine connects each point to the preceding plotted point to form a representation of the graph of f.

EXAMPLE 1 Draw the graph of the function $f(x) = x^2 + 3$ in each of the following viewing rectangles.

(a) $[-2, 2]$ by $[-2, 2]$ (b) $[-4, 4]$ by $[-4, 4]$

(c) $[-10, 10]$ by $[-5, 30]$ (d) $[-50, 50]$ by $[-100, 1000]$

SOLUTION For part (a) we select the range by setting $Xmin = -2$, $Xmax = 2$, $Ymin = -2$, and $Ymax = 2$. The resulting graph is shown in Figure 2(a). The display window is blank! A moment's thought provides the explanation: Notice that $x^2 \geqslant 0$ for all x, so $x^2 + 3 \geqslant 3$ for all x. Thus the range of the function $f(x) = x^2 + 3$ is $[3, \infty)$. This means that the graph of f lies entirely outside the viewing rectangle $[-2, 2]$ by $[-2, 2]$.

The graphs for the viewing rectangles in parts (b), (c), and (d) are also shown in Figure 2. Observe that we get a more complete picture in parts (c) and (d), but in part (d) it is not clear that the y-intercept is 3.

(a) $[-2, 2]$ by $[-2, 2]$

(b) $[-4, 4]$ by $[-4, 4]$

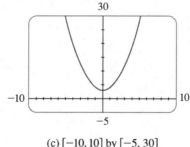

(c) $[-10, 10]$ by $[-5, 30]$

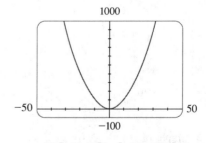

(d) $[-50, 50]$ by $[-100, 1000]$

FIGURE 2 Graphs of $f(x) = x^2 + 3$

We see from Example 1 that the choice of a viewing rectangle can make a big difference in the appearance of a graph. Often it's necessary to change to a larger viewing rectangle to obtain a more complete picture, a more global view, of the graph. In the next example we see that knowledge of the domain and range of a function sometimes provides us with enough information to select a good viewing rectangle.

EXAMPLE 2   Determine an appropriate viewing rectangle for the function $f(x) = \sqrt{8 - 2x^2}$ and use it to graph f.

SOLUTION   The expression for $f(x)$ is defined when

$$8 - 2x^2 \geqslant 0 \quad \Longleftrightarrow \quad 2x^2 \leqslant 8 \quad \Longleftrightarrow \quad x^2 \leqslant 4$$

$$\Longleftrightarrow \quad |x| \leqslant 2 \quad \Longleftrightarrow \quad -2 \leqslant x \leqslant 2$$

Therefore the domain of f is the interval $[-2, 2]$. Also,

$$0 \leqslant \sqrt{8 - 2x^2} \leqslant \sqrt{8} = 2\sqrt{2} \approx 2.83$$

so the range of f is the interval $\left[0, 2\sqrt{2}\,\right]$.

   We choose the viewing rectangle so that the x-interval is somewhat larger than the domain and the y-interval is larger than the range. Taking the viewing rectangle to be $[-3, 3]$ by $[-1, 4]$, we get the graph shown in Figure 3. ∎

FIGURE 3
$f(x) = \sqrt{8 - 2x^2}$

EXAMPLE 3   Graph the function $y = x^3 - 150x$.

SOLUTION   Here the domain is $\mathbb{R}$, the set of all real numbers. That doesn't help us choose a viewing rectangle. Let's experiment. If we start with the viewing rectangle $[-5, 5]$ by $[-5, 5]$, we get the graph in Figure 4. It appears blank, but actually the graph is so nearly vertical that it blends in with the y-axis.

   If we change the viewing rectangle to $[-20, 20]$ by $[-20, 20]$, we get the picture shown in Figure 5(a). The graph appears to consist of vertical lines, but we know that can't be correct. If we look carefully while the graph is being drawn, we see that the graph leaves the screen and reappears during the graphing process. This indicates that we need to see more in the vertical direction, so we change the viewing rectangle to $[-20, 20]$ by $[-500, 500]$. The resulting graph is shown in Figure 5(b). It still doesn't quite reveal all the main features of the function, so we try $[-20, 20]$ by $[-1000, 1000]$ in Figure 5(c). Now we are more confident that we have arrived at an appropriate viewing rectangle. In Chapter 4 we will be able to see that the graph shown in Figure 5(c) does indeed reveal all the main features of the function.

FIGURE 4

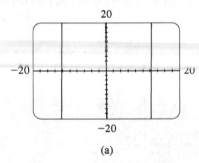

(a)   (b)   (c)

FIGURE 5   Graphs of $y = x^3 - 150x$ ∎

V   **EXAMPLE 4**   Graph the function $f(x) = \sin 50x$ in an appropriate viewing rectangle.

SOLUTION   Figure 6(a) shows the graph of f produced by a graphing calculator using the viewing rectangle $[-12, 12]$ by $[-1.5, 1.5]$. At first glance the graph appears to be reasonable. But if we change the viewing rectangle to the ones shown in the following parts of Figure 6, the graphs look very different. Something strange is happening.

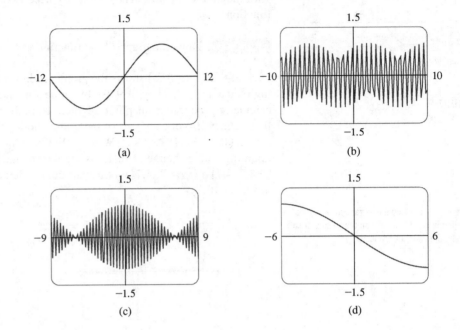

The appearance of the graphs in Figure 6 depends on the machine used. The graphs you get with your own graphing device might not look like these figures, but they will also be quite inaccurate.

FIGURE 6

Graphs of $f(x) = \sin 50x$ in four viewing rectangles

In order to explain the big differences in appearance of these graphs and to find an appropriate viewing rectangle, we need to find the period of the function $y = \sin 50x$. We know that the function $y = \sin x$ has period 2π and the graph of $y = \sin 50x$ is shrunk horizontally by a factor of 50, so the period of $y = \sin 50x$ is

$$\frac{2\pi}{50} = \frac{\pi}{25} \approx 0.126$$

This suggests that we should deal only with small values of x in order to show just a few oscillations of the graph. If we choose the viewing rectangle $[-0.25, 0.25]$ by $[-1.5, 1.5]$, we get the graph shown in Figure 7.

Now we see what went wrong in Figure 6. The oscillations of $y = \sin 50x$ are so rapid that when the calculator plots points and joins them, it misses most of the maximum and minimum points and therefore gives a very misleading impression of the graph. ▬

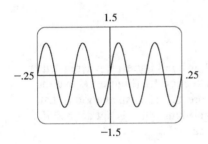

FIGURE 7

$f(x) = \sin 50x$

We have seen that the use of an inappropriate viewing rectangle can give a misleading impression of the graph of a function. In Examples 1 and 3 we solved the problem by changing to a larger viewing rectangle. In Example 4 we had to make the viewing rectangle smaller. In the next example we look at a function for which there is no single viewing rectangle that reveals the true shape of the graph.

V EXAMPLE 5 Graph the function $f(x) = \sin x + \frac{1}{100} \cos 100x$.

SOLUTION Figure 8 shows the graph of f produced by a graphing calculator with viewing rectangle $[-6.5, 6.5]$ by $[-1.5, 1.5]$. It looks much like the graph of $y = \sin x$, but perhaps with some bumps attached. If we zoom in to the viewing rectangle $[-0.1, 0.1]$ by

FIGURE 8

FIGURE 9

Another way to avoid the extraneous line is to change the graphing mode on the calculator so that the dots are not connected.

[−0.1, 0.1], we can see much more clearly the shape of these bumps in Figure 9. The reason for this behavior is that the second term, $\frac{1}{100} \cos 100x$, is very small in comparison with the first term, $\sin x$. Thus we really need two graphs to see the true nature of this function.

EXAMPLE 6 Draw the graph of the function $y = \dfrac{1}{1 - x}$.

SOLUTION Figure 10(a) shows the graph produced by a graphing calculator with viewing rectangle [−9, 9] by [−9, 9]. In connecting successive points on the graph, the calculator produced a steep line segment from the top to the bottom of the screen. That line segment is not truly part of the graph. Notice that the domain of the function $y = 1/(1 - x)$ is $\{x \mid x \neq 1\}$. We can eliminate the extraneous near-vertical line by experimenting with a change of scale. When we change to the smaller viewing rectangle [−4.7, 4.7] by [−4.7, 4.7] on this particular calculator, we obtain the much better graph in Figure 10(b).

FIGURE 10   (a)   (b)

EXAMPLE 7 Graph the function $y = \sqrt[3]{x}$.

SOLUTION Some graphing devices display the graph shown in Figure 11, whereas others produce a graph like that in Figure 12. We know from Section 1.2 (Figure 13) that the graph in Figure 12 is correct, so what happened in Figure 11? The explanation is that some machines compute the cube root of x using a logarithm, which is not defined if x is negative, so only the right half of the graph is produced.

 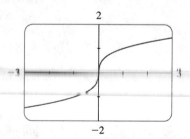

FIGURE 11   **FIGURE 12**

You can get the correct graph with Maple if you first type

```
with(RealDomain);
```

You should experiment with your own machine to see which of these two graphs is produced. If you get the graph in Figure 11, you can obtain the correct picture by graphing the function

$$f(x) = \frac{x}{|x|} \cdot |x|^{1/3}$$

Notice that this function is equal to $\sqrt[3]{x}$ (except when $x = 0$).

To understand how the expression for a function relates to its graph, it's helpful to graph a **family of functions**, that is, a collection of functions whose equations are related. In the next example we graph members of a family of cubic polynomials.

EXAMPLE 8 Graph the function $y = x^3 + cx$ for various values of the number c. How does the graph change when c is changed?

SOLUTION Figure 13 shows the graphs of $y = x^3 + cx$ for $c = 2, 1, 0, -1,$ and -2. We see that, for positive values of c, the graph increases from left to right with no maximum or minimum points (peaks or valleys). When $c = 0$, the curve is flat at the origin. When c is negative, the curve has a maximum point and a minimum point. As c decreases, the maximum point becomes higher and the minimum point lower.

TEC In Visual 1.4 you can see an animation of Figure 13.

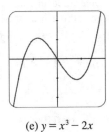

(a) $y = x^3 + 2x$ (b) $y = x^3 + x$ (c) $y = x^3$ (d) $y = x^3 - x$ (e) $y = x^3 - 2x$

FIGURE 13

Several members of the family of functions $y = x^3 + cx$, all graphed in the viewing rectangle $[-2, 2]$ by $[-2.5, 2.5]$

EXAMPLE 9 Find the solution of the equation $\cos x = x$ correct to two decimal places.

SOLUTION The solutions of the equation $\cos x = x$ are the x-coordinates of the points of intersection of the curves $y = \cos x$ and $y = x$. From Figure 14(a) we see that there is only one solution and it lies between 0 and 1. Zooming in to the viewing rectangle $[0, 1]$ by $[0, 1]$, we see from Figure 14(b) that the root lies between 0.7 and 0.8. So we zoom in further to the viewing rectangle $[0.7, 0.8]$ by $[0.7, 0.8]$ in Figure 14(c). By moving the cursor to the intersection point of the two curves, or by inspection and the fact that the x-scale is 0.01, we see that the solution of the equation is about 0.74. (Many calculators have a built-in intersection feature.)

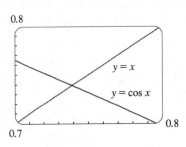

FIGURE 14

Locating the roots of $\cos x = x$

(a) $[-5, 5]$ by $[-1.5, 1.5]$
x-scale $= 1$

(b) $[0, 1]$ by $[0, 1]$
x-scale $= 0.1$

(c) $[0.7, 0.8]$ by $[0.7, 0.8]$
x-scale $= 0.01$

1.4 ⊞ Exercises

1. Use a graphing calculator or computer to determine which of the given viewing rectangles produces the most appropriate graph of the function $f(x) = \sqrt{x^3 - 5x^2}$.
(a) $[-5, 5]$ by $[-5, 5]$ (b) $[0, 10]$ by $[0, 2]$
(c) $[0, 10]$ by $[0, 10]$

2. Use a graphing calculator or computer to determine which of the given viewing rectangles produces the most appropriate graph of the function $f(x) = x^4 - 16x^2 + 20$.
(a) $[-3, 3]$ by $[-3, 3]$ (b) $[-10, 10]$ by $[-10, 10]$
(c) $[-50, 50]$ by $[-50, 50]$ (d) $[-5, 5]$ by $[-50, 50]$

3–14 Determine an appropriate viewing rectangle for the given function and use it to draw the graph.

3. $f(x) = x^2 - 36x + 32$ **4.** $f(x) = x^3 + 15x^2 + 65x$

5. $f(x) = \sqrt{50 - 0.2x}$ **6.** $f(x) = \sqrt{15x - x^2}$

7. $f(x) = x^3 - 225x$ **8.** $f(x) = \dfrac{x}{x^2 + 100}$

9. $f(x) = \sin^2(1000x)$ **10.** $f(x) = \cos(0.001x)$

11. $f(x) = \sin\sqrt{x}$ **12.** $f(x) = \sec(20\pi x)$

13. $y = 10 \sin x + \sin 100x$ **14.** $y = x^2 + 0.02 \sin 50x$

15. (a) Try to find an appropriate viewing rectangle for $f(x) = (x - 10)^3 2^{-x}$.
(b) Do you need more than one window? Why?

16. Graph the function $f(x) = x^2\sqrt{30 - x}$ in an appropriate viewing rectangle. Why does part of the graph appear to be missing?

17. Graph the ellipse $4x^2 + 2y^2 = 1$ by graphing the functions whose graphs are the upper and lower halves of the ellipse.

18. Graph the hyperbola $y^2 - 9x^2 = 1$ by graphing the functions whose graphs are the upper and lower branches of the hyperbola.

19–20 Do the graphs intersect in the given viewing rectangle? If they do, how many points of intersection are there?

19. $y = 3x^2 - 6x + 1$, $y = 0.23x - 2.25$;
$[-1, 3]$ by $[-2.5, 1.5]$

20. $y = 6 - 4x - x^2$, $y = 3x + 18$; $[-6, 2]$ by $[-5, 20]$

21–23 Find all solutions of the equation correct to two decimal places.

21. $x^4 - x = 1$ **22.** $\sqrt{x} = x^3 - 1$

23. $\tan x = \sqrt{1 - x^2}$

24. We saw in Example 9 that the equation $\cos x = x$ has exactly one solution.
(a) Use a graph to show that the equation $\cos x = 0.3x$ has three solutions and find their values correct to two decimal places.
(b) Find an approximate value of m such that the equation $\cos x = mx$ has exactly two solutions.

25. Use graphs to determine which of the functions $f(x) = 10x^2$ and $g(x) = x^3/10$ is eventually larger (that is, larger when x is very large).

26. Use graphs to determine which of the functions $f(x) = x^4 - 100x^3$ and $g(x) = x^3$ is eventually larger.

27. For what values of x is it true that $|\tan x - x| < 0.01$ and $-\pi/2 < x < \pi/2$?

28. Graph the polynomials $P(x) = 3x^5 - 5x^3 + 2x$ and $Q(x) = 3x^5$ on the same screen, first using the viewing rectangle $[-2, 2]$ by $[-2, 2]$ and then changing to $[-10, 10]$ by $[-10,000, 10,000]$. What do you observe from these graphs?

29. In this exercise we consider the family of root functions $f(x) = \sqrt[n]{x}$, where n is a positive integer.
(a) Graph the functions $y = \sqrt{x}$, $y = \sqrt[4]{x}$, and $y = \sqrt[6]{x}$ on the same screen using the viewing rectangle $[-1, 4]$ by $[-1, 3]$.
(b) Graph the functions $y = x$, $y = \sqrt[3]{x}$, and $y = \sqrt[5]{x}$ on the same screen using the viewing rectangle $[-3, 3]$ by $[-2, 2]$. (See Example 7.)
(c) Graph the functions $y = \sqrt{x}$, $y = \sqrt[3]{x}$, $y = \sqrt[4]{x}$, and $y = \sqrt[5]{x}$ on the same screen using the viewing rectangle $[-1, 3]$ by $[-1, 2]$.
(d) What conclusions can you make from these graphs?

30. In this exercise we consider the family of functions $f(x) = 1/x^n$, where n is a positive integer.
(a) Graph the functions $y = 1/x$ and $y = 1/x^3$ on the same screen using the viewing rectangle $[-3, 3]$ by $[-3, 3]$.
(b) Graph the functions $y = 1/x^2$ and $y = 1/x^4$ on the same screen using the same viewing rectangle as in part (a).
(c) Graph all of the functions in parts (a) and (b) on the same screen using the viewing rectangle $[-1, 3]$ by $[-1, 3]$.
(d) What conclusions can you make from these graphs?

31. Graph the function $f(x) = x^4 + cx^2 + x$ for several values of c. How does the graph change when c changes?

32. Graph the function $f(x) = \sqrt{1 + cx^2}$ for various values of c. Describe how changing the value of c affects the graph.

⊞ Graphing calculator or computer required   **1.** Homework Hints available at stewartcalculus.com

33. Graph the function $y = x^n 2^{-x}$, $x \geqslant 0$, for $n = 1, 2, 3, 4, 5$, and 6. How does the graph change as n increases?

34. The curves with equations

$$y = \frac{|x|}{\sqrt{c - x^2}}$$

are called **bullet-nose curves**. Graph some of these curves to see why. What happens as c increases?

35. What happens to the graph of the equation $y^2 = cx^3 + x^2$ as c varies?

36. This exercise explores the effect of the inner function g on a composite function $y = f(g(x))$.
(a) Graph the function $y = \sin(\sqrt{x})$ using the viewing rectangle $[0, 400]$ by $[-1.5, 1.5]$. How does this graph differ from the graph of the sine function?
(b) Graph the function $y = \sin(x^2)$ using the viewing rectangle $[-5, 5]$ by $[-1.5, 1.5]$. How does this graph differ from the graph of the sine function?

37. The figure shows the graphs of $y = \sin 96x$ and $y = \sin 2x$ as displayed by a TI-83 graphing calculator. The first graph is inaccurate. Explain why the two graphs appear identical.

[*Hint:* The TI-83's graphing window is 95 pixels wide. What specific points does the calculator plot?]

$y = \sin 96x$

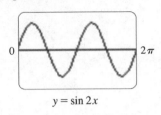
$y = \sin 2x$

38. The first graph in the figure is that of $y = \sin 45x$ as displayed by a TI-83 graphing calculator. It is inaccurate and so, to help explain its appearance, we replot the curve in dot mode in the second graph. What two sine curves does the calculator appear to be plotting? Show that each point on the graph of $y = \sin 45x$ that the TI-83 chooses to plot is in fact on one of these two curves. (The TI-83's graphing window is 95 pixels wide.)

1.5 Exponential Functions

In Appendix G we present an alternative approach to the exponential and logarithmic functions using integral calculus.

The function $f(x) = 2^x$ is called an *exponential function* because the variable, x, is the exponent. It should not be confused with the power function $g(x) = x^2$, in which the variable is the base.

In general, an **exponential function** is a function of the form

$$f(x) = a^x$$

where a is a positive constant. Let's recall what this means.

If $x = n$, a positive integer, then

$$a^n = \underbrace{a \cdot a \cdot \cdots \cdot a}_{n \text{ factors}}$$

If $x = 0$, then $a^0 = 1$, and if $x = -n$, where n is a positive integer, then

$$a^{-n} = \frac{1}{a^n}$$

If x is a rational number, $x = p/q$, where p and q are integers and $q > 0$, then

$$a^x = a^{p/q} = \sqrt[q]{a^p} = \left(\sqrt[q]{a}\right)^p$$

But what is the meaning of a^x if x is an irrational number? For instance, what is meant by $2^{\sqrt{3}}$ or 5^{π}?

To help us answer this question we first look at the graph of the function $y = 2^x$, where x is rational. A representation of this graph is shown in Figure 1. We want to enlarge the domain of $y = 2^x$ to include both rational and irrational numbers.

FIGURE 1
Representation of $y = 2^x$, x rational

There are holes in the graph in Figure 1 corresponding to irrational values of x. We want to fill in the holes by defining $f(x) = 2^x$, where $x \in \mathbb{R}$, so that f is an increasing function. In particular, since the irrational number $\sqrt{3}$ satisfies

$$1.7 < \sqrt{3} < 1.8$$

we must have

$$2^{1.7} < 2^{\sqrt{3}} < 2^{1.8}$$

and we know what $2^{1.7}$ and $2^{1.8}$ mean because 1.7 and 1.8 are rational numbers. Similarly, if we use better approximations for $\sqrt{3}$, we obtain better approximations for $2^{\sqrt{3}}$:

$$1.73 < \sqrt{3} < 1.74 \qquad \Rightarrow \qquad 2^{1.73} < 2^{\sqrt{3}} < 2^{1.74}$$
$$1.732 < \sqrt{3} < 1.733 \qquad \Rightarrow \qquad 2^{1.732} < 2^{\sqrt{3}} < 2^{1.733}$$
$$1.7320 < \sqrt{3} < 1.7321 \qquad \Rightarrow \qquad 2^{1.7320} < 2^{\sqrt{3}} < 2^{1.7321}$$
$$1.73205 < \sqrt{3} < 1.73206 \qquad \Rightarrow \qquad 2^{1.73205} < 2^{\sqrt{3}} < 2^{1.73206}$$
$$\vdots \qquad\qquad \vdots \qquad\qquad\qquad \vdots \qquad\qquad \vdots$$

A proof of this fact is given in J. Marsden and A. Weinstein, *Calculus Unlimited* (Menlo Park, CA, 1981). For an online version, see

caltechbook.library.caltech.edu/197/

It can be shown that there is exactly one number that is greater than all of the numbers

$$2^{1.7}, \quad 2^{1.73}, \quad 2^{1.732}, \quad 2^{1.7320}, \quad 2^{1.73205}, \quad \dots$$

and less than all of the numbers

$$2^{1.8}, \quad 2^{1.74}, \quad 2^{1.733}, \quad 2^{1.7321}, \quad 2^{1.73206}, \quad \dots$$

We define $2^{\sqrt{3}}$ to be this number. Using the preceding approximation process we can compute it correct to six decimal places:

$$2^{\sqrt{3}} \approx 3.321997$$

Similarly, we can define 2^x (or a^x, if $a > 0$) where x is any irrational number. Figure 2 shows how all the holes in Figure 1 have been filled to complete the graph of the function $f(x) = 2^x$, $x \in \mathbb{R}$.

The graphs of members of the family of functions $y = a^x$ are shown in Figure 3 for various values of the base a. Notice that all of these graphs pass through the same point $(0, 1)$ because $a^0 = 1$ for $a \neq 0$. Notice also that as the base a gets larger, the exponential function grows more rapidly (for $x > 0$).

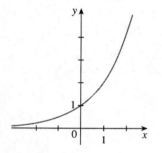

FIGURE 2
$y = 2^x$, x real

If $0 < a < 1$, then a^x approaches 0 as x becomes large. If $a > 1$, then a^x approaches 0 as x decreases through negative values. In both cases the x-axis is a horizontal asymptote. These matters are discussed in Section 2.6.

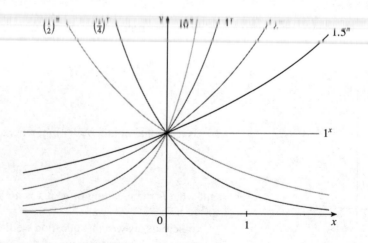

$\left(\frac{1}{2}\right)^x \qquad \left(\frac{1}{4}\right)^x \qquad 10^x \qquad 4^x \qquad 2^x \qquad 1.5^x$

1^x

FIGURE 3

You can see from Figure 3 that there are basically three kinds of exponential functions $y = a^x$. If $0 < a < 1$, the exponential function decreases; if $a = 1$, it is a constant; and if $a > 1$, it increases. These three cases are illustrated in Figure 4. Observe that if $a \neq 1$, then the exponential function $y = a^x$ has domain $\mathbb{R}$ and range $(0, \infty)$. Notice also that, since $(1/a)^x = 1/a^x = a^{-x}$, the graph of $y = (1/a)^x$ is just the reflection of the graph of $y = a^x$ about the y-axis.

FIGURE 4   (a) $y = a^x$, $0 < a < 1$ (b) $y = 1^x$ (c) $y = a^x$, $a > 1$

One reason for the importance of the exponential function lies in the following properties. If x and y are rational numbers, then these laws are well known from elementary algebra. It can be proved that they remain true for arbitrary real numbers x and y.

www.stewartcalculus.com

For review and practice using the Laws of Exponents, click on *Review of Algebra*.

Laws of Exponents If a and b are positive numbers and x and y are any real numbers, then

1. $a^{x+y} = a^x a^y$ **2.** $a^{x-y} = \dfrac{a^x}{a^y}$ **3.** $(a^x)^y = a^{xy}$ **4.** $(ab)^x = a^x b^x$

EXAMPLE 1 Sketch the graph of the function $y = 3 - 2^x$ and determine its domain and range.

SOLUTION First we reflect the graph of $y = 2^x$ [shown in Figures 2 and 5(a)] about the x-axis to get the graph of $y = -2^x$ in Figure 5(b). Then we shift the graph of $y = -2^x$ upward 3 units to obtain the graph of $y = 3 - 2^x$ in Figure 5(c). The domain is $\mathbb{R}$ and the range is $(-\infty, 3)$.

For a review of reflecting and shifting graphs, see Section 1.3.

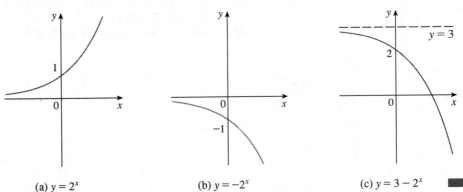

FIGURE 5   (a) $y = 2^x$ (b) $y = -2^x$ (c) $y = 3 - 2^x$

V EXAMPLE 2 Use a graphing device to compare the exponential function $f(x) = 2^x$ and the power function $g(x) = x^2$. Which function grows more quickly when x is large?

Example 2 shows that $y = 2^x$ increases more quickly than $y = x^2$. To demonstrate just how quickly $f(x) = 2^x$ increases, let's perform the following thought experiment. Suppose we start with a piece of paper a tenth of a millimeter thick and we fold it in half 50 times. Each time we fold the paper in half, the thickness of the paper doubles, so the thickness of the resulting paper would be $2^{50}/10$ mm. How thick do you think that is? It works out to be more than a hundred million kilometers!

SOLUTION   Figure 6 shows both functions graphed in the viewing rectangle $[-2, 6]$ by $[0, 40]$. We see that the graphs intersect three times, but for $x > 4$ the graph of $f(x) = 2^x$ stays above the graph of $g(x) = x^2$. Figure 7 gives a more global view and shows that for large values of x, the exponential function $y = 2^x$ grows far more rapidly than the power function $y = x^2$.

FIGURE 6

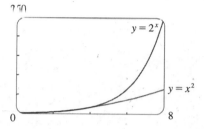

FIGURE 7

Applications of Exponential Functions

The exponential function occurs very frequently in mathematical models of nature and society. Here we indicate briefly how it arises in the description of population growth. In later chapters we will pursue these and other applications in greater detail.

First we consider a population of bacteria in a homogeneous nutrient medium. Suppose that by sampling the population at certain intervals it is determined that the population doubles every hour. If the number of bacteria at time t is $p(t)$, where t is measured in hours, and the initial population is $p(0) = 1000$, then we have

$$p(1) = 2p(0) = 2 \times 1000$$

$$p(2) = 2p(1) = 2^2 \times 1000$$

$$p(3) = 2p(2) = 2^3 \times 1000$$

It seems from this pattern that, in general,

$$p(t) = 2^t \times 1000 = (1000)2^t$$

This population function is a constant multiple of the exponential function $y = 2^t$, so it exhibits the rapid growth that we observed in Figures 2 and 7. Under ideal conditions (unlimited space and nutrition and absence of disease) this exponential growth is typical of what actually occurs in nature.

What about the human population? Table 1 shows data for the population of the world in the 20th century and Figure 8 shows the corresponding scatter plot.

TABLE 1

t	Population (millions)
0	1650
10	1750
20	1860
30	2070
40	2300
50	2560
60	3040
70	3710
80	4450
90	5280
100	6080
110	6870

FIGURE 8 Scatter plot for world population growth

The pattern of the data points in Figure 8 suggests exponential growth, so we use a graphing calculator with exponential regression capability to apply the method of least squares and obtain the exponential model

$$P = (1436.53) \cdot (1.01395)^t$$

where $t = 0$ corresponds to 1900. Figure 9 shows the graph of this exponential function together with the original data points. We see that the exponential curve fits the data reasonably well. The period of relatively slow population growth is explained by the two world wars and the Great Depression of the 1930s.

FIGURE 9
Exponential model for
population growth

The Number e

Of all possible bases for an exponential function, there is one that is most convenient for the purposes of calculus. The choice of a base a is influenced by the way the graph of $y = a^x$ crosses the y-axis. Figures 10 and 11 show the tangent lines to the graphs of $y = 2^x$ and $y = 3^x$ at the point $(0, 1)$. (Tangent lines will be defined precisely in Section 2.7. For present purposes, you can think of the tangent line to an exponential graph at a point as the line that touches the graph only at that point.) If we measure the slopes of these tangent lines at $(0, 1)$, we find that $m \approx 0.7$ for $y = 2^x$ and $m \approx 1.1$ for $y = 3^x$.

FIGURE 10

FIGURE 11

It turns out, as we will see in Chapter 3, that some of the formulas of calculus will be greatly simplified if we choose the base a so that the slope of the tangent line to $y = a^x$ at $(0, 1)$ is *exactly* 1. (See Figure 12.) In fact, there *is* such a number and it is denoted by the letter e. (This notation was chosen by the Swiss mathematician Leonhard Euler in 1727, probably because it is the first letter of the word *exponential*.) In view of Figures 10 and 11, it comes as no surprise that the number e lies between 2 and 3 and the graph of $y = e^x$ lies between the graphs of $y = 2^x$ and $y = 3^x$. (See Figure 13.) In Chapter 3 we will see that the value of e, correct to five decimal places, is

$$e \approx 2.71828$$

FIGURE 12

The natural exponential function
crosses the y-axis with a slope of 1.

We call the function $f(x) = e^x$ the **natural exponential function**.

TEC Module 1.5 enables you to graph exponential functions with various bases and their tangent lines in order to estimate more closely the value of a for which the tangent has slope 1.

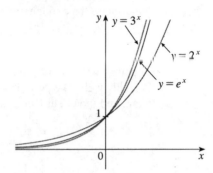

FIGURE 13

V **EXAMPLE 3** Graph the function $y = \frac{1}{2}e^{-x} - 1$ and state the domain and range.

SOLUTION We start with the graph of $y = e^x$ from Figures 12 and 14(a) and reflect about the y-axis to get the graph of $y = e^{-x}$ in Figure 14(b). (Notice that the graph crosses the y-axis with a slope of -1). Then we compress the graph vertically by a factor of 2 to obtain the graph of $y = \frac{1}{2}e^{-x}$ in Figure 14(c). Finally, we shift the graph downward one unit to get the desired graph in Figure 14(d). The domain is $\mathbb{R}$ and the range is $(-1, \infty)$.

(a) $y = e^x$

(b) $y = e^{-x}$

(c) $y = \frac{1}{2}e^{-x}$

(d) $y = \frac{1}{2}e^{-x} - 1$

FIGURE 14

How far to the right do you think we would have to go for the height of the graph of $y = e^x$ to exceed a million? The next example demonstrates the rapid growth of this function by providing an answer that might surprise you.

EXAMPLE 4 Use a graphing device to find the values of x for which $e^x > 1,000,000$.

SOLUTION In Figure 15 we graph both the function $y = e^x$ and the horizontal line $y = 1,000,000$. We see that these curves intersect when $x \approx 13.8$. Thus $e^x > 10^6$ when $x > 13.8$. It is perhaps surprising that the values of the exponential function have already surpassed a million when x is only 14.

FIGURE 15

1.5 Exercises

1–4 Use the Law of Exponents to rewrite and simplify the expression.

1. (a) $\dfrac{4^{-3}}{2^{-8}}$ (b) $\dfrac{1}{\sqrt[3]{x^4}}$

2. (a) $8^{4/3}$ (b) $x(3x^2)^3$

3. (a) $b^8(2b)^4$ (b) $\dfrac{(6y^3)^4}{2y^5}$

4. (a) $\dfrac{x^{2n} \cdot x^{3n-1}}{x^{n+2}}$ (b) $\dfrac{\sqrt{a}\sqrt{b}}{\sqrt[3]{ab}}$

5. (a) Write an equation that defines the exponential function with base $a > 0$.
  (b) What is the domain of this function?
  (c) If $a \neq 1$, what is the range of this function?
  (d) Sketch the general shape of the graph of the exponential function for each of the following cases.
    (i) $a > 1$ (ii) $a = 1$ (iii) $0 < a < 1$

6. (a) How is the number e defined?
  (b) What is an approximate value for e?
  (c) What is the natural exponential function?

7–10 Graph the given functions on a common screen. How are these graphs related?

7. $y = 2^x$, $y = e^x$, $y = 5^x$, $y = 20^x$

8. $y = e^x$, $y = e^{-x}$, $y = 8^x$, $y = 8^{-x}$

9. $y = 3^x$, $y = 10^x$, $y = \left(\tfrac{1}{3}\right)^x$, $y = \left(\tfrac{1}{10}\right)^x$

10. $y = 0.9^x$, $y = 0.6^x$, $y = 0.3^x$, $y = 0.1^x$

11–16 Make a rough sketch of the graph of the function. Do not use a calculator. Just use the graphs given in Figures 3 and 13 and, if necessary, the transformations of Section 1.3.

11. $y = 10^{x+2}$ **12.** $y = (0.5)^x - 2$

13. $y = -2^{-x}$ **14.** $y = e^{|x|}$

15. $y = 1 - \tfrac{1}{2}e^{-x}$ **16.** $y = 2(1 - e^x)$

17. Starting with the graph of $y = e^x$, write the equation of the graph that results from
  (a) shifting 2 units downward
  (b) shifting 2 units to the right
  (c) reflecting about the x-axis
  (d) reflecting about the y-axis
  (e) reflecting about the x-axis and then about the y-axis

18. Starting with the graph of $y = e^x$, find the equation of the graph that results from
  (a) reflecting about the line $y = 4$
  (b) reflecting about the line $x = 2$

19–20 Find the domain of each function.

19. (a) $f(x) = \dfrac{1 - e^{x^2}}{1 - e^{1-x^2}}$ (b) $f(x) = \dfrac{1 + x}{e^{\cos x}}$

20. (a) $g(t) = \sin(e^{-t})$ (b) $g(t) = \sqrt{1 - 2^t}$

21–22 Find the exponential function $f(x) = Ca^x$ whose graph is given.

21.   **22.**

23. If $f(x) = 5^x$, show that

$$\frac{f(x+h) - f(x)}{h} = 5^x\left(\frac{5^h - 1}{h}\right)$$

24. Suppose you are offered a job that lasts one month. Which of the following methods of payment do you prefer?
  I. One million dollars at the end of the month.
  II. One cent on the first day of the month, two cents on the second day, four cents on the third day, and, in general, 2^{n-1} cents on the nth day.

25. Suppose the graphs of $f(x) = x^2$ and $g(x) = 2^x$ are drawn on a coordinate grid where the unit of measurement is 1 cm. Show that, at a distance 1 m to the right of the origin, the height of the graph of f is 100 m but the height of the graph of g is more than 10^{25} km.

26. Compare the functions $f(x) = x^5$ and $g(x) = 5^x$ by graphing both functions in several viewing rectangles. Find all points of intersection of the graphs correct to one decimal place. Which function grows more rapidly when x is large?

27. Compare the functions $f(x) = x^{10}$ and $g(x) = e^x$ by graphing both f and g in several viewing rectangles. When does the graph of g finally surpass the graph of f?

28. Use a graph to estimate the values of x such that $e^x > 1{,}000{,}000{,}000$.

29. Under ideal conditions a certain bacteria population is known to double every three hours. Suppose that there are initially 100 bacteria.
(a) What is the size of the population after 15 hours?
(b) What is the size of the population after t hours?
(c) Estimate the size of the population after 20 hours.
(d) Graph the population function and estimate the time for the population to reach 50,000.

30. A bacterial culture starts with 500 bacteria and doubles in size every half hour.
(a) How many bacteria are there after 3 hours?
(b) How many bacteria are there after t hours?
(c) How many bacteria are there after 40 minutes?
(d) Graph the population function and estimate the time for the population to reach 100,000.

31. Use a graphing calculator with exponential regression capability to model the population of the world with the data from 1950 to 2010 in Table 1 on page 54. Use the model to estimate the population in 1993 and to predict the population in the year 2020.

32. The table gives the population of Malaysia, in millions, for the years 1950–2000. Use a graphing calculator with exponential regression capability to model the Malaysian population since 1950. Use the model to estimate the population in 1975 and to predict the population in the years 2010 and 2020.

Year	Population	Year	Population
1950	6.1	1980	13.8
1955	7.0	1985	15.7
1960	8.1	1990	17.8
1965	9.5	1995	20.4
1970	10.9	2000	23.0
1975	12.3		

33. If you graph the function
$$f(x) = \frac{1 - e^{1/x}}{1 + e^{1/x}}$$
you'll see that f appears to be an odd function. Prove it.

34. Graph several members of the family of functions
$$f(x) = \frac{1}{1 + ae^{bx}}$$
where $a > 0$. How does the graph change when b changes? How does it change when a changes?

1.6   Inverse Functions and Logarithms

Table 1 gives data from an experiment in which a bacteria culture started with 100 bacteria in a limited nutrient medium; the size of the bacteria population was recorded at hourly intervals. The number of bacteria N is a function of the time t: $N = f(t)$.

Suppose, however, that the biologist changes her point of view and becomes interested in the time required for the population to reach various levels. In other words, she is thinking of t as a function of N. This function is called the *inverse function* of f, denoted by f^{-1}, and read "f inverse." Thus $t = f^{-1}(N)$ is the time required for the population level to reach N. The values of f^{-1} can be found by reading Table 1 from right to left or by consulting Table 2. For instance, $f^{-1}(550) = 6$ because $f(6) = 550$.

TABLE 1 N as a function of t

t (hours)	$N = f(t)$ = population at time t
0	100
1	168
2	259
3	358
4	445
5	509
6	550
7	573
8	586

TABLE 2 t as a function of N

N	$t = f^{-1}(N)$ = time to reach N bacteria
100	0
168	1
259	2
358	3
445	4
509	5
550	6
573	7
586	8

Not all functions possess inverses. Let's compare the functions f and g whose arrow diagrams are shown in Figure 1. Note that f never takes on the same value twice (any two inputs in A have different outputs), whereas g does take on the same value twice (both 2 and 3 have the same output, 4). In symbols,

$$g(2) = g(3)$$

but $\qquad\qquad f(x_1) \neq f(x_2) \qquad$ whenever $x_1 \neq x_2$

Functions that share this property with f are called *one-to-one functions*.

 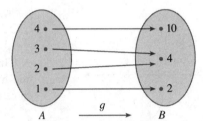

FIGURE 1

f is one-to-one; g is not

In the language of inputs and outputs, this definition says that f is one-to-one if each output corresponds to only one input.

1 **Definition** A function f is called a **one-to-one function** if it never takes on the same value twice; that is,

$$f(x_1) \neq f(x_2) \qquad \text{whenever } x_1 \neq x_2$$

If a horizontal line intersects the graph of f in more than one point, then we see from Figure 2 that there are numbers x_1 and x_2 such that $f(x_1) = f(x_2)$. This means that f is not one-to-one. Therefore we have the following geometric method for determining whether a function is one-to-one.

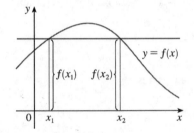

FIGURE 2

This function is not one-to-one because $f(x_1) = f(x_2)$.

Horizontal Line Test A function is one-to-one if and only if no horizontal line intersects its graph more than once.

V **EXAMPLE 1** Is the function $f(x) = x^3$ one-to-one?

SOLUTION 1 If $x_1 \neq x_2$, then $x_1^3 \neq x_2^3$ (two different numbers can't have the same cube). Therefore, by Definition 1, $f(x) = x^3$ is one-to-one.

SOLUTION 2 From Figure 3 we see that no horizontal line intersects the graph of $f(x) = x^3$ more than once. Therefore, by the Horizontal Line Test, f is one-to-one. ▪

EXAMPLE 2 Is the function $g(x) = x^2$ one-to-one?

SOLUTION 1 This function is not one-to-one because, for instance,

$$g(1) = 1 = g(-1)$$

and so 1 and -1 have the same output.

FIGURE 3

$f(x) = x^3$ is one-to-one.

FIGURE 4

$g(x) = x^2$ is not one-to-one.

FIGURE 5

SOLUTION 2 From Figure 4 we see that there are horizontal lines that intersect the graph of g more than once. Therefore, by the Horizontal Line Test, g is not one-to-one. ∎

One-to-one functions are important because they are precisely the functions that possess inverse functions according to the following definition.

> **2** **Definition** Let f be a one-to-one function with domain A and range B. Then its **inverse function** f^{-1} has domain B and range A and is defined by
>
> $$f^{-1}(y) = x \iff f(x) = y$$
>
> for any y in B.

This definition says that if f maps x into y, then f^{-1} maps y back into x. (If f were not one-to-one, then f^{-1} would not be uniquely defined.) The arrow diagram in Figure 5 indicates that f^{-1} reverses the effect of f. Note that

> domain of f^{-1} = range of f
>
> range of f^{-1} = domain of f

For example, the inverse function of $f(x) = x^3$ is $f^{-1}(x) = x^{1/3}$ because if $y = x^3$, then

$$f^{-1}(y) = f^{-1}(x^3) = (x^3)^{1/3} = x$$

⊘   **CAUTION** Do not mistake the -1 in f^{-1} for an exponent. Thus

$$f^{-1}(x) \quad \text{does } not \text{ mean} \quad \frac{1}{f(x)}$$

The reciprocal $1/f(x)$ could, however, be written as $[f(x)]^{-1}$.

V **EXAMPLE 3** If $f(1) = 5$, $f(3) = 7$, and $f(8) = -10$, find $f^{-1}(7)$, $f^{-1}(5)$, and $f^{-1}(-10)$.

SOLUTION From the definition of f^{-1} we have

$$f^{-1}(7) = 3 \qquad \text{because} \qquad f(3) = 7$$

$$f^{-1}(5) = 1 \qquad \text{because} \qquad f(1) = 5$$

$$f^{-1}(-10) = 8 \qquad \text{because} \qquad f(8) = -10$$

The diagram in Figure 6 makes it clear how f^{-1} reverses the effect of f in this case.

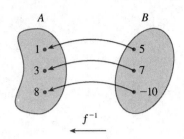

FIGURE 6
The inverse function reverses
inputs and outputs.

The letter x is traditionally used as the independent variable, so when we concentrate on f^{-1} rather than on f, we usually reverse the roles of x and y in Definition 2 and write

$$\boxed{3} \qquad f^{-1}(x) = y \iff f(y) = x$$

By substituting for y in Definition 2 and substituting for x in $\boxed{3}$, we get the following **cancellation equations**:

$$\boxed{4} \qquad \begin{aligned} f^{-1}(f(x)) &= x \quad \text{for every } x \text{ in } A \\ f(f^{-1}(x)) &= x \quad \text{for every } x \text{ in } B \end{aligned}$$

The first cancellation equation says that if we start with x, apply f, and then apply f^{-1}, we arrive back at x, where we started (see the machine diagram in Figure 7). Thus f^{-1} undoes what f does. The second equation says that f undoes what f^{-1} does.

FIGURE 7

$$x \longrightarrow \boxed{f} \longrightarrow f(x) \longrightarrow \boxed{f^{-1}} \longrightarrow x$$

For example, if $f(x) = x^3$, then $f^{-1}(x) = x^{1/3}$ and so the cancellation equations become

$$f^{-1}(f(x)) = (x^3)^{1/3} = x$$
$$f(f^{-1}(x)) = (x^{1/3})^3 = x$$

These equations simply say that the cube function and the cube root function cancel each other when applied in succession.

Now let's see how to compute inverse functions. If we have a function $y = f(x)$ and are able to solve this equation for x in terms of y, then according to Definition 2 we must have $x = f^{-1}(y)$. If we want to call the independent variable x, we then interchange x and y and arrive at the equation $y = f^{-1}(x)$.

$\boxed{5}$ **How to Find the Inverse Function of a One-to-One Function** f

Step 1 Write $y = f(x)$.

Step 2 Solve this equation for x in terms of y (if possible).

Step 3 To express f^{-1} as a function of x, interchange x and y.
The resulting equation is $y = f^{-1}(x)$.

▼ **EXAMPLE 4** Find the inverse function of $f(x) = x^3 + 2$.

SOLUTION According to ⑤ we first write

$$y = x^3 + 2$$

Then we solve this equation for x:

$$x^3 = y - 2$$

$$x = \sqrt[3]{y - 2}$$

Finally, we interchange x and y:

$$y = \sqrt[3]{x - 2}$$

Therefore the inverse function is $f^{-1}(x) = \sqrt[3]{x - 2}$.

In Example 4, notice how f^{-1} reverses the effect of f. The function f is the rule "Cube, then add 2"; f^{-1} is the rule "Subtract 2, then take the cube root."

The principle of interchanging x and y to find the inverse function also gives us the method for obtaining the graph of f^{-1} from the graph of f. Since $f(a) = b$ if and only if $f^{-1}(b) = a$, the point (a, b) is on the graph of f if and only if the point (b, a) is on the graph of f^{-1}. But we get the point (b, a) from (a, b) by reflecting about the line $y = x$. (See Figure 8.)

FIGURE 8   **FIGURE 9**

Therefore, as illustrated by Figure 9:

The graph of f^{-1} is obtained by reflecting the graph of f about the line $y = x$.

FIGURE 10

EXAMPLE 5 Sketch the graphs of $f(x) = \sqrt{-1 - x}$ and its inverse function using the same coordinate axes.

SOLUTION First we sketch the curve $y = \sqrt{-1 - x}$ (the top half of the parabola $y^2 = -1 - x$, or $x = -y^2 - 1$) and then we reflect about the line $y = x$ to get the graph of f^{-1}. (See Figure 10.) As a check on our graph, notice that the expression for f^{-1} is $f^{-1}(x) = -x^2 - 1$, $x \geq 0$. So the graph of f^{-1} is the right half of the parabola $y = -x^2 - 1$ and this seems reasonable from Figure 10.

Logarithmic Functions

If $a > 0$ and $a \neq 1$, the exponential function $f(x) = a^x$ is either increasing or decreasing and so it is one-to-one by the Horizontal Line Test. It therefore has an inverse function f^{-1}, which is called the **logarithmic function with base a** and is denoted by $\log_a$. If we use the formulation of an inverse function given by $\boxed{3}$,

$$f^{-1}(x) = y \iff f(y) = x$$

then we have

$$\boxed{6} \qquad \log_a x = y \iff a^y = x$$

Thus, if $x > 0$, then $\log_a x$ is the exponent to which the base a must be raised to give x. For example, $\log_{10} 0.001 = -3$ because $10^{-3} = 0.001$.

The cancellation equations $\boxed{4}$, when applied to the functions $f(x) = a^x$ and $f^{-1}(x) = \log_a x$, become

$$\boxed{7} \qquad \log_a(a^x) = x \quad \text{for every } x \in \mathbb{R}$$

$$a^{\log_a x} = x \quad \text{for every } x > 0$$

The logarithmic function $\log_a$ has domain $(0, \infty)$ and range $\mathbb{R}$. Its graph is the reflection of the graph of $y = a^x$ about the line $y = x$.

Figure 11 shows the case where $a > 1$. (The most important logarithmic functions have base $a > 1$.) The fact that $y = a^x$ is a very rapidly increasing function for $x > 0$ is reflected in the fact that $y = \log_a x$ is a very slowly increasing function for $x > 1$.

Figure 12 shows the graphs of $y = \log_a x$ with various values of the base $a > 1$. Since $\log_a 1 = 0$, the graphs of all logarithmic functions pass through the point $(1, 0)$.

FIGURE 11

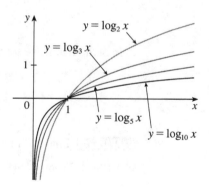

FIGURE 12

The following properties of logarithmic functions follow from the corresponding properties of exponential functions given in Section 1.5.

Laws of Logarithms If x and y are positive numbers, then

1. $\log_a(xy) = \log_a x + \log_a y$

2. $\log_a\left(\dfrac{x}{y}\right) = \log_a x - \log_a y$

3. $\log_a(x^r) = r \log_a x$ \qquad (where r is any real number)

EXAMPLE 6 Use the laws of logarithms to evaluate $\log_2 80 - \log_2 5$.

SOLUTION Using Law 2, we have

$$\log_2 80 - \log_2 5 = \log_2\left(\frac{80}{5}\right) = \log_2 16 = 4$$

because $2^4 = 16$.

Natural Logarithms

Notation for Logarithms

Most textbooks in calculus and the sciences, as well as calculators, use the notation $\ln x$ for the natural logarithm and $\log x$ for the "common logarithm," $\log_{10} x$. In the more advanced mathematical and scientific literature and in computer languages, however, the notation $\log x$ usually denotes the natural logarithm.

Of all possible bases a for logarithms, we will see in Chapter 3 that the most convenient choice of a base is the number e, which was defined in Section 1.5. The logarithm with base e is called the **natural logarithm** and has a special notation:

$$\log_e x = \ln x$$

If we put $a = e$ and replace $\log_e$ with "ln" in $\boxed{6}$ and $\boxed{7}$, then the defining properties of the natural logarithm function become

$\boxed{8}$

$$\ln x = y \iff e^y = x$$

$\boxed{9}$

$$\ln(e^x) = x \qquad x \in \mathbb{R}$$

$$e^{\ln x} = x \qquad x > 0$$

In particular, if we set $x = 1$, we get

$$\ln e = 1$$

EXAMPLE 7 Find x if $\ln x = 5$.

SOLUTION 1 From $\boxed{8}$ we see that

$$\ln x = 5 \qquad \text{means} \qquad e^5 = x$$

Therefore $x = e^5$.

(If you have trouble working with the "ln" notation, just replace it by $\log_e$. Then the equation becomes $\log_e x = 5$; so, by the definition of logarithm, $e^5 = x$.)

SOLUTION 2 Start with the equation

$$\ln x = 5$$

and apply the exponential function to both sides of the equation:

$$e^{\ln x} = e^5$$

But the second cancellation equation in $\boxed{9}$ says that $e^{\ln x} = x$. Therefore $x = e^5$.

EXAMPLE 8 Solve the equation $e^{5-3x} = 10$.

SOLUTION We take natural logarithms of both sides of the equation and use 9:

$$\ln(e^{5-3x}) = \ln 10$$

$$5 - 3x = \ln 10$$

$$3x = 5 - \ln 10$$

$$x = \tfrac{1}{3}(5 - \ln 10)$$

Since the natural logarithm is found on scientific calculators, we can approximate the solution: to four decimal places, $x \approx 0.8991$.

V **EXAMPLE 9** Express $\ln a + \tfrac{1}{2} \ln b$ as a single logarithm.

SOLUTION Using Laws 3 and 1 of logarithms, we have

$$\ln a + \tfrac{1}{2} \ln b = \ln a + \ln b^{1/2}$$

$$= \ln a + \ln \sqrt{b}$$

$$= \ln(a\sqrt{b})$$

The following formula shows that logarithms with any base can be expressed in terms of the natural logarithm.

---

10 **Change of Base Formula** For any positive number a ($a \neq 1$), we have

$$\log_a x = \frac{\ln x}{\ln a}$$

PROOF Let $y = \log_a x$. Then, from 6, we have $a^y = x$. Taking natural logarithms of both sides of this equation, we get $y \ln a = \ln x$. Therefore

$$y = \frac{\ln x}{\ln a}$$

Scientific calculators have a key for natural logarithms, so Formula 10 enables us to use a calculator to compute a logarithm with any base (as shown in the following example). Similarly, Formula 10 allows us to graph any logarithmic function on a graphing calculator or computer (see Exercises 43 and 44).

EXAMPLE 10 Evaluate $\log_8 5$ correct to six decimal places.

SOLUTION Formula 10 gives

$$\log_8 5 = \frac{\ln 5}{\ln 8} \approx 0.773976$$

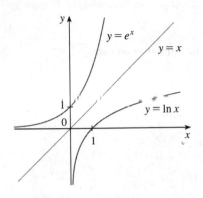

FIGURE 13
The graph of $y = \ln x$ is the reflection of the graph of $y = e^x$ about the line $y = x$

Graph and Growth of the Natural Logarithm

The graphs of the exponential function $y = e^x$ and its inverse function, the natural logarithm function, are shown in Figure 13. Because the curve $y = e^x$ crosses the y-axis with a slope of 1, it follows that the reflected curve $y = \ln x$ crosses the x-axis with a slope of 1.

In common with all other logarithmic functions with base greater than 1, the natural logarithm is an increasing function defined on $(0, \infty)$ and the y axis is a vertical asymptote. (This means that the values of $\ln x$ become very large negative as x approaches 0.)

EXAMPLE 11   Sketch the graph of the function $y = \ln(x - 2) - 1$.

SOLUTION   We start with the graph of $y = \ln x$ as given in Figure 13. Using the transformations of Section 1.3, we shift it 2 units to the right to get the graph of $y = \ln(x - 2)$ and then we shift it 1 unit downward to get the graph of $y = \ln(x - 2) - 1$. (See Figure 14.)

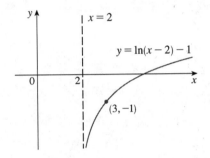

FIGURE 14

Although $\ln x$ is an increasing function, it grows *very* slowly when $x > 1$. In fact, $\ln x$ grows more slowly than any positive power of x. To illustrate this fact, we compare approximate values of the functions $y = \ln x$ and $y = x^{1/2} = \sqrt{x}$ in the following table and we graph them in Figures 15 and 16. You can see that initially the graphs of $y = \sqrt{x}$ and $y = \ln x$ grow at comparable rates, but eventually the root function far surpasses the logarithm.

x	1	2	5	10	50	100	500	1000	10,000	100,000
$\ln x$	0	0.69	1.61	2.30	3.91	4.6	6.2	6.9	9.2	11.5
$\sqrt{x}$	1	1.41	2.24	3.16	7.07	10.0	22.4	31.6	100	316
$\dfrac{\ln x}{\sqrt{x}}$	0	0.49	0.72	0.73	0.55	0.46	0.28	0.22	0.09	0.04

FIGURE 15

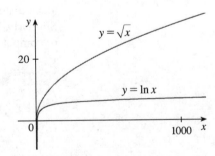

FIGURE 16

Inverse Trigonometric Functions

When we try to find the inverse trigonometric functions, we have a slight difficulty: Because the trigonometric functions are not one-to-one, they don't have inverse functions. The difficulty is overcome by restricting the domains of these functions so that they become one-to-one.

You can see from Figure 17 that the sine function $y = \sin x$ is not one-to-one (use the Horizontal Line Test). But the function $f(x) = \sin x$, $-\pi/2 \le x \le \pi/2$, *is* one-to-one (see Figure 18). The inverse function of this restricted sine function f exists and is denoted by $\sin^{-1}$ or arcsin. It is called the **inverse sine function** or the **arcsine function**.

FIGURE 17

FIGURE 18 $y = \sin x$, $-\frac{\pi}{2} \le x \le \frac{\pi}{2}$

Since the definition of an inverse function says that

$$f^{-1}(x) = y \iff f(y) = x$$

we have

$$\sin^{-1}x = y \iff \sin y = x \quad \text{and} \quad -\frac{\pi}{2} \le y \le \frac{\pi}{2}$$

⊘ $\sin^{-1}x \ne \dfrac{1}{\sin x}$

Thus, if $-1 \le x \le 1$, $\sin^{-1}x$ is the number between $-\pi/2$ and $\pi/2$ whose sine is x.

EXAMPLE 12 Evaluate (a) $\sin^{-1}\left(\frac{1}{2}\right)$ and (b) $\tan\left(\arcsin \frac{1}{3}\right)$.

SOLUTION
(a) We have

$$\sin^{-1}\left(\tfrac{1}{2}\right) = \frac{\pi}{6}$$

because $\sin(\pi/6) = \frac{1}{2}$ and $\pi/6$ lies between $-\pi/2$ and $\pi/2$.

(b) Let $\theta = \arcsin \frac{1}{3}$, so $\sin \theta = \frac{1}{3}$. Then we can draw a right triangle with angle θ as in Figure 19 and deduce from the Pythagorean Theorem that the third side has length $\sqrt{9-1} = 2\sqrt{2}$. This enables us to read from the triangle that

FIGURE 19

$$\tan\left(\arcsin \tfrac{1}{3}\right) = \tan \theta = \frac{1}{2\sqrt{2}}$$

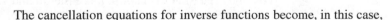

The cancellation equations for inverse functions become, in this case,

$$\sin^{-1}(\sin x) = x \quad \text{for } -\frac{\pi}{2} \le x \le \frac{\pi}{2}$$

$$\sin(\sin^{-1}x) = x \quad \text{for } -1 \le x \le 1$$

FIGURE 20
$y = \sin^{-1}x = \arcsin x$

The inverse sine function, $\sin^{-1}$, has domain $[-1, 1]$ and range $[-\pi/2, \pi/2]$, and its graph, shown in Figure 20, is obtained from that of the restricted sine function (Figure 18) by reflection about the line $y = x$.

The **inverse cosine function** is handled similarly. The restricted cosine function $f(x) = \cos x$, $0 \le x \le \pi$, is one-to-one (see Figure 21) and so it has an inverse function denoted by $\cos^{-1}$ or arccos.

$$\cos^{-1}x = y \quad \Longleftrightarrow \quad \cos y = x \quad \text{and} \quad 0 \le y \le \pi$$

FIGURE 21
$y = \cos x, 0 \le x \le \pi$

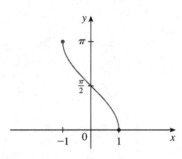

FIGURE 22
$y = \cos^{-1}x = \arccos x$

The cancellation equations are

$$\cos^{-1}(\cos x) = x \quad \text{for } 0 \le x \le \pi$$
$$\cos(\cos^{-1}x) = x \quad \text{for } -1 \le x \le 1$$

The inverse cosine function, $\cos^{-1}$, has domain $[-1, 1]$ and range $[0, \pi]$. Its graph is shown in Figure 22.

The tangent function can be made one-to-one by restricting it to the interval $(-\pi/2, \pi/2)$. Thus the **inverse tangent function** is defined as the inverse of the function $f(x) = \tan x$, $-\pi/2 < x < \pi/2$. (See Figure 23.) It is denoted by $\tan^{-1}$ or arctan.

$$\tan^{-1}x = y \quad \Longleftrightarrow \quad \tan y = x \quad \text{and} \quad -\frac{\pi}{2} < y < \frac{\pi}{2}$$

FIGURE 23
$y = \tan x, -\frac{\pi}{2} < x < \frac{\pi}{2}$

EXAMPLE 13 Simplify the expression $\cos(\tan^{-1}x)$.

SOLUTION 1 Let $y = \tan^{-1}x$. Then $\tan y = x$ and $-\pi/2 < y < \pi/2$. We want to find $\cos y$ but, since $\tan y$ is known, it is easier to find $\sec y$ first:

$$\sec^2 y = 1 + \tan^2 y = 1 + x^2$$

$$\sec y = \sqrt{1 + x^2} \qquad \text{(since } \sec y > 0 \text{ for } -\pi/2 < y < \pi/2)$$

Thus
$$\cos(\tan^{-1}x) = \cos y = \frac{1}{\sec y} = \frac{1}{\sqrt{1 + x^2}}$$

FIGURE 24

SOLUTION 2 Instead of using trigonometric identities as in Solution 1, it is perhaps easier to use a diagram. If $y = \tan^{-1}x$, then $\tan y = x$, and we can read from Figure 24 (which illustrates the case $y > 0$) that

$$\cos(\tan^{-1}x) = \cos y = \frac{1}{\sqrt{1 + x^2}}$$

The inverse tangent function, $\tan^{-1} = \arctan$, has domain $\mathbb{R}$ and range $(-\pi/2, \pi/2)$. Its graph is shown in Figure 25.

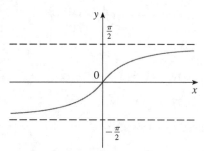

FIGURE 25
$y = \tan^{-1}x = \arctan x$

We know that the lines $x = \pm\pi/2$ are vertical asymptotes of the graph of tan. Since the graph of $\tan^{-1}$ is obtained by reflecting the graph of the restricted tangent function about the line $y = x$, it follows that the lines $y = \pi/2$ and $y = -\pi/2$ are horizontal asymptotes of the graph of $\tan^{-1}$.

The remaining inverse trigonometric functions are not used as frequently and are summarized here.

FIGURE 26
$y = \sec x$

$$\boxed{11} \quad y = \csc^{-1}x \ (|x| \geqslant 1) \quad \Longleftrightarrow \quad \csc y = x \quad \text{and} \quad y \in (0, \pi/2] \cup (\pi, 3\pi/2]$$

$$y = \sec^{-1}x \ (|x| \geqslant 1) \quad \Longleftrightarrow \quad \sec y = x \quad \text{and} \quad y \in [0, \pi/2) \cup [\pi, 3\pi/2)$$

$$y = \cot^{-1}x \ (x \in \mathbb{R}) \quad \Longleftrightarrow \quad \cot y = x \quad \text{and} \quad y \in (0, \pi)$$

The choice of intervals for y in the definitions of $\csc^{-1}$ and $\sec^{-1}$ is not universally agreed upon. For instance, some authors use $y \in [0, \pi/2) \cup (\pi/2, \pi]$ in the definition of $\sec^{-1}$. (You can see from the graph of the secant function in Figure 26 that both this choice and the one in $\boxed{11}$ will work.)

1.6 Exercises

1. (a) What is a one-to-one function?
   (b) How can you tell from the graph of a function whether it is one-to-one?

2. (a) Suppose f is a one-to-one function with domain A and range B. How is the inverse function f^{-1} defined? What is the domain of f^{-1}? What is the range of f^{-1}?
   (b) If you are given a formula for f, how do you find a formula for f^{-1}?
   (c) If you are given the graph of f, how do you find the graph of f^{-1}?

3–14 A function is given by a table of values, a graph, a formula, or a verbal description. Determine whether it is one-to-one.

3.

x	1	2	3	4	5	6
$f(x)$	1.5	2.0	3.6	5.3	2.8	2.0

4.

x	1	2	3	4	5	6
$f(x)$	1.0	1.9	2.8	3.5	3.1	2.9

5.

6.

7.

8.

9. $f(x) = \frac{1}{2}(x + 5)$ **10.** $f(x) = 1 + 4x - x^2$

11. $g(x) = |x|$ **12.** $g(x) = \sqrt{x}$

13. $f(t)$ is the height of a football t seconds after kickoff.

14. $f(t)$ is your height at age t.

---

15. Assume that f is a one-to-one function.
 (a) If $f(6) = 17$, what is $f^{-1}(17)$?
 (b) If $f^{-1}(3) = 2$, what is $f(2)$?

16. If $f(x) = x^5 + x^3 + x$, find $f^{-1}(3)$ and $f(f^{-1}(2))$.

17. If $g(x) = 3 + x + e^x$, find $g^{-1}(4)$.

18. The graph of f is given.
 (a) Why is f one-to-one?
 (b) What are the domain and range of f^{-1}?
 (c) What is the value of $f^{-1}(2)$?
 (d) Estimate the value of $f^{-1}(0)$.

19. The formula $C = \frac{5}{9}(F - 32)$, where $F \geqslant -459.67$, expresses the Celsius temperature C as a function of the Fahrenheit temperature F. Find a formula for the inverse function and interpret it. What is the domain of the inverse function?

20. In the theory of relativity, the mass of a particle with speed v is

$$m = f(v) = \frac{m_0}{\sqrt{1 - v^2/c^2}}$$

where m_0 is the rest mass of the particle and c is the speed of light in a vacuum. Find the inverse function of f and explain its meaning.

21–26 Find a formula for the inverse of the function.

21. $f(x) = 1 + \sqrt{2 + 3x}$ **22.** $f(x) = \dfrac{4x - 1}{2x + 3}$

23. $f(x) = e^{2x-1}$ **24.** $y = x^2 - x$, $x \geqslant \frac{1}{2}$

25. $y = \ln(x + 3)$ **26.** $y = \dfrac{e^x}{1 + 2e^x}$

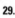 **27–28** Find an explicit formula for f^{-1} and use it to graph f^{-1}, f, and the line $y = x$ on the same screen. To check your work, see whether the graphs of f and f^{-1} are reflections about the line.

27. $f(x) = x^4 + 1$, $x \geqslant 0$ **28.** $f(x) = 2 - e^x$

29–30 Use the given graph of f to sketch the graph of f^{-1}.

29.

30.

31. Let $f(x) = \sqrt{1 - x^2}$, $0 \leqslant x \leqslant 1$.
 (a) Find f^{-1}. How is it related to f?
 (b) Identify the graph of f and explain your answer to part (a).

32. Let $g(x) = \sqrt[3]{1 - x^3}$.
 (a) Find g^{-1}. How is it related to g?
 (b) Graph g. How do you explain your answer to part (a)?

33. (a) How is the logarithmic function $y = \log_a x$ defined?
 (b) What is the domain of this function?
 (c) What is the range of this function?
 (d) Sketch the general shape of the graph of the function $y = \log_a x$ if $a > 1$.

34. (a) What is the natural logarithm?
 (b) What is the common logarithm?
 (c) Sketch the graphs of the natural logarithm function and the natural exponential function with a common set of axes.

35–38 Find the exact value of each expression.

35. (a) $\log_5 125$ (b) $\log_3\left(\frac{1}{27}\right)$

36. (a) $\ln(1/e)$ (b) $\log_{10} \sqrt{10}$

37. (a) $\log_2 6 - \log_2 15 + \log_2 20$
 (b) $\log_3 100 - \log_3 18 - \log_3 50$

38. (a) $e^{-2\ln 5}$ (b) $\ln\left(\ln e^{e^{10}}\right)$

39–41 Express the given quantity as a single logarithm.

39. $\ln 5 + 5 \ln 3$

40. $\ln(a + b) + \ln(a - b) - 2 \ln c$

41. $\frac{1}{3} \ln(x + 2)^3 + \frac{1}{2}[\ln x - \ln(x^2 + 3x + 2)^2]$

42. Use Formula 10 to evaluate each logarithm correct to six decimal places.
 (a) $\log_{12} 10$ (b) $\log_2 8.4$

43–44 Use Formula 10 to graph the given functions on a common screen. How are these graphs related?

43. $y = \log_{1.5} x$, $\quad y = \ln x$, $\quad y = \log_{10} x$, $\quad y = \log_{50} x$

44. $y = \ln x$, $\quad y = \log_{10} x$, $\quad y = e^x$, $\quad y = 10^x$

45. Suppose that the graph of $y = \log_2 x$ is drawn on a coordinate grid where the unit of measurement is a centimeter. How many kilometers to the right of the origin do we have to move before the height of the curve reaches 1 m?

46. Compare the functions $f(x) = x^{0.1}$ and $g(x) = \ln x$ by graphing both f and g in several viewing rectangles. When does the graph of f finally surpass the graph of g?

47–48 Make a rough sketch of the graph of each function. Do not use a calculator. Just use the graphs given in Figures 12 and 13 and, if necessary, the transformations of Section 1.3.

47. (a) $y = \log_{10}(x + 5)$ $\qquad$ (b) $y = -\ln x$

48. (a) $y = \ln(-x)$ $\qquad$ (b) $y = \ln|x|$

49–50 (a) What are the domain and range of f?
(b) What is the x-intercept of the graph of f?
(c) Sketch the graph of f.

49. $f(x) = \ln x + 2$ $\qquad$ **50.** $f(x) = \ln(x - 1) - 1$

51–54 Solve each equation for x.

51. (a) $2 \ln x = 1$ $\qquad$ (b) $e^{-x} = 5$

52. (a) $e^{2x+3} - 7 = 0$ $\qquad$ (b) $\ln(5 - 2x) = -3$

53. (a) $2^{x-5} = 3$ $\qquad$ (b) $\ln x + \ln(x - 1) = 1$

54. (a) $\ln(\ln x) = 1$ $\qquad$ (b) $e^{ax} = Ce^{bx}$, where $a \neq b$

55–56 Solve each inequality for x.

55. (a) $\ln x < 0$ $\qquad$ (b) $e^x > 5$

56. (a) $1 < e^{3x-1} < 2$ $\qquad$ (b) $1 - 2 \ln x < 3$

57. (a) Find the domain of $f(x) = \ln(e^x - 3)$.
(b) Find f^{-1} and its domain.

58. (a) What are the values of $e^{\ln 300}$ and $\ln(e^{300})$?
(b) Use your calculator to evaluate $e^{\ln 300}$ and $\ln(e^{300})$. What do you notice? Can you explain why the calculator has trouble?

59. Graph the function $f(x) = \sqrt{x^3 + x^2 + x + 1}$ and explain why it is one-to-one. Then use a computer algebra system to find an explicit expression for $f^{-1}(x)$. (Your CAS will produce three possible expressions. Explain why two of them are irrelevant in this context.)

60. (a) If $g(x) = x^6 + x^4$, $x \geq 0$, use a computer algebra system to find an expression for $g^{-1}(x)$.

(b) Use the expression in part (a) to graph $y = g(x)$, $y = x$, and $y = g^{-1}(x)$ on the same screen.

61. If a bacteria population starts with 100 bacteria and doubles every three hours, then the number of bacteria after t hours is $n = f(t) = 100 \cdot 2^{t/3}$. (See Exercise 29 in Section 1.5.)
(a) Find the inverse of this function and explain its meaning.
(b) When will the population reach 50,000?

62. When a camera flash goes off, the batteries immediately begin to recharge the flash's capacitor, which stores electric charge given by

$$Q(t) = Q_0(1 - e^{-t/a})$$

(The maximum charge capacity is Q_0 and t is measured in seconds.)
(a) Find the inverse of this function and explain its meaning.
(b) How long does it take to recharge the capacitor to 90% of capacity if $a = 2$?

63–68 Find the exact value of each expression.

63. (a) $\sin^{-1}(\sqrt{3}/2)$ $\qquad$ (b) $\cos^{-1}(-1)$

64. (a) $\tan^{-1}(1/\sqrt{3})$ $\qquad$ (b) $\sec^{-1} 2$

65. (a) $\arctan 1$ $\qquad$ (b) $\sin^{-1}(1/\sqrt{2})$

66. (a) $\cot^{-1}(-\sqrt{3})$ $\qquad$ (b) $\arccos(-\frac{1}{2})$

67. (a) $\tan(\arctan 10)$ $\qquad$ (b) $\sin^{-1}(\sin(7\pi/3))$

68. (a) $\tan(\sec^{-1} 4)$ $\qquad$ (b) $\sin(2 \sin^{-1}(\frac{3}{5}))$

69. Prove that $\cos(\sin^{-1} x) = \sqrt{1 - x^2}$.

70–72 Simplify the expression.

70. $\tan(\sin^{-1} x)$ $\qquad$ **71.** $\sin(\tan^{-1} x)$

72. $\cos(2 \tan^{-1} x)$

73–74 Graph the given functions on the same screen. How are these graphs related?

73. $y = \sin x$, $-\pi/2 \leq x \leq \pi/2$; $\quad y = \sin^{-1} x$; $\quad y = x$

74. $y = \tan x$, $-\pi/2 < x < \pi/2$; $\quad y = \tan^{-1} x$; $\quad y = x$

75. Find the domain and range of the function

$$g(x) = \sin^{-1}(3x + 1)$$

76. (a) Graph the function $f(x) = \sin(\sin^{-1} x)$ and explain the appearance of the graph.
(b) Graph the function $g(x) = \sin^{-1}(\sin x)$. How do you explain the appearance of this graph?

77. (a) If we shift a curve to the left, what happens to its reflection about the line $y = x$? In view of this geometric principle, find an expression for the inverse of $g(x) = f(x + c)$, where f is a one-to-one function.
(b) Find an expression for the inverse of $h(x) = f(cx)$, where $c \neq 0$.

1   Review

Concept Check

1. (a) What is a function? What are its domain and range?
   (b) What is the graph of a function?
   (c) How can you tell whether a given curve is the graph of a function?

2. Discuss four ways of representing a function. Illustrate your discussion with examples.

3. (a) What is an even function? How can you tell if a function is even by looking at its graph? Give three examples of an even function.
   (b) What is an odd function? How can you tell if a function is odd by looking at its graph? Give three examples of an odd function.

4. What is an increasing function?

5. What is a mathematical model?

6. Give an example of each type of function.
   (a) Linear function   (b) Power function
   (c) Exponential function   (d) Quadratic function
   (e) Polynomial of degree 5   (f) Rational function

7. Sketch by hand, on the same axes, the graphs of the following functions.
   (a) $f(x) = x$ (b) $g(x) = x^2$
   (c) $h(x) = x^3$ (d) $j(x) = x^4$

8. Draw, by hand, a rough sketch of the graph of each function.
   (a) $y = \sin x$ (b) $y = \tan x$
   (c) $y = e^x$ (d) $y = \ln x$
   (e) $y = 1/x$ (f) $y = |x|$
   (g) $y = \sqrt{x}$ (h) $y = \tan^{-1}x$

9. Suppose that f has domain A and g has domain B.
   (a) What is the domain of $f + g$?
   (b) What is the domain of fg?
   (c) What is the domain of f/g?

10. How is the composite function $f \circ g$ defined? What is its domain?

11. Suppose the graph of f is given. Write an equation for each of the graphs that are obtained from the graph of f as follows.
   (a) Shift 2 units upward.
   (b) Shift 2 units downward.
   (c) Shift 2 units to the right.
   (d) Shift 2 units to the left.
   (e) Reflect about the x-axis.
   (f) Reflect about the y-axis.
   (g) Stretch vertically by a factor of 2.
   (h) Shrink vertically by a factor of 2.
   (i) Stretch horizontally by a factor of 2.
   (j) Shrink horizontally by a factor of 2.

12. (a) What is a one-to-one function? How can you tell if a function is one-to-one by looking at its graph?
   (b) If f is a one-to-one function, how is its inverse function f^{-1} defined? How do you obtain the graph of f^{-1} from the graph of f?

13. (a) How is the inverse sine function $f(x) = \sin^{-1}x$ defined? What are its domain and range?
   (b) How is the inverse cosine function $f(x) = \cos^{-1}x$ defined? What are its domain and range?
   (c) How is the inverse tangent function $f(x) = \tan^{-1}x$ defined? What are its domain and range?

True-False Quiz

Determine whether the statement is true or false. If it is true, explain why. If it is false, explain why or give an example that disproves the statement.

1. If f is a function, then $f(s + t) = f(s) + f(t)$.

2. If $f(s) = f(t)$, then $s = t$.

3. If f is a function, then $f(3x) = 3f(x)$.

4. If $x_1 < x_2$ and f is a decreasing function, then $f(x_1) > f(x_2)$.

5. A vertical line intersects the graph of a function at most once.

6. If f and g are functions, then $f \circ g = g \circ f$.

7. If f is one-to-one, then $f^{-1}(x) = \dfrac{1}{f(x)}$.

8. You can always divide by e^x.

9. If $0 < a < b$, then $\ln a < \ln b$.

10. If $x > 0$, then $(\ln x)^6 = 6 \ln x$.

11. If $x > 0$ and $a > 1$, then $\dfrac{\ln x}{\ln a} = \ln \dfrac{x}{a}$.

12. $\tan^{-1}(-1) = 3\pi/4$

13. $\tan^{-1}x = \dfrac{\sin^{-1}x}{\cos^{-1}x}$

14. If x is any real number, then $\sqrt{x^2} = x$.

Exercises

1. Let f be the function whose graph is given.
   (a) Estimate the value of $f(2)$.
   (b) Estimate the values of x such that $f(x) = 3$.
   (c) State the domain of f.
   (d) State the range of f.
   (e) On what interval is f increasing?
   (f) Is f one-to-one? Explain.
   (g) Is f even, odd, or neither even nor odd? Explain.

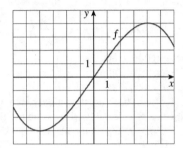

2. The graph of g is given.
   (a) State the value of $g(2)$.
   (b) Why is g one-to-one?
   (c) Estimate the value of $g^{-1}(2)$.
   (d) Estimate the domain of g^{-1}.
   (e) Sketch the graph of g^{-1}.

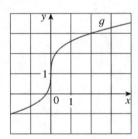

3. If $f(x) = x^2 - 2x + 3$, evaluate the difference quotient

$$\frac{f(a + h) - f(a)}{h}$$

4. Sketch a rough graph of the yield of a crop as a function of the amount of fertilizer used.

5–8 Find the domain and range of the function. Write your answer in interval notation.

5. $f(x) = 2/(3x - 1)$

6. $g(x) = \sqrt{16 - x^4}$

7. $h(x) = \ln(x + 6)$

8. $F(t) = 3 + \cos 2t$

9. Suppose that the graph of f is given. Describe how the graphs of the following functions can be obtained from the graph of f.
   (a) $y = f(x) + 8$ 　　　　　(b) $y = f(x + 8)$
   (c) $y = 1 + 2f(x)$ 　　　　(d) $y = f(x - 2) - 2$
   (e) $y = -f(x)$ 　　　　　　(f) $y = f^{-1}(x)$

10. The graph of f is given. Draw the graphs of the following functions.
    (a) $y = f(x - 8)$ 　　　　(b) $y = -f(x)$
    (c) $y = 2 - f(x)$ 　　　　(d) $y = \frac{1}{2}f(x) - 1$
    (e) $y = f^{-1}(x)$ 　　　　(f) $y = f^{-1}(x + 3)$

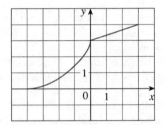

11–16 Use transformations to sketch the graph of the function.

11. $y = -\sin 2x$

12. $y = 3\ln(x - 2)$

13. $y = \frac{1}{2}(1 + e^x)$

14. $y = 2 - \sqrt{x}$

15. $f(x) = \dfrac{1}{x + 2}$

16. $f(x) = \begin{cases} -x & \text{if } x < 0 \\ e^x - 1 & \text{if } x \geq 0 \end{cases}$

17. Determine whether f is even, odd, or neither even nor odd.
    (a) $f(x) = 2x^5 - 3x^2 + 2$
    (b) $f(x) = x^3 - x^7$
    (c) $f(x) = e^{-x^2}$
    (d) $f(x) = 1 + \sin x$

18. Find an expression for the function whose graph consists of the line segment from the point $(-2, 2)$ to the point $(-1, 0)$ together with the top half of the circle with center the origin and radius 1.

19. If $f(x) = \ln x$ and $g(x) = x^2 - 9$, find the functions (a) $f \circ g$, (b) $g \circ f$, (c) $f \circ f$, (d) $g \circ g$, and their domains.

20. Express the function $F(x) = 1/\sqrt{x + \sqrt{x}}$ as a composition of three functions.

⊞ Graphing calculator or computer required

21. The table gives the population of Indonesia (in millions) for the years 1950–2000. Decide what type of model is appropriate and use your model to predict the population of Indonesia in 2010.

Year	Population	Year	Population
1950	80	1980	150
1955	86	1985	166
1960	96	1990	182
1965	107	1995	197
1970	120	2000	212
1975	134		

22. A small-appliance manufacturer finds that it costs \$9000 to produce 1000 toaster ovens a week and \$12,000 to produce 1500 toaster ovens a week.
  (a) Express the cost as a function of the number of toaster ovens produced, assuming that it is linear. Then sketch the graph.
  (b) What is the slope of the graph and what does it represent?
  (c) What is the y-intercept of the graph and what does it represent?

23. If $f(x) = 2x + \ln x$, find $f^{-1}(2)$.

24. Find the inverse function of $f(x) = \dfrac{x + 1}{2x + 1}$.

25. Find the exact value of each expression.
  (a) $e^{2\ln 3}$
  (b) $\log_{10} 25 + \log_{10} 4$
  (c) $\tan\left(\arcsin \frac{1}{2}\right)$
  (d) $\sin\left(\cos^{-1}\left(\frac{4}{5}\right)\right)$

26. Solve each equation for x.
  (a) $e^x = 5$
  (b) $\ln x = 2$
  (c) $e^{e^x} = 2$
  (d) $\tan^{-1} x = 1$

27. The population of a certain species in a limited environment with initial population 100 and carrying capacity 1000 is

$$P(t) = \frac{100{,}000}{100 + 900e^{-t}}$$

where t is measured in years.
  (a) Graph this function and estimate how long it takes for the population to reach 900.
  (b) Find the inverse of this function and explain its meaning.
  (c) Use the inverse function to find the time required for the population to reach 900. Compare with the result of part (a).

28. Graph the three functions $y = x^a$, $y = a^x$, and $y = \log_a x$ on the same screen for two or three values of $a > 1$. For large values of x, which of these functions has the largest values and which has the smallest values?

Principles of Problem Solving

There are no hard and fast rules that will ensure success in solving problems. However, it is possible to outline some general steps in the problem-solving process and to give some principles that may be useful in the solution of certain problems. These steps and principles are just common sense made explicit. They have been adapted from George Polya's book *How To Solve It.*

1 UNDERSTAND THE PROBLEM

The first step is to read the problem and make sure that you understand it clearly. Ask yourself the following questions:

> *What is the unknown?*
> *What are the given quantities?*
> *What are the given conditions?*

For many problems it is useful to

> *draw a diagram*

and identify the given and required quantities on the diagram.
　　Usually it is necessary to

> *introduce suitable notation*

In choosing symbols for the unknown quantities we often use letters such as a, b, c, m, n, x, and y, but in some cases it helps to use initials as suggestive symbols; for instance, V for volume or t for time.

2 THINK OF A PLAN

Find a connection between the given information and the unknown that will enable you to calculate the unknown. It often helps to ask yourself explicitly: "How can I relate the given to the unknown?" If you don't see a connection immediately, the following ideas may be helpful in devising a plan.

Try to Recognize Something Familiar　Relate the given situation to previous knowledge. Look at the unknown and try to recall a more familiar problem that has a similar unknown.

Try to Recognize Patterns　Some problems are solved by recognizing that some kind of pattern is occurring. The pattern could be geometric, or numerical, or algebraic. If you can see regularity or repetition in a problem, you might be able to guess what the continuing pattern is and then prove it.

Use Analogy　Try to think of an analogous problem, that is, a similar problem, a related problem, but one that is easier than the original problem. If you can solve the similar, simpler problem, then it might give you the clues you need to solve the original, more difficult problem. For instance, if a problem involves very large numbers, you could first try a similar problem with smaller numbers. Or if the problem involves three-dimensional geometry, you could look for a similar problem in two-dimensional geometry. Or if the problem you start with is a general one, you could first try a special case.

Introduce Something Extra　It may sometimes be necessary to introduce something new, an auxiliary aid, to help make the connection between the given and the unknown. For instance, in a problem where a diagram is useful the auxiliary aid could be a new line drawn in a diagram. In a more algebraic problem it could be a new unknown that is related to the original unknown.

Take Cases We may sometimes have to split a problem into several cases and give a different argument for each of the cases. For instance, we often have to use this strategy in dealing with absolute value.

Work Backward Sometimes it is useful to imagine that your problem is solved and work backward, step by step, until you arrive at the given data. Then you may be able to reverse your steps and thereby construct a solution to the original problem. This procedure is commonly used in solving equations. For instance, in solving the equation $3x - 5 = 7$, we suppose that x is a number that satisfies $3x - 5 = 7$ and work backward. We add 5 to each side of the equation and then divide each side by 3 to get $x = 4$. Since each of these steps can be reversed, we have solved the problem.

Establish Subgoals In a complex problem it is often useful to set subgoals (in which the desired situation is only partially fulfilled). If we can first reach these subgoals, then we may be able to build on them to reach our final goal.

Indirect Reasoning Sometimes it is appropriate to attack a problem indirectly. In using proof by contradiction to prove that P implies Q, we assume that P is true and Q is false and try to see why this can't happen. Somehow we have to use this information and arrive at a contradiction to what we absolutely know is true.

Mathematical Induction In proving statements that involve a positive integer n, it is frequently helpful to use the following principle.

Principle of Mathematical Induction Let S_n be a statement about the positive integer n. Suppose that

1. S_1 is true.

2. S_{k+1} is true whenever S_k is true.

Then S_n is true for all positive integers n.

This is reasonable because, since S_1 is true, it follows from condition 2 (with $k = 1$) that S_2 is true. Then, using condition 2 with $k = 2$, we see that S_3 is true. Again using condition 2, this time with $k = 3$, we have that S_4 is true. This procedure can be followed indefinitely.

3 CARRY OUT THE PLAN In Step 2 a plan was devised. In carrying out that plan we have to check each stage of the plan and write the details that prove that each stage is correct.

4 LOOK BACK Having completed our solution, it is wise to look back over it, partly to see if we have made errors in the solution and partly to see if we can think of an easier way to solve the problem. Another reason for looking back is that it will familiarize us with the method of solution and this may be useful for solving a future problem. Descartes said, "Every problem that I solved became a rule which served afterwards to solve other problems."

These principles of problem solving are illustrated in the following examples. Before you look at the solutions, try to solve these problems yourself, referring to these Principles of Problem Solving if you get stuck. You may find it useful to refer to this section from time to time as you solve the exercises in the remaining chapters of this book.

EXAMPLE 1 Express the hypotenuse h of a right triangle with area 25 m² as a function of its perimeter P.

PS Understand the problem

SOLUTION Let's first sort out the information by identifying the unknown quantity and the data:

$$Unknown: \quad \text{hypotenuse } h$$

$$Given\ quantities: \quad \text{perimeter } P, \text{ area 25 m}^2$$

PS Draw a diagram

It helps to draw a diagram and we do so in Figure 1.

FIGURE 1

PS Connect the given with the unknown
PS Introduce something extra

In order to connect the given quantities to the unknown, we introduce two extra variables a and b, which are the lengths of the other two sides of the triangle. This enables us to express the given condition, which is that the triangle is right-angled, by the Pythagorean Theorem:

$$h^2 = a^2 + b^2$$

The other connections among the variables come by writing expressions for the area and perimeter:

$$25 = \tfrac{1}{2}ab \qquad P = a + b + h$$

Since P is given, notice that we now have three equations in the three unknowns a, b, and h:

1	$h^2 = a^2 + b^2$
2	$25 = \tfrac{1}{2}ab$
3	$P = a + b + h$

Although we have the correct number of equations, they are not easy to solve in a straightforward fashion. But if we use the problem-solving strategy of trying to recognize something familiar, then we can solve these equations by an easier method. Look at the right sides of Equations 1, 2, and 3. Do these expressions remind you of anything familiar? Notice that they contain the ingredients of a familiar formula:

PS Relate to the familiar

$$(a + b)^2 = a^2 + 2ab + b^2$$

Using this idea, we express $(a + b)^2$ in two ways. From Equations 1 and 2 we have

$$(a + b)^2 = (a^2 + b^2) + 2ab = h^2 + 4(25)$$

From Equation 3 we have

$$(a + b)^2 = (P - h)^2 = P^2 - 2Ph + h^2$$

Thus

$$h^2 + 100 = P^2 - 2Ph + h^2$$

$$2Ph = P^2 - 100$$

$$h = \frac{P^2 - 100}{2P}$$

This is the required expression for h as a function of P.

As the next example illustrates, it is often necessary to use the problem-solving principle of *taking cases* when dealing with absolute values.

EXAMPLE 2 Solve the inequality $|x - 3| + |x + 2| < 11$.

SOLUTION Recall the definition of absolute value:

$$|x| = \begin{cases} x & \text{if } x \geq 0 \\ -x & \text{if } x < 0 \end{cases}$$

It follows that

$$|x - 3| = \begin{cases} x - 3 & \text{if } x - 3 \geq 0 \\ -(x - 3) & \text{if } x - 3 < 0 \end{cases}$$

$$= \begin{cases} x - 3 & \text{if } x \geq 3 \\ -x + 3 & \text{if } x < 3 \end{cases}$$

Similarly

$$|x + 2| = \begin{cases} x + 2 & \text{if } x + 2 \geq 0 \\ -(x + 2) & \text{if } x + 2 < 0 \end{cases}$$

$$= \begin{cases} x + 2 & \text{if } x \geq -2 \\ -x - 2 & \text{if } x < -2 \end{cases}$$

PS Take cases

These expressions show that we must consider three cases:

$$x < -2 \qquad -2 \leq x < 3 \qquad x \geq 3$$

CASE I If $x < -2$, we have

$$|x - 3| + |x + 2| < 11$$
$$-x + 3 - x - 2 < 11$$
$$-2x < 10$$
$$x > -5$$

CASE II If $-2 \leq x < 3$, the given inequality becomes

$$-x + 3 + x + 2 < 11$$
$$5 < 11 \qquad \text{(always true)}$$

CASE III If $x \geq 3$, the inequality becomes

$$x - 3 + x + 2 < 11$$
$$2x < 12$$
$$x < 6$$

Combining cases I, II, and III, we see that the inequality is satisfied when $-5 < x < 6$. So the solution is the interval $(-5, 6)$.

In the following example we first guess the answer by looking at special cases and recognizing a pattern. Then we prove our conjecture by mathematical induction.

In using the Principle of Mathematical Induction, we follow three steps:

Step 1 Prove that S_n is true when $n = 1$.

Step 2 Assume that S_n is true when $n = k$ and deduce that S_n is true when $n = k + 1$.

Step 3 Conclude that S_n is true for all n by the Principle of Mathematical Induction.

EXAMPLE 3 If $f_0(x) = x/(x + 1)$ and $f_{n+1} = f_0 \circ f_n$ for $n = 0, 1, 2, \ldots$, find a formula for $f_n(x)$.

PS Analogy: Try a similar, simpler problem

SOLUTION We start by finding formulas for $f_n(x)$ for the special cases $n = 1, 2,$ and 3.

$$f_1(x) = (f_0 \circ f_0)(x) = f_0(f_0(x)) = f_0\left(\frac{x}{x + 1}\right)$$

$$= \frac{\dfrac{x}{x + 1}}{\dfrac{x}{x + 1} + 1} = \frac{\dfrac{x}{x + 1}}{\dfrac{2x + 1}{x + 1}} = \frac{x}{2x + 1}$$

$$f_2(x) = (f_0 \circ f_1)(x) = f_0(f_1(x)) = f_0\left(\frac{x}{2x + 1}\right)$$

$$= \frac{\dfrac{x}{2x + 1}}{\dfrac{x}{2x + 1} + 1} = \frac{\dfrac{x}{2x + 1}}{\dfrac{3x + 1}{2x + 1}} = \frac{x}{3x + 1}$$

$$f_3(x) = (f_0 \circ f_2)(x) = f_0(f_2(x)) = f_0\left(\frac{x}{3x + 1}\right)$$

PS Look for a pattern

$$= \frac{\dfrac{x}{3x + 1}}{\dfrac{x}{3x + 1} + 1} = \frac{\dfrac{x}{3x + 1}}{\dfrac{4x + 1}{3x + 1}} = \frac{x}{4x + 1}$$

We notice a pattern: The coefficient of x in the denominator of $f_n(x)$ is $n + 1$ in the three cases we have computed. So we make the guess that, in general,

$$\boxed{4} \qquad f_n(x) = \frac{x}{(n + 1)x + 1}$$

To prove this, we use the Principle of Mathematical Induction. We have already verified that $\boxed{4}$ is true for $n = 1$. Assume that it is true for $n = k$, that is,

$$f_k(x) = \frac{x}{(k + 1)x + 1}$$

Then $\quad f_{k+1}(x) = (f_0 \circ f_k)(x) = f_0(f_k(x)) = f_0\left(\dfrac{x}{(k+1)x+1}\right)$

$$= \dfrac{\dfrac{x}{(k+1)x+1}}{\dfrac{x}{(k+1)x+1}+1} = \dfrac{\dfrac{x}{(k+1)x+1}}{\dfrac{(k+2)x+1}{(k+1)x+1}} = \dfrac{x}{(k+2)x+1}$$

This expression shows that $\boxed{4}$ is true for $n = k + 1$. Therefore, by mathematical induction, it is true for all positive integers n. ▬

Problems

1. One of the legs of a right triangle has length 4 cm. Express the length of the altitude perpendicular to the hypotenuse as a function of the length of the hypotenuse.

2. The altitude perpendicular to the hypotenuse of a right triangle is 12 cm. Express the length of the hypotenuse as a function of the perimeter.

3. Solve the equation $|2x - 1| - |x + 5| = 3$.

4. Solve the inequality $|x - 1| - |x - 3| \geq 5$.

5. Sketch the graph of the function $f(x) = |x^2 - 4|x| + 3|$.

6. Sketch the graph of the function $g(x) = |x^2 - 1| - |x^2 - 4|$.

7. Draw the graph of the equation $x + |x| = y + |y|$.

8. Sketch the region in the plane consisting of all points (x, y) such that
$$|x - y| + |x| - |y| \leq 2$$

9. The notation $\max\{a, b, \ldots\}$ means the largest of the numbers $a, b, \ldots$. Sketch the graph of each function.
   (a) $f(x) = \max\{x, 1/x\}$ (b) $f(x) = \max\{\sin x, \cos x\}$ (c) $f(x) = \max\{x^2, 2 + x, 2 - x\}$

10. Sketch the region in the plane defined by each of the following equations or inequalities.
   (a) $\max\{x, 2y\} = 1$ (b) $-1 \leq \max\{x, 2y\} \leq 1$ (c) $\max\{x, y^2\} = 1$

11. Evaluate $(\log_2 3)(\log_3 4)(\log_4 5) \cdots (\log_{31} 32)$.

12. (a) Show that the function $f(x) = \ln\left(x + \sqrt{x^2 + 1}\right)$ is an odd function.
    (b) Find the inverse function of f.

13. Solve the inequality $\ln(x^2 - 2x - 2) \leq 0$.

14. Use indirect reasoning to prove that $\log_2 5$ is an irrational number.

15. A driver sets out on a journey. For the first half of the distance she drives at the leisurely pace of 60 km/h; she drives the second half at 120 km/h. What is her average speed on this trip?

16. Is it true that $f \circ (g + h) = f \circ g + f \circ h$?

17. Prove that if n is a positive integer, then $7^n - 1$ is divisible by 6.

18. Prove that $1 + 3 + 5 + \cdots + (2n - 1) = n^2$.

19. If $f_0(x) = x^2$ and $f_{n+1}(x) = f_0(f_n(x))$ for $n = 0, 1, 2, \ldots$, find a formula for $f_n(x)$.

20. (a) If $f_0(x) = \dfrac{1}{2 - x}$ and $f_{n+1} = f_0 \circ f_n$ for $n = 0, 1, 2, \ldots$, find an expression for $f_n(x)$ and use mathematical induction to prove it.
    (b) Graph f_0, f_1, f_2, f_3 on the same screen and describe the effects of repeated composition.

⌂ Graphing calculator or computer required

80

2 Limits and Derivatives

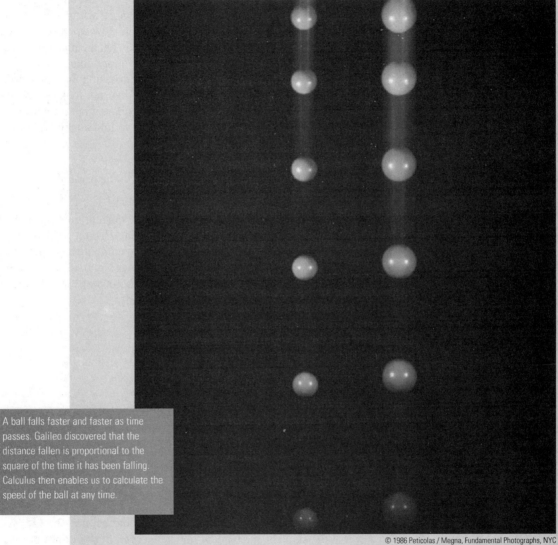

A ball falls faster and faster as time passes. Galileo discovered that the distance fallen is proportional to the square of the time it has been falling. Calculus then enables us to calculate the speed of the ball at any time.

© 1986 Peticolas / Megna, Fundamental Photographs, NYC

In *A Preview of Calculus* (page 1) we saw how the idea of a limit underlies the various branches of calculus. It is therefore appropriate to begin our study of calculus by investigating limits and their properties. The special type of limit that is used to find tangents and velocities gives rise to the central idea in differential calculus, the derivative.

2.1   The Tangent and Velocity Problems

In this section we see how limits arise when we attempt to find the tangent to a curve or the velocity of an object.

The Tangent Problem

The word *tangent* is derived from the Latin word *tangens*, which means "touching." Thus a tangent to a curve is a line that touches the curve. In other words, a tangent line should have the same direction as the curve at the point of contact. How can this idea be made precise?

For a circle we could simply follow Euclid and say that a tangent is a line that intersects the circle once and only once, as in Figure 1(a). For more complicated curves this definition is inadequate. Figure l(b) shows two lines *l* and *t* passing through a point *P* on a curve *C*. The line *l* intersects *C* only once, but it certainly does not look like what we think of as a tangent. The line *t*, on the other hand, looks like a tangent but it intersects *C* twice.

To be specific, let's look at the problem of trying to find a tangent line *t* to the parabola $y = x^2$ in the following example.

(a)

(b)

FIGURE 1

V   EXAMPLE 1   Find an equation of the tangent line to the parabola $y = x^2$ at the point $P(1, 1)$.

SOLUTION   We will be able to find an equation of the tangent line *t* as soon as we know its slope *m*. The difficulty is that we know only one point, *P*, on *t*, whereas we need two points to compute the slope. But observe that we can compute an approximation to *m* by choosing a nearby point $Q(x, x^2)$ on the parabola (as in Figure 2) and computing the slope m_{PQ} of the secant line *PQ*. [A **secant line**, from the Latin word *secans*, meaning cutting, is a line that cuts (intersects) a curve more than once.]

We choose $x \neq 1$ so that $Q \neq P$. Then

$$m_{PQ} = \frac{x^2 - 1}{x - 1}$$

FIGURE 2

For instance, for the point $Q(1.5, 2.25)$ we have

$$m_{PQ} = \frac{2.25 - 1}{1.5 - 1} = \frac{1.25}{0.5} = 2.5$$

x	m_{PQ}
2	3
1.5	2.5
1.1	2.1
1.01	2.01
1.001	2.001

x	m_{PQ}
0	1
0.5	1.5
0.9	1.9
0.99	1.99
0.999	1.999

The tables in the margin show the values of m_{PQ} for several values of *x* close to 1. The closer *Q* is to *P*, the closer *x* is to 1 and, it appears from the tables, the closer m_{PQ} is to 2. This suggests that the slope of the tangent line *t* should be $m = 2$.

We say that the slope of the tangent line is the *limit* of the slopes of the secant lines, and we express this symbolically by writing

$$\lim_{Q \to P} m_{PQ} = m \quad \text{and} \quad \lim_{x \to 1} \frac{x^2 - 1}{x - 1} = 2$$

Assuming that the slope of the tangent line is indeed 2, we use the point-slope form of the equation of a line (see Appendix B) to write the equation of the tangent line through (1, 1) as

$$y - 1 = 2(x - 1) \quad \text{or} \quad y = 2x - 1$$

Figure 3 illustrates the limiting process that occurs in this example. As Q approaches P along the parabola, the corresponding secant lines rotate about P and approach the tangent line t.

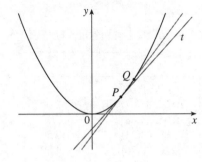

Q approaches P from the right

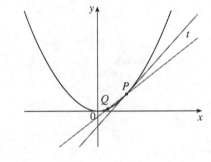

Q approaches P from the left

FIGURE 3

TEC In Visual 2.1 you can see how the process in Figure 3 works for additional functions.

t	Q
0.00	100.00
0.02	81.87
0.04	67.03
0.06	54.88
0.08	44.93
0.10	36.76

Many functions that occur in science are not described by explicit equations; they are defined by experimental data. The next example shows how to estimate the slope of the tangent line to the graph of such a function.

V **EXAMPLE 2** The flash unit on a camera operates by storing charge on a capacitor and releasing it suddenly when the flash is set off. The data in the table describe the charge Q remaining on the capacitor (measured in microcoulombs) at time t (measured in seconds after the flash goes off). Use the data to draw the graph of this function and estimate the slope of the tangent line at the point where $t = 0.04$. [*Note:* The slope of the tangent line represents the electric current flowing from the capacitor to the flash bulb (measured in microamperes).]

SOLUTION In Figure 4 we plot the given data and use them to sketch a curve that approximates the graph of the function.

FIGURE 4

Given the points $P(0.04, 67.03)$ and $R(0.00, 100.00)$ on the graph, we find that the slope of the secant line PR is

$$m_{PR} = \frac{100.00 - 67.03}{0.00 - 0.04} = -824.25$$

R	m_{PR}
(0.00, 100.00)	−824.25
(0.02, 81.87)	−742.00
(0.06, 54.88)	−607.50
(0.08, 44.93)	−552.50
(0.10, 36.76)	−504.50

The physical meaning of the answer in Example 2 is that the electric current flowing from the capacitor to the flash bulb after 0.04 second is about –670 microamperes.

The table at the left shows the results of similar calculations for the slopes of other secant lines. From this table we would expect the slope of the tangent line at $t = 0.04$ to lie somewhere between -742 and -607.5. In fact, the average of the slopes of the two closest secant lines is

$$\tfrac{1}{2}(-742 - 607.5) = -674.75$$

So, by this method, we estimate the slope of the tangent line to be -675.

Another method is to draw an approximation to the tangent line at P and measure the sides of the triangle ABC, as in Figure 4. This gives an estimate of the slope of the tangent line as

$$-\frac{|AB|}{|BC|} \approx -\frac{80.4 - 53.6}{0.06 - 0.02} = -670$$

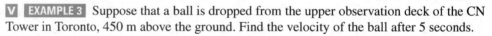

The Velocity Problem

If you watch the speedometer of a car as you travel in city traffic, you see that the needle doesn't stay still for very long; that is, the velocity of the car is not constant. We assume from watching the speedometer that the car has a definite velocity at each moment, but how is the "instantaneous" velocity defined? Let's investigate the example of a falling ball.

V **EXAMPLE 3** Suppose that a ball is dropped from the upper observation deck of the CN Tower in Toronto, 450 m above the ground. Find the velocity of the ball after 5 seconds.

SOLUTION Through experiments carried out four centuries ago, Galileo discovered that the distance fallen by any freely falling body is proportional to the square of the time it has been falling. (This model for free fall neglects air resistance.) If the distance fallen after t seconds is denoted by $s(t)$ and measured in meters, then Galileo's law is expressed by the equation

$$s(t) = 4.9t^2$$

The difficulty in finding the velocity after 5 s is that we are dealing with a single instant of time ($t = 5$), so no time interval is involved. However, we can approximate the desired quantity by computing the average velocity over the brief time interval of a tenth of a second from $t = 5$ to $t = 5.1$:

$$\text{average velocity} = \frac{\text{change in position}}{\text{time elapsed}}$$

$$= \frac{s(5.1) - s(5)}{0.1}$$

$$= \frac{4.9(5.1)^2 - 4.9(5)^2}{0.1} = 49.49 \text{ m/s}$$

The CN Tower in Toronto was the tallest free-standing building in the world for 32 years.

The following table shows the results of similar calculations of the average velocity over successively smaller time periods.

Time interval	Average velocity (m/s)
$5 \leqslant t \leqslant 6$	53.9
$5 \leqslant t \leqslant 5.1$	49.49
$5 \leqslant t \leqslant 5.05$	49.245
$5 \leqslant t \leqslant 5.01$	49.049
$5 \leqslant t \leqslant 5.001$	49.0049

It appears that as we shorten the time period, the average velocity is becoming closer to 49 m/s. The **instantaneous velocity** when $t = 5$ is defined to be the limiting value of these average velocities over shorter and shorter time periods that start at $t = 5$. Thus the (instantaneous) velocity after 5 s is

$$v = 49 \text{ m/s}$$

You may have the feeling that the calculations used in solving this problem are very similar to those used earlier in this section to find tangents. In fact, there is a close connection between the tangent problem and the problem of finding velocities. If we draw the graph of the distance function of the ball (as in Figure 5) and we consider the points $P(a, 4.9a^2)$ and $Q(a + h, 4.9(a + h)^2)$ on the graph, then the slope of the secant line PQ is

$$m_{PQ} = \frac{4.9(a + h)^2 - 4.9a^2}{(a + h) - a}$$

which is the same as the average velocity over the time interval $[a, a + h]$. Therefore the velocity at time $t = a$ (the limit of these average velocities as h approaches 0) must be equal to the slope of the tangent line at P (the limit of the slopes of the secant lines).

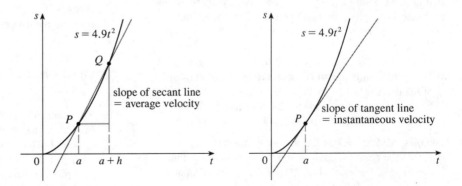

FIGURE 5

Examples 1 and 3 show that in order to solve tangent and velocity problems we must be able to find limits. After studying methods for computing limits in the next five sections, we will return to the problems of finding tangents and velocities in Section 2.7.

Exercises

1. A tank holds 1000 liters of water, which drains from the bottom of the tank in half an hour. The values in the table show the volume V of water remaining in the tank (in liters) after t minutes.

t (min)	5	10	15	20	25	30
V (L)	694	444	250	111	28	0

   (a) If P is the point $(15, 250)$ on the graph of V, find the slopes of the secant lines PQ when Q is the point on the graph with $t = 5, 10, 20, 25,$ and 30.
   (b) Estimate the slope of the tangent line at P by averaging the slopes of two secant lines.
   (c) Use a graph of the function to estimate the slope of the tangent line at P. (This slope represents the rate at which the water is flowing from the tank after 15 minutes.)

2. A cardiac monitor is used to measure the heart rate of a patient after surgery. It compiles the number of heartbeats after t minutes. When the data in the table are graphed, the slope of the tangent line represents the heart rate in beats per minute.

t (min)	36	38	40	42	44
Heartbeats	2530	2661	2806	2948	3080

   The monitor estimates this value by calculating the slope of a secant line. Use the data to estimate the patient's heart rate after 42 minutes using the secant line between the points with the given values of t.
   (a) $t = 36$ and $t = 42$ (b) $t = 38$ and $t = 42$
   (c) $t = 40$ and $t = 42$ (d) $t = 42$ and $t = 44$
   What are your conclusions?

3. The point $P(2, -1)$ lies on the curve $y = 1/(1 - x)$.
   (a) If Q is the point $(x, 1/(1 - x))$, use your calculator to find the slope of the secant line PQ (correct to six decimal places) for the following values of x:
     (i) 1.5   (ii) 1.9   (iii) 1.99   (iv) 1.999
     (v) 2.5   (vi) 2.1   (vii) 2.01   (viii) 2.001
   (b) Using the results of part (a), guess the value of the slope of the tangent line to the curve at $P(2, -1)$.
   (c) Using the slope from part (b), find an equation of the tangent line to the curve at $P(2, -1)$.

4. The point $P(0.5, 0)$ lies on the curve $y = \cos \pi x$.
   (a) If Q is the point $(x, \cos \pi x)$, use your calculator to find the slope of the secant line PQ (correct to six decimal places) for the following values of x:
     (i) 0   (ii) 0.4   (iii) 0.49   (iv) 0.499
     (v) 1   (vi) 0.6   (vii) 0.51   (viii) 0.501
   (b) Using the results of part (a), guess the value of the slope of the tangent line to the curve at $P(0.5, 0)$.

(c) Using the slope from part (b), find an equation of the tangent line to the curve at $P(0.5, 0)$.
(d) Sketch the curve, two of the secant lines, and the tangent line.

5. If a ball is thrown into the air with a velocity of 10 m/s, its height in meters t seconds later is given by $y = 10t - 4.9t^2$.
   (a) Find the average velocity for the time period beginning when $t = 1.5$ and lasting
     (i) 0.5 second   (ii) 0.1 second
     (iii) 0.05 second   (iv) 0.01 second
   (b) Estimate the instantaneous velocity when $t = 1.5$.

6. If a rock is thrown upward on the planet Mars with a velocity of 10 m/s, its height in meters t seconds later is given by $y = 10t - 1.86t^2$.
   (a) Find the average velocity over the given time intervals:
     (i) [1, 2]   (ii) [1, 1.5]   (iii) [1, 1.1]
     (iv) [1, 1.01]   (v) [1, 1.001]
   (b) Estimate the instantaneous velocity when $t = 1$.

7. The table shows the position of a cyclist.

t (seconds)	0	1	2	3	4	5
s (meters)	0	1.4	5.1	10.7	17.7	25.8

   (a) Find the average velocity for each time period:
     (i) [1, 3]   (ii) [2, 3]   (iii) [3, 5]   (iv) [3, 4]
   (b) Use the graph of s as a function of t to estimate the instantaneous velocity when $t = 3$.

8. The displacement (in centimeters) of a particle moving back and forth along a straight line is given by the equation of motion $s = 2 \sin \pi t + 3 \cos \pi t$, where t is measured in seconds.
   (a) Find the average velocity during each time period:
     (i) [1, 2]   (ii) [1, 1.1]
     (iii) [1, 1.01]   (iv) [1, 1.001]
   (b) Estimate the instantaneous velocity of the particle when $t = 1$.

9. The point $P(1, 0)$ lies on the curve $y = \sin(10\pi/x)$.
   (a) If Q is the point $(x, \sin(10\pi/x))$, find the slope of the secant line PQ (correct to four decimal places) for $x = 2, 1.5, 1.4, 1.3, 1.2, 1.1, 0.5, 0.6, 0.7, 0.8,$ and 0.9. Do the slopes appear to be approaching a limit?
   (b) Use a graph of the curve to explain why the slopes of the secant lines in part (a) are not close to the slope of the tangent line at P.
   (c) By choosing appropriate secant lines, estimate the slope of the tangent line at P.

2.2 The Limit of a Function

Having seen in the preceding section how limits arise when we want to find the tangent to a curve or the velocity of an object, we now turn our attention to limits in general and numerical and graphical methods for computing them.

Let's investigate the behavior of the function f defined by $f(x) = x^2 - x + 2$ for values of x near 2. The following table gives values of $f(x)$ for values of x close to 2 but not equal to 2.

x	$f(x)$	x	$f(x)$
1.0	2.000000	3.0	8.000000
1.5	2.750000	2.5	5.750000
1.8	3.440000	2.2	4.640000
1.9	3.710000	2.1	4.310000
1.95	3.852500	2.05	4.152500
1.99	3.970100	2.01	4.030100
1.995	3.985025	2.005	4.015025
1.999	3.997001	2.001	4.003001

FIGURE 1

From the table and the graph of f (a parabola) shown in Figure 1 we see that when x is close to 2 (on either side of 2), $f(x)$ is close to 4. In fact, it appears that we can make the values of $f(x)$ as close as we like to 4 by taking x sufficiently close to 2. We express this by saying "the limit of the function $f(x) = x^2 - x + 2$ as x approaches 2 is equal to 4." The notation for this is

$$\lim_{x \to 2} (x^2 - x + 2) = 4$$

In general, we use the following notation.

---

1 **Definition** Suppose $f(x)$ is defined when x is near the number a. (This means that f is defined on some open interval that contains a, except possibly at a itself.) Then we write

$$\lim_{x \to a} f(x) = L$$

and say   "the limit of $f(x)$, as x approaches a, equals L"

if we can make the values of $f(x)$ arbitrarily close to L (as close to L as we like) by taking x to be sufficiently close to a (on either side of a) but not equal to a.

Roughly speaking, this says that the values of $f(x)$ approach L as x approaches a. In other words, the values of $f(x)$ tend to get closer and closer to the number L as x gets closer and closer to the number a (from either side of a) but $x \neq a$. (A more precise definition will be given in Section 2.4.)

An alternative notation for

$$\lim_{x \to a} f(x) = L$$

is $$f(x) \to L \quad \text{as} \quad x \to a$$

which is usually read "$f(x)$ approaches L as x approaches a."

Notice the phrase "but $x \neq a$" in the definition of limit. This means that in finding the limit of $f(x)$ as x approaches a, we never consider $x = a$. In fact, $f(x)$ need not even be defined when $x = a$. The only thing that matters is how f is defined *near a*.

Figure 2 shows the graphs of three functions. Note that in part (c), $f(a)$ is not defined and in part (b), $f(a) \neq L$. But in each case, regardless of what happens at a, it is true that $\lim_{x \to a} f(x) = L$

(a)

(b)

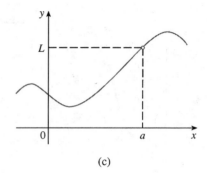
(c)

FIGURE 2 $\lim_{x \to a} f(x) = L$ in all three cases

EXAMPLE 1   Guess the value of $\lim_{x \to 1} \dfrac{x - 1}{x^2 - 1}$.

SOLUTION   Notice that the function $f(x) = (x - 1)/(x^2 - 1)$ is not defined when $x = 1$, but that doesn't matter because the definition of $\lim_{x \to a} f(x)$ says that we consider values of x that are close to a but not equal to a.

The tables at the left give values of $f(x)$ (correct to six decimal places) for values of x that approach 1 (but are not equal to 1). On the basis of the values in the tables, we make the guess that

$$\lim_{x \to 1} \frac{x - 1}{x^2 - 1} = 0.5$$

$x < 1$	$f(x)$
0.5	0.666667
0.9	0.526316
0.99	0.502513
0.999	0.500250
0.9999	0.500025

$x > 1$	$f(x)$
1.5	0.400000
1.1	0.476190
1.01	0.497512
1.001	0.499750
1.0001	0.499975

Example 1 is illustrated by the graph of f in Figure 3. Now let's change f slightly by giving it the value 2 when $x = 1$ and calling the resulting function g:

$$g(x) = \begin{cases} \dfrac{x - 1}{x^2 - 1} & \text{if } x \neq 1 \\ 2 & \text{if } x = 1 \end{cases}$$

This new function g still has the same limit as x approaches 1. (See Figure 4.)

FIGURE 3

FIGURE 4

EXAMPLE 2 Estimate the value of $\lim\limits_{t \to 0} \dfrac{\sqrt{t^2 + 9} - 3}{t^2}$.

SOLUTION The table lists values of the function for several values of t near 0.

t	$\dfrac{\sqrt{t^2 + 9} - 3}{t^2}$
± 1.0	0.16228
± 0.5	0.16553
± 0.1	0.16662
± 0.05	0.16666
± 0.01	0.16667

As t approaches 0, the values of the function seem to approach $0.1666666\ldots$ and so we guess that

$$\lim_{t \to 0} \frac{\sqrt{t^2 + 9} - 3}{t^2} = \frac{1}{6}$$

t	$\dfrac{\sqrt{t^2 + 9} - 3}{t^2}$
± 0.0005	0.16800
± 0.0001	0.20000
± 0.00005	0.00000
± 0.00001	0.00000

www.stewartcalculus.com

For a further explanation of why calculators sometimes give false values, click on *Lies My Calculator and Computer Told Me.* In particular, see the section called *The Perils of Subtraction.*

In Example 2 what would have happened if we had taken even smaller values of t? The table in the margin shows the results from one calculator; you can see that something strange seems to be happening.

If you try these calculations on your own calculator you might get different values, but eventually you will get the value 0 if you make t sufficiently small. Does this mean that the answer is really 0 instead of $\frac{1}{6}$? No, the value of the limit is $\frac{1}{6}$, as we will show in the next section. The problem is that the calculator gave false values because $\sqrt{t^2 + 9}$ is very close to 3 when t is small. (In fact, when t is sufficiently small, a calculator's value for $\sqrt{t^2 + 9}$ is $3.000\ldots$ to as many digits as the calculator is capable of carrying.)

Something similar happens when we try to graph the function

$$f(t) = \frac{\sqrt{t^2 + 9} - 3}{t^2}$$

of Example 2 on a graphing calculator or computer. Parts (a) and (b) of Figure 5 show quite accurate graphs of f, and when we use the trace mode (if available) we can estimate eas-ily that the limit is about $\frac{1}{6}$. But if we zoom in too much, as in parts (c) and (d), then we get in-accurate graphs, again because of problems with subtraction.

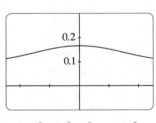

(a) $[-5, 5]$ by $[-0.1, 0.3]$

(b) $[-0.1, 0.1]$ by $[-0.1, 0.3]$

(c) $[-10^{-6}, 10^{-6}]$ by $[-0.1, 0.3]$

(d) $[-10^{-7}, 10^{-7}]$ by $[-0.1, 0.3]$

FIGURE 5

x	$\dfrac{\sin x}{x}$
±1.0	0.84147098
±0.5	0.95885108
±0.4	0.97354586
±0.3	0.98506736
±0.2	0.99334665
±0.1	0.99833417
±0.05	0.99958339
±0.01	0.99998333
±0.005	0.99999583
±0.001	0.99999983

V **EXAMPLE 3** Guess the value of $\displaystyle\lim_{x \to 0} \frac{\sin x}{x}$.

SOLUTION The function $f(x) = (\sin x)/x$ is not defined when $x = 0$. Using a calculator (and remembering that, if $x \in \mathbb{R}$, $\sin x$ means the sine of the angle whose *radian* measure is x), we construct a table of values correct to eight decimal places. From the table at the left and the graph in Figure 6 we guess that

$$\lim_{x \to 0} \frac{\sin x}{x} = 1$$

This guess is in fact correct, as will be proved in Chapter 3 using a geometric argument.

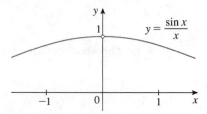

FIGURE 6

V **EXAMPLE 4** Investigate $\displaystyle\lim_{x \to 0} \sin \frac{\pi}{x}$.

SOLUTION Again the function $f(x) = \sin(\pi/x)$ is undefined at 0. Evaluating the function for some small values of x, we get

$$f(1) = \sin \pi = 0 \qquad\qquad f(\tfrac{1}{2}) = \sin 2\pi = 0$$

$$f(\tfrac{1}{3}) = \sin 3\pi = 0 \qquad\qquad f(\tfrac{1}{4}) = \sin 4\pi = 0$$

$$f(0.1) = \sin 10\pi = 0 \qquad f(0.01) = \sin 100\pi = 0$$

Similarly, $f(0.001) = f(0.0001) = 0$. On the basis of this information we might be tempted to guess that

$$\lim_{x \to 0} \sin \frac{\pi}{x} = 0$$

but this time our guess is wrong. Note that although $f(1/n) = \sin n\pi = 0$ for any integer n, it is also true that $f(x) = 1$ for infinitely many values of x that approach 0. You can see this from the graph of f shown in Figure 7.

Computer Algebra Systems

Computer algebra systems (CAS) have commands that compute limits. In order to avoid the types of pitfalls demonstrated in Examples 2, 4, and 5, they don't find limits by numerical experimentation. Instead, they use more sophisticated techniques such as computing infinite series. If you have access to a CAS, use the limit command to compute the limits in the examples of this section and to check your answers in the exercises of this chapter.

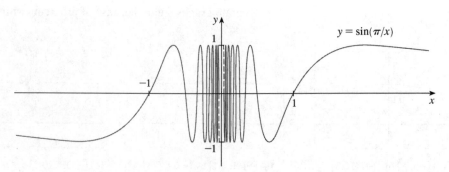

FIGURE 7

The dashed lines near the y-axis indicate that the values of $\sin(\pi/x)$ oscillate between 1 and -1 infinitely often as x approaches 0. (See Exercise 45.)

Since the values of $f(x)$ do not approach a fixed number as x approaches 0,

$$\lim_{x \to 0} \sin \frac{\pi}{x} \quad \text{does not exist} \qquad \blacksquare$$

EXAMPLE 5 Find $\displaystyle\lim_{x \to 0} \left(x^3 + \frac{\cos 5x}{10{,}000} \right)$.

x	$x^3 + \dfrac{\cos 5x}{10{,}000}$
1	1.000028
0.5	0.124920
0.1	0.001088
0.05	0.000222
0.01	0.000101

SOLUTION   As before, we construct a table of values. From the first table in the margin it appears that

$$\lim_{x \to 0} \left(x^3 + \frac{\cos 5x}{10{,}000} \right) = 0$$

But if we persevere with smaller values of x, the second table suggests that

$$\lim_{x \to 0} \left(x^3 + \frac{\cos 5x}{10{,}000} \right) = 0.000100 = \frac{1}{10{,}000}$$

x	$x^3 + \dfrac{\cos 5x}{10{,}000}$
0.005	0.00010009
0.001	0.00010000

Later we will see that $\lim_{x \to 0} \cos 5x = 1$; then it follows that the limit is 0.0001. $\blacksquare$

⊘   Examples 4 and 5 illustrate some of the pitfalls in guessing the value of a limit. It is easy to guess the wrong value if we use inappropriate values of x, but it is difficult to know when to stop calculating values. And, as the discussion after Example 2 shows, sometimes calculators and computers give the wrong values. In the next section, however, we will develop foolproof methods for calculating limits.

V   EXAMPLE 6   The Heaviside function H is defined by

$$H(t) = \begin{cases} 0 & \text{if } t < 0 \\ 1 & \text{if } t \geq 0 \end{cases}$$

[This function is named after the electrical engineer Oliver Heaviside (1850–1925) and can be used to describe an electric current that is switched on at time $t = 0$.] Its graph is shown in Figure 8.

As t approaches 0 from the left, $H(t)$ approaches 0. As t approaches 0 from the right, $H(t)$ approaches 1. There is no single number that $H(t)$ approaches as t approaches 0. Therefore $\lim_{t \to 0} H(t)$ does not exist. $\blacksquare$

FIGURE 8
The Heaviside function

One-Sided Limits

We noticed in Example 6 that $H(t)$ approaches 0 as t approaches 0 from the left and $H(t)$ approaches 1 as t approaches 0 from the right. We indicate this situation symbolically by writing

$$\lim_{t \to 0^-} H(t) = 0 \qquad \text{and} \qquad \lim_{t \to 0^+} H(t) = 1$$

The symbol "$t \to 0^-$" indicates that we consider only values of t that are less than 0. Likewise, "$t \to 0^+$" indicates that we consider only values of t that are greater than 0.

> **2** **Definition** We write
>
> $$\lim_{x \to a^-} f(x) = L$$
>
> and say the **left-hand limit of** $f(x)$ **as** x **approaches** a [or the **limit of** $f(x)$ **as** x **approaches** a **from the left**] is equal to L if we can make the values of $f(x)$ arbitrarily close to L by taking x to be sufficiently close to a and x less than a.

Notice that Definition 2 differs from Definition 1 only in that we require x to be less than a. Similarly, if we require that x be greater than a, we get "the **right-hand limit of** $f(x)$ **as** x **approaches** a is equal to L" and we write

$$\lim_{x \to a^+} f(x) = L$$

Thus the symbol "$x \to a^+$" means that we consider only $x > a$. These definitions are illustrated in Figure 9.

FIGURE 9
(a) $\lim\limits_{x \to a^-} f(x) = L$ (b) $\lim\limits_{x \to a^+} f(x) = L$

By comparing Definition 1 with the definitions of one-sided limits, we see that the following is true.

> **3** $\lim\limits_{x \to a} f(x) = L$ if and only if $\lim\limits_{x \to a^-} f(x) = L$ and $\lim\limits_{x \to a^+} f(x) = L$

V EXAMPLE 7   The graph of a function g is shown in Figure 10. Use it to state the values (if they exist) of the following:

(a) $\lim\limits_{x \to 2^-} g(x)$ (b) $\lim\limits_{x \to 2^+} g(x)$ (c) $\lim\limits_{x \to 2} g(x)$

(d) $\lim\limits_{x \to 5^-} g(x)$ (e) $\lim\limits_{x \to 5^+} g(x)$ (f) $\lim\limits_{x \to 5} g(x)$

FIGURE 10

SOLUTION From the graph we see that the values of $g(x)$ approach 3 as x approaches 2 from the left, but they approach 1 as x approaches 2 from the right. Therefore

$$\text{(a)} \ \lim_{x \to 2^-} g(x) = 3 \quad \text{and} \quad \text{(b)} \ \lim_{x \to 2^+} g(x) = 1$$

(c) Since the left and right limits are different, we conclude from $\boxed{3}$ that $\lim_{x \to 2} g(x)$ does not exist.

The graph also shows that

$$\text{(d)} \ \lim_{x \to 5^-} g(x) = 2 \quad \text{and} \quad \text{(e)} \ \lim_{x \to 5^+} g(x) = 2$$

(f) This time the left and right limits are the same and so, by $\boxed{3}$, we have

$$\lim_{x \to 5} g(x) = 2$$

Despite this fact, notice that $g(5) \neq 2$.

■ Infinite Limits

EXAMPLE 8 Find $\displaystyle\lim_{x \to 0} \frac{1}{x^2}$ if it exists.

SOLUTION As x becomes close to 0, x^2 also becomes close to 0, and $1/x^2$ becomes very large. (See the table in the margin.) In fact, it appears from the graph of the function $f(x) = 1/x^2$ shown in Figure 11 that the values of $f(x)$ can be made arbitrarily large by taking x close enough to 0. Thus the values of $f(x)$ do not approach a number, so $\lim_{x \to 0} (1/x^2)$ does not exist.

To indicate the kind of behavior exhibited in Example 8, we use the notation

$$\lim_{x \to 0} \frac{1}{x^2} = \infty$$

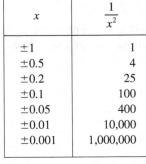

x	$\dfrac{1}{x^2}$
± 1	1
± 0.5	4
± 0.2	25
± 0.1	100
± 0.05	400
± 0.01	10,000
± 0.001	1,000,000

$\oslash$ This does not mean that we are regarding ∞ as a number. Nor does it mean that the limit exists. It simply expresses the particular way in which the limit does not exist: $1/x^2$ can be made as large as we like by taking x close enough to 0.

In general, we write symbolically

$$\lim_{x \to a} f(x) = \infty$$

to indicate that the values of $f(x)$ tend to become larger and larger (or "increase without bound") as x becomes closer and closer to a.

FIGURE 11

$\boxed{4}$ **Definition** Let f be a function defined on both sides of a, except possibly at a itself. Then

$$\lim_{x \to a} f(x) = \infty$$

means that the values of $f(x)$ can be made arbitrarily large (as large as we please) by taking x sufficiently close to a, but not equal to a.

Another notation for $\lim_{x \to a} f(x) = \infty$ is

$$f(x) \to \infty \qquad \text{as} \qquad x \to a$$

Again, the symbol ∞ is not a number, but the expression $\lim_{x \to a} f(x) = \infty$ is often read as

"the limit of $f(x)$, as x approaches a, is infinity"

or "$f(x)$ becomes infinite as x approaches a"

or "$f(x)$ increases without bound as x approaches a"

This definition is illustrated graphically in Figure 12.

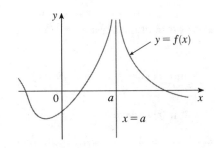

FIGURE 12

$\displaystyle\lim_{x \to a} f(x) = \infty$

When we say a number is "large negative," we mean that it is negative but its magnitude (absolute value) is large.

FIGURE 13
$\lim\limits_{x \to a} f(x) = -\infty$

A similar sort of limit, for functions that become large negative as x gets close to a, is defined in Definition 5 and is illustrated in Figure 13.

> **5**   **Definition**   Let f be defined on both sides of a, except possibly at a itself. Then
> $$\lim_{x \to a} f(x) = -\infty$$
> means that the values of $f(x)$ can be made arbitrarily large negative by taking x sufficiently close to a, but not equal to a.

The symbol $\lim_{x \to a} f(x) = -\infty$ can be read as "the limit of $f(x)$, as x approaches a, is negative infinity" or "$f(x)$ decreases without bound as x approaches a." As an example we have

$$\lim_{x \to 0} \left(-\frac{1}{x^2} \right) = -\infty$$

Similar definitions can be given for the one-sided infinite limits

$$\lim_{x \to a^-} f(x) = \infty \qquad\qquad \lim_{x \to a^+} f(x) = \infty$$

$$\lim_{x \to a^-} f(x) = -\infty \qquad\qquad \lim_{x \to a^+} f(x) = -\infty$$

remembering that "$x \to a^-$" means that we consider only values of x that are less than a, and similarly "$x \to a^+$" means that we consider only $x > a$. Illustrations of these four cases are given in Figure 14.

(a) $\lim\limits_{x \to a^-} f(x) = \infty$

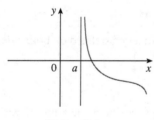

(b) $\lim\limits_{x \to a^+} f(x) = \infty$

(c) $\lim\limits_{x \to a^-} f(x) = -\infty$

(d) $\lim\limits_{x \to a^+} f(x) = -\infty$

FIGURE 14

> **6**   **Definition**   The line $x = a$ is called a **vertical asymptote** of the curve $y = f(x)$ if at least one of the following statements is true:
> $$\lim_{x \to a} f(x) = \infty \qquad \lim_{x \to a^-} f(x) = \infty \qquad \lim_{x \to a^+} f(x) = \infty$$
> $$\lim_{x \to a} f(x) = -\infty \qquad \lim_{x \to a^-} f(x) = -\infty \qquad \lim_{x \to a^+} f(x) = -\infty$$

For instance, the y-axis is a vertical asymptote of the curve $y = 1/x^2$ because $\lim_{x \to 0} (1/x^2) = \infty$. In Figure 14 the line $x = a$ is a vertical asymptote in each of the four cases shown. In general, knowledge of vertical asymptotes is very useful in sketching graphs.

EXAMPLE 9 Find $\lim\limits_{x \to 3^+} \dfrac{2x}{x - 3}$ and $\lim\limits_{x \to 3^-} \dfrac{2x}{x - 3}$.

SOLUTION If x is close to 3 but larger than 3, then the denominator $x - 3$ is a small positive number and $2x$ is close to 6. So the quotient $2x/(x - 3)$ is a large *positive* number. Thus, intuitively, we see that

$$\lim_{x \to 3^+} \frac{2x}{x - 3} = \infty$$

Likewise, if x is close to 3 but smaller than 3, then $x - 3$ is a small negative number but $2x$ is still a positive number (close to 6). So $2x/(x - 3)$ is a numerically large *negative* number. Thus

$$\lim_{x \to 3^-} \frac{2x}{x - 3} = -\infty$$

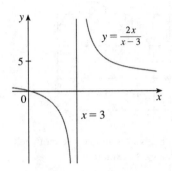

FIGURE 15

The graph of the curve $y = 2x/(x - 3)$ is given in Figure 15. The line $x = 3$ is a vertical asymptote.

EXAMPLE 10 Find the vertical asymptotes of $f(x) = \tan x$.

SOLUTION Because

$$\tan x = \frac{\sin x}{\cos x}$$

there are potential vertical asymptotes where $\cos x = 0$. In fact, since $\cos x \to 0^+$ as $x \to (\pi/2)^-$ and $\cos x \to 0^-$ as $x \to (\pi/2)^+$, whereas $\sin x$ is positive when x is near $\pi/2$, we have

$$\lim_{x \to (\pi/2)^-} \tan x = \infty \qquad \text{and} \qquad \lim_{x \to (\pi/2)^+} \tan x = -\infty$$

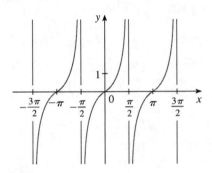

FIGURE 16

$y = \tan x$

This shows that the line $x = \pi/2$ is a vertical asymptote. Similar reasoning shows that the lines $x = (2n + 1)\pi/2$, where n is an integer, are all vertical asymptotes of $f(x) = \tan x$. The graph in Figure 16 confirms this.

Another example of a function whose graph has a vertical asymptote is the natural logarithmic function $y = \ln x$. From Figure 17 we see that

$$\lim_{x \to 0^+} \ln x = -\infty$$

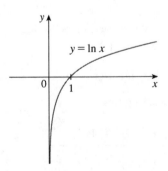

FIGURE 17

The y-axis is a vertical asymptote of the natural logarithmic function.

and so the line $x = 0$ (the y-axis) is a vertical asymptote. In fact, the same is true for $y = \log_a x$ provided that $a > 1$. (See Figures 11 and 12 in Section 1.6.)

| 2.2 | **Exercises** |

1. Explain in your own words what is meant by the equation

$$\lim_{x \to 2} f(x) = 5$$

Is it possible for this statement to be true and yet $f(2) = 3$? Explain.

2. Explain what it means to say that

$$\lim_{x \to 1^-} f(x) = 3 \quad \text{and} \quad \lim_{x \to 1^+} f(x) = 7$$

In this situation is it possible that $\lim_{x \to 1} f(x)$ exists? Explain.

3. Explain the meaning of each of the following.

(a) $\lim_{x \to -3} f(x) = \infty$ (b) $\lim_{x \to 4^+} f(x) = -\infty$

4. Use the given graph of f to state the value of each quantity, if it exists. If it does not exist, explain why.

(a) $\lim_{x \to 2^-} f(x)$ (b) $\lim_{x \to 2^+} f(x)$ (c) $\lim_{x \to 2} f(x)$

(d) $f(2)$ (e) $\lim_{x \to 4} f(x)$ (f) $f(4)$

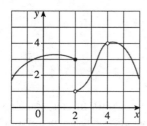

5. For the function f whose graph is given, state the value of each quantity, if it exists. If it does not exist, explain why.

(a) $\lim_{x \to 1} f(x)$ (b) $\lim_{x \to 3^-} f(x)$ (c) $\lim_{x \to 3^+} f(x)$

(d) $\lim_{x \to 3} f(x)$ (e) $f(3)$

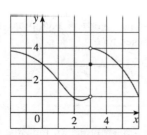

6. For the function h whose graph is given, state the value of each quantity, if it exists. If it does not exist, explain why.

(a) $\lim_{x \to -3^-} h(x)$ (b) $\lim_{x \to -3^+} h(x)$ (c) $\lim_{x \to -3} h(x)$

(d) $h(-3)$ (e) $\lim_{x \to 0^-} h(x)$ (f) $\lim_{x \to 0^+} h(x)$

(g) $\lim_{x \to 0} h(x)$ (h) $h(0)$ (i) $\lim_{x \to 2} h(x)$

(j) $h(2)$ (k) $\lim_{x \to 5^+} h(x)$ (l) $\lim_{x \to 5^-} h(x)$

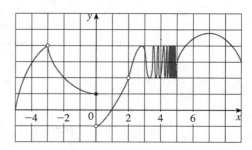

7. For the function g whose graph is given, state the value of each quantity, if it exists. If it does not exist, explain why.

(a) $\lim_{t \to 0^-} g(t)$ (b) $\lim_{t \to 0^+} g(t)$ (c) $\lim_{t \to 0} g(t)$

(d) $\lim_{t \to 2^-} g(t)$ (e) $\lim_{t \to 2^+} g(t)$ (f) $\lim_{t \to 2} g(t)$

(g) $g(2)$ (h) $\lim_{t \to 4} g(t)$

8. For the function R whose graph is shown, state the following.

(a) $\lim_{x \to 2} R(x)$ (b) $\lim_{x \to 5} R(x)$

(c) $\lim_{x \to -3^-} R(x)$ (d) $\lim_{x \to -3^+} R(x)$

(e) The equations of the vertical asymptotes.

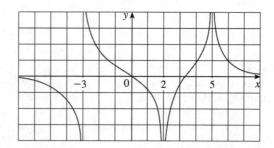

9. For the function f whose graph is shown, state the following.

(a) $\lim\limits_{x \to -7} f(x)$ (b) $\lim\limits_{x \to -3} f(x)$ (c) $\lim\limits_{x \to 0} f(x)$

(d) $\lim\limits_{x \to 6^-} f(x)$ (e) $\lim\limits_{x \to 6^+} f(x)$

(f) The equations of the vertical asymptotes.

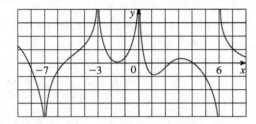

10. A patient receives a 150-mg injection of a drug every 4 hours. The graph shows the amount $f(t)$ of the drug in the bloodstream after t hours. Find

$$\lim_{t \to 12^-} f(t) \qquad \text{and} \qquad \lim_{t \to 12^+} f(t)$$

and explain the significance of these one-sided limits.

11–12 Sketch the graph of the function and use it to determine the values of a for which $\lim_{x \to a} f(x)$ exists.

11. $f(x) = \begin{cases} 1 + x & \text{if } x < -1 \\ x^2 & \text{if } -1 \le x < 1 \\ 2 - x & \text{if } x \ge 1 \end{cases}$

12. $f(x) = \begin{cases} 1 + \sin x & \text{if } x < 0 \\ \cos x & \text{if } 0 \le x \le \pi \\ \sin x & \text{if } x > \pi \end{cases}$

13–14 Use the graph of the function f to state the value of each limit, if it exists. If it does not exist, explain why.

(a) $\lim\limits_{x \to 0^-} f(x)$ (b) $\lim\limits_{x \to 0^+} f(x)$ (c) $\lim\limits_{x \to 0} f(x)$

13. $f(x) = \dfrac{1}{1 + e^{1/x}}$

14. $f(x) = \dfrac{x^2 + x}{\sqrt{x^3 + x^2}}$

15–18 Sketch the graph of an example of a function f that satisfies all of the given conditions.

15. $\lim\limits_{x \to 1^-} f(x) = 2$, $\quad \lim\limits_{x \to 1^+} f(x) = -2$, $\quad f(1) = 2$

16. $\lim\limits_{x \to 0^-} f(x) = 1$, $\quad \lim\limits_{x \to 0^+} f(x) = -1$, $\quad \lim\limits_{x \to 2^-} f(x) = 0$, $\lim\limits_{x \to 2^+} f(x) = 1$, $\quad f(2) = 1$, $\quad f(0)$ is undefined

17. $\lim\limits_{x \to 3^+} f(x) = 4$, $\quad \lim\limits_{x \to 3^-} f(x) = 2$, $\quad \lim\limits_{x \to -2} f(x) = 2$, $f(3) = 3$, $\quad f(-2) = 1$

18. $\lim\limits_{x \to 0^-} f(x) = 2$, $\quad \lim\limits_{x \to 0^+} f(x) = 0$, $\quad \lim\limits_{x \to 4^-} f(x) = 3$, $\lim\limits_{x \to 4^+} f(x) = 0$, $\quad f(0) = 2$, $\quad f(4) = 1$

19–22 Guess the value of the limit (if it exists) by evaluating the function at the given numbers (correct to six decimal places).

19. $\lim\limits_{x \to 2} \dfrac{x^2 - 2x}{x^2 - x - 2}$,
$x = 2.5, 2.1, 2.05, 2.01, 2.005, 2.001,$
$1.9, 1.95, 1.99, 1.995, 1.999$

20. $\lim\limits_{x \to -1} \dfrac{x^2 - 2x}{x^2 - x - 2}$,
$x = 0, -0.5, -0.9, -0.95, -0.99, -0.999,$
$-2, -1.5, -1.1, -1.01, -1.001$

21. $\lim\limits_{x \to 0} \dfrac{e^x - 1 - x}{x^2}$, $\quad x = \pm 1, \pm 0.5, \pm 0.1, \pm 0.05, \pm 0.01$

22. $\lim\limits_{x \to 0^+} x \ln(x + x^2)$, $\quad x = 1, 0.5, 0.1, 0.05, 0.01, 0.005, 0.001$

23–26 Use a table of values to estimate the value of the limit. If you have a graphing device, use it to confirm your result graphically.

23. $\lim\limits_{x \to 0} \dfrac{\sqrt{x + 4} - 2}{x}$

24. $\lim\limits_{x \to 0} \dfrac{\tan 3x}{\tan 5x}$

25. $\lim\limits_{x \to 1} \dfrac{x^6 - 1}{x^{10} - 1}$

26. $\lim\limits_{x \to 0} \dfrac{9^x - 5^x}{x}$

27. (a) By graphing the function $f(x) = (\cos 2x - \cos x)/x^2$ and zooming in toward the point where the graph crosses the y-axis, estimate the value of $\lim_{x \to 0} f(x)$.

(b) Check your answer in part (a) by evaluating $f(x)$ for values of x that approach 0.

28. (a) Estimate the value of

$$\lim_{x \to 0} \frac{\sin x}{\sin \pi x}$$

by graphing the function $f(x) = (\sin x)/(\sin \pi x)$. State your answer correct to two decimal places.

(b) Check your answer in part (a) by evaluating $f(x)$ for values of x that approach 0.

29–37 Determine the infinite limit.

29. $\lim\limits_{x \to -3^+} \dfrac{x + 2}{x + 3}$

30. $\lim\limits_{x \to -3^-} \dfrac{x + 2}{x + 3}$

31. $\lim\limits_{x \to 1} \dfrac{2 - x}{(x - 1)^2}$

32. $\lim\limits_{x \to 5^-} \dfrac{e^x}{(x - 5)^3}$

33. $\lim\limits_{x \to 3^+} \ln(x^2 - 9)$

34. $\lim\limits_{x \to \pi^-} \cot x$

35. $\lim\limits_{x \to 2\pi^-} x \csc x$

36. $\lim\limits_{x \to 2^-} \dfrac{x^2 - 2x}{x^2 - 4x + 4}$

37. $\lim\limits_{x \to 2^+} \dfrac{x^2 - 2x - 8}{x^2 - 5x + 6}$

38. (a) Find the vertical asymptotes of the function

$$y = \frac{x^2 + 1}{3x - 2x^2}$$

(b) Confirm your answer to part (a) by graphing the function.

39. Determine $\lim\limits_{x \to 1^-} \dfrac{1}{x^3 - 1}$ and $\lim\limits_{x \to 1^+} \dfrac{1}{x^3 - 1}$

(a) by evaluating $f(x) = 1/(x^3 - 1)$ for values of x that approach 1 from the left and from the right,

(b) by reasoning as in Example 9, and

(c) from a graph of f.

40. (a) By graphing the function $f(x) = (\tan 4x)/x$ and zooming in toward the point where the graph crosses the y-axis, estimate the value of $\lim_{x \to 0} f(x)$.

(b) Check your answer in part (a) by evaluating $f(x)$ for values of x that approach 0.

41. (a) Estimate the value of the limit $\lim_{x \to 0} (1 + x)^{1/x}$ to five decimal places. Does this number look familiar?

(b) Illustrate part (a) by graphing the function $y = (1 + x)^{1/x}$.

42. (a) Graph the function $f(x) = e^x + \ln|x - 4|$ for $0 \le x \le 5$. Do you think the graph is an accurate representation of f?

(b) How would you get a graph that represents f better?

43. (a) Evaluate the function $f(x) = x^2 - (2^x/1000)$ for $x = 1$, 0.8, 0.6, 0.4, 0.2, 0.1, and 0.05, and guess the value of

$$\lim_{x \to 0} \left(x^2 - \frac{2^x}{1000} \right)$$

(b) Evaluate $f(x)$ for $x = 0.04, 0.02, 0.01, 0.005, 0.003$, and 0.001. Guess again.

44. (a) Evaluate $h(x) = (\tan x - x)/x^3$ for $x = 1, 0.5, 0.1, 0.05, 0.01$, and 0.005.

(b) Guess the value of $\lim\limits_{x \to 0} \dfrac{\tan x - x}{x^3}$.

(c) Evaluate $h(x)$ for successively smaller values of x until you finally reach a value of 0 for $h(x)$. Are you still confident that your guess in part (b) is correct? Explain why you eventually obtained 0 values. (In Section 4.4 a method for evaluating the limit will be explained.)

(d) Graph the function h in the viewing rectangle $[-1, 1]$ by $[0, 1]$. Then zoom in toward the point where the graph crosses the y-axis to estimate the limit of $h(x)$ as x approaches 0. Continue to zoom in until you observe distortions in the graph of h. Compare with the results of part (c).

45. Graph the function $f(x) = \sin(\pi/x)$ of Example 4 in the viewing rectangle $[-1, 1]$ by $[-1, 1]$. Then zoom in toward the origin several times. Comment on the behavior of this function.

46. In the theory of relativity, the mass of a particle with velocity v is

$$m = \frac{m_0}{\sqrt{1 - v^2/c^2}}$$

where m_0 is the mass of the particle at rest and c is the speed of light. What happens as $v \to c^-$?

47. Use a graph to estimate the equations of all the vertical asymptotes of the curve

$$y = \tan(2 \sin x) \qquad -\pi \le x \le \pi$$

Then find the exact equations of these asymptotes.

48. (a) Use numerical and graphical evidence to guess the value of the limit

$$\lim_{x \to 1} \frac{x^3 - 1}{\sqrt{x} - 1}$$

(b) How close to 1 does x have to be to ensure that the function in part (a) is within a distance 0.5 of its limit?

2.3   Calculating Limits Using the Limit Laws

In Section 2.2 we used calculators and graphs to guess the values of limits, but we saw that such methods don't always lead to the correct answer. In this section we use the following properties of limits, called the *Limit Laws,* to calculate limits.

Limit Laws   Suppose that c is a constant and the limits

$$\lim_{x \to a} f(x) \quad \text{and} \quad \lim_{x \to a} g(x)$$

exist. Then

1. $\displaystyle\lim_{x \to a} [f(x) + g(x)] = \lim_{x \to a} f(x) + \lim_{x \to a} g(x)$

2. $\displaystyle\lim_{x \to a} [f(x) - g(x)] = \lim_{x \to a} f(x) - \lim_{x \to a} g(x)$

3. $\displaystyle\lim_{x \to a} [cf(x)] = c \lim_{x \to a} f(x)$

4. $\displaystyle\lim_{x \to a} [f(x)\,g(x)] = \lim_{x \to a} f(x) \cdot \lim_{x \to a} g(x)$

5. $\displaystyle\lim_{x \to a} \frac{f(x)}{g(x)} = \frac{\displaystyle\lim_{x \to a} f(x)}{\displaystyle\lim_{x \to a} g(x)}$ if $\displaystyle\lim_{x \to a} g(x) \neq 0$

These five laws can be stated verbally as follows:

Sum Law

1. The limit of a sum is the sum of the limits.

Difference Law

2. The limit of a difference is the difference of the limits.

Constant Multiple Law

3. The limit of a constant times a function is the constant times the limit of the function.

Product Law

4. The limit of a product is the product of the limits.

Quotient Law

5. The limit of a quotient is the quotient of the limits (provided that the limit of the denominator is not 0).

It is easy to believe that these properties are true. For instance, if $f(x)$ is close to L and $g(x)$ is close to M, it is reasonable to conclude that $f(x) + g(x)$ is close to $L + M$. This gives us an intuitive basis for believing that Law 1 is true. In Section 2.4 we give a precise definition of a limit and use it to prove this law. The proofs of the remaining laws are given in Appendix F.

EXAMPLE 1   Use the Limit Laws and the graphs of f and g in Figure 1 to evaluate the following limits, if they exist.

(a) $\displaystyle\lim_{x \to -2} [f(x) + 5g(x)]$ (b) $\displaystyle\lim_{x \to 1} [f(x)g(x)]$ (c) $\displaystyle\lim_{x \to 2} \frac{f(x)}{g(x)}$

SOLUTION

(a) From the graphs of f and g we see that

$$\lim_{x \to -2} f(x) = 1 \quad \text{and} \quad \lim_{x \to -2} g(x) = -1$$

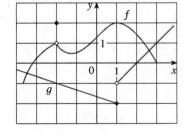

FIGURE 1

Therefore we have

$$\lim_{x \to -2} [f(x) + 5g(x)] = \lim_{x \to -2} f(x) + \lim_{x \to -2} [5g(x)] \qquad \text{(by Law 1)}$$

$$= \lim_{x \to -2} f(x) + 5 \lim_{x \to -2} g(x) \qquad \text{(by Law 3)}$$

$$= 1 + 5(-1) = -4$$

(b) We see that $\lim_{x \to 1} f(x) = 2$. But $\lim_{x \to 1} g(x)$ does not exist because the left and right limits are different:

$$\lim_{x \to 1^-} g(x) = -2 \qquad \lim_{x \to 1^+} g(x) = -1$$

So we can't use Law 4 for the desired limit. But we *can* use Law 4 for the one-sided limits:

$$\lim_{x \to 1^-} [f(x)g(x)] = 2 \cdot (-2) = -4 \qquad \lim_{x \to 1^+} [f(x)g(x)] = 2 \cdot (-1) = -2 .$$

The left and right limits aren't equal, so $\lim_{x \to 1} [f(x)g(x)]$ does not exist.

(c) The graphs show that

$$\lim_{x \to 2} f(x) \approx 1.4 \qquad \text{and} \qquad \lim_{x \to 2} g(x) = 0$$

Because the limit of the denominator is 0, we can't use Law 5. The given limit does not exist because the denominator approaches 0 while the numerator approaches a nonzero number.

If we use the Product Law repeatedly with $g(x) = f(x)$, we obtain the following law.

Power Law

> **6.** $\lim_{x \to a} [f(x)]^n = \left[\lim_{x \to a} f(x)\right]^n$ where n is a positive integer

In applying these six limit laws, we need to use two special limits:

> **7.** $\lim_{x \to a} c = c$ **8.** $\lim_{x \to a} x = a$

These limits are obvious from an intuitive point of view (state them in words or draw graphs of $y = c$ and $y = x$), but proofs based on the precise definition are requested in the exercises for Section 2.4.

If we now put $f(x) = x$ in Law 6 and use Law 8, we get another useful special limit.

> **9.** $\lim_{x \to a} x^n = a^n$ where n is a positive integer

A similar limit holds for roots as follows. (For square roots the proof is outlined in Exercise 37 in Section 2.4.)

> **10.** $\lim_{x \to a} \sqrt[n]{x} = \sqrt[n]{a}$ where n is a positive integer
>
> (If n is even, we assume that $a > 0$.)

More generally, we have the following law, which is proved in Section 2.5 as a consequence of Law 10.

Root Law

11. $\lim\limits_{x \to a} \sqrt[n]{f(x)} = \sqrt[n]{\lim\limits_{x \to a} f(x)}$ where n is a positive integer

$\left[\text{If } n \text{ is even, we assume that } \lim\limits_{x \to a} f(x) > 0. \right]$

Newton and Limits

Isaac Newton was born on Christmas Day in 1642, the year of Galileo's death. When he entered Cambridge University in 1661 Newton didn't know much mathematics, but he learned quickly by reading Euclid and Descartes and by attending the lectures of Isaac Barrow. Cambridge was closed because of the plague in 1665 and 1666, and Newton returned home to reflect on what he had learned. Those two years were amazingly productive for at that time he made four of his major discoveries: (1) his representation of functions as sums of infinite series, including the binomial theorem; (2) his work on differential and integral calculus; (3) his laws of motion and law of universal gravitation; and (4) his prism experiments on the nature of light and color. Because of a fear of controversy and criticism, he was reluctant to publish his discoveries and it wasn't until 1687, at the urging of the astronomer Halley, that Newton published *Principia Mathematica*. In this work, the greatest scientific treatise ever written, Newton set forth his version of calculus and used it to investigate mechanics, fluid dynamics, and wave motion, and to explain the motion of planets and comets.

The beginnings of calculus are found in the calculations of areas and volumes by ancient Greek scholars such as Eudoxus and Archimedes. Although aspects of the idea of a limit are implicit in their "method of exhaustion," Eudoxus and Archimedes never explicitly formulated the concept of a limit. Likewise, mathematicians such as Cavalieri, Fermat, and Barrow, the immediate precursors of Newton in the development of calculus, did not actually use limits. It was Isaac Newton who was the first to talk explicitly about limits. He explained that the main idea behind limits is that quantities "approach nearer than by any given difference." Newton stated that the limit was the basic concept in calculus, but it was left to later mathematicians like Cauchy to clarify his ideas about limits.

EXAMPLE 2 Evaluate the following limits and justify each step.

(a) $\lim\limits_{x \to 5} (2x^2 - 3x + 4)$

(b) $\lim\limits_{x \to -2} \dfrac{x^3 + 2x^2 - 1}{5 - 3x}$

SOLUTION

(a)
$$\lim_{x \to 5} (2x^2 - 3x + 4) = \lim_{x \to 5} (2x^2) - \lim_{x \to 5} (3x) + \lim_{x \to 5} 4 \quad \text{(by Laws 2 and 1)}$$

$$= 2 \lim_{x \to 5} x^2 - 3 \lim_{x \to 5} x + \lim_{x \to 5} 4 \quad \text{(by 3)}$$

$$= 2(5^2) - 3(5) + 4 \quad \text{(by 9, 8, and 7)}$$

$$= 39$$

(b) We start by using Law 5, but its use is fully justified only at the final stage when we see that the limits of the numerator and denominator exist and the limit of the denominator is not 0.

$$\lim_{x \to -2} \frac{x^3 + 2x^2 - 1}{5 - 3x} = \frac{\lim\limits_{x \to -2} (x^3 + 2x^2 - 1)}{\lim\limits_{x \to -2} (5 - 3x)} \quad \text{(by Law 5)}$$

$$= \frac{\lim\limits_{x \to -2} x^3 + 2 \lim\limits_{x \to -2} x^2 - \lim\limits_{x \to -2} 1}{\lim\limits_{x \to -2} 5 - 3 \lim\limits_{x \to -2} x} \quad \text{(by 1, 2, and 3)}$$

$$= \frac{(-2)^3 + 2(-2)^2 - 1}{5 - 3(-2)} \quad \text{(by 9, 8, and 7)}$$

$$= -\frac{1}{11}$$

NOTE If we let $f(x) = 2x^2 - 3x + 4$, then $f(5) = 39$. In other words, we would have gotten the correct answer in Example 2(a) by substituting 5 for x. Similarly, direct substitution provides the correct answer in part (b). The functions in Example 2 are a polynomial and a rational function, respectively, and similar use of the Limit Laws proves that direct substitution always works for such functions (see Exercises 55 and 56). We state this fact as follows.

Direct Substitution Property If f is a polynomial or a rational function and a is in the domain of f, then

$$\lim_{x \to a} f(x) = f(a)$$

Functions with the Direct Substitution Property are called *continuous at a* and will be studied in Section 2.5. However, not all limits can be evaluated by direct substitution, as the following examples show.

EXAMPLE 3 Find $\lim\limits_{x \to 1} \dfrac{x^2 - 1}{x - 1}$.

SOLUTION Let $f(x) = (x^2 - 1)/(x - 1)$. We can't find the limit by substituting $x = 1$ because $f(1)$ isn't defined. Nor can we apply the Quotient Law, because the limit of the denominator is 0. Instead, we need to do some preliminary algebra. We factor the numerator as a difference of squares:

$$\frac{x^2 - 1}{x - 1} = \frac{(x - 1)(x + 1)}{x - 1}$$

The numerator and denominator have a common factor of $x - 1$. When we take the limit as x approaches 1, we have $x \neq 1$ and so $x - 1 \neq 0$. Therefore we can cancel the common factor and compute the limit as follows:

$$\lim_{x \to 1} \frac{x^2 - 1}{x - 1} = \lim_{x \to 1} \frac{(x - 1)(x + 1)}{x - 1}$$

$$= \lim_{x \to 1} (x + 1)$$

$$= 1 + 1 = 2$$

The limit in this example arose in Section 2.1 when we were trying to find the tangent to the parabola $y = x^2$ at the point $(1, 1)$.

NOTE In Example 3 we were able to compute the limit by replacing the given function $f(x) = (x^2 - 1)/(x - 1)$ by a simpler function, $g(x) = x + 1$, with the same limit. This is valid because $f(x) = g(x)$ except when $x = 1$, and in computing a limit as x approaches 1 we don't consider what happens when x is actually *equal* to 1. In general, we have the following useful fact.

If $f(x) = g(x)$ when $x \neq a$, then $\lim\limits_{x \to a} f(x) = \lim\limits_{x \to a} g(x)$, provided the limits exist.

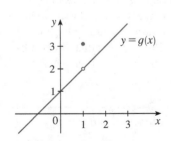

FIGURE 2
The graphs of the functions f (from Example 3) and g (from Example 4)

EXAMPLE 4 Find $\lim\limits_{x \to 1} g(x)$ where

$$g(x) = \begin{cases} x + 1 & \text{if } x \neq 1 \\ \pi & \text{if } x = 1 \end{cases}$$

SOLUTION Here g is defined at $x = 1$ and $g(1) = \pi$, but the value of a limit as x approaches 1 does not depend on the value of the function at 1. Since $g(x) = x + 1$ for $x \neq 1$, we have

$$\lim_{x \to 1} g(x) = \lim_{x \to 1} (x + 1) = 2$$

Note that the values of the functions in Examples 3 and 4 are identical except when $x = 1$ (see Figure 2) and so they have the same limit as x approaches 1.

V **EXAMPLE 5** Evaluate $\lim\limits_{h \to 0} \dfrac{(3 + h)^2 - 9}{h}$.

SOLUTION If we define

$$F(h) = \frac{(3 + h)^2 - 9}{h}$$

then, as in Example 3, we can't compute $\lim_{h \to 0} F(h)$ by letting $h = 0$ since $F(0)$ is undefined. But if we simplify $F(h)$ algebraically, we find that

$$F(h) = \frac{(9 + 6h + h^2) - 9}{h} = \frac{6h + h^2}{h} = 6 + h$$

(Recall that we consider only $h \neq 0$ when letting h approach 0.) Thus

$$\lim_{h \to 0} \frac{(3 + h)^2 - 9}{h} = \lim_{h \to 0} (6 + h) = 6$$

EXAMPLE 6 Find $\lim\limits_{t \to 0} \dfrac{\sqrt{t^2 + 9} - 3}{t^2}$.

SOLUTION We can't apply the Quotient Law immediately, since the limit of the denominator is 0. Here the preliminary algebra consists of rationalizing the numerator:

$$\begin{aligned}
\lim_{t \to 0} \frac{\sqrt{t^2 + 9} - 3}{t^2} &= \lim_{t \to 0} \frac{\sqrt{t^2 + 9} - 3}{t^2} \cdot \frac{\sqrt{t^2 + 9} + 3}{\sqrt{t^2 + 9} + 3} \\
&= \lim_{t \to 0} \frac{(t^2 + 9) - 9}{t^2 \left(\sqrt{t^2 + 9} + 3\right)} \\
&= \lim_{t \to 0} \frac{t^2}{t^2 \left(\sqrt{t^2 + 9} + 3\right)} \\
&= \lim_{t \to 0} \frac{1}{\sqrt{t^2 + 9} + 3} \\
&= \frac{1}{\sqrt{\lim\limits_{t \to 0} (t^2 + 9)} + 3} \\
&= \frac{1}{3 + 3} = \frac{1}{6}
\end{aligned}$$

This calculation confirms the guess that we made in Example 2 in Section 2.2.

Some limits are best calculated by first finding the left- and right-hand limits. The following theorem is a reminder of what we discovered in Section 2.2. It says that a two-sided limit exists if and only if both of the one-sided limits exist and are equal.

---

1 **Theorem** $\quad \lim\limits_{x \to a} f(x) = L \quad$ if and only if $\quad \lim\limits_{x \to a^-} f(x) = L = \lim\limits_{x \to a^+} f(x)$

When computing one-sided limits, we use the fact that the Limit Laws also hold for one-sided limits.

EXAMPLE 7   Show that $\lim\limits_{x \to 0} |x| = 0$.

SOLUTION   Recall that

$$|x| = \begin{cases} x & \text{if } x \geq 0 \\ -x & \text{if } x < 0 \end{cases}$$

The result of Example 7 looks plausible from Figure 3.

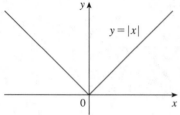

FIGURE 3

Since $|x| = x$ for $x > 0$, we have

$$\lim\limits_{x \to 0^+} |x| = \lim\limits_{x \to 0^+} x = 0$$

For $x < 0$ we have $|x| = -x$ and so

$$\lim\limits_{x \to 0^-} |x| = \lim\limits_{x \to 0^-} (-x) = 0$$

Therefore, by Theorem 1,

$$\lim\limits_{x \to 0} |x| = 0$$

V **EXAMPLE 8**   Prove that $\lim\limits_{x \to 0} \dfrac{|x|}{x}$ does not exist.

SOLUTION
$$\lim\limits_{x \to 0^+} \frac{|x|}{x} = \lim\limits_{x \to 0^+} \frac{x}{x} = \lim\limits_{x \to 0^+} 1 = 1$$

$$\lim\limits_{x \to 0^-} \frac{|x|}{x} = \lim\limits_{x \to 0^-} \frac{-x}{x} = \lim\limits_{x \to 0^-} (-1) = -1$$

Since the right- and left-hand limits are different, it follows from Theorem 1 that $\lim_{x \to 0} |x|/x$ does not exist. The graph of the function $f(x) = |x|/x$ is shown in Figure 4 and supports the one-sided limits that we found.

FIGURE 4

EXAMPLE 9   If

$$f(x) = \begin{cases} \sqrt{x - 4} & \text{if } x > 4 \\ 8 - 2x & \text{if } x < 4 \end{cases}$$

determine whether $\lim_{x \to 4} f(x)$ exists.

It is shown in Example 3 in Section 2.4 that $\lim_{x \to 0^+} \sqrt{x} = 0$.

SOLUTION   Since $f(x) = \sqrt{x - 4}$ for $x > 4$, we have

$$\lim\limits_{x \to 4^+} f(x) = \lim\limits_{x \to 4^+} \sqrt{x - 4} = \sqrt{4 - 4} = 0$$

Since $f(x) = 8 - 2x$ for $x < 4$, we have

$$\lim\limits_{x \to 4^-} f(x) = \lim\limits_{x \to 4^-} (8 - 2x) = 8 - 2 \cdot 4 = 0$$

The right- and left-hand limits are equal. Thus the limit exists and

$$\lim\limits_{x \to 4} f(x) = 0$$

FIGURE 5

The graph of f is shown in Figure 5.

Other notations for $[\![x]\!]$ are $[x]$ and $\lfloor x \rfloor$. The greatest integer function is sometimes called the *floor function*.

FIGURE 6
Greatest integer function

EXAMPLE 10 The **greatest integer function** is defined by $[\![x]\!] = $ the largest integer that is less than or equal to x. (For instance, $[\![4]\!] = 4$, $[\![4.8]\!] = 4$, $[\![\pi]\!] = 3$, $[\![\sqrt{2}]\!] = 1$, $[\![-\frac{1}{2}]\!] = -1$.) Show that $\lim_{x \to 3} [\![x]\!]$ does not exist.

SOLUTION The graph of the greatest integer function is shown in Figure 6. Since $[\![x]\!] = 3$ for $3 \le x < 4$, we have

$$\lim_{x \to 3^+} [\![x]\!] = \lim_{x \to 3^+} 3 = 3$$

Since $[\![x]\!] = 2$ for $2 \le x < 3$, we have

$$\lim_{x \to 3^-} [\![x]\!] = \lim_{x \to 3^-} 2 = 2$$

Because these one-sided limits are not equal, $\lim_{x \to 3} [\![x]\!]$ does not exist by Theorem 1.

The next two theorems give two additional properties of limits. Their proofs can be found in Appendix F.

> **2 Theorem** If $f(x) \le g(x)$ when x is near a (except possibly at a) and the limits of f and g both exist as x approaches a, then
>
> $$\lim_{x \to a} f(x) \le \lim_{x \to a} g(x)$$

> **3 The Squeeze Theorem** If $f(x) \le g(x) \le h(x)$ when x is near a (except possibly at a) and
>
> $$\lim_{x \to a} f(x) = \lim_{x \to a} h(x) = L$$
>
> then
> $$\lim_{x \to a} g(x) = L$$

FIGURE 7

The Squeeze Theorem, which is sometimes called the Sandwich Theorem or the Pinching Theorem, is illustrated by Figure 7. It says that if $g(x)$ is squeezed between $f(x)$ and $h(x)$ near a, and if f and h have the same limit L at a, then g is forced to have the same limit L at a.

V **EXAMPLE 11** Show that $\lim_{x \to 0} x^2 \sin \dfrac{1}{x} = 0$.

SOLUTION First note that we **cannot** use

$$\lim_{x \to 0} x^2 \sin \frac{1}{x} = \lim_{x \to 0} x^2 \cdot \lim_{x \to 0} \sin \frac{1}{x}$$

because $\lim_{x \to 0} \sin(1/x)$ does not exist (see Example 4 in Section 2.2).

Instead we apply the Squeeze Theorem, and so we need to find a function f smaller than $g(x) = x^2 \sin(1/x)$ and a function h bigger than g such that both $f(x)$ and $h(x)$

approach 0. To do this we use our knowledge of the sine function. Because the sine of any number lies between -1 and 1, we can write

$$\boxed{4} \qquad\qquad -1 \le \sin\frac{1}{x} \le 1$$

Any inequality remains true when multiplied by a positive number. We know that $x^2 \ge 0$ for all x and so, multiplying each side of the inequalities in $\boxed{4}$ by x^2, we get

$$-x^2 \le x^2 \sin\frac{1}{x} \le x^2$$

as illustrated by Figure 8. We know that

$$\lim_{x \to 0} x^2 = 0 \qquad \text{and} \qquad \lim_{x \to 0} (-x^2) = 0$$

Taking $f(x) = -x^2$, $g(x) = x^2 \sin(1/x)$, and $h(x) = x^2$ in the Squeeze Theorem, we obtain

$$\lim_{x \to 0} x^2 \sin\frac{1}{x} = 0$$

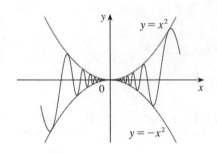

FIGURE 8
$y = x^2 \sin(1/x)$

2.3 Exercises

1. Given that

$$\lim_{x \to 2} f(x) = 4 \qquad \lim_{x \to 2} g(x) = -2 \qquad \lim_{x \to 2} h(x) = 0$$

find the limits that exist. If the limit does not exist, explain why.

(a) $\displaystyle\lim_{x \to 2} [f(x) + 5g(x)]$ (b) $\displaystyle\lim_{x \to 2} [g(x)]^3$

(c) $\displaystyle\lim_{x \to 2} \sqrt{f(x)}$ (d) $\displaystyle\lim_{x \to 2} \frac{3f(x)}{g(x)}$

(e) $\displaystyle\lim_{x \to 2} \frac{g(x)}{h(x)}$ (f) $\displaystyle\lim_{x \to 2} \frac{g(x)h(x)}{f(x)}$

2. The graphs of f and g are given. Use them to evaluate each limit, if it exists. If the limit does not exist, explain why.

(a) $\displaystyle\lim_{x \to 2} [f(x) + g(x)]$ (b) $\displaystyle\lim_{x \to 1} [f(x) + g(x)]$

(c) $\displaystyle\lim_{x \to 0} [f(x)g(x)]$ (d) $\displaystyle\lim_{x \to -1} \frac{f(x)}{g(x)}$

(e) $\displaystyle\lim_{x \to 2} [x^3 f(x)]$ (f) $\displaystyle\lim_{x \to 1} \sqrt{3 + f(x)}$

3–9 Evaluate the limit and justify each step by indicating the appropriate Limit Law(s).

3. $\displaystyle\lim_{x \to -2} (3x^4 + 2x^2 - x + 1)$

4. $\displaystyle\lim_{x \to -1} (x^4 - 3x)(x^2 + 5x + 3)$

5. $\displaystyle\lim_{t \to -2} \frac{t^4 - 2}{2t^2 - 3t + 2}$ **6.** $\displaystyle\lim_{u \to -2} \sqrt{u^4 + 3u + 6}$

7. $\displaystyle\lim_{x \to 8} (1 + \sqrt[3]{x})(2 - 6x^2 + x^3)$ **8.** $\displaystyle\lim_{t \to 2} \left(\frac{t^2 - 2}{t^3 - 3t + 5}\right)^2$

9. $\displaystyle\lim_{x \to 2} \sqrt{\frac{2x^2 + 1}{3x - 2}}$

---

10. (a) What is wrong with the following equation?

$$\frac{x^2 + x - 6}{x - 2} = x + 3$$

(b) In view of part (a), explain why the equation

$$\lim_{x \to 2} \frac{x^2 + x - 6}{x - 2} = \lim_{x \to 2} (x + 3)$$

is correct.

11–32 Evaluate the limit, if it exists.

11. $\lim\limits_{x \to 2} \dfrac{x^2 + x - 6}{x - 2}$

12. $\lim\limits_{x \to -4} \dfrac{x^2 + 5x + 4}{x^2 + 3x - 4}$

13. $\lim\limits_{x \to 2} \dfrac{x^2 - x + 6}{x - 2}$

14. $\lim\limits_{x \to -1} \dfrac{x^2 - 4x}{x^2 - 3x - 4}$

15. $\lim\limits_{t \to -3} \dfrac{t^2 - 9}{2t^2 + 7t + 3}$

16. $\lim\limits_{x \to -1} \dfrac{2x^2 + 3x + 1}{x^2 - 2x - 3}$

17. $\lim\limits_{h \to 0} \dfrac{(-5 + h)^2 - 25}{h}$

18. $\lim\limits_{h \to 0} \dfrac{(2 + h)^3 - 8}{h}$

19. $\lim\limits_{x \to -2} \dfrac{x + 2}{x^3 + 8}$

20. $\lim\limits_{t \to 1} \dfrac{t^4 - 1}{t^3 - 1}$

21. $\lim\limits_{h \to 0} \dfrac{\sqrt{9 + h} - 3}{h}$

22. $\lim\limits_{u \to 2} \dfrac{\sqrt{4u + 1} - 3}{u - 2}$

23. $\lim\limits_{x \to -4} \dfrac{\frac{1}{4} + \frac{1}{x}}{4 + x}$

24. $\lim\limits_{x \to -1} \dfrac{x^2 + 2x + 1}{x^4 - 1}$

25. $\lim\limits_{t \to 0} \dfrac{\sqrt{1 + t} - \sqrt{1 - t}}{t}$

26. $\lim\limits_{t \to 0} \left(\dfrac{1}{t} - \dfrac{1}{t^2 + t} \right)$

27. $\lim\limits_{x \to 16} \dfrac{4 - \sqrt{x}}{16x - x^2}$

28. $\lim\limits_{h \to 0} \dfrac{(3 + h)^{-1} - 3^{-1}}{h}$

29. $\lim\limits_{t \to 0} \left(\dfrac{1}{t\sqrt{1 + t}} - \dfrac{1}{t} \right)$

30. $\lim\limits_{x \to -4} \dfrac{\sqrt{x^2 + 9} - 5}{x + 4}$

31. $\lim\limits_{h \to 0} \dfrac{(x + h)^3 - x^3}{h}$

32. $\lim\limits_{h \to 0} \dfrac{\frac{1}{(x + h)^2} - \frac{1}{x^2}}{h}$

---

33. (a) Estimate the value of
$$\lim_{x \to 0} \frac{x}{\sqrt{1 + 3x} - 1}$$
by graphing the function $f(x) = x/(\sqrt{1 + 3x} - 1)$.
(b) Make a table of values of $f(x)$ for x close to 0 and guess the value of the limit.
(c) Use the Limit Laws to prove that your guess is correct.

34. (a) Use a graph of
$$f(x) = \frac{\sqrt{3 + x} - \sqrt{3}}{x}$$
to estimate the value of $\lim_{x \to 0} f(x)$ to two decimal places.
(b) Use a table of values of $f(x)$ to estimate the limit to four decimal places.
(c) Use the Limit Laws to find the exact value of the limit.

35. Use the Squeeze Theorem to show that $\lim_{x \to 0} (x^2 \cos 20\pi x) = 0$. Illustrate by graphing the functions $f(x) = -x^2$, $g(x) = x^2 \cos 20\pi x$, and $h(x) = x^2$ on the same screen.

36. Use the Squeeze Theorem to show that
$$\lim_{x \to 0} \sqrt{x^3 + x^2} \, \sin \frac{\pi}{x} = 0$$
Illustrate by graphing the functions f, g, and h (in the notation of the Squeeze Theorem) on the same screen.

37. If $4x - 9 \leqslant f(x) \leqslant x^2 - 4x + 7$ for $x \geqslant 0$, find $\lim\limits_{x \to 4} f(x)$.

38. If $2x \leqslant g(x) \leqslant x^4 - x^2 + 2$ for all x, evaluate $\lim\limits_{x \to 1} g(x)$.

39. Prove that $\lim\limits_{x \to 0} x^4 \cos \dfrac{2}{x} = 0$.

40. Prove that $\lim\limits_{x \to 0^+} \sqrt{x} \, e^{\sin(\pi/x)} = 0$.

41–46 Find the limit, if it exists. If the limit does not exist, explain why.

41. $\lim\limits_{x \to 3} (2x + |x - 3|)$

42. $\lim\limits_{x \to -6} \dfrac{2x + 12}{|x + 6|}$

43. $\lim\limits_{x \to 0.5^-} \dfrac{2x - 1}{|2x^3 - x^2|}$

44. $\lim\limits_{x \to -2} \dfrac{2 - |x|}{2 + x}$

45. $\lim\limits_{x \to 0^-} \left(\dfrac{1}{x} - \dfrac{1}{|x|} \right)$

46. $\lim\limits_{x \to 0^+} \left(\dfrac{1}{x} - \dfrac{1}{|x|} \right)$

---

47. The *signum* (or sign) *function*, denoted by sgn, is defined by
$$\operatorname{sgn} x = \begin{cases} -1 & \text{if } x < 0 \\ 0 & \text{if } x = 0 \\ 1 & \text{if } x > 0 \end{cases}$$

(a) Sketch the graph of this function.
(b) Find each of the following limits or explain why it does not exist.
  (i) $\lim\limits_{x \to 0^+} \operatorname{sgn} x$
  (ii) $\lim\limits_{x \to 0^-} \operatorname{sgn} x$
  (iii) $\lim\limits_{x \to 0} \operatorname{sgn} x$
  (iv) $\lim\limits_{x \to 0} |\operatorname{sgn} x|$

48. Let
$$f(x) = \begin{cases} x^2 + 1 & \text{if } x < 1 \\ (x - 2)^2 & \text{if } x \geqslant 1 \end{cases}$$

(a) Find $\lim_{x \to 1^-} f(x)$ and $\lim_{x \to 1^+} f(x)$.
(b) Does $\lim_{x \to 1} f(x)$ exist?
(c) Sketch the graph of f.

49. Let $g(x) = \dfrac{x^2 + x - 6}{|x - 2|}$.

(a) Find
  (i) $\lim\limits_{x \to 2^+} g(x)$
  (ii) $\lim\limits_{x \to 2^-} g(x)$
(b) Does $\lim_{x \to 2} g(x)$ exist?
(c) Sketch the graph of g.

50. Let

$$g(x) = \begin{cases} x & \text{if } x < 1 \\ 3 & \text{if } x = 1 \\ 2 - x^2 & \text{if } 1 < x \leqslant 2 \\ x - 3 & \text{if } x > 2 \end{cases}$$

(a) Evaluate each of the following, if it exists.

(i) $\lim_{x \to 1^-} g(x)$ (ii) $\lim_{x \to 1} g(x)$ (iii) $g(1)$

(iv) $\lim_{x \to 2^-} g(x)$ (v) $\lim_{x \to 2^+} g(x)$ (vi) $\lim_{x \to 2} g(x)$

(b) Sketch the graph of g.

51. (a) If the symbol $[\![\ ]\!]$ denotes the greatest integer function defined in Example 10, evaluate

(i) $\lim_{x \to -2^+} [\![x]\!]$ (ii) $\lim_{x \to -2} [\![x]\!]$ (iii) $\lim_{x \to -2.4} [\![x]\!]$

(b) If n is an integer, evaluate

(i) $\lim_{x \to n^-} [\![x]\!]$ (ii) $\lim_{x \to n^+} [\![x]\!]$

(c) For what values of a does $\lim_{x \to a} [\![x]\!]$ exist?

52. Let $f(x) = [\![\cos x]\!]$, $-\pi \leqslant x \leqslant \pi$.

(a) Sketch the graph of f.

(b) Evaluate each limit, if it exists.

(i) $\lim_{x \to 0} f(x)$ (ii) $\lim_{x \to (\pi/2)^-} f(x)$

(iii) $\lim_{x \to (\pi/2)^+} f(x)$ (iv) $\lim_{x \to \pi/2} f(x)$

(c) For what values of a does $\lim_{x \to a} f(x)$ exist?

53. If $f(x) = [\![x]\!] + [\![-x]\!]$, show that $\lim_{x \to 2} f(x)$ exists but is not equal to $f(2)$.

54. In the theory of relativity, the Lorentz contraction formula

$$L = L_0 \sqrt{1 - v^2/c^2}$$

expresses the length L of an object as a function of its velocity v with respect to an observer, where L_0 is the length of the object at rest and c is the speed of light. Find $\lim_{v \to c^-} L$ and interpret the result. Why is a left-hand limit necessary?

55. If p is a polynomial, show that $\lim_{x \to a} p(x) = p(a)$.

56. If r is a rational function, use Exercise 55 to show that $\lim_{x \to a} r(x) = r(a)$ for every number a in the domain of r.

57. If $\lim_{x \to 1} \dfrac{f(x) - 8}{x - 1} = 10$, find $\lim_{x \to 1} f(x)$.

58. If $\lim_{x \to 0} \dfrac{f(x)}{x^2} = 5$, find the following limits.

(a) $\lim_{x \to 0} f(x)$ (b) $\lim_{x \to 0} \dfrac{f(x)}{x}$

59. If

$$f(x) = \begin{cases} x^2 & \text{if } x \text{ is rational} \\ 0 & \text{if } x \text{ is irrational} \end{cases}$$

prove that $\lim_{x \to 0} f(x) = 0$.

60. Show by means of an example that $\lim_{x \to a} [f(x) + g(x)]$ may exist even though neither $\lim_{x \to a} f(x)$ nor $\lim_{x \to a} g(x)$ exists.

61. Show by means of an example that $\lim_{x \to a} [f(x) g(x)]$ may exist even though neither $\lim_{x \to a} f(x)$ nor $\lim_{x \to a} g(x)$ exists.

62. Evaluate $\lim_{x \to 2} \dfrac{\sqrt{6 - x} - 2}{\sqrt{3 - x} - 1}$.

63. Is there a number a such that

$$\lim_{x \to -2} \frac{3x^2 + ax + a + 3}{x^2 + x - 2}$$

exists? If so, find the value of a and the value of the limit.

64. The figure shows a fixed circle C_1 with equation $(x - 1)^2 + y^2 = 1$ and a shrinking circle C_2 with radius r and center the origin. P is the point $(0, r)$, Q is the upper point of intersection of the two circles, and R is the point of intersection of the line PQ and the x-axis. What happens to R as C_2 shrinks, that is, as $r \to 0^+$?

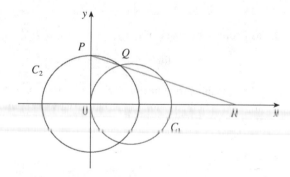

2.4   The Precise Definition of a Limit

The intuitive definition of a limit given in Section 2.2 is inadequate for some purposes because such phrases as "x is close to 2" and "$f(x)$ gets closer and closer to L" are vague. In order to be able to prove conclusively that

$$\lim_{x \to 0} \left(x^3 + \frac{\cos 5x}{10,000} \right) = 0.0001 \qquad \text{or} \qquad \lim_{x \to 0} \frac{\sin x}{x} = 1$$

we must make the definition of a limit precise.

To motivate the precise definition of a limit, let's consider the function

$$f(x) = \begin{cases} 2x - 1 & \text{if } x \neq 3 \\ 6 & \text{if } x = 3 \end{cases}$$

Intuitively, it is clear that when x is close to 3 but $x \neq 3$, then $f(x)$ is close to 5, and so $\lim_{x \to 3} f(x) = 5$.

To obtain more detailed information about how $f(x)$ varies when x is close to 3, we ask the following question:

How close to 3 does x have to be so that $f(x)$ differs from 5 by less than 0.1?

The distance from x to 3 is $|x - 3|$ and the distance from $f(x)$ to 5 is $|f(x) - 5|$, so our problem is to find a number δ such that

$$|f(x) - 5| < 0.1 \quad \text{if} \quad |x - 3| < \delta \quad \text{but } x \neq 3$$

It is traditional to use the Greek letter δ (delta) in this situation.

If $|x - 3| > 0$, then $x \neq 3$, so an equivalent formulation of our problem is to find a number δ such that

$$|f(x) - 5| < 0.1 \quad \text{if} \quad 0 < |x - 3| < \delta$$

Notice that if $0 < |x - 3| < (0.1)/2 = 0.05$, then

$$|f(x) - 5| = |(2x - 1) - 5| = |2x - 6| = 2|x - 3| < 2(0.05) = 0.1$$

that is,
$$|f(x) - 5| < 0.1 \quad \text{if} \quad 0 < |x - 3| < 0.05$$

Thus an answer to the problem is given by $\delta = 0.05$; that is, if x is within a distance of 0.05 from 3, then $f(x)$ will be within a distance of 0.1 from 5.

If we change the number 0.1 in our problem to the smaller number 0.01, then by using the same method we find that $f(x)$ will differ from 5 by less than 0.01 provided that x differs from 3 by less than $(0.01)/2 = 0.005$:

$$|f(x) - 5| < 0.01 \quad \text{if} \quad 0 < |x - 3| < 0.005$$

Similarly,

$$|f(x) - 5| < 0.001 \quad \text{if} \quad 0 < |x - 3| < 0.0005$$

The numbers 0.1, 0.01, and 0.001 that we have considered are *error tolerances* that we might allow. For 5 to be the precise limit of $f(x)$ as x approaches 3, we must not only be able to bring the difference between $f(x)$ and 5 below each of these three numbers; we must be able to bring it below *any* positive number. And, by the same reasoning, we can! If we write ε (the Greek letter epsilon) for an arbitrary positive number, then we find as before that

$$\boxed{1} \qquad |f(x) - 5| < \varepsilon \quad \text{if} \quad 0 < |x - 3| < \delta = \frac{\varepsilon}{2}$$

This is a precise way of saying that $f(x)$ is close to 5 when x is close to 3 because $\boxed{1}$ says that we can make the values of $f(x)$ within an arbitrary distance ε from 5 by taking the values of x within a distance $\varepsilon/2$ from 3 (but $x \neq 3$).

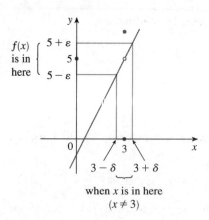

$f(x)$ is in here

FIGURE 1

when x is in here
$(x \neq 3)$

Note that 1 can be rewritten as follows:

$$\text{if} \quad 3 - \delta < x < 3 + \delta \quad (x \neq 3) \qquad \text{then} \qquad 5 - \varepsilon < f(x) < 5 + \varepsilon$$

and this is illustrated in Figure 1. By taking the values of x ($\neq 3$) to lie in the interval $(3 - \delta, 3 + \delta)$ we can make the values of $f(x)$ lie in the interval $(5 - \varepsilon, 5 + \varepsilon)$.

Using 1 as a model, we give a precise definition of a limit.

---

2 Definition Let f be a function defined on some open interval that contains the number a, except possibly at a itself. Then we say that the **limit of $f(x)$ as x approaches a is L**, and we write

$$\lim_{x \to a} f(x) = L$$

if for every number $\varepsilon > 0$ there is a number $\delta > 0$ such that

$$\text{if} \quad 0 < |x - a| < \delta \qquad \text{then} \qquad |f(x) - L| < \varepsilon$$

Since $|x - a|$ is the distance from x to a and $|f(x) - L|$ is the distance from $f(x)$ to L, and since ε can be arbitrarily small, the definition of a limit can be expressed in words as follows:

$\lim_{x \to a} f(x) = L$ means that the distance between $f(x)$ and L can be made arbitrarily small by taking the distance from x to a sufficiently small (but not 0).

Alternatively,

$\lim_{x \to a} f(x) = L$ means that the values of $f(x)$ can be made as close as we please to L by taking x close enough to a (but not equal to a).

We can also reformulate Definition 2 in terms of intervals by observing that the inequality $|x - a| < \delta$ is equivalent to $-\delta < x - a < \delta$, which in turn can be written as $a - \delta < x < a + \delta$. Also $0 < |x - a|$ is true if and only if $x - a \neq 0$, that is, $x \neq a$. Similarly, the inequality $|f(x) - L| < \varepsilon$ is equivalent to the pair of inequalities $L - \varepsilon < f(x) < L + \varepsilon$. Therefore, in terms of intervals, Definition 2 can be stated as follows:

$\lim_{x \to a} f(x) = L$ means that for every $\varepsilon > 0$ (no matter how small ε is) we can find $\delta > 0$ such that if x lies in the open interval $(a - \delta, a + \delta)$ and $x \neq a$, then $f(x)$ lies in the open interval $(L - \varepsilon, L + \varepsilon)$.

We interpret this statement geometrically by representing a function by an arrow diagram as in Figure 2, where f maps a subset of $\mathbb{R}$ onto another subset of $\mathbb{R}$.

FIGURE 2

f

x a $f(a)$ $f(x)$

The definition of limit says that if any small interval $(L - \varepsilon, L + \varepsilon)$ is given around L, then we can find an interval $(a - \delta, a + \delta)$ around a such that f maps all the points in $(a - \delta, a + \delta)$ (except possibly a) into the interval $(L - \varepsilon, L + \varepsilon)$. (See Figure 3.)

FIGURE 3

Another geometric interpretation of limits can be given in terms of the graph of a function. If $\varepsilon > 0$ is given, then we draw the horizontal lines $y = L + \varepsilon$ and $y = L - \varepsilon$ and the graph of f. (See Figure 4.) If $\lim_{x \to a} f(x) = L$, then we can find a number $\delta > 0$ such that if we restrict x to lie in the interval $(a - \delta, a + \delta)$ and take $x \neq a$, then the curve $y = f(x)$ lies between the lines $y = L - \varepsilon$ and $y = L + \varepsilon$. (See Figure 5.) You can see that if such a δ has been found, then any smaller δ will also work.

It is important to realize that the process illustrated in Figures 4 and 5 must work for *every* positive number ε, no matter how small it is chosen. Figure 6 shows that if a smaller ε is chosen, then a smaller δ may be required.

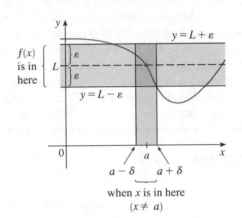

FIGURE 4

FIGURE 5

FIGURE 6

EXAMPLE 1 Use a graph to find a number δ such that

$$\text{if} \quad |x - 1| < \delta \quad \text{then} \quad |(x^3 - 5x + 6) - 2| < 0.2$$

In other words, find a number δ that corresponds to $\varepsilon = 0.2$ in the definition of a limit for the function $f(x) = x^3 - 5x + 6$ with $a = 1$ and $L = 2$.

SOLUTION A graph of f is shown in Figure 7; we are interested in the region near the point $(1, 2)$. Notice that we can rewrite the inequality

$$|(x^3 - 5x + 6) - 2| < 0.2$$

as

$$1.8 < x^3 - 5x + 6 < 2.2$$

So we need to determine the values of x for which the curve $y = x^3 - 5x + 6$ lies between the horizontal lines $y = 1.8$ and $y = 2.2$. Therefore we graph the curves $y = x^3 - 5x + 6$, $y = 1.8$, and $y = 2.2$ near the point $(1, 2)$ in Figure 8. Then we use the cursor to estimate that the x-coordinate of the point of intersection of the line $y = 2.2$ and the curve $y = x^3 - 5x + 6$ is about 0.911. Similarly, $y = x^3 - 5x + 6$ intersects the line $y = 1.8$ when $x \approx 1.124$. So, rounding to be safe, we can say that

$$\text{if} \quad 0.92 < x < 1.12 \quad \text{then} \quad 1.8 < x^3 - 5x + 6 < 2.2$$

FIGURE 7

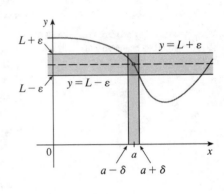

FIGURE 8

This interval (0.92, 1.12) is not symmetric about $x = 1$. The distance from $x = 1$ to the left endpoint is $1 - 0.92 = 0.08$ and the distance to the right endpoint is 0.12. We can choose δ to be the smaller of these numbers, that is, $\delta = 0.08$. Then we can rewrite our inequalities in terms of distances as follows:

$$\text{if} \quad |x - 1| < 0.08 \quad \text{then} \quad |(x^3 - 5x + 6) - 2| < 0.2$$

This just says that by keeping x within 0.08 of 1, we are able to keep $f(x)$ within 0.2 of 2.

Although we chose $\delta = 0.08$, any smaller positive value of δ would also have worked.

The graphical procedure in Example 1 gives an illustration of the definition for $\varepsilon = 0.2$, but it does not *prove* that the limit is equal to 2. A proof has to provide a δ for *every* ε.

In proving limit statements it may be helpful to think of the definition of limit as a challenge. First it challenges you with a number ε. Then you must be able to produce a suitable δ. You have to be able to do this for *every* $\varepsilon > 0$, not just a particular ε.

TEC In Module 2.4/2.6 you can explore the precise definition of a limit both graphically and numerically.

Imagine a contest between two people, A and B, and imagine yourself to be B. Person A stipulates that the fixed number L should be approximated by the values of $f(x)$ to within a degree of accuracy ε (say, 0.01). Person B then responds by finding a number δ such that if $0 < |x - a| < \delta$, then $|f(x) - L| < \varepsilon$. Then A may become more exacting and challenge B with a smaller value of ε (say, 0.0001). Again B has to respond by finding a corresponding δ. Usually the smaller the value of ε, the smaller the corresponding value of δ must be. If B always wins, no matter how small A makes ε, then $\lim_{x \to a} f(x) = L$.

V   EXAMPLE 2 Prove that $\lim_{x \to 3} (4x - 5) = 7$.

SOLUTION

1. *Preliminary analysis of the problem (guessing a value for δ).* Let ε be a given positive number. We want to find a number δ such that

$$\text{if} \quad 0 < |x - 3| < \delta \quad \text{then} \quad |(4x - 5) - 7| < \varepsilon$$

But $|(4x - 5) - 7| = |4x - 12| = |4(x - 3)| = 4|x - 3|$. Therefore we want δ such that

$$\text{if} \quad 0 < |x - 3| < \delta \quad \text{then} \quad 4|x - 3| < \varepsilon$$

that is,

$$\text{if} \quad 0 < |x - 3| < \delta \quad \text{then} \quad |x - 3| < \frac{\varepsilon}{4}$$

This suggests that we should choose $\delta = \varepsilon/4$.

2. *Proof (showing that this δ works).* Given $\varepsilon > 0$, choose $\delta = \varepsilon/4$. If $0 < |x - 3| < \delta$, then

$$|(4x - 5) - 7| = |4x - 12| = 4|x - 3| < 4\delta = 4\left(\frac{\varepsilon}{4}\right) = \varepsilon$$

Thus

$$\text{if} \quad 0 < |x - 3| < \delta \quad \text{then} \quad |(4x - 5) - 7| < \varepsilon$$

Therefore, by the definition of a limit,

$$\lim_{x \to 3} (4x - 5) = 7$$

FIGURE 9

This example is illustrated by Figure 9.

Note that in the solution of Example 2 there were two stages—guessing and proving. We made a preliminary analysis that enabled us to guess a value for δ. But then in the second stage we had to go back and prove in a careful, logical fashion that we had made a correct guess. This procedure is typical of much of mathematics. Sometimes it is necessary to first make an intelligent guess about the answer to a problem and then prove that the guess is correct.

The intuitive definitions of one-sided limits that were given in Section 2.2 can be precisely reformulated as follows.

---

3 **Definition of Left-Hand Limit**

$$\lim_{x \to a^-} f(x) = L$$

if for every number $\varepsilon > 0$ there is a number $\delta > 0$ such that

$$\text{if} \quad a - \delta < x < a \quad \text{then} \quad |f(x) - L| < \varepsilon$$

---

4 **Definition of Right-Hand Limit**

$$\lim_{x \to a^+} f(x) = L$$

if for every number $\varepsilon > 0$ there is a number $\delta > 0$ such that

$$\text{if} \quad a < x < a + \delta \quad \text{then} \quad |f(x) - L| < \varepsilon$$

Notice that Definition 3 is the same as Definition 2 except that x is restricted to lie in the *left* half $(a - \delta, a)$ of the interval $(a - \delta, a + \delta)$. In Definition 4, x is restricted to lie in the *right* half $(a, a + \delta)$ of the interval $(a - \delta, a + \delta)$.

V **EXAMPLE 3**   Use Definition 4 to prove that $\lim_{x \to 0^+} \sqrt{x} = 0$.

SOLUTION

1. *Guessing a value for δ.* Let ε be a given positive number. Here $a = 0$ and $L = 0$, so we want to find a number δ such that

$$\text{if} \quad 0 < x < \delta \quad \text{then} \quad |\sqrt{x} - 0| < \varepsilon$$

that is,

$$\text{if} \quad 0 < x < \delta \quad \text{then} \quad \sqrt{x} < \varepsilon$$

or, squaring both sides of the inequality $\sqrt{x} < \varepsilon$, we get

$$\text{if} \quad 0 < x < \delta \quad \text{then} \quad x < \varepsilon^2$$

This suggests that we should choose $\delta = \varepsilon^2$.

2. *Showing that this δ works.* Given $\varepsilon > 0$, let $\delta = \varepsilon^2$. If $0 < x < \delta$, then

$$\sqrt{x} < \sqrt{\delta} = \sqrt{\varepsilon^2} = \varepsilon$$

so

$$|\sqrt{x} - 0| < \varepsilon$$

According to Definition 4, this shows that $\lim_{x \to 0^+} \sqrt{x} = 0$.

Cauchy and Limits

After the invention of calculus in the 17th century, there followed a period of free development of the subject in the 18th century. Mathematicians like the Bernoulli brothers and Euler were eager to exploit the power of calculus and boldly explored the consequences of this new and wonderful mathematical theory without worrying too much about whether their proofs were completely correct.

The 19th century, by contrast, was the Age of Rigor in mathematics. There was a movement to go back to the foundations of the subject—to provide careful definitions and rigorous proofs. At the forefront of this movement was the French mathematician Augustin-Louis Cauchy (1789–1857), who started out as a military engineer before becoming a mathematics professor in Paris. Cauchy took Newton's idea of a limit, which was kept alive in the 18th century by the French mathematician Jean d'Alembert, and made it more precise. His definition of a limit reads as follows: "When the successive values attributed to a variable approach indefinitely a fixed value so as to end by differing from it by as little as one wishes, this last is called the *limit* of all the others." But when Cauchy used this definition in examples and proofs, he often employed delta-epsilon inequalities similar to the ones in this section. A typical Cauchy proof starts with: "Designate by δ and ε two very small numbers; . . ." He used ε because of the correspondence between epsilon and the French word *erreur* and δ because delta corresponds to *différence*. Later, the German mathematician Karl Weierstrass (1815–1897) stated the definition of a limit exactly as in our Definition 2.

EXAMPLE 4 Prove that $\lim\limits_{x\to 3} x^2 = 9$.

SOLUTION

1. *Guessing a value for* δ. Let $\varepsilon > 0$ be given. We have to find a number $\delta > 0$ such that

$$\text{if} \quad 0 < |x - 3| < \delta \quad \text{then} \quad |x^2 - 9| < \varepsilon$$

To connect $|x^2 - 9|$ with $|x - 3|$ we write $|x^2 - 9| = |(x + 3)(x - 3)|$. Then we want

$$\text{if} \quad 0 < |x - 3| < \delta \quad \text{then} \quad |x + 3||x - 3| < \varepsilon$$

Notice that if we can find a positive constant C such that $|x + 3| < C$, then

$$|x + 3||x - 3| < C|x - 3|$$

and we can make $C|x - 3| < \varepsilon$ by taking $|x - 3| < \varepsilon/C = \delta$.

We can find such a number C if we restrict x to lie in some interval centered at 3. In fact, since we are interested only in values of x that are close to 3, it is reasonable to assume that x is within a distance 1 from 3, that is, $|x - 3| < 1$. Then $2 < x < 4$, so $5 < x + 3 < 7$. Thus we have $|x + 3| < 7$, and so $C = 7$ is a suitable choice for the constant.

But now there are two restrictions on $|x - 3|$, namely

$$|x - 3| < 1 \quad \text{and} \quad |x - 3| < \frac{\varepsilon}{C} = \frac{\varepsilon}{7}$$

To make sure that both of these inequalities are satisfied, we take δ to be the smaller of the two numbers 1 and $\varepsilon/7$. The notation for this is $\delta = \min\{1, \varepsilon/7\}$.

2. *Showing that this* δ *works.* Given $\varepsilon > 0$, let $\delta = \min\{1, \varepsilon/7\}$. If $0 < |x - 3| < \delta$, then $|x - 3| < 1 \Rightarrow 2 < x < 4 \Rightarrow |x + 3| < 7$ (as in part 1). We also have $|x - 3| < \varepsilon/7$, so

$$|x^2 - 9| = |x + 3||x - 3| < 7 \cdot \frac{\varepsilon}{7} = \varepsilon$$

This shows that $\lim_{x\to 3} x^2 = 9$. ▬

As Example 4 shows, it is not always easy to prove that limit statements are true using the ε, δ definition. In fact, if we had been given a more complicated function such as $f(x) = (6x^2 - 8x + 9)/(2x^2 - 1)$, a proof would require a great deal of ingenuity. Fortunately this is unnecessary because the Limit Laws stated in Section 2.3 can be proved using Definition 2, and then the limits of complicated functions can be found rigorously from the Limit Laws without resorting to the definition directly.

For instance, we prove the Sum Law: If $\lim_{x\to a} f(x) = L$ and $\lim_{x\to a} g(x) = M$ both exist, then

$$\lim_{x\to a} [f(x) + g(x)] = L + M$$

The remaining laws are proved in the exercises and in Appendix F.

PROOF OF THE SUM LAW Let $\varepsilon > 0$ be given. We must find $\delta > 0$ such that

$$\text{if} \quad 0 < |x - a| < \delta \quad \text{then} \quad |f(x) + g(x) - (L + M)| < \varepsilon$$

Triangle Inequality:

$$|a + b| \leq |a| + |b|$$

(See Appendix A.)

Using the Triangle Inequality we can write

$$\boxed{5} \qquad |f(x) + g(x) - (L + M)| = |(f(x) - L) + (g(x) - M)|$$
$$\leq |f(x) - L| + |g(x) - M|$$

We make $|f(x) + g(x) - (L + M)|$ less than ε by making each of the terms $|f(x) - L|$ and $|g(x) - M|$ less than $\varepsilon/2$.

Since $\varepsilon/2 > 0$ and $\lim_{x \to a} f(x) = L$, there exists a number $\delta_1 > 0$ such that

$$\text{if} \qquad 0 < |x - a| < \delta_1 \qquad \text{then} \qquad |f(x) - L| < \frac{\varepsilon}{2}$$

Similarly, since $\lim_{x \to a} g(x) = M$, there exists a number $\delta_2 > 0$ such that

$$\text{if} \qquad 0 < |x - a| < \delta_2 \qquad \text{then} \qquad |g(x) - M| < \frac{\varepsilon}{2}$$

Let $\delta = \min\{\delta_1, \delta_2\}$, the smaller of the numbers δ_1 and δ_2. Notice that

$$\text{if} \qquad 0 < |x - a| < \delta \quad \text{then} \quad 0 < |x - a| < \delta_1 \quad \text{and} \quad 0 < |x - a| < \delta_2$$

and so

$$|f(x) - L| < \frac{\varepsilon}{2} \qquad \text{and} \qquad |g(x) - M| < \frac{\varepsilon}{2}$$

Therefore, by $\boxed{5}$,

$$|f(x) + g(x) - (L + M)| \leq |f(x) - L| + |g(x) - M|$$
$$< \frac{\varepsilon}{2} + \frac{\varepsilon}{2} = \varepsilon$$

To summarize,

$$\text{if} \qquad 0 < |x - a| < \delta \qquad \text{then} \qquad |f(x) + g(x) - (L + M)| < \varepsilon$$

Thus, by the definition of a limit,

$$\lim_{x \to a} [f(x) + g(x)] = L + M \qquad \blacksquare$$

Infinite Limits

Infinite limits can also be defined in a precise way. The following is a precise version of Definition 4 in Section 2.2.

$\boxed{6}$ **Definition** Let f be a function defined on some open interval that contains the number a, except possibly at a itself. Then

$$\lim_{x \to a} f(x) = \infty$$

means that for every positive number M there is a positive number δ such that

$$\text{if} \qquad 0 < |x - a| < \delta \qquad \text{then} \qquad f(x) > M$$

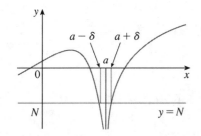

FIGURE 10

This says that the values of $f(x)$ can be made arbitrarily large (larger than any given number M) by taking x close enough to a (within a distance δ, where δ depends on M, but with $x \neq a$). A geometric illustration is shown in Figure 10.

Given any horizontal line $y = M$, we can find a number $\delta > 0$ such that if we restrict x to lie in the interval $(a - \delta, a + \delta)$ but $x \neq a$, then the curve $y = f(x)$ lies above the line $y = M$. You can see that if a larger M is chosen, then a smaller δ may be required.

V **EXAMPLE 5** Use Definition 6 to prove that $\displaystyle\lim_{x \to 0} \frac{1}{x^2} = \infty$.

SOLUTION Let M be a given positive number. We want to find a number δ such that

$$\text{if} \quad 0 < |x| < \delta \quad \text{then} \quad 1/x^2 > M$$

But

$$\frac{1}{x^2} > M \quad \Longleftrightarrow \quad x^2 < \frac{1}{M} \quad \Longleftrightarrow \quad |x| < \frac{1}{\sqrt{M}}$$

So if we choose $\delta = 1/\sqrt{M}$ and $0 < |x| < \delta = 1/\sqrt{M}$, then $1/x^2 > M$. This shows that $1/x^2 \to \infty$ as $x \to 0$. ∎

Similarly, the following is a precise version of Definition 5 in Section 2.2. It is illustrated by Figure 11.

FIGURE 11

---

7 **Definition** Let f be a function defined on some open interval that contains the number a, except possibly at a itself. Then

$$\lim_{x \to a} f(x) = -\infty$$

means that for every negative number N there is a positive number δ such that

$$\text{if} \quad 0 < |x - a| < \delta \quad \text{then} \quad f(x) < N$$

2.4 Exercises

1. Use the given graph of f to find a number δ such that

$$\text{if} \quad |x - 1| < \delta \quad \text{then} \quad |f(x) - 1| < 0.2$$

2. Use the given graph of f to find a number δ such that

$$\text{if} \quad 0 < |x - 3| < \delta \quad \text{then} \quad |f(x) - 2| < 0.5$$

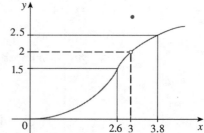

---

3. Use the given graph of $f(x) = \sqrt{x}$ to find a number δ such that

$$\text{if} \quad |x - 4| < \delta \quad \text{then} \quad |\sqrt{x} - 2| < 0.4$$

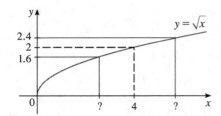

4. Use the given graph of $f(x) = x^2$ to find a number δ such that

$$\text{if} \quad |x - 1| < \delta \quad \text{then} \quad |x^2 - 1| < \tfrac{1}{2}$$

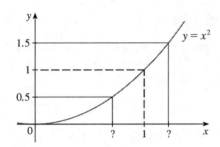

5. Use a graph to find a number δ such that

$$\text{if} \quad \left|x - \frac{\pi}{4}\right| < \delta \quad \text{then} \quad |\tan x - 1| < 0.2$$

6. Use a graph to find a number δ such that

$$\text{if} \quad |x - 1| < \delta \quad \text{then} \quad \left|\frac{2x}{x^2 + 4} - 0.4\right| < 0.1$$

7. For the limit

$$\lim_{x \to 2} (x^3 - 3x + 4) = 6$$

illustrate Definition 2 by finding values of δ that correspond to $\varepsilon = 0.2$ and $\varepsilon = 0.1$.

8. For the limit

$$\lim_{x \to 0} \frac{e^{2x} - 1}{x} = 2$$

illustrate Definition 2 by finding values of δ that correspond to $\varepsilon = 0.5$ and $\varepsilon = 0.1$.

9. Given that $\lim_{x \to \pi/2} \tan^2 x = \infty$, illustrate Definition 6 by finding values of δ that correspond to (a) $M = 1000$ and (b) $M = 10,000$.

10. Use a graph to find a number δ such that

$$\text{if} \quad 5 < x < 5 + \delta \quad \text{then} \quad \frac{x^2}{\sqrt{x - 5}} > 100$$

11. A machinist is required to manufacture a circular metal disk with area 1000 cm².
(a) What radius produces such a disk?
(b) If the machinist is allowed an error tolerance of ± 5 cm² in the area of the disk, how close to the ideal radius in part (a) must the machinist control the radius?
(c) In terms of the ε, δ definition of $\lim_{x \to a} f(x) = L$, what is x? What is $f(x)$? What is a? What is L? What value of ε is given? What is the corresponding value of δ?

12. A crystal growth furnace is used in research to determine how best to manufacture crystals used in electronic components for the space shuttle. For proper growth of the crystal, the temperature must be controlled accurately by adjusting the input power. Suppose the relationship is given by

$$T(w) = 0.1w^2 + 2.155w + 20$$

where T is the temperature in degrees Celsius and w is the power input in watts.
(a) How much power is needed to maintain the temperature at 200°C?
(b) If the temperature is allowed to vary from 200°C by up to ± 1°C, what range of wattage is allowed for the input power?
(c) In terms of the ε, δ definition of $\lim_{x \to a} f(x) = L$, what is x? What is $f(x)$? What is a? What is L? What value of ε is given? What is the corresponding value of δ?

13. (a) Find a number δ such that if $|x - 2| < \delta$, then $|4x - 8| < \varepsilon$, where $\varepsilon = 0.1$.
(b) Repeat part (a) with $\varepsilon = 0.01$.

14. Given that $\lim_{x \to 2} (5x - 7) = 3$, illustrate Definition 2 by finding values of δ that correspond to $\varepsilon = 0.1$, $\varepsilon = 0.05$, and $\varepsilon = 0.01$.

15–18 Prove the statement using the ε, δ definition of a limit and illustrate with a diagram like Figure 9.

15. $\lim_{x \to 1} (2x + 3) = 5$

16. $\lim_{x \to -2} \left(\tfrac{1}{2}x + 3\right) = 2$

17. $\lim_{x \to -3} (1 - 4x) = 13$

18. $\lim_{x \to -2} (3x + 5) = -1$

19–32 Prove the statement using the ε, δ definition of a limit.

19. $\lim_{x \to 1} \frac{2 + 4x}{3} = 2$

20. $\lim_{x \to 10} \left(3 - \tfrac{4}{5}x\right) = -5$

21. $\lim_{x \to 2} \frac{x^2 + x - 6}{x - 2} = 5$

22. $\lim_{x \to -1.5} \frac{9 - 4x^2}{3 + 2x} = 6$

23. $\lim_{x \to a} x = a$

24. $\lim_{x \to a} c = c$

25. $\lim_{x \to 0} x^2 = 0$

26. $\lim_{x \to 0} x^3 = 0$

27. $\lim_{x \to 0} |x| = 0$

28. $\lim_{x \to -6^+} \sqrt[8]{6 + x} = 0$

29. $\lim_{x \to 2} (x^2 - 4x + 5) = 1$

30. $\lim_{x \to 2} (x^2 + 2x - 7) = 1$

31. $\lim\limits_{x \to -2} (x^2 - 1) = 3$

32. $\lim\limits_{x \to 2} x^3 = 8$

33. Verify that another possible choice of δ for showing that $\lim_{x \to 3} x^2 = 9$ in Example 4 is $\delta = \min\{2, \varepsilon/8\}$.

34. Verify, by a geometric argument, that the largest possible choice of δ for showing that $\lim_{x \to 3} x^2 = 9$ is $\delta = \sqrt{9 + \varepsilon} - 3$.

CAS **35.** (a) For the limit $\lim_{x \to 1} (x^3 + x + 1) = 3$, use a graph to find a value of δ that corresponds to $\varepsilon = 0.4$.
(b) By using a computer algebra system to solve the cubic equation $x^3 + x + 1 = 3 + \varepsilon$, find the largest possible value of δ that works for any given $\varepsilon > 0$.
(c) Put $\varepsilon = 0.4$ in your answer to part (b) and compare with your answer to part (a).

36. Prove that $\lim\limits_{x \to 2} \dfrac{1}{x} = \dfrac{1}{2}$.

37. Prove that $\lim\limits_{x \to a} \sqrt{x} = \sqrt{a}$ if $a > 0$.

$$\left[Hint:\ \text{Use}\ \left| \sqrt{x} - \sqrt{a} \right| = \frac{|x - a|}{\sqrt{x} + \sqrt{a}}. \right]$$

38. If H is the Heaviside function defined in Example 6 in Section 2.2, prove, using Definition 2, that $\lim_{t \to 0} H(t)$ does not exist. [*Hint:* Use an indirect proof as follows. Suppose that

the limit is L. Take $\varepsilon = \frac{1}{2}$ in the definition of a limit and try to arrive at a contradiction.]

39. If the function f is defined by

$$f(x) = \begin{cases} 0 & \text{if } x \text{ is rational} \\ 1 & \text{if } x \text{ is irrational} \end{cases}$$

prove that $\lim_{x \to 0} f(x)$ does not exist.

40. By comparing Definitions 2, 3, and 4, prove Theorem 1 in Section 2.3.

41. How close to -3 do we have to take x so that

$$\frac{1}{(x + 3)^4} > 10,000$$

42. Prove, using Definition 6, that $\lim\limits_{x \to -3} \dfrac{1}{(x + 3)^4} = \infty$.

43. Prove that $\lim\limits_{x \to 0^+} \ln x = -\infty$.

44. Suppose that $\lim_{x \to a} f(x) = \infty$ and $\lim_{x \to a} g(x) = c$, where c is a real number. Prove each statement.
(a) $\lim\limits_{x \to a} [f(x) + g(x)] = \infty$
(b) $\lim\limits_{x \to a} [f(x)g(x)] = \infty$ if $c > 0$
(c) $\lim\limits_{x \to a} [f(x)g(x)] = -\infty$ if $c < 0$

2.5 Continuity

We noticed in Section 2.3 that the limit of a function as x approaches a can often be found simply by calculating the value of the function at a. Functions with this property are called *continuous at a*. We will see that the mathematical definition of continuity corresponds closely with the meaning of the word *continuity* in everyday language. (A continuous process is one that takes place gradually, without interruption or abrupt change.)

As illustrated in Figure 1, if f is continuous, then the points $(x, f(x))$ on the graph of f approach the point $(a, f(a))$ on the graph. So there is no gap in the curve.

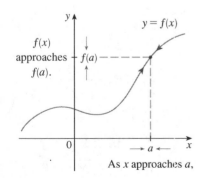

FIGURE 1

---

1 **Definition** A function f is **continuous at a number a** if

$$\lim_{x \to a} f(x) = f(a)$$

Notice that Definition 1 implicitly requires three things if f is continuous at a:

1. $f(a)$ is defined (that is, a is in the domain of f)

2. $\lim\limits_{x \to a} f(x)$ exists

3. $\lim\limits_{x \to a} f(x) = f(a)$

The definition says that f is continuous at a if $f(x)$ approaches $f(a)$ as x approaches a. Thus a continuous function f has the property that a small change in x produces only a small change in $f(x)$. In fact, the change in $f(x)$ can be kept as small as we please by keeping the change in x sufficiently small.

If f is defined near a (in other words, f is defined on an open interval containing a, except perhaps at a), we say that f is **discontinuous at** a (or f has a **discontinuity** at a) if f is not continuous at a.

Physical phenomena are usually continuous. For instance, the displacement or velocity of a vehicle varies continuously with time, as does a person's height. But discontinuities do occur in such situations as electric currents. [See Example 6 in Section 2.2, where the Heaviside function is discontinuous at 0 because $\lim_{t \to 0} H(t)$ does not exist.]

Geometrically, you can think of a function that is continuous at every number in an interval as a function whose graph has no break in it. The graph can be drawn without removing your pen from the paper.

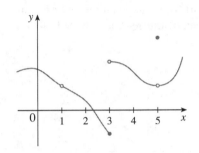

FIGURE 2

EXAMPLE 1 Figure 2 shows the graph of a function f. At which numbers is f discontinuous? Why?

SOLUTION It looks as if there is a discontinuity when $a = 1$ because the graph has a break there. The official reason that f is discontinuous at 1 is that $f(1)$ is not defined.

The graph also has a break when $a = 3$, but the reason for the discontinuity is different. Here, $f(3)$ is defined, but $\lim_{x \to 3} f(x)$ does not exist (because the left and right limits are different). So f is discontinuous at 3.

What about $a = 5$? Here, $f(5)$ is defined and $\lim_{x \to 5} f(x)$ exists (because the left and right limits are the same). But

$$\lim_{x \to 5} f(x) \neq f(5)$$

So f is discontinuous at 5.

Now let's see how to detect discontinuities when a function is defined by a formula.

V EXAMPLE 2 Where are each of the following functions discontinuous?

(a) $f(x) = \dfrac{x^2 - x - 2}{x - 2}$

(b) $f(x) = \begin{cases} \dfrac{1}{x^2} & \text{if } x \neq 0 \\ 1 & \text{if } x = 0 \end{cases}$

(c) $f(x) = \begin{cases} \dfrac{x^2 - x - 2}{x - 2} & \text{if } x \neq 2 \\ 1 & \text{if } x = 2 \end{cases}$

(d) $f(x) = [\![x]\!]$

SOLUTION

(a) Notice that $f(2)$ is not defined, so f is discontinuous at 2. Later we'll see why f is continuous at all other numbers.

(b) Here $f(0) = 1$ is defined but

$$\lim_{x \to 0} f(x) = \lim_{x \to 0} \frac{1}{x^2}$$

does not exist. (See Example 8 in Section 2.2.) So f is discontinuous at 0.

(c) Here $f(2) = 1$ is defined and

$$\lim_{x \to 2} f(x) = \lim_{x \to 2} \frac{x^2 - x - 2}{x - 2} = \lim_{x \to 2} \frac{(x - 2)(x + 1)}{x - 2} = \lim_{x \to 2} (x + 1) = 3$$

exists. But

$$\lim_{x \to 2} f(x) \neq f(2)$$

so f is not continuous at 2.

(d) The greatest integer function $f(x) = [\![x]\!]$ has discontinuities at all of the integers because $\lim_{x \to n} [\![x]\!]$ does not exist if n is an integer. (See Example 10 and Exercise 51 in Section 2.3.)

Figure 3 shows the graphs of the functions in Example 2. In each case the graph can't be drawn without lifting the pen from the paper because a hole or break or jump occurs in the graph. The kind of discontinuity illustrated in parts (a) and (c) is called **removable** because we could remove the discontinuity by redefining f at just the single number 2. [The function $g(x) = x + 1$ is continuous.] The discontinuity in part (b) is called an **infinite discontinuity**. The discontinuities in part (d) are called **jump discontinuities** because the function "jumps" from one value to another.

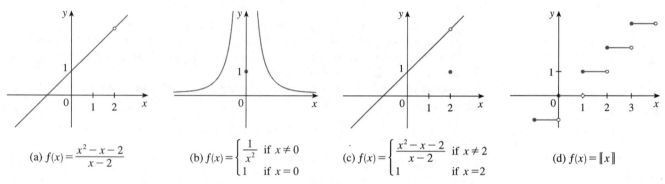

(a) $f(x) = \dfrac{x^2 - x - 2}{x - 2}$

(b) $f(x) = \begin{cases} \dfrac{1}{x^2} & \text{if } x \neq 0 \\ 1 & \text{if } x = 0 \end{cases}$

(c) $f(x) = \begin{cases} \dfrac{x^2 - x - 2}{x - 2} & \text{if } x \neq 2 \\ 1 & \text{if } x = 2 \end{cases}$

(d) $f(x) = [\![x]\!]$

FIGURE 3
Graphs of the functions in Example 2

---

2   **Definition**   A function f is **continuous from the right at a number a** if

$$\lim_{x \to a^+} f(x) = f(a)$$

and f is **continuous from the left at a** if

$$\lim_{x \to a^-} f(x) = f(a)$$

EXAMPLE 3   At each integer n, the function $f(x) = [\![x]\!]$ [see Figure 3(d)] is continuous from the right but discontinuous from the left because

$$\lim_{x \to n^+} f(x) = \lim_{x \to n^+} [\![x]\!] = n = f(n)$$

but

$$\lim_{x \to n^-} f(x) = \lim_{x \to n^-} [\![x]\!] = n - 1 \neq f(n)$$

---

3   **Definition**   A function f is **continuous on an interval** if it is continuous at every number in the interval. (If f is defined only on one side of an endpoint of the interval, we understand *continuous* at the endpoint to mean *continuous from the right* or *continuous from the left*.)

EXAMPLE 4 Show that the function $f(x) = 1 - \sqrt{1 - x^2}$ is continuous on the interval $[-1, 1]$.

SOLUTION If $-1 < a < 1$, then using the Limit Laws, we have

$$\lim_{x \to a} f(x) = \lim_{x \to a} \left(1 - \sqrt{1 - x^2}\right)$$

$$= 1 - \lim_{x \to a} \sqrt{1 - x^2} \qquad \text{(by Laws 2 and 7)}$$

$$= 1 - \sqrt{\lim_{x \to a} (1 - x^2)} \qquad \text{(by 11)}$$

$$= 1 - \sqrt{1 - a^2} \qquad \text{(by 2, 7, and 9)}$$

$$= f(a)$$

Thus, by Definition 1, f is continuous at a if $-1 < a < 1$. Similar calculations show that

$$\lim_{x \to -1^+} f(x) = 1 = f(-1) \qquad \text{and} \qquad \lim_{x \to 1^-} f(x) = 1 = f(1)$$

so f is continuous from the right at -1 and continuous from the left at 1. Therefore, according to Definition 3, f is continuous on $[-1, 1]$.

The graph of f is sketched in Figure 4. It is the lower half of the circle

$$x^2 + (y - 1)^2 = 1$$

FIGURE 4

Instead of always using Definitions 1, 2, and 3 to verify the continuity of a function as we did in Example 4, it is often convenient to use the next theorem, which shows how to build up complicated continuous functions from simple ones.

---

4 Theorem If f and g are continuous at a and c is a constant, then the following functions are also continuous at a:

1. $f + g$ 2. $f - g$ 3. cf

4. fg 5. $\dfrac{f}{g}$ if $g(a) \neq 0$

PROOF Each of the five parts of this theorem follows from the corresponding Limit Law in Section 2.3. For instance, we give the proof of part 1. Since f and g are continuous at a, we have

$$\lim_{x \to a} f(x) = f(a) \qquad \text{and} \qquad \lim_{x \to a} g(x) = g(a)$$

Therefore

$$\lim_{x \to a} (f + g)(x) = \lim_{x \to a} [f(x) + g(x)]$$

$$= \lim_{x \to a} f(x) + \lim_{x \to a} g(x) \qquad \text{(by Law 1)}$$

$$= f(a) + g(a)$$

$$= (f + g)(a)$$

This shows that $f + g$ is continuous at a.

It follows from Theorem 4 and Definition 3 that if f and g are continuous on an interval, then so are the functions $f + g$, $f - g$, cf, fg, and (if g is never 0) f/g. The following theorem was stated in Section 2.3 as the Direct Substitution Property.

---

5   Theorem

(a) Any polynomial is continuous everywhere; that is, it is continuous on $\mathbb{R} = (-\infty, \infty)$.

(b) Any rational function is continuous wherever it is defined; that is, it is continuous on its domain.

PROOF

(a) A polynomial is a function of the form

$$P(x) = c_n x^n + c_{n-1} x^{n-1} + \cdots + c_1 x + c_0$$

where $c_0, c_1, \ldots, c_n$ are constants. We know that

$$\lim_{x \to a} c_0 = c_0 \qquad \text{(by Law 7)}$$

and

$$\lim_{x \to a} x^m = a^m \qquad m = 1, 2, \ldots, n \qquad \text{(by 9)}$$

This equation is precisely the statement that the function $f(x) = x^m$ is a continuous function. Thus, by part 3 of Theorem 4, the function $g(x) = cx^m$ is continuous. Since P is a sum of functions of this form and a constant function, it follows from part 1 of Theorem 4 that P is continuous.

(b) A rational function is a function of the form

$$f(x) = \frac{P(x)}{Q(x)}$$

where P and Q are polynomials. The domain of f is $D = \{x \in \mathbb{R} \mid Q(x) \neq 0\}$. We know from part (a) that P and Q are continuous everywhere. Thus, by part 5 of Theorem 4, f is continuous at every number in D. ∎

As an illustration of Theorem 5, observe that the volume of a sphere varies continuously with its radius because the formula $V(r) = \frac{4}{3}\pi r^3$ shows that V is a polynomial function of r. Likewise, if a ball is thrown vertically into the air with a velocity of 20 m/s, then the height of the ball in meters t seconds later is given by the formula $h = 20t - 4.9t^2$. Again this is a polynomial function, so the height is a continuous function of the elapsed time.

Knowledge of which functions are continuous enables us to evaluate some limits very quickly, as the following example shows. Compare it with Example 2(b) in Section 2.3.

EXAMPLE 5   Find $\displaystyle\lim_{x \to -2} \frac{x^3 + 2x^2 - 1}{5 - 3x}$.

SOLUTION The function

$$f(x) = \frac{x^3 + 2x^2 - 1}{5 - 3x}$$

is rational, so by Theorem 5 it is continuous on its domain, which is $\left\{x \mid x \neq \frac{5}{3}\right\}$.

Therefore

$$\lim_{x \to -2} \frac{x^3 + 2x^2 - 1}{5 - 3x} = \lim_{x \to -2} f(x) = f(-2)$$

$$= \frac{(-2)^3 + 2(-2)^2 - 1}{5 - 3(-2)} = -\frac{1}{11}$$

FIGURE 5

Another way to establish the limits in $\boxed{6}$ is to use the Squeeze Theorem with the inequality $\sin \theta < \theta$ (for $\theta > 0$), which is proved in Section 3.3.

It turns out that most of the familiar functions are continuous at every number in their domains. For instance, Limit Law 10 (page 100) is exactly the statement that root functions are continuous.

From the appearance of the graphs of the sine and cosine functions (Figure 18 in Section 1.2), we would certainly guess that they are continuous. We know from the definitions of $\sin \theta$ and $\cos \theta$ that the coordinates of the point P in Figure 5 are $(\cos \theta, \sin \theta)$. As $\theta \to 0$, we see that P approaches the point $(1, 0)$ and so $\cos \theta \to 1$ and $\sin \theta \to 0$. Thus

$$\boxed{6} \qquad \lim_{\theta \to 0} \cos \theta = 1 \qquad \lim_{\theta \to 0} \sin \theta = 0$$

Since $\cos 0 = 1$ and $\sin 0 = 0$, the equations in $\boxed{6}$ assert that the cosine and sine functions are continuous at 0. The addition formulas for cosine and sine can then be used to deduce that these functions are continuous everywhere (see Exercises 60 and 61).

It follows from part 5 of Theorem 4 that

$$\tan x = \frac{\sin x}{\cos x}$$

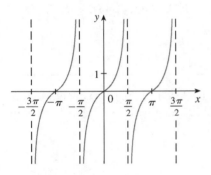

FIGURE 6 $y = \tan x$

The inverse trigonometric functions are reviewed in Section 1.6.

is continuous except where $\cos x = 0$. This happens when x is an odd integer multiple of $\pi/2$, so $y = \tan x$ has infinite discontinuities when $x = \pm\pi/2, \pm 3\pi/2, \pm 5\pi/2$, and so on (see Figure 6).

The inverse function of any continuous one-to-one function is also continuous. (This fact is proved in Appendix F, but our geometric intuition makes it seem plausible: The graph of f^{-1} is obtained by reflecting the graph of f about the line $y = x$. So if the graph of f has no break in it, neither does the graph of f^{-1}.) Thus the inverse trigonometric functions are continuous.

In Section 1.5 we defined the exponential function $y = a^x$ so as to fill in the holes in the graph of $y = a^x$ where x is rational. In other words, the very definition of $y = a^x$ makes it a continuous function on $\mathbb{R}$. Therefore its inverse function $y = \log_a x$ is continuous on $(0, \infty)$.

$\boxed{7}$ **Theorem** The following types of functions are continuous at every number in their domains:

polynomials	rational functions	root functions
trigonometric functions		inverse trigonometric functions
exponential functions		logarithmic functions

EXAMPLE 6 Where is the function $f(x) = \dfrac{\ln x + \tan^{-1}x}{x^2 - 1}$ continuous?

SOLUTION We know from Theorem 7 that the function $y = \ln x$ is continuous for $x > 0$ and $y = \tan^{-1}x$ is continuous on $\mathbb{R}$. Thus, by part 1 of Theorem 4, $y = \ln x + \tan^{-1}x$ is continuous on $(0, \infty)$. The denominator, $y = x^2 - 1$, is a polynomial, so it is continuous everywhere. Therefore, by part 5 of Theorem 4, f is continuous at all positive numbers x except where $x^2 - 1 = 0$. So f is continuous on the intervals $(0, 1)$ and $(1, \infty)$. ▊

EXAMPLE 7 Evaluate $\displaystyle\lim_{x \to \pi} \frac{\sin x}{2 + \cos x}$.

SOLUTION Theorem 7 tells us that $y = \sin x$ is continuous. The function in the denominator, $y = 2 + \cos x$, is the sum of two continuous functions and is therefore continuous. Notice that this function is never 0 because $\cos x \geq -1$ for all x and so $2 + \cos x > 0$ everywhere. Thus the ratio

$$f(x) = \frac{\sin x}{2 + \cos x}$$

is continuous everywhere. Hence, by the definition of a continuous function,

$$\lim_{x \to \pi} \frac{\sin x}{2 + \cos x} = \lim_{x \to \pi} f(x) = f(\pi) = \frac{\sin \pi}{2 + \cos \pi} = \frac{0}{2 - 1} = 0$$ ▊

Another way of combining continuous functions f and g to get a new continuous function is to form the composite function $f \circ g$. This fact is a consequence of the following theorem.

> **8 Theorem** If f is continuous at b and $\displaystyle\lim_{x \to a} g(x) = b$, then $\displaystyle\lim_{x \to a} f(g(x)) = f(b)$. In other words,
>
> $$\lim_{x \to a} f(g(x)) = f\left(\lim_{x \to a} g(x)\right)$$

This theorem says that a limit symbol can be moved through a function symbol if the function is continuous and the limit exists. In other words, the order of these two symbols can be reversed.

Intuitively, Theorem 8 is reasonable because if x is close to a, then $g(x)$ is close to b, and since f is continuous at b, if $g(x)$ is close to b, then $f(g(x))$ is close to $f(b)$. A proof of Theorem 8 is given in Appendix F.

EXAMPLE 8 Evaluate $\displaystyle\lim_{x \to 1} \arcsin\left(\frac{1 - \sqrt{x}}{1 - x}\right)$.

SOLUTION Because arcsin is a continuous function, we can apply Theorem 8:

$$\lim_{x \to 1} \arcsin\left(\frac{1 - \sqrt{x}}{1 - x}\right) = \arcsin\left(\lim_{x \to 1} \frac{1 - \sqrt{x}}{1 - x}\right)$$

$$= \arcsin\left(\lim_{x \to 1} \frac{1 - \sqrt{x}}{(1 - \sqrt{x})(1 + \sqrt{x})}\right)$$

$$= \arcsin\left(\lim_{x \to 1} \frac{1}{1 + \sqrt{x}}\right)$$

$$= \arcsin \frac{1}{2} = \frac{\pi}{6}$$ ▊

Let's now apply Theorem 8 in the special case where $f(x) = \sqrt[n]{x}$, with n being a positive integer. Then

$$f(g(x)) = \sqrt[n]{g(x)}$$

and

$$f\left(\lim_{x \to a} g(x)\right) = \sqrt[n]{\lim_{x \to a} g(x)}$$

If we put these expressions into Theorem 8, we get

$$\lim_{x \to a} \sqrt[n]{g(x)} = \sqrt[n]{\lim_{x \to a} g(x)}$$

and so Limit Law 11 has now been proved. (We assume that the roots exist.)

> **9** **Theorem** If g is continuous at a and f is continuous at $g(a)$, then the composite function $f \circ g$ given by $(f \circ g)(x) = f(g(x))$ is continuous at a.

This theorem is often expressed informally by saying "a continuous function of a continuous function is a continuous function."

PROOF Since g is continuous at a, we have

$$\lim_{x \to a} g(x) = g(a)$$

Since f is continuous at $b = g(a)$, we can apply Theorem 8 to obtain

$$\lim_{x \to a} f(g(x)) = f(g(a))$$

which is precisely the statement that the function $h(x) = f(g(x))$ is continuous at a; that is, $f \circ g$ is continuous at a. ∎

V **EXAMPLE 9** Where are the following functions continuous?
(a) $h(x) = \sin(x^2)$ (b) $F(x) = \ln(1 + \cos x)$

SOLUTION
(a) We have $h(x) = f(g(x))$, where

$$g(x) = x^2 \quad \text{and} \quad f(x) = \sin x$$

Now g is continuous on $\mathbb{R}$ since it is a polynomial, and f is also continuous everywhere. Thus $h = f \circ g$ is continuous on $\mathbb{R}$ by Theorem 9.

(b) We know from Theorem 7 that $f(x) = \ln x$ is continuous and $g(x) = 1 + \cos x$ is continuous (because both $y = 1$ and $y = \cos x$ are continuous). Therefore, by Theorem 9, $F(x) = f(g(x))$ is continuous wherever it is defined. Now $\ln(1 + \cos x)$ is defined when $1 + \cos x > 0$. So it is undefined when $\cos x = -1$, and this happens when $x = \pm\pi, \pm3\pi, \ldots$. Thus F has discontinuities when x is an odd multiple of π and is continuous on the intervals between these values (see Figure 7). ∎

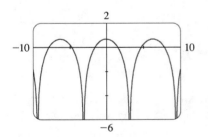

FIGURE 7
$y = \ln(1 + \cos x)$

An important property of continuous functions is expressed by the following theorem, whose proof is found in more advanced books on calculus.

> **10** **The Intermediate Value Theorem** Suppose that f is continuous on the closed interval $[a, b]$ and let N be any number between $f(a)$ and $f(b)$, where $f(a) \neq f(b)$. Then there exists a number c in (a, b) such that $f(c) = N$.

The Intermediate Value Theorem states that a continuous function takes on every intermediate value between the function values $f(a)$ and $f(b)$. It is illustrated by Figure 8. Note that the value N can be taken on once [as in part (a)] or more than once [as in part (b)].

FIGURE 8   (a)   (b)

If we think of a continuous function as a function whose graph has no hole or break, then it is easy to believe that the Intermediate Value Theorem is true. In geometric terms it says that if any horizontal line $y = N$ is given between $y = f(a)$ and $y = f(b)$ as in Figure 9, then the graph of f can't jump over the line. It must intersect $y = N$ somewhere.

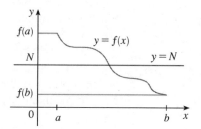

FIGURE 9

It is important that the function f in Theorem 10 be continuous. The Intermediate Value Theorem is not true in general for discontinuous functions (see Exercise 48).

One use of the Intermediate Value Theorem is in locating roots of equations as in the following example.

V EXAMPLE 10 Show that there is a root of the equation

$$4x^3 - 6x^2 + 3x - 2 = 0$$

between 1 and 2.

SOLUTION Let $f(x) = 4x^3 - 6x^2 + 3x - 2$. We are looking for a solution of the given equation, that is, a number c between 1 and 2 such that $f(c) = 0$. Therefore we take $a = 1, b = 2$, and $N = 0$ in Theorem 10. We have

$$f(1) = 4 - 6 + 3 - 2 = -1 < 0$$

and

$$f(2) = 32 - 24 + 6 - 2 = 12 > 0$$

Thus $f(1) < 0 < f(2)$; that is, $N = 0$ is a number between $f(1)$ and $f(2)$. Now f is continuous since it is a polynomial, so the Intermediate Value Theorem says there is a number c between 1 and 2 such that $f(c) = 0$. In other words, the equation $4x^3 - 6x^2 + 3x - 2 = 0$ has at least one root c in the interval $(1, 2)$.

In fact, we can locate a root more precisely by using the Intermediate Value Theorem again. Since

$$f(1.2) = -0.128 < 0 \qquad \text{and} \qquad f(1.3) = 0.548 > 0$$

a root must lie between 1.2 and 1.3. A calculator gives, by trial and error,

$$f(1.22) = -0.007008 < 0 \quad \text{and} \quad f(1.23) = 0.056068 > 0$$

so a root lies in the interval $(1.22, 1.23)$.

We can use a graphing calculator or computer to illustrate the use of the Intermediate Value Theorem in Example 10. Figure 10 shows the graph of f in the viewing rectangle $[-1, 3]$ by $[-3, 3]$ and you can see that the graph crosses the x-axis between 1 and 2. Figure 11 shows the result of zooming in to the viewing rectangle $[1.2, 1.3]$ by $[-0.2, 0.2]$.

FIGURE 10   **FIGURE 11**

In fact, the Intermediate Value Theorem plays a role in the very way these graphing devices work. A computer calculates a finite number of points on the graph and turns on the pixels that contain these calculated points. It assumes that the function is continuous and takes on all the intermediate values between two consecutive points. The computer therefore connects the pixels by turning on the intermediate pixels.

2.5 Exercises

1. Write an equation that expresses the fact that a function f is continuous at the number 4.

2. If f is continuous on $(-\infty, \infty)$, what can you say about its graph?

3. (a) From the graph of f, state the numbers at which f is discontinuous and explain why.
   (b) For each of the numbers stated in part (a), determine whether f is continuous from the right, or from the left, or neither.

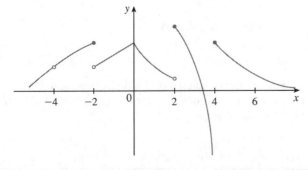

4. From the graph of g, state the intervals on which g is continuous.

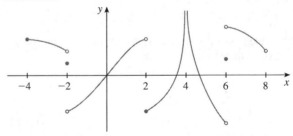

5–8 Sketch the graph of a function f that is continuous except for the stated discontinuity.

5. Discontinuous, but continuous from the right, at 2

6. Discontinuities at -1 and 4, but continuous from the left at -1 and from the right at 4

7. Removable discontinuity at 3, jump discontinuity at 5

8. Neither left nor right continuous at -2, continuous only from the left at 2

9. The toll T charged for driving on a certain stretch of a toll road is \$5 except during rush hours (between 7 AM and 10 AM and between 4 PM and 7 PM) when the toll is \$7.
   (a) Sketch a graph of T as a function of the time t, measured in hours past midnight.
   (b) Discuss the discontinuities of this function and their significance to someone who uses the road.

10. Explain why each function is continuous or discontinuous.
   (a) The temperature at a specific location as a function of time
   (b) The temperature at a specific time as a function of the distance due west from Paris
   (c) The altitude above sea level as a function of the distance due west from Paris
   (d) The cost of a taxi ride as a function of the distance traveled
   (e) The current in the circuit for the lights in a room as a function of time

11. Suppose f and g are continuous functions such that $g(2) = 6$ and $\lim_{x \to 2} [3f(x) + f(x)g(x)] = 36$. Find $f(2)$.

12–14 Use the definition of continuity and the properties of limits to show that the function is continuous at the given number a.

12. $f(x) = x^2 + \sqrt{7 - x}, \quad a = 4$

13. $f(x) = (x + 2x^3)^4, \quad a = -1$

14. $h(t) = \dfrac{2t - 3t^2}{1 + t^3}, \quad a = 1$

15–16 Use the definition of continuity and the properties of limits to show that the function is continuous on the given interval.

15. $f(x) = \dfrac{2x + 3}{x - 2}, \quad (2, \infty)$

16. $g(x) = 2\sqrt{3 - x}, \quad (-\infty, 3]$

17–22 Explain why the function is discontinuous at the given number a. Sketch the graph of the function.

17. $f(x) = \dfrac{1}{x + 2} \qquad a = -2$

18. $f(x) = \begin{cases} \dfrac{1}{x + 2} & \text{if } x \neq -2 \\ 1 & \text{if } x = -2 \end{cases} \qquad a = -2$

19. $f(x) = \begin{cases} e^x & \text{if } x < 0 \\ x^2 & \text{if } x \geq 0 \end{cases} \qquad a = 0$

20. $f(x) = \begin{cases} \dfrac{x^2 - x}{x^2 - 1} & \text{if } x \neq 1 \\ 1 & \text{if } x = 1 \end{cases} \qquad a = 1$

21. $f(x) = \begin{cases} \cos x & \text{if } x < 0 \\ 0 & \text{if } x = 0 \\ 1 - x^2 & \text{if } x > 0 \end{cases} \qquad a = 0$

22. $f(x) = \begin{cases} \dfrac{2x^2 - 5x - 3}{x - 3} & \text{if } x \neq 3 \\ 6 & \text{if } x = 3 \end{cases} \qquad a = 3$

23–24 How would you "remove the discontinuity" of f? In other words, how would you define $f(2)$ in order to make f continuous at 2?

23. $f(x) = \dfrac{x^2 - x - 2}{x - 2}$

24. $f(x) = \dfrac{x^3 - 8}{x^2 - 4}$

25–32 Explain, using Theorems 4, 5, 7, and 9, why the function is continuous at every number in its domain. State the domain.

25. $F(x) = \dfrac{x}{x^2 + 5x + 6}$

26. $G(x) = \sqrt[3]{x}\,(1 + x^3)$

27. $R(x) = x^2 + \sqrt{2x - 1}$

28. $h(x) = \dfrac{\sin x}{x + 1}$

29. $A(t) = \arcsin(1 + 2t)$

30. $B(x) = \dfrac{\tan x}{\sqrt{4 - x^2}}$

31. $M(x) = \sqrt{1 + \dfrac{1}{x}}$

32. $N(r) = \tan^{-1}(1 + e^{-r^2})$

33–34 Locate the discontinuities of the function and illustrate by graphing.

33. $y = \dfrac{1}{1 + e^{1/x}}$

34. $y = \ln(\tan^2 x)$

35–38 Use continuity to evaluate the limit.

35. $\displaystyle\lim_{x \to 4} \dfrac{5 + \sqrt{x}}{\sqrt{5 + x}}$

36. $\displaystyle\lim_{x \to \pi} \sin(x + \sin x)$

37. $\displaystyle\lim_{x \to 1} e^{x^2 - x}$

38. $\displaystyle\lim_{x \to 2} \arctan\left(\dfrac{x^2 - 4}{3x^2 - 6x}\right)$

39–40 Show that f is continuous on $(-\infty, \infty)$.

39. $f(x) = \begin{cases} x^2 & \text{if } x < 1 \\ \sqrt{x} & \text{if } x \geq 1 \end{cases}$

40. $f(x) = \begin{cases} \sin x & \text{if } x < \pi/4 \\ \cos x & \text{if } x \geq \pi/4 \end{cases}$

41–43 Find the numbers at which f is discontinuous. At which of these numbers is f continuous from the right, from the left, or neither? Sketch the graph of f.

41. $f(x) = \begin{cases} 1 + x^2 & \text{if } x \leq 0 \\ 2 - x & \text{if } 0 < x \leq 2 \\ (x - 2)^2 & \text{if } x > 2 \end{cases}$

42. $f(x) = \begin{cases} x + 1 & \text{if } x \le 1 \\ 1/x & \text{if } 1 < x < 3 \\ \sqrt{x - 3} & \text{if } x \ge 3 \end{cases}$

43. $f(x) = \begin{cases} x + 2 & \text{if } x < 0 \\ e^x & \text{if } 0 \le x \le 1 \\ 2 - x & \text{if } x > 1 \end{cases}$

44. The gravitational force exerted by the planet Earth on a unit mass at a distance r from the center of the planet is

$$F(r) = \begin{cases} \dfrac{GMr}{R^3} & \text{if } r < R \\ \dfrac{GM}{r^2} & \text{if } r \ge R \end{cases}$$

where M is the mass of Earth, R is its radius, and G is the gravitational constant. Is F a continuous function of r?

45. For what value of the constant c is the function f continuous on $(-\infty, \infty)$?

$$f(x) = \begin{cases} cx^2 + 2x & \text{if } x < 2 \\ x^3 - cx & \text{if } x \ge 2 \end{cases}$$

46. Find the values of a and b that make f continuous everywhere.

$$f(x) = \begin{cases} \dfrac{x^2 - 4}{x - 2} & \text{if } x < 2 \\ ax^2 - bx + 3 & \text{if } 2 \le x < 3 \\ 2x - a + b & \text{if } x \ge 3 \end{cases}$$

47. Which of the following functions f has a removable discontinuity at a? If the discontinuity is removable, find a function g that agrees with f for $x \ne a$ and is continuous at a.

(a) $f(x) = \dfrac{x^4 - 1}{x - 1}, \quad a = 1$

(b) $f(x) = \dfrac{x^3 - x^2 - 2x}{x - 2}, \quad a = 2$

(c) $f(x) = [\![\sin x]\!], \quad a = \pi$

48. Suppose that a function f is continuous on $[0, 1]$ except at 0.25 and that $f(0) = 1$ and $f(1) = 3$. Let $N = 2$. Sketch two possible graphs of f, one showing that f might not satisfy the conclusion of the Intermediate Value Theorem and one showing that f might still satisfy the conclusion of the Intermediate Value Theorem (even though it doesn't satisfy the hypothesis).

49. If $f(x) = x^2 + 10 \sin x$, show that there is a number c such that $f(c) = 1000$.

50. Suppose f is continuous on $[1, 5]$ and the only solutions of the equation $f(x) = 6$ are $x = 1$ and $x = 4$. If $f(2) = 8$, explain why $f(3) > 6$.

51–54 Use the Intermediate Value Theorem to show that there is a root of the given equation in the specified interval.

51. $x^4 + x - 3 = 0, \quad (1, 2)$ **52.** $\sqrt[3]{x} = 1 - x, \quad (0, 1)$

53. $e^x = 3 - 2x, \quad (0, 1)$ **54.** $\sin x = x^2 - x, \quad (1, 2)$

55–56 (a) Prove that the equation has at least one real root. (b) Use your calculator to find an interval of length 0.01 that contains a root.

55. $\cos x = x^3$ **56.** $\ln x = 3 - 2x$

57–58 (a) Prove that the equation has at least one real root. (b) Use your graphing device to find the root correct to three decimal places.

57. $100e^{-x/100} = 0.01x^2$ **58.** $\arctan x = 1 - x$

59. Prove that f is continuous at a if and only if

$$\lim_{h \to 0} f(a + h) = f(a)$$

60. To prove that sine is continuous, we need to show that $\lim_{x \to a} \sin x = \sin a$ for every real number a. By Exercise 59 an equivalent statement is that

$$\lim_{h \to 0} \sin(a + h) = \sin a$$

Use $\boxed{6}$ to show that this is true.

61. Prove that cosine is a continuous function.

62. (a) Prove Theorem 4, part 3.
(b) Prove Theorem 4, part 5.

63. For what values of x is f continuous?

$$f(x) = \begin{cases} 0 & \text{if } x \text{ is rational} \\ 1 & \text{if } x \text{ is irrational} \end{cases}$$

64. For what values of x is g continuous?

$$g(x) = \begin{cases} 0 & \text{if } x \text{ is rational} \\ x & \text{if } x \text{ is irrational} \end{cases}$$

65. Is there a number that is exactly 1 more than its cube?

66. If a and b are positive numbers, prove that the equation

$$\frac{a}{x^3 + 2x^2 - 1} + \frac{b}{x^3 + x - 2} = 0$$

has at least one solution in the interval $(-1, 1)$.

67. Show that the function

$$f(x) = \begin{cases} x^4 \sin(1/x) & \text{if } x \neq 0 \\ 0 & \text{if } x = 0 \end{cases}$$

is continuous on $(-\infty, \infty)$.

68. (a) Show that the absolute value function $F(x) = |x|$ is continuous everywhere.
(b) Prove that if f is a continuous function on an interval, then so is $|f|$.

(c) Is the converse of the statement in part (b) also true? In other words, if $|f|$ is continuous, does it follow that f is continuous? If so, prove it. If not, find a counterexample.

69. A Tibetan monk leaves the monastery at 7:00 AM and takes his usual path to the top of the mountain, arriving at 7:00 PM. The following morning, he starts at 7:00 AM at the top and takes the same path back, arriving at the monastery at 7:00 PM. Use the Intermediate Value Theorem to show that there is a point on the path that the monk will cross at exactly the same time of day on both days.

2.6 Limits at Infinity; Horizontal Asymptotes

In Sections 2.2 and 2.4 we investigated infinite limits and vertical asymptotes. There we let x approach a number and the result was that the values of y became arbitrarily large (positive or negative). In this section we let x become arbitrarily large (positive or negative) and see what happens to y.

Let's begin by investigating the behavior of the function f defined by

$$f(x) = \frac{x^2 - 1}{x^2 + 1}$$

as x becomes large. The table at the left gives values of this function correct to six decimal places, and the graph of f has been drawn by a computer in Figure 1.

x	$f(x)$
0	-1
± 1	0
± 2	0.600000
± 3	0.800000
± 4	0.882353
± 5	0.923077
± 10	0.980198
± 50	0.999200
± 100	0.999800
± 1000	0.999998

FIGURE 1

As x grows larger and larger you can see that the values of $f(x)$ get closer and closer to 1. In fact, it seems that we can make the values of $f(x)$ as close as we like to 1 by taking x sufficiently large. This situation is expressed symbolically by writing

$$\lim_{x \to \infty} \frac{x^2 - 1}{x^2 + 1} = 1$$

In general, we use the notation

$$\lim_{x \to \infty} f(x) = L$$

to indicate that the values of $f(x)$ approach L as x becomes larger and larger.

> **1   Definition**   Let f be a function defined on some interval (a, ∞). Then
> $$\lim_{x \to \infty} f(x) = L$$
> means that the values of $f(x)$ can be made arbitrarily close to L by taking x sufficiently large.

Another notation for $\lim_{x\to\infty} f(x) = L$ is

$$f(x) \to L \quad \text{as} \quad x \to \infty$$

The symbol ∞ does not represent a number. Nonetheless, the expression $\lim_{x\to\infty} f(x) = L$ is often read as

"the limit of $f(x)$, as x approaches infinity, is L"

or   "the limit of $f(x)$, as x becomes infinite, is L"

or   "the limit of $f(x)$, as x increases without bound, is L"

The meaning of such phrases is given by Definition 1. A more precise definition, similar to the ε, δ definition of Section 2.4, is given at the end of this section.

Geometric illustrations of Definition 1 are shown in Figure 2. Notice that there are many ways for the graph of f to approach the line $y = L$ (which is called a *horizontal asymptote*) as we look to the far right of each graph.

FIGURE 2
Examples illustrating $\lim_{x\to\infty} f(x) = L$

Referring back to Figure 1, we see that for numerically large negative values of x, the values of $f(x)$ are close to 1. By letting x decrease through negative values without bound, we can make $f(x)$ as close to 1 as we like. This is expressed by writing

$$\lim_{x\to-\infty} \frac{x^2 - 1}{x^2 + 1} = 1$$

The general definition is as follows.

---

2 Definition Let f be a function defined on some interval $(-\infty, a)$. Then

$$\lim_{x\to-\infty} f(x) = L$$

means that the values of $f(x)$ can be made arbitrarily close to L by taking x sufficiently large negative.

Again, the symbol $-\infty$ does not represent a number, but the expression $\lim_{x\to-\infty} f(x) = L$ is often read as

"the limit of $f(x)$, as x approaches negative infinity, is L"

Definition 2 is illustrated in Figure 3. Notice that the graph approaches the line $y = L$ as we look to the far left of each graph.

---

3 Definition The line $y = L$ is called a **horizontal asymptote** of the curve $y = f(x)$ if either

$$\lim_{x\to\infty} f(x) = L \quad \text{or} \quad \lim_{x\to-\infty} f(x) = L$$

FIGURE 3
Examples illustrating $\lim_{x\to-\infty} f(x) = L$

For instance, the curve illustrated in Figure 1 has the line $y = 1$ as a horizontal asymptote because

$$\lim_{x \to \infty} \frac{x^2 - 1}{x^2 + 1} = 1$$

An example of a curve with two horizontal asymptotes is $y = \tan^{-1} x$. (See Figure 4.) In fact,

$$\boxed{4} \qquad \lim_{x \to -\infty} \tan^{-1} x = -\frac{\pi}{2} \qquad \lim_{x \to \infty} \tan^{-1} x = \frac{\pi}{2}$$

so both of the lines $y = -\pi/2$ and $y = \pi/2$ are horizontal asymptotes. (This follows from the fact that the lines $x = \pm\pi/2$ are vertical asymptotes of the graph of tan.)

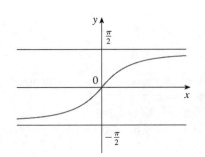

FIGURE 4
$y = \tan^{-1} x$

EXAMPLE 1   Find the infinite limits, limits at infinity, and asymptotes for the function f whose graph is shown in Figure 5.

SOLUTION   We see that the values of $f(x)$ become large as $x \to -1$ from both sides, so

$$\lim_{x \to -1} f(x) = \infty$$

Notice that $f(x)$ becomes large negative as x approaches 2 from the left, but large positive as x approaches 2 from the right. So

$$\lim_{x \to 2^-} f(x) = -\infty \qquad \text{and} \qquad \lim_{x \to 2^+} f(x) = \infty$$

Thus both of the lines $x = -1$ and $x = 2$ are vertical asymptotes.

As x becomes large, it appears that $f(x)$ approaches 4. But as x decreases through negative values, $f(x)$ approaches 2. So

$$\lim_{x \to \infty} f(x) = 4 \qquad \text{and} \qquad \lim_{x \to -\infty} f(x) = 2$$

This means that both $y = 4$ and $y = 2$ are horizontal asymptotes.

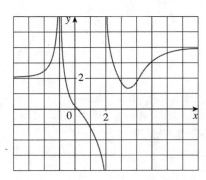

FIGURE 5

EXAMPLE 2   Find $\lim$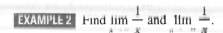

SOLUTION   Observe that when x is large, $1/x$ is small. For instance,

$$\frac{1}{100} = 0.01 \qquad \frac{1}{10,000} = 0.0001 \qquad \frac{1}{1,000,000} = 0.000001$$

In fact, by taking x large enough, we can make $1/x$ as close to 0 as we please. Therefore, according to Definition 1, we have

$$\lim_{x \to \infty} \frac{1}{x} = 0$$

Similar reasoning shows that when x is large negative, $1/x$ is small negative, so we also have

$$\lim_{x \to -\infty} \frac{1}{x} = 0$$

It follows that the line $y = 0$ (the x-axis) is a horizontal asymptote of the curve $y = 1/x$. (This is an equilateral hyperbola; see Figure 6.)

Most of the Limit Laws that were given in Section 2.3 also hold for limits at infinity. It can be proved that the *Limit Laws listed in Section 2.3 (with the exception of Laws 9 and 10) are also valid if "$x \to a$" is replaced by "$x \to \infty$" or "$x \to -\infty$."* In particular, if we combine Laws 6 and 11 with the results of Example 2, we obtain the following important rule for calculating limits.

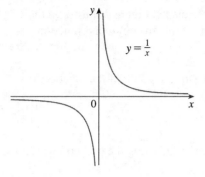

FIGURE 6

$\lim\limits_{x \to \infty} \dfrac{1}{x} = 0, \quad \lim\limits_{x \to -\infty} \dfrac{1}{x} = 0$

---

5 **Theorem** If $r > 0$ is a rational number, then

$$\lim_{x \to \infty} \frac{1}{x^r} = 0$$

If $r > 0$ is a rational number such that x^r is defined for all x, then

$$\lim_{x \to -\infty} \frac{1}{x^r} = 0$$

V **EXAMPLE 3** Evaluate

$$\lim_{x \to \infty} \frac{3x^2 - x - 2}{5x^2 + 4x + 1}$$

and indicate which properties of limits are used at each stage.

SOLUTION As x becomes large, both numerator and denominator become large, so it isn't obvious what happens to their ratio. We need to do some preliminary algebra.

To evaluate the limit at infinity of any rational function, we first divide both the numerator and denominator by the highest power of x that occurs in the denominator. (We may assume that $x \neq 0$, since we are interested only in large values of x.) In this case the highest power of x in the denominator is x^2, so we have

$$\lim_{x \to \infty} \frac{3x^2 - x - 2}{5x^2 + 4x + 1} = \lim_{x \to \infty} \frac{\dfrac{3x^2 - x - 2}{x^2}}{\dfrac{5x^2 + 4x + 1}{x^2}} = \lim_{x \to \infty} \frac{3 - \dfrac{1}{x} - \dfrac{2}{x^2}}{5 + \dfrac{4}{x} + \dfrac{1}{x^2}}$$

$$= \frac{\displaystyle\lim_{x \to \infty}\left(3 - \frac{1}{x} - \frac{2}{x^2}\right)}{\displaystyle\lim_{x \to \infty}\left(5 + \frac{4}{x} + \frac{1}{x^2}\right)} \qquad \text{(by Limit Law 5)}$$

$$= \frac{\displaystyle\lim_{x \to \infty} 3 - \lim_{x \to \infty} \frac{1}{x} - 2\lim_{x \to \infty} \frac{1}{x^2}}{\displaystyle\lim_{x \to \infty} 5 + 4\lim_{x \to \infty} \frac{1}{x} + \lim_{x \to \infty} \frac{1}{x^2}} \qquad \text{(by 1, 2, and 3)}$$

$$= \frac{3 - 0 - 0}{5 + 0 + 0} \qquad \text{(by 7 and Theorem 5)}$$

$$= \frac{3}{5}$$

FIGURE 7

$$y = \frac{3x^2 - x - 2}{5x^2 + 4x + 1}$$

A similar calculation shows that the limit as $x \to -\infty$ is also $\frac{3}{5}$. Figure 7 illustrates the results of these calculations by showing how the graph of the given rational function approaches the horizontal asymptote $y = \frac{3}{5}$.

EXAMPLE 4 Find the horizontal and vertical asymptotes of the graph of the function

$$f(x) = \frac{\sqrt{2x^2 + 1}}{3x - 5}$$

SOLUTION Dividing both numerator and denominator by x and using the properties of limits, we have

$$\lim_{x \to \infty} \frac{\sqrt{2x^2 + 1}}{3x - 5} = \lim_{x \to \infty} \frac{\sqrt{2 + \dfrac{1}{x^2}}}{3 - \dfrac{5}{x}} \qquad \text{(since } \sqrt{x^2} = x \text{ for } x > 0\text{)}$$

$$= \frac{\lim\limits_{x \to \infty} \sqrt{2 + \dfrac{1}{x^2}}}{\lim\limits_{x \to \infty} \left(3 - \dfrac{5}{x}\right)} = \frac{\sqrt{\lim\limits_{x \to \infty} 2 + \lim\limits_{x \to \infty} \dfrac{1}{x^2}}}{\lim\limits_{x \to \infty} 3 - 5 \lim\limits_{x \to \infty} \dfrac{1}{x}} = \frac{\sqrt{2 + 0}}{3 - 5 \cdot 0} = \frac{\sqrt{2}}{3}$$

Therefore the line $y = \sqrt{2}/3$ is a horizontal asymptote of the graph of f.

In computing the limit as $x \to -\infty$, we must remember that for $x < 0$, we have $\sqrt{x^2} = |x| = -x$. So when we divide the numerator by x, for $x < 0$ we get

$$\frac{1}{x} \sqrt{2x^2 + 1} = -\frac{1}{\sqrt{x^2}} \sqrt{2x^2 + 1} = -\sqrt{2 + \frac{1}{x^2}}$$

Therefore

$$\lim_{x \to -\infty} \frac{\sqrt{2x^2 + 1}}{3x - 5} = \lim_{x \to -\infty} \frac{-\sqrt{2 + \dfrac{1}{x^2}}}{3 - \dfrac{5}{x}} = \frac{-\sqrt{2 + \lim\limits_{x \to -\infty} \dfrac{1}{x^2}}}{3 - 5 \lim\limits_{x \to -\infty} \dfrac{1}{x}} = -\frac{\sqrt{2}}{3}$$

FIGURE 8

$$y = \frac{\sqrt{2x^2 + 1}}{3x - 5}$$

Thus the line $y = -\sqrt{2}/3$ is also a horizontal asymptote.

A vertical asymptote is likely to occur when the denominator, $3x - 5$, is 0, that is, when $x = \frac{5}{3}$. If x is close to $\frac{5}{3}$ and $x > \frac{5}{3}$, then the denominator is close to 0 and $3x - 5$ is positive. The numerator $\sqrt{2x^2 + 1}$ is always positive, so $f(x)$ is positive. Therefore

$$\lim_{x \to (5/3)^+} \frac{\sqrt{2x^2 + 1}}{3x - 5} = \infty$$

If x is close to $\frac{5}{3}$ but $x < \frac{5}{3}$, then $3x - 5 < 0$ and so $f(x)$ is large negative. Thus

$$\lim_{x \to (5/3)^-} \frac{\sqrt{2x^2 + 1}}{3x - 5} = -\infty$$

The vertical asymptote is $x = \frac{5}{3}$. All three asymptotes are shown in Figure 8.

EXAMPLE 5 Compute $\lim\limits_{x\to\infty}\left(\sqrt{x^2+1}-x\right)$.

SOLUTION Because both $\sqrt{x^2+1}$ and x are large when x is large, it's difficult to see what happens to their difference, so we use algebra to rewrite the function. We first multiply numerator and denominator by the conjugate radical:

$$\lim_{x\to\infty}\left(\sqrt{x^2+1}-x\right)=\lim_{x\to\infty}\left(\sqrt{x^2+1}-x\right)\frac{\sqrt{x^2+1}+x}{\sqrt{x^2+1}+x}$$

$$=\lim_{x\to\infty}\frac{(x^2+1)-x^2}{\sqrt{x^2+1}+x}=\lim_{x\to\infty}\frac{1}{\sqrt{x^2+1}+x}$$

Notice that the denominator of this last expression $\left(\sqrt{x^2+1}+x\right)$ becomes large as $x\to\infty$ (it's bigger than x). So

$$\lim_{x\to\infty}\left(\sqrt{x^2+1}-x\right)=\lim_{x\to\infty}\frac{1}{\sqrt{x^2+1}+x}=0$$

Figure 9 illustrates this result.

We can think of the given function as having a denominator of 1.

$$y=\sqrt{x^2+1}-x$$

FIGURE 9

EXAMPLE 6 Evaluate $\lim\limits_{x\to 2^+}\arctan\left(\dfrac{1}{x-2}\right)$.

SOLUTION If we let $t=1/(x-2)$, we know that $t\to\infty$ as $x\to 2^+$. Therefore, by the second equation in $\boxed{4}$, we have

$$\lim_{x\to 2^+}\arctan\left(\frac{1}{x-2}\right)=\lim_{t\to\infty}\arctan t=\frac{\pi}{2}$$

The graph of the natural exponential function $y=e^x$ has the line $y=0$ (the x-axis) as a horizontal asymptote. (The same is true of any exponential function with base $a>1$.) In fact, from the graph in Figure 10 and the corresponding table of values, we see that

$\boxed{6}$

$$\lim_{x\to-\infty}e^x=0$$

Notice that the values of e^x approach 0 very rapidly.

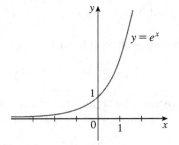

$$y=e^x$$

FIGURE 10

x	e^x
0	1.00000
-1	0.36788
-2	0.13534
-3	0.04979
-5	0.00674
-8	0.00034
-10	0.00005

PS The problem-solving strategy for Examples 6 and 7 is *introducing something extra* (see page 75). Here, the something extra, the auxiliary aid, is the new variable *t*.

V **EXAMPLE 7** Evaluate $\lim_{x \to 0^-} e^{1/x}$.

SOLUTION If we let $t = 1/x$, we know that $t \to -\infty$ as $x \to 0^-$. Therefore, by $\boxed{6}$,

$$\lim_{x \to 0^-} e^{1/x} = \lim_{t \to -\infty} e^t = 0$$

(See Exercise 75.)

EXAMPLE 8 Evaluate $\lim_{x \to \infty} \sin x$.

SOLUTION As x increases, the values of $\sin x$ oscillate between 1 and -1 infinitely often and so they don't approach any definite number. Thus $\lim_{x \to \infty} \sin x$ does not exist.

▓ Infinite Limits at Infinity

The notation

$$\lim_{x \to \infty} f(x) = \infty$$

is used to indicate that the values of $f(x)$ become large as x becomes large. Similar meanings are attached to the following symbols:

$$\lim_{x \to -\infty} f(x) = \infty \qquad \lim_{x \to \infty} f(x) = -\infty \qquad \lim_{x \to -\infty} f(x) = -\infty$$

EXAMPLE 9 Find $\lim_{x \to \infty} x^3$ and $\lim_{x \to -\infty} x^3$.

SOLUTION When x becomes large, x^3 also becomes large. For instance,

$$10^3 = 1000 \qquad 100^3 = 1{,}000{,}000 \qquad 1000^3 = 1{,}000{,}000{,}000$$

In fact, we can make x^3 as big as we like by taking x large enough. Therefore we can write

$$\lim_{x \to \infty} x^3 = \infty$$

Similarly, when x is large negative, so is x^3. Thus

$$\lim_{x \to -\infty} x^3 = -\infty$$

These limit statements can also be seen from the graph of $y = x^3$ in Figure 11.

Looking at Figure 10 we see that

$$\lim_{x \to \infty} e^x = \infty$$

but, as Figure 12 demonstrates, $y = e^x$ becomes large as $x \to \infty$ at a much faster rate than $y = x^3$.

EXAMPLE 10 Find $\lim_{x \to \infty} (x^2 - x)$.

⊘ SOLUTION It would be **wrong** to write

$$\lim_{x \to \infty} (x^2 - x) = \lim_{x \to \infty} x^2 - \lim_{x \to \infty} x = \infty - \infty$$

The Limit Laws can't be applied to infinite limits because ∞ is not a number ($\infty - \infty$ can't be defined). However, we *can* write

$$\lim_{x \to \infty} (x^2 - x) = \lim_{x \to \infty} x(x - 1) = \infty$$

because both x and $x - 1$ become arbitrarily large and so their product does too.

FIGURE 11

$\lim_{x \to \infty} x^3 = \infty, \ \lim_{x \to -\infty} x^3 = -\infty$

FIGURE 12

e^x is much larger than x^3 when x is large.

EXAMPLE 11 Find $\lim\limits_{x \to \infty} \dfrac{x^2 + x}{3 - x}$.

SOLUTION As in Example 3, we divide the numerator and denominator by the highest power of x in the denominator, which is just x:

$$\lim_{x \to \infty} \frac{x^2 + x}{3 - x} = \lim_{x \to \infty} \frac{x + 1}{\dfrac{3}{x} - 1} = -\infty$$

because $x + 1 \to \infty$ and $3/x - 1 \to -1$ as $x \to \infty$.   ▅▅▅

The next example shows that by using infinite limits at infinity, together with intercepts, we can get a rough idea of the graph of a polynomial without having to plot a large number of points.

V **EXAMPLE 12** Sketch the graph of $y = (x - 2)^4(x + 1)^3(x - 1)$ by finding its intercepts and its limits as $x \to \infty$ and as $x \to -\infty$.

SOLUTION The y-intercept is $f(0) = (-2)^4(1)^3(-1) = -16$ and the x-intercepts are found by setting $y = 0$: $x = 2, -1, 1$. Notice that since $(x - 2)^4$ is positive, the function doesn't change sign at 2; thus the graph doesn't cross the x-axis at 2. The graph crosses the axis at -1 and 1.

When x is large positive, all three factors are large, so

$$\lim_{x \to \infty} (x - 2)^4(x + 1)^3(x - 1) = \infty$$

When x is large negative, the first factor is large positive and the second and third factors are both large negative, so

$$\lim_{x \to -\infty} (x - 2)^4(x + 1)^3(x - 1) = \infty$$

Combining this information, we give a rough sketch of the graph in Figure 13.   ▅▅▅

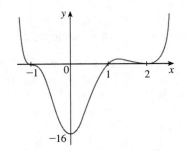

FIGURE 13
$y = (x - 2)^4(x + 1)^3(x - 1)$

�▩ **Precise Definitions**

Definition 1 can be stated precisely as follows.

> **7** **Definition** Let f be a function defined on some interval (a, ∞). Then
>
> $$\lim_{x \to \infty} f(x) = L$$
>
> means that for every $\varepsilon > 0$ there is a corresponding number N such that
>
> $$\text{if} \quad x > N \quad \text{then} \quad |f(x) - L| < \varepsilon$$

In words, this says that the values of $f(x)$ can be made arbitrarily close to L (within a distance ε, where ε is any positive number) by taking x sufficiently large (larger than N, where N depends on ε). Graphically it says that by choosing x large enough (larger than some number N) we can make the graph of f lie between the given horizontal lines

$y = L - \varepsilon$ and $y = L + \varepsilon$ as in Figure 14. This must be true no matter how small we choose ε. Figure 15 shows that if a smaller value of ε is chosen, then a larger value of N may be required.

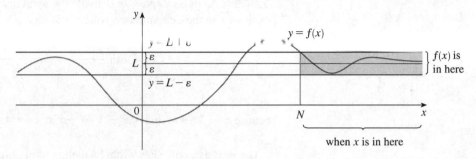

FIGURE 14

$\lim\limits_{x \to \infty} f(x) = L$

FIGURE 15

$\lim\limits_{x \to \infty} f(x) = L$

Similarly, a precise version of Definition 2 is given by Definition 8, which is illustrated in Figure 16.

---

8 Definition Let f be a function defined on some interval $(-\infty, a)$. Then

$$\lim_{x \to -\infty} f(x) = L$$

means that for every $\varepsilon > 0$ there is a corresponding number N such that

$$\text{if} \quad x < N \qquad \text{then} \qquad |f(x) - L| < \varepsilon$$

FIGURE 16

$\lim\limits_{x \to -\infty} f(x) = L$

In Example 3 we calculated that

$$\lim_{x \to \infty} \frac{3x^2 - x - 2}{5x^2 + 4x + 1} = \frac{3}{5}$$

In the next example we use a graphing device to relate this statement to Definition 7 with $L = \frac{3}{5}$ and $\varepsilon = 0.1$.

TEC In Module 2.4/2.6 you can explore the precise definition of a limit both graphically and numerically.

EXAMPLE 13 Use a graph to find a number N such that

$$\text{if} \quad x > N \quad \text{then} \quad \left| \frac{3x^2 - x - 2}{5x^2 + 4x + 1} - 0.6 \right| < 0.1$$

SOLUTION We rewrite the given inequality as

$$0.5 < \frac{3x^2 - x - 2}{5x^2 + 4x + 1} < 0.7$$

We need to determine the values of x for which the given curve lies between the horizontal lines $y = 0.5$ and $y = 0.7$. So we graph the curve and these lines in Figure 17. Then we use the cursor to estimate that the curve crosses the line $y = 0.5$ when $x \approx 6.7$. To the right of this number it seems that the curve stays between the lines $y = 0.5$ and $y = 0.7$. Rounding to be safe, we can say that

$$\text{if} \quad x > 7 \quad \text{then} \quad \left| \frac{3x^2 - x - 2}{5x^2 + 4x + 1} - 0.6 \right| < 0.1$$

In other words, for $\varepsilon = 0.1$ we can choose $N = 7$ (or any larger number) in Definition 7.

FIGURE 17

EXAMPLE 14 Use Definition 7 to prove that $\lim\limits_{x \to \infty} \dfrac{1}{x} = 0$.

SOLUTION Given $\varepsilon > 0$, we want to find N such that

$$\text{if} \quad x > N \quad \text{then} \quad \left| \frac{1}{x} - 0 \right| < \varepsilon$$

In computing the limit we may assume that $x > 0$. Then $1/x < \varepsilon \iff x > 1/\varepsilon$. Let's choose $N = 1/\varepsilon$. So

$$\text{if} \quad x > N = \frac{1}{\varepsilon} \quad \text{then} \quad \left| \frac{1}{x} - 0 \right| = \frac{1}{x} < \varepsilon$$

Therefore, by Definition 7,

$$\lim_{x \to \infty} \frac{1}{x} = 0$$

Figure 18 illustrates the proof by showing some values of ε and the corresponding values of N.

FIGURE 18

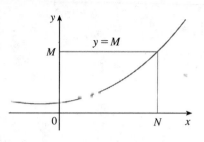

FIGURE 19
$\lim\limits_{x\to\infty} f(x) = \infty$

Finally we note that an infinite limit at infinity can be defined as follows. The geometric illustration is given in Figure 19.

> **9 Definition** Let f be a function defined on some interval (a, ∞). Then
> $$\lim_{x\to\infty} f(x) = \infty$$
> means that for every positive number M there is a corresponding positive number N such that
> $$\text{if} \quad x > N \quad \text{then} \quad f(x) > M$$

Similar definitions apply when the symbol ∞ is replaced by $-\infty$. (See Exercise 74.)

2.6 Exercises

1. Explain in your own words the meaning of each of the following.
(a) $\lim\limits_{x\to\infty} f(x) = 5$
(b) $\lim\limits_{x\to-\infty} f(x) = 3$

2. (a) Can the graph of $y = f(x)$ intersect a vertical asymptote? Can it intersect a horizontal asymptote? Illustrate by sketching graphs.
(b) How many horizontal asymptotes can the graph of $y = f(x)$ have? Sketch graphs to illustrate the possibilities.

3. For the function f whose graph is given, state the following.
(a) $\lim\limits_{x\to 2} f(x)$
(b) $\lim\limits_{x\to-1^-} f(x)$
(c) $\lim\limits_{x\to-1^+} f(x)$
(d) $\lim\limits_{x\to\infty} f(x)$
(e) $\lim\limits_{x\to-\infty} f(x)$
(f) The equations of the asymptotes

4. For the function g whose graph is given, state the following.
(a) $\lim\limits_{x\to\infty} g(x)$
(b) $\lim\limits_{x\to-\infty} g(x)$
(c) $\lim\limits_{x\to 3} g(x)$
(d) $\lim\limits_{x\to 0} g(x)$
(e) $\lim\limits_{x\to-2^+} g(x)$
(f) The equations of the asymptotes

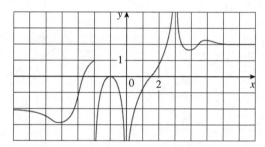

5–10 Sketch the graph of an example of a function f that satisfies all of the given conditions.

5. $\lim\limits_{x\to 0} f(x) = -\infty$, $\lim\limits_{x\to-\infty} f(x) = 5$, $\lim\limits_{x\to\infty} f(x) = -5$

6. $\lim\limits_{x\to 2} f(x) = \infty$, $\lim\limits_{x\to-2^+} f(x) = \infty$, $\lim\limits_{x\to-2^-} f(x) = -\infty$,
$\lim\limits_{x\to-\infty} f(x) = 0$, $\lim\limits_{x\to\infty} f(x) = 0$, $f(0) = 0$

7. $\lim\limits_{x\to 2} f(x) = \infty$, $\lim\limits_{x\to\infty} f(x) = \infty$, $\lim\limits_{x\to-\infty} f(x) = 0$,
$\lim\limits_{x\to 0^+} f(x) = \infty$, $\lim\limits_{x\to 0^-} f(x) = -\infty$

8. $\lim\limits_{x\to\infty} f(x) = 3$, $\lim\limits_{x\to 2^-} f(x) = \infty$, $\lim\limits_{x\to 2^+} f(x) = -\infty$, f is odd

9. $f(0) = 3$, $\lim\limits_{x\to 0^-} f(x) = 4$, $\lim\limits_{x\to 0^+} f(x) = 2$,
$\lim\limits_{x\to-\infty} f(x) = -\infty$, $\lim\limits_{x\to 4^-} f(x) = -\infty$, $\lim\limits_{x\to 4^+} f(x) = \infty$,
$\lim\limits_{x\to\infty} f(x) = 3$

10. $\lim\limits_{x\to 3} f(x) = -\infty$, $\lim\limits_{x\to\infty} f(x) = 2$, $f(0) = 0$, f is even

---

11. Guess the value of the limit

$$\lim_{x \to \infty} \frac{x^2}{2^x}$$

by evaluating the function $f(x) = x^2/2^x$ for $x = 0, 1, 2, 3,$ 4, 5, 6, 7, 8, 9, 10, 20, 50, and 100. Then use a graph of f to support your guess.

12. (a) Use a graph of

$$f(x) = \left(1 - \frac{2}{x}\right)^x$$

to estimate the value of $\lim_{x \to \infty} f(x)$ correct to two decimal places.
(b) Use a table of values of $f(x)$ to estimate the limit to four decimal places.

13–14 Evaluate the limit and justify each step by indicating the appropriate properties of limits.

13. $\lim\limits_{x \to \infty} \dfrac{3x^2 - x + 4}{2x^2 + 5x - 8}$

14. $\lim\limits_{x \to \infty} \sqrt{\dfrac{12x^3 - 5x + 2}{1 + 4x^2 + 3x^3}}$

15–38 Find the limit or show that it does not exist.

15. $\lim\limits_{x \to \infty} \dfrac{1}{2x + 3}$

16. $\lim\limits_{x \to \infty} \dfrac{3x + 5}{x - 4}$

17. $\lim\limits_{x \to -\infty} \dfrac{1 - x - x^2}{2x^2 - 7}$

18. $\lim\limits_{y \to \infty} \dfrac{2 - 3y^2}{5y^2 + 4y}$

19. $\lim\limits_{t \to \infty} \dfrac{\sqrt{t} + t^2}{2t - t^2}$

20. $\lim\limits_{t \to \infty} \dfrac{t - t\sqrt{t}}{2t^{3/2} + 3t - 5}$

21. $\lim\limits_{x \to \infty} \dfrac{(2x^2 + 1)^2}{(x - 1)^2(x^2 + x)}$

22. $\lim\limits_{x \to \infty} \dfrac{x^2}{\sqrt{x^4 + 1}}$

23. $\lim\limits_{x \to \infty} \dfrac{\sqrt{9x^6 - x}}{x^3 + 1}$

24. $\lim\limits_{x \to -\infty} \dfrac{\sqrt{9x^6 - x}}{x^3 + 1}$

25. $\lim\limits_{x \to \infty} \left(\sqrt{9x^2 + x} - 3x\right)$

26. $\lim\limits_{x \to -\infty} \left(x + \sqrt{x^2 + 2x}\right)$

27. $\lim\limits_{x \to \infty} \left(\sqrt{x^2 + ax} - \sqrt{x^2 + bx}\right)$

28. $\lim\limits_{x \to \infty} \sqrt{x^2 + 1}$

29. $\lim\limits_{x \to \infty} \dfrac{x^4 - 3x^2 + x}{x^3 - x + 2}$

30. $\lim\limits_{x \to \infty} (e^{-x} + 2 \cos 3x)$

31. $\lim\limits_{x \to -\infty} (x^4 + x^5)$

32. $\lim\limits_{x \to -\infty} \dfrac{1 + x^6}{x^4 + 1}$

33. $\lim\limits_{x \to \infty} \arctan(e^x)$

34. $\lim\limits_{x \to \infty} \dfrac{e^{3x} - e^{-3x}}{e^{3x} + e^{-3x}}$

35. $\lim\limits_{x \to \infty} \dfrac{1 - e^x}{1 + 2e^x}$

36. $\lim\limits_{x \to \infty} \dfrac{\sin^2 x}{x^2 + 1}$

37. $\lim\limits_{x \to \infty} (e^{-2x} \cos x)$

38. $\lim\limits_{x \to 0^+} \tan^{-1}(\ln x)$

39. (a) Estimate the value of

$$\lim_{x \to -\infty} \left(\sqrt{x^2 + x + 1} + x\right)$$

by graphing the function $f(x) = \sqrt{x^2 + x + 1} + x$.
(b) Use a table of values of $f(x)$ to guess the value of the limit.
(c) Prove that your guess is correct.

40. (a) Use a graph of

$$f(x) = \sqrt{3x^2 + 8x + 6} - \sqrt{3x^2 + 3x + 1}$$

to estimate the value of $\lim_{x \to \infty} f(x)$ to one decimal place.
(b) Use a table of values of $f(x)$ to estimate the limit to four decimal places.
(c) Find the exact value of the limit.

41–46 Find the horizontal and vertical asymptotes of each curve. If you have a graphing device, check your work by graphing the curve and estimating the asymptotes.

41. $y = \dfrac{2x + 1}{x - 2}$

42. $y = \dfrac{x^2 + 1}{2x^2 - 3x - 2}$

43. $y = \dfrac{2x^2 + x - 1}{x^2 + x - 2}$

44. $y = \dfrac{1 + x^4}{x^2 - x^4}$

45. $y = \dfrac{x^3 - x}{x^2 - 6x + 5}$

46. $y = \dfrac{2e^x}{e^x - 5}$

47. Estimate the horizontal asymptote of the function

$$f(x) = \frac{3x^3 + 500x^2}{x^3 + 500x^2 + 100x + 2000}$$

by graphing f for $-10 \le x \le 10$. Then calculate the equation of the asymptote by evaluating the limit. How do you explain the discrepancy?

48. (a) Graph the function

$$f(x) = \frac{\sqrt{2x^2 + 1}}{3x - 5}$$

How many horizontal and vertical asymptotes do you observe? Use the graph to estimate the values of the limits

$$\lim_{x \to \infty} \frac{\sqrt{2x^2 + 1}}{3x - 5} \quad \text{and} \quad \lim_{x \to -\infty} \frac{\sqrt{2x^2 + 1}}{3x - 5}$$

(b) By calculating values of $f(x)$, give numerical estimates of the limits in part (a).
(c) Calculate the exact values of the limits in part (a). Did you get the same value or different values for these two limits? [In view of your answer to part (a), you might have to check your calculation for the second limit.]

49. Find a formula for a function f that satisfies the following conditions:

$$\lim_{x \to \pm\infty} f(x) = 0, \quad \lim_{x \to 0} f(x) = -\infty, \quad f(2) = 0,$$

$$\lim_{x \to 3^-} f(x) = \infty, \quad \lim_{x \to 3^+} f(x) = -\infty$$

50. Find a formula for a function that has vertical asymptotes $x = 1$ and $x = 3$ and horizontal asymptote $y = 1$.

51. A function f is a ratio of quadratic functions and has a vertical asymptote $x = 4$ and just one x-intercept, $x = 1$. It is known that f has a removable discontinuity at $x = -1$ and $\lim_{x \to -1} f(x) = 2$. Evaluate
    (a) $f(0)$
    (b) $\lim_{x \to \infty} f(x)$

52–56 Find the limits as $x \to \infty$ and as $x \to -\infty$. Use this information, together with intercepts, to give a rough sketch of the graph as in Example 12.

52. $y = 2x^3 - x^4$

53. $y = x^4 - x^6$

54. $y = x^3(x + 2)^2(x - 1)$

55. $y = (3 - x)(1 + x)^2(1 - x)^4$

56. $y = x^2(x^2 - 1)^2(x + 2)$

---

57. (a) Use the Squeeze Theorem to evaluate $\lim_{x \to \infty} \dfrac{\sin x}{x}$.

(b) Graph $f(x) = (\sin x)/x$. How many times does the graph cross the asymptote?

58. By the *end behavior* of a function we mean the behavior of its values as $x \to \infty$ and as $x \to -\infty$.
    (a) Describe and compare the end behavior of the functions

$$P(x) = 3x^5 - 5x^3 + 2x \qquad Q(x) = 3x^5$$

by graphing both functions in the viewing rectangles $[-2, 2]$ by $[-2, 2]$ and $[-10, 10]$ by $[-10,000, 10,000]$.
    (b) Two functions are said to have the *same end behavior* if their ratio approaches 1 as $x \to \infty$. Show that P and Q have the same end behavior.

59 Let P and Q be polynomials. Find

$$\lim_{x \to \infty} \frac{P(x)}{Q(x)}$$

if the degree of P is (a) less than the degree of Q and (b) greater than the degree of Q.

60. Make a rough sketch of the curve $y = x^n$ (n an integer) for the following five cases:
    (i) $n = 0$
    (ii) $n > 0, n$ odd
    (iii) $n > 0, n$ even
    (iv) $n < 0, n$ odd
    (v) $n < 0, n$ even
    Then use these sketches to find the following limits.
    (a) $\lim_{x \to 0^+} x^n$
    (b) $\lim_{x \to 0^-} x^n$
    (c) $\lim_{x \to \infty} x^n$
    (d) $\lim_{x \to -\infty} x^n$

61. Find $\lim_{x \to \infty} f(x)$ if, for all $x > 1$,

$$\frac{10e^x - 21}{2e^x} < f(x) < \frac{5\sqrt{x}}{\sqrt{x - 1}}$$

62. (a) A tank contains 5000 L of pure water. Brine that contains 30 g of salt per liter of water is pumped into the tank at a rate of 25 L/min. Show that the concentration of salt after t minutes (in grams per liter) is

$$C(t) = \frac{30t}{200 + t}$$

(b) What happens to the concentration as $t \to \infty$?

63. In Chapter 9 we will be able to show, under certain assumptions, that the velocity $v(t)$ of a falling raindrop at time t is

$$v(t) = v*(1 - e^{-gt/v*})$$

where g is the acceleration due to gravity and $v*$ is the *terminal velocity* of the raindrop.
    (a) Find $\lim_{t \to \infty} v(t)$.
    (b) Graph $v(t)$ if $v* = 1$ m/s and $g = 9.8$ m/s^2. How long does it take for the velocity of the raindrop to reach 99% of its terminal velocity?

64. (a) By graphing $y = e^{-x/10}$ and $y = 0.1$ on a common screen, discover how large you need to make x so that $e^{-x/10} < 0.1$.
    (b) Can you solve part (a) without using a graphing device?

65. Use a graph to find a number N such that

$$\text{if} \quad x > N \quad \text{then} \quad \left| \frac{3x^2 + 1}{2x^2 + x + 1} - 1.5 \right| < 0.05$$

66. For the limit

$$\lim_{x \to \infty} \frac{\sqrt{4x^2 + 1}}{x + 1} = 2$$

illustrate Definition 7 by finding values of N that correspond to $\varepsilon = 0.5$ and $\varepsilon = 0.1$.

67. For the limit

$$\lim_{x \to -\infty} \frac{\sqrt{4x^2 + 1}}{x + 1} = -2$$

illustrate Definition 8 by finding values of N that correspond to $\varepsilon = 0.5$ and $\varepsilon = 0.1$.

68. For the limit

$$\lim_{x \to \infty} \frac{2x + 1}{\sqrt{x + 1}} = \infty$$

illustrate Definition 9 by finding a value of N that corresponds to $M = 100$.

69. (a) How large do we have to take x so that $1/x^2 < 0.0001$?

(b) Taking $r = 2$ in Theorem 5, we have the statement

$$\lim_{x \to \infty} \frac{1}{x^2} = 0$$

Prove this directly using Definition 7.

70. (a) How large do we have to take x so that $1/\sqrt{x} < 0.0001$?

(b) Taking $r = \frac{1}{2}$ in Theorem 5, we have the statement

$$\lim_{x \to \infty} \frac{1}{\sqrt{x}} = 0$$

Prove this directly using Definition 7.

71. Use Definition 8 to prove that $\lim\limits_{x \to -\infty} \dfrac{1}{x} = 0$.

72. Prove, using Definition 9, that $\lim\limits_{x \to \infty} x^3 = \infty$.

73. Use Definition 9 to prove that $\lim\limits_{x \to \infty} e^x = \infty$.

74. Formulate a precise definition of

$$\lim_{x \to -\infty} f(x) = -\infty$$

Then use your definition to prove that

$$\lim_{x \to -\infty} (1 + x^3) = -\infty$$

75. Prove that

$$\lim_{x \to \infty} f(x) = \lim_{t \to 0^+} f(1/t)$$

and

$$\lim_{x \to -\infty} f(x) = \lim_{t \to 0^-} f(1/t)$$

if these limits exist.

2.7 Derivatives and Rates of Change

The problem of finding the tangent line to a curve and the problem of finding the velocity of an object both involve finding the same type of limit, as we saw in Section 2.1. This special type of limit is called a *derivative* and we will see that it can be interpreted as a rate of change in any of the sciences or engineering.

Tangents

If a curve C has equation $y = f(x)$ and we want to find the tangent line to C at the point $P(a, f(a))$, then we consider a nearby point $Q(x, f(x))$, where $x \neq a$, and compute the slope of the secant line PQ:

$$m_{PQ} = \frac{f(x) - f(a)}{x - a}$$

Then we let Q approach P along the curve C by letting x approach a. If m_{PQ} approaches a number m, then we define the *tangent* t to be the line through P with slope m. (This amounts to saying that the tangent line is the limiting position of the secant line PQ as Q approaches P. See Figure 1.)

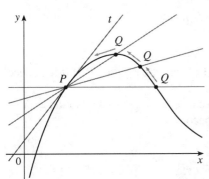

FIGURE 1

> **1** **Definition** The **tangent line** to the curve $y = f(x)$ at the point $P(a, f(a))$ is the line through P with slope
>
> $$m = \lim_{x \to a} \frac{f(x) - f(a)}{x - a}$$
>
> provided that this limit exists.

In our first example we confirm the guess we made in Example 1 in Section 2.1.

V **EXAMPLE 1** Find an equation of the tangent line to the parabola $y = x^2$ at the point $P(1, 1)$.

SOLUTION Here we have $a = 1$ and $f(x) = x^2$, so the slope is

$$m = \lim_{x \to 1} \frac{f(x) - f(1)}{x - 1} = \lim_{x \to 1} \frac{x^2 - 1}{x - 1}$$

$$= \lim_{x \to 1} \frac{(x - 1)(x + 1)}{x - 1}$$

$$= \lim_{x \to 1} (x + 1) = 1 + 1 = 2$$

Point-slope form for a line through the point (x_1, y_1) with slope m:

$$y - y_1 = m(x - x_1)$$

Using the point-slope form of the equation of a line, we find that an equation of the tangent line at $(1, 1)$ is

$$y - 1 = 2(x - 1) \qquad \text{or} \qquad y = 2x - 1 \qquad \blacksquare$$

We sometimes refer to the slope of the tangent line to a curve at a point as the **slope of the curve** at the point. The idea is that if we zoom in far enough toward the point, the curve looks almost like a straight line. Figure 2 illustrates this procedure for the curve $y = x^2$ in Example 1. The more we zoom in, the more the parabola looks like a line. In other words, the curve becomes almost indistinguishable from its tangent line.

TEC Visual 2.7 shows an animation of Figure 2.

FIGURE 2 Zooming in toward the point $(1, 1)$ on the parabola $y = x^2$

FIGURE 3

There is another expression for the slope of a tangent line that is sometimes easier to use. If $h = x - a$, then $x = a + h$ and so the slope of the secant line PQ is

$$m_{PQ} = \frac{f(a + h) - f(a)}{h}$$

(See Figure 3 where the case $h > 0$ is illustrated and Q is to the right of P. If it happened that $h < 0$, however, Q would be to the left of P.)

Notice that as x approaches a, h approaches 0 (because $h = x - a$) and so the expression for the slope of the tangent line in Definition 1 becomes

2
$$m = \lim_{h \to 0} \frac{f(a + h) - f(a)}{h}$$

EXAMPLE 2 Find an equation of the tangent line to the hyperbola $y = 3/x$ at the point $(3, 1)$.

SOLUTION Let $f(x) = 3/x$. Then the slope of the tangent at $(3, 1)$ is

$$m = \lim_{h \to 0} \frac{f(3 + h) - f(3)}{h} = \lim_{h \to 0} \frac{\dfrac{3}{3 + h} - 1}{h} = \lim_{h \to 0} \frac{\dfrac{3 - (3 + h)}{3 + h}}{h}$$

$$= \lim_{h \to 0} \frac{-h}{h(3 + h)} = \lim_{h \to 0} -\frac{1}{3 + h} = -\frac{1}{3}$$

Therefore an equation of the tangent at the point $(3, 1)$ is

$$y - 1 = -\tfrac{1}{3}(x - 3)$$

which simplifies to

$$x + 3y - 6 = 0$$

The hyperbola and its tangent are shown in Figure 4.

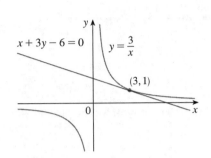

FIGURE 4

Velocities

In Section 2.1 we investigated the motion of a ball dropped from the CN Tower and defined its velocity to be the limiting value of average velocities over shorter and shorter time periods.

In general, suppose an object moves along a straight line according to an equation of motion $s = f(t)$, where s is the displacement (directed distance) of the object from the origin at time t. The function f that describes the motion is called the **position function** of the object. In the time interval from $t = a$ to $t = a + h$ the change in position is $f(a + h) - f(a)$. (See Figure 5.) The average velocity over this time interval is

$$\text{average velocity} = \frac{\text{displacement}}{\text{time}} = \frac{f(a + h) - f(a)}{h}$$

FIGURE 5

which is the same as the slope of the secant line PQ in Figure 6.

Now suppose we compute the average velocities over shorter and shorter time intervals $[a, a + h]$. In other words, we let h approach 0. As in the example of the falling ball, we define the **velocity** (or **instantaneous velocity**) $v(a)$ at time $t = a$ to be the limit of these average velocities:

$$\boxed{3} \qquad v(a) = \lim_{h \to 0} \frac{f(a + h) - f(a)}{h}$$

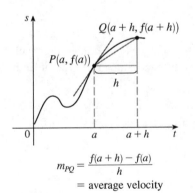

FIGURE 6

This means that the velocity at time $t = a$ is equal to the slope of the tangent line at P (compare Equations 2 and 3).

Now that we know how to compute limits, let's reconsider the problem of the falling ball.

V **EXAMPLE 3** Suppose that a ball is dropped from the upper observation deck of the CN Tower, 450 m above the ground.

(a) What is the velocity of the ball after 5 seconds?

(b) How fast is the ball traveling when it hits the ground?

Recall from Section 2.1: The distance (in meters) fallen after t seconds is $4.9t^2$.

SOLUTION We will need to find the velocity both when $t = 5$ and when the ball hits the ground, so it's efficient to start by finding the velocity at a general time $t = a$. Using the equation of motion $s = f(t) = 4.9t^2$, we have

$$v(a) = \lim_{h \to 0} \frac{f(a+h) - f(a)}{h} = \lim_{h \to 0} \frac{4.9(a+h)^2 - 4.9a^2}{h}$$

$$\lim_{h \to 0} \frac{4.9(a^2 + 2ah + h^2 - a^2)}{h} - \lim_{h \to 0} \frac{4.9(2ah + h^2)}{h}$$

$$= \lim_{h \to 0} 4.9(2a + h) = 9.8a$$

(a) The velocity after 5 s is $v(5) = (9.8)(5) = 49$ m/s.

(b) Since the observation deck is 450 m above the ground, the ball will hit the ground at the time t_1 when $s(t_1) = 450$, that is,

$$4.9t_1^2 = 450$$

This gives

$$t_1^2 = \frac{450}{4.9} \qquad \text{and} \qquad t_1 = \sqrt{\frac{450}{4.9}} \approx 9.6 \text{ s}$$

The velocity of the ball as it hits the ground is therefore

$$v(t_1) = 9.8t_1 = 9.8\sqrt{\frac{450}{4.9}} \approx 94 \text{ m/s}$$

Derivatives

We have seen that the same type of limit arises in finding the slope of a tangent line (Equation 2) or the velocity of an object (Equation 3). In fact, limits of the form

$$\lim_{h \to 0} \frac{f(a+h) - f(a)}{h}$$

arise whenever we calculate a rate of change in any of the sciences or engineering, such as a rate of reaction in chemistry or a marginal cost in economics. Since this type of limit occurs so widely, it is given a special name and notation.

> **4** **Definition** The **derivative of a function f at a number a**, denoted by $f'(a)$, is
>
> $$f'(a) = \lim_{h \to 0} \frac{f(a+h) - f(a)}{h}$$
>
> if this limit exists.

$f'(a)$ is read "f prime of a."

If we write $x = a + h$, then we have $h = x - a$ and h approaches 0 if and only if x approaches a. Therefore an equivalent way of stating the definition of the derivative, as we saw in finding tangent lines, is

5
$$f'(a) = \lim_{x \to a} \frac{f(x) - f(a)}{x - a}$$

V **EXAMPLE 4** Find the derivative of the function $f(x) = x^2 - 8x + 9$ at the number a.

SOLUTION From Definition 4 we have

$$f'(a) = \lim_{h \to 0} \frac{f(a + h) - f(a)}{h}$$

$$= \lim_{h \to 0} \frac{[(a + h)^2 - 8(a + h) + 9] - [a^2 - 8a + 9]}{h}$$

$$= \lim_{h \to 0} \frac{a^2 + 2ah + h^2 - 8a - 8h + 9 - a^2 + 8a - 9}{h}$$

$$= \lim_{h \to 0} \frac{2ah + h^2 - 8h}{h} = \lim_{h \to 0} (2a + h - 8)$$

$$= 2a - 8$$

We defined the tangent line to the curve $y = f(x)$ at the point $P(a, f(a))$ to be the line that passes through P and has slope m given by Equation 1 or 2. Since, by Definition 4, this is the same as the derivative $f'(a)$, we can now say the following.

> The tangent line to $y = f(x)$ at $(a, f(a))$ is the line through $(a, f(a))$ whose slope is equal to $f'(a)$, the derivative of f at a.

If we use the point-slope form of the equation of a line, we can write an equation of the tangent line to the curve $y = f(x)$ at the point $(a, f(a))$:

$$y - f(a) = f'(a)(x - a)$$

V **EXAMPLE 5** Find an equation of the tangent line to the parabola $y = x^2 - 8x + 9$ at the point $(3, -6)$.

SOLUTION From Example 4 we know that the derivative of $f(x) = x^2 - 8x + 9$ at the number a is $f'(a) = 2a - 8$. Therefore the slope of the tangent line at $(3, -6)$ is $f'(3) = 2(3) - 8 = -2$. Thus an equation of the tangent line, shown in Figure 7, is

$$y - (-6) = (-2)(x - 3) \qquad \text{or} \qquad y = -2x$$

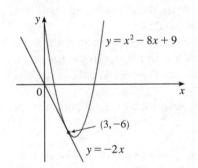

FIGURE 7

Rates of Change

Suppose y is a quantity that depends on another quantity x. Thus y is a function of x and we write $y = f(x)$. If x changes from x_1 to x_2, then the change in x (also called the **increment** of x) is

$$\Delta x = x_2 - x_1$$

and the corresponding change in y is

$$\Delta y = f(x_2) - f(x_1)$$

The difference quotient

$$\frac{\Delta y}{\Delta x} = \frac{f(x_2) - f(x_1)}{x_2 - x_1}$$

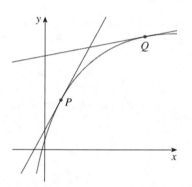

average rate of change $= m_{PQ}$

instantaneous rate of change $=$
            slope of tangent at P

FIGURE 8

FIGURE 9
The y-values are changing rapidly
at P and slowly at Q.

is called the **average rate of change of y with respect to x** over the interval $[x_1, x_2]$ and can be interpreted as the slope of the secant line PQ in Figure 8.

By analogy with velocity, we consider the average rate of change over smaller and smaller intervals by letting x_2 approach x_1 and therefore letting Δx approach 0. The limit of these average rates of change is called the **(instantaneous) rate of change of y with respect to x at $x = x_1$**, which is interpreted as the slope of the tangent to the curve $y = f(x)$ at $P(x_1, f(x_1))$:

$$\boxed{6} \qquad \text{instantaneous rate of change} = \lim_{\Delta x \to 0} \frac{\Delta y}{\Delta x} = \lim_{x_2 \to x_1} \frac{f(x_2) - f(x_1)}{x_2 - x_1}$$

We recognize this limit as being the derivative $f'(x_1)$.

We know that one interpretation of the derivative $f'(a)$ is as the slope of the tangent line to the curve $y = f(x)$ when $x = a$. We now have a second interpretation:

> The derivative $f'(a)$ is the instantaneous rate of change of $y = f(x)$ with respect to x when $x = a$.

The connection with the first interpretation is that if we sketch the curve $y = f(x)$, then the instantaneous rate of change is the slope of the tangent to this curve at the point where $x = a$. This means that when the derivative is large (and therefore the curve is steep, as at the point P in Figure 9), the y-values change rapidly. When the derivative is small, the curve is relatively flat (as at point Q) and the y-values change slowly.

In particular, if $s = f(t)$ is the position function of a particle that moves along a straight line, then $f'(a)$ is the rate of change of the displacement s with respect to the time t. In other words, $f'(a)$ *is the velocity of the particle at time $t = a$*. The **speed** of the particle is the absolute value of the velocity, that is, $|f'(a)|$.

In the next example we discuss the meaning of the derivative of a function that is defined verbally.

▼ EXAMPLE 6   A manufacturer produces bolts of a fabric with a fixed width. The cost of producing x meters of this fabric is $C = f(x)$ dollars.
(a) What is the meaning of the derivative $f'(x)$? What are its units?
(b) In practical terms, what does it mean to say that $f'(1000) = 9$?
(c) Which do you think is greater, $f'(50)$ or $f'(500)$? What about $f'(5000)$?

SOLUTION
(a) The derivative $f'(x)$ is the instantaneous rate of change of C with respect to x; that is, $f'(x)$ means the rate of change of the production cost with respect to the number of meters produced. (Economists call this rate of change the *marginal cost*. This idea is discussed in more detail in Sections 3.7 and 4.7.)
Because

$$f'(x) = \lim_{\Delta x \to 0} \frac{\Delta C}{\Delta x}$$

the units for $f'(x)$ are the same as the units for the difference quotient $\Delta C / \Delta x$. Since ΔC is measured in dollars and Δx in meters, it follows that the units for $f'(x)$ are dollars per meter.

(b) The statement that $f'(1000) = 9$ means that, after 1000 meters of fabric have been manufactured, the rate at which the production cost is increasing is $9/m. (When $x = 1000$, C is increasing 9 times as fast as x.)

Here we are assuming that the cost function is well behaved; in other words, $C(x)$ doesn't oscillate rapidly near $x = 1000$.

Since $\Delta x = 1$ is small compared with $x = 1000$, we could use the approximation

$$f'(1000) \approx \frac{\Delta C}{\Delta x} = \frac{\Delta C}{1} = \Delta C$$

and say that the cost of manufacturing the 1000th meter (or the 1001st) is about $9.

(c) The rate at which the production cost is increasing (per meter) is probably lower when $x = 500$ than when $x = 50$ (the cost of making the 500th meter is less than the cost of the 50th meter) because of economies of scale. (The manufacturer makes more efficient use of the fixed costs of production.) So

$$f'(50) > f'(500)$$

But, as production expands, the resulting large-scale operation might become inefficient and there might be overtime costs. Thus it is possible that the rate of increase of costs will eventually start to rise. So it may happen that

$$f'(5000) > f'(500)$$

In the following example we estimate the rate of change of the national debt with respect to time. Here the function is defined not by a formula but by a table of values.

EXAMPLE 7 Let $D(t)$ be the Canadian gross public debt at time t. The table in the margin gives approximate values of this function by providing midyear estimates, in billions of dollars, from 1994 to 2002. Interpret and estimate the value of $D'(1998)$.

t	$D(t)$
1994	414.0
1996	469.5
1998	467.3
2000	456.4
2002	442.3

SOLUTION The derivative $D'(1998)$ means the rate of change of D with respect to t when $t = 1998$, that is, the rate of increase of the national debt in 1998.

According to Equation 3,

$$D'(1998) = \lim_{t \to 1998} \frac{D(t) - D(1998)}{t - 1998}$$

So we compute and tabulate values of the difference quotient (the average rates of change) as follows.

t	$\dfrac{D(t) - D(1998)}{t - 1998}$
1994	13.3
1996	−1.1
2000	−5.5
2002	−6.3

From this table we see that $D'(1998)$ lies somewhere between −1.1 and −5.5 billion dollars per year. [Here we are making the reasonable assumption that the debt didn't fluctuate wildly between 1998 and 2002.] We estimate that the rate of change of the Canadian debt in 1998 was the average of these two numbers, namely

$$D'(1998) \approx -3.3 \text{ billion dollars per year}$$

A Note on Units

The units for the average rate of change $\Delta D / \Delta t$ are the units for ΔD divided by the units for Δt, namely, billions of dollars per year. The instantaneous rate of change is the limit of the average rates of change, so it is measured in the same units: billions of dollars per year.

The minus sign means that the debt was *decreasing* at that time.

Another method would be to plot the debt function and estimate the slope of the tangent line when $t = 1998$.

In Examples 3, 6, and 7 we saw three specific examples of rates of change: the velocity of an object is the rate of change of displacement with respect to time; marginal cost is the rate of change of production cost with respect to the number of items produced; the rate of change of the debt with respect to time is of interest in economics. Here is a small sample of other rates of change: In physics, the rate of change of work with respect to time is called *power*. Chemists who study a chemical reaction are interested in the rate of change in the concentration of a reactant with respect to time (called the *rate of reaction*). A biologist is interested in the rate of change of the population of a colony of bacteria with respect to time. In fact, the computation of rates of change is important in all of the natural sciences, in engineering, and even in the social sciences. Further examples will be given in Section 3.7.

All these rates of change are derivatives and can therefore be interpreted as slopes of tangents. This gives added significance to the solution of the tangent problem. Whenever we solve a problem involving tangent lines, we are not just solving a problem in geometry. We are also implicitly solving a great variety of problems involving rates of change in science and engineering.

2.7 Exercises

1. A curve has equation $y = f(x)$.
  (a) Write an expression for the slope of the secant line through the points $P(3, f(3))$ and $Q(x, f(x))$.
  (b) Write an expression for the slope of the tangent line at P.

2. Graph the curve $y = e^x$ in the viewing rectangles $[-1, 1]$ by $[0, 2]$, $[-0.5, 0.5]$ by $[0.5, 1.5]$, and $[-0.1, 0.1]$ by $[0.9, 1.1]$. What do you notice about the curve as you zoom in toward the point $(0, 1)$?

3. (a) Find the slope of the tangent line to the parabola $y = 4x - x^2$ at the point $(1, 3)$
    (i) using Definition 1   (ii) using Equation 2
  (b) Find an equation of the tangent line in part (a).
  (c) Graph the parabola and the tangent line. As a check on your work, zoom in toward the point $(1, 3)$ until the parabola and the tangent line are indistinguishable.

4. (a) Find the slope of the tangent line to the curve $y = x - x^3$ at the point $(1, 0)$
    (i) using Definition 1   (ii) using Equation 2
  (b) Find an equation of the tangent line in part (a).
  (c) Graph the curve and the tangent line in successively smaller viewing rectangles centered at $(1, 0)$ until the curve and the line appear to coincide.

5–8 Find an equation of the tangent line to the curve at the given point.

5. $y = 4x - 3x^2$, $(2, -4)$ **6.** $y = x^3 - 3x + 1$, $(2, 3)$

7. $y = \sqrt{x}$, $(1, 1)$ **8.** $y = \dfrac{2x + 1}{x + 2}$, $(1, 1)$

9. (a) Find the slope of the tangent to the curve $y = 3 + 4x^2 - 2x^3$ at the point where $x = a$.

  (b) Find equations of the tangent lines at the points $(1, 5)$ and $(2, 3)$.
  (c) Graph the curve and both tangents on a common screen.

10. (a) Find the slope of the tangent to the curve $y = 1/\sqrt{x}$ at the point where $x = a$.
  (b) Find equations of the tangent lines at the points $(1, 1)$ and $\left(4, \frac{1}{2}\right)$.
  (c) Graph the curve and both tangents on a common screen.

11. (a) A particle starts by moving to the right along a horizontal line; the graph of its position function is shown. When is the particle moving to the right? Moving to the left? Standing still?
  (b) Draw a graph of the velocity function.

12. Shown are graphs of the position functions of two runners, A and B, who run a 100-m race and finish in a tie.

(a) Describe and compare how the runners run the race.
(b) At what time is the distance between the runners the greatest?
(c) At what time do they have the same velocity?

13. If a ball is thrown into the air with a velocity of 10 m/s, its height (in meters) after t seconds is given by $y = 10t - 4.9t^2$. Find the velocity when $t = 2$.

14. If a rock is thrown upward on the planet Mars with a velocity of 10 m/s, its height (in meters) after t seconds is given by $H = 10t - 1.86t^2$.
(a) Find the velocity of the rock after one second.
(b) Find the velocity of the rock when $t = a$.
(c) When will the rock hit the surface?
(d) With what velocity will the rock hit the surface?

15. The displacement (in meters) of a particle moving in a straight line is given by the equation of motion $s = 1/t^2$, where t is measured in seconds. Find the velocity of the particle at times $t = a$, $t = 1$, $t = 2$, and $t = 3$.

16. The displacement (in meters) of a particle moving in a straight line is given by $s = t^2 - 8t + 18$, where t is measured in seconds.
(a) Find the average velocity over each time interval:
  (i) $[3, 4]$ (ii) $[3.5, 4]$
  (iii) $[4, 5]$ (iv) $[4, 4.5]$
(b) Find the instantaneous velocity when $t = 4$.
(c) Draw the graph of s as a function of t and draw the secant lines whose slopes are the average velocities in part (a) and the tangent line whose slope is the instantaneous velocity in part (b).

17. For the function g whose graph is given, arrange the following numbers in increasing order and explain your reasoning:

$$0 \quad g'(-2) \quad g'(0) \quad g'(2) \quad g'(4)$$

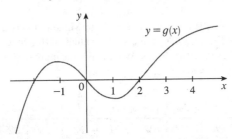

18. Find an equation of the tangent line to the graph of $y = g(x)$ at $x = 5$ if $g(5) = -3$ and $g'(5) = 4$.

19. If an equation of the tangent line to the curve $y = f(x)$ at the point where $a = 2$ is $y = 4x - 5$, find $f(2)$ and $f'(2)$.

20. If the tangent line to $y = f(x)$ at $(4, 3)$ passes through the point $(0, 2)$, find $f(4)$ and $f'(4)$.

21. Sketch the graph of a function f for which $f(0) = 0$, $f'(0) = 3$, $f'(1) = 0$, and $f'(2) = -1$.

22. Sketch the graph of a function g for which $g(0) = g(2) = g(4) = 0$, $g'(1) = g'(3) = 0$, $g'(0) = g'(4) = 1$, $g'(2) = -1$, $\lim_{x \to \infty} g(x) = \infty$, and $\lim_{x \to -\infty} g(x) = -\infty$.

23. If $f(x) = 3x^2 - x^3$, find $f'(1)$ and use it to find an equation of the tangent line to the curve $y = 3x^2 - x^3$ at the point $(1, 2)$.

24. If $g(x) = x^4 - 2$, find $g'(1)$ and use it to find an equation of the tangent line to the curve $y = x^4 - 2$ at the point $(1, -1)$.

25. (a) If $F(x) = 5x/(1 + x^2)$, find $F'(2)$ and use it to find an equation of the tangent line to the curve $y = 5x/(1 + x^2)$ at the point $(2, 2)$.
(b) Illustrate part (a) by graphing the curve and the tangent line on the same screen.

26. (a) If $G(x) = 4x^2 - x^3$, find $G'(a)$ and use it to find equations of the tangent lines to the curve $y = 4x^2 - x^3$ at the points $(2, 8)$ and $(3, 9)$.
(b) Illustrate part (a) by graphing the curve and the tangent lines on the same screen.

27–32 Find $f'(a)$.

27. $f(x) = 3x^2 - 4x + 1$

28. $f(t) = 2t^3 + t$

29. $f(t) = \dfrac{2t + 1}{t + 3}$

30. $f(x) = x^{-2}$

31. $f(x) = \sqrt{1 - 2x}$

32. $f(x) = \dfrac{4}{\sqrt{1 - x}}$

33–38 Each limit represents the derivative of some function f at some number a. State such an f and a in each case.

33. $\displaystyle\lim_{h \to 0} \frac{(1 + h)^{10} - 1}{h}$

34. $\displaystyle\lim_{h \to 0} \frac{\sqrt[4]{16 + h} - 2}{h}$

35. $\displaystyle\lim_{x \to 5} \frac{2^x - 32}{x - 5}$

36. $\displaystyle\lim_{x \to \pi/4} \frac{\tan x - 1}{x - \pi/4}$

37. $\displaystyle\lim_{h \to 0} \frac{\cos(\pi + h) + 1}{h}$

38. $\displaystyle\lim_{t \to 1} \frac{t^4 + t - 2}{t - 1}$

39–40 A particle moves along a straight line with equation of motion $s = f(t)$, where s is measured in meters and t in seconds. Find the velocity and the speed when $t = 5$.

39. $f(t) = 100 + 50t - 4.9t^2$

40. $f(t) = t^{-1} - t$

41. A warm can of soda is placed in a cold refrigerator. Sketch the graph of the temperature of the soda as a function of time. Is the initial rate of change of temperature greater or less than the rate of change after an hour?

42. A roast turkey is taken from an oven when its temperature has reached 85°C and is placed on a table in a room where the temperature is 24°C. The graph shows how the temperature of the turkey decreases and eventually approaches room temperature. By measuring the slope of the tangent, estimate the rate of change of the temperature after an hour.

43. The table shows the number of passengers P that arrived in Ireland by air, in millions.

Year	2001	2003	2005	2007	2009
P	8.49	9.65	11.78	14.54	12.84

(a) Find the average rate of increase of P
   (i) from 2001 to 2005   (ii) from 2003 to 2005
   (iii) from 2005 to 2007
   In each case, include the units.
(b) Estimate the instantaneous rate of growth in 2005 by taking the average of two average rates of change. What are its units?

44. The number N of locations of a popular coffeehouse chain is given in the table. (The numbers of locations as of October 1 are given.)

Year	2004	2005	2006	2007	2008
N	8569	10,241	12,440	15,011	16,680

(a) Find the average rate of growth
   (i) from 2006 to 2008   (ii) from 2006 to 2007
   (iii) from 2005 to 2006
   In each case, include the units.
(b) Estimate the instantaneous rate of growth in 2006 by taking the average of two average rates of change. What are its units?
(c) Estimate the instantaneous rate of growth in 2006 by measuring the slope of a tangent.
(d) Estimate the intantaneous rate of growth in 2007 and compare it with the growth rate in 2006. What do you conclude?

45. The cost (in dollars) of producing x units of a certain commodity is $C(x) = 5000 + 10x + 0.05x^2$.
(a) Find the average rate of change of C with respect to x when the production level is changed
   (i) from $x = 100$ to $x = 105$
   (ii) from $x = 100$ to $x = 101$

(b) Find the instantaneous rate of change of C with respect to x when $x = 100$. (This is called the *marginal cost*. Its significance will be explained in Section 3.7.)

46. If a cylindrical tank holds 100,000 liters of water, which can be drained from the bottom of the tank in an hour, then Torricelli's Law gives the volume V of water remaining in the tank after t minutes as

$$V(t) = 100,000\left(1 - \tfrac{1}{60}t\right)^2 \qquad 0 \le t \le 60$$

Find the rate at which the water is flowing out of the tank (the instantaneous rate of change of V with respect to t) as a function of t. What are its units? For times $t = 0, 10, 20, 30, 40, 50,$ and 60 min, find the flow rate and the amount of water remaining in the tank. Summarize your findings in a sentence or two. At what time is the flow rate the greatest? The least?

47. The cost of producing x kilograms of gold from a new gold mine is $C = f(x)$ dollars.
(a) What is the meaning of the derivative $f'(x)$? What are its units?
(b) What does the statement $f'(50) = 36$ mean?
(c) Do you think the values of $f'(x)$ will increase or decrease in the short term? What about the long term? Explain.

48. The number of bacteria after t hours in a controlled laboratory experiment is $n = f(t)$.
(a) What is the meaning of the derivative $f'(5)$? What are its units?
(b) Suppose there is an unlimited amount of space and nutrients for the bacteria. Which do you think is larger, $f'(5)$ or $f'(10)$? If the supply of nutrients is limited, would that affect your conclusion? Explain.

49. Let $T(t)$ be the temperature (in °C) in Manila t hours after noon on July 19, 2011. The table shows values of this function recorded every two hours. What is the meaning of $T''(5)$? Estimate its value.

t	1	3	5	7	9	11
T	32	32	31	27	26	25

50. The quantity (in kilograms) of a gourmet ground coffee that is sold by a coffee company at a price of p dollars per kilogram is $Q = f(p)$.
(a) What is the meaning of the derivative $f'(8)$? What are its units?
(b) Is $f'(8)$ positive or negative? Explain.

51. The quantity of oxygen that can dissolve in water depends on the temperature of the water. (So thermal pollution influences the oxygen content of water.) The graph shows how oxygen solubility S varies as a function of the water temperature T.

(a) What is the meaning of the derivative $S'(T)$? What are its units?

(b) Estimate the value of $S'(16)$ and interpret it.

Adapted from Kupchella & Hyland, *Environmental Science: Living Within the System of Nature*, 2d ed.; © 1989. Printed and electronically reproduced by permission of Pearson Education, Inc., Upper Saddle River, NJ.

52. The graph shows the influence of the temperature T on the maximum sustainable swimming speed S of Coho salmon.

(a) What is the meaning of the derivative $S'(T)$? What are its units?

(b) Estimate the values of $S'(15)$ and $S'(25)$ and interpret them.

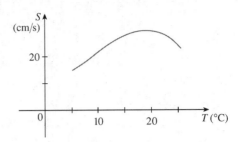

53–54 Determine whether $f'(0)$ exists.

53. $f(x) = \begin{cases} x \sin \dfrac{1}{x} & \text{if } x \neq 0 \\ 0 & \text{if } x = 0 \end{cases}$

54. $f(x) = \begin{cases} x^2 \sin \dfrac{1}{x} & \text{if } x \neq 0 \\ 0 & \text{if } x = 0 \end{cases}$

EARLY METHODS FOR FINDING TANGENTS

The first person to formulate explicitly the ideas of limits and derivatives was Sir Isaac Newton in the 1660s. But Newton acknowledged that "If I have seen further than other men, it is because I have stood on the shoulders of giants." Two of those giants were Pierre Fermat (1601–1665) and Newton's mentor at Cambridge, Isaac Barrow (1630–1677). Newton was familiar with the methods that these men used to find tangent lines, and their methods played a role in Newton's eventual formulation of calculus.

The following references contain explanations of these methods. Read one or more of the references and write a report comparing the methods of either Fermat or Barrow to modern methods. In particular, use the method of Section 2.7 to find an equation of the tangent line to the curve $y = x^3 + 2x$ at the point $(1, 3)$ and show how either Fermat or Barrow would have solved the same problem. Although you used derivatives and they did not, point out similarities between the methods.

1. Carl Boyer and Uta Merzbach, *A History of Mathematics* (New York: Wiley, 1989), pp. 389, 432.

2. C. H. Edwards, *The Historical Development of the Calculus* (New York: Springer-Verlag, 1979), pp. 124, 132.

3. Howard Eves, *An Introduction to the History of Mathematics*, 6th ed. (New York: Saunders, 1990), pp. 391, 395.

4. Morris Kline, *Mathematical Thought from Ancient to Modern Times* (New York: Oxford University Press, 1972), pp. 344, 346.

2.8 The Derivative as a Function

In the preceding section we considered the derivative of a function f at a fixed number a:

$$\boxed{1} \qquad f'(a) = \lim_{h \to 0} \frac{f(a + h) - f(a)}{h}$$

Here we change our point of view and let the number a vary. If we replace a in Equation 1 by a variable x, we obtain

$$\boxed{2} \qquad f'(x) = \lim_{h \to 0} \frac{f(x + h) - f(x)}{h}$$

Given any number x for which this limit exists, we assign to x the number $f'(x)$. So we can regard f' as a new function, called the **derivative of f** and defined by Equation 2. We know that the value of f' at x, $f'(x)$, can be interpreted geometrically as the slope of the tangent line to the graph of f at the point $(x, f(x))$.

The function f' is called the derivative of f because it has been "derived" from f by the limiting operation in Equation 2. The domain of f' is the set $\{x \mid f'(x) \text{ exists}\}$ and may be smaller than the domain of f.

V **EXAMPLE 1** The graph of a function f is given in Figure 1. Use it to sketch the graph of the derivative f'.

FIGURE 1

SOLUTION We can estimate the value of the derivative at any value of x by drawing the tangent at the point $(x, f(x))$ and estimating its slope. For instance, for $x = 5$ we draw the tangent at P in Figure 2(a) and estimate its slope to be about $\frac{3}{2}$, so $f'(5) \approx 1.5$. This allows us to plot the point $P'(5, 1.5)$ on the graph of f' directly beneath P. Repeating this procedure at several points, we get the graph shown in Figure 2(b). Notice that the tangents at A, B, and C are horizontal, so the derivative is 0 there and the graph of f' crosses the x-axis at the points A', B', and C', directly beneath A, B, and C. Between A and B the tangents have positive slope, so $f'(x)$ is positive there. But between B and C the tangents have negative slope, so $f'(x)$ is negative there.

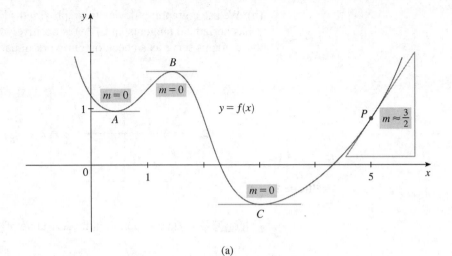

(a)

TEC Visual 2.8 shows an animation of Figure 2 for several functions.

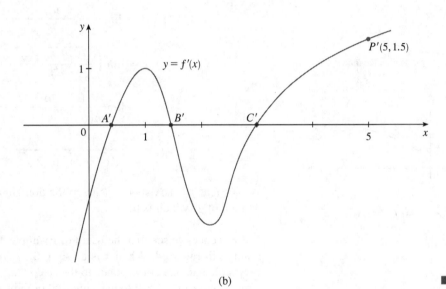

(b)

FIGURE 2

V **EXAMPLE 2**

(a) If $f(x) = x^3 - x$, find a formula for $f'(x)$.

(b) Illustrate by comparing the graphs of f and f'.

SOLUTION

(a) When using Equation 2 to compute a derivative, we must remember that the variable is h and that x is temporarily regarded as a constant during the calculation of the limit.

$$f'(x) = \lim_{h \to 0} \frac{f(x+h) - f(x)}{h} = \lim_{h \to 0} \frac{[(x+h)^3 - (x+h)] - [x^3 - x]}{h}$$

$$= \lim_{h \to 0} \frac{x^3 + 3x^2h + 3xh^2 + h^3 - x - h - x^3 + x}{h}$$

$$= \lim_{h \to 0} \frac{3x^2h + 3xh^2 + h^3 - h}{h} = \lim_{h \to 0} (3x^2 + 3xh + h^2 - 1) = 3x^2 - 1$$

(b) We use a graphing device to graph f and f' in Figure 3. Notice that $f'(x) = 0$ when f has horizontal tangents and $f'(x)$ is positive when the tangents have positive slope. So these graphs serve as a check on our work in part (a).

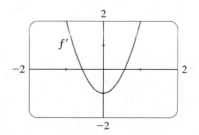

FIGURE 3

EXAMPLE 3 If $f(x) = \sqrt{x}$, find the derivative of f. State the domain of f'.

SOLUTION

$$f'(x) = \lim_{h \to 0} \frac{f(x+h) - f(x)}{h} = \lim_{h \to 0} \frac{\sqrt{x+h} - \sqrt{x}}{h}$$

Here we rationalize the numerator.

$$= \lim_{h \to 0} \left(\frac{\sqrt{x+h} - \sqrt{x}}{h} \cdot \frac{\sqrt{x+h} + \sqrt{x}}{\sqrt{x+h} + \sqrt{x}} \right)$$

$$= \lim_{h \to 0} \frac{(x+h) - x}{h(\sqrt{x+h} + \sqrt{x})} = \lim_{h \to 0} \frac{1}{\sqrt{x+h} + \sqrt{x}}$$

$$= \frac{1}{\sqrt{x} + \sqrt{x}} = \frac{1}{2\sqrt{x}}$$

We see that $f'(x)$ exists if $x > 0$, so the domain of f' is $(0, \infty)$. This is smaller than the domain of f, which is $[0, \infty)$.

(a) $f(x) = \sqrt{x}$

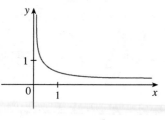

(b) $f'(x) = \dfrac{1}{2\sqrt{x}}$

FIGURE 4

Let's check to see that the result of Example 3 is reasonable by looking at the graphs of f and f' in Figure 4. When x is close to 0, $\sqrt{x}$ is also close to 0, so $f'(x) = 1/(2\sqrt{x})$ is very large and this corresponds to the steep tangent lines near $(0, 0)$ in Figure 4(a) and the large values of $f'(x)$ just to the right of 0 in Figure 4(b). When x is large, $f'(x)$ is very small and this corresponds to the flatter tangent lines at the far right of the graph of f and the horizontal asymptote of the graph of f'.

EXAMPLE 4 Find f' if $f(x) = \dfrac{1 - x}{2 + x}$.

SOLUTION

$$f'(x) = \lim_{h \to 0} \frac{f(x+h) - f(x)}{h} = \lim_{h \to 0} \frac{\dfrac{1 - (x+h)}{2 + (x+h)} - \dfrac{1 - x}{2 + x}}{h}$$

$$\frac{\dfrac{a}{b} - \dfrac{c}{d}}{e} = \frac{ad - bc}{bd} \cdot \frac{1}{e}$$

$$= \lim_{h \to 0} \frac{(1 - x - h)(2 + x) - (1 - x)(2 + x + h)}{h(2 + x + h)(2 + x)}$$

$$= \lim_{h \to 0} \frac{(2 - x - 2h - x^2 - xh) - (2 - x + h - x^2 - xh)}{h(2 + x + h)(2 + x)}$$

$$= \lim_{h \to 0} \frac{-3h}{h(2 + x + h)(2 + x)} = \lim_{h \to 0} \frac{-3}{(2 + x + h)(2 + x)} = -\frac{3}{(2 + x)^2}$$

Other Notations

If we use the traditional notation $y = f(x)$ to indicate that the independent variable is x and the dependent variable is y, then some common alternative notations for the derivative are as follows:

$$f'(x) = y' = \frac{dy}{dx} = \frac{df}{dx} = \frac{d}{dx} f(x) = Df(x) = D_x f(x)$$

The symbols D and d/dx are called **differentiation operators** because they indicate the operation of **differentiation**, which is the process of calculating a derivative.

The symbol dy/dx, which was introduced by Leibniz, should not be regarded as a ratio (for the time being); it is simply a synonym for $f'(x)$. Nonetheless, it is a very useful and suggestive notation, especially when used in conjunction with increment notation. Referring to Equation 2.7.6, we can rewrite the definition of derivative in Leibniz notation in the form

$$\frac{dy}{dx} = \lim_{\Delta x \to 0} \frac{\Delta y}{\Delta x}$$

If we want to indicate the value of a derivative dy/dx in Leibniz notation at a specific number a, we use the notation

$$\frac{dy}{dx}\bigg|_{x=a} \qquad \text{or} \qquad \frac{dy}{dx}\bigg]_{x=a}$$

which is a synonym for $f'(a)$.

---

3 **Definition** A function f is **differentiable at a** if $f'(a)$ exists. It is **differentiable on an open interval** (a, b) [or (a, ∞) or $(-\infty, a)$ or $(-\infty, \infty)$] if it is differentiable at every number in the interval.

V EXAMPLE 5 Where is the function $f(x) = |x|$ differentiable?

SOLUTION If $x > 0$, then $|x| = x$ and we can choose h small enough that $x + h > 0$ and hence $|x + h| = x + h$. Therefore, for $x > 0$, we have

$$f'(x) = \lim_{h \to 0} \frac{|x + h| - |x|}{h} = \lim_{h \to 0} \frac{(x + h) - x}{h}$$

$$= \lim_{h \to 0} \frac{h}{h} = \lim_{h \to 0} 1 = 1$$

and so f is differentiable for any $x > 0$.

Similarly, for $x < 0$ we have $|x| = -x$ and h can be chosen small enough that $x + h < 0$ and so $|x + h| = -(x + h)$. Therefore, for $x < 0$,

$$f'(x) = \lim_{h \to 0} \frac{|x + h| - |x|}{h} = \lim_{h \to 0} \frac{-(x + h) - (-x)}{h}$$

$$= \lim_{h \to 0} \frac{-h}{h} = \lim_{h \to 0} (-1) = -1$$

and so f is differentiable for any $x < 0$.

Leibniz

Gottfried Wilhelm Leibniz was born in Leipzig in 1646 and studied law, theology, philosophy, and mathematics at the university there, graduating with a bachelor's degree at age 17. After earning his doctorate in law at age 20, Leibniz entered the diplomatic service and spent most of his life traveling to the capitals of Europe on political missions. In particular, he worked to avert a French military threat against Germany and attempted to reconcile the Catholic and Protestant churches.

His serious study of mathematics did not begin until 1672 while he was on a diplomatic mission in Paris. There he built a calculating machine and met scientists, like Huygens, who directed his attention to the latest developments in mathematics and science. Leibniz sought to develop a symbolic logic and system of notation that would simplify logical reasoning. In particular, the version of calculus that he published in 1684 established the notation and the rules for finding derivatives that we use today.

Unfortunately, a dreadful priority dispute arose in the 1690s between the followers of Newton and those of Leibniz as to who had invented calculus first. Leibniz was even accused of plagiarism by members of the Royal Society in England. The truth is that each man invented calculus independently. Newton arrived at his version of calculus first but, because of his fear of controversy, did not publish it immediately. So Leibniz's 1684 account of calculus was the first to be published.

For $x = 0$ we have to investigate

$$f'(0) = \lim_{h \to 0} \frac{f(0 + h) - f(0)}{h}$$

$$= \lim_{h \to 0} \frac{|0 + h| - |0|}{h} \qquad \text{(if it exists)}$$

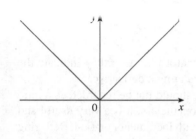

(a) $y = f(x) = |x|$

Let's compute the left and right limits separately:

$$\lim_{h \to 0^+} \frac{|0 + h| - |0|}{h} = \lim_{h \to 0^+} \frac{|h|}{h} = \lim_{h \to 0^+} \frac{h}{h} = \lim_{h \to 0^+} 1 = 1$$

and $\quad \lim_{h \to 0^-} \frac{|0 + h| - |0|}{h} = \lim_{h \to 0^-} \frac{|h|}{h} = \lim_{h \to 0^-} \frac{-h}{h} = \lim_{h \to 0^-} (-1) = -1$

Since these limits are different, $f'(0)$ does not exist. Thus f is differentiable at all x except 0.

A formula for f' is given by

$$f'(x) = \begin{cases} 1 & \text{if } x > 0 \\ -1 & \text{if } x < 0 \end{cases}$$

(b) $y = f'(x)$

FIGURE 5

and its graph is shown in Figure 5(b). The fact that $f'(0)$ does not exist is reflected geometrically in the fact that the curve $y = |x|$ does not have a tangent line at $(0, 0)$. [See Figure 5(a).]

Both continuity and differentiability are desirable properties for a function to have. The following theorem shows how these properties are related.

---

4 **Theorem** If f is differentiable at a, then f is continuous at a.

PROOF To prove that f is continuous at a, we have to show that $\lim_{x \to a} f(x) = f(a)$. We do this by showing that the difference $f(x) - f(a)$ approaches 0.

The given information is that f is differentiable at a, that is,

$$f'(a) = \lim_{x \to a} \frac{f(x) - f(a)}{x - a}$$

PS An important aspect of problem solving is trying to find a connection between the given and the unknown. See Step 2 (Think of a Plan) in *Principles of Problem Solving* on page 75.

exists (see Equation 2.7.5). To connect the given and the unknown, we divide and multiply $f(x) - f(a)$ by $x - a$ (which we can do when $x \neq a$):

$$f(x) - f(a) = \frac{f(x) - f(a)}{x - a} (x - a)$$

Thus, using the Product Law and (2.7.5), we can write

$$\lim_{x \to a} [f(x) - f(a)] = \lim_{x \to a} \frac{f(x) - f(a)}{x - a} (x - a)$$

$$= \lim_{x \to a} \frac{f(x) - f(a)}{x - a} \cdot \lim_{x \to a} (x - a)$$

$$= f'(a) \cdot 0 = 0$$

To use what we have just proved, we start with $f(x)$ and add and subtract $f(a)$:

$$\lim_{x \to a} f(x) = \lim_{x \to a} [f(a) + (f(x) - f(a))]$$

$$= \lim_{x \to a} f(a) + \lim_{x \to a} [f(x) - f(a)]$$

$$= f(a) + 0 = f(a)$$

Therefore f is continuous at a.

⊘   **NOTE** The converse of Theorem 4 is false; that is, there are functions that are continuous but not differentiable. For instance, the function $f(x) = |x|$ is continuous at 0 because

$$\lim_{x \to 0} f(x) = \lim_{x \to 0} |x| = 0 = f(0)$$

(See Example 7 in Section 2.3.) But in Example 5 we showed that f is not differentiable at 0.

How Can a Function Fail to Be Differentiable?

We saw that the function $y = |x|$ in Example 5 is not differentiable at 0 and Figure 5(a) shows that its graph changes direction abruptly when $x = 0$. In general, if the graph of a function f has a "corner" or "kink" in it, then the graph of f has no tangent at this point and f is not differentiable there. [In trying to compute $f'(a)$, we find that the left and right limits are different.]

    Theorem 4 gives another way for a function not to have a derivative. It says that if f is not continuous at a, then f is not differentiable at a. So at any discontinuity (for instance, a jump discontinuity) f fails to be differentiable.

    A third possibility is that the curve has a **vertical tangent line** when $x = a$; that is, f is continuous at a and

$$\lim_{x \to a} |f'(x)| = \infty$$

This means that the tangent lines become steeper and steeper as $x \to a$. Figure 6 shows one way that this can happen; Figure 7(c) shows another. Figure 7 illustrates the three possibilities that we have discussed.

FIGURE 6

FIGURE 7
Three ways for f not to be differentiable at a

(a) A corner   (b) A discontinuity   (c) A vertical tangent

A graphing calculator or computer provides another way of looking at differentiability. If f is differentiable at a, then when we zoom in toward the point $(a, f(a))$ the graph straightens out and appears more and more like a line. (See Figure 8. We saw a specific example of this in Figure 2 in Section 2.7.) But no matter how much we zoom in toward a point like the ones in Figures 6 and 7(a), we can't eliminate the sharp point or corner (see Figure 9).

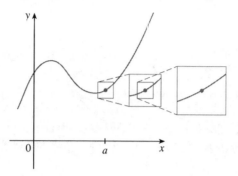

FIGURE 8
f is differentiable at a.

FIGURE 9
f is not differentiable at a.

Higher Derivatives

If f is a differentiable function, then its derivative f' is also a function, so f' may have a derivative of its own, denoted by $(f')' = f''$. This new function f'' is called the **second derivative** of f because it is the derivative of the derivative of f. Using Leibniz notation, we write the second derivative of $y = f(x)$ as

$$\frac{d}{dx}\left(\frac{dy}{dx}\right) = \frac{d^2y}{dx^2}$$

EXAMPLE 6 If $f(x) = x^3 - x$, find and interpret $f''(x)$.

SOLUTION In Example 2 we found that the first derivative is $f'(x) = 3x^2 - 1$. So the second derivative is

$$f''(x) = (f')'(x) = \lim_{h \to 0} \frac{f'(x+h) - f'(x)}{h}$$

$$= \lim_{h \to 0} \frac{[3(x+h)^2 - 1] - [3x^2 - 1]}{h}$$

$$= \lim_{h \to 0} \frac{3x^2 + 6xh + 3h^2 - 1 - 3x^2 + 1}{h}$$

$$= \lim_{h \to 0} (6x + 3h) = 6x$$

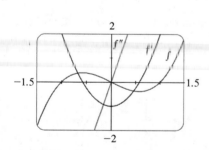

FIGURE 10

TEC In Module 2.8 you can see how changing the coefficients of a polynomial f affects the appearance of the graphs of f, f', and f''.

The graphs of f, f', and f'' are shown in Figure 10.

We can interpret $f''(x)$ as the slope of the curve $y = f'(x)$ at the point $(x, f'(x))$. In other words, it is the rate of change of the slope of the original curve $y = f(x)$.

Notice from Figure 10 that $f''(x)$ is negative when $y = f'(x)$ has negative slope and positive when $y = f'(x)$ has positive slope. So the graphs serve as a check on our calculations.

In general, we can interpret a second derivative as a rate of change of a rate of change. The most familiar example of this is *acceleration*, which we define as follows.

If $s = s(t)$ is the position function of an object that moves in a straight line, we know that its first derivative represents the velocity $v(t)$ of the object as a function of time:

$$v(t) = s'(t) = \frac{ds}{dt}$$

The instantaneous rate of change of velocity with respect to time is called the **acceleration** $a(t)$ of the object. Thus the acceleration function is the derivative of the velocity function and is therefore the second derivative of the position function:

$$a(t) = v'(t) = s''(t)$$

or, in Leibniz notation,

$$a = \frac{dv}{dt} = \frac{d^2s}{dt^2}$$

The **third derivative** f''' is the derivative of the second derivative: $f''' = (f'')'$. So $f'''(x)$ can be interpreted as the slope of the curve $y = f''(x)$ or as the rate of change of $f''(x)$. If $y = f(x)$, then alternative notations for the third derivative are

$$y''' = f'''(x) = \frac{d}{dx}\left(\frac{d^2y}{dx^2}\right) = \frac{d^3y}{dx^3}$$

The process can be continued. The fourth derivative f'''' is usually denoted by $f^{(4)}$. In general, the nth derivative of f is denoted by $f^{(n)}$ and is obtained from f by differentiating n times. If $y = f(x)$, we write

$$y^{(n)} = f^{(n)}(x) = \frac{d^n y}{dx^n}$$

EXAMPLE 7 If $f(x) = x^3 - x$, find $f'''(x)$ and $f^{(4)}(x)$.

SOLUTION In Example 6 we found that $f''(x) = 6x$. The graph of the second derivative has equation $y = 6x$ and so it is a straight line with slope 6. Since the derivative $f'''(x)$ is the slope of $f''(x)$, we have

$$f'''(x) = 6$$

for all values of x. So f''' is a constant function and its graph is a horizontal line. Therefore, for all values of x,

$$f^{(4)}(x) = 0$$

We can also interpret the third derivative physically in the case where the function is the position function $s = s(t)$ of an object that moves along a straight line. Because $s''' = (s'')' = a'$, the third derivative of the position function is the derivative of the acceleration function and is called the **jerk**:

$$j = \frac{da}{dt} = \frac{d^3s}{dt^3}$$

Thus the jerk j is the rate of change of acceleration. It is aptly named because a large jerk means a sudden change in acceleration, which causes an abrupt movement in a vehicle.

We have seen that one application of second and third derivatives occurs in analyzing the motion of objects using acceleration and jerk. We will investigate another application of second derivatives in Section 4.3, where we show how knowledge of f'' gives us information about the shape of the graph of f. In Chapter 11 we will see how second and higher derivatives enable us to represent functions as sums of infinite series.

1–2 Use the given graph to estimate the value of each derivative. Then sketch the graph of f'.

1. (a) $f'(-3)$
(b) $f'(-2)$
(c) $f'(-1)$
(d) $f'(0)$
(e) $f'(1)$
(f) $f'(2)$
(g) $f'(3)$

2. (a) $f'(0)$
(b) $f'(1)$
(c) $f'(2)$
(d) $f'(3)$
(e) $f'(4)$
(f) $f'(5)$
(g) $f'(6)$
(h) $f'(7)$

3. Match the graph of each function in (a)–(d) with the graph of its derivative in I–IV. Give reasons for your choices.

(a)

(b)

(c)

(d)

I

II

III

IV

4–11 Trace or copy the graph of the given function f. (Assume that the axes have equal scales.) Then use the method of Example 1 to sketch the graph of f' below it.

4.

5.

6.

7.

8.

9.

10.

11.

12. Shown is the graph of the population function $P(t)$ for yeast cells in a laboratory culture. Use the method of Example 1 to

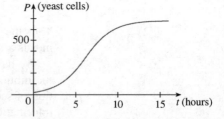

graph the derivative $P'(t)$. What does the graph of P' tell us about the yeast population?

13. A rechargeable battery is plugged into a charger. The graph shows $C(t)$, the percentage of full capacity that the battery reaches as a function of time t elapsed (in hours).

(a) What is the meaning of the derivative $C'(t)$?

(b) Sketch the graph of $C'(t)$. What does the graph tell you?

14. The graph (from the US Department of Energy) shows how driving speed affects gas mileage. Fuel economy F is measured in miles per gallon and speed v is measured in miles per hour.

(a) What is the meaning of the derivative $F'(v)$?

(b) Sketch the graph of $F'(v)$.

(c) At what speed should you drive if you want to save on gas?

15. The graph shows how the average age of first marriage of Japanese men varied in the last half of the 20th century. Sketch the graph of the derivative function $M'(t)$. During which years was the derivative negative?

16–18 Make a careful sketch of the graph of f and below it sketch the graph of f' in the same manner as in Exercises 4–11. Can you guess a formula for $f'(x)$ from its graph?

16. $f(x) = \sin x$

17. $f(x) = e^x$

18. $f(x) = \ln x$

19. Let $f(x) = x^2$.

(a) Estimate the values of $f'(0)$, $f'(\frac{1}{2})$, $f'(1)$, and $f'(2)$ by using a graphing device to zoom in on the graph of f.

(b) Use symmetry to deduce the values of $f'(-\frac{1}{2})$, $f'(-1)$, and $f'(-2)$.

(c) Use the results from parts (a) and (b) to guess a formula for $f'(x)$.

(d) Use the definition of derivative to prove that your guess in part (c) is correct.

20. Let $f(x) = x^3$.

(a) Estimate the values of $f'(0)$, $f'(\frac{1}{2})$, $f'(1)$, $f'(2)$, and $f'(3)$ by using a graphing device to zoom in on the graph of f.

(b) Use symmetry to deduce the values of $f'(-\frac{1}{2})$, $f'(-1)$, $f'(-2)$, and $f'(-3)$.

(c) Use the values from parts (a) and (b) to graph f'.

(d) Guess a formula for $f'(x)$.

(e) Use the definition of derivative to prove that your guess in part (d) is correct.

21–31 Find the derivative of the function using the definition of derivative. State the domain of the function and the domain of its derivative.

21. $f(x) = \frac{1}{2}x - \frac{1}{3}$ **22.** $f(x) = mx + b$

23. $f(t) = 5t - 9t^2$ **24.** $f(x) = 1.5x^2 - x + 3.7$

25. $f(x) = x^3 - 3x + 5$ **26.** $f(x) = x + \sqrt{x}$

27. $g(x) = \sqrt{9 - x}$ **28.** $f(x) = \dfrac{x^2 - 1}{2x - 3}$

29. $G(t) = \dfrac{1 - 2t}{3 + t}$ **30.** $f(x) = x^{3/2}$

31. $f(x) = x^4$

32. (a) Sketch the graph of $f(x) = \sqrt{6 - x}$ by starting with the graph of $y = \sqrt{x}$ and using the transformations of Section 1.3.

(b) Use the graph from part (a) to sketch the graph of f'.

(c) Use the definition of a derivative to find $f'(x)$. What are the domains of f and f'?

(d) Use a graphing device to graph f' and compare with your sketch in part (b).

33. (a) If $f(x) = x^4 + 2x$, find $f'(x)$.

(b) Check to see that your answer to part (a) is reasonable by comparing the graphs of f and f'.

34. (a) If $f(x) = x + 1/x$, find $f'(x)$.

(b) Check to see that your answer to part (a) is reasonable by comparing the graphs of f and f'.

35. The unemployment rate $U(t)$ varies with time. The table gives the percentage of unemployed in the Australian labor force measured at midyear from 1995 to 2004.

t	$U(t)$	t	$U(t)$
1995	8.1	2000	6.2
1996	8.0	2001	6.9
1997	8.2	2002	6.5
1998	7.9	2003	6.2
1999	6.7	2004	5.6

(a) What is the meaning of $U'(t)$? What are its units?
(b) Construct a table of estimated values for $U'(t)$.

36. Let $P(t)$ be the percentage of the population of the Philippines over the age of 60 at time t. The table gives projections of values of this function from 1995 to 2020.

t	$P(t)$	t	$P(t)$
1995	5.2	2010	6.7
2000	5.5	2015	7.7
2005	6.1	2020	8.9

(a) What is the meaning of $P'(t)$? What are its units?
(b) Construct a table of estimated values for $P'(t)$.
(c) Graph P and P'.

37–40 The graph of f is given. State, with reasons, the numbers at which f is not differentiable.

37.

38.

39.

40.

41. Graph the function $f(x) = x + \sqrt{|x|}$. Zoom in repeatedly, first toward the point $(-1, 0)$ and then toward the origin. What is different about the behavior of f in the vicinity of these two points? What do you conclude about the differentiability of f?

42. Zoom in toward the points $(1, 0)$, $(0, 1)$, and $(-1, 0)$ on the graph of the function $g(x) = (x^2 - 1)^{2/3}$. What do you notice? Account for what you see in terms of the differentiability of g.

43. The figure shows the graphs of f, f', and f''. Identify each curve, and explain your choices.

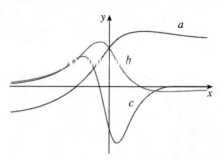

44. The figure shows graphs of f, f', f'', and f'''. Identify each curve, and explain your choices.

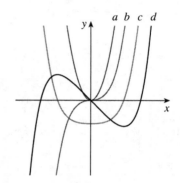

45. The figure shows the graphs of three functions. One is the position function of a car, one is the velocity of the car, and one is its acceleration. Identify each curve, and explain your choices.

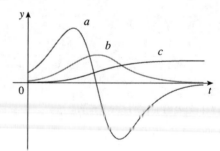

46. The figure shows the graphs of four functions. One is the position function of a car, one is the velocity of the car, one is its acceleration, and one is its jerk. Identify each curve, and explain your choices.

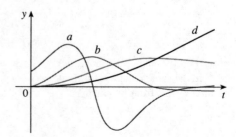

47–48 Use the definition of a derivative to find $f'(x)$ and $f''(x)$. Then graph f, f', and f'' on a common screen and check to see if your answers are reasonable.

47. $f(x) = 3x^2 + 2x + 1$ **48.** $f(x) = x^3 - 3x$

---

49. If $f(x) = 2x^2 - x^3$, find $f'(x)$, $f''(x)$, $f'''(x)$, and $f^{(4)}(x)$. Graph f, f', f'', and f''' on a common screen. Are the graphs consistent with the geometric interpretations of these derivatives?

50. (a) The graph of a position function of a car is shown, where s is measured in meters and t in seconds. Use it to graph the velocity and acceleration of the car. What is the acceleration at $t = 10$ seconds?

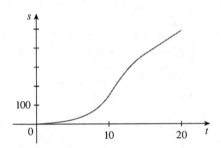

(b) Use the acceleration curve from part (a) to estimate the jerk at $t = 10$ seconds. What are the units for jerk?

51. Let $f(x) = \sqrt[3]{x}$.
(a) If $a \neq 0$, use Equation 2.7.5 to find $f'(a)$.
(b) Show that $f'(0)$ does not exist.
(c) Show that $y = \sqrt[3]{x}$ has a vertical tangent line at $(0, 0)$. (Recall the shape of the graph of f. See Figure 13 in Section 1.2.)

52. (a) If $g(x) = x^{2/3}$, show that $g'(0)$ does not exist.
(b) If $a \neq 0$, find $g'(a)$.
(c) Show that $y = x^{2/3}$ has a vertical tangent line at $(0, 0)$.
(d) Illustrate part (c) by graphing $y = x^{2/3}$.

53. Show that the function $f(x) = |x - 6|$ is not differentiable at 6. Find a formula for f' and sketch its graph.

54. Where is the greatest integer function $f(x) = [\![x]\!]$ not differentiable? Find a formula for f' and sketch its graph.

55. (a) Sketch the graph of the function $f(x) = x\,|x|$.
(b) For what values of x is f differentiable?
(c) Find a formula for f'.

56. The **left-hand** and **right-hand derivatives** of f at a are defined by

$$f'_-(a) = \lim_{h \to 0^-} \frac{f(a + h) - f(a)}{h}$$

and $$f'_+(a) = \lim_{h \to 0^+} \frac{f(a + h) - f(a)}{h}$$

if these limits exist. Then $f'(a)$ exists if and only if these one-sided derivatives exist and are equal.
(a) Find $f'_-(4)$ and $f'_+(4)$ for the function

$$f(x) = \begin{cases} 0 & \text{if } x \leq 0 \\ 5 - x & \text{if } 0 < x < 4 \\ \dfrac{1}{5 - x} & \text{if } x \geq 4 \end{cases}$$

(b) Sketch the graph of f.
(c) Where is f discontinuous?
(d) Where is f not differentiable?

57. Recall that a function f is called *even* if $f(-x) = f(x)$ for all x in its domain and *odd* if $f(-x) = -f(x)$ for all such x. Prove each of the following.
(a) The derivative of an even function is an odd function.
(b) The derivative of an odd function is an even function.

58. When you turn on a hot-water faucet, the temperature T of the water depends on how long the water has been running.
(a) Sketch a possible graph of T as a function of the time t that has elapsed since the faucet was turned on.
(b) Describe how the rate of change of T with respect to t varies as t increases.
(c) Sketch a graph of the derivative of T.

59. Let ℓ be the tangent line to the parabola $y = x^2$ at the point $(1, 1)$. The *angle of inclination* of ℓ is the angle ϕ that ℓ makes with the positive direction of the x-axis. Calculate ϕ correct to the nearest degree.

---

2   Review

Concept Check

1. Explain what each of the following means and illustrate with a sketch.
(a) $\lim_{x \to a} f(x) = L$ (b) $\lim_{x \to a^+} f(x) = L$
(c) $\lim_{x \to a^-} f(x) = L$ (d) $\lim_{x \to a} f(x) = \infty$
(e) $\lim_{x \to \infty} f(x) = L$

2. Describe several ways in which a limit can fail to exist. Illustrate with sketches.

3. State the following Limit Laws.
(a) Sum Law   (b) Difference Law
(c) Constant Multiple Law   (d) Product Law
(e) Quotient Law   (f) Power Law
(g) Root Law

4. What does the Squeeze Theorem say?

5. (a) What does it mean to say that the line $x = a$ is a vertical asymptote of the curve $y = f(x)$? Draw curves to illustrate the various possibilities.
   (b) What does it mean to say that the line $y = L$ is a horizontal asymptote of the curve $y = f(x)$? Draw curves to illustrate the various possibilities.

6. Which of the following curves have vertical asymptotes? Which have horizontal asymptotes?
   (a) $y = x^4$
   (b) $y = \sin x$
   (c) $y = \tan x$
   (d) $y = \tan^{-1} x$
   (e) $y = e^x$
   (f) $y = \ln x$
   (g) $y = 1/x$
   (h) $y = \sqrt{x}$

7. (a) What does it mean for f to be continuous at a?
   (b) What does it mean for f to be continuous on the interval $(-\infty, \infty)$? What can you say about the graph of such a function?

8. What does the Intermediate Value Theorem say?

9. Write an expression for the slope of the tangent line to the curve $y = f(x)$ at the point $(a, f(a))$.

10. Suppose an object moves along a straight line with position $f(t)$ at time t. Write an expression for the instantaneous veloc-ity of the object at time $t = a$. How can you interpret this velocity in terms of the graph of f?

11. If $y = f(x)$ and x changes from x_1 to x_2, write expressions for the following.
   (a) The average rate of change of y with respect to x over the interval $[x_1, x_2]$.
   (b) The instantaneous rate of change of y with respect to x at $x = x_1$.

12. Define the derivative $f'(a)$. Discuss two ways of interpreting this number.

13. Define the second derivative of f. If $f(t)$ is the position function of a particle, how can you interpret the second derivative?

14. (a) What does it mean for f to be differentiable at a?
   (b) What is the relation between the differentiability and continuity of a function?
   (c) Sketch the graph of a function that is continuous but not differentiable at $a = 2$.

15. Describe several ways in which a function can fail to be differentiable. Illustrate with sketches.

True-False Quiz

Determine whether the statement is true or false. If it is true, explain why. If it is false, explain why or give an example that disproves the statement.

1. $\lim\limits_{x \to 4} \left(\dfrac{2x}{x-4} - \dfrac{8}{x-4} \right) = \lim\limits_{x \to 4} \dfrac{2x}{x-4} - \lim\limits_{x \to 4} \dfrac{8}{x-4}$

2. $\lim\limits_{x \to 1} \dfrac{x^2 + 6x - 7}{x^2 + 5x - 6} = \dfrac{\lim\limits_{x \to 1} (x^2 + 6x - 7)}{\lim\limits_{x \to 1} (x^2 + 5x - 6)}$

3. $\lim\limits_{x \to 1} \dfrac{x - 3}{x^2 + 2x - 4} = \dfrac{\lim\limits_{x \to 1} (x - 3)}{\lim\limits_{x \to 1} (x^2 + 2x - 4)}$

4. If $\lim\limits_{x \to 5} f(x) = 2$ and $\lim\limits_{x \to 5} g(x) = 0$, then $\lim\limits_{x \to 5} [f(x)/g(x)]$ does not exist.

5. If $\lim\limits_{x \to 5} f(x) = 0$ and $\lim\limits_{x \to 5} g(x) = 0$, then $\lim\limits_{x \to 5} [f(x)/g(x)]$ does not exist.

6. If neither $\lim\limits_{x \to a} f(x)$ nor $\lim\limits_{x \to a} g(x)$ exists, then $\lim\limits_{x \to a} [f(x) + g(x)]$ does not exist.

7. If $\lim\limits_{x \to a} f(x)$ exists but $\lim\limits_{x \to a} g(x)$ does not exist, then $\lim\limits_{x \to a} [f(x) + g(x)]$ does not exist.

8. If $\lim\limits_{x \to 6} [f(x) g(x)]$ exists, then the limit must be $f(6) g(6)$.

9. If p is a polynomial, then $\lim\limits_{x \to b} p(x) = p(b)$.

10. If $\lim\limits_{x \to 0} f(x) = \infty$ and $\lim\limits_{x \to 0} g(x) = \infty$, then $\lim\limits_{x \to 0} [f(x) - g(x)] = 0$.

11. A function can have two different horizontal asymptotes.

12. If f has domain $[0, \infty)$ and has no horizontal asymptote, then $\lim\limits_{x \to \infty} f(x) = \infty$ or $\lim\limits_{x \to \infty} f(x) = -\infty$.

13. If the line $x = 1$ is a vertical asymptote of $y = f(x)$, then f is not defined at 1.

14. If $f(1) > 0$ and $f(3) < 0$, then there exists a number c between 1 and 3 such that $f(c) = 0$.

15. If f is continuous at 5 and $f(5) = 2$ and $f(4) = 3$, then $\lim\limits_{x \to 2} f(4x^2 - 11) = 2$.

16. If f is continuous on $[-1, 1]$ and $f(-1) = 4$ and $f(1) = 3$, then there exists a number r such that $|r| < 1$ and $f(r) = \pi$.

17. Let f be a function such that $\lim\limits_{x \to 0} f(x) = 6$. Then there exists a number δ such that if $0 < |x| < \delta$, then $|f(x) - 6| < 1$.

18. If $f(x) > 1$ for all x and $\lim\limits_{x \to 0} f(x)$ exists, then $\lim\limits_{x \to 0} f(x) > 1$.

19. If f is continuous at a, then f is differentiable at a.

20. If $f'(r)$ exists, then $\lim\limits_{x \to r} f(x) = f(r)$.

21. $\dfrac{d^2 y}{dx^2} = \left(\dfrac{dy}{dx} \right)^2$

22. The equation $x^{10} - 10x^2 + 5 = 0$ has a root in the interval $(0, 2)$.

23. If f is continuous at a, so is $|f|$.

24. If $|f|$ is continuous at a, so is f.

Exercises

1. The graph of f is given.

(a) Find each limit, or explain why it does not exist.

    (i) $\displaystyle\lim_{x \to 2^+} f(x)$ (ii) $\displaystyle\lim_{x \to -3^+} f(x)$

    (iii) $\displaystyle\lim_{x \to -3} f(x)$ (iv) $\displaystyle\lim_{x \to 4} f(x)$

    (v) $\displaystyle\lim_{x \to 0} f(x)$ (vi) $\displaystyle\lim_{x \to 2^-} f(x)$

    (vii) $\displaystyle\lim_{x \to \infty} f(x)$ (viii) $\displaystyle\lim_{x \to -\infty} f(x)$

(b) State the equations of the horizontal asymptotes.

(c) State the equations of the vertical asymptotes.

(d) At what numbers is f discontinuous? Explain.

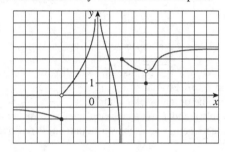

2. Sketch the graph of an example of a function f that satisfies all of the following conditions:

$$\lim_{x \to -\infty} f(x) = -2, \quad \lim_{x \to \infty} f(x) = 0, \quad \lim_{x \to -3} f(x) = \infty,$$

$$\lim_{x \to 3^-} f(x) = -\infty, \quad \lim_{x \to 3^+} f(x) = 2,$$

f is continuous from the right at 3

3–20 Find the limit.

3. $\displaystyle\lim_{x \to 1} e^{x^3 - x}$

4. $\displaystyle\lim_{x \to 3} \frac{x^2 - 9}{x^2 + 2x - 3}$

5. $\displaystyle\lim_{x \to -3} \frac{x^2 - 9}{x^2 + 2x - 3}$

6. $\displaystyle\lim_{x \to 1^+} \frac{x^2 - 9}{x^2 + 2x - 3}$

7. $\displaystyle\lim_{h \to 0} \frac{(h - 1)^3 + 1}{h}$

8. $\displaystyle\lim_{t \to 2} \frac{t^2 - 4}{t^3 - 8}$

9. $\displaystyle\lim_{r \to 9} \frac{\sqrt{r}}{(r - 9)^4}$

10. $\displaystyle\lim_{v \to 4^+} \frac{4 - v}{|4 - v|}$

11. $\displaystyle\lim_{u \to 1} \frac{u^4 - 1}{u^3 + 5u^2 - 6u}$

12. $\displaystyle\lim_{x \to 3} \frac{\sqrt{x + 6} - x}{x^3 - 3x^2}$

13. $\displaystyle\lim_{x \to \infty} \frac{\sqrt{x^2 - 9}}{2x - 6}$

14. $\displaystyle\lim_{x \to -\infty} \frac{\sqrt{x^2 - 9}}{2x - 6}$

15. $\displaystyle\lim_{x \to \pi^-} \ln(\sin x)$

16. $\displaystyle\lim_{x \to -\infty} \frac{1 - 2x^2 - x^4}{5 + x - 3x^4}$

17. $\displaystyle\lim_{x \to \infty} \left(\sqrt{x^2 + 4x + 1} - x\right)$

18. $\displaystyle\lim_{x \to \infty} e^{x - x^2}$

19. $\displaystyle\lim_{x \to 0^+} \tan^{-1}(1/x)$

20. $\displaystyle\lim_{x \to 1} \left(\frac{1}{x - 1} + \frac{1}{x^2 - 3x + 2}\right)$

⊞ **21–22** Use graphs to discover the asymptotes of the curve. Then prove what you have discovered.

21. $y = \dfrac{\cos^2 x}{x^2}$

22. $y = \sqrt{x^2 + x + 1} - \sqrt{x^2 - x}$

23. If $2x - 1 \le f(x) \le x^2$ for $0 < x < 3$, find $\lim_{x \to 1} f(x)$.

24. Prove that $\lim_{x \to 0} x^2 \cos(1/x^2) = 0$.

25–28 Prove the statement using the precise definition of a limit.

25. $\displaystyle\lim_{x \to 2} (14 - 5x) = 4$

26. $\displaystyle\lim_{x \to 0} \sqrt[3]{x} = 0$

27. $\displaystyle\lim_{x \to 2} (x^2 - 3x) = -2$

28. $\displaystyle\lim_{x \to 4^+} \frac{2}{\sqrt{x - 4}} = \infty$

29. Let

$$f(x) = \begin{cases} \sqrt{-x} & \text{if } x < 0 \\ 3 - x & \text{if } 0 \le x < 3 \\ (x - 3)^2 & \text{if } x > 3 \end{cases}$$

(a) Evaluate each limit, if it exists.

    (i) $\displaystyle\lim_{x \to 0^+} f(x)$ (ii) $\displaystyle\lim_{x \to 0^-} f(x)$ (iii) $\displaystyle\lim_{x \to 0} f(x)$

    (iv) $\displaystyle\lim_{x \to 3^-} f(x)$ (v) $\displaystyle\lim_{x \to 3^+} f(x)$ (vi) $\displaystyle\lim_{x \to 3} f(x)$

(b) Where is f discontinuous?

(c) Sketch the graph of f.

30. Let

$$g(x) = \begin{cases} 2x - x^2 & \text{if } 0 \le x \le 2 \\ 2 - x & \text{if } 2 < x \le 3 \\ x - 4 & \text{if } 3 < x < 4 \\ \pi & \text{if } x \ge 4 \end{cases}$$

(a) For each of the numbers 2, 3, and 4, discover whether g is continuous from the left, continuous from the right, or continuous at the number.

(b) Sketch the graph of g.

31–32 Show that the function is continuous on its domain. State the domain.

31. $h(x) = xe^{\sin x}$

32. $g(x) = \dfrac{\sqrt{x^2 - 9}}{x^2 - 2}$

33–34 Use the Intermediate Value Theorem to show that there is a root of the equation in the given interval.

33. $x^5 - x^3 + 3x - 5 = 0, \quad (1, 2)$

34. $\cos\sqrt{x} = e^x - 2, \quad (0, 1)$

---

35. (a) Find the slope of the tangent line to the curve $y = 9 - 2x^2$ at the point $(2, 1)$.
     (b) Find an equation of this tangent line.

36. Find equations of the tangent lines to the curve

$$y = \frac{2}{1 - 3x}$$

at the points with x-coordinates 0 and -1.

37. The displacement (in meters) of an object moving in a straight line is given by $s = 1 + 2t + \frac{1}{4}t^2$, where t is measured in seconds.
     (a) Find the average velocity over each time period.
        (i) $[1, 3]$ (ii) $[1, 2]$
        (iii) $[1, 1.5]$ (iv) $[1, 1.1]$
     (b) Find the instantaneous velocity when $t = 1$.

38. According to Boyle's Law, if the temperature of a confined gas is held fixed, then the product of the pressure P and the volume V is a constant. Suppose that, for a certain gas, $PV = 4000$, where P is measured in pascals and V is measured in liters.
     (a) Find the average rate of change of P as V increases from 3 L to 4 L.
     (b) Express V as a function of P and show that the instantaneous rate of change of V with respect to P is inversely proportional to the square of P.

39. (a) Use the definition of a derivative to find $f'(2)$, where $f(x) = x^3 - 2x$.
     (b) Find an equation of the tangent line to the curve $y = x^3 - 2x$ at the point $(2, 4)$.
      (c) Illustrate part (b) by graphing the curve and the tangent line on the same screen.

40. Find a function f and a number a such that

$$\lim_{h \to 0} \frac{(2 + h)^6 - 64}{h} = f'(a)$$

41. The total cost of repaying a student loan at an interest rate of $r\%$ per year is $C = f(r)$.
     (a) What is the meaning of the derivative $f'(r)$? What are its units?
     (b) What does the statement $f'(10) = 1200$ mean?
     (c) Is $f'(r)$ always positive or does it change sign?

42–44 Trace or copy the graph of the function. Then sketch a graph of its derivative directly beneath.

42.

43.

44.

---

45. (a) If $f(x) = \sqrt{3 - 5x}$, use the definition of a derivative to find $f'(x)$.
     (b) Find the domains of f and f'.
      (c) Graph f and f' on a common screen. Compare the graphs to see whether your answer to part (a) is reasonable.

46. (a) Find the asymptotes of the graph of $f(x) = \dfrac{4 - x}{3 + x}$ and use them to sketch the graph.
     (b) Use your graph from part (a) to sketch the graph of f'.
     (c) Use the definition of a derivative to find $f'(x)$.
      (d) Use a graphing device to graph f' and compare with your sketch in part (b).

47. The graph of f is shown. State, with reasons, the numbers at which f is not differentiable.

48. The figure shows the graphs of f, f', and f''. Identify each curve, and explain your choices.

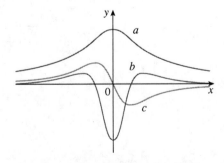

49. Let $E(t)$ be the value of the euro (the European currency) in terms of the US dollar at time t. The table gives values of this function, as of midyear, from 2000 to 2004. Interpret $E'(2002)$ and estimate its value.

t	2000	2001	2002	2003	2004
$E(t)$	0.955	0.847	0.986	1.149	1.218

50. The *total fertility rate* at time t, denoted by $F(t)$, is an estimate of the average number of children born to each woman (assuming that current birth rates remain constant). The graph of the total fertility rate in the United States shows the fluctuations from 1940 to 1990.
   (a) Estimate the values of $F'(1950)$, $F'(1965)$, and $F'(1987)$.
   (b) What are the meanings of these derivatives?
   (c) Can you suggest reasons for the values of these derivatives?

51. Suppose that $|f(x)| \leq g(x)$ for all x, where $\lim_{x \to a} g(x) = 0$. Find $\lim_{x \to a} f(x)$.

52. Let $f(x) = [\![x]\!] + [\![-x]\!]$.
   (a) For what values of a does $\lim_{x \to a} f(x)$ exist?
   (b) At what numbers is f discontinuous?

Problems Plus

In our discussion of the principles of problem solving we considered the problem-solving strategy of *introducing something extra* (see page 75). In the following example we show how this principle is sometimes useful when we evaluate limits. The idea is to change the variable—to introduce a new variable that is related to the original variable—in such a way as to make the problem simpler. Later, in Section 5.5, we will make more extensive use of this general idea.

EXAMPLE 1 Evaluate $\lim\limits_{x \to 0} \dfrac{\sqrt[3]{1 + cx} - 1}{x}$, where c is a constant.

SOLUTION As it stands, this limit looks challenging. In Section 2.3 we evaluated several limits in which both numerator and denominator approached 0. There our strategy was to perform some sort of algebraic manipulation that led to a simplifying cancellation, but here it's not clear what kind of algebra is necessary.

So we introduce a new variable t by the equation

$$t = \sqrt[3]{1 + cx}$$

We also need to express x in terms of t, so we solve this equation:

$$t^3 = 1 + cx \qquad x = \frac{t^3 - 1}{c} \quad \text{(if } c \neq 0\text{)}$$

Notice that $x \to 0$ is equivalent to $t \to 1$. This allows us to convert the given limit into one involving the variable t:

$$\lim_{x \to 0} \frac{\sqrt[3]{1 + cx} - 1}{x} = \lim_{t \to 1} \frac{t - 1}{(t^3 - 1)/c}$$

$$= \lim_{t \to 1} \frac{c(t - 1)}{t^3 - 1}$$

The change of variable allowed us to replace a relatively complicated limit by a simpler one of a type that we have seen before. Factoring the denominator as a difference of cubes, we get

$$\lim_{t \to 1} \frac{c(t - 1)}{t^3 - 1} = \lim_{t \to 1} \frac{c(t - 1)}{(t - 1)(t^2 + t + 1)}$$

$$= \lim_{t \to 1} \frac{c}{t^2 + t + 1} = \frac{c}{3}$$

In making the change of variable we had to rule out the case $c = 0$. But if $c = 0$, the function is 0 for all nonzero x and so its limit is 0. Therefore, in all cases, the limit is $c/3$.

The following problems are meant to test and challenge your problem-solving skills. Some of them require a considerable amount of time to think through, so don't be discouraged if you can't solve them right away. If you get stuck, you might find it helpful to refer to the discussion of the principles of problem solving on page 75.

Problems

1. Evaluate $\lim\limits_{x \to 1} \dfrac{\sqrt[3]{x} - 1}{\sqrt{x} - 1}$.

2. Find numbers a and b such that $\lim\limits_{x \to 0} \dfrac{\sqrt{ax + b} - 2}{x} = 1$.

3. Evaluate $\lim\limits_{x\to 0}\dfrac{|2x-1|-|2x+1|}{x}$.

4. The figure shows a point P on the parabola $y=x^2$ and the point Q where the perpendicular bisector of OP intersects the y-axis. As P approaches the origin along the parabola, what happens to Q? Does it have a limiting position? If so, find it.

5. Evaluate the following limits, if they exist, where $[\![x]\!]$ denotes the greatest integer function.

(a) $\lim\limits_{x\to 0}\dfrac{[\![x]\!]}{x}$ (b) $\lim\limits_{x\to 0} x[\![1/x]\!]$

6. Sketch the region in the plane defined by each of the following equations.

(a) $[\![x]\!]^2+[\![y]\!]^2=1$ (b) $[\![x]\!]^2-[\![y]\!]^2=3$ (c) $[\![x+y]\!]^2=1$ (d) $[\![x]\!]+[\![y]\!]=1$

7. Find all values of a such that f is continuous on $\mathbb{R}$:

$$f(x)=\begin{cases}x+1 & \text{if } x\leqslant a\\ x^2 & \text{if } x>a\end{cases}$$

8. A **fixed point** of a function f is a number c in its domain such that $f(c)=c$. (The function doesn't move c; it stays fixed.)

(a) Sketch the graph of a continuous function with domain $[0,1]$ whose range also lies in $[0,1]$. Locate a fixed point of f.

(b) Try to draw the graph of a continuous function with domain $[0,1]$ and range in $[0,1]$ that does *not* have a fixed point. What is the obstacle?

(c) Use the Intermediate Value Theorem to prove that any continuous function with domain $[0,1]$ and range in $[0,1]$ must have a fixed point.

9. If $\lim_{x\to a}[f(x)+g(x)]=2$ and $\lim_{x\to a}[f(x)-g(x)]=1$, find $\lim_{x\to a}[f(x)g(x)]$.

10. (a) The figure shows an isosceles triangle ABC with $\angle B=\angle C$. The bisector of angle B intersects the side AC at the point P. Suppose that the base BC remains fixed but the altitude $|AM|$ of the triangle approaches 0, so A approaches the midpoint M of BC. What happens to P during this process? Does it have a limiting position? If so, find it.

(b) Try to sketch the path traced out by P during this process. Then find an equation of this curve and use this equation to sketch the curve.

11. (a) If we start from $0°$ latitude and proceed in a westerly direction, we can let $T(x)$ denote the temperature at the point x at any given time. Assuming that T is a continuous function of x, show that at any fixed time there are at least two diametrically opposite points on the equator that have exactly the same temperature.

(b) Does the result in part (a) hold for points lying on any circle on the earth's surface?

(c) Does the result in part (a) hold for barometric pressure and for altitude above sea level?

12. If f is a differentiable function and $g(x)=xf(x)$, use the definition of a derivative to show that $g'(x)=xf'(x)+f(x)$.

13. Suppose f is a function that satisfies the equation

$$f(x+y)=f(x)+f(y)+x^2y+xy^2$$

for all real numbers x and y. Suppose also that

$$\lim\limits_{x\to 0}\dfrac{f(x)}{x}=1$$

(a) Find $f(0)$.   (b) Find $f'(0)$.   (c) Find $f'(x)$.

14. Suppose f is a function with the property that $|f(x)|\leqslant x^2$ for all x. Show that $f(0)=0$. Then show that $f'(0)=0$.

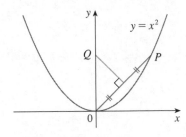

$y=x^2$

FIGURE FOR PROBLEM 4

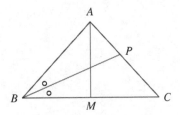

FIGURE FOR PROBLEM 10

3 Differentiation Rules

For a roller coaster ride to be smooth, the straight stretches of the track need to be connected to the curved segments so that there are no abrupt changes in direction. In the project on page 184 you will see how to design the first ascent and drop of a new coaster for a smooth ride.

We have seen how to interpret derivatives as slopes and rates of change. We have seen how to estimate derivatives of functions given by tables of values. We have learned how to graph derivatives of functions that are defined graphically. We have used the definition of a derivative to calculate the derivatives of functions defined by formulas. But it would be tedious if we always had to use the definition, so in this chapter we develop rules for finding derivatives without having to use the definition directly. These differentiation rules enable us to calculate with relative ease the derivatives of polynomials, rational functions, algebraic functions, exponential and logarithmic functions, and trigonometric and inverse trigonometric functions. We then use these rules to solve problems involving rates of change and the approximation of functions.

3.1   Derivatives of Polynomials and Exponential Functions

In this section we learn how to differentiate constant functions, power functions, polynomials, and exponential functions.

Let's start with the simplest of all functions, the constant function $f(x) = c$. The graph of this function is the horizontal line $y = c$, which has slope 0, so we must have $f'(x) = 0$. (See Figure 1.) A formal proof, from the definition of a derivative, is also easy:

$$f'(x) = \lim_{h \to 0} \frac{f(x+h) - f(x)}{h} = \lim_{h \to 0} \frac{c - c}{h} = \lim_{h \to 0} 0 = 0$$

In Leibniz notation, we write this rule as follows.

FIGURE 1
The graph of $f(x) = c$ is the line $y = c$, so $f'(x) = 0$.

Derivative of a Constant Function
$$\frac{d}{dx}(c) = 0$$

Power Functions

We next look at the functions $f(x) = x^n$, where n is a positive integer. If $n = 1$, the graph of $f(x) = x$ is the line $y = x$, which has slope 1. (See Figure 2.) So

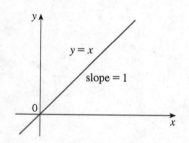

FIGURE 2
The graph of $f(x) = x$ is the line $y = x$, so $f'(x) = 1$.

$$\boxed{1} \qquad \frac{d}{dx}(x) = 1$$

(You can also verify Equation 1 from the definition of a derivative.) We have already investigated the cases $n = 2$ and $n = 3$. In fact, in Section 2.8 (Exercises 19 and 20) we found that

$$\boxed{2} \qquad \frac{d}{dx}(x^2) = 2x \qquad \frac{d}{dx}(x^3) = 3x^2$$

For $n = 4$ we find the derivative of $f(x) = x^4$ as follows:

$$f'(x) = \lim_{h \to 0} \frac{f(x+h) - f(x)}{h} = \lim_{h \to 0} \frac{(x+h)^4 - x^4}{h}$$

$$= \lim_{h \to 0} \frac{x^4 + 4x^3h + 6x^2h^2 + 4xh^3 + h^4 - x^4}{h}$$

$$= \lim_{h \to 0} \frac{4x^3h + 6x^2h^2 + 4xh^3 + h^4}{h}$$

$$= \lim_{h \to 0} (4x^3 + 6x^2h + 4xh^2 + h^3) = 4x^3$$

Thus

$$\boxed{3} \qquad \frac{d}{dx}(x^4) = 4x^3$$

Comparing the equations in $\boxed{1}$, $\boxed{2}$, and $\boxed{3}$, we see a pattern emerging. It seems to be a reasonable guess that, when n is a positive integer, $(d/dx)(x^n) = nx^{n-1}$. This turns out to be true.

The Power Rule If n is a positive integer, then

$$\frac{d}{dx}(x^n) = nx^{n-1}$$

FIRST PROOF The formula

$$x^n - a^n = (x - a)(x^{n-1} + x^{n-2}a + \cdots + xa^{n-2} + a^{n-1})$$

can be verified simply by multiplying out the right-hand side (or by summing the second factor as a geometric series). If $f(x) = x^n$, we can use Equation 2.7.5 for $f'(a)$ and the equation above to write

$$f'(a) = \lim_{x \to a} \frac{f(x) - f(a)}{x - a} = \lim_{x \to a} \frac{x^n - a^n}{x - a}$$

$$= \lim_{x \to a} (x^{n-1} + x^{n-2}a + \cdots + xa^{n-2} + a^{n-1})$$

$$= a^{n-1} + a^{n-2}a + \cdots + aa^{n-2} + a^{n-1}$$

$$= na^{n-1}$$

SECOND PROOF

$$f'(x) = \lim_{h \to 0} \frac{f(x + h) - f(x)}{h} = \lim_{h \to 0} \frac{(x + h)^n - x^n}{h}$$

The Binomial Theorem is given on Reference Page 1.

In finding the derivative of x^4 we had to expand $(x + h)^4$. Here we need to expand $(x + h)^n$ and we use the Binomial Theorem to do so:

$$f'(x) = \lim_{h \to 0} \frac{\left[x^n + nx^{n-1}h + \dfrac{n(n-1)}{2}x^{n-2}h^2 + \cdots + nxh^{n-1} + h^n \right] - x^n}{h}$$

$$= \lim_{h \to 0} \frac{nx^{n-1}h + \dfrac{n(n-1)}{2}x^{n-2}h^2 + \cdots + nxh^{n-1} + h^n}{h}$$

$$= \lim_{h \to 0} \left[nx^{n-1} + \frac{n(n-1)}{2}x^{n-2}h + \cdots + nxh^{n-2} + h^{n-1} \right]$$

$$= nx^{n-1}$$

because every term except the first has h as a factor and therefore approaches 0. ∎

We illustrate the Power Rule using various notations in Example 1.

EXAMPLE 1

(a) If $f(x) = x^6$, then $f'(x) = 6x^5$.   (b) If $y = x^{1000}$, then $y' = 1000x^{999}$.

(c) If $y = t^4$, then $\dfrac{dy}{dt} = 4t^3$.   (d) $\dfrac{d}{dr}(r^3) = 3r^2$

What about power functions with negative integer exponents? In Exercise 61 we ask you to verify from the definition of a derivative that

$$\frac{d}{dx}\left(\frac{1}{x}\right) = -\frac{1}{x^2}$$

We can rewrite this equation as

$$\frac{d}{dx}(x^{-1}) = (-1)x^{-2}$$

and so the Power Rule is true when $n = -1$. In fact, we will show in the next section [Exercise 62(c)] that it holds for all negative integers.

What if the exponent is a fraction? In Example 3 in Section 2.8 we found that

$$\frac{d}{dx}\sqrt{x} = \frac{1}{2\sqrt{x}}$$

which can be written as

$$\frac{d}{dx}(x^{1/2}) = \tfrac{1}{2}x^{-1/2}$$

This shows that the Power Rule is true even when $n = \tfrac{1}{2}$. In fact, we will show in Section 3.6 that it is true for all real numbers n.

> **The Power Rule (General Version)** If n is any real number, then
>
> $$\frac{d}{dx}(x^n) = nx^{n-1}$$

Figure 3 shows the function y in Example 2(b) and its derivative y'. Notice that y is not differentiable at 0 (y' is not defined there). Observe that y' is positive when y increases and is negative when y decreases.

FIGURE 3
$y = \sqrt[3]{x^2}$

EXAMPLE 2 Differentiate:

(a) $f(x) = \dfrac{1}{x^2}$

(b) $y = \sqrt[3]{x^2}$

SOLUTION In each case we rewrite the function as a power of x.

(a) Since $f(x) = x^{-2}$, we use the Power Rule with $n = -2$:

$$f'(x) = \frac{d}{dx}(x^{-2}) = -2x^{-2-1} = -2x^{-3} = -\frac{2}{x^3}$$

(b)
$$\frac{dy}{dx} = \frac{d}{dx}\left(\sqrt[3]{x^2}\right) = \frac{d}{dx}(x^{2/3}) = \tfrac{2}{3}x^{(2/3)-1} = \tfrac{2}{3}x^{-1/3}$$ ▪

The Power Rule enables us to find tangent lines without having to resort to the definition of a derivative. It also enables us to find *normal lines*. The **normal line** to a curve C at a point P is the line through P that is perpendicular to the tangent line at P. (In the study of optics, one needs to consider the angle between a light ray and the normal line to a lens.)

▼ EXAMPLE 3 Find equations of the tangent line and normal line to the curve $y = x\sqrt{x}$ at the point $(1, 1)$. Illustrate by graphing the curve and these lines.

SOLUTION The derivative of $f(x) = x\sqrt{x} = xx^{1/2} = x^{3/2}$ is

$$f'(x) = \tfrac{3}{2}x^{(3/2)-1} = \tfrac{3}{2}x^{1/2} = \tfrac{3}{2}\sqrt{x}$$

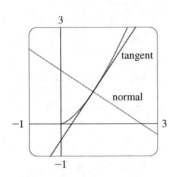

FIGURE 4
$y = x\sqrt{x}$

So the slope of the tangent line at $(1, 1)$ is $f'(1) = \tfrac{3}{2}$. Therefore an equation of the tangent line is

$$y - 1 = \tfrac{3}{2}(x - 1) \qquad \text{or} \qquad y = \tfrac{3}{2}x - \tfrac{1}{2}$$

The normal line is perpendicular to the tangent line, so its slope is the negative reciprocal of $\tfrac{3}{2}$, that is, $-\tfrac{2}{3}$. Thus an equation of the normal line is

$$y - 1 = -\tfrac{2}{3}(x - 1) \qquad \text{or} \qquad y = -\tfrac{2}{3}x + \tfrac{5}{3}$$

We graph the curve and its tangent line and normal line in Figure 4.

New Derivatives from Old

When new functions are formed from old functions by addition, subtraction, or multiplication by a constant, their derivatives can be calculated in terms of derivatives of the old functions. In particular, the following formula says that *the derivative of a constant times a function is the constant times the derivative of the function.*

> **The Constant Multiple Rule** If c is a constant and f is a differentiable function, then
> $$\frac{d}{dx}[cf(x)] = c\frac{d}{dx}f(x)$$

GEOMETRIC INTERPRETATION OF
THE CONSTANT MULTIPLE RULE

Multiplying by $c = 2$ stretches the graph vertically by a factor of 2. All the rises have been doubled but the runs stay the same. So the slopes are doubled too.

PROOF Let $g(x) = cf(x)$. Then

$$g'(x) = \lim_{h \to 0} \frac{g(x + h) - g(x)}{h} = \lim_{h \to 0} \frac{cf(x + h) - cf(x)}{h}$$

$$= \lim_{h \to 0} c\left[\frac{f(x + h) - f(x)}{h}\right]$$

$$= c \lim_{h \to 0} \frac{f(x + h) - f(x)}{h} \qquad \text{(by Law 3 of limits)}$$

$$= cf'(x)$$

EXAMPLE 4

(a) $\dfrac{d}{dx}(3x^4) = 3\dfrac{d}{dx}(x^4) = 3(4x^3) = 12x^3$

(b) $\dfrac{d}{dx}(-x) = \dfrac{d}{dx}[(-1)x] = (-1)\dfrac{d}{dx}(x) = -1(1) = -1$

The next rule tells us that *the derivative of a sum of functions is the sum of the derivatives.*

Using prime notation, we can write the Sum Rule as

$$(f + g)' = f' + g'$$

> **The Sum Rule** If f and g are both differentiable, then
> $$\frac{d}{dx}[f(x) + g(x)] = \frac{d}{dx}f(x) + \frac{d}{dx}g(x)$$

PROOF Let $F(x) = f(x) + g(x)$. Then

$$F'(x) = \lim_{h \to 0} \frac{F(x + h) - F(x)}{h}$$

$$= \lim_{h \to 0} \frac{[f(x + h) + g(x + h)] - [f(x) + g(x)]}{h}$$

$$= \lim_{h \to 0} \left[\frac{f(x + h) - f(x)}{h} + \frac{g(x + h) - g(x)}{h} \right]$$

$$= \lim_{h \to 0} \frac{f(x + h) - f(x)}{h} + \lim_{h \to 0} \frac{g(x + h) - g(x)}{h} \qquad \text{(by Law 1)}$$

$$= f'(x) + g'(x)$$

The Sum Rule can be extended to the sum of any number of functions. For instance, using this theorem twice, we get

$$(f + g + h)' = [(f + g) + h]' = (f + g)' + h' = f' + g' + h'$$

By writing $f - g$ as $f + (-1)g$ and applying the Sum Rule and the Constant Multiple Rule, we get the following formula.

The Difference Rule If f and g are both differentiable, then

$$\frac{d}{dx}[f(x) - g(x)] = \frac{d}{dx}f(x) - \frac{d}{dx}g(x)$$

The Constant Multiple Rule, the Sum Rule, and the Difference Rule can be combined with the Power Rule to differentiate any polynomial, as the following examples demonstrate.

EXAMPLE 5

$$\frac{d}{dx}(x^8 + 12x^5 - 4x^4 + 10x^3 - 6x + 5)$$

$$= \frac{d}{dx}(x^8) + 12\frac{d}{dx}(x^5) - 4\frac{d}{dx}(x^4) + 10\frac{d}{dx}(x^3) - 6\frac{d}{dx}(x) + \frac{d}{dx}(5)$$

$$= 8x^7 + 12(5x^4) - 4(4x^3) + 10(3x^2) - 6(1) + 0$$

$$= 8x^7 + 60x^4 - 16x^3 + 30x^2 - 6$$

V **EXAMPLE 6** Find the points on the curve $y = x^4 - 6x^2 + 4$ where the tangent line is horizontal.

SOLUTION Horizontal tangents occur where the derivative is zero. We have

$$\frac{dy}{dx} = \frac{d}{dx}(x^4) - 6\frac{d}{dx}(x^2) + \frac{d}{dx}(4)$$

$$= 4x^3 - 12x + 0 = 4x(x^2 - 3)$$

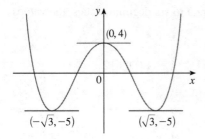

FIGURE 5
The curve $y = x^4 - 6x^2 + 4$ and
its horizontal tangents

Thus $dy/dx = 0$ if $x = 0$ or $x^2 - 3 = 0$, that is, $x = \pm\sqrt{3}$. So the given curve has horizontal tangents when $x = 0$, $\sqrt{3}$, and $-\sqrt{3}$. The corresponding points are $(0, 4)$, $(\sqrt{3}, -5)$, and $(-\sqrt{3}, -5)$. (See Figure 5.)

EXAMPLE 7 The equation of motion of a particle is $s = 2t^3 - 5t^2 + 3t + 4$, where s is measured in centimeters and t in seconds. Find the acceleration as a function of time. What is the acceleration after 2 seconds?

SOLUTION The velocity and acceleration are

$$v(t) = \frac{ds}{dt} = 6t^2 - 10t + 3$$

$$a(t) = \frac{dv}{dt} = 12t - 10$$

The acceleration after 2 s is $a(2) = 14 \text{ cm/s}^2$.

Exponential Functions

Let's try to compute the derivative of the exponential function $f(x) = a^x$ using the definition of a derivative:

$$f'(x) = \lim_{h \to 0} \frac{f(x + h) - f(x)}{h} = \lim_{h \to 0} \frac{a^{x+h} - a^x}{h}$$

$$= \lim_{h \to 0} \frac{a^x a^h - a^x}{h} = \lim_{h \to 0} \frac{a^x(a^h - 1)}{h}$$

The factor a^x doesn't depend on h, so we can take it in front of the limit:

$$f'(x) = a^x \lim_{h \to 0} \frac{a^h - 1}{h}$$

Notice that the limit is the value of the derivative of f at 0, that is,

$$\lim_{h \to 0} \frac{a^h - 1}{h} = f'(0)$$

Therefore we have shown that if the exponential function $f(x) = a^x$ is differentiable at 0, then it is differentiable everywhere and

$$\boxed{4} \qquad\qquad f'(x) = f'(0)a^x$$

This equation says that *the rate of change of any exponential function is proportional to the function itself.* (The slope is proportional to the height.)

Numerical evidence for the existence of $f'(0)$ is given in the table at the left for the cases $a = 2$ and $a = 3$. (Values are stated correct to four decimal places.) It appears that the limits exist and

for $a = 2$, $\quad f'(0) = \lim_{h \to 0} \dfrac{2^h - 1}{h} \approx 0.69$

for $a = 3$, $\quad f'(0) = \lim_{h \to 0} \dfrac{3^h - 1}{h} \approx 1.10$

h	$\dfrac{2^h - 1}{h}$	$\dfrac{3^h - 1}{h}$
0.1	0.7177	1.1612
0.01	0.6956	1.1047
0.001	0.6934	1.0992
0.0001	0.6932	1.0987

In fact, it can be proved that these limits exist and, correct to six decimal places, the values are

$$\frac{d}{dx}(2^x)\Big|_{x=0} \approx 0.693147 \qquad \frac{d}{dx}(3^x)\Big|_{x=0} \approx 1.098612$$

Thus, from Equation 4, we have

5
$$\frac{d}{dx}(2^x) \approx (0.69)2^x \qquad \frac{d}{dx}(3^x) \approx (1.10)3^x$$

Of all possible choices for the base a in Equation 4, the simplest differentiation formula occurs when $f'(0) = 1$. In view of the estimates of $f'(0)$ for $a = 2$ and $a = 3$, it seems reasonable that there is a number a between 2 and 3 for which $f'(0) = 1$. It is traditional to denote this value by the letter e. (In fact, that is how we introduced e in Section 1.5.) Thus we have the following definition.

In Exercise 1 we will see that e lies between 2.7 and 2.8. Later we will be able to show that, correct to five decimal places,

$$e \approx 2.71828$$

Definition of the Number e

$$e \text{ is the number such that } \lim_{h \to 0} \frac{e^h - 1}{h} = 1$$

Geometrically, this means that of all the possible exponential functions $y = a^x$, the function $f(x) = e^x$ is the one whose tangent line at $(0, 1)$ has a slope $f'(0)$ that is exactly 1. (See Figures 6 and 7.)

FIGURE 6   **FIGURE 7**

If we put $a = e$ and, therefore, $f'(0) = 1$ in Equation 4, it becomes the following important differentiation formula.

TEC Visual 3.1 uses the slope-a-scope to illustrate this formula.

Derivative of the Natural Exponential Function

$$\frac{d}{dx}(e^x) = e^x$$

Thus the exponential function $f(x) = e^x$ has the property that it is its own derivative. The geometrical significance of this fact is that the slope of a tangent line to the curve $y = e^x$ is equal to the y-coordinate of the point (see Figure 7).

V **EXAMPLE 8** If $f(x) = e^x - x$, find f' and f''. Compare the graphs of f and f'.

SOLUTION Using the Difference Rule, we have

$$f'(x) = \frac{d}{dx}(e^x - x) = \frac{d}{dx}(e^x) - \frac{d}{dx}(x) = e^x - 1$$

In Section 2.8 we defined the second derivative as the derivative of f', so

$$f''(x) = \frac{d}{dx}(e^x - 1) = \frac{d}{dx}(e^x) - \frac{d}{dx}(1) = e^x$$

FIGURE 8

The function f and its derivative f' are graphed in Figure 8. Notice that f has a horizontal tangent when $x = 0$; this corresponds to the fact that $f'(0) = 0$. Notice also that, for $x > 0$, $f'(x)$ is positive and f is increasing. When $x < 0$, $f'(x)$ is negative and f is decreasing.

EXAMPLE 9 At what point on the curve $y = e^x$ is the tangent line parallel to the line $y = 2x$?

SOLUTION Since $y = e^x$, we have $y' = e^x$. Let the x-coordinate of the point in question be a. Then the slope of the tangent line at that point is e^a. This tangent line will be parallel to the line $y = 2x$ if it has the same slope, that is, 2. Equating slopes, we get

$$e^a = 2 \qquad a = \ln 2$$

Therefore the required point is $(a, e^a) = (\ln 2, 2)$. (See Figure 9.)

FIGURE 9

3.1   Exercises

1. (a) How is the number e defined?
   (b) Use a calculator to estimate the values of the limits

$$\lim_{h \to 0} \frac{2.7^h - 1}{h} \quad \text{and} \quad \lim_{h \to 0} \frac{2.8^h - 1}{h}$$

   correct to two decimal places. What can you conclude about the value of e?

2. (a) Sketch, by hand, the graph of the function $f(x) = e^x$, paying particular attention to how the graph crosses the y-axis. What fact allows you to do this?
   (b) What types of functions are $f(x) = e^x$ and $g(x) = x^e$? Compare the differentiation formulas for f and g.
   (c) Which of the two functions in part (b) grows more rapidly when x is large?

3–32 Differentiate the function.

3. $f(x) = 186.5$

4. $f(x) = \sqrt{30}$

5. $f(x) = 5x - 1$

6. $F(x) = -4x^{10}$

7. $f(x) = x^3 - 4x + 6$

8. $f(t) = 1.4t^5 - 2.5t^2 + 6.7$

9. $g(x) = x^2(1 - 2x)$

10. $h(x) = (x - 2)(2x + 3)$

11. $y = x^{-2/5}$

12. $B(y) = cy^{-6}$

13. $A(s) = -\dfrac{12}{s^5}$

14. $y = x^{5/3} - x^{2/3}$

15. $R(a) = (3a + 1)^2$

16. $h(t) = \sqrt[4]{t} - 4e^t$

17. $S(p) = \sqrt{p} - p$

18. $y = \sqrt{x}\,(x - 1)$

19. $y = 3e^x + \dfrac{4}{\sqrt[3]{x}}$

20. $S(R) = 4\pi R^2$

21. $h(u) = Au^3 + Bu^2 + Cu$

22. $y = \dfrac{\sqrt{x} + x}{x^2}$

23. $y = \dfrac{x^2 + 4x + 3}{\sqrt{x}}$

24. $g(u) = \sqrt{2}\,u + \sqrt{3u}$

25. $j(x) = x^{2.4} + e^{2.4}$

26. $k(r) = e^r + r^e$

27. $H(x) = (x + x^{-1})^3$

28. $y = ae^v + \dfrac{b}{v} + \dfrac{c}{v^2}$

🖩 Graphing calculator or computer required   **1.** Homework Hints available at stewartcalculus.com

29. $u = \sqrt[5]{t} + 4\sqrt{t^5}$

30. $v = \left(\sqrt{x} + \dfrac{1}{\sqrt[3]{x}}\right)^2$

31. $z = \dfrac{A}{y^{10}} + Be^y$

32. $y = e^{x+1} + 1$

33–34 Find an equation of the tangent line to the curve at the given point.

33. $y = \sqrt[4]{x}, \quad (1, 1)$

34. $y = x^4 + 2x^2 - x, \quad (1, 2)$

35–36 Find equations of the tangent line and normal line to the curve at the given point.

35. $y = x^4 + 2e^x, \quad (0, 2)$

36. $y = x^2 - x^4, \quad (1, 0)$

37–38 Find an equation of the tangent line to the curve at the given point. Illustrate by graphing the curve and the tangent line on the same screen.

37. $y = 3x^2 - x^3, \quad (1, 2)$

38. $y = x - \sqrt{x}, \quad (1, 0)$

39–40 Find $f'(x)$. Compare the graphs of f and f' and use them to explain why your answer is reasonable.

39. $f(x) = x^4 - 2x^3 + x^2$

40. $f(x) = x^5 - 2x^3 + x - 1$

---

41. (a) Use a graphing calculator or computer to graph the function $f(x) = x^4 - 3x^3 - 6x^2 + 7x + 30$ in the viewing rectangle $[-3, 5]$ by $[-10, 50]$.

(b) Using the graph in part (a) to estimate slopes, make a rough sketch, by hand, of the graph of f'. (See Example 1 in Section 2.8.)

(c) Calculate $f'(x)$ and use this expression, with a graphing device, to graph f'. Compare with your sketch in part (b).

42. (a) Use a graphing calculator or computer to graph the function $g(x) = e^x - 3x^2$ in the viewing rectangle $[-1, 4]$ by $[-8, 8]$

(b) Using the graph in part (a) to estimate slopes, make a rough sketch, by hand, of the graph of g'. (See Example 1 in Section 2.8.)

(c) Calculate $g'(x)$ and use this expression, with a graphing device, to graph g'. Compare with your sketch in part (b).

43–44 Find the first and second derivatives of the function.

43. $f(x) = 10x^{10} + 5x^5 - x$

44. $G(r) = \sqrt{r} + \sqrt[3]{r}$

45–46 Find the first and second derivatives of the function. Check to see that your answers are reasonable by comparing the graphs of f, f', and f''.

45. $f(x) = 2x - 5x^{3/4}$

46. $f(x) = e^x - x^3$

---

47. The equation of motion of a particle is $s = t^3 - 3t$, where s is in meters and t is in seconds. Find

(a) the velocity and acceleration as functions of t,

(b) the acceleration after 2 s, and

(c) the acceleration when the velocity is 0.

48. The equation of motion of a particle is $s = t^4 - 2t^3 + t^2 - t$, where s is in meters and t is in seconds.

(a) Find the velocity and acceleration as functions of t.

(b) Find the acceleration after 1 s.

(c) Graph the position, velocity, and acceleration functions on the same screen.

49. Boyle's Law states that when a sample of gas is compressed at a constant temperature, the pressure P of the gas is inversely proportional to the volume V of the gas.

(a) Suppose that the pressure of a sample of air that occupies 0.106 m^3 at $25°C$ is 50 kPa. Write V as a function of P.

(b) Calculate dV/dP when $P = 50$ kPa. What is the meaning of the derivative? What are its units?

50. Car tires need to be inflated properly because overinflation or underinflation can cause premature treadwear. The data in the table show tire life L (in thousands of kilometers) for a certain type of tire at various pressures P (in kPa).

P	179	193	214	242	262	290	311
L	80	106	126	130	119	113	95

(a) Use a graphing calculator or computer to model tire life with a quadratic function of the pressure.

(b) Use the model to estimate dL/dP when $P = 200$ and when $P = 300$. What is the meaning of the derivative? What are the units? What is the significance of the signs of the derivatives?

51. Find the points on the curve $y = 2x^3 + 3x^2 - 12x + 1$ where the tangent is horizontal.

52. For what value of x does the graph of $f(x) = e^x - 2x$ have a horizontal tangent?

53. Show that the curve $y = 2e^x + 3x + 5x^3$ has no tangent line with slope 2.

54. Find an equation of the tangent line to the curve $y = x\sqrt{x}$ that is parallel to the line $y = 1 + 3x$.

55. Find equations of both lines that are tangent to the curve $y = 1 + x^3$ and parallel to the line $12x - y = 1$.

56. At what point on the curve $y = 1 + 2e^x - 3x$ is the tangent line parallel to the line $3x - y = 5$? Illustrate by graphing the curve and both lines.

57. Find an equation of the normal line to the parabola $y = x^2 - 5x + 4$ that is parallel to the line $x - 3y = 5$.

58. Where does the normal line to the parabola $y = x - x^2$ at the point $(1, 0)$ intersect the parabola a second time? Illustrate with a sketch.

59. Draw a diagram to show that there are two tangent lines to the parabola $y = x^2$ that pass through the point $(0, -4)$. Find the coordinates of the points where these tangent lines intersect the parabola.

60. (a) Find equations of both lines through the point $(2, -3)$ that are tangent to the parabola $y = x^2 + x$.
(b) Show that there is no line through the point $(2, 7)$ that is tangent to the parabola. Then draw a diagram to see why.

61. Use the definition of a derivative to show that if $f(x) = 1/x$, then $f'(x) = -1/x^2$. (This proves the Power Rule for the case $n = -1$.)

62. Find the nth derivative of each function by calculating the first few derivatives and observing the pattern that occurs.
(a) $f(x) = x^n$ (b) $f(x) = 1/x$

63. Find a second-degree polynomial P such that $P(2) = 5$, $P'(2) = 3$, and $P''(2) = 2$.

64. The equation $y'' + y' - 2y = x^2$ is called a **differential equation** because it involves an unknown function y and its derivatives y' and y''. Find constants A, B, and C such that the function $y = Ax^2 + Bx + C$ satisfies this equation. (Differential equations will be studied in detail in Chapter 9.)

65. Find a cubic function $y = ax^3 + bx^2 + cx + d$ whose graph has horizontal tangents at the points $(-2, 6)$ and $(2, 0)$.

66. Find a parabola with equation $y = ax^2 + bx + c$ that has slope 4 at $x = 1$, slope -8 at $x = -1$, and passes through the point $(2, 15)$.

67. Let
$$f(x) = \begin{cases} x^2 + 1 & \text{if } x < 1 \\ x + 1 & \text{if } x \geq 1 \end{cases}$$

Is f differentiable at 1? Sketch the graphs of f and f'.

68. At what numbers is the following function g differentiable?
$$g(x) = \begin{cases} 2x & \text{if } x \leq 0 \\ 2x - x^2 & \text{if } 0 < x < 2 \\ 2 - x & \text{if } x \geq 2 \end{cases}$$

Give a formula for g' and sketch the graphs of g and g'.

69. (a) For what values of x is the function $f(x) = |x^2 - 9|$ differentiable? Find a formula for f'.
(b) Sketch the graphs of f and f'.

70. Where is the function $h(x) = |x - 1| + |x + 2|$ differentiable? Give a formula for h' and sketch the graphs of h and h'.

71. Find the parabola with equation $y = ax^2 + bx$ whose tangent line at $(1, 1)$ has equation $y = 3x - 2$.

72. Suppose the curve $y = x^4 + ax^3 + bx^2 + cx + d$ has a tangent line when $x = 0$ with equation $y = 2x + 1$ and a tangent line when $x = 1$ with equation $y = 2 - 3x$. Find the values of a, b, c, and d.

73. For what values of a and b is the line $2x + y = b$ tangent to the parabola $y = ax^2$ when $x = 2$?

74. Find the value of c such that the line $y = \frac{3}{2}x + 6$ is tangent to the curve $y = c\sqrt{x}$.

75. Let
$$f(x) = \begin{cases} x^2 & \text{if } x \leq 2 \\ mx + b & \text{if } x > 2 \end{cases}$$

Find the values of m and b that make f differentiable everywhere.

76. A tangent line is drawn to the hyperbola $xy = c$ at a point P.
(a) Show that the midpoint of the line segment cut from this tangent line by the coordinate axes is P.
(b) Show that the triangle formed by the tangent line and the coordinate axes always has the same area, no matter where P is located on the hyperbola.

77. Evaluate $\lim\limits_{x \to 1} \dfrac{x^{1000} - 1}{x - 1}$.

78. Draw a diagram showing two perpendicular lines that intersect on the y-axis and are both tangent to the parabola $y = x^2$. Where do these lines intersect?

79. If $c > \frac{1}{2}$, how many lines through the point $(0, c)$ are normal lines to the parabola $y = x^2$? What if $c \leq \frac{1}{2}$?

80. Sketch the parabolas $y = x^2$ and $y = x^2 - 2x + 2$. Do you think there is a line that is tangent to both curves? If so, find its equation. If not, why not?

BUILDING A BETTER ROLLER COASTER

Suppose you are asked to design the first ascent and drop for a new roller coaster. By studying photographs of your favorite coasters, you decide to make the slope of the ascent 0.8 and the slope of the drop -1.6. You decide to connect these two straight stretches $y = L_1(x)$ and $y = L_2(x)$ with part of a parabola $y = f(x) = ax^2 + bx + c$, where x and $f(x)$ are measured in meters. For the track to be smooth there can't be abrupt changes in direction, so you want the linear segments L_1 and L_2 to be tangent to the parabola at the transition points P and Q. (See the figure.) To simplify the equations, you decide to place the origin at P.

1. (a) Suppose the horizontal distance between P and Q is 30 m. Write equations in a, b, and c that will ensure that the track is smooth at the transition points.
   (b) Solve the equations in part (a) for a, b, and c to find a formula for $f(x)$.
   (c) Plot L_1, f, and L_2 to verify graphically that the transitions are smooth.
   (d) Find the difference in elevation between P and Q.

2. The solution in Problem 1 might *look* smooth, but it might not *feel* smooth because the piecewise defined function [consisting of $L_1(x)$ for $x < 0$, $f(x)$ for $0 \le x \le 30$, and $L_2(x)$ for $x > 30$] doesn't have a continuous second derivative. So you decide to improve the design by using a quadratic function $q(x) = ax^2 + bx + c$ only on the interval $3 \le x \le 27$ and connecting it to the linear functions by means of two cubic functions:

$$g(x) = kx^3 + lx^2 + mx + n \qquad 0 \le x < 3$$
$$h(x) = px^3 + qx^2 + rx + s \qquad 27 < x \le 30$$

   (a) Write a system of equations in 11 unknowns that ensure that the functions and their first two derivatives agree at the transition points.
   (b) Solve the equations in part (a) with a computer algebra system to find formulas for $q(x)$, $g(x)$, and $h(x)$.
   (c) Plot L_1, g, q, h, and L_2, and compare with the plot in Problem 1(c).

Graphing calculator or computer required

CAS Computer algebra system required

3.2 The Product and Quotient Rules

The formulas of this section enable us to differentiate new functions formed from old functions by multiplication or division.

The Product Rule

By analogy with the Sum and Difference Rules, one might be tempted to guess, as Leibniz did three centuries ago, that the derivative of a product is the product of the derivatives. We can see, however, that this guess is wrong by looking at a particular example. Let $f(x) = x$ and $g(x) = x^2$. Then the Power Rule gives $f'(x) = 1$ and $g'(x) = 2x$. But $(fg)(x) = x^3$, so $(fg)'(x) = 3x^2$. Thus $(fg)' \ne f'g'$. The correct formula was discovered by Leibniz (soon after his false start) and is called the Product Rule.

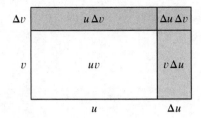

FIGURE 1

The geometry of the Product Rule

Before stating the Product Rule, let's see how we might discover it. We start by assuming that $u = f(x)$ and $v = g(x)$ are both positive differentiable functions. Then we can interpret the product uv as an area of a rectangle (see Figure 1). If x changes by an amount Δx, then the corresponding changes in u and v are

$$\Delta u = f(x + \Delta x) - f(x) \qquad \Delta v = g(x + \Delta x) - g(x)$$

and the new value of the product, $(u + \Delta u)(v + \Delta v)$, can be interpreted as the area of the large rectangle in Figure 1 (provided that Δu and Δv happen to be positive).

The change in the area of the rectangle is

$$\boxed{1} \qquad \Delta(uv) = (u + \Delta u)(v + \Delta v) - uv = u\,\Delta v + v\,\Delta u + \Delta u\,\Delta v$$

$$= \text{the sum of the three shaded areas}$$

If we divide by Δx, we get

$$\frac{\Delta(uv)}{\Delta x} = u\,\frac{\Delta v}{\Delta x} + v\,\frac{\Delta u}{\Delta x} + \Delta u\,\frac{\Delta v}{\Delta x}$$

Recall that in Leibniz notation the definition of a derivative can be written as

$$\frac{dy}{dx} = \lim_{\Delta x \to 0} \frac{\Delta y}{\Delta x}$$

If we now let $\Delta x \to 0$, we get the derivative of uv:

$$\frac{d}{dx}(uv) = \lim_{\Delta x \to 0} \frac{\Delta(uv)}{\Delta x} = \lim_{\Delta x \to 0}\left(u\,\frac{\Delta v}{\Delta x} + v\,\frac{\Delta u}{\Delta x} + \Delta u\,\frac{\Delta v}{\Delta x} \right)$$

$$= u \lim_{\Delta x \to 0} \frac{\Delta v}{\Delta x} + v \lim_{\Delta x \to 0} \frac{\Delta u}{\Delta x} + \left(\lim_{\Delta x \to 0} \Delta u \right)\left(\lim_{\Delta x \to 0} \frac{\Delta v}{\Delta x} \right)$$

$$= u\,\frac{dv}{dx} + v\,\frac{du}{dx} + 0 \cdot \frac{dv}{dx}$$

$$\boxed{2} \qquad \frac{d}{dx}(uv) = u\,\frac{dv}{dx} + v\,\frac{du}{dx}$$

(Notice that $\Delta u \to 0$ as $\Delta x \to 0$ since f is differentiable and therefore continuous.)

Although we started by assuming (for the geometric interpretation) that all the quantities are positive, we notice that Equation 1 is always true. (The algebra is valid whether u, v, Δu, and Δv are positive or negative.) So we have proved Equation 2, known as the Product Rule, for all differentiable functions u and v.

In prime notation:

$$(fg)' = fg' + gf'$$

The Product Rule If f and g are both differentiable, then

$$\frac{d}{dx}[f(x)g(x)] = f(x)\,\frac{d}{dx}[g(x)] + g(x)\,\frac{d}{dx}[f(x)]$$

In words, the Product Rule says that *the derivative of a product of two functions is the first function times the derivative of the second function plus the second function times the derivative of the first function.*

Figure 2 shows the graphs of the function f of Example 1 and its derivative f'. Notice that $f'(x)$ is positive when f is increasing and negative when f is decreasing.

3

f' f

-3 1.5

-1

FIGURE 2

In Example 2, a and b are constants. It is customary in mathematics to use letters near the beginning of the alphabet to represent constants and letters near the end of the alphabet to represent variables.

EXAMPLE 1

(a) If $f(x) = xe^x$, find $f'(x)$.

(b) Find the nth derivative, $f^{(n)}(x)$.

SOLUTION

(a) By the Product Rule, we have

$$f'(x) = \frac{d}{dx}(xe^x)$$

$$= x\frac{d}{dx}(e^x) + e^x\frac{d}{dx}(x)$$

$$= xe^x + e^x \cdot 1 = (x + 1)e^x$$

(b) Using the Product Rule a second time, we get

$$f''(x) = \frac{d}{dx}[(x + 1)e^x]$$

$$= (x + 1)\frac{d}{dx}(e^x) + e^x\frac{d}{dx}(x + 1)$$

$$= (x + 1)e^x + e^x \cdot 1 = (x + 2)e^x$$

Further applications of the Product Rule give

$$f'''(x) = (x + 3)e^x \qquad f^{(4)}(x) = (x + 4)e^x$$

In fact, each successive differentiation adds another term e^x, so

$$f^{(n)}(x) = (x + n)e^x$$

EXAMPLE 2   Differentiate the function $f(t) = \sqrt{t}\,(a + bt)$.

SOLUTION 1   Using the Product Rule, we have

$$f'(t) = \sqrt{t}\,\frac{d}{dt}(a + bt) + (a + bt)\frac{d}{dt}(\sqrt{t})$$

$$= \sqrt{t} \cdot b + (a + bt) \cdot \tfrac{1}{2}t^{-1/2}$$

$$= b\sqrt{t} + \frac{a + bt}{2\sqrt{t}} = \frac{a + 3bt}{2\sqrt{t}}$$

SOLUTION 2   If we first use the laws of exponents to rewrite $f(t)$, then we can proceed directly without using the Product Rule.

$$f(t) = a\sqrt{t} + bt\sqrt{t} = at^{1/2} + bt^{3/2}$$

$$f'(t) = \tfrac{1}{2}at^{-1/2} + \tfrac{3}{2}bt^{1/2}$$

which is equivalent to the answer given in Solution 1.

Example 2 shows that it is sometimes easier to simplify a product of functions before differentiating than to use the Product Rule. In Example 1, however, the Product Rule is the only possible method.

EXAMPLE 3 If $f(x) = \sqrt{x}\, g(x)$, where $g(4) = 2$ and $g'(4) = 3$, find $f'(4)$.

SOLUTION Applying the Product Rule, we get

$$f'(x) = \frac{d}{dx}\left[\sqrt{x}\, g(x)\right] = \sqrt{x}\, \frac{d}{dx}\left[g(x)\right] + g(x)\frac{d}{dx}\left[\sqrt{x}\right]$$

$$= \sqrt{x}\, g'(x) + g(x) \cdot \tfrac{1}{2}x^{-1/2}$$

$$= \sqrt{x}\, g'(x) + \frac{g(x)}{2\sqrt{x}}$$

So

$$f'(4) = \sqrt{4}\, g'(4) + \frac{g(4)}{2\sqrt{4}} = 2\cdot 3 + \frac{2}{2\cdot 2} = 6.5$$

The Quotient Rule

We find a rule for differentiating the quotient of two differentiable functions $u = f(x)$ and $v = g(x)$ in much the same way that we found the Product Rule. If x, u, and v change by amounts Δx, Δu, and Δv, then the corresponding change in the quotient u/v is

$$\Delta\left(\frac{u}{v}\right) = \frac{u + \Delta u}{v + \Delta v} - \frac{u}{v} = \frac{(u + \Delta u)v - u(v + \Delta v)}{v(v + \Delta v)}$$

$$= \frac{v\,\Delta u - u\,\Delta v}{v(v + \Delta v)}$$

so

$$\frac{d}{dx}\left(\frac{u}{v}\right) = \lim_{\Delta x \to 0}\frac{\Delta(u/v)}{\Delta x} = \lim_{\Delta x \to 0}\frac{v\dfrac{\Delta u}{\Delta x} - u\dfrac{\Delta v}{\Delta x}}{v(v + \Delta v)}$$

As $\Delta x \to 0$, $\Delta v \to 0$ also, because $v = g(x)$ is differentiable and therefore continuous. Thus, using the Limit Laws, we get

$$\frac{d}{dx}\left(\frac{u}{v}\right) = \frac{v \lim\limits_{\Delta x \to 0}\dfrac{\Delta u}{\Delta x} - u \lim\limits_{\Delta x \to 0}\dfrac{\Delta v}{\Delta x}}{v \lim\limits_{\Delta x \to 0}(v + \Delta v)} = \frac{v\dfrac{du}{dx} - u\dfrac{dv}{dx}}{v^2}$$

In prime notation:

$$\left(\frac{f}{g}\right)' = \frac{gf' - fg'}{g^2}$$

> **The Quotient Rule** If f and g are differentiable, then
>
> $$\frac{d}{dx}\left[\frac{f(x)}{g(x)}\right] = \frac{g(x)\dfrac{d}{dx}\left[f(x)\right] - f(x)\dfrac{d}{dx}\left[g(x)\right]}{\left[g(x)\right]^2}$$

In words, the Quotient Rule says that the *derivative of a quotient is the denominator times the derivative of the numerator minus the numerator times the derivative of the denominator, all divided by the square of the denominator.*

The Quotient Rule and the other differentiation formulas enable us to compute the derivative of any rational function, as the next example illustrates.

We can use a graphing device to check that the answer to Example 4 is plausible. Figure 3 shows the graphs of the function of Example 4 and its derivative. Notice that when y grows rapidly (near -2), y' is large. And when y grows slowly, y' is near 0.

FIGURE 3

V **EXAMPLE 4**   Let $y = \dfrac{x^2 + x - 2}{x^3 + 6}$. Then

$$y' = \frac{(x^3 + 6)\dfrac{d}{dx}(x^2 + x - 2) - (x^2 + x - 2)\dfrac{d}{dx}(x^3 + 6)}{(x^3 + 6)^2}$$

$$= \frac{(x^3 + 6)(2x + 1) - (x^2 + x - 2)(3x^2)}{(x^3 + 6)^2}$$

$$= \frac{(2x^4 + x^3 + 12x + 6) - (3x^4 + 3x^3 - 6x^2)}{(x^3 + 6)^2}$$

$$= \frac{-x^4 - 2x^3 + 6x^2 + 12x + 6}{(x^3 + 6)^2}$$

V **EXAMPLE 5**   Find an equation of the tangent line to the curve $y = e^x/(1 + x^2)$ at the point $\left(1, \frac{1}{2}e\right)$.

SOLUTION   According to the Quotient Rule, we have

$$\frac{dy}{dx} = \frac{(1 + x^2)\dfrac{d}{dx}(e^x) - e^x \dfrac{d}{dx}(1 + x^2)}{(1 + x^2)^2}$$

$$= \frac{(1 + x^2)e^x - e^x(2x)}{(1 + x^2)^2}$$

$$= \frac{e^x(1 - x)^2}{(1 + x^2)^2}$$

So the slope of the tangent line at $\left(1, \frac{1}{2}e\right)$ is

$$\left.\frac{dy}{dx}\right|_{x=1} = 0$$

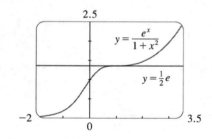

FIGURE 4

This means that the tangent line at $\left(1, \frac{1}{2}e\right)$ is horizontal and its equation is $y = \frac{1}{2}e$. [See Figure 4. Notice that the function is increasing and crosses its tangent line at $\left(1, \frac{1}{2}e\right)$.]

NOTE   Don't use the Quotient Rule *every* time you see a quotient. Sometimes it's easier to rewrite a quotient first to put it in a form that is simpler for the purpose of differentiation. For instance, although it is possible to differentiate the function

$$F(x) = \frac{3x^2 + 2\sqrt{x}}{x}$$

using the Quotient Rule, it is much easier to perform the division first and write the function as

$$F(x) = 3x + 2x^{-1/2}$$

before differentiating.

We summarize the differentiation formulas we have learned so far as follows.

Table of Differentiation Formulas

$$\frac{d}{dx}(c) = 0 \qquad \frac{d}{dx}(x^n) = nx^{n-1} \qquad \frac{d}{dx}(e^x) = e^x$$

$$(cf)' = cf' \qquad (f + g)' = f' + g' \qquad (f - g)' = f' - g'$$

$$(fg)' = fg' + gf' \qquad \left(\frac{f}{g}\right)' = \frac{gf' - fg'}{g^2}$$

3.2 Exercises

1. Find the derivative of $f(x) = (1 + 2x^2)(x - x^2)$ in two ways: by using the Product Rule and by performing the multiplication first. Do your answers agree?

2. Find the derivative of the function

$$F(x) = \frac{x^4 - 5x^3 + \sqrt{x}}{x^2}$$

in two ways: by using the Quotient Rule and by simplifying first. Show that your answers are equivalent. Which method do you prefer?

3–26 Differentiate.

3. $f(x) = (x^3 + 2x)e^x$

4. $g(x) = \sqrt{x}\, e^x$

5. $y = \dfrac{e^x}{x^2}$

6. $y = \dfrac{e^x}{1 + x}$

7. $g(x) = \dfrac{3x - 1}{2x + 1}$

8. $f(t) = \dfrac{2t}{4 + t^2}$

9. $H(u) = (u - \sqrt{u})(u + \sqrt{u})$

10. $J(v) = (v^3 - 2v)(v^{-4} + v^{-2})$

11. $F(y) = \left(\dfrac{1}{y^2} - \dfrac{3}{y^4}\right)(y + 5y^3)$

12. $f(z) = (1 - e^z)(z + e^z)$

13. $y = \dfrac{x^3}{1 - x^2}$

14. $y = \dfrac{x + 1}{x^3 + x - 2}$

15. $y = \dfrac{t^2 + 2}{t^4 - 3t^2 + 1}$

16. $y = \dfrac{t}{(t - 1)^2}$

17. $y = e^p(p + p\sqrt{p})$

18. $y = \dfrac{1}{s + ke^s}$

19. $y = \dfrac{v^3 - 2v\sqrt{v}}{v}$

20. $z = w^{3/2}(w + ce^w)$

21. $f(t) = \dfrac{2t}{2 + \sqrt{t}}$

22. $g(t) = \dfrac{t - \sqrt{t}}{t^{1/3}}$

23. $f(x) = \dfrac{A}{B + Ce^x}$

24. $f(x) = \dfrac{1 - xe^x}{x + e^x}$

25. $f(x) = \dfrac{x}{x + \dfrac{c}{x}}$

26. $f(x) = \dfrac{ax + b}{cx + d}$

27–30 Find $f'(x)$ and $f''(x)$.

27. $f(x) = x^4 e^x$

28. $f(x) = x^{5/2} e^x$

29. $f(x) = \dfrac{x^2}{1 + 2x}$

30. $f(x) = \dfrac{x}{x^2 - 1}$

31–32 Find an equation of the tangent line to the given curve at the specified point.

31. $y = \dfrac{x^2 - 1}{x^2 + x + 1}$, $(1, 0)$

32. $y = \dfrac{e^x}{x}$, $(1, e)$

33–34 Find equations of the tangent line and normal line to the given curve at the specified point.

33. $y = 2xe^x$, $(0, 0)$

34. $y = \dfrac{2x}{x^2 + 1}$, $(1, 1)$

35. (a) The curve $y = 1/(1 + x^2)$ is called a **witch of Maria Agnesi**. Find an equation of the tangent line to this curve at the point $\left(-1, \frac{1}{2}\right)$.

(b) Illustrate part (a) by graphing the curve and the tangent line on the same screen.

36. (a) The curve $y = x/(1 + x^2)$ is called a **serpentine**. Find an equation of the tangent line to this curve at the point $(3, 0.3)$.

(b) Illustrate part (a) by graphing the curve and the tangent line on the same screen.

37. (a) If $f(x) = (x^3 - x)e^x$, find $f'(x)$.

(b) Check to see that your answer to part (a) is reasonable by comparing the graphs of f and f'.

38. (a) If $f(x) = e^x/(2x^2 + x + 1)$, find $f'(x)$.

(b) Check to see that your answer to part (a) is reasonable by comparing the graphs of f and f'.

Graphing calculator or computer required   **1.** Homework Hints available at stewartcalculus.com

39. (a) If $f(x) = (x^2 - 1)/(x^2 + 1)$, find $f'(x)$ and $f''(x)$.

(b) Check to see that your answers to part (a) are reasonable by comparing the graphs of f, f', and f''.

40. (a) If $f(x) = (x^2 - 1)e^x$, find $f'(x)$ and $f''(x)$.

(b) Check to see that your answers to part (a) are reasonable by comparing the graphs of f, f', and f''.

41. If $f(x) = x^2/(1 + x)$, find $f''(1)$.

42. If $g(x) = x/e^x$, find $g^{(n)}(x)$.

43. Suppose that $f(5) = 1$, $f'(5) = 6$, $g(5) = -3$, and $g'(5) = 2$. Find the following values.

(a) $(fg)'(5)$ (b) $(f/g)'(5)$ (c) $(g/f)'(5)$

44. Suppose that $f(2) = -3$, $g(2) = 4$, $f'(2) = -2$, and $g'(2) = 7$. Find $h'(2)$.

(a) $h(x) = 5f(x) - 4g(x)$ (b) $h(x) = f(x)g(x)$

(c) $h(x) = \dfrac{f(x)}{g(x)}$ (d) $h(x) = \dfrac{g(x)}{1 + f(x)}$

45. If $f(x) = e^x g(x)$, where $g(0) = 2$ and $g'(0) = 5$, find $f'(0)$.

46. If $h(2) = 4$ and $h'(2) = -3$, find

$$\frac{d}{dx}\left(\frac{h(x)}{x}\right)\bigg|_{x=2}$$

47. If $g(x) = xf(x)$, where $f(3) = 4$ and $f'(3) = -2$, find an equation of the tangent line to the graph of g at the point where $x = 3$.

48. If $f(2) = 10$ and $f'(x) = x^2 f(x)$ for all x, find $f''(2)$.

49. If f and g are the functions whose graphs are shown, let $u(x) = f(x)g(x)$ and $v(x) = f(x)/g(x)$.

(a) Find $u'(1)$.   (b) Find $v'(5)$.

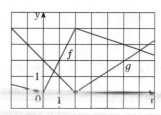

50. Let $P(x) = F(x)G(x)$ and $Q(x) = F(x)/G(x)$, where F and G are the functions whose graphs are shown.

(a) Find $P'(2)$.   (b) Find $Q'(7)$.

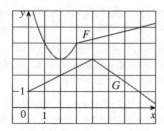

51. If g is a differentiable function, find an expression for the derivative of each of the following functions.

(a) $y = xg(x)$ (b) $y = \dfrac{x}{g(x)}$ (c) $y = \dfrac{g(x)}{x}$

52. If f is a differentiable function, find an expression for the derivative of each of the following functions.

(a) $y = x^2 f(x)$ (b) $y = \dfrac{f(x)}{x^2}$

(c) $y = \dfrac{x^2}{f(x)}$ (d) $y = \dfrac{1 + xf(x)}{\sqrt{x}}$

53. How many tangent lines to the curve $y = x/(x + 1)$ pass through the point $(1, 2)$? At which points do these tangent lines touch the curve?

54. Find equations of the tangent lines to the curve

$$y = \frac{x - 1}{x + 1}$$

that are parallel to the line $x - 2y = 2$.

55. Find $R'(0)$, where

$$R(x) = \frac{x - 3x^3 + 5x^5}{1 + 3x^3 + 6x^6 + 9x^9}$$

Hint: Instead of finding $R'(x)$ first, let $f(x)$ be the numerator and $g(x)$ the denominator of $R(x)$ and compute $R'(0)$ from $f(0), f'(0), g(0),$ and $g'(0)$.

56. Use the method of Exercise 55 to compute $Q'(0)$, where

$$Q(x) = \frac{1 + x + x^2 + xe^x}{1 - x + x^2 - xe^x}$$

57. In this exercise we estimate the rate at which the total personal income is rising in the Richmond-Petersburg, Virginia, metropolitan area. In 1999, the population of this area was 961,400, and the population was increasing at roughly 9200 people per year. The average annual income was $30,593 per capita, and this average was increasing at about $1400 per year (a little above the national average of about $1225 yearly). Use the Product Rule and these figures to estimate the rate at which total personal income was rising in the Richmond-Petersburg area in 1999. Explain the meaning of each term in the Product Rule.

58. A manufacturer produces bolts of a fabric with a fixed width. The quantity q of this fabric (measured in meters) that is sold is a function of the selling price p (in dollars per meter), so we can write $q = f(p)$. Then the total revenue earned with selling price p is $R(p) = pf(p)$.

(a) What does it mean to say that $f(20) = 10,000$ and $f'(20) = -350$?

(b) Assuming the values in part (a), find $R'(20)$ and interpret your answer.

59. (a) Use the Product Rule twice to prove that if f, g, and h are differentiable, then $(fgh)' = f'gh + fg'h + fgh'$.

   (b) Taking $f = g = h$ in part (a), show that

$$\frac{d}{dx}\,[f(x)]^3 = 3[f(x)]^2 f'(x)$$

   (c) Use part (b) to differentiate $y = e^{3x}$.

60. (a) If $F(x) = f(x)\,g(x)$, where f and g have derivatives of all orders, show that $F'' = f''g + 2f'g' + fg''$.

   (b) Find similar formulas for F''' and $F^{(4)}$.

   (c) Guess a formula for $F^{(n)}$.

61. Find expressions for the first five derivatives of $f(x) = x^2 e^x$. Do you see a pattern in these expressions? Guess a formula for $f^{(n)}(x)$ and prove it using mathematical induction.

62. (a) If g is differentiable, the **Reciprocal Rule** says that

$$\frac{d}{dx}\left[\frac{1}{g(x)}\right] = -\frac{g'(x)}{[g(x)]^2}$$

   Use the Quotient Rule to prove the Reciprocal Rule.

   (b) Use the Reciprocal Rule to differentiate the function in Exercise 18.

   (c) Use the Reciprocal Rule to verify that the Power Rule is valid for negative integers, that is,

$$\frac{d}{dx}\,(x^{-n}) = -nx^{-n-1}$$

   for all positive integers n.

3.3   Derivatives of Trigonometric Functions

A review of the trigonometric functions is given in Appendix D.

Before starting this section, you might need to review the trigonometric functions. In particular, it is important to remember that when we talk about the function f defined for all real numbers x by

$$f(x) = \sin x$$

it is understood that $\sin x$ means the sine of the angle whose *radian* measure is x. A similar convention holds for the other trigonometric functions cos, tan, csc, sec, and cot. Recall from Section 2.5 that all of the trigonometric functions are continuous at every number in their domains.

If we sketch the graph of the function $f(x) = \sin x$ and use the interpretation of $f'(x)$ as the slope of the tangent to the sine curve in order to sketch the graph of f' (see Exercise 16 in Section 2.8), then it looks as if the graph of f' may be the same as the cosine curve (see Figure 1).

TEC Visual 3.3 shows an animation of Figure 1.

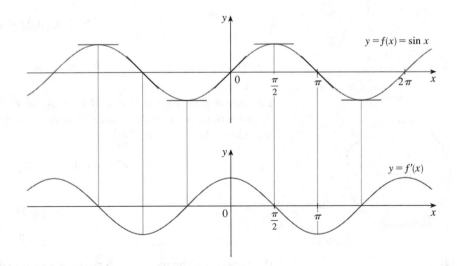

FIGURE 1

Let's try to confirm our guess that if $f(x) = \sin x$, then $f'(x) = \cos x$. From the definition of a derivative, we have

$$f'(x) = \lim_{h \to 0} \frac{f(x+h) - f(x)}{h} = \lim_{h \to 0} \frac{\sin(x+h) - \sin x}{h}$$

We have used the addition formula for sine. See Appendix D.

$$= \lim_{h \to 0} \frac{\sin x \cos h + \cos x \sin h - \sin x}{h}$$

$$= \lim_{h \to 0} \left[\frac{\sin x \cos h - \sin x}{h} + \frac{\cos x \sin h}{h} \right]$$

$$= \lim_{h \to 0} \left[\sin x \left(\frac{\cos h - 1}{h} \right) + \cos x \left(\frac{\sin h}{h} \right) \right]$$

$$\boxed{1} \qquad = \lim_{h \to 0} \sin x \cdot \lim_{h \to 0} \frac{\cos h - 1}{h} + \lim_{h \to 0} \cos x \cdot \lim_{h \to 0} \frac{\sin h}{h}$$

Two of these four limits are easy to evaluate. Since we regard x as a constant when computing a limit as $h \to 0$, we have

$$\lim_{h \to 0} \sin x = \sin x \qquad \text{and} \qquad \lim_{h \to 0} \cos x = \cos x$$

The limit of $(\sin h)/h$ is not so obvious. In Example 3 in Section 2.2 we made the guess, on the basis of numerical and graphical evidence, that

$$\boxed{2} \qquad \lim_{\theta \to 0} \frac{\sin \theta}{\theta} = 1$$

We now use a geometric argument to prove Equation 2. Assume first that θ lies between 0 and $\pi/2$. Figure 2(a) shows a sector of a circle with center O, central angle θ, and radius 1. BC is drawn perpendicular to OA. By the definition of radian measure, we have arc $AB = \theta$. Also $|BC| = |OB| \sin \theta = \sin \theta$. From the diagram we see that

$$|BC| < |AB| < \text{arc } AB$$

(a)

Therefore $\sin \theta < \theta$ so $\dfrac{\sin \theta}{\theta} < 1$

Let the tangent lines at A and B intersect at E. You can see from Figure 2(b) that the circumference of a circle is smaller than the length of a circumscribed polygon, and so arc $AB < |AE| + |EB|$. Thus

$$\theta = \text{arc } AB < |AE| + |EB|$$
$$< |AE| + |ED|$$
$$= |AD| = |OA| \tan \theta$$
$$= \tan \theta$$

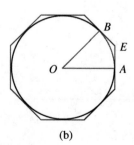

(b)

FIGURE 2

(In Appendix F the inequality $\theta \leqslant \tan \theta$ is proved directly from the definition of the length of an arc without resorting to geometric intuition as we did here.) Therefore we have

$$\theta < \frac{\sin \theta}{\cos \theta}$$

so

$$\cos \theta < \frac{\sin \theta}{\theta} < 1$$

We know that $\lim_{\theta \to 0} 1 = 1$ and $\lim_{\theta \to 0} \cos \theta = 1$, so by the Squeeze Theorem, we have

$$\lim_{\theta \to 0^+} \frac{\sin \theta}{\theta} = 1$$

But the function $(\sin \theta)/\theta$ is an even function, so its right and left limits must be equal. Hence, we have

$$\lim_{\theta \to 0} \frac{\sin \theta}{\theta} = 1$$

so we have proved Equation 2.

We can deduce the value of the remaining limit in $\boxed{1}$ as follows:

We multiply numerator and denominator by $\cos \theta + 1$ in order to put the function in a form in which we can use the limits we know.

$$\lim_{\theta \to 0} \frac{\cos \theta - 1}{\theta} = \lim_{\theta \to 0} \left(\frac{\cos \theta - 1}{\theta} \cdot \frac{\cos \theta + 1}{\cos \theta + 1} \right) = \lim_{\theta \to 0} \frac{\cos^2 \theta - 1}{\theta (\cos \theta + 1)}$$

$$= \lim_{\theta \to 0} \frac{-\sin^2 \theta}{\theta (\cos \theta + 1)} = -\lim_{\theta \to 0} \left(\frac{\sin \theta}{\theta} \cdot \frac{\sin \theta}{\cos \theta + 1} \right)$$

$$= -\lim_{\theta \to 0} \frac{\sin \theta}{\theta} \cdot \lim_{\theta \to 0} \frac{\sin \theta}{\cos \theta + 1}$$

$$= -1 \cdot \left(\frac{0}{1 + 1} \right) = 0 \qquad \text{(by Equation 2)}$$

$\boxed{3}$
$$\boxed{\lim_{\theta \to 0} \frac{\cos \theta - 1}{\theta} = 0}$$

If we now put the limits $\boxed{2}$ and $\boxed{3}$ in $\boxed{1}$, we get

$$f'(x) = \lim_{h \to 0} \sin x \cdot \lim_{h \to 0} \frac{\cos h - 1}{h} + \lim_{h \to 0} \cos x \cdot \lim_{h \to 0} \frac{\sin h}{h}$$

$$= (\sin x) \cdot 0 + (\cos x) \cdot 1 = \cos x$$

So we have proved the formula for the derivative of the sine function:

$\boxed{4}$
$$\boxed{\frac{d}{dx} (\sin x) = \cos x}$$

Figure 3 shows the graphs of the function of Example 1 and its derivative. Notice that $y' = 0$ whenever y has a horizontal tangent.

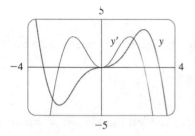

FIGURE 3

V **EXAMPLE 1** Differentiate $y = x^2 \sin x$.

SOLUTION Using the Product Rule and Formula 4, we have

$$\frac{dy}{dx} = x^2 \frac{d}{dx}(\sin x) + \sin x \frac{d}{dx}(x^2)$$

$$= x^2 \cos x + 2x \sin x \qquad \blacksquare$$

Using the same methods as in the proof of Formula 4, one can prove (see Exercise 20) that

5
$$\boxed{\frac{d}{dx}(\cos x) = -\sin x}$$

The tangent function can also be differentiated by using the definition of a derivative, but it is easier to use the Quotient Rule together with Formulas 4 and 5:

$$\frac{d}{dx}(\tan x) = \frac{d}{dx}\left(\frac{\sin x}{\cos x}\right)$$

$$= \frac{\cos x \dfrac{d}{dx}(\sin x) - \sin x \dfrac{d}{dx}(\cos x)}{\cos^2 x}$$

$$= \frac{\cos x \cdot \cos x - \sin x(-\sin x)}{\cos^2 x}$$

$$= \frac{\cos^2 x + \sin^2 x}{\cos^2 x}$$

$$= \frac{1}{\cos^2 x} = \sec^2 x$$

6
$$\boxed{\frac{d}{dx}(\tan x) = \sec^2 x}$$

The derivatives of the remaining trigonometric functions, csc, sec, and cot, can also be found easily using the Quotient Rule (see Exercises 17–19). We collect all the differentiation formulas for trigonometric functions in the following table. Remember that they are valid only when x is measured in radians.

When you memorize this table, it is helpful to notice that the minus signs go with the derivatives of the "cofunctions," that is, cosine, cosecant, and cotangent.

Derivatives of Trigonometric Functions	
$\dfrac{d}{dx}(\sin x) = \cos x$	$\dfrac{d}{dx}(\csc x) = -\csc x \cot x$
$\dfrac{d}{dx}(\cos x) = -\sin x$	$\dfrac{d}{dx}(\sec x) = \sec x \tan x$
$\dfrac{d}{dx}(\tan x) = \sec^2 x$	$\dfrac{d}{dx}(\cot x) = -\csc^2 x$

EXAMPLE 2 Differentiate $f(x) = \dfrac{\sec x}{1 + \tan x}$. For what values of x does the graph of f have a horizontal tangent?

SOLUTION The Quotient Rule gives

$$f'(x) = \frac{(1 + \tan x)\dfrac{d}{dx}(\sec x) - \sec x\dfrac{d}{dx}(1 + \tan x)}{(1 + \tan x)^2}$$

$$= \frac{(1 + \tan x)\sec x \tan x - \sec x \cdot \sec^2 x}{(1 + \tan x)^2}$$

$$= \frac{\sec x (\tan x + \tan^2 x - \sec^2 x)}{(1 + \tan x)^2}$$

$$= \frac{\sec x (\tan x - 1)}{(1 + \tan x)^2}$$

In simplifying the answer we have used the identity $\tan^2 x + 1 = \sec^2 x$.

Since $\sec x$ is never 0, we see that $f'(x) = 0$ when $\tan x = 1$, and this occurs when $x = n\pi + \pi/4$, where n is an integer (see Figure 4).

FIGURE 4

The horizontal tangents in Example 2

Trigonometric functions are often used in modeling real-world phenomena. In particular, vibrations, waves, elastic motions, and other quantities that vary in a periodic manner can be described using trigonometric functions. In the following example we discuss an instance of simple harmonic motion.

V **EXAMPLE 3** An object at the end of a vertical spring is stretched 4 cm beyond its rest position and released at time $t = 0$. (See Figure 5 and note that the downward direction is positive.) Its position at time t is

$$s = f(t) = 4 \cos t$$

Find the velocity and acceleration at time t and use them to analyze the motion of the object.

SOLUTION The velocity and acceleration are

$$v = \frac{ds}{dt} = \frac{d}{dt}(4 \cos t) = 4\frac{d}{dt}(\cos t) = -4 \sin t$$

$$a = \frac{dv}{dt} = \frac{d}{dt}(-4 \sin t) = -4\frac{d}{dt}(\sin t) = -4 \cos t$$

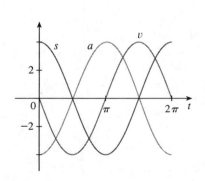

FIGURE 5

The object oscillates from the lowest point ($s = 4$ cm) to the highest point ($s = -4$ cm). The period of the oscillation is 2π, the period of $\cos t$.

The speed is $|v| = 4|\sin t|$, which is greatest when $|\sin t| = 1$, that is, when $\cos t = 0$. So the object moves fastest as it passes through its equilibrium position ($s = 0$). Its speed is 0 when $\sin t = 0$, that is, at the high and low points.

The acceleration $a = -4 \cos t = 0$ when $s = 0$. It has greatest magnitude at the high and low points. See the graphs in Figure 6.

FIGURE 6

EXAMPLE 4 Find the 27th derivative of $\cos x$.

SOLUTION The first few derivatives of $f(x) = \cos x$ are as follows:

PS Look for a pattern.

$$f'(x) = -\sin x$$
$$f''(x) = -\cos x$$
$$f'''(x) = \sin x$$
$$f^{(4)}(x) = \cos x$$
$$f^{(5)}(x) = -\sin x$$

We see that the successive derivatives occur in a cycle of length 4 and, in particular, $f^{(n)}(x) = \cos x$ whenever n is a multiple of 4. Therefore

$$f^{(24)}(x) = \cos x$$

and, differentiating three more times, we have

$$f^{(27)}(x) = \sin x$$

Our main use for the limit in Equation 2 has been to prove the differentiation formula for the sine function. But this limit is also useful in finding certain other trigonometric limits, as the following two examples show.

EXAMPLE 5 Find $\displaystyle\lim_{x \to 0} \frac{\sin 7x}{4x}$.

SOLUTION In order to apply Equation 2, we first rewrite the function by multiplying and dividing by 7:

Note that $\sin 7x \neq 7 \sin x$.

$$\frac{\sin 7x}{4x} = \frac{7}{4}\left(\frac{\sin 7x}{7x}\right)$$

If we let $\theta = 7x$, then $\theta \to 0$ as $x \to 0$, so by Equation 2 we have

$$\lim_{x \to 0} \frac{\sin 7x}{4x} = \frac{7}{4} \lim_{x \to 0}\left(\frac{\sin 7x}{7x}\right)$$

$$= \frac{7}{4} \lim_{\theta \to 0} \frac{\sin \theta}{\theta} = \frac{7}{4} \cdot 1 = \frac{7}{4}$$

V **EXAMPLE 6** Calculate $\displaystyle\lim_{x \to 0} x \cot x$.

SOLUTION Here we divide numerator and denominator by x:

$$\lim_{x \to 0} x \cot x = \lim_{x \to 0} \frac{x \cos x}{\sin x}$$

$$= \lim_{x \to 0} \frac{\cos x}{\dfrac{\sin x}{x}} = \frac{\displaystyle\lim_{x \to 0} \cos x}{\displaystyle\lim_{x \to 0} \dfrac{\sin x}{x}}$$

$$= \frac{\cos 0}{1} \qquad \text{(by the continuity of cosine and Equation 2)}$$

$$= 1$$

3.3 Exercises

1–16 Differentiate.

1. $f(x) = 3x^2 - 2\cos x$

2. $f(x) = \sqrt{x}\,\sin x$

3. $f(x) = \sin x + \frac{1}{2}\cot x$

4. $y = 2\sec x - \csc x$

5. $g(t) = t^3\cos t$

6. $g(t) = 4\sec t + \tan t$

7. $h(\theta) = \csc\theta + e^\theta\cot\theta$

8. $y = e^u(\cos u + cu)$

9. $y = \dfrac{x}{2 - \tan x}$

10. $y = \sin\theta\cos\theta$

11. $f(\theta) = \dfrac{\sec\theta}{1 + \sec\theta}$

12. $y = \dfrac{\cos x}{1 - \sin x}$

13. $y = \dfrac{t\sin t}{1 + t}$

14. $y = \dfrac{1 - \sec x}{\tan x}$

15. $f(x) = xe^x\csc x$

16. $y = x^2\sin x\tan x$

---

17. Prove that $\dfrac{d}{dx}(\csc x) = -\csc x\cot x$.

18. Prove that $\dfrac{d}{dx}(\sec x) = \sec x\tan x$.

19. Prove that $\dfrac{d}{dx}(\cot x) = -\csc^2 x$.

20. Prove, using the definition of derivative, that if $f(x) = \cos x$, then $f'(x) = -\sin x$.

21–24 Find an equation of the tangent line to the curve at the given point.

21. $y = \sec x$, $(\pi/3, 2)$

22. $y = e^x\cos x$, $(0, 1)$

23. $y = \cos x - \sin x$, $(\pi, -1)$

24. $y = x + \tan x$, (π, π)

---

25. (a) Find an equation of the tangent line to the curve $y = 2x\sin x$ at the point $(\pi/2, \pi)$.

 (b) Illustrate part (a) by graphing the curve and the tangent line on the same screen.

26. (a) Find an equation of the tangent line to the curve $y = 3x + 6\cos x$ at the point $(\pi/3, \pi + 3)$.

 (b) Illustrate part (a) by graphing the curve and the tangent line on the same screen.

27. (a) If $f(x) = \sec x - x$, find $f'(x)$.

 (b) Check to see that your answer to part (a) is reasonable by graphing both f and f' for $|x| < \pi/2$.

28. (a) If $f(x) = e^x\cos x$, find $f'(x)$ and $f''(x)$.

(b) Check to see that your answers to part (a) are reasonable by graphing f, f', and f''.

29. If $H(\theta) = \theta\sin\theta$, find $H'(\theta)$ and $H''(\theta)$.

30. If $f(t) = \csc t$, find $f''(\pi/6)$.

31. (a) Use the Quotient Rule to differentiate the function
$$f(x) = \frac{\tan x - 1}{\sec x}$$

(b) Simplify the expression for $f(x)$ by writing it in terms of $\sin x$ and $\cos x$, and then find $f'(x)$.

(c) Show that your answers to parts (a) and (b) are equivalent.

32. Suppose $f(\pi/3) = 4$ and $f'(\pi/3) = -2$, and let $g(x) = f(x)\sin x$ and $h(x) = (\cos x)/f(x)$. Find
(a) $g'(\pi/3)$ (b) $h'(\pi/3)$

33–34 For what values of x does the graph of f have a horizontal tangent?

33. $f(x) = x + 2\sin x$

34. $f(x) = e^x\cos x$

35. A mass on a spring vibrates horizontally on a smooth level surface (see the figure). Its equation of motion is $x(t) = 8\sin t$, where t is in seconds and x in centimeters.
(a) Find the velocity and acceleration at time t.
(b) Find the position, velocity, and acceleration of the mass at time $t = 2\pi/3$. In what direction is it moving at that time?

36. An elastic band is hung on a hook and a mass is hung on the lower end of the band. When the mass is pulled downward and then released, it vibrates vertically. The equation of motion is $s = 2\cos t + 3\sin t$, $t \geq 0$, where s is measured in centimeters and t in seconds. (Take the positive direction to be downward.)
(a) Find the velocity and acceleration at time t.
(b) Graph the velocity and acceleration functions.
(c) When does the mass pass through the equilibrium position for the first time?
(d) How far from its equilibrium position does the mass travel?
(e) When is the speed the greatest?

37. A ladder 6 m long rests against a vertical wall. Let θ be the angle between the top of the ladder and the wall and let x be the distance from the bottom of the ladder to the wall. If the bottom of the ladder slides away from the wall, how fast does x change with respect to θ when $\theta = \pi/3$?

 Graphing calculator or computer required   **1.** Homework Hints available at stewartcalculus.com

38. An object with mass m is dragged along a horizontal plane by a force acting along a rope attached to the object. If the rope makes an angle θ with the plane, then the magnitude of the force is

$$F = \frac{\mu mg}{\mu \sin\theta + \cos\theta}$$

where μ is a constant called the *coefficient of friction*.

(a) Find the rate of change of F with respect to θ.

(b) When is this rate of change equal to 0?

(c) If $m = 20$ kg, $g = 9.8$ m/s^2, and $\mu = 0.6$, draw the graph of F as a function of θ and use it to locate the value of θ for which $dF/d\theta = 0$. Is the value consistent with your answer to part (b)?

39–48 Find the limit.

39. $\displaystyle\lim_{x\to0} \frac{\sin 3x}{x}$

40. $\displaystyle\lim_{x\to0} \frac{\sin 4x}{\sin 6x}$

41. $\displaystyle\lim_{t\to0} \frac{\tan 6t}{\sin 2t}$

42. $\displaystyle\lim_{\theta\to0} \frac{\cos\theta - 1}{\sin\theta}$

43. $\displaystyle\lim_{x\to0} \frac{\sin 3x}{5x^3 - 4x}$

44. $\displaystyle\lim_{x\to0} \frac{\sin 3x \sin 5x}{x^2}$

45. $\displaystyle\lim_{\theta\to0} \frac{\sin\theta}{\theta + \tan\theta}$

46. $\displaystyle\lim_{x\to0} \frac{\sin(x^2)}{x}$

47. $\displaystyle\lim_{x\to\pi/4} \frac{1 - \tan x}{\sin x - \cos x}$

48. $\displaystyle\lim_{x\to1} \frac{\sin(x - 1)}{x^2 + x - 2}$

49–50 Find the given derivative by finding the first few derivatives and observing the pattern that occurs.

49. $\dfrac{d^{99}}{dx^{99}} (\sin x)$

50. $\dfrac{d^{35}}{dx^{35}} (x \sin x)$

51. Find constants A and B such that the function $y = A \sin x + B \cos x$ satisfies the differential equation $y'' + y' - 2y = \sin x$.

52. (a) Evaluate $\displaystyle\lim_{x\to\infty} x \sin \frac{1}{x}$.

(b) Evaluate $\displaystyle\lim_{x\to0} x \sin \frac{1}{x}$.

(c) Illustrate parts (a) and (b) by graphing $y = x \sin(1/x)$.

53. Differentiate each trigonometric identity to obtain a new (or familiar) identity.

(a) $\tan x = \dfrac{\sin x}{\cos x}$

(b) $\sec x = \dfrac{1}{\cos x}$

(c) $\sin x + \cos x = \dfrac{1 + \cot x}{\csc x}$

54. A semicircle with diameter PQ sits on an isosceles triangle PQR to form a region shaped like a two-dimensional ice-cream cone, as shown in the figure. If $A(\theta)$ is the area of the semicircle and $B(\theta)$ is the area of the triangle, find

$$\lim_{\theta\to0^+} \frac{A(\theta)}{B(\theta)}$$

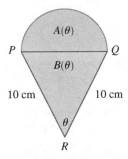

55. The figure shows a circular arc of length s and a chord of length d, both subtended by a central angle θ. Find

$$\lim_{\theta\to0^+} \frac{s}{d}$$

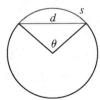

56. Let $f(x) = \dfrac{x}{\sqrt{1 - \cos 2x}}$.

(a) Graph f. What type of discontinuity does it appear to have at 0?

(b) Calculate the left and right limits of f at 0. Do these values confirm your answer to part (a)?

3.4 The Chain Rule

Suppose you are asked to differentiate the function

$$F(x) = \sqrt{x^2 + 1}$$

The differentiation formulas you learned in the previous sections of this chapter do not enable you to calculate $F'(x)$.

See Section 1.3 for a review of composite functions.

Observe that F is a composite function. In fact, if we let $y = f(u) = \sqrt{u}$ and let $u = g(x) = x^2 + 1$, then we can write $y = F(x) = f(g(x))$, that is, $F = f \circ g$. We know how to differentiate both f and g, so it would be useful to have a rule that tells us how to find the derivative of $F = f \circ g$ in terms of the derivatives of f and g.

It turns out that the derivative of the composite function $f \circ g$ is the product of the derivatives of f and g. This fact is one of the most important of the differentiation rules and is called the *Chain Rule*. It seems plausible if we interpret derivatives as rates of change. Regard du/dx as the rate of change of u with respect to x, dy/du as the rate of change of y with respect to u, and dy/dx as the rate of change of y with respect to x. If u changes twice as fast as x and y changes three times as fast as u, then it seems reasonable that y changes six times as fast as x, and so we expect that

$$\frac{dy}{dx} = \frac{dy}{du}\frac{du}{dx}$$

The Chain Rule If g is differentiable at x and f is differentiable at $g(x)$, then the composite function $F = f \circ g$ defined by $F(x) = f(g(x))$ is differentiable at x and F' is given by the product

$$F'(x) = f'(g(x)) \cdot g'(x)$$

In Leibniz notation, if $y = f(u)$ and $u = g(x)$ are both differentiable functions, then

$$\frac{dy}{dx} = \frac{dy}{du}\frac{du}{dx}$$

James Gregory

The first person to formulate the Chain Rule was the Scottish mathematician James Gregory (1638–1675), who also designed the first practical reflecting telescope. Gregory discovered the basic ideas of calculus at about the same time as Newton. He became the first Professor of Mathematics at the University of St. Andrews and later held the same position at the University of Edinburgh. But one year after accepting that position he died at the age of 36.

COMMENTS ON THE PROOF OF THE CHAIN RULE Let Δu be the change in u corresponding to a change of Δx in x, that is,

$$\Delta u = g(x + \Delta x) - g(x)$$

Then the corresponding change in y is

$$\Delta y = f(u + \Delta u) - f(u)$$

It is tempting to write

$$\frac{dy}{dx} = \lim_{\Delta x \to 0} \frac{\Delta y}{\Delta x}$$

1

$$= \lim_{\Delta x \to 0} \frac{\Delta y}{\Delta u} \cdot \frac{\Delta u}{\Delta x}$$

$$= \lim_{\Delta x \to 0} \frac{\Delta y}{\Delta u} \cdot \lim_{\Delta x \to 0} \frac{\Delta u}{\Delta x}$$

$$= \lim_{\Delta u \to 0} \frac{\Delta y}{\Delta u} \cdot \lim_{\Delta x \to 0} \frac{\Delta u}{\Delta x} \qquad \text{(Note that } \Delta u \to 0 \text{ as } \Delta x \to 0 \text{ since } g \text{ is continuous.)}$$

$$= \frac{dy}{du}\frac{du}{dx}$$

The only flaw in this reasoning is that in $\boxed{1}$ it might happen that $\Delta u = 0$ (even when $\Delta x \neq 0$) and, of course, we can't divide by 0. Nonetheless, this reasoning does at least *suggest* that the Chain Rule is true. A full proof of the Chain Rule is given at the end of this section. ▬

The Chain Rule can be written either in the prime notation

$$\boxed{2} \qquad (f \circ g)'(x) = f'(g(x)) \cdot g'(x)$$

or, if $y = f(u)$ and $u = g(x)$, in Leibniz notation:

$$\boxed{3} \qquad \frac{dy}{dx} = \frac{dy}{du}\frac{du}{dx}$$

Equation 3 is easy to remember because if dy/du and du/dx were quotients, then we could cancel du. Remember, however, that du has not been defined and du/dx should not be thought of as an actual quotient.

EXAMPLE 1 Find $F'(x)$ if $F(x) = \sqrt{x^2 + 1}$.

SOLUTION 1 (using Equation 2): At the beginning of this section we expressed F as $F(x) = (f \circ g)(x) = f(g(x))$ where $f(u) = \sqrt{u}$ and $g(x) = x^2 + 1$. Since

$$f'(u) = \tfrac{1}{2}u^{-1/2} = \frac{1}{2\sqrt{u}} \qquad \text{and} \qquad g'(x) = 2x$$

we have

$$F'(x) = f'(g(x)) \cdot g'(x)$$

$$= \frac{1}{2\sqrt{x^2 + 1}} \cdot 2x = \frac{x}{\sqrt{x^2 + 1}}$$

SOLUTION 2 (using Equation 3): If we let $u = x^2 + 1$ and $y = \sqrt{u}$, then

$$F'(x) = \frac{dy}{du}\frac{du}{dx} = \frac{1}{2\sqrt{u}}\,(2x) = \frac{1}{2\sqrt{x^2 + 1}}(2x) = \frac{x}{\sqrt{x^2 + 1}} \qquad ▬$$

When using Formula 3 we should bear in mind that dy/dx refers to the derivative of y when y is considered as a function of x (called the *derivative of y with respect to x*), whereas dy/du refers to the derivative of y when considered as a function of u (the derivative of y with respect to u). For instance, in Example 1, y can be considered as a function of x $\left(y = \sqrt{x^2 + 1}\right)$ and also as a function of u $\left(y = \sqrt{u}\right)$. Note that

$$\frac{dy}{dx} = F'(x) = \frac{x}{\sqrt{x^2 + 1}} \qquad \text{whereas} \qquad \frac{dy}{du} = f'(u) = \frac{1}{2\sqrt{u}}$$

NOTE In using the Chain Rule we work from the outside to the inside. Formula 2 says that *we differentiate the outer function f [at the inner function $g(x)$] and then we multiply by the derivative of the inner function.*

$$\frac{d}{dx} \quad \underbrace{f}_{\substack{\text{outer} \\ \text{function}}} \quad \underbrace{(g(x))}_{\substack{\text{evaluated} \\ \text{at inner} \\ \text{function}}} \quad = \quad \underbrace{f'}_{\substack{\text{derivative} \\ \text{of outer} \\ \text{function}}} \quad \underbrace{(g(x))}_{\substack{\text{evaluated} \\ \text{at inner} \\ \text{function}}} \quad \cdot \quad \underbrace{g'(x)}_{\substack{\text{derivative} \\ \text{of inner} \\ \text{function}}}$$

V **EXAMPLE 2** Differentiate (a) $y = \sin(x^2)$ and (b) $y = \sin^2 x$.

SOLUTION

(a) If $y = \sin(x^2)$, then the outer function is the sine function and the inner function is the squaring function, so the Chain Rule gives

$$\frac{dy}{dx} = \frac{d}{dx} \underbrace{\sin}_{\substack{\text{outer} \\ \text{function}}} \underbrace{(x^2)}_{\substack{\text{evaluated} \\ \text{at inner} \\ \text{function}}} = \underbrace{\cos}_{\substack{\text{derivative} \\ \text{of outer} \\ \text{function}}} \underbrace{(x^2)}_{\substack{\text{evaluated} \\ \text{at inner} \\ \text{function}}} \cdot \underbrace{2x}_{\substack{\text{derivative} \\ \text{of inner} \\ \text{function}}}$$

$$= 2x \cos(x^2)$$

(b) Note that $\sin^2 x = (\sin x)^2$. Here the outer function is the squaring function and the inner function is the sine function. So

$$\frac{dy}{dx} = \frac{d}{dx} \underbrace{(\sin x)^2}_{\substack{\text{inner} \\ \text{function}}} = \underbrace{2}_{\substack{\text{derivative} \\ \text{of outer} \\ \text{function}}} \cdot \underbrace{(\sin x)}_{\substack{\text{evaluated} \\ \text{at inner} \\ \text{function}}} \cdot \underbrace{\cos x}_{\substack{\text{derivative} \\ \text{of inner} \\ \text{function}}}$$

The answer can be left as $2 \sin x \cos x$ or written as $\sin 2x$ (by a trigonometric identity known as the double-angle formula).

See Reference Page 2 or Appendix D.

In Example 2(a) we combined the Chain Rule with the rule for differentiating the sine function. In general, if $y = \sin u$, where u is a differentiable function of x, then, by the Chain Rule,

$$\frac{dy}{dx} = \frac{dy}{du} \frac{du}{dx} = \cos u \frac{du}{dx}$$

Thus

$$\frac{d}{dx}(\sin u) = \cos u \frac{du}{dx}$$

In a similar fashion, all of the formulas for differentiating trigonometric functions can be combined with the Chain Rule.

Let's make explicit the special case of the Chain Rule where the outer function f is a power function. If $y = [g(x)]^n$, then we can write $y = f(u) = u^n$ where $u = g(x)$. By using the Chain Rule and then the Power Rule, we get

$$\frac{dy}{dx} = \frac{dy}{du} \frac{du}{dx} = nu^{n-1} \frac{du}{dx} = n[g(x)]^{n-1} g'(x)$$

---

4 **The Power Rule Combined with the Chain Rule** If n is any real number and $u = g(x)$ is differentiable, then

$$\frac{d}{dx}(u^n) = nu^{n-1} \frac{du}{dx}$$

Alternatively,
$$\frac{d}{dx}[g(x)]^n = n[g(x)]^{n-1} \cdot g'(x)$$

Notice that the derivative in Example 1 could be calculated by taking $n = \frac{1}{2}$ in Rule 4.

EXAMPLE 3   Differentiate $y = (x^3 - 1)^{100}$.

SOLUTION   Taking $u = g(x) = x^3 - 1$ and $n = 100$ in ④, we have

$$\frac{dy}{dx} = \frac{d}{dx}(x^3 - 1)^{100} = 100(x^3 - 1)^{99}\frac{d}{dx}(x^3 - 1)$$

$$= 100(x^3 - 1)^{99} \cdot 3x^2 = 300x^2(x^3 - 1)^{99}$$

V   EXAMPLE 4   Find $f'(x)$ if $f(x) = \dfrac{1}{\sqrt[3]{x^2 + x + 1}}$.

SOLUTION   First rewrite f: $f(x) = (x^2 + x + 1)^{-1/3}$

Thus $f'(x) = -\tfrac{1}{3}(x^2 + x + 1)^{-4/3}\dfrac{d}{dx}(x^2 + x + 1)$

$$= -\tfrac{1}{3}(x^2 + x + 1)^{-4/3}(2x + 1)$$

EXAMPLE 5   Find the derivative of the function

$$g(t) = \left(\frac{t - 2}{2t + 1}\right)^9$$

SOLUTION   Combining the Power Rule, Chain Rule, and Quotient Rule, we get

$$g'(t) = 9\left(\frac{t - 2}{2t + 1}\right)^8 \frac{d}{dt}\left(\frac{t - 2}{2t + 1}\right)$$

$$= 9\left(\frac{t - 2}{2t + 1}\right)^8 \frac{(2t + 1) \cdot 1 - 2(t - 2)}{(2t + 1)^2} = \frac{45(t - 2)^8}{(2t + 1)^{10}}$$

EXAMPLE 6   Differentiate $y = (2x + 1)^5(x^3 - x + 1)^4$.

SOLUTION   In this example we must use the Product Rule before using the Chain Rule:

$$\frac{dy}{dx} = (2x + 1)^5\frac{d}{dx}(x^3 - x + 1)^4 + (x^3 - x + 1)^4\frac{d}{dx}(2x + 1)^5$$

$$= (2x + 1)^5 \cdot 4(x^3 - x + 1)^3\frac{d}{dx}(x^3 - x + 1)$$

$$+ (x^3 - x + 1)^4 \cdot 5(2x + 1)^4\frac{d}{dx}(2x + 1)$$

$$= 4(2x + 1)^5(x^3 - x + 1)^3(3x^2 - 1) + 5(x^3 - x + 1)^4(2x + 1)^4 \cdot 2$$

Noticing that each term has the common factor $2(2x + 1)^4(x^3 - x + 1)^3$, we could factor it out and write the answer as

$$\frac{dy}{dx} = 2(2x + 1)^4(x^3 - x + 1)^3(17x^3 + 6x^2 - 9x + 3)$$

The graphs of the functions y and y' in Example 6 are shown in Figure 1. Notice that y' is large when y increases rapidly and $y' = 0$ when y has a horizontal tangent. So our answer appears to be reasonable.

FIGURE 1

EXAMPLE 7   Differentiate $y = e^{\sin x}$.

SOLUTION Here the inner function is $g(x) = \sin x$ and the outer function is the exponential function $f(x) = e^x$. So, by the Chain Rule,

$$\frac{dy}{dx} = \frac{d}{dx}\left(e^{\sin x}\right) = e^{\sin x}\frac{d}{dx}\left(\sin x\right) = e^{\sin x}\cos x$$
∎

More generally, the Chain Rule gives
$$\frac{d}{dx}\left(e^u\right) = e^u\frac{du}{dx}$$

We can use the Chain Rule to differentiate an exponential function with any base $a > 0$. Recall from Section 1.6 that $a = e^{\ln a}$. So

$$a^x = \left(e^{\ln a}\right)^x = e^{(\ln a)x}$$

and the Chain Rule gives

$$\frac{d}{dx}\left(a^x\right) = \frac{d}{dx}\left(e^{(\ln a)x}\right) = e^{(\ln a)x}\frac{d}{dx}\left(\ln a\right)x$$
$$= e^{(\ln a)x} \cdot \ln a = a^x\ln a$$

because $\ln a$ is a constant. So we have the formula

Don't confuse Formula 5 (where x is the *exponent*) with the Power Rule (where x is the *base*):
$$\frac{d}{dx}\left(x^n\right) = nx^{n-1}$$

5

$$\frac{d}{dx}\left(a^x\right) = a^x\ln a$$

In particular, if $a = 2$, we get

6

$$\frac{d}{dx}\left(2^x\right) = 2^x\ln 2$$

In Section 3.1 we gave the estimate

$$\frac{d}{dx}\left(2^x\right) \approx (0.69)2^x$$

This is consistent with the exact formula **6** because $\ln 2 \approx 0.693147$.

The reason for the name "Chain Rule" becomes clear when we make a longer chain by adding another link. Suppose that $y = f(u)$, $u = g(x)$, and $x = h(t)$, where f, g, and h are differentiable functions. Then, to compute the derivative of y with respect to t, we use the Chain Rule twice:

$$\frac{dy}{dt} = \frac{dy}{dx}\frac{dx}{dt} = \frac{dy}{du}\frac{du}{dx}\frac{dx}{dt}$$

V **EXAMPLE 8** If $f(x) = \sin(\cos(\tan x))$, then

$$f'(x) = \cos(\cos(\tan x))\frac{d}{dx}\cos(\tan x)$$

$$= \cos(\cos(\tan x))[-\sin(\tan x)]\frac{d}{dx}\left(\tan x\right)$$

$$= -\cos(\cos(\tan x))\sin(\tan x)\sec^2 x$$

Notice that we used the Chain Rule twice. ∎

EXAMPLE 9 Differentiate $y = e^{\sec 3\theta}$.

SOLUTION The outer function is the exponential function, the middle function is the secant function, and the inner function is the tripling function. So we have

$$\frac{dy}{d\theta} = e^{\sec 3\theta} \frac{d}{d\theta} (\sec 3\theta)$$

$$= e^{\sec 3\theta} \sec 3\theta \tan 3\theta \frac{d}{d\theta} (3\theta)$$

$$= 3e^{\sec 3\theta} \sec 3\theta \tan 3\theta$$

How to Prove the Chain Rule

Recall that if $y = f(x)$ and x changes from a to $a + \Delta x$, we define the increment of y as

$$\Delta y = f(a + \Delta x) - f(a)$$

According to the definition of a derivative, we have

$$\lim_{\Delta x \to 0} \frac{\Delta y}{\Delta x} = f'(a)$$

So if we denote by ε the difference between the difference quotient and the derivative, we obtain

$$\lim_{\Delta x \to 0} \varepsilon = \lim_{\Delta x \to 0} \left(\frac{\Delta y}{\Delta x} - f'(a) \right) = f'(a) - f'(a) = 0$$

But

$$\varepsilon = \frac{\Delta y}{\Delta x} - f'(a) \quad \Rightarrow \quad \Delta y = f'(a)\, \Delta x + \varepsilon\, \Delta x$$

If we define ε to be 0 when $\Delta x = 0$, then ε becomes a continuous function of Δx. Thus, for a differentiable function f, we can write

$$\boxed{7} \qquad \Delta y = f'(a)\, \Delta x + \varepsilon\, \Delta x \qquad \text{where} \quad \varepsilon \to 0 \text{ as } \Delta x \to 0$$

and ε is a continuous function of Δx. This property of differentiable functions is what enables us to prove the Chain Rule.

PROOF OF THE CHAIN RULE Suppose $u = g(x)$ is differentiable at a and $y = f(u)$ is differentiable at $b = g(a)$. If Δx is an increment in x and Δu and Δy are the corresponding increments in u and y, then we can use Equation 7 to write

$$\boxed{8} \qquad \Delta u = g'(a)\, \Delta x + \varepsilon_1\, \Delta x = [g'(a) + \varepsilon_1]\, \Delta x$$

where $\varepsilon_1 \to 0$ as $\Delta x \to 0$. Similarly

$$\boxed{9} \qquad \Delta y = f'(b)\, \Delta u + \varepsilon_2\, \Delta u = [f'(b) + \varepsilon_2]\, \Delta u$$

where $\varepsilon_2 \to 0$ as $\Delta u \to 0$. If we now substitute the expression for Δu from Equation 8 into Equation 9, we get

$$\Delta y = [f'(b) + \varepsilon_2][g'(a) + \varepsilon_1]\, \Delta x$$

so
$$\frac{\Delta y}{\Delta x} = [f'(b) + \varepsilon_2][g'(a) + \varepsilon_1]$$

As $\Delta x \to 0$, Equation 8 shows that $\Delta u \to 0$. So both $\varepsilon_1 \to 0$ and $\varepsilon_2 \to 0$ as $\Delta x \to 0$. Therefore

$$\frac{dy}{dx} = \lim_{\Delta x \to 0} \frac{\Delta y}{\Delta x} = \lim_{\Delta x \to 0} [f'(b) + \varepsilon_2][g'(a) + \varepsilon_1]$$

$$= f'(b)\,g'(a) = f'(g(a))\,g'(a)$$

This proves the Chain Rule.

3.4 Exercises

1–6 Write the composite function in the form $f(g(x))$. [Identify the inner function $u = g(x)$ and the outer function $y = f(u)$.] Then find the derivative dy/dx.

1. $y = \sin 4x$

2. $y = \sqrt{4 + 3x}$

3. $y = (1 - x^2)^{10}$

4. $y = \tan(\sin x)$

5. $y = e^{\sqrt{x}}$

6. $y = \sqrt{2 - e^x}$

7–46 Find the derivative of the function.

7. $F(x) = (x^4 + 3x^2 - 2)^5$

8. $F(x) = (4x - x^2)^{100}$

9. $F(x) = \sqrt[4]{1 + 2x + x^3}$

10. $f(x) = (1 + x^4)^{2/3}$

11. $g(t) = \dfrac{1}{(t^4 + 1)^3}$

12. $f(t) = \sqrt[3]{1 + \tan t}$

13. $y = \cos(a^3 + x^3)$

14. $y = a^3 + \cos^3 x$

15. $y = xe^{-kx}$

16. $y = e^{-2t} \cos 4t$

17. $f(x) = (2x - 3)^4(x^2 + x + 1)^5$

18. $g(x) = (x^2 + 1)^3(x^2 + 2)^6$

19. $h(t) = (t + 1)^{2/3}(2t^2 - 1)^3$

20. $F(t) = (3t - 1)^4(2t + 1)^{-3}$

21. $y = \left(\dfrac{x^2 + 1}{x^2 - 1}\right)^3$

22. $f(s) = \sqrt{\dfrac{s^2 + 1}{s^2 + 4}}$

23. $y = \sqrt{1 + 2e^{3x}}$

24. $y = 10^{1-x^2}$

25. $y = 5^{-1/x}$

26. $G(y) = \dfrac{(y - 1)^4}{(y^2 + 2y)^5}$

27. $y = \dfrac{r}{\sqrt{r^2 + 1}}$

28. $y = \dfrac{e^u - e^{-u}}{e^u + e^{-u}}$

29. $F(t) = e^{t\sin 2t}$

30. $F(v) = \left(\dfrac{v}{v^3 + 1}\right)^6$

31. $y = \sin(\tan 2x)$

32. $y = \sec^2(m\theta)$

33. $y = 2^{\sin \pi x}$

34. $y = x^2 e^{-1/x}$

35. $y = \cos\left(\dfrac{1 - e^{2x}}{1 + e^{2x}}\right)$

36. $y = \sqrt{1 + xe^{-2x}}$

37. $y = \cot^2(\sin \theta)$

38. $y = e^{k \tan \sqrt{x}}$

39. $f(t) = \tan(e^t) + e^{\tan t}$

40. $y = \sin(\sin(\sin x))$

41. $f(t) = \sin^2(e^{\sin^2 t})$

42. $y = \sqrt{x + \sqrt{x + \sqrt{x}}}$

43. $g(x) = (2ra^{rx} + n)^p$

44. $y = 2^{3^{x^2}}$

45. $y = \cos\sqrt{\sin(\tan \pi x)}$

46. $y = [x + (x + \sin^2 x)^3]^4$

47–50 Find y' and y''.

47. $y = \cos(x^2)$

48. $y = \cos^2 x$

49. $y = e^{\alpha x} \sin \beta x$

50. $y = e^{e^x}$

51–54 Find an equation of the tangent line to the curve at the given point.

51. $y = (1 + 2x)^{10}$, $(0, 1)$

52. $y = \sqrt{1 + x^3}$, $(2, 3)$

53. $y = \sin(\sin x)$, $(\pi, 0)$

54. $y = \sin x + \sin^2 x$, $(0, 0)$

55. (a) Find an equation of the tangent line to the curve $y = 2/(1 + e^{-x})$ at the point $(0, 1)$.
(b) Illustrate part (a) by graphing the curve and the tangent line on the same screen.

56. (a) The curve $y = |x|/\sqrt{2 - x^2}$ is called a *bullet-nose curve*. Find an equation of the tangent line to this curve at the point $(1, 1)$.
(b) Illustrate part (a) by graphing the curve and the tangent line on the same screen.

57. (a) If $f(x) = x\sqrt{2 - x^2}$, find $f'(x)$.
(b) Check to see that your answer to part (a) is reasonable by comparing the graphs of f and f'.

58. The function $f(x) = \sin(x + \sin 2x)$, $0 \le x \le \pi$, arises in applications to frequency modulation (FM) synthesis.
   (a) Use a graph of f produced by a graphing device to make a rough sketch of the graph of f'.
   (b) Calculate $f'(x)$ and use this expression, with a graphing device, to graph f'. Compare with your sketch in part (a).

59. Find all points on the graph of the function $f(x) = 2 \sin x + \sin^2 x$ at which the tangent line is horizontal.

60. Find the x-coordinates of all points on the curve $y = \sin 2x - 2 \sin x$ at which the tangent line is horizontal.

61. If $F(x) = f(g(x))$, where $f(-2) = 8$, $f'(-2) = 4$, $f'(5) = 3$, $g(5) = -2$, and $g'(5) = 6$, find $F'(5)$.

62. If $h(x) = \sqrt{4 + 3f(x)}$, where $f(1) = 7$ and $f'(1) = 4$, find $h'(1)$.

63. A table of values for f, g, f', and g' is given.

x	$f(x)$	$g(x)$	$f'(x)$	$g'(x)$
1	3	2	4	6
2	1	8	5	7
3	7	2	7	9

   (a) If $h(x) = f(g(x))$, find $h'(1)$.
   (b) If $H(x) = g(f(x))$, find $H'(1)$.

64. Let f and g be the functions in Exercise 63.
   (a) If $F(x) = f(f(x))$, find $F'(2)$.
   (b) If $G(x) = g(g(x))$, find $G'(3)$.

65. If f and g are the functions whose graphs are shown, let $u(x) = f(g(x))$, $v(x) = g(f(x))$, and $w(x) = g(g(x))$. Find each derivative, if it exists. If it does not exist, explain why.
   (a) $u'(1)$ (b) $v'(1)$ (c) $w'(1)$

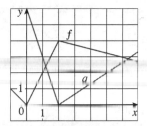

66. If f is the function whose graph is shown, let $h(x) = f(f(x))$ and $g(x) = f(x^2)$. Use the graph of f to estimate the value of each derivative.
   (a) $h'(2)$ (b) $g'(2)$

67. If $g(x) = \sqrt{f(x)}$, where the graph of f is shown, evaluate $g'(3)$.

68. Suppose f is differentiable on $\mathbb{R}$ and α is a real number. Let $F(x) = f(x^\alpha)$ and $G(x) = [f(x)]^\alpha$. Find expressions for (a) $F'(x)$ and (b) $G'(x)$.

69. Suppose f is differentiable on $\mathbb{R}$. Let $F(x) = f(e^x)$ and $G(x) = e^{f(x)}$. Find expressions for (a) $F'(x)$ and (b) $G'(x)$.

70. Let $g(x) = e^{cx} + f(x)$ and $h(x) = e^{kx}f(x)$, where $f(0) = 3$, $f'(0) = 5$, and $f''(0) = -2$.
   (a) Find $g'(0)$ and $g''(0)$ in terms of c.
   (b) In terms of k, find an equation of the tangent line to the graph of h at the point where $x = 0$.

71. Let $r(x) = f(g(h(x)))$, where $h(1) = 2$, $g(2) = 3$, $h'(1) = 4$, $g'(2) = 5$, and $f'(3) = 6$. Find $r'(1)$.

72. If g is a twice differentiable function and $f(x) = xg(x^2)$, find f'' in terms of g, g', and g''.

73. If $F(x) = f(3f(4f(x)))$, where $f(0) = 0$ and $f'(0) = 2$, find $F'(0)$.

74. If $F(x) = f(xf(xf(x)))$, where $f(1) = 2$, $f(2) = 3$, $f'(1) = 4$, $f'(2) = 5$, and $f'(3) = 6$, find $F'(1)$.

75. Show that the function $y = e^{2x}(A \cos 3x + B \sin 3x)$ satisfies the differential equation $y'' - 4y' + 13y = 0$.

76. For what values of r does the function $y = e^{rx}$ satisfy the differential equation $y'' - 4y' + y = 0$?

77. Find the 50th derivative of $y = \cos 2x$.

78. Find the 1000th derivative of $f(x) = xe^{-x}$.

79. The displacement of a particle on a vibrating string is given by the equation $s(t) = 10 + \frac{1}{4}\sin(10\pi t)$ where s is measured in centimeters and t in seconds. Find the velocity of the particle after t seconds.

80. If the equation of motion of a particle is given by $s = A \cos(\omega t + \delta)$, the particle is said to undergo *simple harmonic motion*.
   (a) Find the velocity of the particle at time t.
   (b) When is the velocity 0?

81. A Cepheid variable star is a star whose brightness alternately increases and decreases. The most easily visible such star is Delta Cephei, for which the interval between times of maximum brightness is 5.4 days. The average brightness of this star is 4.0 and its brightness changes by ± 0.35. In view of these data, the brightness of Delta Cephei at time t, where t is measured in days, has been modeled by the function

$$B(t) = 4.0 + 0.35 \sin\left(\frac{2\pi t}{5.4}\right)$$

(a) Find the rate of change of the brightness after t days.
(b) Find, correct to two decimal places, the rate of increase after one day.

82. In Example 4 in Section 1.3 we arrived at a model for the length of daylight (in hours) in Ankara, Turkey, on the tth day of the year:

$$L(t) = 12 + 2.8 \sin\left[\frac{2\pi}{365}(t - 80)\right]$$

Use this model to compare how the number of hours of daylight is increasing in Ankara on March 21 and May 21.

83. The motion of a spring that is subject to a frictional force or a damping force (such as a shock absorber in a car) is often modeled by the product of an exponential function and a sine or cosine function. Suppose the equation of motion of a point on such a spring is

$$s(t) = 2e^{-1.5t} \sin 2\pi t$$

where s is measured in centimeters and t in seconds. Find the velocity after t seconds and graph both the position and velocity functions for $0 \leqslant t \leqslant 2$.

84. Under certain circumstances a rumor spreads according to the equation

$$p(t) = \frac{1}{1 + ae^{-kt}}$$

where $p(t)$ is the proportion of the population that knows the rumor at time t and a and k are positive constants. [In Section 9.4 we will see that this is a reasonable equation for $p(t)$.]

(a) Find $\lim_{t \to \infty} p(t)$.
(b) Find the rate of spread of the rumor.
(c) Graph p for the case $a = 10$, $k = 0.5$ with t measured in hours. Use the graph to estimate how long it will take for 80% of the population to hear the rumor.

85. A particle moves along a straight line with displacement $s(t)$, velocity $v(t)$, and acceleration $a(t)$. Show that

$$a(t) = v(t) \frac{dv}{ds}$$

Explain the difference between the meanings of the derivatives dv/dt and dv/ds.

86. Air is being pumped into a spherical weather balloon. At any time t, the volume of the balloon is $V(t)$ and its radius is $r(t)$.
(a) What do the derivatives dV/dr and dV/dt represent?
(b) Express dV/dt in terms of dr/dt.

87. The flash unit on a camera operates by storing charge on a capacitor and releasing it suddenly when the flash is set off.

The following data describe the charge Q remaining on the capacitor (measured in microcoulombs, μC) at time t (measured in seconds).

t	0.00	0.02	0.04	0.06	0.08	0.10
Q	100.00	81.87	67.03	54.88	44.93	36.76

(a) Use a graphing calculator or computer to find an exponential model for the charge.
(b) The derivative $Q'(t)$ represents the electric current (measured in microamperes, μA) flowing from the capacitor to the flash bulb. Use part (a) to estimate the current when $t = 0.04$ s. Compare with the result of Example 2 in Section 2.1.

88. The table gives the population of Mexico (in millions) in the 20th century census years.

Year	Population	Year	Population
1900	13.6	1960	34.9
1910	15.2	1970	48.2
1920	14.3	1980	66.8
1930	16.6	1990	81.2
1940	19.7	2000	97.5
1950	25.8		

(a) Use a graphing calculator or computer to fit an exponential function to the data. Graph the data points and the exponential model. How good is the fit?
(b) Estimate the rates of population growth in 1950 and 1960 by averaging slopes of secant lines.
(c) Use your exponential model in part (a) to find a model for the rate of growth of the Mexican population in the 20th century.
(d) Use your model in part (c) to estimate the rates of growth in 1950 and 1960. Compare with your estimates in part (b).

89. Computer algebra systems have commands that differentiate functions, but the form of the answer may not be convenient and so further commands may be necessary to simplify the answer.
(a) Use a CAS to find the derivative in Example 5 and compare with the answer in that example. Then use the simplify command and compare again.
(b) Use a CAS to find the derivative in Example 6. What happens if you use the simplify command? What happens if you use the factor command? Which form of the answer would be best for locating horizontal tangents?

90. (a) Use a CAS to differentiate the function

$$f(x) = \sqrt{\frac{x^4 - x + 1}{x^4 + x + 1}}$$

and to simplify the result.
(b) Where does the graph of f have horizontal tangents?

(c) Graph f and f' on the same screen. Are the graphs consistent with your answer to part (b)?

91. Use the Chain Rule to prove the following.
(a) The derivative of an even function is an odd function.
(b) The derivative of an odd function is an even function.

92. Use the Chain Rule and the Product Rule to give an alternative proof of the Quotient Rule.
[*Hint:* Write $f(x)/g(x) = f(x)[g(x)]^{-1}$.]

93. (a) If n is a positive integer, prove that

$$\frac{d}{dx}(\sin^n x \cos nx) = n \sin^{n-1} x \cos(n + 1)x$$

(b) Find a formula for the derivative of $y = \cos^n x \cos nx$ that is similar to the one in part (a).

94. Suppose $y = f(x)$ is a curve that always lies above the x-axis and never has a horizontal tangent, where f is differentiable everywhere. For what value of y is the rate of change of y^5 with respect to x eighty times the rate of change of y with respect to x?

95. Use the Chain Rule to show that if θ is measured in degrees, then

$$\frac{d}{d\theta}(\sin \theta) = \frac{\pi}{180} \cos \theta$$

(This gives one reason for the convention that radian measure is always used when dealing with trigonometric functions in calculus: The differentiation formulas would not be as simple if we used degree measure.)

96. (a) Write $|x| = \sqrt{x^2}$ and use the Chain Rule to show that

$$\frac{d}{dx}|x| = \frac{x}{|x|}$$

(b) If $f(x) = |\sin x|$, find $f'(x)$ and sketch the graphs of f and f'. Where is f not differentiable?
(c) If $g(x) = \sin|x|$, find $g'(x)$ and sketch the graphs of g and g'. Where is g not differentiable?

97. If $y = f(u)$ and $u = g(x)$, where f and g are twice differentiable functions, show that

$$\frac{d^2y}{dx^2} = \frac{d^2y}{du^2}\left(\frac{du}{dx}\right)^2 + \frac{dy}{du}\frac{d^2u}{dx^2}$$

98. If $y = f(u)$ and $u = g(x)$, where f and g possess third derivatives, find a formula for d^3y/dx^3 similar to the one given in Exercise 97.

APPLIED PROJECT WHERE SHOULD A PILOT START DESCENT?

$y = P(x)$

An approach path for an aircraft landing is shown in the figure and satisfies the following conditions:

(i) The cruising altitude is h when descent starts at a horizontal distance ℓ from touchdown at the origin.

(ii) The pilot must maintain a constant horizontal speed v throughout descent.

(iii) The absolute value of the vertical acceleration should not exceed a constant k (which is much less than the acceleration due to gravity).

1. Find a cubic polynomial $P(x) = ax^3 + bx^2 + cx + d$ that satisfies condition (i) by imposing suitable conditions on $P(x)$ and $P'(x)$ at the start of descent and at touchdown.

2. Use conditions (ii) and (iii) to show that

$$\frac{6hv^2}{\ell^2} \leq k$$

3. Suppose that an airline decides not to allow vertical acceleration of a plane to exceed $k = 1385$ km/h^2. If the cruising altitude of a plane is 11,000 m and the speed is 480 km/h, how far away from the airport should the pilot start descent?

4. Graph the approach path if the conditions stated in Problem 3 are satisfied.

Graphing calculator or computer required

3.5 Implicit Differentiation

The functions that we have met so far can be described by expressing one variable explicitly in terms of another variable—for example,

$$y = \sqrt{x^3 + 1} \quad \text{or} \quad y = x \sin x$$

or, in general, $y = f(x)$. Some functions, however, are defined implicitly by a relation between x and y such as

$$\boxed{1} \qquad\qquad x^2 + y^2 = 25$$

or

$$\boxed{2} \qquad\qquad x^3 + y^3 = 6xy$$

In some cases it is possible to solve such an equation for y as an explicit function (or several functions) of x. For instance, if we solve Equation 1 for y, we get $y = \pm\sqrt{25 - x^2}$, so two of the functions determined by the implicit Equation 1 are $f(x) = \sqrt{25 - x^2}$ and $g(x) = -\sqrt{25 - x^2}$. The graphs of f and g are the upper and lower semicircles of the circle $x^2 + y^2 = 25$. (See Figure 1.)

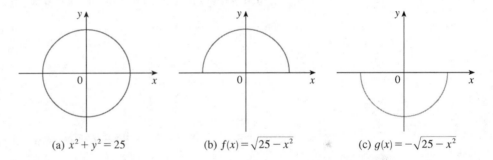

FIGURE 1 (a) $x^2 + y^2 = 25$ (b) $f(x) = \sqrt{25 - x^2}$ (c) $g(x) = -\sqrt{25 - x^2}$

It's not easy to solve Equation 2 for y explicitly as a function of x by hand. (A computer algebra system has no trouble, but the expressions it obtains are very complicated.) Nonetheless, $\boxed{2}$ is the equation of a curve called the **folium of Descartes** shown in Figure 2 and it implicitly defines y as several functions of x. The graphs of three such functions are shown in Figure 3. When we say that f is a function defined implicitly by Equation 2, we mean that the equation

$$x^3 + [f(x)]^3 = 6xf(x)$$

is true for all values of x in the domain of f.

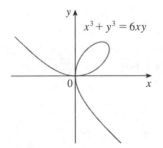

FIGURE 2 The folium of Descartes

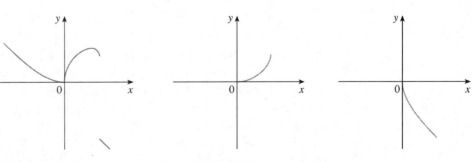

FIGURE 3 Graphs of three functions defined by the folium of Descartes

Fortunately, we don't need to solve an equation for y in terms of x in order to find the derivative of y. Instead we can use the method of **implicit differentiation**. This consists of differentiating both sides of the equation with respect to x and then solving the resulting equation for y'. In the examples and exercises of this section it is always assumed that the given equation determines y implicitly as a differentiable function of x so that the method of implicit differentiation can be applied.

V EXAMPLE 1

(a) If $x^2 + y^2 = 25$, find $\dfrac{dy}{dx}$.

(b) Find an equation of the tangent to the circle $x^2 + y^2 = 25$ at the point $(3, 4)$.

SOLUTION 1

(a) Differentiate both sides of the equation $x^2 + y^2 = 25$:

$$\frac{d}{dx}(x^2 + y^2) = \frac{d}{dx}(25)$$

$$\frac{d}{dx}(x^2) + \frac{d}{dx}(y^2) = 0$$

Remembering that y is a function of x and using the Chain Rule, we have

$$\frac{d}{dx}(y^2) = \frac{d}{dy}(y^2)\frac{dy}{dx} = 2y\frac{dy}{dx}$$

Thus
$$2x + 2y\frac{dy}{dx} = 0$$

Now we solve this equation for dy/dx:

$$\frac{dy}{dx} = -\frac{x}{y}$$

(b) At the point $(3, 4)$ we have $x = 3$ and $y = 4$, so

$$\frac{dy}{dx} = -\frac{3}{4}$$

An equation of the tangent to the circle at $(3, 4)$ is therefore

$$y - 4 = -\tfrac{3}{4}(x - 3) \qquad \text{or} \qquad 3x + 4y = 25$$

SOLUTION 2

(b) Solving the equation $x^2 + y^2 = 25$, we get $y = \pm\sqrt{25 - x^2}$. The point $(3, 4)$ lies on the upper semicircle $y = \sqrt{25 - x^2}$ and so we consider the function $f(x) = \sqrt{25 - x^2}$. Differentiating f using the Chain Rule, we have

$$f'(x) = \tfrac{1}{2}(25 - x^2)^{-1/2}\frac{d}{dx}(25 - x^2)$$

$$= \tfrac{1}{2}(25 - x^2)^{-1/2}(-2x) = -\frac{x}{\sqrt{25 - x^2}}$$

Example 1 illustrates that even when it is possible to solve an equation explicitly for y in terms of x, it may be easier to use implicit differentiation.

So
$$f'(3) = -\frac{3}{\sqrt{25 - 3^2}} = -\frac{3}{4}$$

and, as in Solution 1, an equation of the tangent is $3x + 4y = 25$. ▬

NOTE 1 The expression $dy/dx = -x/y$ in Solution 1 gives the derivative in terms of both x and y. It is correct no matter which function y is determined by the given equation. For instance, for $y = f(x) = \sqrt{25 - x^2}$ we have

$$\frac{dy}{dx} = -\frac{x}{y} = -\frac{x}{\sqrt{25 - x^2}}$$

whereas for $y = g(x) = -\sqrt{25 - x^2}$ we have

$$\frac{dy}{dx} = -\frac{x}{y} = -\frac{x}{-\sqrt{25 - x^2}} = \frac{x}{\sqrt{25 - x^2}}$$

V EXAMPLE 2
(a) Find y' if $x^3 + y^3 = 6xy$.
(b) Find the tangent to the folium of Descartes $x^3 + y^3 = 6xy$ at the point $(3, 3)$.
(c) At what point in the first quadrant is the tangent line horizontal?

SOLUTION
(a) Differentiating both sides of $x^3 + y^3 = 6xy$ with respect to x, regarding y as a function of x, and using the Chain Rule on the term y^3 and the Product Rule on the term $6xy$, we get

$$3x^2 + 3y^2 y' = 6xy' + 6y$$

or
$$x^2 + y^2 y' = 2xy' + 2y$$

We now solve for y':
$$y^2 y' - 2xy' = 2y - x^2$$
$$(y^2 - 2x)y' = 2y - x^2$$
$$y' = \frac{2y - x^2}{y^2 - 2x}$$

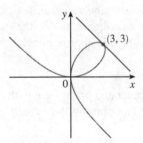

(b) When $x = y = 3$,
$$y' = \frac{2 \cdot 3 - 3^2}{3^2 - 2 \cdot 3} = -1$$

FIGURE 4

and a glance at Figure 4 confirms that this is a reasonable value for the slope at $(3, 3)$. So an equation of the tangent to the folium at $(3, 3)$ is

$$y - 3 = -1(x - 3) \qquad \text{or} \qquad x + y = 6$$

(c) The tangent line is horizontal if $y' = 0$. Using the expression for y' from part (a), we see that $y' = 0$ when $2y - x^2 = 0$ (provided that $y^2 - 2x \neq 0$). Substituting $y = \frac{1}{2}x^2$ in the equation of the curve, we get

$$x^3 + \left(\tfrac{1}{2}x^2\right)^3 = 6x\left(\tfrac{1}{2}x^2\right)$$

FIGURE 5

which simplifies to $x^6 = 16x^3$. Since $x \neq 0$ in the first quadrant, we have $x^3 = 16$. If $x = 16^{1/3} = 2^{4/3}$, then $y = \frac{1}{2}(2^{8/3}) = 2^{5/3}$. Thus the tangent is horizontal at $(2^{4/3}, 2^{5/3})$, which is approximately $(2.5198, 3.1748)$. Looking at Figure 5, we see that our answer is reasonable. ▬

NOTE 2 There is a formula for the three roots of a cubic equation that is like the quadratic formula but much more complicated. If we use this formula (or a computer algebra system) to solve the equation $x^3 + y^3 = 6xy$ for y in terms of x, we get three functions determined by the equation:

$$y = f(x) = \sqrt[3]{-\tfrac{1}{2}x^3 + \sqrt{\tfrac{1}{4}x^6 - 8x^3}} + \sqrt[3]{-\tfrac{1}{2}x^3 - \sqrt{\tfrac{1}{4}x^6 - 8x^3}}$$

and

$$y = \tfrac{1}{2}\left[-f(x) \pm \sqrt{-3}\left(\sqrt[3]{-\tfrac{1}{2}x^3 + \sqrt{\tfrac{1}{4}x^6 - 8x^3}} - \sqrt[3]{-\tfrac{1}{2}x^3 - \sqrt{\tfrac{1}{4}x^6 - 8x^3}} \right) \right]$$

(These are the three functions whose graphs are shown in Figure 3.) You can see that the method of implicit differentiation saves an enormous amount of work in cases such as this. Moreover, implicit differentiation works just as easily for equations such as

$$y^5 + 3x^2y^2 + 5x^4 = 12$$

for which it is *impossible* to find a similar expression for y in terms of x.

EXAMPLE 3   Find y' if $\sin(x + y) = y^2 \cos x$.

SOLUTION Differentiating implicitly with respect to x and remembering that y is a function of x, we get

$$\cos(x + y) \cdot (1 + y') = y^2(-\sin x) + (\cos x)(2yy')$$

(Note that we have used the Chain Rule on the left side and the Product Rule and Chain Rule on the right side.) If we collect the terms that involve y', we get

$$\cos(x + y) + y^2 \sin x = (2y \cos x)y' - \cos(x + y) \cdot y'$$

So

$$y' = \frac{y^2 \sin x + \cos(x + y)}{2y \cos x - \cos(x + y)}$$

Figure 6, drawn with the implicit-plotting command of a computer algebra system, shows part of the curve $\sin(x + y) = y^2 \cos x$. As a check on our calculation, notice that $y' = -1$ when $x = y = 0$ and it appears from the graph that the slope is approximately -1 at the origin.

Figures 7, 8, and 9 show three more curves produced by a computer algebra system with an implicit-plotting command. In Exercises 41–42 you will have an opportunity to create and examine unusual curves of this nature.

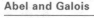

Abel and Galois

The Norwegian mathematician Niels Abel proved in 1824 that no general formula can be given for the roots of a fifth-degree equation in terms of radicals. Later the French mathematician Evariste Galois proved that it is impossible to find a general formula for the roots of an nth-degree equation (in terms of algebraic operations on the coefficients) if n is any integer larger than 4.

FIGURE 6

FIGURE 7
$(y^2 - 1)(y^2 - 4) = x^2(x^2 - 4)$

FIGURE 8
$(y^2 - 1)\sin(xy) = x^2 - 4$

FIGURE 9
$y \sin 3x = x \cos 3y$

The following example shows how to find the second derivative of a function that is defined implicitly.

EXAMPLE 4 Find y'' if $x^4 + y^4 = 16$.

SOLUTION Differentiating the equation implicitly with respect to x, we get

$$4x^3 + 4y^3 y' = 0$$

Solving for y' gives

$$\boxed{3} \qquad\qquad y' = -\frac{x^3}{y^3}$$

Figure 10 shows the graph of the curve $x^4 + y^4 = 16$ of Example 4. Notice that it's a stretched and flattened version of the circle $x^2 + y^2 = 4$. For this reason it's sometimes called a *fat circle*. It starts out very steep on the left but quickly becomes very flat. This can be seen from the expression

$$y' = -\frac{x^3}{y^3} = -\left(\frac{x}{y}\right)^3$$

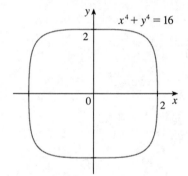

FIGURE 10

To find y'' we differentiate this expression for y' using the Quotient Rule and remembering that y is a function of x:

$$y'' = \frac{d}{dx}\left(-\frac{x^3}{y^3}\right) = -\frac{y^3 \, (d/dx)(x^3) - x^3 \, (d/dx)(y^3)}{(y^3)^2}$$

$$= -\frac{y^3 \cdot 3x^2 - x^3(3y^2 y')}{y^6}$$

If we now substitute Equation 3 into this expression, we get

$$y'' = -\frac{3x^2 y^3 - 3x^3 y^2\left(-\dfrac{x^3}{y^3}\right)}{y^6}$$

$$= -\frac{3(x^2 y^4 + x^6)}{y^7} = -\frac{3x^2(y^4 + x^4)}{y^7}$$

But the values of x and y must satisfy the original equation $x^4 + y^4 = 16$. So the answer simplifies to

$$y'' = -\frac{3x^2(16)}{y^7} = -48\frac{x^2}{y^7} \qquad\qquad\blacksquare$$

■ Derivatives of Inverse Trigonometric Functions

The inverse trigonometric functions were reviewed in Section 1.6. We discussed their continuity in Section 2.5 and their asymptotes in Section 2.6. Here we use implicit differentiation to find the derivatives of the inverse trigonometric functions, assuming that these functions are differentiable. [In fact, if f is any one-to-one differentiable function, it can be proved that its inverse function f^{-1} is also differentiable, except where its tangents are vertical. This is plausible because the graph of a differentiable function has no corner or kink and so if we reflect it about $y = x$, the graph of its inverse function also has no corner or kink.]

Recall the definition of the arcsine function:

$$y = \sin^{-1} x \qquad \text{means} \qquad \sin y = x \quad \text{and} \quad -\frac{\pi}{2} \leqslant y \leqslant \frac{\pi}{2}$$

Differentiating $\sin y = x$ implicitly with respect to x, we obtain

$$\cos y \,\frac{dy}{dx} = 1 \qquad \text{or} \qquad \frac{dy}{dx} = \frac{1}{\cos y}$$

Now $\cos y \geq 0$, since $-\pi/2 \leq y \leq \pi/2$, so

$$\cos y = \sqrt{1 - \sin^2 y} = \sqrt{1 - x^2}$$

The same method can be used to find a formula for the derivative of any inverse function. See Exercise 77.

Therefore

$$\frac{dy}{dx} = \frac{1}{\cos y} = \frac{1}{\sqrt{1 - x^2}}$$

$$\boxed{\frac{d}{dx}(\sin^{-1}x) = \frac{1}{\sqrt{1 - x^2}}}$$

Figure 11 shows the graph of $f(x) = \tan^{-1}x$ and its derivative $f'(x) = 1/(1 + x^2)$. Notice that f is increasing and $f'(x)$ is always positive. The fact that $\tan^{-1}x \to \pm\pi/2$ as $x \to \pm\infty$ is reflected in the fact that $f'(x) \to 0$ as $x \to \pm\infty$.

The formula for the derivative of the arctangent function is derived in a similar way. If $y = \tan^{-1}x$, then $\tan y = x$. Differentiating this latter equation implicitly with respect to x, we have

$$\sec^2 y \frac{dy}{dx} = 1$$

$$\frac{dy}{dx} = \frac{1}{\sec^2 y} = \frac{1}{1 + \tan^2 y} = \frac{1}{1 + x^2}$$

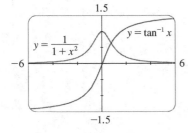

$$\boxed{\frac{d}{dx}(\tan^{-1}x) = \frac{1}{1 + x^2}}$$

FIGURE 11

V EXAMPLE 5 Differentiate (a) $y = \dfrac{1}{\sin^{-1}x}$ and (b) $f(x) = x \arctan\sqrt{x}$.

SOLUTION

(a)
$$\frac{dy}{dx} = \frac{d}{dx}(\sin^{-1}x)^{-1} = -(\sin^{-1}x)^{-2}\frac{d}{dx}(\sin^{-1}x)$$

$$= -\frac{1}{(\sin^{-1}x)^2\sqrt{1 - x^2}}$$

Recall that arctan x is an alternative notation for $\tan^{-1}x$.

(b)
$$f'(x) = x\frac{1}{1 + (\sqrt{x})^2}\left(\tfrac{1}{2}x^{-1/2}\right) + \arctan\sqrt{x}$$

$$= \frac{\sqrt{x}}{2(1 + x)} + \arctan\sqrt{x}$$

The inverse trigonometric functions that occur most frequently are the ones that we have just discussed. The derivatives of the remaining four are given in the following table. The proofs of the formulas are left as exercises.

The formulas for the derivatives of $\csc^{-1}x$ and $\sec^{-1}x$ depend on the definitions that are used for these functions. See Exercise 64.

Derivatives of Inverse Trigonometric Functions	
$\dfrac{d}{dx}(\sin^{-1}x) = \dfrac{1}{\sqrt{1 - x^2}}$	$\dfrac{d}{dx}(\csc^{-1}x) = -\dfrac{1}{x\sqrt{x^2 - 1}}$
$\dfrac{d}{dx}(\cos^{-1}x) = -\dfrac{1}{\sqrt{1 - x^2}}$	$\dfrac{d}{dx}(\sec^{-1}x) = \dfrac{1}{x\sqrt{x^2 - 1}}$
$\dfrac{d}{dx}(\tan^{-1}x) = \dfrac{1}{1 + x^2}$	$\dfrac{d}{dx}(\cot^{-1}x) = -\dfrac{1}{1 + x^2}$

3.5 Exercises

1–4
(a) Find y' by implicit differentiation.
(b) Solve the equation explicitly for y and differentiate to get y' in terms of x.
(c) Check that your solutions to parts (a) and (b) are consistent by substituting the expression for y into your solution for part (a).

1. $xy + 2x + 3x^2 = 4$ **2.** $4x^2 + 9y^2 = 36$

3. $\dfrac{1}{x} + \dfrac{1}{y} = 1$ **4.** $\cos x + \sqrt{y} = 5$

5–20 Find dy/dx by implicit differentiation.

5. $x^3 + y^3 = 1$ **6.** $2\sqrt{x} + \sqrt{y} = 3$

7. $x^2 + xy - y^2 = 4$ **8.** $2x^3 + x^2y - xy^3 = 2$

9. $x^4(x + y) = y^2(3x - y)$ **10.** $xe^y = x - y$

11. $x^2y^2 + x \sin y = 4$ **12.** $1 + x = \sin(xy^2)$

13. $4 \cos x \sin y = 1$ **14.** $e^y \sin x = x + xy$

15. $e^{x/y} = x - y$ **16.** $\sqrt{x + y} = 1 + x^2y^2$

17. $\tan^{-1}(x^2y) = x + xy^2$ **18.** $x \sin y + y \sin x = 1$

19. $e^y \cos x = 1 + \sin(xy)$ **20.** $\tan(x - y) = \dfrac{y}{1 + x^2}$

21. If $f(x) + x^2[f(x)]^3 = 10$ and $f(1) = 2$, find $f'(1)$.

22. If $g(x) + x \sin g(x) = x^2$, find $g'(0)$.

23–24 Regard y as the independent variable and x as the dependent variable and use implicit differentiation to find dx/dy.

23. $x^4y^2 - x^3y + 2xy^3 = 0$ **24.** $y \sec x = x \tan y$

25–32 Use implicit differentiation to find an equation of the tangent line to the curve at the given point.

25. $y \sin 2x = x \cos 2y$, $(\pi/2, \pi/4)$

26. $\sin(x + y) = 2x - 2y$, (π, π)

27. $x^2 + xy + y^2 = 3$, $(1, 1)$ (ellipse)

28. $x^2 + 2xy - y^2 + x = 2$, $(1, 2)$ (hyperbola)

29. $x^2 + y^2 = (2x^2 + 2y^2 - x)^2$
$(0, \frac{1}{2})$
(cardioid)

30. $x^{2/3} + y^{2/3} = 4$
$(-3\sqrt{3}, 1)$
(astroid)

31. $2(x^2 + y^2)^2 = 25(x^2 - y^2)$
(3, 1)
(lemniscate)

32. $y^2(y^2 - 4) = x^2(x^2 - 5)$
(0, −2)
(devil's curve)

33. (a) The curve with equation $y^2 = 5x^4 - x^2$ is called a **kampyle of Eudoxus**. Find an equation of the tangent line to this curve at the point $(1, 2)$.
(b) Illustrate part (a) by graphing the curve and the tangent line on a common screen. (If your graphing device will graph implicitly defined curves, then use that capability. If not, you can still graph this curve by graphing its upper and lower halves separately.)

34. (a) The curve with equation $y^2 = x^3 + 3x^2$ is called the **Tschirnhausen cubic**. Find an equation of the tangent line to this curve at the point $(1, -2)$.
(b) At what points does this curve have horizontal tangents?
(c) Illustrate parts (a) and (b) by graphing the curve and the tangent lines on a common screen.

35–38 Find y'' by implicit differentiation.

35. $9x^2 + y^2 = 9$ **36.** $\sqrt{x} + \sqrt{y} = 1$

37. $x^3 + y^3 = 1$ **38.** $x^4 + y^4 = a^4$

39. If $xy + e^y = e$, find the value of y'' at the point where $x = 0$.

40. If $x^2 + xy + y^3 = 1$, find the value of y''' at the point where $x = 1$.

[CAS] **41.** Fanciful shapes can be created by using the implicit plotting capabilities of computer algebra systems.
(a) Graph the curve with equation

$$y(y^2 - 1)(y - 2) = x(x - 1)(x - 2)$$

At how many points does this curve have horizontal tangents? Estimate the x-coordinates of these points.
(b) Find equations of the tangent lines at the points $(0, 1)$ and $(0, 2)$.
(c) Find the exact x-coordinates of the points in part (a).
(d) Create even more fanciful curves by modifying the equation in part (a).

42. (a) The curve with equation

$$2y^3 + y^2 - y^5 = x^4 - 2x^3 + x^2$$

has been likened to a bouncing wagon. Use a computer algebra system to graph this curve and discover why.

(b) At how many points does this curve have horizontal tangent lines? Find the x-coordinates of these points.

43. Find the points on the lemniscate in Exercise 31 where the tangent is horizontal.

44. Show by implicit differentiation that the tangent to the ellipse

$$\frac{x^2}{a^2} + \frac{y^2}{b^2} = 1$$

at the point (x_0, y_0) is

$$\frac{x_0 x}{a^2} + \frac{y_0 y}{b^2} = 1$$

45. Find an equation of the tangent line to the hyperbola

$$\frac{x^2}{a^2} - \frac{y^2}{b^2} = 1$$

at the point (x_0, y_0).

46. Show that the sum of the x- and y-intercepts of any tangent line to the curve $\sqrt{x} + \sqrt{y} = \sqrt{c}$ is equal to c.

47. Show, using implicit differentiation, that any tangent line at a point P to a circle with center O is perpendicular to the radius OP.

48. The Power Rule can be proved using implicit differentiation for the case where n is a rational number, $n = p/q$, and $y = f(x) = x^n$ is assumed beforehand to be a differentiable function. If $y = x^{p/q}$, then $y^q = x^p$. Use implicit differentiation to show that

$$y' = \frac{p}{q} x^{(p/q)-1}$$

49–60 Find the derivative of the function. Simplify where possible.

49. $y = \tan^{-1}\sqrt{x}$

50. $y = \sqrt{\tan^{-1} r}$

51. $y = \sin^{-1}(2x + 1)$

52. $g(x) = \sqrt{x^2 - 1} \; \sec^{-1} x$

53. $G(x) = \sqrt{1 - x^2} \arccos x$

54. $y = \tan^{-1}(x - \sqrt{1 + x^2})$

55. $h(t) = \cot^{-1}(t) + \cot^{-1}(1/t)$

56. $F(\theta) = \arcsin \sqrt{\sin \theta}$

57. $y = x \sin^{-1}x + \sqrt{1 - x^2}$

58. $y = \cos^{-1}(\sin^{-1} t)$

59. $y = \arccos\left(\dfrac{b + a \cos x}{a + b \cos x}\right), \quad 0 \leq x \leq \pi, \; a > b > 0$

60. $y = \arctan\sqrt{\dfrac{1 - x}{1 + x}}$

61–62 Find $f'(x)$. Check that your answer is reasonable by comparing the graphs of f and f'.

61. $f(x) = \sqrt{1 - x^2} \arcsin x$

62. $f(x) = \arctan(x^2 - x)$

63. Prove the formula for $(d/dx)(\cos^{-1}x)$ by the same method as for $(d/dx)(\sin^{-1}x)$.

64. (a) One way of defining $\sec^{-1}x$ is to say that $y = \sec^{-1}x \iff \sec y = x$ and $0 \leq y < \pi/2$ or $\pi \leq y < 3\pi/2$. Show that, with this definition,

$$\frac{d}{dx}(\sec^{-1}x) = \frac{1}{x\sqrt{x^2 - 1}}$$

(b) Another way of defining $\sec^{-1}x$ that is sometimes used is to say that $y = \sec^{-1}x \iff \sec y = x$ and $0 \leq y \leq \pi$, $y \neq 0$. Show that, with this definition,

$$\frac{d}{dx}(\sec^{-1}x) = \frac{1}{|x|\sqrt{x^2 - 1}}$$

65–68 Two curves are **orthogonal** if their tangent lines are perpendicular at each point of intersection. Show that the given families of curves are **orthogonal trajectories** of each other; that is, every curve in one family is orthogonal to every curve in the other family. Sketch both families of curves on the same axes.

65. $x^2 + y^2 = r^2, \quad ax + by = 0$

66. $x^2 + y^2 = ax, \quad x^2 + y^2 = by$

67. $y = cx^2, \quad x^2 + 2y^2 = k$

68. $y = ax^3, \quad x^2 + 3y^2 = b$

69. Show that the ellipse $x^2/a^2 + y^2/b^2 = 1$ and the hyperbola $x^2/A^2 - y^2/B^2 = 1$ are orthogonal trajectories if $A^2 < a^2$ and $a^2 - b^2 = A^2 + B^2$ (so the ellipse and hyperbola have the same foci).

70. Find the value of the number a such that the families of curves $y = (x + c)^{-1}$ and $y = a(x + k)^{1/3}$ are orthogonal trajectories.

71. (a) The *van der Waals equation* for n moles of a gas is

$$\left(P + \frac{n^2 a}{V^2}\right)(V - nb) = nRT$$

where P is the pressure, V is the volume, and T is the temperature of the gas. The constant R is the universal gas constant and a and b are positive constants that are characteristic of a particular gas. If T remains constant, use implicit differentiation to find dV/dP.

(b) Find the rate of change of volume with respect to pressure of 1 mole of carbon dioxide at a volume of $V = 10$ L and a pressure of $P = 2.5$ atm. Use $a = 3.592$ L^2-atm/mole^2 and $b = 0.04267$ L/mole.

72. (a) Use implicit differentiation to find y' if
$x^2 + xy + y^2 + 1 = 0$.

 (b) Plot the curve in part (a). What do you see? Prove that what you see is correct.

(c) In view of part (b), what can you say about the expression for y' that you found in part (a)?

73. The equation $x^2 - xy + y^2 = 3$ represents a "rotated ellipse," that is, an ellipse whose axes are not parallel to the coordinate axes. Find the points at which this ellipse crosses the x-axis and show that the tangent lines at these points are parallel.

74. (a) Where does the normal line to the ellipse $x^2 - xy + y^2 = 3$ at the point $(-1, 1)$ intersect the ellipse a second time?

 (b) Illustrate part (a) by graphing the ellipse and the normal line.

75. Find all points on the curve $x^2 y^2 + xy = 2$ where the slope of the tangent line is -1.

76. Find equations of both the tangent lines to the ellipse $x^2 + 4y^2 = 36$ that pass through the point $(12, 3)$.

77. (a) Suppose f is a one-to-one differentiable function and its inverse function f^{-1} is also differentiable. Use implicit differentiation to show that

$$(f^{-1})'(x) = \frac{1}{f'(f^{-1}(x))}$$

provided that the denominator is not 0.

(b) If $f(4) = 5$ and $f'(4) = \frac{2}{3}$, find $(f^{-1})'(5)$.

78. (a) Show that $f(x) = x + e^x$ is one-to-one.

(b) What is the value of $f^{-1}(1)$?

(c) Use the formula from Exercise 77(a) to find $(f^{-1})'(1)$.

79. The **Bessel function** of order 0, $y = J(x)$, satisfies the differential equation $xy'' + y' + xy = 0$ for all values of x and its value at 0 is $J(0) = 1$.

(a) Find $J'(0)$.

(b) Use implicit differentiation to find $J''(0)$.

80. The figure shows a lamp located three units to the right of the y-axis and a shadow created by the elliptical region $x^2 + 4y^2 \le 5$. If the point $(-5, 0)$ is on the edge of the shadow, how far above the x-axis is the lamp located?

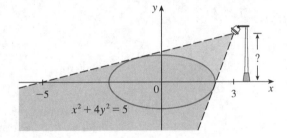

LABORATORY PROJECT [CAS] FAMILIES OF IMPLICIT CURVES

In this project you will explore the changing shapes of implicitly defined curves as you vary the constants in a family, and determine which features are common to all members of the family.

1. Consider the family of curves

$$y^2 - 2x^2(x + 8) = c[(y + 1)^2(y + 9) - x^2]$$

(a) By graphing the curves with $c = 0$ and $c = 2$, determine how many points of intersection there are. (You might have to zoom in to find all of them.)

(b) Now add the curves with $c = 5$ and $c = 10$ to your graphs in part (a). What do you notice? What about other values of c?

2. (a) Graph several members of the family of curves

$$x^2 + y^2 + cx^2y^2 = 1$$

Describe how the graph changes as you change the value of c.

(b) What happens to the curve when $c = -1$? Describe what appears on the screen. Can you prove it algebraically?

(c) Find y' by implicit differentiation. For the case $c = -1$, is your expression for y' consistent with what you discovered in part (b)?

[CAS] Computer algebra system required

3.6 Derivatives of Logarithmic Functions

In this section we use implicit differentiation to find the derivatives of the logarithmic functions $y = \log_a x$ and, in particular, the natural logarithmic function $y = \ln x$. [It can be proved that logarithmic functions are differentiable; this is certainly plausible from their graphs (see Figure 12 in Section 1.6).]

$$\boxed{1} \qquad \frac{d}{dx}(\log_a x) = \frac{1}{x \ln a}$$

PROOF Let $y = \log_a x$. Then

$$a^y = x$$

Formula 3.4.5 says that

$$\frac{d}{dx}(a^x) = a^x \ln a$$

Differentiating this equation implicitly with respect to x, using Formula 3.4.5, we get

$$a^y(\ln a)\frac{dy}{dx} = 1$$

and so

$$\frac{dy}{dx} = \frac{1}{a^y \ln a} = \frac{1}{x \ln a}$$

If we put $a = e$ in Formula 1, then the factor $\ln a$ on the right side becomes $\ln e = 1$ and we get the formula for the derivative of the natural logarithmic function $\log_e x = \ln x$:

$$\boxed{2} \qquad \frac{d}{dx}(\ln x) = \frac{1}{x}$$

By comparing Formulas 1 and 2, we see one of the main reasons that natural logarithms (logarithms with base e) are used in calculus: The differentiation formula is simplest when $a = e$ because $\ln e = 1$.

▼ EXAMPLE 1 Differentiate $y = \ln(x^3 + 1)$.

SOLUTION To use the Chain Rule, we let $u = x^3 + 1$. Then $y = \ln u$, so

$$\frac{dy}{dx} = \frac{dy}{du}\frac{du}{dx} = \frac{1}{u}\frac{du}{dx}$$

$$= \frac{1}{x^3 + 1}(3x^2) = \frac{3x^2}{x^3 + 1}$$

In general, if we combine Formula 2 with the Chain Rule as in Example 1, we get

$$\boxed{3} \qquad \frac{d}{dx}(\ln u) = \frac{1}{u}\frac{du}{dx} \qquad \text{or} \qquad \frac{d}{dx}[\ln g(x)] = \frac{g'(x)}{g(x)}$$

EXAMPLE 2 Find $\dfrac{d}{dx}\ln(\sin x)$.

SOLUTION Using $\boxed{3}$, we have

$$\frac{d}{dx}\ln(\sin x) = \frac{1}{\sin x}\frac{d}{dx}(\sin x) = \frac{1}{\sin x}\cos x = \cot x$$

EXAMPLE 3 Differentiate $f(x) = \sqrt{\ln x}$.

SOLUTION This time the logarithm is the inner function, so the Chain Rule gives

$$f'(x) = \tfrac{1}{2}(\ln x)^{-1/2}\frac{d}{dx}(\ln x) = \frac{1}{2\sqrt{\ln x}}\cdot\frac{1}{x} = \frac{1}{2x\sqrt{\ln x}}$$

EXAMPLE 4 Differentiate $f(x) = \log_{10}(2 + \sin x)$.

SOLUTION Using Formula 1 with $a = 10$, we have

$$f'(x) = \frac{d}{dx}\log_{10}(2 + \sin x)$$

$$= \frac{1}{(2 + \sin x)\ln 10}\frac{d}{dx}(2 + \sin x)$$

$$= \frac{\cos x}{(2 + \sin x)\ln 10}$$

EXAMPLE 5 Find $\dfrac{d}{dx}\ln\dfrac{x + 1}{\sqrt{x - 2}}$.

SOLUTION 1

$$\frac{d}{dx}\ln\frac{x + 1}{\sqrt{x - 2}} = \frac{1}{\dfrac{x + 1}{\sqrt{x - 2}}}\frac{d}{dx}\frac{x + 1}{\sqrt{x - 2}}$$

$$= \frac{\sqrt{x - 2}}{x + 1}\frac{\sqrt{x - 2}\cdot 1 - (x + 1)(\tfrac{1}{2})(x - 2)^{-1/2}}{x - 2}$$

$$= \frac{x - 2 - \tfrac{1}{2}(x + 1)}{(x + 1)(x - 2)}$$

$$= \frac{x - 5}{2(x + 1)(x - 2)}$$

Figure 1 shows the graph of the function f of Example 5 together with the graph of its derivative. It gives a visual check on our calculation. Notice that $f'(x)$ is large negative when f is rapidly decreasing.

FIGURE 1

SOLUTION 2 If we first simplify the given function using the laws of logarithms, then the differentiation becomes easier:

$$\frac{d}{dx}\ln\frac{x + 1}{\sqrt{x - 2}} = \frac{d}{dx}\left[\ln(x + 1) - \tfrac{1}{2}\ln(x - 2)\right]$$

$$= \frac{1}{x + 1} - \frac{1}{2}\left(\frac{1}{x - 2}\right)$$

(This answer can be left as written, but if we used a common denominator we would see that it gives the same answer as in Solution 1.)

Figure 2 shows the graph of the function $f(x) = \ln|x|$ in Example 6 and its derivative $f'(x) = 1/x$. Notice that when x is small, the graph of $y = \ln|x|$ is steep and so $f'(x)$ is large (positive or negative).

FIGURE 2

V EXAMPLE 6 Find $f'(x)$ if $f(x) = \ln|x|$.

SOLUTION Since

$$f(x) = \begin{cases} \ln x & \text{if } x > 0 \\ \ln(-x) & \text{if } x < 0 \end{cases}$$

it follows that

$$f'(x) = \begin{cases} \dfrac{1}{x} & \text{if } x > 0 \\ \dfrac{1}{-x}(-1) = \dfrac{1}{x} & \text{if } x < 0 \end{cases}$$

Thus $f'(x) = 1/x$ for all $x \neq 0$.

The result of Example 6 is worth remembering:

4
$$\frac{d}{dx}\ln|x| = \frac{1}{x}$$

Logarithmic Differentiation

The calculation of derivatives of complicated functions involving products, quotients, or powers can often be simplified by taking logarithms. The method used in the following example is called **logarithmic differentiation**.

EXAMPLE 7 Differentiate $y = \dfrac{x^{3/4}\sqrt{x^2 + 1}}{(3x + 2)^5}$.

SOLUTION We take logarithms of both sides of the equation and use the Laws of Logarithms to simplify:

$$\ln y = \tfrac{3}{4}\ln x + \tfrac{1}{2}\ln(x^2 + 1) - 5\ln(3x + 2)$$

Differentiating implicitly with respect to x gives

$$\frac{1}{y}\frac{dy}{dx} = \frac{3}{4}\cdot\frac{1}{x} + \frac{1}{2}\cdot\frac{2x}{x^2 + 1} - 5\cdot\frac{3}{3x + 2}$$

Solving for dy/dx, we get

$$\frac{dy}{dx} = y\left(\frac{3}{4x} + \frac{x}{x^2 + 1} - \frac{15}{3x + 2}\right)$$

If we hadn't used logarithmic differentiation in Example 7, we would have had to use both the Quotient Rule and the Product Rule. The resulting calculation would have been horrendous.

Because we have an explicit expression for y, we can substitute and write

$$\frac{dy}{dx} = \frac{x^{3/4}\sqrt{x^2 + 1}}{(3x + 2)^5}\left(\frac{3}{4x} + \frac{x}{x^2 + 1} - \frac{15}{3x + 2}\right)$$

Steps in Logarithmic Differentiation

1. Take natural logarithms of both sides of an equation $y = f(x)$ and use the Laws of Logarithms to simplify.

2. Differentiate implicitly with respect to x.

3. Solve the resulting equation for y'.

If $f(x) < 0$ for some values of x, then $\ln f(x)$ is not defined, but we can write $|y| = |f(x)|$ and use Equation 4. We illustrate this procedure by proving the general version of the Power Rule, as promised in Section 3.1.

The Power Rule If n is any real number and $f(x) = x^n$, then

$$f'(x) = nx^{n-1}$$

PROOF Let $y = x^n$ and use logarithmic differentiation:

$$\ln|y| = \ln|x|^n = n\ln|x| \qquad x \neq 0$$

Therefore

$$\frac{y'}{y} = \frac{n}{x}$$

Hence

$$y' = n\frac{y}{x} = n\frac{x^n}{x} = nx^{n-1}$$

■

If $x = 0$, we can show that $f'(0) = 0$ for $n > 1$ directly from the definition of a derivative.

⊘ You should distinguish carefully between the Power Rule $[(x^n)' = nx^{n-1}]$, where the base is variable and the exponent is constant, and the rule for differentiating exponential functions $[(a^x)' = a^x \ln a]$, where the base is constant and the exponent is variable.

In general there are four cases for exponents and bases:

Constant base, constant exponent

1. $\dfrac{d}{dx}(a^b) = 0 \qquad$ (a and b are constants)

Variable base, constant exponent

2. $\dfrac{d}{dx}[f(x)]^b = b[f(x)]^{b-1}f'(x)$

Constant base, variable exponent

3. $\dfrac{d}{dx}[a^{g(x)}] = a^{g(x)}(\ln a)g'(x)$

Variable base, variable exponent

4. To find $(d/dx)[f(x)]^{g(x)}$, logarithmic differentiation can be used, as in the next example.

V **EXAMPLE 8** Differentiate $y = x^{\sqrt{x}}$.

SOLUTION 1 Since both the base and the exponent are variable, we use logarithmic differentiation:

$$\ln y = \ln x^{\sqrt{x}} = \sqrt{x}\,\ln x$$

$$\frac{y'}{y} = \sqrt{x} \cdot \frac{1}{x} + (\ln x)\frac{1}{2\sqrt{x}}$$

$$y' = y\left(\frac{1}{\sqrt{x}} + \frac{\ln x}{2\sqrt{x}}\right) = x^{\sqrt{x}}\left(\frac{2 + \ln x}{2\sqrt{x}}\right)$$

Figure 3 illustrates Example 8 by showing the graphs of $f(x) = x^{\sqrt{x}}$ and its derivative.

FIGURE 3

SOLUTION 2 Another method is to write $x^{\sqrt{x}} = (e^{\ln x})^{\sqrt{x}}$:

$$\frac{d}{dx}\left(x^{\sqrt{x}}\right) = \frac{d}{dx}\left(e^{\sqrt{x}\,\ln x}\right) = e^{\sqrt{x}\,\ln x}\frac{d}{dx}\left(\sqrt{x}\,\ln x\right)$$

$$= x^{\sqrt{x}}\left(\frac{2 + \ln x}{2\sqrt{x}}\right) \qquad \text{(as in Solution 1)}$$

The Number e as a Limit

We have shown that if $f(x) = \ln x$, then $f'(x) = 1/x$. Thus $f'(1) = 1$. We now use this fact to express the number e as a limit.

From the definition of a derivative as a limit, we have

$$f'(1) = \lim_{h \to 0}\frac{f(1+h) - f(1)}{h} = \lim_{x \to 0}\frac{f(1+x) - f(1)}{x}$$

$$= \lim_{x \to 0}\frac{\ln(1+x) - \ln 1}{x} = \lim_{x \to 0}\frac{1}{x}\ln(1+x)$$

$$= \lim_{x \to 0}\ln(1+x)^{1/x}$$

Because $f'(1) = 1$, we have

$$\lim_{x \to 0}\ln(1+x)^{1/x} = 1$$

Then, by Theorem 2.5.8 and the continuity of the exponential function, we have

$$e = e^1 = e^{\lim_{x \to 0}\ln(1+x)^{1/x}} = \lim_{x \to 0}e^{\ln(1+x)^{1/x}} = \lim_{x \to 0}(1+x)^{1/x}$$

$y = (1+x)^{1/x}$

FIGURE 4

$$\boxed{5} \qquad \boxed{e = \lim_{x \to 0}(1+x)^{1/x}}$$

Formula 5 is illustrated by the graph of the function $y = (1 + x)^{1/x}$ in Figure 4 and a table of values for small values of x. This illustrates the fact that, correct to seven decimal places,

$$e \approx 2.7182818$$

If we put $n = 1/x$ in Formula 5, then $n \to \infty$ as $x \to 0^+$ and so an alternative expression for e is

$$\boxed{6} \qquad \boxed{e = \lim_{n \to \infty}\left(1 + \frac{1}{n}\right)^n}$$

x	$(1 + x)^{1/x}$
0.1	2.59374246
0.01	2.70481383
0.001	2.71692393
0.0001	2.71814593
0.00001	2.71826824
0.000001	2.71828047
0.0000001	2.71828169
0.00000001	2.71828181

3.6 Exercises

1. Explain why the natural logarithmic function $y = \ln x$ is used much more frequently in calculus than the other logarithmic functions $y = \log_a x$.

2–22 Differentiate the function.

2. $f(x) = x \ln x - x$

3. $f(x) = \sin(\ln x)$

4. $f(x) = \ln(\sin^2 x)$

5. $f(x) = \sqrt[5]{\ln x}$

6. $f(x) = \ln \sqrt[5]{x}$

7. $f(x) = \log_{10}(x^3 + 1)$

8. $f(x) = \log_5(xe^x)$

9. $f(x) = \sin x \ln(5x)$

10. $f(u) = \dfrac{u}{1 + \ln u}$

11. $g(x) = \ln\left(x\sqrt{x^2 - 1}\right)$

12. $h(x) = \ln\left(x + \sqrt{x^2 - 1}\right)$

13. $G(y) = \ln \dfrac{(2y + 1)^5}{\sqrt{y^2 + 1}}$

14. $g(r) = r^2 \ln(2r + 1)$

15. $F(s) = \ln \ln s$

16. $y = \ln\left|1 + t - t^3\right|$

17. $y = \tan[\ln(ax + b)]$

18. $y = \ln\left|\cos(\ln x)\right|$

19. $y = \ln(e^{-x} + xe^{-x})$

20. $H(z) = \ln \sqrt{\dfrac{a^2 - z^2}{a^2 + z^2}}$

21. $y = 2x \log_{10} \sqrt{x}$

22. $y = \log_2(e^{-x} \cos \pi x)$

23–26 Find y' and y''.

23. $y = x^2 \ln(2x)$

24. $y = \dfrac{\ln x}{x^2}$

25. $y = \ln\left(x + \sqrt{1 + x^2}\right)$

26. $y = \ln(\sec x + \tan x)$

27–30 Differentiate f and find the domain of f.

27. $f(x) = \dfrac{x}{1 - \ln(x - 1)}$

28. $f(x) = \sqrt{2 + \ln x}$

29. $f(x) = \ln(x^2 - 2x)$

30. $f(x) = \ln \ln \ln x$

31. If $f(x) = \dfrac{\ln x}{x^2}$, find $f'(1)$.

32. If $f(x) = \ln(1 + e^{2x})$, find $f'(0)$.

33–34 Find an equation of the tangent line to the curve at the given point.

33. $y = \ln(x^2 - 3x + 1)$, $(3, 0)$ 34. $y = x^2 \ln x$, $(1, 0)$

35. If $f(x) = \sin x + \ln x$, find $f'(x)$. Check that your answer is reasonable by comparing the graphs of f and f'.

36. Find equations of the tangent lines to the curve $y = (\ln x)/x$ at the points $(1, 0)$ and $(e, 1/e)$. Illustrate by graphing the curve and its tangent lines.

37. Let $f(x) = cx + \ln(\cos x)$. For what value of c is $f'(\pi/4) = 6$?

38. Let $f(x) = \log_a(3x^2 - 2)$. For what value of a is $f'(1) = 3$?

39–50 Use logarithmic differentiation to find the derivative of the function.

39. $y = (2x + 1)^5(x^4 - 3)^6$

40. $y = \sqrt{x}\, e^{x^2}(x^2 + 1)^{10}$

41. $y = \sqrt{\dfrac{x - 1}{x^4 + 1}}$

42. $y = \sqrt{x}\, e^{x^2 - x}(x + 1)^{2/3}$

43. $y = x^x$

44. $y = x^{\cos x}$

45. $y = x^{\sin x}$

46. $y = \sqrt{x}^{\,x}$

47. $y = (\cos x)^x$

48. $y = (\sin x)^{\ln x}$

49. $y = (\tan x)^{1/x}$

50. $y = (\ln x)^{\cos x}$

51. Find y' if $y = \ln(x^2 + y^2)$.

52. Find y' if $x^y = y^x$.

53. Find a formula for $f^{(n)}(x)$ if $f(x) = \ln(x - 1)$.

54. Find $\dfrac{d^9}{dx^9}(x^8 \ln x)$.

55. Use the definition of derivative to prove that

$$\lim_{x \to 0} \frac{\ln(1 + x)}{x} = 1$$

56. Show that $\displaystyle\lim_{n \to \infty}\left(1 + \frac{x}{n}\right)^n = e^x$ for any $x > 0$.

3.7 Rates of Change in the Natural and Social Sciences

We know that if $y = f(x)$, then the derivative dy/dx can be interpreted as the rate of change of y with respect to x. In this section we examine some of the applications of this idea to physics, chemistry, biology, economics, and other sciences.

Let's recall from Section 2.7 the basic idea behind rates of change. If x changes from x_1 to x_2, then the change in x is

$$\Delta x = x_2 - x_1$$

and the corresponding change in y is

$$\Delta y = f(x_2) - f(x_1)$$

The difference quotient

$$\frac{\Delta y}{\Delta x} = \frac{f(x_2) - f(x_1)}{x_2 - x_1}$$

is the **average rate of change of y with respect to x** over the interval $[x_1, x_2]$ and can be interpreted as the slope of the secant line PQ in Figure 1. Its limit as $\Delta x \to 0$ is the derivative $f'(x_1)$, which can therefore be interpreted as the **instantaneous rate of change of y with respect to x** or the slope of the tangent line at $P(x_1, f(x_1))$. Using Leibniz notation, we write the process in the form

$$\frac{dy}{dx} = \lim_{\Delta x \to 0} \frac{\Delta y}{\Delta x}$$

Whenever the function $y = f(x)$ has a specific interpretation in one of the sciences, its derivative will have a specific interpretation as a rate of change. (As we discussed in Section 2.7, the units for dy/dx are the units for y divided by the units for x.) We now look at some of these interpretations in the natural and social sciences.

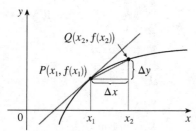

m_{PQ} = average rate of change
$m = f'(x_1)$ = instantaneous rate of change

FIGURE 1

Physics

If $s = f(t)$ is the position function of a particle that is moving in a straight line, then $\Delta s/\Delta t$ represents the average velocity over a time period Δt, and $v = ds/dt$ represents the instantaneous **velocity** (the rate of change of displacement with respect to time). The instantaneous rate of change of velocity with respect to time is **acceleration**: $a(t) = v'(t) = s''(t)$. This was discussed in Sections 2.7 and 2.8, but now that we know the differentiation formulas, we are able to solve problems involving the motion of objects more easily.

V EXAMPLE 1 The position of a particle is given by the equation

$$s = f(t) = t^3 - 6t^2 + 9t$$

where t is measured in seconds and s in meters.
(a) Find the velocity at time t.
(b) What is the velocity after 2 s? After 4 s?
(c) When is the particle at rest?
(d) When is the particle moving forward (that is, in the positive direction)?
(e) Draw a diagram to represent the motion of the particle.
(f) Find the total distance traveled by the particle during the first five seconds.
(g) Find the acceleration at time t and after 4 s.

(h) Graph the position, velocity, and acceleration functions for $0 \leqslant t \leqslant 5$.

(i) When is the particle speeding up? When is it slowing down?

SOLUTION

(a) The velocity function is the derivative of the position function.

$$s = f(t) = t^3 - 6t^2 + 9t$$

$$v(t) = \frac{ds}{dt} = 3t^2 - 12t + 9$$

(b) The velocity after 2 s means the instantaneous velocity when $t = 2$, that is,

$$v(2) = \left.\frac{ds}{dt}\right|_{t=2} = 3(2)^2 - 12(2) + 9 = -3 \text{ m/s}$$

The velocity after 4 s is

$$v(4) = 3(4)^2 - 12(4) + 9 = 9 \text{ m/s}$$

(c) The particle is at rest when $v(t) = 0$, that is,

$$3t^2 - 12t + 9 = 3(t^2 - 4t + 3) = 3(t - 1)(t - 3) = 0$$

and this is true when $t = 1$ or $t = 3$. Thus the particle is at rest after 1 s and after 3 s.

(d) The particle moves in the positive direction when $v(t) > 0$, that is,

$$3t^2 - 12t + 9 = 3(t - 1)(t - 3) > 0$$

This inequality is true when both factors are positive $(t > 3)$ or when both factors are negative $(t < 1)$. Thus the particle moves in the positive direction in the time intervals $t < 1$ and $t > 3$. It moves backward (in the negative direction) when $1 < t < 3$.

(e) Using the information from part (d) we make a schematic sketch in Figure 2 of the motion of the particle back and forth along a line (the s-axis).

(f) Because of what we learned in parts (d) and (e), we need to calculate the distances traveled during the time intervals [0, 1], [1, 3], and [3, 5] separately.

The distance traveled in the first second is

$$|f(1) - f(0)| = |4 - 0| = 4 \text{ m}$$

From $t = 1$ to $t = 3$ the distance traveled is

$$|f(3) - f(1)| = |0 - 4| = 4 \text{ m}$$

From $t = 3$ to $t = 5$ the distance traveled is

$$|f(5) - f(3)| = |20 - 0| = 20 \text{ m}$$

The total distance is $4 + 4 + 20 = 28$ m.

(g) The acceleration is the derivative of the velocity function:

$$a(t) = \frac{d^2s}{dt^2} = \frac{dv}{dt} = 6t - 12$$

$$a(4) = 6(4) - 12 = 12 \text{ m/s}^2$$

(h) Figure 3 shows the graphs of s, v, and a.

$t = 3$
$s = 0$

$t = 0$ $t = 1$
$s = 0$ $s = 4$

FIGURE 2

25

v s a

0   5

-12

FIGURE 3

(i) The particle speeds up when the velocity is positive and increasing (v and a are both positive) and also when the velocity is negative and decreasing (v and a are both negative). In other words, the particle speeds up when the velocity and acceleration have the same sign. (The particle is pushed in the same direction it is moving.) From Figure 3 we see that this happens when $1 < t < 2$ and when $t > 3$. The particle slows down when v and a have opposite signs, that is, when $0 \leq t < 1$ and when $2 < t < 3$. Figure 4 summarizes the motion of the particle.

TEC In Module 3.7 you can see an animation of Figure 4 with an expression for s that you can choose yourself.

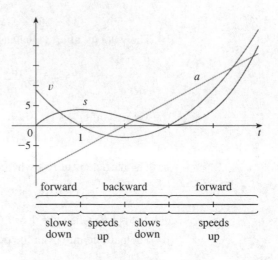

FIGURE 4

EXAMPLE 2 If a rod or piece of wire is homogeneous, then its linear density is uniform and is defined as the mass per unit length ($\rho = m/l$) and measured in kilograms per meter. Suppose, however, that the rod is not homogeneous but that its mass measured from its left end to a point x is $m = f(x)$, as shown in Figure 5.

FIGURE 5   This part of the rod has mass $f(x)$.

The mass of the part of the rod that lies between $x = x_1$ and $x = x_2$ is given by $\Delta m = f(x_2) - f(x_1)$, so the average density of that part of the rod is

$$\text{average density} = \frac{\Delta m}{\Delta x} = \frac{f(x_2) - f(x_1)}{x_2 - x_1}$$

If we now let $\Delta x \to 0$ (that is, $x_2 \to x_1$), we are computing the average density over smaller and smaller intervals. The **linear density** ρ at x_1 is the limit of these average densities as $\Delta x \to 0$; that is, the linear density is the rate of change of mass with respect to length. Symbolically,

$$\rho = \lim_{\Delta x \to 0} \frac{\Delta m}{\Delta x} = \frac{dm}{dx}$$

Thus the linear density of the rod is the derivative of mass with respect to length.

For instance, if $m = f(x) = \sqrt{x}$, where x is measured in meters and m in kilograms, then the average density of the part of the rod given by $1 \leqslant x \leqslant 1.2$ is

$$\frac{\Delta m}{\Delta x} = \frac{f(1.2) - f(1)}{1.2 - 1} = \frac{\sqrt{1.2} - 1}{0.2} \approx 0.48 \text{ kg/m}$$

while the density right at $x = 1$ is

$$\rho = \frac{dm}{dx}\bigg|_{x=1} = \frac{1}{2\sqrt{x}}\bigg|_{x=1} = 0.50 \text{ kg/m}$$

FIGURE 6

▼ EXAMPLE 3 A current exists whenever electric charges move. Figure 6 shows part of a wire and electrons moving through a plane surface, shaded red. If ΔQ is the net charge that passes through this surface during a time period Δt, then the average current during this time interval is defined as

$$\text{average current} = \frac{\Delta Q}{\Delta t} = \frac{Q_2 - Q_1}{t_2 - t_1}$$

If we take the limit of this average current over smaller and smaller time intervals, we get what is called the **current** I at a given time t_1:

$$I = \lim_{\Delta t \to 0} \frac{\Delta Q}{\Delta t} = \frac{dQ}{dt}$$

Thus the current is the rate at which charge flows through a surface. It is measured in units of charge per unit time (often coulombs per second, called amperes).

Velocity, density, and current are not the only rates of change that are important in physics. Others include power (the rate at which work is done), the rate of heat flow, temperature gradient (the rate of change of temperature with respect to position), and the rate of decay of a radioactive substance in nuclear physics.

Chemistry

EXAMPLE 4 A chemical reaction results in the formation of one or more substances (called *products*) from one or more starting materials (called *reactants*). For instance, the "equation"

$$2H_2 + O_2 \rightarrow 2H_2O$$

indicates that two molecules of hydrogen and one molecule of oxygen form two molecules of water. Let's consider the reaction

$$A + B \rightarrow C$$

where A and B are the reactants and C is the product. The **concentration** of a reactant A is the number of moles (1 mole = 6.022×10^{23} molecules) per liter and is denoted by [A]. The concentration varies during a reaction, so [A], [B], and [C] are all functions of time (t). The average rate of reaction of the product C over a time interval $t_1 \leqslant t \leqslant t_2$ is

$$\frac{\Delta[C]}{\Delta t} = \frac{[C](t_2) - [C](t_1)}{t_2 - t_1}$$

But chemists are more interested in the **instantaneous rate of reaction**, which is obtained by taking the limit of the average rate of reaction as the time interval Δt approaches 0:

$$\text{rate of reaction} = \lim_{\Delta t \to 0} \frac{\Delta[C]}{\Delta t} = \frac{d[C]}{dt}$$

Since the concentration of the product increases as the reaction proceeds, the derivative $d[C]/dt$ will be positive, and so the rate of reaction of C is positive. The concentrations of the reactants, however, decrease during the reaction, so, to make the rates of reaction of A and B positive numbers, we put minus signs in front of the derivatives $d[A]/dt$ and $d[B]/dt$. Since [A] and [B] each decrease at the same rate that [C] increases, we have

$$\text{rate of reaction} = \frac{d[C]}{dt} = -\frac{d[A]}{dt} = -\frac{d[B]}{dt}$$

More generally, it turns out that for a reaction of the form

$$a\text{A} + b\text{B} \to c\text{C} + d\text{D}$$

we have

$$-\frac{1}{a}\frac{d[A]}{dt} = -\frac{1}{b}\frac{d[B]}{dt} = \frac{1}{c}\frac{d[C]}{dt} = \frac{1}{d}\frac{d[D]}{dt}$$

The rate of reaction can be determined from data and graphical methods. In some cases there are explicit formulas for the concentrations as functions of time, which enable us to compute the rate of reaction (see Exercise 24). ▬

EXAMPLE 5 One of the quantities of interest in thermodynamics is compressibility. If a given substance is kept at a constant temperature, then its volume V depends on its pressure P. We can consider the rate of change of volume with respect to pressure—namely, the derivative dV/dP. As P increases, V decreases, so $dV/dP < 0$. The **compressibility** is defined by introducing a minus sign and dividing this derivative by the volume V:

$$\text{isothermal compressibility} = \beta = -\frac{1}{V}\frac{dV}{dP}$$

Thus β measures how fast, per unit volume, the volume of a substance decreases as the pressure on it increases at constant temperature.

For instance, the volume V (in cubic meters) of a sample of air at 25°C was found to be related to the pressure P (in kilopascals) by the equation

$$V = \frac{5.3}{P}$$

The rate of change of V with respect to P when $P = 50$ kPa is

$$\frac{dV}{dP}\bigg|_{P=50} = -\frac{5.3}{P^2}\bigg|_{P=50}$$

$$= -\frac{5.3}{2500} = -0.00212 \ \text{m}^3/\text{kPa}$$

The compressibility at that pressure is

$$\beta = -\frac{1}{V}\frac{dV}{dP}\bigg|_{P=50} = \frac{0.00212}{\dfrac{5.3}{50}} = 0.02 \ (\text{m}^3/\text{kPa})/\text{m}^3$$

Biology

EXAMPLE 6 Let $n = f(t)$ be the number of individuals in an animal or plant population at time t. The change in the population size between the times $t = t_1$ and $t = t_2$ is $\Delta n = f(t_2) - f(t_1)$, and so the average rate of growth during the time period $t_1 \leqslant t \leqslant t_2$ is

$$\text{average rate of growth} = \frac{\Delta n}{\Delta t} = \frac{f(t_2) - f(t_1)}{t_2 - t_1}$$

The **instantaneous rate of growth** is obtained from this average rate of growth by letting the time period Δt approach 0:

$$\text{growth rate} = \lim_{\Delta t \to 0} \frac{\Delta n}{\Delta t} = \frac{dn}{dt}$$

Strictly speaking, this is not quite accurate because the actual graph of a population function $n = f(t)$ would be a step function that is discontinuous whenever a birth or death occurs and therefore not differentiable. However, for a large animal or plant population, we can replace the graph by a smooth approximating curve as in Figure 7.

FIGURE 7

A smooth curve approximating a growth function

E. coli bacteria are about 2 micrometers (μm) long and 0.75 μm wide. The image was produced with a scanning electron microscope.

To be more specific, consider a population of bacteria in a homogeneous nutrient medium. Suppose that by sampling the population at certain intervals it is determined that the population doubles every hour. If the initial population is n_0 and the time t is measured in hours, then

$$f(1) = 2f(0) = 2n_0$$

$$f(2) = 2f(1) = 2^2 n_0$$

$$f(3) = 2f(2) = 2^3 n_0$$

and, in general,

$$f(t) = 2^t n_0$$

The population function is $n = n_0 2^t$.

In Section 3.4 we showed that

$$\frac{d}{dx}(a^x) = a^x \ln a$$

So the rate of growth of the bacteria population at time t is

$$\frac{dn}{dt} = \frac{d}{dt}(n_0 2^t) = n_0 2^t \ln 2$$

For example, suppose that we start with an initial population of $n_0 = 100$ bacteria. Then the rate of growth after 4 hours is

$$\frac{dn}{dt}\bigg|_{t=4} = 100 \cdot 2^4 \ln 2 = 1600 \ln 2 \approx 1109$$

This means that, after 4 hours, the bacteria population is growing at a rate of about 1109 bacteria per hour.

EXAMPLE 7 When we consider the flow of blood through a blood vessel, such as a vein or artery, we can model the shape of the blood vessel by a cylindrical tube with radius R and length l as illustrated in Figure 8.

FIGURE 8

Blood flow in an artery

Because of friction at the walls of the tube, the velocity v of the blood is greatest along the central axis of the tube and decreases as the distance r from the axis increases until v becomes 0 at the wall. The relationship between v and r is given by the **law of laminar flow** discovered by the French physician Jean-Louis-Marie Poiseuille in 1840. This law states that

$$\boxed{1} \qquad v = \frac{P}{4\eta l}(R^2 - r^2)$$

For more detailed information, see W. Nichols and M. O'Rourke (eds.), *McDonald's Blood Flow in Arteries: Theoretical, Experimental, and Clinical Principles*, 5th ed. (New York, 2005).

where η is the viscosity of the blood and P is the pressure difference between the ends of the tube. If P and l are constant, then v is a function of r with domain $[0, R]$.

The average rate of change of the velocity as we move from $r = r_1$ outward to $r = r_2$ is given by

$$\frac{\Delta v}{\Delta r} = \frac{v(r_2) - v(r_1)}{r_2 - r_1}$$

and if we let $\Delta r \to 0$, we obtain the **velocity gradient**, that is, the instantaneous rate of change of velocity with respect to r:

$$\text{velocity gradient} = \lim_{\Delta r \to 0} \frac{\Delta v}{\Delta r} = \frac{dv}{dr}$$

Using Equation 1, we obtain

$$\frac{dv}{dr} = \frac{P}{4\eta l}(0 - 2r) = -\frac{Pr}{2\eta l}$$

For one of the smaller human arteries we can take $\eta = 0.027$, $R = 0.008$ cm, $l = 2$ cm, and $P = 4000$ dynes/cm^2, which gives

$$v = \frac{4000}{4(0.027)2}(0.000064 - r^2)$$

$$\approx 1.85 \times 10^4 (6.4 \times 10^{-5} - r^2)$$

At $r = 0.002$ cm the blood is flowing at a speed of

$$v(0.002) \approx 1.85 \times 10^4 (64 \times 10^{-6} - 4 \times 10^{-6})$$

$$= 1.11 \text{ cm/s}$$

and the velocity gradient at that point is

$$\left. \frac{dv}{dr} \right|_{r=0.002} = -\frac{4000(0.002)}{2(0.027)2} \approx -74 \text{ (cm/s)/cm}$$

To get a feeling for what this statement means, let's change our units from centimeters to micrometers (1 cm $=$ 10,000 μm). Then the radius of the artery is 80 μm. The velocity at the central axis is 11,850 μm/s, which decreases to 11,110 μm/s at a distance of $r = 20$ μm. The fact that $dv/dr = -74$ (μm/s)/μm means that, when $r = 20$ μm, the velocity is decreasing at a rate of about 74 μm/s for each micrometer that we proceed away from the center. ▬▬

▬ Economics

V **EXAMPLE 8** Suppose $C(x)$ is the total cost that a company incurs in producing x units of a certain commodity. The function C is called a **cost function**. If the number of items produced is increased from x_1 to x_2, then the additional cost is $\Delta C = C(x_2) - C(x_1)$, and the average rate of change of the cost is

$$\frac{\Delta C}{\Delta x} = \frac{C(x_2) - C(x_1)}{x_2 - x_1} = \frac{C(x_1 + \Delta x) - C(x_1)}{\Delta x}$$

The limit of this quantity as $\Delta x \to 0$, that is, the instantaneous rate of change of cost with respect to the number of items produced, is called the **marginal cost** by economists:

$$\text{marginal cost} = \lim_{\Delta x \to 0} \frac{\Delta C}{\Delta x} = \frac{dC}{dx}$$

[Since x often takes on only integer values, it may not make literal sense to let Δx approach 0, but we can always replace $C(x)$ by a smooth approximating function as in Example 6.]

Taking $\Delta x = 1$ and n large (so that Δx is small compared to n), we have

$$C'(n) \approx C(n + 1) - C(n)$$

Thus the marginal cost of producing n units is approximately equal to the cost of producing one more unit [the $(n + 1)$st unit].

It is often appropriate to represent a total cost function by a polynomial

$$C(x) = a + bx + cx^2 + dx^3$$

where a represents the overhead cost (rent, heat, maintenance) and the other terms represent the cost of raw materials, labor, and so on. (The cost of raw materials may be proportional to x, but labor costs might depend partly on higher powers of x because of overtime costs and inefficiencies involved in large-scale operations.)

For instance, suppose a company has estimated that the cost (in dollars) of producing x items is

$$C(x) = 10{,}000 + 5x + 0.01x^2$$

Then the marginal cost function is

$$C'(x) = 5 + 0.02x$$

The marginal cost at the production level of 500 items is

$$C'(500) = 5 + 0.02(500) = \$15/\text{item}$$

This gives the rate at which costs are increasing with respect to the production level when $x = 500$ and predicts the cost of the 501st item.

The actual cost of producing the 501st item is

$$C(501) - C(500) = [10{,}000 + 5(501) + 0.01(501)^2]$$
$$- [10{,}000 + 5(500) + 0.01(500)^2]$$
$$= \$15.01$$

Notice that $C'(500) \approx C(501) - C(500)$.

Economists also study marginal demand, marginal revenue, and marginal profit, which are the derivatives of the demand, revenue, and profit functions. These will be considered in Chapter 4 after we have developed techniques for finding the maximum and minimum values of functions.

Other Sciences

Rates of change occur in all the sciences. A geologist is interested in knowing the rate at which an intruded body of molten rock cools by conduction of heat into surrounding rocks. An engineer wants to know the rate at which water flows into or out of a reservoir. An urban geographer is interested in the rate of change of the population density in a city as the distance from the city center increases. A meteorologist is concerned with the rate of change of atmospheric pressure with respect to height (see Exercise 17 in Section 3.8).

In psychology, those interested in learning theory study the so-called learning curve, which graphs the performance $P(t)$ of someone learning a skill as a function of the training time t. Of particular interest is the rate at which performance improves as time passes, that is, dP/dt.

In sociology, differential calculus is used in analyzing the spread of rumors (or innovations or fads or fashions). If $p(t)$ denotes the proportion of a population that knows a rumor by time t, then the derivative dp/dt represents the rate of spread of the rumor (see Exercise 84 in Section 3.4).

■ A Single Idea, Many Interpretations

Velocity, density, current, power, and temperature gradient in physics; rate of reaction and compressibility in chemistry; rate of growth and blood velocity gradient in biology; marginal cost and marginal profit in economics; rate of heat flow in geology; rate of improvement of performance in psychology; rate of spread of a rumor in sociology—these are all special cases of a single mathematical concept, the derivative.

This is an illustration of the fact that part of the power of mathematics lies in its abstractness. A single abstract mathematical concept (such as the derivative) can have different interpretations in each of the sciences. When we develop the properties of the mathematical concept once and for all, we can then turn around and apply these results to all of the sciences. This is much more efficient than developing properties of special concepts in each separate science. The French mathematician Joseph Fourier (1768–1830) put it succinctly: "Mathematics compares the most diverse phenomena and discovers the secret analogies that unite them."

3.7 Exercises

1–4 A particle moves according to a law of motion $s = f(t)$, $t \geqslant 0$, where t is measured in seconds and s in meters.
(a) Find the velocity at time t.
(b) What is the velocity after 3 s?
(c) When is the particle at rest?
(d) When is the particle moving in the positive direction?
(e) Find the total distance traveled during the first 8 s.
(f) Draw a diagram like Figure 2 to illustrate the motion of the particle.
(g) Find the acceleration at time t and after 3 s.
▦ (h) Graph the position, velocity, and acceleration functions for $0 \leqslant t \leqslant 8$.
(i) When is the particle speeding up? When is it slowing down?

1. $f(t) = t^3 - 12t^2 + 36t$

2. $f(t) = 0.01t^4 - 0.04t^3$

3. $f(t) = \cos(\pi t/4), \quad t \leqslant 10$

4. $f(t) = te^{-t/2}$

5. Graphs of the *velocity* functions of two particles are shown, where t is measured in seconds. When is each particle speeding up? When is it slowing down? Explain.

6. Graphs of the *position* functions of two particles are shown, where t is measured in seconds. When is each particle speeding up? When is it slowing down? Explain.

▦ Graphing calculator or computer required   **1.** Homework Hints available at stewartcalculus.com

7. The height (in meters) of a projectile shot vertically upward from a point 2 m above ground level with an initial velocity of 24.5 m/s is $h = 2 + 24.5t - 4.9t^2$ after t seconds.
   (a) Find the velocity after 2 s and after 4 s.
   (b) When does the projectile reach its maximum height?
   (c) What is the maximum height?
   (d) When does it hit the ground?
   (e) With what velocity does it hit the ground?

8. If a ball is thrown vertically upward with a velocity of 24.5 m/s, then its height after t seconds is $s = 24.5t - 4.9t^2$.
   (a) What is the maximum height reached by the ball?
   (b) What is the velocity of the ball when it is 29.4 m above the ground on its way up? On its way down?

9. If a rock is thrown vertically upward from the surface of Mars with velocity 15 m/s, its height after t seconds is $h = 15t - 1.86t^2$.
   (a) What is the velocity of the rock after 2 s?
   (b) What is the velocity of the rock when its height is 25 m on its way up? On its way down?

10. A particle moves with position function
    $$s = t^4 - 4t^3 - 20t^2 + 20t \qquad t \geq 0$$
    (a) At what time does the particle have a velocity of 20 m/s?
    (b) At what time is the acceleration 0? What is the significance of this value of t?

11. (a) A company makes computer chips from square wafers of silicon. It wants to keep the side length of a wafer very close to 15 mm and it wants to know how the area $A(x)$ of a wafer changes when the side length x changes. Find $A'(15)$ and explain its meaning in this situation.
    (b) Show that the rate of change of the area of a square with respect to its side length is half its perimeter. Try to explain geometrically why this is true by drawing a square whose side length x is increased by an amount Δx. How can you approximate the resulting change in area ΔA if Δx is small?

12. (a) Sodium chlorate crystals are easy to grow in the shape of cubes by allowing a solution of water and sodium chlorate to evaporate slowly. If V is the volume of such a cube with side length x, calculate dV/dx when $x = 3$ mm and explain its meaning.
    (b) Show that the rate of change of the volume of a cube with respect to its edge length is equal to half the surface area of the cube. Explain geometrically why this result is true by arguing by analogy with Exercise 11(b).

13. (a) Find the average rate of change of the area of a circle with respect to its radius r as r changes from
    (i) 2 to 3   (ii) 2 to 2.5   (iii) 2 to 2.1
    (b) Find the instantaneous rate of change when $r = 2$.
    (c) Show that the rate of change of the area of a circle with respect to its radius (at any r) is equal to the circumference of the circle. Try to explain geometrically why this is true by drawing a circle whose radius is increased by an

amount Δr. How can you approximate the resulting change in area ΔA if Δr is small?

14. A stone is dropped into a lake, creating a circular ripple that travels outward at a speed of 60 cm/s. Find the rate at which the area within the circle is increasing after (a) 1 s, (b) 3 s, and (c) 5 s. What can you conclude?

15. A spherical balloon is being inflated. Find the rate of increase of the surface area ($S = 4\pi r^2$) with respect to the radius r when r is (a) 20 cm, (b) 40 cm, and (c) 60 cm. What conclusion can you make?

16. (a) The volume of a growing spherical cell is $V = \frac{4}{3}\pi r^3$, where the radius r is measured in micrometers (1 μm $= 10^{-6}$ m). Find the average rate of change of V with respect to r when r changes from
    (i) 5 to 8 μm   (ii) 5 to 6 μm   (iii) 5 to 5.1 μm
    (b) Find the instantaneous rate of change of V with respect to r when $r = 5$ μm.
    (c) Show that the rate of change of the volume of a sphere with respect to its radius is equal to its surface area. Explain geometrically why this result is true. Argue by analogy with Exercise 13(c).

17. The mass of the part of a metal rod that lies between its left end and a point x meters to the right is $3x^2$ kg. Find the linear density (see Example 2) when x is (a) 1 m, (b) 2 m, and (c) 3 m. Where is the density the highest? The lowest?

18. If a tank holds 5000 liters of water, which drains from the bottom of the tank in 40 minutes, then Torricelli's Law gives the volume V of water remaining in the tank after t minutes as
    $$V = 5000\left(1 - \tfrac{1}{40}t\right)^2 \qquad 0 \leq t \leq 40$$
    Find the rate at which water is draining from the tank after (a) 5 min, (b) 10 min, (c) 20 min, and (d) 40 min. At what time is the water flowing out the fastest? The slowest? Summarize your findings.

19. The quantity of charge Q in coulombs (C) that has passed through a point in a wire up to time t (measured in seconds) is given by $Q(t) = t^3 - 2t^2 + 6t + 2$. Find the current when
    (a) $t = 0.5$ s and (b) $t = 1$ s. [See Example 3. The unit of current is an ampere (1 A $= 1$ C/s).] At what time is the current lowest?

20. Newton's Law of Gravitation says that the magnitude F of the force exerted by a body of mass m on a body of mass M is
    $$F = \frac{GmM}{r^2}$$
    where G is the gravitational constant and r is the distance between the bodies.
    (a) Find dF/dr and explain its meaning. What does the minus sign indicate?
    (b) Suppose it is known that the earth attracts an object with a force that decreases at the rate of 2 N/km when $r = 20,000$ km. How fast does this force change when $r = 10,000$ km?

21. The force F acting on a body with mass m and velocity v is the rate of change of momentum: $F = (d/dt)(mv)$. If m is constant, this becomes $F = ma$, where $a = dv/dt$ is the acceleration. But in the theory of relativity the mass of a particle varies with v as follows: $m = m_0/\sqrt{1 - v^2/c^2}$, where m_0 is the mass of the particle at rest and c is the speed of light. Show that

$$F = \frac{m_0 a}{(1 - v^2/c^2)^{3/2}}$$

22. Some of the highest tides in the world occur in the Bay of Fundy on the Atlantic Coast of Canada. At Hopewell Cape the water depth at low tide is about 2.0 m and at high tide it is about 12.0 m. The natural period of oscillation is a little more than 12 hours and on June 30, 2009, high tide occurred at 6:45 AM. This helps explain the following model for the water depth D (in meters) as a function of the time t (in hours after midnight) on that day:

$$D(t) = 7 + 5\cos[0.503(t - 6.75)]$$

How fast was the tide rising (or falling) at the following times?
(a) 3:00 AM (b) 6:00 AM
(c) 9:00 AM (d) Noon

23. Boyle's Law states that when a sample of gas is compressed at a constant temperature, the product of the pressure and the volume remains constant: $PV = C$.
(a) Find the rate of change of volume with respect to pressure.
(b) A sample of gas is in a container at low pressure and is steadily compressed at constant temperature for 10 minutes. Is the volume decreasing more rapidly at the beginning or the end of the 10 minutes? Explain.
(c) Prove that the isothermal compressibility (see Example 5) is given by $\beta = 1/P$.

24. If, in Example 4, one molecule of the product C is formed from one molecule of the reactant A and one molecule of the reactant B, and the initial concentrations of A and B have a common value $[A] = [B] = a$ moles/L, then

$$[C] = a^2kt/(akt + 1)$$

where k is a constant.
(a) Find the rate of reaction at time t.
(b) Show that if $x = [C]$, then

$$\frac{dx}{dt} = k(a - x)^2$$

(c) What happens to the concentration as $t \to \infty$?
(d) What happens to the rate of reaction as $t \to \infty$?
(e) What do the results of parts (c) and (d) mean in practical terms?

25. In Example 6 we considered a bacteria population that doubles every hour. Suppose that another population of bacteria triples every hour and starts with 400 bacteria. Find an expression for the number n of bacteria after t hours and use it to estimate the rate of growth of the bacteria population after 2.5 hours.

26. The number of yeast cells in a laboratory culture increases rapidly initially but levels off eventually. The population is modeled by the function

$$n = f(t) = \frac{a}{1 + be^{-0.7t}}$$

where t is measured in hours. At time $t = 0$ the population is 20 cells and is increasing at a rate of 12 cells/hour. Find the values of a and b. According to this model, what happens to the yeast population in the long run?

27. The table gives the population of the world in the 20th century.

Year	Population (in millions)	Year	Population (in millions)
1900	1650	1960	3040
1910	1750	1970	3710
1920	1860	1980	4450
1930	2070	1990	5280
1940	2300	2000	6080
1950	2560		

(a) Estimate the rate of population growth in 1920 and in 1980 by averaging the slopes of two secant lines.
(b) Use a graphing calculator or computer to find a cubic function (a third-degree polynomial) that models the data.
(c) Use your model in part (b) to find a model for the rate of population growth in the 20th century.
(d) Use part (c) to estimate the rates of growth in 1920 and 1980. Compare with your estimates in part (a).
(e) Estimate the rate of growth in 1985.

28. The table shows how the average age of first marriage of Japanese women varied in the last half of the 20th century.

t	$A(t)$	t	$A(t)$
1950	23.0	1980	25.2
1955	23.8	1985	25.5
1960	24.4	1990	25.9
1965	24.5	1995	26.3
1970	24.2	2000	27.0
1975	24.7		

(a) Use a graphing calculator or computer to model these data with a fourth-degree polynomial.
(b) Use part (a) to find a model for $A'(t)$.
(c) Estimate the rate of change of marriage age for women in 1990.
(d) Graph the data points and the models for A and A'.

29. Refer to the law of laminar flow given in Example 7. Consider a blood vessel with radius 0.01 cm, length 3 cm, pressure difference 3000 dynes/cm^2, and viscosity $\eta = 0.027$.
(a) Find the velocity of the blood along the centerline $r = 0$, at radius $r = 0.005$ cm, and at the wall $r = R = 0.01$ cm.

(b) Find the velocity gradient at $r = 0$, $r = 0.005$, and $r = 0.01$.

(c) Where is the velocity the greatest? Where is the velocity changing most?

30. The frequency of vibrations of a vibrating violin string is given by

$$f = \frac{1}{2L} \sqrt{\frac{T}{\rho}}$$

where L is the length of the string, T is its tension, and ρ is its linear density. [See Chapter 11 in D. E. Hall, *Musical Acoustics,* 3rd ed. (Pacific Grove, CA, 2002).]

(a) Find the rate of change of the frequency with respect to
   (i) the length (when T and ρ are constant),
   (ii) the tension (when L and ρ are constant), and
   (iii) the linear density (when L and T are constant).

(b) The pitch of a note (how high or low the note sounds) is determined by the frequency f. (The higher the frequency, the higher the pitch.) Use the signs of the derivatives in part (a) to determine what happens to the pitch of a note
   (i) when the effective length of a string is decreased by placing a finger on the string so a shorter portion of the string vibrates,
   (ii) when the tension is increased by turning a tuning peg,
   (iii) when the linear density is increased by switching to another string.

31. The cost, in dollars, of producing x meters of a certain fabric is

$$C(x) = 1200 + 12x - 0.1x^2 + 0.0005x^3$$

(a) Find the marginal cost function.

(b) Find $C'(200)$ and explain its meaning. What does it predict?

(c) Compare $C'(200)$ with the cost of manufacturing the 201st meter of fabric.

32. The cost function for production of a commodity is

$$C(x) = 339 + 25x - 0.09x^2 + 0.0004x^3$$

(a) Find and interpret $C'(100)$.

(b) Compare $C'(100)$ with the cost of producing the 101st item.

33. If $p(x)$ is the total value of the production when there are x workers in a plant, then the *average productivity* of the workforce at the plant is

$$A(x) = \frac{p(x)}{x}$$

(a) Find $A'(x)$. Why does the company want to hire more workers if $A'(x) > 0$?

(b) Show that $A'(x) > 0$ if $p'(x)$ is greater than the average productivity.

34. If R denotes the reaction of the body to some stimulus of strength x, the *sensitivity* S is defined to be the rate of change

of the reaction with respect to x. A particular example is that when the brightness x of a light source is increased, the eye reacts by decreasing the area R of the pupil. The experimental formula

$$R = \frac{40 + 24x^{0.4}}{1 + 4x^{0.4}}$$

has been used to model the dependence of R on x when R is measured in square millimeters and x is measured in appropriate units of brightness.

(a) Find the sensitivity.

(b) Illustrate part (a) by graphing both R and S as functions of x. Comment on the values of R and S at low levels of brightness. Is this what you would expect?

35. The gas law for an ideal gas at absolute temperature T (in kelvins), pressure P (in atmospheres), and volume V (in liters) is $PV = nRT$, where n is the number of moles of the gas and $R = 0.0821$ is the gas constant. Suppose that, at a certain instant, $P = 8.0$ atm and is increasing at a rate of 0.10 atm/min and $V = 10$ L and is decreasing at a rate of 0.15 L/min. Find the rate of change of T with respect to time at that instant if $n = 10$ mol.

36. In a fish farm, a population of fish is introduced into a pond and harvested regularly. A model for the rate of change of the fish population is given by the equation

$$\frac{dP}{dt} = r_0 \left(1 - \frac{P(t)}{P_c}\right) P(t) - \beta P(t)$$

where r_0 is the birth rate of the fish, P_c is the maximum population that the pond can sustain (called the *carrying capacity*), and β is the percentage of the population that is harvested.

(a) What value of dP/dt corresponds to a stable population?

(b) If the pond can sustain 10,000 fish, the birth rate is 5%, and the harvesting rate is 4%, find the stable population level.

(c) What happens if β is raised to 5%?

37. In the study of ecosystems, *predator-prey models* are often used to study the interaction between species. Consider populations of tundra wolves, given by $W(t)$, and caribou, given by $C(t)$, in northern Canada. The interaction has been modeled by the equations

$$\frac{dC}{dt} = aC - bCW \qquad \frac{dW}{dt} = -cW + dCW$$

(a) What values of dC/dt and dW/dt correspond to stable populations?

(b) How would the statement "The caribou go extinct" be represented mathematically?

(c) Suppose that $a = 0.05$, $b = 0.001$, $c = 0.05$, and $d = 0.0001$. Find all population pairs (C, W) that lead to stable populations. According to this model, is it possible for the two species to live in balance or will one or both species become extinct?

3.8 Exponential Growth and Decay

In many natural phenomena, quantities grow or decay at a rate proportional to their size. For instance, if $y = f(t)$ is the number of individuals in a population of animals or bacteria at time t, then it seems reasonable to expect that the rate of growth $f'(t)$ is proportional to the population $f(t)$; that is, $f'(t) = kf(t)$ for some constant k. Indeed, under ideal conditions (unlimited environment, adequate nutrition, immunity to disease) the mathematical model given by the equation $f'(t) = kf(t)$ predicts what actually happens fairly accurately. Another example occurs in nuclear physics where the mass of a radioactive substance decays at a rate proportional to the mass. In chemistry, the rate of a unimolecular first-order reaction is proportional to the concentration of the substance. In finance, the value of a savings account with continuously compounded interest increases at a rate proportional to that value.

In general, if $y(t)$ is the value of a quantity y at time t and if the rate of change of y with respect to t is proportional to its size $y(t)$ at any time, then

$$\boxed{1} \qquad \boxed{\dfrac{dy}{dt} = ky}$$

where k is a constant. Equation 1 is sometimes called the **law of natural growth** (if $k > 0$) or the **law of natural decay** (if $k < 0$). It is called a **differential equation** because it involves an unknown function y and its derivative dy/dt.

It's not hard to think of a solution of Equation 1. This equation asks us to find a function whose derivative is a constant multiple of itself. We have met such functions in this chapter. Any exponential function of the form $y(t) = Ce^{kt}$, where C is a constant, satisfies

$$y'(t) = C(ke^{kt}) = k(Ce^{kt}) = ky(t)$$

We will see in Section 9.4 that *any* function that satisfies $dy/dt = ky$ must be of the form $y = Ce^{kt}$. To see the significance of the constant C, we observe that

$$y(0) = Ce^{k\cdot 0} = C$$

Therefore C is the initial value of the function.

> $\boxed{2}$ **Theorem** The only solutions of the differential equation $dy/dt = ky$ are the exponential functions
>
> $$y(t) = y(0)e^{kt}$$

■ Population Growth

What is the significance of the proportionality constant k? In the context of population growth, where $P(t)$ is the size of a population at time t, we can write

$$\boxed{3} \qquad \dfrac{dP}{dt} = kP \qquad \text{or} \qquad \dfrac{1}{P}\dfrac{dP}{dt} = k$$

The quantity

$$\dfrac{1}{P}\dfrac{dP}{dt}$$

is the growth rate divided by the population size; it is called the **relative growth rate**. According to $\boxed{3}$, instead of saying "the growth rate is proportional to population size" we could say "the relative growth rate is constant." Then $\boxed{2}$ says that a population with constant relative growth rate must grow exponentially. Notice that the relative growth rate k appears as the coefficient of t in the exponential function Ce^{kt}. For instance, if

$$\frac{dP}{dt} = 0.02P$$

and t is measured in years, then the relative growth rate is $k = 0.02$ and the population grows at a relative rate of 2% per year. If the population at time 0 is P_0, then the expression for the population is

$$P(t) = P_0 e^{0.02t}$$

V **EXAMPLE 1** Use the fact that the world population was 2560 million in 1950 and 3040 million in 1960 to model the population of the world in the second half of the 20th century. (Assume that the growth rate is proportional to the population size.) What is the relative growth rate? Use the model to estimate the world population in 1993 and to predict the population in the year 2020.

SOLUTION We measure the time t in years and let $t = 0$ in the year 1950. We measure the population $P(t)$ in millions of people. Then $P(0) = 2560$ and $P(10) = 3040$. Since we are assuming that $dP/dt = kP$, Theorem 2 gives

$$P(t) = P(0)e^{kt} = 2560e^{kt}$$

$$P(10) = 2560e^{10k} = 3040$$

$$k = \frac{1}{10} \ln \frac{3040}{2560} \approx 0.017185$$

The relative growth rate is about 1.7% per year and the model is

$$P(t) = 2560e^{0.017185t}$$

We estimate that the world population in 1993 was

$$P(43) = 2560e^{0.017185(43)} \approx 5360 \text{ million}$$

The model predicts that the population in 2020 will be

$$P(70) = 2560e^{0.017185(70)} \approx 8524 \text{ million}$$

The graph in Figure 1 shows that the model is fairly accurate to the end of the 20th century (the dots represent the actual population), so the estimate for 1993 is quite reliable. But the prediction for 2020 is riskier.

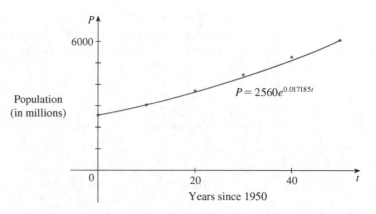

FIGURE 1

A model for world population growth in the second half of the 20th century

Radioactive Decay

Radioactive substances decay by spontaneously emitting radiation. If $m(t)$ is the mass remaining from an initial mass m_0 of the substance after time t, then the relative decay rate

$$-\frac{1}{m}\frac{dm}{dt}$$

has been found experimentally to be constant. (Since dm/dt is negative, the relative decay rate is positive.) It follows that

$$\frac{dm}{dt} = km$$

where k is a negative constant. In other words, radioactive substances decay at a rate proportional to the remaining mass. This means that we can use $\boxed{2}$ to show that the mass decays exponentially:

$$m(t) = m_0 e^{kt}$$

Physicists express the rate of decay in terms of **half-life**, the time required for half of any given quantity to decay.

V EXAMPLE 2 The half-life of radium-226 is 1590 years.
(a) A sample of radium-226 has a mass of 100 mg. Find a formula for the mass of the sample that remains after t years.
(b) Find the mass after 1000 years correct to the nearest milligram.
(c) When will the mass be reduced to 30 mg?

SOLUTION
(a) Let $m(t)$ be the mass of radium-226 (in milligrams) that remains after t years. Then $dm/dt = km$ and $y(0) = 100$, so $\boxed{2}$ gives

$$m(t) = m(0)e^{kt} = 100e^{kt}$$

In order to determine the value of k, we use the fact that $y(1590) = \frac{1}{2}(100)$. Thus

$$100e^{1590k} = 50 \qquad \text{so} \qquad e^{1590k} = \tfrac{1}{2}$$

and

$$1590k = \ln\tfrac{1}{2} = -\ln 2$$

$$k = -\frac{\ln 2}{1590}$$

Therefore

$$m(t) = 100e^{-(\ln 2)t/1590}$$

We could use the fact that $e^{\ln 2} = 2$ to write the expression for $m(t)$ in the alternative form

$$m(t) = 100 \times 2^{-t/1590}$$

(b) The mass after 1000 years is

$$m(1000) = 100e^{-(\ln 2)1000/1590} \approx 65 \text{ mg}$$

(c) We want to find the value of t such that $m(t) = 30$, that is,

$$100e^{-(\ln 2)t/1590} = 30 \qquad \text{or} \qquad e^{-(\ln 2)t/1590} = 0.3$$

We solve this equation for t by taking the natural logarithm of both sides:

$$-\frac{\ln 2}{1590}t = \ln 0.3$$

Thus

$$t = -1590\,\frac{\ln 0.3}{\ln 2} \approx 2762 \text{ years}$$

150

$m = 100e^{-(\ln 2)t/1590}$

$m = 30$

0   4000

FIGURE 2

As a check on our work in Example 2, we use a graphing device to draw the graph of $m(t)$ in Figure 2 together with the horizontal line $m = 30$. These curves intersect when $t \approx 2800$, and this agrees with the answer to part (c).

Newton's Law of Cooling

Newton's Law of Cooling states that the rate of cooling of an object is proportional to the temperature difference between the object and its surroundings, provided that this difference is not too large. (This law also applies to warming.) If we let $T(t)$ be the temperature of the object at time t and T_s be the temperature of the surroundings, then we can formulate Newton's Law of Cooling as a differential equation:

$$\frac{dT}{dt} = k(T - T_s)$$

where k is a constant. This equation is not quite the same as Equation 1, so we make the change of variable $y(t) = T(t) - T_s$. Because T_s is constant, we have $y'(t) = T'(t)$ and so the equation becomes

$$\frac{dy}{dt} = ky$$

We can then use $\boxed{2}$ to find an expression for y, from which we can find T.

EXAMPLE 3 A bottle of soda pop at room temperature (22°C) is placed in a refrigerator where the temperature is 7°C. After half an hour the soda pop has cooled to 16°C.
(a) What is the temperature of the soda pop after another half hour?
(b) How long does it take for the soda pop to cool to 10°C?

SOLUTION
(a) Let $T(t)$ be the temperature of the soda after t minutes. The surrounding temperature is $T_s = 7°C$, so Newton's Law of Cooling states that

$$\frac{dT}{dt} = k(T - 7)$$

If we let $y = T - 7$, then $y(0) = T(0) - 7 = 22 - 7 = 15$, so y is a solution of the initial-value problem

$$\frac{dy}{dt} = ky \qquad y(0) = 15$$

and by $\boxed{2}$ we have

$$y(t) = y(0)e^{kt} = 15e^{kt}$$

We are given that $T(30) = 16$, so $y(30) = 16 - 7 = 9$ and

$$15e^{30k} = 9 \qquad e^{30k} = \tfrac{3}{5}$$

Taking logarithms, we have

$$k = \frac{\ln\left(\frac{3}{5}\right)}{30} \approx -0.01703$$

Thus

$$y(t) = 15e^{-0.01703t}$$

$$T(t) = 7 + 15e^{-0.01703t}$$

$$T(60) = 7 + 15e^{-0.01703(60)} \approx 12.4$$

So after another half hour the pop has cooled to about 12°C.

(b) We have $T(t) = 10$ when

$$7 + 15e^{-0.01703t} = 10$$

$$e^{-0.01703t} = \tfrac{3}{15} = \tfrac{1}{5}$$

$$t = \frac{\ln\left(\frac{1}{5}\right)}{-0.01703} \approx 94.5$$

The pop cools to 10°C after about 1 hour 35 minutes.

Notice that in Example 3, we have

$$\lim_{t\to\infty} T(t) = \lim_{t\to\infty} (7 + 15e^{-0.01703t}) = 7 + 15 \cdot 0 = 7$$

which is to be expected. The graph of the temperature function is shown in Figure 3.

FIGURE 3

■ Continuously Compounded Interest

EXAMPLE 4 If $1000 is invested at 6% interest, compounded annually, then after 1 year the investment is worth $1000(1.06) = $1060, after 2 years it's worth $[1000(1.06)]1.06 = $1123.60, and after t years it's worth $1000(1.06)^t$. In general, if an amount A_0 is invested at an interest rate r ($r = 0.06$ in this example), then after t years it's worth $A_0(1 + r)^t$. Usually, however, interest is compounded more frequently, say, n times a year. Then in each compounding period the interest rate is r/n and there are nt compounding periods in t years, so the value of the investment is

$$A_0\left(1 + \frac{r}{n}\right)^{nt}$$

For instance, after 3 years at 6% interest a $1000 investment will be worth

$$\$1000(1.06)^3 = \$1191.02 \quad \text{with annual compounding}$$

$$\$1000(1.03)^6 = \$1194.05 \quad \text{with semiannual compounding}$$

$$\$1000(1.015)^{12} = \$1195.62 \quad \text{with quarterly compounding}$$

$$\$1000(1.005)^{36} = \$1196.68 \quad \text{with monthly compounding}$$

$$\$1000\left(1 + \frac{0.06}{365}\right)^{365\cdot 3} = \$1197.20 \quad \text{with daily compounding}$$

You can see that the interest paid increases as the number of compounding periods (n) increases. If we let $n \to \infty$, then we will be compounding the interest **continuously** and the value of the investment will be

$$A(t) = \lim_{n \to \infty} A_0 \left(1 + \frac{r}{n} \right)^{nt}$$

$$= \lim_{n \to \infty} A_0 \left[\left(1 + \frac{r}{n} \right)^{n/r} \right]^{rt}$$

$$= A_0 \left[\lim_{n \to \infty} \left(1 + \frac{r}{n} \right)^{n/r} \right]^{rt}$$

$$= A_0 \left[\lim_{m \to \infty} \left(1 + \frac{1}{m} \right)^{m} \right]^{rt} \qquad \text{(where } m = n/r\text{)}$$

But the limit in this expression is equal to the number e (see Equation 3.6.6). So with continuous compounding of interest at interest rate r, the amount after t years is

$$A(t) = A_0 e^{rt}$$

If we differentiate this equation, we get

$$\frac{dA}{dt} = rA_0 e^{rt} = rA(t)$$

which says that, with continuous compounding of interest, the rate of increase of an investment is proportional to its size.

Returning to the example of $1000 invested for 3 years at 6% interest, we see that with continuous compounding of interest the value of the investment will be

$$A(3) = \$1000 e^{(0.06)3} = \$1197.22$$

Notice how close this is to the amount we calculated for daily compounding, $1197.20. But the amount is easier to compute if we use continuous compounding. ▬

3.8 Exercises

1. A population of protozoa develops with a constant relative growth rate of 0.7944 per member per day. On day zero the population consists of two members. Find the population size after six days.

2. A common inhabitant of human intestines is the bacterium *Escherichia coli*. A cell of this bacterium in a nutrient-broth medium divides into two cells every 20 minutes. The initial population of a culture is 60 cells.
(a) Find the relative growth rate.
(b) Find an expression for the number of cells after t hours.

(c) Find the number of cells after 8 hours.
(d) Find the rate of growth after 8 hours.
(e) When will the population reach 20,000 cells?

3. A bacteria culture initially contains 100 cells and grows at a rate proportional to its size. After an hour the population has increased to 420.
(a) Find an expression for the number of bacteria after t hours.
(b) Find the number of bacteria after 3 hours.
(c) Find the rate of growth after 3 hours.
(d) When will the population reach 10,000?

Graphing calculator or computer required   1. Homework Hints available at stewartcalculus.com

4. A bacteria culture grows with constant relative growth rate. The bacteria count was 400 after 2 hours and 25,600 after 6 hours.
   (a) What is the relative growth rate? Express your answer as a percentage.
   (b) What was the intitial size of the culture?
   (c) Find an expression for the number of bacteria after t hours.
   (d) Find the number of cells after 4.5 hours.
   (e) Find the rate of growth after 4.5 hours.
   (f) When will the population reach 50,000?

5. The table gives estimates of the world population, in millions, from 1750 to 2000.
   (a) Use the exponential model and the population figures for 1750 and 1800 to predict the world population in 1900 and 1950. Compare with the actual figures.
   (b) Use the exponential model and the population figures for 1850 and 1900 to predict the world population in 1950. Compare with the actual population.
   (c) Use the exponential model and the population figures for 1900 and 1950 to predict the world population in 2000. Compare with the actual population and try to explain the discrepancy.

Year	Population	Year	Population
1750	790	1900	1650
1800	980	1950	2560
1850	1260	2000	6080

6. The table gives the population of India, in millions, for the second half of the 20th century.

Year	Population
1951	361
1961	439
1971	548
1981	683
1991	846
2001	1029

   (a) Use the exponential model and the census figures for 1951 and 1961 to predict the population in 2001. Compare with the actual figure.
   (b) Use the exponential model and the census figures for 1961 and 1981 to predict the population in 2001. Compare with the actual population. Then use this model to predict the population in the years 2010 and 2020.
   (c) Graph both of the exponential functions in parts (a) and (b) together with a plot of the actual population. Are these models reasonable ones?

7. Experiments show that if the chemical reaction

$$N_2O_5 \rightarrow 2NO_2 + \tfrac{1}{2}O_2$$

takes place at 45°C, the rate of reaction of dinitrogen pent-

oxide is proportional to its concentration as follows:

$$-\frac{d[N_2O_5]}{dt} = 0.0005[N_2O_5]$$

(See Example 4 in Section 3.7.)
   (a) Find an expression for the concentration $[N_2O_5]$ after t seconds if the initial concentration is C.
   (b) How long will the reaction take to reduce the concentration of N_2O_5 to 90% of its original value?

8. Strontium-90 has a half-life of 28 days.
   (a) A sample has a mass of 50 mg initially. Find a formula for the mass remaining after t days.
   (b) Find the mass remaining after 40 days.
   (c) How long does it take the sample to decay to a mass of 2 mg?
   (d) Sketch the graph of the mass function.

9. The half-life of cesium-137 is 30 years. Suppose we have a 100-mg sample.
   (a) Find the mass that remains after t years.
   (b) How much of the sample remains after 100 years?
   (c) After how long will only 1 mg remain?

10. A sample of tritium-3 decayed to 94.5% of its original amount after a year.
   (a) What is the half-life of tritium-3?
   (b) How long would it take the sample to decay to 20% of its original amount?

11. Scientists can determine the age of ancient objects by the method of *radiocarbon dating*. The bombardment of the upper atmosphere by cosmic rays converts nitrogen to a radioactive isotope of carbon, ^{14}C, with a half-life of about 5730 years. Vegetation absorbs carbon dioxide through the atmosphere and animal life assimilates ^{14}C through food chains. When a plant or animal dies, it stops replacing its carbon and the amount of ^{14}C begins to decrease through radioactive decay. Therefore the level of radioactivity must also decay exponentially.

A parchment fragment was discovered that had about 74% as much ^{14}C radioactivity as does plant material on the earth today. Estimate the age of the parchment.

12. A curve passes through the point $(0, 5)$ and has the property that the slope of the curve at every point P is twice the y-coordinate of P. What is the equation of the curve?

13. A roast turkey is taken from an oven when its temperature has reached 85°C and is placed on a table in a room where the temperature is 22°C.
   (a) If the temperature of the turkey is 65°C after half an hour, what is the temperature after 45 minutes?
   (b) When will the turkey have cooled to 40°C?

14. In a murder investigation, the temperature of the corpse was 32.5°C at 1:30 PM and 30.3°C an hour later. Normal body temperature is 37.0°C and the temperature of the surroundings was 20.0°C. When did the murder take place?

15. When a cold drink is taken from a refrigerator, its temperature is 5°C. After 25 minutes in a 20°C room its temperature has increased to 10°C.
(a) What is the temperature of the drink after 50 minutes?
(b) When will its temperature be 15°C?

16. A freshly brewed cup of coffee has temperature 95°C in a 20°C room. When its temperature is 70°C, it is cooling at a rate of 1°C per minute. When does this occur?

17. The rate of change of atmospheric pressure P with respect to altitude h is proportional to P, provided that the temperature is constant. At 15°C the pressure is 101.3 kPa at sea level and 87.14 kPa at $h = 1000$ m.
(a) What is the pressure at an altitude of 3000 m?
(b) What is the pressure at the top of Mount McKinley, at an altitude of 6187 m?

18. (a) If $1000 is borrowed at 8% interest, find the amounts due at the end of 3 years if the interest is compounded (i) annually, (ii) quarterly, (iii) monthly, (iv) weekly, (v) daily, (vi) hourly, and (vii) continuously.
(b) Suppose $1000 is borrowed and the interest is compounded continuously. If $A(t)$ is the amount due after t years, where $0 \leq t \leq 3$, graph $A(t)$ for each of the interest rates 6%, 8%, and 10% on a common screen.

19. (a) If $3000 is invested at 5% interest, find the value of the investment at the end of 5 years if the interest is compounded (i) annually, (ii) semiannually, (iii) monthly, (iv) weekly, (v) daily, and (vi) continuously.
(b) If $A(t)$ is the amount of the investment at time t for the case of continuous compounding, write a differential equation and an initial condition satisfied by $A(t)$.

20. (a) How long will it take an investment to double in value if the interest rate is 6% compounded continuously?
(b) What is the equivalent annual interest rate?

3.9 Related Rates

If we are pumping air into a balloon, both the volume and the radius of the balloon are increasing and their rates of increase are related to each other. But it is much easier to measure directly the rate of increase of the volume than the rate of increase of the radius.

In a related rates problem the idea is to compute the rate of change of one quantity in terms of the rate of change of another quantity (which may be more easily measured). The procedure is to find an equation that relates the two quantities and then use the Chain Rule to differentiate both sides with respect to time.

V EXAMPLE 1 Air is being pumped into a spherical balloon so that its volume increases at a rate of 100 cm³/s. How fast is the radius of the balloon increasing when the diameter is 50 cm?

SOLUTION We start by identifying two things:

the *given information:*

the rate of increase of the volume of air is 100 cm³/s

and the *unknown:*

the rate of increase of the radius when the diameter is 50 cm

PS According to the Principles of Problem Solving discussed on page 75, the first step is to understand the problem. This includes reading the problem carefully, identifying the given and the unknown, and introducing suitable notation.

In order to express these quantities mathematically, we introduce some suggestive *notation:*

Let V be the volume of the balloon and let r be its radius.

The key thing to remember is that rates of change are derivatives. In this problem, the volume and the radius are both functions of the time t. The rate of increase of the volume with respect to time is the derivative dV/dt, and the rate of increase of the radius is dr/dt. We can therefore restate the given and the unknown as follows:

$$\text{Given:} \quad \frac{dV}{dt} = 100 \text{ cm}^3/\text{s}$$

$$\text{Unknown:} \quad \frac{dr}{dt} \quad \text{when } r = 25 \text{ cm}$$

PS The second stage of problem solving is to think of a plan for connecting the given and the unknown.

In order to connect dV/dt and dr/dt, we first relate V and r by the formula for the volume of a sphere:

$$V = \tfrac{4}{3}\pi r^3$$

In order to use the given information, we differentiate each side of this equation with respect to t. To differentiate the right side, we need to use the Chain Rule:

$$\frac{dV}{dt} = \frac{dV}{dr}\frac{dr}{dt} = 4\pi r^2 \frac{dr}{dt}$$

Now we solve for the unknown quantity:

Notice that, although dV/dt is constant, dr/dt is *not* constant.

$$\frac{dr}{dt} = \frac{1}{4\pi r^2}\frac{dV}{dt}$$

If we put $r = 25$ and $dV/dt = 100$ in this equation, we obtain

$$\frac{dr}{dt} = \frac{1}{4\pi(25)^2}100 = \frac{1}{25\pi}$$

The radius of the balloon is increasing at the rate of $1/(25\pi) \approx 0.0127$ cm/s. ▬

EXAMPLE 2 A ladder 5 m long rests against a vertical wall. If the bottom of the ladder slides away from the wall at a rate of 1 m/s, how fast is the top of the ladder sliding down the wall when the bottom of the ladder is 3 m from the wall?

SOLUTION We first draw a diagram and label it as in Figure 1. Let x meters be the distance from the bottom of the ladder to the wall and y meters the distance from the top of the ladder to the ground. Note that x and y are both functions of t (time, measured in seconds).

We are given that $dx/dt = 1$ m/s and we are asked to find dy/dt when $x = 3$ m (see Figure 2). In this problem, the relationship between x and y is given by the Pythagorean Theorem:

$$x^2 + y^2 = 25$$

Differentiating each side with respect to t using the Chain Rule, we have

$$2x\frac{dx}{dt} + 2y\frac{dy}{dt} = 0$$

and solving this equation for the desired rate, we obtain

$$\frac{dy}{dt} = -\frac{x}{y}\frac{dx}{dt}$$

When $x = 3$, the Pythagorean Theorem gives $y = 4$ and so, substituting these values and $dx/dt = 1$, we have

$$\frac{dy}{dt} = -\frac{3}{4}(1) = -\frac{3}{4} \text{ m/s}$$

The fact that dy/dt is negative means that the distance from the top of the ladder to the ground is *decreasing* at a rate of $\tfrac{3}{4}$ m/s. In other words, the top of the ladder is sliding down the wall at a rate of $\tfrac{3}{4}$ m/s. ▬

FIGURE 1

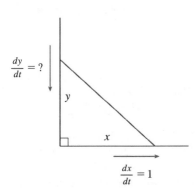

FIGURE 2

EXAMPLE 3 A water tank has the shape of an inverted circular cone with base radius 2 m and height 4 m. If water is being pumped into the tank at a rate of 2 m³/min, find the rate at which the water level is rising when the water is 3 m deep.

FIGURE 3

SOLUTION We first sketch the cone and label it as in Figure 3. Let V, r, and h be the volume of the water, the radius of the surface, and the height of the water at time t, where t is measured in minutes.

We are given that $dV/dt = 2 \text{ m}^3/\text{min}$ and we are asked to find dh/dt when h is 3 m. The quantities V and h are related by the equation

$$V = \tfrac{1}{3}\pi r^2 h$$

but it is very useful to express V as a function of h alone. In order to eliminate r, we use the similar triangles in Figure 3 to write

$$\frac{r}{h} = \frac{2}{4} \qquad r = \frac{h}{2}$$

and the expression for V becomes

$$V = \frac{1}{3}\pi \left(\frac{h}{2}\right)^2 h = \frac{\pi}{12}h^3$$

Now we can differentiate each side with respect to t:

$$\frac{dV}{dt} = \frac{\pi}{4}h^2 \frac{dh}{dt}$$

so

$$\frac{dh}{dt} = \frac{4}{\pi h^2}\frac{dV}{dt}$$

Substituting $h = 3$ m and $dV/dt = 2 \text{ m}^3/\text{min}$, we have

$$\frac{dh}{dt} = \frac{4}{\pi(3)^2} \cdot 2 = \frac{8}{9\pi}$$

The water level is rising at a rate of $8/(9\pi) \approx 0.28 \text{ m/min}$.

PS Look back: What have we learned from Examples 1–3 that will help us solve future problems?

⊘ **WARNING** A common error is to substitute the given numerical information (for quantities that vary with time) too early. This should be done only *after* the differentiation. (Step 7 follows Step 6.) For instance, in Example 3 we dealt with general values of h until we finally substituted $h = 3$ at the last stage. (If we had put $h = 3$ earlier, we would have gotten $dV/dt = 0$, which is clearly wrong.)

Problem Solving Strategy   It is useful to recall some of the problem-solving principles from page 75 and adapt them to related rates in light of our experience in Examples 1–3:

1. Read the problem carefully.

2. Draw a diagram if possible.

3. Introduce notation. Assign symbols to all quantities that are functions of time.

4. Express the given information and the required rate in terms of derivatives.

5. Write an equation that relates the various quantities of the problem. If necessary, use the geometry of the situation to eliminate one of the variables by substitution (as in Example 3).

6. Use the Chain Rule to differentiate both sides of the equation with respect to t.

7. Substitute the given information into the resulting equation and solve for the unknown rate.

The following examples are further illustrations of the strategy.

V **EXAMPLE 4** Car A is traveling west at 90 km/h and car B is traveling north at 100 km/h. Both are headed for the intersection of the two roads. At what rate are the cars approaching each other when car A is 60 m and car B is 80 m from the intersection?

SOLUTION We draw Figure 4, where C is the intersection of the roads. At a given time t, let x be the distance from car A to C, let y be the distance from car B to C, and let z be the distance between the cars, where x, y, and z are measured in kilometers.

We are given that $dx/dt = -90$ km/h and $dy/dt = -100$ km/h. (The derivatives are negative because x and y are decreasing.) We are asked to find dz/dt. The equation that relates x, y, and z is given by the Pythagorean Theorem:

$$z^2 = x^2 + y^2$$

Differentiating each side with respect to t, we have

$$2z \frac{dz}{dt} = 2x \frac{dx}{dt} + 2y \frac{dy}{dt}$$

$$\frac{dz}{dt} = \frac{1}{z} \left(x \frac{dx}{dt} + y \frac{dy}{dt} \right)$$

When $x = 0.06$ km and $y = 0.08$ km, the Pythagorean Theorem gives $z = 0.1$ km, so

$$\frac{dz}{dt} = \frac{1}{0.1} [0.06(-90) + 0.08(-100)]$$

$$= -134 \text{ km/h}$$

The cars are approaching each other at a rate of 134 km/h. ▬

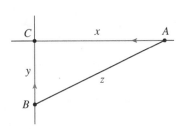

FIGURE 4

V **EXAMPLE 5** A man walks along a straight path at a speed of 1.5 m/s. A searchlight is located on the ground 6 m from the path and is kept focused on the man. At what rate is the searchlight rotating when the man is 8 m from the point on the path closest to the searchlight?

SOLUTION We draw Figure 5 and let x be the distance from the man to the point on the path closest to the searchlight. We let θ be the angle between the beam of the searchlight and the perpendicular to the path.

We are given that $dx/dt = 1.5$ m/s and are asked to find $d\theta/dt$ when $x = 8$. The equation that relates x and θ can be written from Figure 5:

$$\frac{x}{6} = \tan\theta \qquad x = 6\tan\theta$$

Differentiating each side with respect to t, we get

$$\frac{dx}{dt} = 6\sec^2\theta \frac{d\theta}{dt}$$

so

$$\frac{d\theta}{dt} = \frac{1}{6}\cos^2\theta \frac{dx}{dt}$$

$$= \frac{1}{6}\cos^2\theta\,(1.5) = \frac{1}{4}\cos^2\theta$$

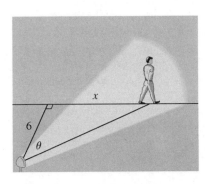

FIGURE 5

When $x = 8$, the length of the beam is 10, so $\cos\theta = \frac{3}{5}$ and

$$\frac{d\theta}{dt} = \frac{1}{4}\left(\frac{3}{5}\right)^2 = \frac{9}{100} = 0.09$$

The searchlight is rotating at a rate of 0.09 rad/s.

3.9 Exercises

1. If V is the volume of a cube with edge length x and the cube expands as time passes, find dV/dt in terms of dx/dt.

2. (a) If A is the area of a circle with radius r and the circle expands as time passes, find dA/dt in terms of dr/dt.
(b) Suppose oil spills from a ruptured tanker and spreads in a circular pattern. If the radius of the oil spill increases at a constant rate of 1 m/s, how fast is the area of the spill increasing when the radius is 30 m?

3. Each side of a square is increasing at a rate of 6 cm/s. At what rate is the area of the square increasing when the area of the square is 16 cm^2?

4. The length of a rectangle is increasing at a rate of 8 cm/s and its width is increasing at a rate of 3 cm/s. When the length is 20 cm and the width is 10 cm, how fast is the area of the rectangle increasing?

5. A cylindrical tank with radius 5 m is being filled with water at a rate of $3\text{ m}^3/\text{min}$. How fast is the height of the water increasing?

6. The radius of a sphere is increasing at a rate of 4 mm/s. How fast is the volume increasing when the diameter is 80 mm?

7. Suppose $y = \sqrt{2x + 1}$, where x and y are functions of t.
(a) If $dx/dt = 3$, find dy/dt when $x = 4$.
(b) If $dy/dt = 5$, find dx/dt when $x = 12$.

8. Suppose $4x^2 + 9y^2 = 36$, where x and y are functions of t.
(a) If $dy/dt = \frac{1}{3}$, find dx/dt when $x = 2$ and $y = \frac{2}{3}\sqrt{5}$.
(b) If $dx/dt = 3$, find dy/dt when $x = -2$ and $y = \frac{2}{3}\sqrt{5}$.

9. If $x^2 + y^2 + z^2 = 9$, $dx/dt = 5$, and $dy/dt = 4$, find dz/dt when $(x, y, z) = (2, 2, 1)$.

10. A particle is moving along a hyperbola $xy = 8$. As it reaches the point $(4, 2)$, the y-coordinate is decreasing at a rate of 3 cm/s. How fast is the x-coordinate of the point changing at that instant?

11–14
(a) What quantities are given in the problem?
(b) What is the unknown?
(c) Draw a picture of the situation for any time t.
(d) Write an equation that relates the quantities.
(e) Finish solving the problem.

11. A plane flying horizontally at an altitude of 2 km and a speed of 800 km/h passes directly over a radar station. Find the rate at which the distance from the plane to the station is increasing when it is 3 km away from the station.

12. If a snowball melts so that its surface area decreases at a rate of $1\text{ cm}^2/\text{min}$, find the rate at which the diameter decreases when the diameter is 10 cm.

13. A street light is mounted at the top of a 6-meter-tall pole. A man 2 m tall walks away from the pole with a speed of 1.5 m/s along a straight path. How fast is the tip of his shadow moving when he is 10 m from the pole?

14. At noon, ship A is 150 km west of ship B. Ship A is sailing east at 35 km/h and ship B is sailing north at 25 km/h. How fast is the distance between the ships changing at 4:00 PM?

---

15. Two cars start moving from the same point. One travels south at 30 km/h and the other travels west at 72 km/h. At what rate is the distance between the cars increasing two hours later?

16. A spotlight on the ground shines on a wall 12 m away. If a man 2 m tall walks from the spotlight toward the building at a speed of 1.6 m/s, how fast is the length of his shadow on the building decreasing when he is 4 m from the building?

17. A man starts walking north at 1.2 m/s from a point P. Five minutes later a woman starts walking south at 1.6 m/s from a point 200 m due east of P. At what rate are the people moving apart 15 min after the woman starts walking?

18. A baseball diamond is a square with side 90 ft. A batter hits the ball and runs toward first base with a speed of 24 ft/s.
(a) At what rate is his distance from second base decreasing when he is halfway to first base?
(b) At what rate is his distance from third base increasing at the same moment?

19. The altitude of a triangle is increasing at a rate of 1 cm/min while the area of the triangle is increasing at a rate of

---

2 cm²/min. At what rate is the base of the triangle changing when the altitude is 10 cm and the area is 100 cm²?

20. A boat is pulled into a dock by a rope attached to the bow of the boat and passing through a pulley on the dock that is 1 m higher than the bow of the boat. If the rope is pulled in at a rate of 1 m/s, how fast is the boat approaching the dock when it is 8 m from the dock?

21. At noon, ship A is 100 km west of ship B. Ship A is sailing south at 35 km/h and ship B is sailing north at 25 km/h. How fast is the distance between the ships changing at 4:00 PM?

22. A particle moves along the curve $y = 2 \sin(\pi x/2)$. As the particle passes through the point $\left(\frac{1}{3}, 1\right)$, its x-coordinate increases at a rate of $\sqrt{10}$ cm/s. How fast is the distance from the particle to the origin changing at this instant?

23. Water is leaking out of an inverted conical tank at a rate of 10,000 cm³/min at the same time that water is being pumped into the tank at a constant rate. The tank has height 6 m and the diameter at the top is 4 m. If the water level is rising at a rate of 20 cm/min when the height of the water is 2 m, find the rate at which water is being pumped into the tank.

24. A trough is 6 m long and its ends have the shape of isosceles triangles that are 1 m across at the top and have a height of 50 cm. If the trough is being filled with water at a rate of 1.2 m³/min, how fast is the water level rising when the water is 30 cm deep?

25. A water trough is 10 m long and a cross-section has the shape of an isosceles trapezoid that is 30 cm wide at the bottom, 80 cm wide at the top, and has height 50 cm. If the trough is being filled with water at the rate of 0.2 m³/min, how fast is the water level rising when the water is 30 cm deep?

26. A swimming pool is 5 m wide, 10 m long, 1 m deep at the shallow end, and 3 m deep at its deepest point. A cross-section is shown in the figure. If the pool is being filled at a rate of 0.1 m³/min, how fast is the water level rising when the depth at the deepest point is 1 m?

27. Gravel is being dumped from a conveyor belt at a rate of 3 m³/min, and its coarseness is such that it forms a pile in the shape of a cone whose base diameter and height are always

equal. How fast is the height of the pile increasing when the pile is 3 m high?

28. A kite 50 m above the ground moves horizontally at a speed of 2 m/s. At what rate is the angle between the string and the horizontal decreasing when 100 m of string has been let out?

29. Two sides of a triangle are 4 m and 5 m in length and the angle between them is increasing at a rate of 0.06 rad/s. Find the rate at which the area of the triangle is increasing when the angle between the sides of fixed length is $\pi/3$.

30. How fast is the angle between the ladder and the ground changing in Example 2 when the bottom of the ladder is 3 m from the wall?

31. The top of a ladder slides down a vertical wall at a rate of 0.15 m/s. At the moment when the bottom of the ladder is 3 m from the wall, it slides away from the wall at a rate of 0.2 m/s. How long is the ladder?

32. A faucet is filling a hemispherical basin of diameter 60 cm with water at a rate of 2 L/min. Find the rate at which the water is rising in the basin when it is half full. [Use the following facts: 1 L is 1000 cm³. The volume of the portion of a sphere with radius r from the bottom to a height h is $V = \pi\left(rh^2 - \frac{1}{3}h^3\right)$, as we will show in Chapter 6.]

33. Boyle's Law states that when a sample of gas is compressed at a constant temperature, the pressure P and volume V satisfy the equation $PV = C$, where C is a constant. Suppose that at a certain instant the volume is 600 cm³, the pressure is 150 kPa, and the pressure is increasing at a rate of 20 kPa/min. At what rate is the volume decreasing at this instant?

34. When air expands adiabatically (without gaining or losing heat), its pressure P and volume V are related by the equation $PV^{1.4} = C$, where C is a constant. Suppose that at a certain instant the volume is 400 cm³ and the pressure is 80 kPa and is decreasing at a rate of 10 kPa/min. At what rate is the volume increasing at this instant?

35. If two resistors with resistances R_1 and R_2 are connected in parallel, as in the figure, then the total resistance R, measured in ohms (Ω), is given by

$$\frac{1}{R} = \frac{1}{R_1} + \frac{1}{R_2}$$

If R_1 and R_2 are increasing at rates of 0.3 Ω/s and 0.2 Ω/s, respectively, how fast is R changing when $R_1 = 80 \ \Omega$ and $R_2 = 100 \ \Omega$?

36. Brain weight B as a function of body weight W in fish has been modeled by the power function $B = 0.007W^{2/3}$, where B and W are measured in grams. A model for body weight as a function of body length L (measured in centimeters) is $W = 0.12L^{2.53}$. If, over 10 million years, the average length of a certain species of fish evolved from 15 cm to 20 cm at a constant rate, how fast was this species' brain growing when the average length was 18 cm?

37. Two sides of a triangle have lengths 12 m and 15 m. The angle between them is increasing at a rate of $2°/\text{min}$. How fast is the length of the third side increasing when the angle between the sides of fixed length is $60°$?

38. Two carts, A and B, are connected by a rope 12 m long that passes over a pulley P (see the figure). The point Q is on the floor 4 m directly beneath P and between the carts. Cart A is being pulled away from Q at a speed of 0.5 m/s. How fast is cart B moving toward Q at the instant when cart A is 3 m from Q?

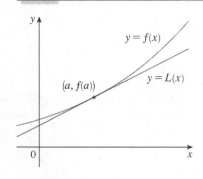

39. A television camera is positioned 1200 m from the base of a rocket launching pad. The angle of elevation of the camera has to change at the correct rate in order to keep the rocket in sight. Also, the mechanism for focusing the camera has to take into account the increasing distance from the camera to the rising rocket. Let's assume the rocket rises vertically and its speed is 200 m/s when it has risen 900 m.

(a) How fast is the distance from the television camera to the rocket changing at that moment?

(b) If the television camera is always kept aimed at the rocket, how fast is the camera's angle of elevation changing at that same moment?

40. A lighthouse is located on a small island 3 km away from the nearest point P on a straight shoreline and its light makes four revolutions per minute. How fast is the beam of light moving along the shoreline when it is 1 km from P?

41. A plane flies horizontally at an altitude of 5 km and passes directly over a tracking telescope on the ground. When the angle of elevation is $\pi/3$, this angle is decreasing at a rate of $\pi/6$ rad/min. How fast is the plane traveling at that time?

42. A Ferris wheel with a radius of 10 m is rotating at a rate of one revolution every 2 minutes. How fast is a rider rising when his seat is 16 m above ground level?

43. A plane flying with a constant speed of 300 km/h passes over a ground radar station at an altitude of 1 km and climbs at an angle of $30°$. At what rate is the distance from the plane to the radar station increasing a minute later?

44. Two people start from the same point. One walks east at 4 km/h and the other walks northeast at 2 km/h. How fast is the distance between the people changing after 15 minutes?

45. A runner sprints around a circular track of radius 100 m at a constant speed of 7 m/s. The runner's friend is standing at a distance 200 m from the center of the track. How fast is the distance between the friends changing when the distance between them is 200 m?

46. The minute hand on a watch is 8 mm long and the hour hand is 4 mm long. How fast is the distance between the tips of the hands changing at one o'clock?

Linear Approximations and Differentials

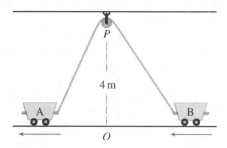

FIGURE 1

We have seen that a curve lies very close to its tangent line near the point of tangency. In fact, by zooming in toward a point on the graph of a differentiable function, we noticed that the graph looks more and more like its tangent line. (See Figure 2 in Section 2.7.) This observation is the basis for a method of finding approximate values of functions.

The idea is that it might be easy to calculate a value $f(a)$ of a function, but difficult (or even impossible) to compute nearby values of f. So we settle for the easily computed values of the linear function L whose graph is the tangent line of f at $(a, f(a))$. (See Figure 1.)

In other words, we use the tangent line at $(a, f(a))$ as an approximation to the curve $y = f(x)$ when x is near a. An equation of this tangent line is

$$y = f(a) + f'(a)(x - a)$$

and the approximation

$$\boxed{1} \qquad f(x) \approx f(a) + f'(a)(x - a)$$

is called the **linear approximation** or **tangent line approximation** of f at a. The linear function whose graph is this tangent line, that is,

$$\boxed{2} \qquad L(x) = f(a) + f'(a)(x - a)$$

is called the **linearization** of f at a.

V EXAMPLE 1 Find the linearization of the function $f(x) = \sqrt{x + 3}$ at $a = 1$ and use it to approximate the numbers $\sqrt{3.98}$ and $\sqrt{4.05}$. Are these approximations overestimates or underestimates?

SOLUTION The derivative of $f(x) = (x + 3)^{1/2}$ is

$$f'(x) = \tfrac{1}{2}(x + 3)^{-1/2} = \frac{1}{2\sqrt{x + 3}}$$

and so we have $f(1) = 2$ and $f'(1) = \tfrac{1}{4}$. Putting these values into Equation 2, we see that the linearization is

$$L(x) = f(1) + f'(1)(x - 1) = 2 + \tfrac{1}{4}(x - 1) = \frac{7}{4} + \frac{x}{4}$$

The corresponding linear approximation $\boxed{1}$ is

$$\sqrt{x + 3} \approx \frac{7}{4} + \frac{x}{4} \qquad \text{(when } x \text{ is near 1)}$$

In particular, we have

$$\sqrt{3.98} \approx \tfrac{7}{4} + \tfrac{0.98}{4} = 1.995 \qquad \text{and} \qquad \sqrt{4.05} \approx \tfrac{7}{4} + \tfrac{1.05}{4} = 2.0125$$

The linear approximation is illustrated in Figure 2. We see that, indeed, the tangent line approximation is a good approximation to the given function when x is near 1. We also see that our approximations are overestimates because the tangent line lies above the curve.

Of course, a calculator could give us approximations for $\sqrt{3.98}$ and $\sqrt{4.05}$, but the linear approximation gives an approximation *over an entire interval*.

In the following table we compare the estimates from the linear approximation in Example 1 with the true values. Notice from this table, and also from Figure 2, that the tangent line approximation gives good estimates when x is close to 1 but the accuracy of the approximation deteriorates when x is farther away from 1.

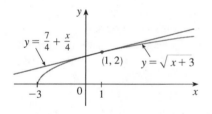

FIGURE 2

	x	From $L(x)$	Actual value
$\sqrt{3.9}$	0.9	1.975	1.97484176...
$\sqrt{3.98}$	0.98	1.995	1.99499373...
$\sqrt{4}$	1	2	2.00000000...
$\sqrt{4.05}$	1.05	2.0125	2.01246117...
$\sqrt{4.1}$	1.1	2.025	2.02484567...
$\sqrt{5}$	2	2.25	2.23606797...
$\sqrt{6}$	3	2.5	2.44948974...

How good is the approximation that we obtained in Example 1? The next example shows that by using a graphing calculator or computer we can determine an interval throughout which a linear approximation provides a specified accuracy.

EXAMPLE 2   For what values of x is the linear approximation

$$\sqrt{x + 3} \approx \frac{7}{4} + \frac{x}{4}$$

accurate to within 0.5? What about accuracy to within 0.1?

SOLUTION   Accuracy to within 0.5 means that the functions should differ by less than 0.5:

$$\left| \sqrt{x + 3} - \left(\frac{7}{4} + \frac{x}{4} \right) \right| < 0.5$$

Equivalently, we could write

$$\sqrt{x + 3} - 0.5 < \frac{7}{4} + \frac{x}{4} < \sqrt{x + 3} + 0.5$$

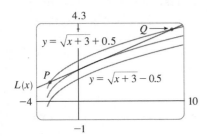

FIGURE 3

This says that the linear approximation should lie between the curves obtained by shifting the curve $y = \sqrt{x + 3}$ upward and downward by an amount 0.5. Figure 3 shows the tangent line $y = (7 + x)/4$ intersecting the upper curve $y = \sqrt{x + 3} + 0.5$ at P and Q. Zooming in and using the cursor, we estimate that the x-coordinate of P is about -2.66 and the x-coordinate of Q is about 8.66. Thus we see from the graph that the approximation

$$\sqrt{x + 3} \approx \frac{7}{4} + \frac{x}{4}$$

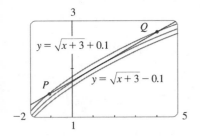

FIGURE 4

is accurate to within 0.5 when $-2.6 < x < 8.6$. (We have rounded to be safe.)

Similarly, from Figure 4 we see that the approximation is accurate to within 0.1 when $-1.1 < x < 3.9$.   ▅

▅ Applications to Physics

Linear approximations are often used in physics. In analyzing the consequences of an equation, a physicist sometimes needs to simplify a function by replacing it with its linear approximation. For instance, in deriving a formula for the period of a pendulum, physics textbooks obtain the expression $a_T = -g \sin \theta$ for tangential acceleration and then replace $\sin \theta$ by θ with the remark that $\sin \theta$ is very close to θ if θ is not too large. [See, for example, *Physics: Calculus,* 2d ed., by Eugene Hecht (Pacific Grove, CA, 2000), p. 431.] You can verify that the linearization of the function $f(x) = \sin x$ at $a = 0$ is $L(x) = x$ and so the linear approximation at 0 is

$$\sin x \approx x$$

(see Exercise 42). So, in effect, the derivation of the formula for the period of a pendulum uses the tangent line approximation for the sine function.

Another example occurs in the theory of optics, where light rays that arrive at shallow angles relative to the optical axis are called *paraxial rays*. In paraxial (or Gaussian) optics, both $\sin \theta$ and $\cos \theta$ are replaced by their linearizations. In other words, the linear approximations

$$\sin \theta \approx \theta \qquad \text{and} \qquad \cos \theta \approx 1$$

are used because θ is close to 0. The results of calculations made with these approximations became the basic theoretical tool used to design lenses. [See *Optics*, 4th ed., by Eugene Hecht (San Francisco, 2002), p. 154.]

In Section 11.11 we will present several other applications of the idea of linear approximations to physics and engineering.

▨ Differentials

The ideas behind linear approximations are sometimes formulated in the terminology and notation of *differentials*. If $y = f(x)$, where f is a differentiable function, then the **differential** dx is an independent variable; that is, dx can be given the value of any real number. The **differential** dy is then defined in terms of dx by the equation

> If $dx \neq 0$, we can divide both sides of Equation 3 by dx to obtain
>
> $$\frac{dy}{dx} = f'(x)$$
>
> We have seen similar equations before, but now the left side can genuinely be interpreted as a ratio of differentials.

$$\boxed{3} \qquad dy = f'(x)\, dx$$

So dy is a dependent variable; it depends on the values of x and dx. If dx is given a specific value and x is taken to be some specific number in the domain of f, then the numerical value of dy is determined.

The geometric meaning of differentials is shown in Figure 5. Let $P(x, f(x))$ and $Q(x + \Delta x, f(x + \Delta x))$ be points on the graph of f and let $dx = \Delta x$. The corresponding change in y is

$$\Delta y = f(x + \Delta x) - f(x)$$

The slope of the tangent line PR is the derivative $f'(x)$. Thus the directed distance from S to R is $f'(x)\, dx = dy$. Therefore dy represents the amount that the tangent line rises or falls (the change in the linearization), whereas Δy represents the amount that the curve $y = f(x)$ rises or falls when x changes by an amount dx.

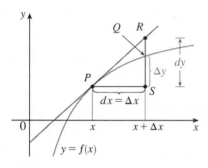

FIGURE 5

EXAMPLE 3 Compare the values of Δy and dy if $y = f(x) = x^3 + x^2 - 2x + 1$ and x changes (a) from 2 to 2.05 and (b) from 2 to 2.01.

SOLUTION
(a) We have

$$f(2) = 2^3 + 2^2 - 2(2) + 1 = 9$$

$$f(2.05) = (2.05)^3 + (2.05)^2 - 2(2.05) + 1 = 9.717625$$

$$\Delta y = f(2.05) - f(2) = 0.717625$$

In general,

$$dy = f'(x)\, dx = (3x^2 + 2x - 2)\, dx$$

When $x = 2$ and $dx = \Delta x = 0.05$, this becomes

$$dy = [3(2)^2 + 2(2) - 2]0.05 = 0.7$$

(b)

$$f(2.01) = (2.01)^3 + (2.01)^2 - 2(2.01) + 1 = 9.140701$$

$$\Delta y = f(2.01) - f(2) = 0.140701$$

> Figure 6 shows the function in Example 3 and a comparison of dy and Δy when $a = 2$. The viewing rectangle is $[1.8, 2.5]$ by $[6, 18]$.
>
>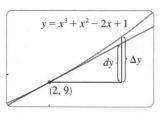
>
> **FIGURE 6**

When $dx = \Delta x = 0.01$,

$$dy = [3(2)^2 + 2(2) - 2]0.01 = 0.14$$

Notice that the approximation $\Delta y \approx dy$ becomes better as Δx becomes smaller in Example 3. Notice also that dy was easier to compute than Δy. For more complicated functions it may be impossible to compute Δy exactly. In such cases the approximation by differentials is especially useful.

In the notation of differentials, the linear approximation $\boxed{1}$ can be written as

$$f(a + dx) \approx f(a) + dy$$

For instance, for the function $f(x) = \sqrt{x + 3}$ in Example 1, we have

$$dy = f'(x)\,dx = \frac{dx}{2\sqrt{x + 3}}$$

If $a = 1$ and $dx = \Delta x = 0.05$, then

$$dy = \frac{0.05}{2\sqrt{1 + 3}} = 0.0125$$

and

$$\sqrt{4.05} = f(1.05) \approx f(1) + dy = 2.0125$$

just as we found in Example 1.

Our final example illustrates the use of differentials in estimating the errors that occur because of approximate measurements.

V **EXAMPLE 4** The radius of a sphere was measured and found to be 21 cm with a possible error in measurement of at most 0.05 cm. What is the maximum error in using this value of the radius to compute the volume of the sphere?

SOLUTION If the radius of the sphere is r, then its volume is $V = \frac{4}{3}\pi r^3$. If the error in the measured value of r is denoted by $dr = \Delta r$, then the corresponding error in the calculated value of V is ΔV, which can be approximated by the differential

$$dV = 4\pi r^2\,dr$$

When $r = 21$ and $dr = 0.05$, this becomes

$$dV = 4\pi(21)^2 0.05 \approx 277$$

The maximum error in the calculated volume is about 277 cm^3.

NOTE Although the possible error in Example 4 may appear to be rather large, a better picture of the error is given by the **relative error**, which is computed by dividing the error by the total volume:

$$\frac{\Delta V}{V} \approx \frac{dV}{V} = \frac{4\pi r^2\,dr}{\frac{4}{3}\pi r^3} = 3\,\frac{dr}{r}$$

Thus the relative error in the volume is about three times the relative error in the radius. In Example 4 the relative error in the radius is approximately $dr/r = 0.05/21 \approx 0.0024$ and it produces a relative error of about 0.007 in the volume. The errors could also be expressed as **percentage errors** of 0.24% in the radius and 0.7% in the volume.

3.10 **Exercises**

1–4 Find the linearization $L(x)$ of the function at a.

1. $f(x) = x^4 + 3x^2$, $\quad a = -1$ **2.** $f(x) = \sin x$, $\quad a = \pi/6$

3. $f(x) = \sqrt{x}$, $\quad a = 4$ **4.** $f(x) = x^{3/4}$, $\quad a = 16$

 5. Find the linear approximation of the function $f(x) = \sqrt{1 - x}$ at $a = 0$ and use it to approximate the numbers $\sqrt{0.9}$ and $\sqrt{0.99}$. Illustrate by graphing f and the tangent line.

6. Find the linear approximation of the function $g(x) = \sqrt[3]{1 + x}$ at $a = 0$ and use it to approximate the numbers $\sqrt[3]{0.95}$ and $\sqrt[3]{1.1}$. Illustrate by graphing g and the tangent line.

7–10 Verify the given linear approximation at $a = 0$. Then determine the values of x for which the linear approximation is accurate to within 0.1.

7. $\ln(1 + x) \approx x$ **8.** $\tan x \approx x$

9. $1/(1 + 2x)^4 \approx 1 - 8x$ **10.** $e^x \cos x \approx 1 + x$

11–14 Find the differential of each function.

11. (a) $y = x^2 \sin 2x$ (b) $y = \ln\sqrt{1 + t^2}$

12. (a) $y = s/(1 + 2s)$ (b) $y = e^{-u} \cos u$

13. (a) $y = \tan \sqrt{t}$ (b) $y = \dfrac{1 - v^2}{1 + v^2}$

14. (a) $y = e^{\tan \pi t}$ (b) $y = \sqrt{1 + \ln z}$

15–18 (a) Find the differential dy and (b) evaluate dy for the given values of x and dx.

15. $y = e^{x/10}$, $\quad x = 0$, $\quad dx = 0.1$

16. $y = \cos \pi x$, $\quad x = \frac{1}{3}$, $\quad dx = -0.02$

17. $y = \sqrt{3 + x^2}$, $\quad x = 1$, $\quad dx = -0.1$

18. $y = \dfrac{x + 1}{x - 1}$, $\quad x = 2$, $\quad dx = 0.05$

19–22 Compute Δy and dy for the given values of x and $dx = \Delta x$. Then sketch a diagram like Figure 5 showing the line segments with lengths dx, dy, and Δy.

19. $y = 2x - x^2$, $\quad x = 2$, $\quad \Delta x = -0.4$

20. $y = \sqrt{x}$, $\quad x = 1$, $\quad \Delta x = 1$

21. $y = 2/x$, $\quad x = 4$, $\quad \Delta x = 1$

22. $y = e^x$, $\quad x = 0$, $\quad \Delta x = 0.5$

23–28 Use a linear approximation (or differentials) to estimate the given number.

23. $(1.999)^4$

24. $e^{-0.015}$

25. $\sqrt[3]{1001}$ **26.** $1/4.002$

27. $\tan 44°$ **28.** $\sqrt{99.8}$

29–31 Explain, in terms of linear approximations or differentials, why the approximation is reasonable.

29. $\sec 0.08 \approx 1$ **30.** $(1.01)^6 \approx 1.06$

31. $\ln 1.05 \approx 0.05$

32. Let
$$f(x) = (x - 1)^2 \qquad g(x) = e^{-2x}$$
and
$$h(x) = 1 + \ln(1 - 2x)$$

    (a) Find the linearizations of f, g, and h at $a = 0$. What do you notice? How do you explain what happened?

    (b) Graph f, g, and h and their linear approximations. For which function is the linear approximation best? For which is it worst? Explain.

33. The edge of a cube was found to be 30 cm with a possible error in measurement of 0.1 cm. Use differentials to estimate the maximum possible error, relative error, and percentage error in computing (a) the volume of the cube and (b) the surface area of the cube.

34. The radius of a circular disk is given as 24 cm with a maximum error in measurement of 0.2 cm.

    (a) Use differentials to estimate the maximum error in the calculated area of the disk.

    (b) What is the relative error? What is the percentage error?

35. The circumference of a sphere was measured to be 84 cm with a possible error of 0.5 cm.

    (a) Use differentials to estimate the maximum error in the calculated surface area. What is the relative error?

    (b) Use differentials to estimate the maximum error in the calculated volume. What is the relative error?

36. Use differentials to estimate the amount of paint needed to apply a coat of paint 0.05 cm thick to a hemispherical dome with diameter 50 m.

37. (a) Use differentials to find a formula for the approximate volume of a thin cylindrical shell with height h, inner radius r, and thickness Δr.

    (b) What is the error involved in using the formula from part (a)?

38. One side of a right triangle is known to be 20 cm long and the opposite angle is measured as 30°, with a possible error of $\pm 1°$.

    (a) Use differentials to estimate the error in computing the length of the hypotenuse.

    (b) What is the percentage error?

Graphing calculator or computer required   **1.** Homework Hints available at stewartcalculus.com

39. If a current I passes through a resistor with resistance R, Ohm's Law states that the voltage drop is $V = RI$. If V is constant and R is measured with a certain error, use differentials to show that the relative error in calculating I is approximately the same (in magnitude) as the relative error in R.

40. When blood flows along a blood vessel, the flux F (the volume of blood per unit time that flows past a given point) is proportional to the fourth power of the radius R of the blood vessel:

$$F = kR^4$$

(This is known as Poiseuille's Law; we will show why it is true in Section 8.4.) A partially clogged artery can be expanded by an operation called angioplasty, in which a balloon-tipped catheter is inflated inside the artery in order to widen it and restore the normal blood flow.

Show that the relative change in F is about four times the relative change in R. How will a 5% increase in the radius affect the flow of blood?

41. Establish the following rules for working with differentials (where c denotes a constant and u and v are functions of x).

(a) $dc = 0$
(b) $d(cu) = c\,du$
(c) $d(u + v) = du + dv$
(d) $d(uv) = u\,dv + v\,du$
(e) $d\left(\dfrac{u}{v}\right) = \dfrac{v\,du - u\,dv}{v^2}$
(f) $d(x^n) = nx^{n-1}\,dx$

42. On page 431 of *Physics: Calculus,* 2d ed., by Eugene Hecht (Pacific Grove, CA, 2000), in the course of deriving the formula $T = 2\pi\sqrt{L/g}$ for the period of a pendulum of length L, the author obtains the equation $a_T = -g\sin\theta$ for the tangen-

tial acceleration of the bob of the pendulum. He then says, "for small angles, the value of θ in radians is very nearly the value of $\sin\theta$; they differ by less than 2% out to about 20°."

(a) Verify the linear approximation at 0 for the sine function:

$$\sin x \approx x$$

 (b) Use a graphing device to determine the values of x for which $\sin x$ and x differ by less than 2%. Then verify Hecht's statement by converting from radians to degrees.

43. Suppose that the only information we have about a function f is that $f(1) = 5$ and the graph of its *derivative* is as shown.

(a) Use a linear approximation to estimate $f(0.9)$ and $f(1.1)$.

(b) Are your estimates in part (a) too large or too small? Explain.

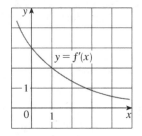

44. Suppose that we don't have a formula for $g(x)$ but we know that $g(2) = -4$ and $g'(x) = \sqrt{x^2 + 5}$ for all x.

(a) Use a linear approximation to estimate $g(1.95)$ and $g(2.05)$.

(b) Are your estimates in part (a) too large or too small? Explain.

LABORATORY PROJECT TAYLOR POLYNOMIALS

The tangent line approximation $L(x)$ is the best first-degree (linear) approximation to $f(x)$ near $x = a$ because $f(x)$ and $L(x)$ have the same rate of change (derivative) at a. For a better approximation than a linear one, let's try a second-degree (quadratic) approximation $P(x)$. In other words, we approximate a curve by a parabola instead of by a straight line. To make sure that the approximation is a good one, we stipulate the following:

(i) $P(a) = f(a)$ (P and f should have the same value at a.)

(ii) $P'(a) = f'(a)$ (P and f should have the same rate of change at a.)

(iii) $P''(a) = f''(a)$ (The slopes of P and f should change at the same rate at a.)

1. Find the quadratic approximation $P(x) = A + Bx + Cx^2$ to the function $f(x) = \cos x$ that satisfies conditions (i), (ii), and (iii) with $a = 0$. Graph P, f, and the linear approximation $L(x) = 1$ on a common screen. Comment on how well the functions P and L approximate f.

2. Determine the values of x for which the quadratic approximation $f(x) \approx P(x)$ in Problem 1 is accurate to within 0.1. [*Hint:* Graph $y = P(x)$, $y = \cos x - 0.1$, and $y = \cos x + 0.1$ on a common screen.]

 Graphing calculator or computer required

3. To approximate a function f by a quadratic function P near a number a, it is best to write P in the form

$$P(x) = A + B(x - a) + C(x - a)^2$$

Show that the quadratic function that satisfies conditions (i), (ii), and (iii) is

$$P(x) = f(a) + f'(a)(x - a) + \tfrac{1}{2}f''(a)(x - a)^2$$

4. Find the quadratic approximation to $f(x) = \sqrt{x + 3}$ near $a = 1$. Graph f, the quadratic approximation, and the linear approximation from Example 2 in Section 3.10 on a common screen. What do you conclude?

5. Instead of being satisfied with a linear or quadratic approximation to $f(x)$ near $x = a$, let's try to find better approximations with higher-degree polynomials. We look for an nth-degree polynomial

$$T_n(x) = c_0 + c_1(x - a) + c_2(x - a)^2 + c_3(x - a)^3 + \cdots + c_n(x - a)^n$$

such that T_n and its first n derivatives have the same values at $x = a$ as f and its first n derivatives. By differentiating repeatedly and setting $x = a$, show that these conditions are satisfied if $c_0 = f(a)$, $c_1 = f'(a)$, $c_2 = \tfrac{1}{2}f''(a)$, and in general

$$c_k = \frac{f^{(k)}(a)}{k!}$$

where $k! = 1 \cdot 2 \cdot 3 \cdot 4 \cdot \cdots \cdot k$. The resulting polynomial

$$T_n(x) = f(a) + f'(a)(x - a) + \frac{f''(a)}{2!}(x - a)^2 + \cdots + \frac{f^{(n)}(a)}{n!}(x - a)^n$$

is called the **nth-degree Taylor polynomial of f centered at a.**

6. Find the 8th-degree Taylor polynomial centered at $a = 0$ for the function $f(x) = \cos x$. Graph f together with the Taylor polynomials T_2, T_4, T_6, T_8 in the viewing rectangle $[-5, 5]$ by $[-1.4, 1.4]$ and comment on how well they approximate f.

3.11 Hyperbolic Functions

Certain even and odd combinations of the exponential functions e^x and e^{-x} arise so frequently in mathematics and its applications that they deserve to be given special names. In many ways they are analogous to the trigonometric functions, and they have the same relationship to the hyperbola that the trigonometric functions have to the circle. For this reason they are collectively called **hyperbolic functions** and individually called **hyperbolic sine**, **hyperbolic cosine**, and so on.

Definition of the Hyperbolic Functions

$$\sinh x = \frac{e^x - e^{-x}}{2} \qquad\qquad \operatorname{csch} x = \frac{1}{\sinh x}$$

$$\cosh x = \frac{e^x + e^{-x}}{2} \qquad\qquad \operatorname{sech} x = \frac{1}{\cosh x}$$

$$\tanh x = \frac{\sinh x}{\cosh x} \qquad\qquad \coth x = \frac{\cosh x}{\sinh x}$$

The graphs of hyperbolic sine and cosine can be sketched using graphical addition as in Figures 1 and 2.

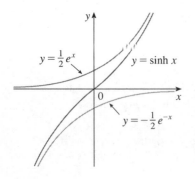

FIGURE 1
$y = \sinh x = \frac{1}{2}e^x - \frac{1}{2}e^{-x}$

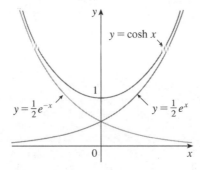

FIGURE 2
$y = \cosh x = \frac{1}{2}e^x + \frac{1}{2}e^{-x}$

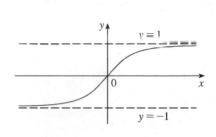

FIGURE 3
$y = \tanh x$

FIGURE 4
A catenary $y = c + a\cosh(x/a)$

FIGURE 5
Idealized ocean wave

Note that sinh has domain $\mathbb{R}$ and range $\mathbb{R}$, while cosh has domain $\mathbb{R}$ and range $[1, \infty)$. The graph of tanh is shown in Figure 3. It has the horizontal asymptotes $y = \pm 1$. (See Exercise 23.)

Some of the mathematical uses of hyperbolic functions will be seen in Chapter 7. Applications to science and engineering occur whenever an entity such as light, velocity, electricity, or radioactivity is gradually absorbed or extinguished, for the decay can be represented by hyperbolic functions. The most famous application is the use of hyperbolic cosine to describe the shape of a hanging wire. It can be proved that if a heavy flexible cable (such as a telephone or power line) is suspended between two points at the same height, then it takes the shape of a curve with equation $y = c + a\cosh(x/a)$ called a *catenary* (see Figure 4). (The Latin word *catena* means "chain.")

Another application of hyperbolic functions occurs in the description of ocean waves: The velocity of a water wave with length L moving across a body of water with depth d is modeled by the function

$$v = \sqrt{\frac{gL}{2\pi}\tanh\left(\frac{2\pi d}{L}\right)}$$

where g is the acceleration due to gravity. (See Figure 5 and Exercise 49.)

The hyperbolic functions satisfy a number of identities that are similar to well-known trigonometric identities. We list some of them here and leave most of the proofs to the exercises.

Hyperbolic Identities

$$\sinh(-x) = -\sinh x \qquad\qquad \cosh(-x) = \cosh x$$

$$\cosh^2 x - \sinh^2 x = 1 \qquad\qquad 1 - \tanh^2 x = \operatorname{sech}^2 x$$

$$\sinh(x + y) = \sinh x \cosh y + \cosh x \sinh y$$

$$\cosh(x + y) = \cosh x \cosh y + \sinh x \sinh y$$

The Gateway Arch in St. Louis was designed using a hyperbolic cosine function (Exercise 48).

V **EXAMPLE 1** Prove (a) $\cosh^2 x - \sinh^2 x = 1$ and (b) $1 - \tanh^2 x = \text{sech}^2 x$.

SOLUTION

(a)
$$\cosh^2 x - \sinh^2 x = \left(\frac{e^x + e^{-x}}{2}\right)^2 - \left(\frac{e^x - e^{-x}}{2}\right)^2$$

$$= \frac{e^{2x} + 2 + e^{-2x}}{4} - \frac{e^{2x} - 2 + e^{-2x}}{4} = \frac{4}{4} = 1$$

(b) We start with the identity proved in part (a):

$$\cosh^2 x - \sinh^2 x = 1$$

If we divide both sides by $\cosh^2 x$, we get

$$1 - \frac{\sinh^2 x}{\cosh^2 x} = \frac{1}{\cosh^2 x}$$

or
$$1 - \tanh^2 x = \text{sech}^2 x$$

The identity proved in Example 1(a) gives a clue to the reason for the name "hyperbolic" functions:

If t is any real number, then the point $P(\cos t, \sin t)$ lies on the unit circle $x^2 + y^2 = 1$ because $\cos^2 t + \sin^2 t = 1$. In fact, t can be interpreted as the radian measure of $\angle POQ$ in Figure 6. For this reason the trigonometric functions are sometimes called *circular* functions.

Likewise, if t is any real number, then the point $P(\cosh t, \sinh t)$ lies on the right branch of the hyperbola $x^2 - y^2 = 1$ because $\cosh^2 t - \sinh^2 t = 1$ and $\cosh t \geq 1$. This time, t does not represent the measure of an angle. However, it turns out that t represents twice the area of the shaded hyperbolic sector in Figure 7, just as in the trigonometric case t represents twice the area of the shaded circular sector in Figure 6.

The derivatives of the hyperbolic functions are easily computed. For example,

$$\frac{d}{dx}(\sinh x) = \frac{d}{dx}\left(\frac{e^x - e^{-x}}{2}\right) = \frac{e^x + e^{-x}}{2} = \cosh x$$

We list the differentiation formulas for the hyperbolic functions as Table 1. The remaining proofs are left as exercises. Note the analogy with the differentiation formulas for trigonometric functions, but beware that the signs are different in some cases.

FIGURE 6

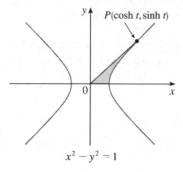

FIGURE 7

---

1 **Derivatives of Hyperbolic Functions**

$$\frac{d}{dx}(\sinh x) = \cosh x \qquad \frac{d}{dx}(\text{csch } x) = -\text{csch } x \coth x$$

$$\frac{d}{dx}(\cosh x) = \sinh x \qquad \frac{d}{dx}(\text{sech } x) = -\text{sech } x \tanh x$$

$$\frac{d}{dx}(\tanh x) = \text{sech}^2 x \qquad \frac{d}{dx}(\coth x) = -\text{csch}^2 x$$

EXAMPLE 2   Any of these differentiation rules can be combined with the Chain Rule. For instance,

$$\frac{d}{dx}\left(\cosh \sqrt{x}\,\right) = \sinh \sqrt{x} \cdot \frac{d}{dx}\sqrt{x} = \frac{\sinh \sqrt{x}}{2\sqrt{x}}$$

Inverse Hyperbolic Functions

You can see from Figures 1 and 3 that sinh and tanh are one-to-one functions and so they have inverse functions denoted by $\sinh^{-1}$ and $\tanh^{-1}$. Figure 2 shows that cosh is not one-to-one, but when restricted to the domain $[0, \infty)$ it becomes one-to-one. The inverse hyperbolic cosine function is defined as the inverse of this restricted function.

$$\boxed{2}\qquad
\begin{aligned}
y &= \sinh^{-1}x &\iff&\quad \sinh y = x \\
y &= \cosh^{-1}x &\iff&\quad \cosh y = x \quad \text{and} \quad y \geq 0 \\
y &= \tanh^{-1}x &\iff&\quad \tanh y = x
\end{aligned}$$

The remaining inverse hyperbolic functions are defined similarly (see Exercise 28).

We can sketch the graphs of $\sinh^{-1}$, $\cosh^{-1}$, and $\tanh^{-1}$ in Figures 8, 9, and 10 by using Figures 1, 2, and 3.

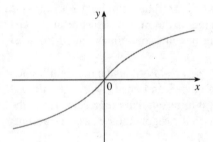

FIGURE 8 $y = \sinh^{-1}x$
domain $= \mathbb{R}$ range $= \mathbb{R}$

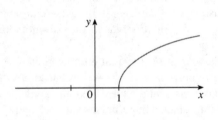

FIGURE 9 $y = \cosh^{-1}x$
domain $= [1, \infty)$ range $= [0, \infty)$

FIGURE 10 $y = \tanh^{-1}x$
domain $= (-1, 1)$ range $= \mathbb{R}$

Since the hyperbolic functions are defined in terms of exponential functions, it's not surprising to learn that the inverse hyperbolic functions can be expressed in terms of logarithms. In particular, we have:

Formula 3 is proved in Example 3. The proofs of Formulas 4 and 5 are requested in Exercises 26 and 27.

$$\boxed{3}\qquad \sinh^{-1}x = \ln\left(x + \sqrt{x^2 + 1}\,\right) \qquad x \in \mathbb{R}$$

$$\boxed{4}\qquad \cosh^{-1}x = \ln\left(x + \sqrt{x^2 - 1}\,\right) \qquad x \geq 1$$

$$\boxed{5}\qquad \tanh^{-1}x = \tfrac{1}{2}\ln\left(\frac{1 + x}{1 - x}\right) \qquad -1 < x < 1$$

EXAMPLE 3   Show that $\sinh^{-1}x = \ln\left(x + \sqrt{x^2 + 1}\,\right)$.

SOLUTION   Let $y = \sinh^{-1}x$. Then

$$x = \sinh y = \frac{e^y - e^{-y}}{2}$$

so
$$e^y - 2x - e^{-y} = 0$$

or, multiplying by e^y,
$$e^{2y} - 2xe^y - 1 = 0$$

This is really a quadratic equation in e^y:
$$(e^y)^2 - 2x(e^y) - 1 = 0$$

Solving by the quadratic formula, we get
$$e^y = \frac{2x \pm \sqrt{4x^2 + 4}}{2} = x \pm \sqrt{x^2 + 1}$$

Note that $e^y > 0$, but $x - \sqrt{x^2 + 1} < 0$ $\left(\text{because } x < \sqrt{x^2 + 1}\right)$. Thus the minus sign is inadmissible and we have
$$e^y = x + \sqrt{x^2 + 1}$$

Therefore
$$y = \ln(e^y) = \ln\left(x + \sqrt{x^2 + 1}\right)$$

(See Exercise 25 for another method.) ▬

---

6 | **Derivatives of Inverse Hyperbolic Functions**

$$\frac{d}{dx}(\sinh^{-1}x) = \frac{1}{\sqrt{1 + x^2}} \qquad\qquad \frac{d}{dx}(\operatorname{csch}^{-1}x) = -\frac{1}{|x|\sqrt{x^2 + 1}}$$

$$\frac{d}{dx}(\cosh^{-1}x) = \frac{1}{\sqrt{x^2 - 1}} \qquad\qquad \frac{d}{dx}(\operatorname{sech}^{-1}x) = -\frac{1}{x\sqrt{1 - x^2}}$$

$$\frac{d}{dx}(\tanh^{-1}x) = \frac{1}{1 - x^2} \qquad\qquad \frac{d}{dx}(\coth^{-1}x) = \frac{1}{1 - x^2}$$

Notice that the formulas for the derivatives of $\tanh^{-1}x$ and $\coth^{-1}x$ appear to be identical. But the domains of these functions have no numbers in common: $\tanh^{-1}x$ is defined for $|x| < 1$, whereas $\coth^{-1}x$ is defined for $|x| > 1$.

The inverse hyperbolic functions are all differentiable because the hyperbolic functions are differentiable. The formulas in Table 6 can be proved either by the method for inverse functions or by differentiating Formulas 3, 4, and 5.

V **EXAMPLE 4** Prove that $\dfrac{d}{dx}(\sinh^{-1}x) = \dfrac{1}{\sqrt{1 + x^2}}$.

SOLUTION 1 Let $y = \sinh^{-1}x$. Then $\sinh y = x$. If we differentiate this equation implicitly with respect to x, we get
$$\cosh y\, \frac{dy}{dx} = 1$$

Since $\cosh^2 y - \sinh^2 y = 1$ and $\cosh y \geqslant 0$, we have $\cosh y = \sqrt{1 + \sinh^2 y}$, so
$$\frac{dy}{dx} = \frac{1}{\cosh y} = \frac{1}{\sqrt{1 + \sinh^2 y}} = \frac{1}{\sqrt{1 + x^2}}$$

SOLUTION 2 From Equation 3 (proved in Example 3), we have

$$\frac{d}{dx}(\sinh^{-1}x) = \frac{d}{dx}\ln\left(x + \sqrt{x^2 + 1}\right)$$

$$= \frac{1}{x + \sqrt{x^2 + 1}}\frac{d}{dx}\left(x + \sqrt{x^2 + 1}\right)$$

$$= \frac{1}{x + \sqrt{x^2 + 1}}\left(1 + \frac{x}{\sqrt{x^2 + 1}}\right)$$

$$= \frac{\sqrt{x^2 + 1} + x}{\left(x + \sqrt{x^2 + 1}\right)\sqrt{x^2 + 1}}$$

$$= \frac{1}{\sqrt{x^2 + 1}}$$

V **EXAMPLE 5** Find $\dfrac{d}{dx}[\tanh^{-1}(\sin x)]$.

SOLUTION Using Table 6 and the Chain Rule, we have

$$\frac{d}{dx}[\tanh^{-1}(\sin x)] = \frac{1}{1 - (\sin x)^2}\frac{d}{dx}(\sin x)$$

$$= \frac{1}{1 - \sin^2 x}\cos x = \frac{\cos x}{\cos^2 x} = \sec x$$

3.11 Exercises

1–6 Find the numerical value of each expression.

1. (a) $\sinh 0$ (b) $\cosh 0$

2. (a) $\tanh 0$ (b) $\tanh 1$

3. (a) $\sinh(\ln 2)$ (b) $\sinh 2$

4. (a) $\cosh 3$ (b) $\cosh(\ln 3)$

5. (a) $\operatorname{sech} 0$ (b) $\cosh^{-1}1$

6. (a) $\sinh 1$ (b) $\sinh^{-1}1$

7–19 Prove the identity.

7. $\sinh(-x) = -\sinh x$
(This shows that sinh is an odd function.)

8. $\cosh(-x) = \cosh x$
(This shows that cosh is an even function.)

9. $\cosh x + \sinh x = e^x$

10. $\cosh x - \sinh x = e^{-x}$

11. $\sinh(x + y) = \sinh x \cosh y + \cosh x \sinh y$

12. $\cosh(x + y) = \cosh x \cosh y + \sinh x \sinh y$

13. $\coth^2 x - 1 = \operatorname{csch}^2 x$

14. $\tanh(x + y) = \dfrac{\tanh x + \tanh y}{1 + \tanh x \tanh y}$

15. $\sinh 2x = 2 \sinh x \cosh x$

16. $\cosh 2x = \cosh^2 x + \sinh^2 x$

17. $\tanh(\ln x) = \dfrac{x^2 - 1}{x^2 + 1}$

18. $\dfrac{1 + \tanh x}{1 - \tanh x} = e^{2x}$

19. $(\cosh x + \sinh x)^n = \cosh nx + \sinh nx$
(n any real number)

20. If $\tanh x = \frac{12}{13}$, find the values of the other hyperbolic functions at x.

21. If $\cosh x = \frac{5}{3}$ and $x > 0$, find the values of the other hyperbolic functions at x.

22. (a) Use the graphs of sinh, cosh, and tanh in Figures 1–3 to draw the graphs of csch, sech, and coth.

(b) Check the graphs that you sketched in part (a) by using a graphing device to produce them.

23. Use the definitions of the hyperbolic functions to find each of the following limits.

(a) $\lim\limits_{x \to \infty} \tanh x$

(b) $\lim\limits_{x \to -\infty} \tanh x$

(c) $\lim\limits_{x \to \infty} \sinh x$

(d) $\lim\limits_{x \to -\infty} \sinh x$

(e) $\lim\limits_{x \to \infty} \operatorname{sech} x$

(f) $\lim\limits_{x \to \infty} \coth x$

(g) $\lim\limits_{x \to 0^+} \coth x$

(h) $\lim\limits_{x \to 0^-} \coth x$

(i) $\lim\limits_{x \to -\infty} \operatorname{csch} x$

24. Prove the formulas given in Table 1 for the derivatives of the functions (a) cosh, (b) tanh, (c) csch, (d) sech, and (e) coth.

25. Give an alternative solution to Example 3 by letting $y = \sinh^{-1} x$ and then using Exercise 9 and Example 1(a) with x replaced by y.

26. Prove Equation 4.

27. Prove Equation 5 using (a) the method of Example 3 and (b) Exercise 18 with x replaced by y.

28. For each of the following functions (i) give a definition like those in $\boxed{2}$, (ii) sketch the graph, and (iii) find a formula similar to Equation 3.

(a) csch^{-1}　　(b) sech^{-1}　　(c) $\coth^{-1}$

29. Prove the formulas given in Table 6 for the derivatives of the following functions.

(a) $\cosh^{-1}$　　(b) $\tanh^{-1}$　　(c) csch^{-1}

(d) sech^{-1}　　(e) $\coth^{-1}$

30–45 Find the derivative. Simplify where possible.

30. $f(x) = \tanh(1 + e^{2x})$

31. $f(x) = x \sinh x - \cosh x$

32. $g(x) = \cosh(\ln x)$

33. $h(x) = \ln(\cosh x)$

34. $y = x \coth(1 + x^2)$

35. $y = e^{\cosh 3x}$

36. $f(t) = \operatorname{csch} t (1 - \ln \operatorname{csch} t)$

37. $f(t) = \operatorname{sech}^2(e^t)$

38. $y = \sinh(\cosh x)$

39. $G(x) = \dfrac{1 - \cosh x}{1 + \cosh x}$

40. $y = \sinh^{-1}(\tan x)$

41. $y = \cosh^{-1}\sqrt{x}$

42. $y = x \tanh^{-1} x + \ln \sqrt{1 - x^2}$

43. $y = x \sinh^{-1}(x/3) - \sqrt{9 + x^2}$

44. $y = \operatorname{sech}^{-1}(e^{-x})$

45. $y = \coth^{-1}(\sec x)$

46. Show that $\dfrac{d}{dx} \sqrt[4]{\dfrac{1 + \tanh x}{1 - \tanh x}} = \tfrac{1}{2} e^{x/2}$

47. Show that $\dfrac{d}{dx} \arctan(\tanh x) = \operatorname{sech} 2x$.

48. The Gateway Arch in St. Louis was designed by Eero Saarinen and was constructed using the equation

$$y = 211.49 - 20.96 \cosh 0.03291765x$$

for the central curve of the arch, where x and y are measured in meters and $|x| \leqslant 91.20$.

(a) Graph the central curve.

(b) What is the height of the arch at its center?

(c) At what points is the height 100 m?

(d) What is the slope of the arch at the points in part (c)?

49. If a water wave with length L moves with velocity v in a body of water with depth d, then

$$v = \sqrt{\frac{gL}{2\pi} \tanh\left(\frac{2\pi d}{L}\right)}$$

where g is the acceleration due to gravity. (See Figure 5.) Explain why the approximation

$$v \approx \sqrt{\frac{gL}{2\pi}}$$

is appropriate in deep water.

50. A flexible cable always hangs in the shape of a catenary $y = c + a \cosh(x/a)$, where c and a are constants and $a > 0$ (see Figure 4 and Exercise 52). Graph several members of the family of functions $y = a \cosh(x/a)$. How does the graph change as a varies?

51. A telephone line hangs between two poles 14 m apart in the shape of the catenary $y = 20 \cosh(x/20) - 15$, where x and y are measured in meters.

(a) Find the slope of this curve where it meets the right pole.

(b) Find the angle θ between the line and the pole.

52. Using principles from physics it can be shown that when a cable is hung between two poles, it takes the shape of a curve $y = f(x)$ that satisfies the differential equation

$$\frac{d^2 y}{dx^2} = \frac{\rho g}{T} \sqrt{1 + \left(\frac{dy}{dx}\right)^2}$$

where ρ is the linear density of the cable, g is the acceleration due to gravity, T is the tension in the cable at its lowest point, and the coordinate system is chosen appropriately. Verify that the function

$$y = f(x) = \frac{T}{\rho g} \cosh\left(\frac{\rho g x}{T}\right)$$

is a solution of this differential equation.

53. A cable with linear density $\rho = 2$ kg/m is strung from the tops of two poles that are 200 m apart.

(a) Use Exercise 52 to find the tension T so that the cable is 60 m above the ground at its lowest point. How tall are the poles?

(b) If the tension is doubled, what is the new low point of the cable? How tall are the poles now?

54. Evaluate $\displaystyle\lim_{x \to \infty} \frac{\sinh x}{e^x}$.

55. (a) Show that any function of the form

$$y = A \sinh mx + B \cosh mx$$

satisfies the differential equation $y'' = m^2 y$.

(b) Find $y = y(x)$ such that $y'' = 9y$, $y(0) = -4$, and $y'(0) = 6$.

56. If $x = \ln(\sec \theta + \tan \theta)$, show that $\sec \theta = \cosh x$.

57. At what point of the curve $y = \cosh x$ does the tangent have slope 1?

58. Investigate the family of functions

$$f_n(x) = \tanh(n \sin x)$$

where n is a positive integer. Describe what happens to the graph of f_n when n becomes large.

59. Show that if $a \neq 0$ and $b \neq 0$, then there exist numbers α and β such that $ae^x + be^{-x}$ equals either $\alpha \sinh(x + \beta)$ or $\alpha \cosh(x + \beta)$. In other words, almost every function of the form $f(x) = ae^x + be^{-x}$ is a shifted and stretched hyperbolic sine or cosine function.

---

3   Review

Concept Check

1. State each differentiation rule both in symbols and in words.

(a) The Power Rule   (b) The Constant Multiple Rule

(c) The Sum Rule   (d) The Difference Rule

(e) The Product Rule   (f) The Quotient Rule

(g) The Chain Rule

2. State the derivative of each function.

(a) $y = x^n$ (b) $y = e^x$ (c) $y = a^x$

(d) $y = \ln x$ (e) $y = \log_a x$ (f) $y = \sin x$

(g) $y = \cos x$ (h) $y = \tan x$ (i) $y = \csc x$

(j) $y = \sec x$ (k) $y = \cot x$ (l) $y = \sin^{-1} x$

(m) $y = \cos^{-1} x$ (n) $y = \tan^{-1} x$ (o) $y = \sinh x$

(p) $y = \cosh x$ (q) $y = \tanh x$ (r) $y = \sinh^{-1} x$

(s) $y = \cosh^{-1} x$ (t) $y = \tanh^{-1} x$

3. (a) How is the number e defined?

(b) Express e as a limit.

(c) Why is the natural exponential function $y = e^x$ used more often in calculus than the other exponential functions $y = a^x$?

(d) Why is the natural logarithmic function $y = \ln x$ used more often in calculus than the other logarithmic functions $y = \log_a x$?

4. (a) Explain how implicit differentiation works.

(b) Explain how logarithmic differentiation works.

5. Give several examples of how the derivative can be interpreted as a rate of change in physics, chemistry, biology, economics, or other sciences.

6. (a) Write a differential equation that expresses the law of natural growth.

(b) Under what circumstances is this an appropriate model for population growth?

(c) What are the solutions of this equation?

7. (a) Write an expression for the linearization of f at a.

(b) If $y = f(x)$, write an expression for the differential dy.

(c) If $dx = \Delta x$, draw a picture showing the geometric meanings of Δy and dy.

True-False Quiz

Determine whether the statement is true or false. If it is true, explain why. If it is false, explain why or give an example that disproves the statement.

1. If f and g are differentiable, then

$$\frac{d}{dx}[f(x) + g(x)] = f'(x) + g'(x)$$

2. If f and g are differentiable, then

$$\frac{d}{dx}[f(x)g(x)] = f'(x)g'(x)$$

3. If f and g are differentiable, then

$$\frac{d}{dx}[f(g(x))] = f'(g(x))g'(x)$$

4. If f is differentiable, then $\displaystyle\frac{d}{dx}\sqrt{f(x)} = \frac{f'(x)}{2\sqrt{f(x)}}$.

5. If f is differentiable, then $\displaystyle\frac{d}{dx}f(\sqrt{x}) = \frac{f'(x)}{2\sqrt{x}}$.

6. If $y = e^2$, then $y' = 2e$.

7. $\dfrac{d}{dx}(10^x) = x10^{x-1}$

8. $\dfrac{d}{dx}(\ln 10) = \dfrac{1}{10}$

9. $\dfrac{d}{dx}(\tan^2 x) = \dfrac{d}{dx}(\sec^2 x)$

10. $\dfrac{d}{dx}|x^2 + x| = |2x + 1|$

11. The derivative of a polynomial is a polynomial.

12. If $f(x) = (x^6 - x^4)^5$, then $f^{(31)}(x) = 0$.

13. The derivative of a rational function is a rational function.

14. An equation of the tangent line to the parabola $y = x^2$ at $(-2, 4)$ is $y - 4 = 2x(x + 2)$.

15. If $g(x) = x^5$, then $\displaystyle\lim_{x\to 2}\frac{g(x) - g(2)}{x - 2} = 80$

Exercises

1–50 Calculate y'.

1. $y = (x^4 - 3x^2 + 5)^3$

2. $y = \cos(\tan x)$

3. $y = \sqrt{x} + \dfrac{1}{\sqrt[3]{x^4}}$

4. $y = \dfrac{3x - 2}{\sqrt{2x + 1}}$

5. $y = x^2 \sin \pi x$

6. $y = x \cos^{-1} x$

7. $y = \dfrac{t^4 - 1}{t^4 + 1}$

8. $xe^y = y \sin x$

9. $y = \ln(x \ln x)$

10. $y = e^{mx} \cos nx$

11. $y = \sqrt{x} \cos \sqrt{x}$

12. $y = (\arcsin 2x)^2$

13. $y = \dfrac{e^{1/x}}{x^2}$

14. $y = \ln \sec x$

15. $y + x \cos y = x^2 y$

16. $y = \left(\dfrac{u - 1}{u^2 + u + 1}\right)^4$

17. $y = \sqrt{\arctan x}$

18. $y = \cot(\csc x)$

19. $y = \tan\left(\dfrac{t}{1 + t^2}\right)$

20. $y = e^{x \sec x}$

21. $y = 3^{x \ln x}$

22. $y = \sec(1 + x^2)$

23. $y = (1 - x^{-1})^{-1}$

24. $y = 1/\sqrt[3]{x + \sqrt{x}}$

25. $\sin(xy) = x^2 - y$

26. $y = \sqrt{\sin \sqrt{x}}$

27. $y = \log_5(1 + 2x)$

28. $y = (\cos x)^x$

29. $y = \ln \sin x - \tfrac{1}{2}\sin^2 x$

30. $y = \dfrac{(x^2 + 1)^4}{(2x + 1)^3(3x - 1)^5}$

31. $y = x \tan^{-1}(4x)$

32. $y = e^{\cos x} + \cos(e^x)$

33. $y = \ln|\sec 5x + \tan 5x|$

34. $y = 10^{\tan \pi\theta}$

35. $y = \cot(3x^2 + 5)$

36. $y = \sqrt{t \ln(t^4)}$

37. $y = \sin(\tan\sqrt{1 + x^3})$

38. $y = \arctan(\arcsin\sqrt{x})$

39. $y = \tan^2(\sin\theta)$

40. $xe^y = y - 1$

41. $y = \dfrac{\sqrt{x + 1}\,(2 - x)^5}{(x + 3)^7}$

42. $y = \dfrac{(x + \lambda)^4}{x^4 + \lambda^4}$

43. $y = x \sinh(x^2)$

44. $y = \dfrac{\sin mx}{x}$

45. $y = \ln(\cosh 3x)$

46. $y = \ln\left|\dfrac{x^2 - 4}{2x + 5}\right|$

47. $y = \cosh^{-1}(\sinh x)$

48. $y = x \tanh^{-1}\sqrt{x}$

49. $y = \cos(e^{\sqrt{\tan 3x}})$

50. $y = \sin^2(\cos\sqrt{\sin \pi x})$

51. If $f(t) = \sqrt{4t + 1}$, find $f''(2)$.

52. If $g(\theta) = \theta \sin\theta$, find $g''(\pi/6)$.

53. Find y'' if $x^6 + y^6 = 1$.

54. Find $f^{(n)}(x)$ if $f(x) = 1/(2 - x)$.

55. Use mathematical induction (page 76) to show that if $f(x) = xe^x$, then $f^{(n)}(x) = (x + n)e^x$.

56. Evaluate $\displaystyle\lim_{t\to 0}\frac{t^3}{\tan^3(2t)}$.

57–59 Find an equation of the tangent to the curve at the given point.

57. $y = 4\sin^2 x$, $(\pi/6, 1)$

58. $y = \dfrac{x^2 - 1}{x^2 + 1}$, $(0, -1)$

59. $y = \sqrt{1 + 4\sin x}$, $(0, 1)$

60–61 Find equations of the tangent line and normal line to the curve at the given point.

60. $x^2 + 4xy + y^2 = 13$, $(2, 1)$

61. $y = (2 + x)e^{-x}$, $(0, 2)$

62. If $f(x) = xe^{\sin x}$, find $f'(x)$. Graph f and f' on the same screen and comment.

63. (a) If $f(x) = x\sqrt{5 - x}$, find $f'(x)$.
(b) Find equations of the tangent lines to the curve $y = x\sqrt{5 - x}$ at the points $(1, 2)$ and $(4, 4)$.
(c) Illustrate part (b) by graphing the curve and tangent lines on the same screen.
(d) Check to see that your answer to part (a) is reasonable by comparing the graphs of f and f'.

Graphing calculator or computer required

64. (a) If $f(x) = 4x - \tan x$, $-\pi/2 < x < \pi/2$, find f' and f''.
(b) Check to see that your answers to part (a) are reasonable by comparing the graphs of f, f', and f''.

65. At what points on the curve $y = \sin x + \cos x$, $0 \leq x \leq 2\pi$, is the tangent line horizontal?

66. Find the points on the ellipse $x^2 + 2y^2 = 1$ where the tangent line has slope 1.

67. If $f(x) = (x - a)(x - b)(x - c)$, show that

$$\frac{f'(x)}{f(x)} = \frac{1}{x - a} + \frac{1}{x - b} + \frac{1}{x - c}$$

68. (a) By differentiating the double-angle formula

$$\cos 2x = \cos^2 x - \sin^2 x$$

obtain the double-angle formula for the sine function.
(b) By differentiating the addition formula

$$\sin(x + a) = \sin x \cos a + \cos x \sin a$$

obtain the addition formula for the cosine function.

69. Suppose that $h(x) = f(x)g(x)$ and $F(x) = f(g(x))$, where $f(2) = 3$, $g(2) = 5$, $g'(2) = 4$, $f'(2) = -2$, and $f'(5) = 11$. Find (a) $h'(2)$ and (b) $F'(2)$.

70. If f and g are the functions whose graphs are shown, let $P(x) = f(x)g(x)$, $Q(x) = f(x)/g(x)$, and $C(x) = f(g(x))$. Find (a) $P'(2)$, (b) $Q'(2)$, and (c) $C'(2)$.

71–78 Find f' in terms of g'.

71. $f(x) = x^2 g(x)$

72. $f(x) = g(x^2)$

73. $f(x) = [g(x)]^2$

74. $f(x) = g(g(x))$

75. $f(x) = g(e^x)$

76. $f(x) = e^{g(x)}$

77. $f(x) = \ln |g(x)|$

78. $f(x) = g(\ln x)$

79–81 Find h' in terms of f' and g'.

79. $h(x) = \dfrac{f(x)g(x)}{f(x) + g(x)}$

80. $h(x) = \sqrt{\dfrac{f(x)}{g(x)}}$

81. $h(x) = f(g(\sin 4x))$

82. (a) Graph the function $f(x) = x - 2 \sin x$ in the viewing rectangle $[0, 8]$ by $[-2, 8]$.
(b) On which interval is the average rate of change larger: $[1, 2]$ or $[2, 3]$?
(c) At which value of x is the instantaneous rate of change larger: $x = 2$ or $x = 5$?
(d) Check your visual estimates in part (c) by computing $f'(x)$ and comparing the numerical values of $f'(2)$ and $f'(5)$.

83. At what point on the curve $y = [\ln(x + 4)]^2$ is the tangent horizontal?

84. (a) Find an equation of the tangent to the curve $y = e^x$ that is parallel to the line $x - 4y = 1$.
(b) Find an equation of the tangent to the curve $y = e^x$ that passes through the origin.

85. Find a parabola $y = ax^2 + bx + c$ that passes through the point $(1, 4)$ and whose tangent lines at $x = -1$ and $x = 5$ have slopes 6 and -2, respectively.

86. The function $C(t) = K(e^{-at} - e^{-bt})$, where a, b, and K are positive constants and $b > a$, is used to model the concentration at time t of a drug injected into the bloodstream.
(a) Show that $\lim_{t \to \infty} C(t) = 0$.
(b) Find $C'(t)$, the rate at which the drug is cleared from circulation.
(c) When is this rate equal to 0?

87. An equation of motion of the form $s = Ae^{-ct}\cos(\omega t + \delta)$ represents damped oscillation of an object. Find the velocity and acceleration of the object.

88. A particle moves along a horizontal line so that its coordinate at time t is $x = \sqrt{b^2 + c^2 t^2}$, $t \geq 0$, where b and c are positive constants.
(a) Find the velocity and acceleration functions.
(b) Show that the particle always moves in the positive direction.

89. A particle moves on a vertical line so that its coordinate at time t is $y = t^3 - 12t + 3$, $t \geq 0$.
(a) Find the velocity and acceleration functions.
(b) When is the particle moving upward and when is it moving downward?
(c) Find the distance that the particle travels in the time interval $0 \leq t \leq 3$.
(d) Graph the position, velocity, and acceleration functions for $0 \leq t \leq 3$.
(e) When is the particle speeding up? When is it slowing down?

90. The volume of a right circular cone is $V = \frac{1}{3}\pi r^2 h$, where r is the radius of the base and h is the height.
(a) Find the rate of change of the volume with respect to the height if the radius is constant.

(b) Find the rate of change of the volume with respect to the radius if the height is constant.

91. The mass of part of a wire is $x\left(1 + \sqrt{x}\,\right)$ kilograms, where x is measured in meters from one end of the wire. Find the linear density of the wire when $x = 4$ m.

92. The cost, in dollars, of producing x units of a certain commodity is
$$C(x) = 920 + 2x - 0.02x^2 + 0.00007x^3$$
(a) Find the marginal cost function.
(b) Find $C'(100)$ and explain its meaning.
(c) Compare $C'(100)$ with the cost of producing the 101st item.

93. A bacteria culture contains 200 cells initially and grows at a rate proportional to its size. After half an hour the population has increased to 360 cells.
(a) Find the number of bacteria after t hours.
(b) Find the number of bacteria after 4 hours.
(c) Find the rate of growth after 4 hours.
(d) When will the population reach 10,000?

94. Cobalt-60 has a half-life of 5.24 years.
(a) Find the mass that remains from a 100-mg sample after 20 years.
(b) How long would it take for the mass to decay to 1 mg?

95. Let $C(t)$ be the concentration of a drug in the bloodstream. As the body eliminates the drug, $C(t)$ decreases at a rate that is proportional to the amount of the drug that is present at the time. Thus $C'(t) = -kC(t)$, where k is a positive number called the *elimination constant* of the drug.
(a) If C_0 is the concentration at time $t = 0$, find the concentration at time t.
(b) If the body eliminates half the drug in 30 hours, how long does it take to eliminate 90% of the drug?

96. A cup of hot chocolate has temperature 80°C in a room kept at 20°C. After half an hour the hot chocolate cools to 60°C.
(a) What is the temperature of the chocolate after another half hour?
(b) When will the chocolate have cooled to 40°C?

97. The volume of a cube is increasing at a rate of 10 cm³/min. How fast is the surface area increasing when the length of an edge is 30 cm?

98. A paper cup has the shape of a cone with height 10 cm and radius 3 cm (at the top). If water is poured into the cup at a rate of 2 cm³/s, how fast is the water level rising when the water is 5 cm deep?

99. A balloon is rising at a constant speed of 2 m/s. A boy is cycling along a straight road at a speed of 5 m/s. When he passes under the balloon, it is 15 m above him. How fast is the distance between the boy and the balloon increasing 3 s later?

100. A waterskier skis over the ramp shown in the figure at a speed of 10 m/s. How fast is she rising as she leaves the ramp?

101. The angle of elevation of the sun is decreasing at a rate of 0.25 rad/h. How fast is the shadow cast by a 400-ft-tall building increasing when the angle of elevation of the sun is $\pi/6$?

102. (a) Find the linear approximation to $f(x) = \sqrt{25 - x^2}$ near 3.
(b) Illustrate part (a) by graphing f and the linear approximation.
(c) For what values of x is the linear approximation accurate to within 0.1?

103. (a) Find the linearization of $f(x) = \sqrt[3]{1 + 3x}$ at $a = 0$. State the corresponding linear approximation and use it to give an approximate value for $\sqrt[3]{1.03}$.
(b) Determine the values of x for which the linear approximation given in part (a) is accurate to within 0.1.

104. Evaluate dy if $y = x^3 - 2x^2 + 1$, $x = 2$, and $dx = 0.2$.

105. A window has the shape of a square surmounted by a semicircle. The base of the window is measured as having width 60 cm with a possible error in measurement of 0.1 cm. Use differentials to estimate the maximum error possible in computing the area of the window.

106–108 Express the limit as a derivative and evaluate.

106. $\displaystyle \lim_{x \to 1} \frac{x^{17} - 1}{x - 1}$

107. $\displaystyle \lim_{h \to 0} \frac{\sqrt[4]{16 + h} - 2}{h}$

108. $\displaystyle \lim_{\theta \to \pi/3} \frac{\cos \theta - 0.5}{\theta - \pi/3}$

109. Evaluate $\displaystyle \lim_{x \to 0} \frac{\sqrt{1 + \tan x} - \sqrt{1 + \sin x}}{x^3}$.

110. Suppose f is a differentiable function such that $f(g(x)) = x$ and $f'(x) = 1 + [f(x)]^2$. Show that $g'(x) = 1/(1 + x^2)$.

111. Find $f'(x)$ if it is known that
$$\frac{d}{dx}[f(2x)] = x^2$$

112. Show that the length of the portion of any tangent line to the astroid $x^{2/3} + y^{2/3} = a^{2/3}$ cut off by the coordinate axes is constant.

Before you look at the examples, cover up the solutions and try them yourself first.

EXAMPLE 1 How many lines are tangent to both of the parabolas $y = -1 - x^2$ and $y = 1 + x^2$? Find the coordinates of the points at which these tangents touch the parabolas.

SOLUTION To gain insight into this problem, it is essential to draw a diagram. So we sketch the parabolas $y = 1 + x^2$ (which is the standard parabola $y = x^2$ shifted 1 unit upward) and $y = -1 - x^2$ (which is obtained by reflecting the first parabola about the x-axis). If we try to draw a line tangent to both parabolas, we soon discover that there are only two possibilities, as illustrated in Figure 1.

Let P be a point at which one of these tangents touches the upper parabola and let a be its x-coordinate. (The choice of notation for the unknown is important. Of course we could have used b or c or x_0 or x_1 instead of a. However, it's not advisable to use x in place of a because that x could be confused with the variable x in the equation of the parabola.) Then, since P lies on the parabola $y = 1 + x^2$, its y-coordinate must be $1 + a^2$. Because of the symmetry shown in Figure 1, the coordinates of the point Q where the tangent touches the lower parabola must be $(-a, -(1 + a^2))$.

To use the given information that the line is a tangent, we equate the slope of the line PQ to the slope of the tangent line at P. We have

$$m_{PQ} = \frac{1 + a^2 - (-1 - a^2)}{a - (-a)} = \frac{1 + a^2}{a}$$

If $f(x) = 1 + x^2$, then the slope of the tangent line at P is $f'(a) = 2a$. Thus the condition that we need to use is that

$$\frac{1 + a^2}{a} = 2a$$

Solving this equation, we get $1 + a^2 = 2a^2$, so $a^2 = 1$ and $a = \pm1$. Therefore the points are $(1, 2)$ and $(-1, -2)$. By symmetry, the two remaining points are $(-1, 2)$ and $(1, -2)$.

EXAMPLE 2 For what values of c does the equation $\ln x = cx^2$ have exactly one solution?

SOLUTION One of the most important principles of problem solving is to draw a diagram, even if the problem as stated doesn't explicitly mention a geometric situation. Our present problem can be reformulated geometrically as follows: For what values of c does the curve $y = \ln x$ intersect the curve $y = cx^2$ in exactly one point?

Let's start by graphing $y = \ln x$ and $y = cx^2$ for various values of c. We know that, for $c \neq 0$, $y = cx^2$ is a parabola that opens upward if $c > 0$ and downward if $c < 0$. Figure 2 shows the parabolas $y = cx^2$ for several positive values of c. Most of them don't intersect $y = \ln x$ at all and one intersects twice. We have the feeling that there must be a value of c (somewhere between 0.1 and 0.3) for which the curves intersect exactly once, as in Figure 3.

To find that particular value of c, we let a be the x-coordinate of the single point of intersection. In other words, $\ln a = ca^2$, so a is the unique solution of the given equation. We see from Figure 3 that the curves just touch, so they have a common tangent line when $x = a$. That means the curves $y = \ln x$ and $y = cx^2$ have the same slope when $x = a$. Therefore

$$\frac{1}{a} = 2ca$$

FIGURE 1

$3x^2 \quad x^2 \quad \frac{1}{2}x^2 \quad 0.3x^2$

$0.1x^2$

$y = \ln x$

FIGURE 2

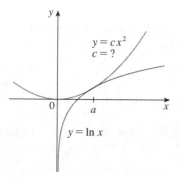

$y = cx^2$
$c = ?$

$y = \ln x$

FIGURE 3

Solving the equations $\ln a = ca^2$ and $1/a = 2ca$, we get

$$\ln a = ca^2 = c \cdot \frac{1}{2c} = \frac{1}{2}$$

Thus $a = e^{1/2}$ and

$$c = \frac{\ln a}{a^2} = \frac{\ln e^{1/2}}{e} = \frac{1}{2e}$$

For negative values of c we have the situation illustrated in Figure 4: All parabolas $y = cx^2$ with negative values of c intersect $y = \ln x$ exactly once. And let's not forget about $c = 0$: The curve $y = 0x^2 = 0$ is just the x-axis, which intersects $y = \ln x$ exactly once.

To summarize, the required values of c are $c = 1/(2e)$ and $c \le 0$. ▬

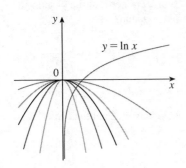

FIGURE 4

Problems

1. Find points P and Q on the parabola $y = 1 - x^2$ so that the triangle ABC formed by the x-axis and the tangent lines at P and Q is an equilateral triangle. (See the figure.)

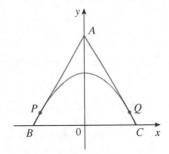

2. Find the point where the curves $y = x^3 - 3x + 4$ and $y = 3(x^2 - x)$ are tangent to each other, that is, have a common tangent line. Illustrate by sketching both curves and the common tangent.

3. Show that the tangent lines to the parabola $y = ax^2 + bx + c$ at any two points with x-coordinates p and q must intersect at a point whose x-coordinate is halfway between p and q.

4. Show that

$$\frac{d}{dx}\left(\frac{\sin^2 x}{1 + \cot x} + \frac{\cos^2 x}{1 + \tan x}\right) = -\cos 2x$$

5. If $f(x) = \lim\limits_{t \to x} \dfrac{\sec t - \sec x}{t - x}$, find the value of $f'(\pi/4)$.

6. Find the values of the constants a and b such that

$$\lim_{x \to 0} \frac{\sqrt[3]{ax + b} - 2}{x} = \frac{5}{12}$$

7. Show that $\sin^{-1}(\tanh x) = \tan^{-1}(\sinh x)$.

⊞ Graphing calculator or computer required

CAS Computer algebra system required

FIGURE FOR PROBLEM 8

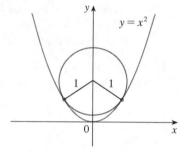

FIGURE FOR PROBLEM 13

8. A car is traveling at night along a highway shaped like a parabola with its vertex at the origin (see the figure). The car starts at a point 100 m west and 100 m north of the origin and travels in an easterly direction. There is a statue located 100 m east and 50 m north of the origin. At what point on the highway will the car's headlights illuminate the statue?

9. Prove that $\dfrac{d^n}{dx^n}(\sin^4 x + \cos^4 x) = 4^{n-1}\cos(4x + n\pi/2)$.

10. Find the nth derivative of the function $f(x) = x^n/(1 - x)$.

11. The figure shows a circle with radius 1 inscribed in the parabola $y = x^2$. Find the center of the circle.

12. If f is differentiable at a, where $a > 0$, evaluate the following limit in terms of $f'(a)$:

$$\lim_{x \to a} \frac{f(x) - f(a)}{\sqrt{x} - \sqrt{a}}$$

13. The figure shows a rotating wheel with radius 40 cm and a connecting rod AP with length 1.2 m. The pin P slides back and forth along the x-axis as the wheel rotates counterclockwise at a rate of 360 revolutions per minute.
   (a) Find the angular velocity of the connecting rod, $d\alpha/dt$, in radians per second, when $\theta = \pi/3$.
   (b) Express the distance $x = |OP|$ in terms of θ.
   (c) Find an expression for the velocity of the pin P in terms of θ.

14. Tangent lines T_1 and T_2 are drawn at two points P_1 and P_2 on the parabola $y = x^2$ and they intersect at a point P. Another tangent line T is drawn at a point between P_1 and P_2; it intersects T_1 at Q_1 and T_2 at Q_2. Show that

$$\frac{|PQ_1|}{|PP_1|} + \frac{|PQ_2|}{|PP_2|} = 1$$

15. Show that

$$\frac{d^n}{dx^n}(e^{ax}\sin bx) = r^n e^{ax}\sin(bx + n\theta)$$

where a and b are positive numbers, $r^2 = a^2 + b^2$, and $\theta = \tan^{-1}(b/a)$.

16. Evaluate $\displaystyle\lim_{x \to \pi} \frac{e^{\sin x} - 1}{x - \pi}$.

17. Let T and N be the tangent and normal lines to the ellipse $x^2/9 + y^2/4 = 1$ at any point P on the ellipse in the first quadrant. Let x_T and y_T be the x- and y-intercepts of T and x_N and y_N be the intercepts of N. As P moves along the ellipse in the first quadrant (but not on the axes), what values can x_T, y_T, x_N, and y_N take on? First try to guess the answers just by looking at the figure. Then use calculus to solve the problem and see how good your intuition is.

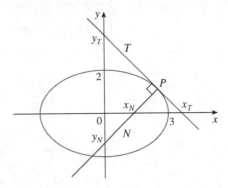

18. Evaluate $\displaystyle\lim_{x \to 0} \frac{\sin(3 + x)^2 - \sin 9}{x}$.

19. (a) Use the identity for $\tan(x - y)$ (see Equation 14b in Appendix D) to show that if two lines L_1 and L_2 intersect at an angle α, then

$$\tan \alpha = \frac{m_2 - m_1}{1 + m_1 m_2}$$

where m_1 and m_2 are the slopes of L_1 and L_2, respectively.

(b) The **angle between the curves** C_1 and C_2 at a point of intersection P is defined to be the angle between the tangent lines to C_1 and C_2 at P (if these tangent lines exist). Use part (a) to find, correct to the nearest degree, the angle between each pair of curves at each point of intersection.

(i) $y = x^2$ and $y = (x - 2)^2$

(ii) $x^2 - y^2 = 3$ and $x^2 - 4x + y^2 + 3 = 0$

20. Let $P(x_1, y_1)$ be a point on the parabola $y^2 = 4px$ with focus $F(p, 0)$. Let α be the angle between the parabola and the line segment FP, and let β be the angle between the horizontal line $y = y_1$ and the parabola as in the figure. Prove that $\alpha = \beta$. (Thus, by a principle of geometrical optics, light from a source placed at F will be reflected along a line parallel to the x-axis. This explains why *paraboloids*, the surfaces obtained by rotating parabolas about their axes, are used as the shape of some automobile headlights and mirrors for telescopes.)

FIGURE FOR PROBLEM 21

21. Suppose that we replace the parabolic mirror of Problem 20 by a spherical mirror. Although the mirror has no focus, we can show the existence of an *approximate* focus. In the figure, C is a semicircle with center O. A ray of light coming in toward the mirror parallel to the axis along the line PQ will be reflected to the point R on the axis so that $\angle PQO = \angle OQR$ (the angle of incidence is equal to the angle of reflection). What happens to the point R as P is taken closer and closer to the axis?

22. If f and g are differentiable functions with $f(0) = g(0) = 0$ and $g'(0) \neq 0$, show that
$$\lim_{x \to 0} \frac{f(x)}{g(x)} = \frac{f'(0)}{g'(0)}$$

23. Evaluate $\displaystyle\lim_{x \to 0} \frac{\sin(a + 2x) - 2\sin(a + x) + \sin a}{x^2}$.

CAS 24. (a) The cubic function $f(x) = x(x - 2)(x - 6)$ has three distinct zeros: 0, 2, and 6. Graph f and its tangent lines at the *average* of each pair of zeros. What do you notice?
    (b) Suppose the cubic function $f(x) = (x - a)(x - b)(x - c)$ has three distinct zeros: a, b, and c. Prove, with the help of a computer algebra system, that a tangent line drawn at the average of the zeros a and b intersects the graph of f at the third zero.

25. For what value of k does the equation $e^{2x} = k\sqrt{x}$ have exactly one solution?

26. For which positive numbers a is it true that $a^x \geq 1 + x$ for all x?

27. If
$$y = \frac{x}{\sqrt{a^2 - 1}} - \frac{2}{\sqrt{a^2 - 1}} \arctan \frac{\sin x}{a + \sqrt{a^2 - 1} + \cos x}$$
show that $y' = \dfrac{1}{a + \cos x}$.

28. Given an ellipse $x^2/a^2 + y^2/b^2 = 1$, where $a \neq b$, find the equation of the set of all points from which there are two tangents to the curve whose slopes are (a) reciprocals and (b) negative reciprocals.

29. Find the two points on the curve $y = x^4 - 2x^2 - x$ that have a common tangent line.

30. Suppose that three points on the parabola $y = x^2$ have the property that their normal lines intersect at a common point. Show that the sum of their x-coordinates is 0.

31. A *lattice point* in the plane is a point with integer coordinates. Suppose that circles with radius r are drawn using all lattice points as centers. Find the smallest value of r such that any line with slope $\frac{2}{5}$ intersects some of these circles.

32. A cone of radius r centimeters and height h centimeters is lowered point first at a rate of 1 cm/s into a tall cylinder of radius R centimeters that is partially filled with water. How fast is the water level rising at the instant the cone is completely submerged?

33. A container in the shape of an inverted cone has height 16 cm and radius 5 cm at the top. It is partially filled with a liquid that oozes through the sides at a rate proportional to the area of the container that is in contact with the liquid. (The surface area of a cone is $\pi r l$, where r is the radius and l is the slant height.) If we pour the liquid into the container at a rate of 2 cm³/min, then the height of the liquid decreases at a rate of 0.3 cm/min when the height is 10 cm. If our goal is to keep the liquid at a constant height of 10 cm, at what rate should we pour the liquid into the container?

4 Applications of Differentiation

The calculus that you learn in this chapter will enable you to explain the location of rainbows in the sky and why the colors in the secondary rainbow appear in the opposite order to those in the primary rainbow. (See the project on pages 282–283.)

© Pichugin Dmitry / Shutterstock

We have already investigated some of the applications of derivatives, but now that we know the differentiation rules we are in a better position to pursue the applications of differentiation in greater depth. Here we learn how derivatives affect the shape of a graph of a function and, in particular, how they help us locate maximum and minimum values of functions. Many practical problems require us to minimize a cost or maximize an area or somehow find the best possible outcome of a situation. In particular, we will be able to investigate the optimal shape of a can and to explain the location of rainbows in the sky.

4.1 Maximum and Minimum Values

Some of the most important applications of differential calculus are *optimization problems*, in which we are required to find the optimal (best) way of doing something. Here are examples of such problems that we will solve in this chapter:

- What is the shape of a can that minimizes manufacturing costs?
- What is the maximum acceleration of a space shuttle? (This is an important question to the astronauts who have to withstand the effects of acceleration.)
- What is the radius of a contracted windpipe that expels air most rapidly during a cough?
- At what angle should blood vessels branch so as to minimize the energy expended by the heart in pumping blood?

These problems can be reduced to finding the maximum or minimum values of a function. Let's first explain exactly what we mean by maximum and minimum values.

We see that the highest point on the graph of the function f shown in Figure 1 is the point $(3, 5)$. In other words, the largest value of f is $f(3) = 5$. Likewise, the smallest value is $f(6) = 2$. We say that $f(3) = 5$ is the *absolute maximum* of f and $f(6) = 2$ is the *absolute minimum*. In general, we use the following definition.

FIGURE 1

---

1 **Definition** Let c be a number in the domain D of a function f. Then $f(c)$ is the

- **absolute maximum** value of f on D if $f(c) \geq f(x)$ for all x in D.
- **absolute minimum** value of f on D if $f(c) \leq f(x)$ for all x in D.

An absolute maximum or minimum is sometimes called a **global** maximum or minimum. The maximum and minimum values of f are called **extreme values** of f.

Figure 2 shows the graph of a function f with absolute maximum at d and absolute minimum at a. Note that $(d, f(d))$ is the highest point on the graph and $(a, f(a))$ is the lowest point. In Figure 2, if we consider only values of x near b [for instance, if we restrict our attention to the interval (a, c)], then $f(b)$ is the largest of those values of $f(x)$ and is called a *local maximum value* of f. Likewise, $f(c)$ is called a *local minimum value* of f because $f(c) \leq f(x)$ for x near c [in the interval (b, d), for instance]. The function f also has a local minimum at e. In general, we have the following definition.

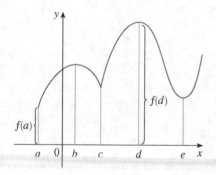

FIGURE 2
Abs min $f(a)$, abs max $f(d)$,
loc min $f(c)$, $f(e)$, loc max $f(b)$, $f(d)$

---

2 **Definition** The number $f(c)$ is a

- **local maximum** value of f if $f(c) \geq f(x)$ when x is near c.
- **local minimum** value of f if $f(c) \leq f(x)$ when x is near c.

In Definition 2 (and elsewhere), if we say that something is true **near** c, we mean that it is true on some open interval containing c. For instance, in Figure 3 we see that $f(4) = 5$ is a local minimum because it's the smallest value of f on the interval I. It's not the absolute minimum because $f(x)$ takes smaller values when x is near 12 (in the interval K, for instance). In fact $f(12) = 3$ is both a local minimum and the absolute minimum. Similarly, $f(8) = 7$ is a local maximum, but not the absolute maximum because f takes larger values near 1.

FIGURE 3

EXAMPLE 1 The function $f(x) = \cos x$ takes on its (local and absolute) maximum value of 1 infinitely many times, since $\cos 2n\pi = 1$ for any integer n and $-1 \le \cos x \le 1$ for all x. Likewise, $\cos(2n + 1)\pi = -1$ is its minimum value, where n is any integer. ▬

EXAMPLE 2 If $f(x) = x^2$, then $f(x) \ge f(0)$ because $x^2 \ge 0$ for all x. Therefore $f(0) = 0$ is the absolute (and local) minimum value of f. This corresponds to the fact that the origin is the lowest point on the parabola $y = x^2$. (See Figure 4.) However, there is no highest point on the parabola and so this function has no maximum value. ▬

FIGURE 4
Minimum value 0, no maximum

EXAMPLE 3 From the graph of the function $f(x) = x^3$, shown in Figure 5, we see that this function has neither an absolute maximum value nor an absolute minimum value. In fact, it has no local extreme values either.

FIGURE 5
No minimum, no maximum

V EXAMPLE 4 The graph of the function

$$f(x) = 3x^4 - 16x^3 + 18x^2 \qquad -1 \le x \le 4$$

is shown in Figure 6. You can see that $f(1) = 5$ is a local maximum, whereas the absolute maximum is $f(-1) = 37$. (This absolute maximum is not a local maximum because it occurs at an endpoint.) Also, $f(0) = 0$ is a local minimum and $f(3) = -27$ is both a local and an absolute minimum. Note that f has neither a local nor an absolute maximum at $x = 4$. ▬

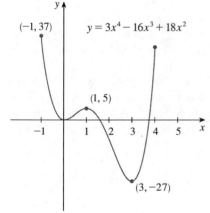

FIGURE 6

We have seen that some functions have extreme values, whereas others do not. The following theorem gives conditions under which a function is guaranteed to possess extreme values.

> **3** **The Extreme Value Theorem** If f is continuous on a closed interval $[a, b]$, then f attains an absolute maximum value $f(c)$ and an absolute minimum value $f(d)$ at some numbers c and d in $[a, b]$.

The Extreme Value Theorem is illustrated in Figure 7. Note that an extreme value can be taken on more than once. Although the Extreme Value Theorem is intuitively very plausible, it is difficult to prove and so we omit the proof.

FIGURE 7

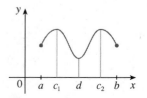

Figures 8 and 9 show that a function need not possess extreme values if either hypothesis (continuity or closed interval) is omitted from the Extreme Value Theorem.

FIGURE 8

This function has minimum value $f(2) = 0$, but no maximum value.

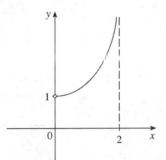

FIGURE 9

This continuous function g has no maximum or minimum.

The function f whose graph is shown in Figure 8 is defined on the closed interval $[0, 2]$ but has no maximum value. (Notice that the range of f is $[0, 3)$. The function takes on values arbitrarily close to 3, but never actually attains the value 3.) This does not contradict the Extreme Value Theorem because f is not continuous. [Nonetheless, a discontinuous function *could* have maximum and minimum values. See Exercise 13(b).]

The function g shown in Figure 9 is continuous on the open interval $(0, 2)$ but has neither a maximum nor a minimum value. [The range of g is $(1, \infty)$. The function takes on arbitrarily large values.] This does not contradict the Extreme Value Theorem because the interval $(0, 2)$ is not closed.

The Extreme Value Theorem says that a continuous function on a closed interval has a maximum value and a minimum value, but it does not tell us how to find these extreme values. We start by looking for local extreme values.

Figure 10 shows the graph of a function f with a local maximum at c and a local minimum at d. It appears that at the maximum and minimum points the tangent lines are horizontal and therefore each has slope 0. We know that the derivative is the slope of the tangent line, so it appears that $f'(c) = 0$ and $f'(d) = 0$. The following theorem says that this is always true for differentiable functions.

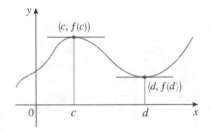

FIGURE 10

Fermat

Fermat's Theorem is named after Pierre Fermat (1601–1665), a French lawyer who took up mathematics as a hobby. Despite his amateur status, Fermat was one of the two inventors of analytic geometry (Descartes was the other). His methods for finding tangents to curves and maximum and minimum values (before the invention of limits and derivatives) made him a forerunner of Newton in the creation of differential calculus.

> **4**   **Fermat's Theorem**   If f has a local maximum or minimum at c, and if $f'(c)$ exists, then $f'(c) = 0$.

PROOF   Suppose, for the sake of definiteness, that f has a local maximum at c. Then, according to Definition 2, $f(c) \geqslant f(x)$ if x is sufficiently close to c. This implies that if h is sufficiently close to 0, with h being positive or negative, then

$$f(c) \geqslant f(c + h)$$

and therefore

$$\boxed{5} \qquad\qquad f(c + h) - f(c) \leqslant 0$$

We can divide both sides of an inequality by a positive number. Thus, if $h > 0$ and h is sufficiently small, we have

$$\frac{f(c + h) - f(c)}{h} \leqslant 0$$

Taking the right-hand limit of both sides of this inequality (using Theorem 2.3.2), we get

$$\lim_{h\to 0^+} \frac{f(c+h) - f(c)}{h} \le \lim_{h\to 0^+} 0 = 0$$

But since $f'(c)$ exists, we have

$$f'(c) = \lim_{h\to 0} \frac{f(c+h) - f(c)}{h} = \lim_{h\to 0^+} \frac{f(c+h) - f(c)}{h}$$

and so we have shown that $f'(c) \le 0$.

If $h < 0$, then the direction of the inequality $\boxed{5}$ is reversed when we divide by h:

$$\frac{f(c+h) - f(c)}{h} \ge 0 \qquad h < 0$$

So, taking the left-hand limit, we have

$$f'(c) = \lim_{h\to 0} \frac{f(c+h) - f(c)}{h} = \lim_{h\to 0^-} \frac{f(c+h) - f(c)}{h} \ge 0$$

We have shown that $f'(c) \ge 0$ and also that $f'(c) \le 0$. Since both of these inequalities must be true, the only possibility is that $f'(c) = 0$.

We have proved Fermat's Theorem for the case of a local maximum. The case of a local minimum can be proved in a similar manner, or we could use Exercise 76 to deduce it from the case we have just proved (see Exercise 77). ■

The following examples caution us against reading too much into Fermat's Theorem: We can't expect to locate extreme values simply by setting $f'(x) = 0$ and solving for x.

FIGURE 11
If $f(x) = x^3$, then $f'(0) = 0$ but f has no maximum or minimum.

EXAMPLE 5 If $f(x) = x^3$, then $f'(x) = 3x^2$, so $f'(0) = 0$. But f has no maximum or minimum at 0, as you can see from its graph in Figure 11. (Or observe that $x^3 > 0$ for $x > 0$ but $x^3 < 0$ for $x < 0$.) The fact that $f'(0) = 0$ simply means that the curve $y = x^3$ has a horizontal tangent at $(0, 0)$. Instead of having a maximum or minimum at $(0, 0)$, the curve crosses its horizontal tangent there. ■

EXAMPLE 6 The function $f(x) = |x|$ has its (local and absolute) minimum value at 0, but that value can't be found by setting $f'(x) = 0$ because, as was shown in Example 5 in Section 2.8, $f'(0)$ does not exist. (See Figure 12.) ■

WARNING Examples 5 and 6 show that we must be careful when using Fermat's Theorem. Example 5 demonstrates that even when $f'(c) = 0$ there need not be a maximum or minimum at c. (In other words, the converse of Fermat's Theorem is false in general.) Furthermore, there may be an extreme value even when $f'(c)$ does not exist (as in Example 6).

Fermat's Theorem does suggest that we should at least *start* looking for extreme values of f at the numbers c where $f'(c) = 0$ or where $f'(c)$ does not exist. Such numbers are given a special name.

FIGURE 12
If $f(x) = |x|$, then $f(0) = 0$ is a minimum value, but $f'(0)$ does not exist.

$\boxed{6}$ **Definition** A **critical number** of a function f is a number c in the domain of f such that either $f'(c) = 0$ or $f'(c)$ does not exist.

Figure 13 shows a graph of the function f in Example 7. It supports our answer because there is a horizontal tangent when $x = 1.5$ and a vertical tangent when $x = 0$.

FIGURE 13

V **EXAMPLE 7** Find the critical numbers of $f(x) = x^{3/5}(4 - x)$.

SOLUTION The Product Rule gives

$$f'(x) = x^{3/5}(-1) + (4 - x)\left(\tfrac{3}{5}x^{-2/5}\right) = -x^{3/5} + \frac{3(4 - x)}{5x^{2/5}}$$

$$= \frac{-5x + 3(4 - x)}{5x^{2/5}} = \frac{12 - 8x}{5x^{2/5}}$$

[The same result could be obtained by first writing $f(x) = 4x^{3/5} - x^{8/5}$.] Therefore $f'(x) = 0$ if $12 - 8x = 0$, that is, $x = \tfrac{3}{2}$, and $f'(x)$ does not exist when $x = 0$. Thus the critical numbers are $\tfrac{3}{2}$ and 0.

In terms of critical numbers, Fermat's Theorem can be rephrased as follows (compare Definition 6 with Theorem 4):

> **7** If f has a local maximum or minimum at c, then c is a critical number of f.

To find an absolute maximum or minimum of a continuous function on a closed interval, we note that either it is local [in which case it occurs at a critical number by **7**] or it occurs at an endpoint of the interval. Thus the following three-step procedure always works.

> **The Closed Interval Method**   To find the *absolute* maximum and minimum values of a continuous function f on a closed interval $[a, b]$:
>
> **1.** Find the values of f at the critical numbers of f in (a, b).
>
> **2.** Find the values of f at the endpoints of the interval.
>
> **3.** The largest of the values from Steps 1 and 2 is the absolute maximum value; the smallest of these values is the absolute minimum value.

V **EXAMPLE 8** Find the absolute maximum and minimum values of the function

$$f(x) = x^3 - 3x^2 + 1 \qquad -\tfrac{1}{2} \le x \le 4$$

SOLUTION Since f is continuous on $\left[-\tfrac{1}{2}, 4\right]$, we can use the Closed Interval Method:

$$f(x) = x^3 - 3x^2 + 1$$

$$f'(x) = 3x^2 - 6x = 3x(x - 2)$$

Since $f'(x)$ exists for all x, the only critical numbers of f occur when $f'(x) = 0$, that is, $x = 0$ or $x = 2$. Notice that each of these critical numbers lies in the interval $\left(-\tfrac{1}{2}, 4\right)$. The values of f at these critical numbers are

$$f(0) = 1 \qquad f(2) = -3$$

The values of f at the endpoints of the interval are

$$f\left(-\tfrac{1}{2}\right) = \tfrac{1}{8} \qquad f(4) = 17$$

Comparing these four numbers, we see that the absolute maximum value is $f(4) = 17$ and the absolute minimum value is $f(2) = -3$.

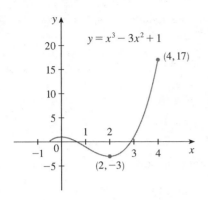

FIGURE 14

Note that in this example the absolute maximum occurs at an endpoint, whereas the absolute minimum occurs at a critical number. The graph of f is sketched in Figure 14.

If you have a graphing calculator or a computer with graphing software, it is possible to estimate maximum and minimum values very easily. But, as the next example shows, calculus is needed to find the *exact* values.

EXAMPLE 9
(a) Use a graphing device to estimate the absolute minimum and maximum values of the function $f(x) = x - 2 \sin x$, $0 \le x \le 2\pi$.
(b) Use calculus to find the exact minimum and maximum values.

SOLUTION
(a) Figure 15 shows a graph of f in the viewing rectangle $[0, 2\pi]$ by $[-1, 8]$. By moving the cursor close to the maximum point, we see that the y-coordinates don't change very much in the vicinity of the maximum. The absolute maximum value is about 6.97 and it occurs when $x \approx 5.2$. Similarly, by moving the cursor close to the minimum point, we see that the absolute minimum value is about -0.68 and it occurs when $x \approx 1.0$. It is possible to get more accurate estimates by zooming in toward the maximum and minimum points, but instead let's use calculus.

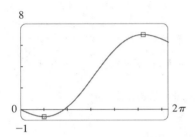

FIGURE 15

(b) The function $f(x) = x - 2 \sin x$ is continuous on $[0, 2\pi]$. Since $f'(x) = 1 - 2 \cos x$, we have $f'(x) = 0$ when $\cos x = \frac{1}{2}$ and this occurs when $x = \pi/3$ or $5\pi/3$. The values of f at these critical numbers are

$$f(\pi/3) = \frac{\pi}{3} - 2 \sin \frac{\pi}{3} = \frac{\pi}{3} - \sqrt{3} \approx -0.684853$$

and

$$f(5\pi/3) = \frac{5\pi}{3} - 2 \sin \frac{5\pi}{3} = \frac{5\pi}{3} + \sqrt{3} \approx 6.968039$$

The values of f at the endpoints are

$$f(0) = 0 \quad \text{and} \quad f(2\pi) = 2\pi \approx 6.28$$

Comparing these four numbers and using the Closed Interval Method, we see that the absolute minimum value is $f(\pi/3) = \pi/3 - \sqrt{3}$ and the absolute maximum value is $f(5\pi/3) = 5\pi/3 + \sqrt{3}$. The values from part (a) serve as a check on our work.

EXAMPLE 10 The Hubble Space Telescope was deployed on April 24, 1990, by the space shuttle *Discovery*. A model for the velocity of the shuttle during this mission, from liftoff at $t = 0$ until the solid rocket boosters were jettisoned at $t = 126$ s, is given by

$$v(t) = 0.0003968t^3 - 0.02752t^2 + 7.196t - 0.9397$$

(in meters per second). Using this model, estimate the absolute maximum and minimum values of the *acceleration* of the shuttle between liftoff and the jettisoning of the boosters.

SOLUTION We are asked for the extreme values not of the given velocity function, but rather of the acceleration function. So we first need to differentiate to find the acceleration:

$$a(t) = v'(t) = \frac{d}{dt}(0.0003968t^3 - 0.02752t^2 + 7.196t - 0.9397)$$

$$= 0.0011904t^2 - 0.05504t + 7.196$$

NASA

We now apply the Closed Interval Method to the continuous function a on the interval $0 \le t \le 126$. Its derivative is

$$a'(t) = 0.0023808t - 0.05504$$

The only critical number occurs when $a'(t) = 0$:

$$t_1 = \frac{0.05504}{0.0023808} \approx 23.12$$

Evaluating $a(t)$ at the critical number and at the endpoints, we have

$$a(0) = 7.196 \qquad a(t_1) \approx 6.56 \qquad a(126) \approx 19.16$$

So the maximum acceleration is about 19.16 m/s² and the minimum acceleration is about 6.56 m/s².

4.1   Exercises

1. Explain the difference between an absolute minimum and a local minimum.

2. Suppose f is a continuous function defined on a closed interval $[a, b]$.
   (a) What theorem guarantees the existence of an absolute maximum value and an absolute minimum value for f?
   (b) What steps would you take to find those maximum and minimum values?

3–4 For each of the numbers a, b, c, d, r, and s, state whether the function whose graph is shown has an absolute maximum or minimum, a local maximum or minimum, or neither a maximum nor a minimum.

3.

4.

5–6 Use the graph to state the absolute and local maximum and minimum values of the function.

5.

6.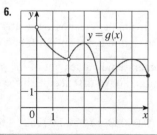

7–10 Sketch the graph of a function f that is continuous on $[1, 5]$ and has the given properties.

7. Absolute minimum at 2, absolute maximum at 3, local minimum at 4

8. Absolute minimum at 1, absolute maximum at 5, local maximum at 2, local minimum at 4

9. Absolute maximum at 5, absolute minimum at 2, local maximum at 3, local minima at 2 and 4

10. f has no local maximum or minimum, but 2 and 4 are critical numbers

11. (a) Sketch the graph of a function that has a local maximum at 2 and is differentiable at 2.
    (b) Sketch the graph of a function that has a local maximum at 2 and is continuous but not differentiable at 2.
    (c) Sketch the graph of a function that has a local maximum at 2 and is not continuous at 2.

12. (a) Sketch the graph of a function on $[-1, 2]$ that has an absolute maximum but no local maximum.
    (b) Sketch the graph of a function on $[-1, 2]$ that has a local maximum but no absolute maximum.

13. (a) Sketch the graph of a function on $[-1, 2]$ that has an absolute maximum but no absolute minimum.
    (b) Sketch the graph of a function on $[-1, 2]$ that is discontinuous but has both an absolute maximum and an absolute minimum.

14. (a) Sketch the graph of a function that has two local maxima, one local minimum, and no absolute minimum.
    (b) Sketch the graph of a function that has three local minima, two local maxima, and seven critical numbers.

15–28 Sketch the graph of f by hand and use your sketch to find the absolute and local maximum and minimum values of f. (Use the graphs and transformations of Sections 1.2 and 1.3.)

15. $f(x) = \frac{1}{2}(3x - 1), \quad x \le 3$

16. $f(x) = 2 - \frac{1}{3}x, \quad x \ge -2$

17. $f(x) = 1/x, \quad x \ge 1$

18. $f(x) = 1/x, \quad 1 < x < 3$

19. $f(x) = \sin x, \quad 0 \le x < \pi/2$

20. $f(x) = \sin x, \quad 0 < x \le \pi/2$

21. $f(x) = \sin x, \quad -\pi/2 \le x \le \pi/2$

22. $f(t) = \cos t, \quad -3\pi/2 \le t \le 3\pi/2$

23. $f(x) = \ln x, \quad 0 < x \le 2$

24. $f(x) = |x|$

25. $f(x) = 1 - \sqrt{x}$

26. $f(x) = e^x$

27. $f(x) = \begin{cases} 1 - x & \text{if } 0 \le x < 2 \\ 2x - 4 & \text{if } 2 \le x \le 3 \end{cases}$

28. $f(x) = \begin{cases} 4 - x^2 & \text{if } -2 \le x < 0 \\ 2x - 1 & \text{if } 0 \le x \le 2 \end{cases}$

29–44 Find the critical numbers of the function.

29. $f(x) = 5x^2 + 4x$

30. $f(x) = x^3 + x^2 - x$

31. $f(x) = 2x^3 - 3x^2 - 36x$

32. $f(x) = 2x^3 + x^2 + 2x$

33. $g(t) = t^4 + t^3 + t^2 + 1$

34. $g(t) = |3t - 4|$

35. $g(y) = \dfrac{y - 1}{y^2 - y + 1}$

36. $h(p) = \dfrac{p - 1}{p^2 + 4}$

37. $h(t) = t^{3/4} - 2t^{1/4}$

38. $g(x) = x^{1/3} - x^{-2/3}$

39. $F(x) = x^{4/5}(x - 4)^2$

40. $g(\theta) = 4\theta - \tan\theta$

41. $f(\theta) = 2\cos\theta + \sin^2\theta$

42. $h(t) = 3t - \arcsin t$

43. $f(x) = x^2 e^{-3x}$

44. $f(x) = x^{-2}\ln x$

45–46 A formula for the *derivative* of a function f is given. How many critical numbers does f have?

45. $f'(x) = 5e^{-0.1|x|}\sin x - 1$

46. $f'(x) = \dfrac{100\cos^2 x}{10 + x^2} - 1$

47–62 Find the absolute maximum and absolute minimum values of f on the given interval.

47. $f(x) = 3x^2 - 12x + 5, \quad [0, 3]$

48. $f(x) = x^3 - 3x + 1, \quad [0, 3]$

49. $f(x) = 2x^3 - 3x^2 - 12x + 1, \quad [-2, 3]$

50. $f(x) = x^3 - 6x^2 + 5, \quad [-3, 5]$

51. $f(x) = 3x^4 - 4x^3 - 12x^2 + 1, \quad [-2, 3]$

52. $f(x) = (x^2 - 1)^3, \quad [-1, 2]$

53. $f(x) = x + \dfrac{1}{x}, \quad [0.2, 4]$

54. $f(x) = \dfrac{x}{x^2 - x + 1}, \quad [0, 3]$

55. $f(t) = t\sqrt{4 - t^2}, \quad [-1, 2]$

56. $f(t) = \sqrt[3]{t}(8 - t), \quad [0, 8]$

57. $f(t) = 2\cos t + \sin 2t, \quad [0, \pi/2]$

58. $f(t) = t + \cot(t/2), \quad [\pi/4, 7\pi/4]$

59. $f(x) = xe^{-x^2/8}, \quad [-1, 4]$

60. $f(x) = x - \ln x, \quad \left[\frac{1}{2}, 2\right]$

61. $f(x) = \ln(x^2 + x + 1), \quad [-1, 1]$

62. $f(x) = x - 2\tan^{-1}x, \quad [0, 4]$

63. If a and b are positive numbers, find the maximum value of $f(x) = x^a(1 - x)^b, 0 \le x \le 1$.

64. Use a graph to estimate the critical numbers of $f(x) = |x^3 - 3x^2 + 2|$ correct to one decimal place.

65–68
(a) Use a graph to estimate the absolute maximum and minimum values of the function to two decimal places.
(b) Use calculus to find the exact maximum and minimum values.

65. $f(x) = x^5 - x^3 + 2, \quad -1 \le x \le 1$

66. $f(x) = e^x + e^{-2x}, \quad 0 \le x \le 1$

67. $f(x) = x\sqrt{x - x^2}$

68. $f(x) = x - 2\cos x, \quad -2 \le x \le 0$

69. Between 0°C and 30°C, the volume V (in cubic centimeters) of 1 kg of water at a temperature T is given approximately by the formula

$$V = 999.87 - 0.06426T + 0.0085043T^2 - 0.0000679T^3$$

Find the temperature at which water has its maximum density.

70. An object with mass m is dragged along a horizontal plane by a force acting along a rope attached to the object. If the rope makes an angle θ with the plane, then the magnitude of the force is

$$F = \frac{\mu mg}{\mu \sin\theta + \cos\theta}$$

where μ is a positive constant called the *coefficient of friction* and where $0 \le \theta \le \pi/2$. Show that F is minimized when $\tan\theta = \mu$.

71. A model for the US average price of a pound of white sugar from 1993 to 2003 is given by the function

$$S(t) = -0.00003237t^5 + 0.0009037t^4 - 0.008956t^3$$
$$+ 0.03629t^2 - 0.04458t + 0.4074$$

where t is measured in years since August of 1993. Estimate the times when sugar was cheapest and most expensive during the period 1993–2003.

72. On May 7, 1992, the space shuttle *Endeavour* was launched on mission STS-49, the purpose of which was to install a new perigee kick motor in an Intelsat communications satellite. The table gives the velocity data for the shuttle between liftoff and the jettisoning of the solid rocket boosters.

Event	Time (s)	Velocity (m/s)
Launch	0	0
Begin roll maneuver	10	56.4
End roll maneuver	15	97.2
Throttle to 89%	20	136.2
Throttle to 67%	32	226.2
Throttle to 104%	59	403.9
Maximum dynamic pressure	62	440.4
Solid rocket booster separation	125	1265.2

(a) Use a graphing calculator or computer to find the cubic polynomial that best models the velocity of the shuttle for the time interval $t \in [0, 125]$. Then graph this polynomial.

(b) Find a model for the acceleration of the shuttle and use it to estimate the maximum and minimum values of the acceleration during the first 125 seconds.

73. When a foreign object lodged in the trachea (windpipe) forces a person to cough, the diaphragm thrusts upward causing an increase in pressure in the lungs. This is accompanied by a contraction of the trachea, making a narrower channel for the expelled air to flow through. For a given amount of air to escape in a fixed time, it must move faster through the narrower channel than the wider one. The greater the velocity of the airstream, the greater the force on the foreign object. X rays show that the radius of the circular tracheal tube contracts to about two-thirds of its normal radius during a cough. According to a mathematical model of coughing, the velocity v of the airstream is related to the radius r of the trachea by the equation

$$v(r) = k(r_0 - r)r^2 \qquad \tfrac{1}{2}r_0 \leq r \leq r_0$$

where k is a constant and r_0 is the normal radius of the trachea. The restriction on r is due to the fact that the tracheal wall stiffens under pressure and a contraction greater than $\frac{1}{2}r_0$ is prevented (otherwise the person would suffocate).

(a) Determine the value of r in the interval $\left[\frac{1}{2}r_0, r_0\right]$ at which v has an absolute maximum. How does this compare with experimental evidence?

(b) What is the absolute maximum value of v on the interval?

(c) Sketch the graph of v on the interval $[0, r_0]$.

74. Show that 5 is a critical number of the function

$$g(x) = 2 + (x - 5)^3$$

but g does not have a local extreme value at 5.

75. Prove that the function

$$f(x) = x^{101} + x^{51} + x + 1$$

has neither a local maximum nor a local minimum.

76. If f has a local minimum value at c, show that the function $g(x) = -f(x)$ has a local maximum value at c.

77. Prove Fermat's Theorem for the case in which f has a local minimum at c.

78. A cubic function is a polynomial of degree 3; that is, it has the form $f(x) = ax^3 + bx^2 + cx + d$, where $a \neq 0$.

(a) Show that a cubic function can have two, one, or no critical number(s). Give examples and sketches to illustrate the three possibilities.

(b) How many local extreme values can a cubic function have?

APPLIED PROJECT   **THE CALCULUS OF RAINBOWS**

Rainbows are created when raindrops scatter sunlight. They have fascinated mankind since ancient times and have inspired attempts at scientific explanation since the time of Aristotle. In this project we use the ideas of Descartes and Newton to explain the shape, location, and colors of rainbows.

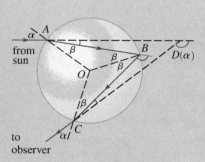

Formation of the primary rainbow

1. The figure shows a ray of sunlight entering a spherical raindrop at A. Some of the light is reflected, but the line AB shows the path of the part that enters the drop. Notice that the light is refracted toward the normal line AO and in fact Snell's Law says that $\sin \alpha = k \sin \beta$, where α is the angle of incidence, β is the angle of refraction, and $k \approx \frac{4}{3}$ is the index of refraction for water. At B some of the light passes through the drop and is refracted into the air, but the line BC shows the part that is reflected. (The angle of incidence equals the angle of reflection.) When the ray reaches C, part of it is reflected, but for the time being we are

rays from sun

138°

rays from sun

42°

observer

more interested in the part that leaves the raindrop at C. (Notice that it is refracted away from the normal line.) The *angle of deviation* $D(\alpha)$ is the amount of clockwise rotation that the ray has undergone during this three-stage process. Thus

$$D(\alpha) = (\alpha - \beta) + (\pi - 2\beta) + (\alpha - \beta) = \pi + 2\alpha - 4\beta$$

Show that the minimum value of the deviation is $D(\alpha) \approx 138°$ and occurs when $\alpha \approx 59.4°$.
 The significance of the minimum deviation is that when $\alpha \approx 59.4°$ we have $D'(\alpha) \approx 0$, so $\Delta D/\Delta \alpha \approx 0$. This means that many rays with $\alpha \approx 59.4°$ become deviated by approximately the same amount. It is the *concentration* of rays coming from near the direction of minimum deviation that creates the brightness of the primary rainbow. The figure at the left shows that the angle of elevation from the observer up to the highest point on the rainbow is $180° - 138° = 42°$. (This angle is called the *rainbow angle*.)

2. Problem 1 explains the location of the primary rainbow, but how do we explain the colors? Sunlight comprises a range of wavelengths, from the red range through orange, yellow, green, blue, indigo, and violet. As Newton discovered in his prism experiments of 1666, the index of refraction is different for each color. (The effect is called *dispersion*.) For red light the refractive index is $k \approx 1.3318$ whereas for violet light it is $k \approx 1.3435$. By repeating the calculation of Problem 1 for these values of k, show that the rainbow angle is about 42.3° for the red bow and 40.6° for the violet bow. So the rainbow really consists of seven individual bows corresponding to the seven colors.

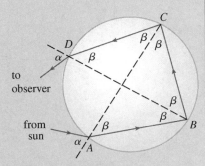

to observer

from sun

Formation of the secondary rainbow

3. Perhaps you have seen a fainter secondary rainbow above the primary bow. That results from the part of a ray that enters a raindrop and is refracted at A, reflected twice (at B and C), and refracted as it leaves the drop at D (see the figure at the left). This time the deviation angle $D(\alpha)$ is the total amount of counterclockwise rotation that the ray undergoes in this four-stage process. Show that

$$D(\alpha) = 2\alpha - 6\beta + 2\pi$$

and $D(\alpha)$ has a minimum value when

$$\cos \alpha = \sqrt{\frac{k^2 - 1}{8}}$$

Taking $k = \frac{4}{3}$, show that the minimum deviation is about 129° and so the rainbow angle for the secondary rainbow is about 51°, as shown in the figure at the left.

4. Show that the colors in the secondary rainbow appear in the opposite order from those in the primary rainbow.

42°   51°

4.2 The Mean Value Theorem

Rolle

Rolle's Theorem was first published in 1691 by the French mathematician Michel Rolle (1652–1719) in a book entitled *Méthode pour resoudre les Egalitez*. He was a vocal critic of the methods of his day and attacked calculus as being a "collection of ingenious fallacies." Later, however, he became convinced of the essential correctness of the methods of calculus.

We will see that many of the results of this chapter depend on one central fact, which is called the Mean Value Theorem. But to arrive at the Mean Value Theorem we first need the following result.

> **Rolle's Theorem** Let f be a function that satisfies the following three hypotheses:
>
> 1. f is continuous on the closed interval $[a, b]$.
> 2. f is differentiable on the open interval (a, b).
> 3. $f(a) = f(b)$
>
> Then there is a number c in (a, b) such that $f'(c) = 0$.

Before giving the proof let's take a look at the graphs of some typical functions that satisfy the three hypotheses. Figure 1 shows the graphs of four such functions. In each case it appears that there is at least one point $(c, f(c))$ on the graph where the tangent is horizontal and therefore $f'(c) = 0$. Thus Rolle's Theorem is plausible.

(a)

(b)

(c)

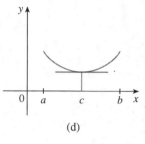
(d)

FIGURE 1

PS Take cases

PROOF There are three cases:

CASE I $f(x) = k$, a constant
Then $f'(x) = 0$, so the number c can be taken to be *any* number in (a, b).

CASE II $f(x) > f(a)$ for some x in (a, b) [as in Figure 1(b) or (c)]
By the Extreme Value Theorem (which we can apply by hypothesis 1), f has a maximum value somewhere in $[a, b]$. Since $f(a) = f(b)$, it must attain this maximum value at a number c in the open interval (a, b). Then f has a *local maximum* at c and, by hypothesis 2, f is differentiable at c. Therefore $f'(c) = 0$ by Fermat's Theorem.

CASE III $f(x) < f(a)$ for some x in (a, b) [as in Figure 1(c) or (d)]
By the Extreme Value Theorem, f has a minimum value in $[a, b]$ and, since $f(a) = f(b)$, it attains this minimum value at a number c in (a, b). Again $f'(c) = 0$ by Fermat's Theorem.

EXAMPLE 1 Let's apply Rolle's Theorem to the position function $s = f(t)$ of a moving object. If the object is in the same place at two different instants $t = a$ and $t = b$, then $f(a) = f(b)$. Rolle's Theorem says that there is some instant of time $t = c$ between a and b when $f'(c) = 0$; that is, the velocity is 0. (In particular, you can see that this is true when a ball is thrown directly upward.)

EXAMPLE 2 Prove that the equation $x^3 + x - 1 = 0$ has exactly one real root.

SOLUTION First we use the Intermediate Value Theorem (2.5.10) to show that a root exists. Let $f(x) = x^3 + x - 1$. Then $f(0) = -1 < 0$ and $f(1) = 1 > 0$. Since f is a

Figure 2 shows a graph of the function $f(x) = x^3 + x - 1$ discussed in Example 2. Rolle's Theorem shows that, no matter how much we enlarge the viewing rectangle, we can never find a second x-intercept.

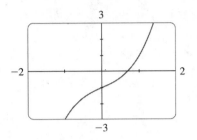

FIGURE 2

The Mean Value Theorem is an example of what is called an existence theorem. Like the Intermediate Value Theorem, the Extreme Value Theorem, and Rolle's Theorem, it guarantees that there *exists* a number with a certain property, but it doesn't tell us how to find the number.

polynomial, it is continuous, so the Intermediate Value Theorem states that there is a number c between 0 and 1 such that $f(c) = 0$. Thus the given equation has a root.

To show that the equation has no other real root, we use Rolle's Theorem and argue by contradiction. Suppose that it had two roots a and b. Then $f(a) = 0 = f(b)$ and, since f is a polynomial, it is differentiable on (a, b) and continuous on $[a, b]$. Thus, by Rolle's Theorem, there is a number c between a and b such that $f'(c) = 0$. But

$$f'(x) = 3x^2 + 1 \geq 1 \qquad \text{for all } x$$

(since $x^2 \geq 0$) so $f'(x)$ can never be 0. This gives a contradiction. Therefore the equation can't have two real roots. ∎

Our main use of Rolle's Theorem is in proving the following important theorem, which was first stated by another French mathematician, Joseph-Louis Lagrange.

The Mean Value Theorem   Let f be a function that satisfies the following hypotheses:

1. f is continuous on the closed interval $[a, b]$.

2. f is differentiable on the open interval (a, b).

Then there is a number c in (a, b) such that

$$\boxed{1} \qquad f'(c) = \frac{f(b) - f(a)}{b - a}$$

or, equivalently,

$$\boxed{2} \qquad f(b) - f(a) = f'(c)(b - a)$$

Before proving this theorem, we can see that it is reasonable by interpreting it geometrically. Figures 3 and 4 show the points $A(a, f(a))$ and $B(b, f(b))$ on the graphs of two differentiable functions. The slope of the secant line AB is

$$\boxed{3} \qquad m_{AB} = \frac{f(b) - f(a)}{b - a}$$

which is the same expression as on the right side of Equation 1. Since $f'(c)$ is the slope of the tangent line at the point $(c, f(c))$, the Mean Value Theorem, in the form given by Equation 1, says that there is at least one point $P(c, f(c))$ on the graph where the slope of the tangent line is the same as the slope of the secant line AB. In other words, there is a point P where the tangent line is parallel to the secant line AB. (Imagine a line parallel to AB, starting far away and moving parallel to itself until it touches the graph for the first time.)

FIGURE 3   **FIGURE 4**

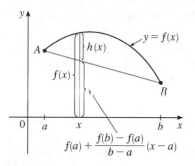

FIGURE 5

Lagrange and the Mean Value Theorem

The Mean Value Theorem was first formulated by Joseph-Louis Lagrange (1736–1813), born in Italy of a French father and an Italian mother. He was a child prodigy and became a professor in Turin at the tender age of 19. Lagrange made great contributions to number theory, theory of functions, theory of equations, and analytical and celestial mechanics. In particular, he applied calculus to the analysis of the stability of the solar system. At the invitation of Frederick the Great, he succeeded Euler at the Berlin Academy and, when Frederick died, Lagrange accepted King Louis XVI's invitation to Paris, where he was given apartments in the Louvre and became a professor at the Ecole Polytechnique. Despite all the trappings of luxury and fame, he was a kind and quiet man, living only for science.

PROOF We apply Rolle's Theorem to a new function h defined as the difference between f and the function whose graph is the secant line AB. Using Equation 3, we see that the equation of the line AB can be written as

$$y - f(a) = \frac{f(b) - f(a)}{b - a} (x - a)$$

or as

$$y = f(a) + \frac{f(b) - f(a)}{b - a} (x - a)$$

So, as shown in Figure 5,

$$\boxed{4} \qquad h(x) = f(x) - f(a) - \frac{f(b) - f(a)}{b - a} (x - a)$$

First we must verify that h satisfies the three hypotheses of Rolle's Theorem.

1. The function h is continuous on $[a, b]$ because it is the sum of f and a first-degree polynomial, both of which are continuous.

2. The function h is differentiable on (a, b) because both f and the first-degree polynomial are differentiable. In fact, we can compute h' directly from Equation 4:

$$h'(x) = f'(x) - \frac{f(b) - f(a)}{b - a}$$

(Note that $f(a)$ and $[f(b) - f(a)]/(b - a)$ are constants.)

3.
$$h(a) = f(a) - f(a) - \frac{f(b) - f(a)}{b - a} (a - a) = 0$$

$$h(b) = f(b) - f(a) - \frac{f(b) - f(a)}{b - a} (b - a)$$

$$= f(b) - f(a) - [f(b) - f(a)] = 0$$

Therefore $h(a) = h(b)$.

Since h satisfies the hypotheses of Rolle's Theorem, that theorem says there is a number c in (a, b) such that $h'(c) = 0$. Therefore

$$0 = h'(c) = f'(c) - \frac{f(b) - f(a)}{b - a}$$

and so

$$f'(c) = \frac{f(b) - f(a)}{b - a}$$

▼ **EXAMPLE 3** To illustrate the Mean Value Theorem with a specific function, let's consider $f(x) = x^3 - x$, $a = 0$, $b = 2$. Since f is a polynomial, it is continuous and differentiable for all x, so it is certainly continuous on $[0, 2]$ and differentiable on $(0, 2)$. Therefore, by the Mean Value Theorem, there is a number c in $(0, 2)$ such that

$$f(2) - f(0) = f'(c)(2 - 0)$$

Now $f(2) = 6$, $f(0) = 0$, and $f'(x) = 3x^2 - 1$, so this equation becomes

$$6 = (3c^2 - 1)2 = 6c^2 - 2$$

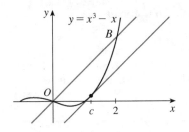

FIGURE 6

which gives $c^2 = \frac{4}{3}$, that is, $c = \pm 2/\sqrt{3}$. But c must lie in $(0, 2)$, so $c = 2/\sqrt{3}$. Figure 6 illustrates this calculation: The tangent line at this value of c is parallel to the secant line OB.

V **EXAMPLE 4** If an object moves in a straight line with position function $s = f(t)$, then the average velocity between $t = a$ and $t = b$ is

$$\frac{f(b) - f(a)}{b - a}$$

and the velocity at $t = c$ is $f'(c)$. Thus the Mean Value Theorem (in the form of Equation 1) tells us that at some time $t = c$ between a and b the instantaneous velocity $f'(c)$ is equal to that average velocity. For instance, if a car traveled 180 km in 2 hours, then the speedometer must have read 90 km/h at least once.

In general, the Mean Value Theorem can be interpreted as saying that there is a number at which the instantaneous rate of change is equal to the average rate of change over an interval.

The main significance of the Mean Value Theorem is that it enables us to obtain information about a function from information about its derivative. The next example provides an instance of this principle.

V **EXAMPLE 5** Suppose that $f(0) = -3$ and $f'(x) \leqslant 5$ for all values of x. How large can $f(2)$ possibly be?

SOLUTION We are given that f is differentiable (and therefore continuous) everywhere. In particular, we can apply the Mean Value Theorem on the interval $[0, 2]$. There exists a number c such that

$$f(2) - f(0) = f'(c)(2 - 0)$$

so

$$f(2) = f(0) + 2f'(c) = -3 + 2f'(c)$$

We are given that $f'(x) \leqslant 5$ for all x, so in particular we know that $f'(c) \leqslant 5$. Multiplying both sides of this inequality by 2, we have $2f'(c) \leqslant 10$, so

$$f(2) = -3 + 2f'(c) \leqslant -3 + 10 = 7$$

The largest possible value for $f(2)$ is 7.

The Mean Value Theorem can be used to establish some of the basic facts of differential calculus. One of these basic facts is the following theorem. Others will be found in the following sections.

| **5** | **Theorem** If $f'(x) = 0$ for all x in an interval (a, b), then f is constant on (a, b). |

PROOF Let x_1 and x_2 be any two numbers in (a, b) with $x_1 < x_2$. Since f is differentiable on (a, b), it must be differentiable on (x_1, x_2) and continuous on $[x_1, x_2]$. By applying the Mean Value Theorem to f on the interval $[x_1, x_2]$, we get a number c such that $x_1 < c < x_2$ and

| **6** | $$f(x_2) - f(x_1) = f'(c)(x_2 - x_1)$$ |

Since $f'(x) = 0$ for all x, we have $f'(c) = 0$, and so Equation 6 becomes

$$f(x_2) - f(x_1) = 0 \qquad \text{or} \qquad f(x_2) = f(x_1)$$

Therefore f has the same value at *any* two numbers x_1 and x_2 in (a, b). This means that f is constant on (a, b).

> **7** **Corollary** If $f'(x) = g'(x)$ for all x in an interval (a, b), then $f - g$ is constant on (a, b); that is, $f(x) = g(x) + c$ where c is a constant.

PROOF Let $F(x) = f(x) - g(x)$. Then

$$F'(x) = f'(x) - g'(x) = 0$$

for all x in (a, b). Thus, by Theorem 5, F is constant; that is, $f - g$ is constant.

NOTE Care must be taken in applying Theorem 5. Let

$$f(x) = \frac{x}{|x|} = \begin{cases} 1 & \text{if } x > 0 \\ -1 & \text{if } x < 0 \end{cases}$$

The domain of f is $D = \{x \mid x \neq 0\}$ and $f'(x) = 0$ for all x in D. But f is obviously not a constant function. This does not contradict Theorem 5 because D is not an interval. Notice that f is constant on the interval $(0, \infty)$ and also on the interval $(-\infty, 0)$.

EXAMPLE 6 Prove the identity $\tan^{-1}x + \cot^{-1}x = \pi/2$.

SOLUTION Although calculus isn't needed to prove this identity, the proof using calculus is quite simple. If $f(x) = \tan^{-1}x + \cot^{-1}x$, then

$$f'(x) = \frac{1}{1 + x^2} - \frac{1}{1 + x^2} = 0$$

for all values of x. Therefore $f(x) = C$, a constant. To determine the value of C, we put $x = 1$ [because we can evaluate $f(1)$ exactly]. Then

$$C = f(1) = \tan^{-1}1 + \cot^{-1}1 = \frac{\pi}{4} + \frac{\pi}{4} = \frac{\pi}{2}$$

Thus $\tan^{-1}x + \cot^{-1}x = \pi/2$.

4.2 Exercises

1–4 Verify that the function satisfies the three hypotheses of Rolle's Theorem on the given interval. Then find all numbers c that satisfy the conclusion of Rolle's Theorem.

1. $f(x) = 5 - 12x + 3x^2$, $\quad [1, 3]$

2. $f(x) = x^3 - x^2 - 6x + 2$, $\quad [0, 3]$

3. $f(x) = \sqrt{x} - \frac{1}{3}x$, $\quad [0, 9]$

4. $f(x) = \cos 2x$, $\quad [\pi/8, 7\pi/8]$

---

5. Let $f(x) = 1 - x^{2/3}$. Show that $f(-1) = f(1)$ but there is no number c in $(-1, 1)$ such that $f'(c) = 0$. Why does this not contradict Rolle's Theorem?

6. Let $f(x) = \tan x$. Show that $f(0) = f(\pi)$ but there is no number c in $(0, \pi)$ such that $f'(c) = 0$. Why does this not contradict Rolle's Theorem?

⊞ Graphing calculator or computer required   **1.** Homework Hints available at stewartcalculus.com

7. Use the graph of f to estimate the values of c that satisfy the conclusion of the Mean Value Theorem for the interval $[0, 8]$.

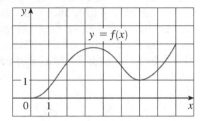

8. Use the graph of f given in Exercise 7 to estimate the values of c that satisfy the conclusion of the Mean Value Theorem for the interval $[1, 7]$.

9–12 Verify that the function satisfies the hypotheses of the Mean Value Theorem on the given interval. Then find all numbers c that satisfy the conclusion of the Mean Value Theorem.

9. $f(x) = 2x^2 - 3x + 1$, $\quad [0, 2]$

10. $f(x) = x^3 + x - 1$, $\quad [0, 2]$

11. $f(x) = e^{-2x}$, $\quad [0, 3]$

12. $f(x) = \dfrac{x}{x + 2}$, $\quad [1, 4]$

13–14 Find the number c that satisfies the conclusion of the Mean Value Theorem on the given interval. Graph the function, the secant line through the endpoints, and the tangent line at $(c, f(c))$. Are the secant line and the tangent line parallel?

13. $f(x) = \sqrt{x}$, $\quad [0, 4]$ **14.** $f(x) = e^{-x}$, $\quad [0, 2]$

15. Let $f(x) = (x - 3)^{-2}$. Show that there is no value of c in $(1, 4)$ such that $f(4) - f(1) = f'(c)(4 - 1)$. Why does this not contradict the Mean Value Theorem?

16. Let $f(x) = 2 - |2x - 1|$. Show that there is no value of c such that $f(3) - f(0) = f'(c)(3 - 0)$. Why does this not contradict the Mean Value Theorem?

17–18 Show that the equation has exactly one real root.

17. $2x + \cos x = 0$ **18.** $x^3 + e^x = 0$

19. Show that the equation $x^3 - 15x + c = 0$ has at most one root in the interval $[-2, 2]$.

20. Show that the equation $x^4 + 4x + c = 0$ has at most two real roots.

21. (a) Show that a polynomial of degree 3 has at most three real roots.
(b) Show that a polynomial of degree n has at most n real roots.

22. (a) Suppose that f is differentiable on $\mathbb{R}$ and has two roots. Show that f' has at least one root.

(b) Suppose f is twice differentiable on $\mathbb{R}$ and has three roots. Show that f'' has at least one real root.
(c) Can you generalize parts (a) and (b)?

23. If $f(1) = 10$ and $f'(x) \geqslant 2$ for $1 \leqslant x \leqslant 4$, how small can $f(4)$ possibly be?

24. Suppose that $3 \leqslant f'(x) \leqslant 5$ for all values of x. Show that $18 \leqslant f(8) - f(2) \leqslant 30$.

25. Does there exist a function f such that $f(0) = -1$, $f(2) = 4$, and $f'(x) \leqslant 2$ for all x?

26. Suppose that f and g are continuous on $[a, b]$ and differentiable on (a, b). Suppose also that $f(a) = g(a)$ and $f'(x) < g'(x)$ for $a < x < b$. Prove that $f(b) < g(b)$. [*Hint:* Apply the Mean Value Theorem to the function $h = f - g$.]

27. Show that $\sqrt{1 + x} < 1 + \frac{1}{2}x$ if $x > 0$.

28. Suppose f is an odd function and is differentiable everywhere. Prove that for every positive number b, there exists a number c in $(-b, b)$ such that $f'(c) = f(b)/b$.

29. Use the Mean Value Theorem to prove the inequality
$$|\sin a - \sin b| \leqslant |a - b| \qquad \text{for all } a \text{ and } b$$

30. If $f'(x) = c$ (c a constant) for all x, use Corollary 7 to show that $f(x) = cx + d$ for some constant d.

31. Let $f(x) = 1/x$ and
$$g(x) = \begin{cases} \dfrac{1}{x} & \text{if } x > 0 \\[2mm] 1 + \dfrac{1}{x} & \text{if } x < 0 \end{cases}$$

Show that $f'(x) = g'(x)$ for all x in their domains. Can we conclude from Corollary 7 that $f - g$ is constant?

32. Use the method of Example 6 to prove the identity
$$2 \sin^{-1}x = \cos^{-1}(1 - 2x^2) \qquad x \geqslant 0$$

33. Prove the identity
$$\arcsin \frac{x - 1}{x + 1} = 2 \arctan \sqrt{x} - \frac{\pi}{2}$$

34. At 2:00 PM a car's speedometer reads 50 km/h. At 2:10 PM it reads 65 km/h. Show that at some time between 2:00 and 2:10 the acceleration is exactly 90 km/h^2.

35. Two runners start a race at the same time and finish in a tie. Prove that at some time during the race they have the same speed. [*Hint:* Consider $f(t) = g(t) - h(t)$, where g and h are the position functions of the two runners.]

36. A number a is called a **fixed point** of a function f if $f(a) = a$. Prove that if $f'(x) \neq 1$ for all real numbers x, then f has at most one fixed point.

4.3   How Derivatives Affect the Shape of a Graph

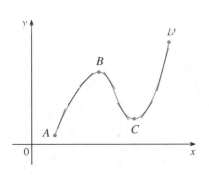

FIGURE 1

Let's abbreviate the name of this test to the I/D Test.

Many of the applications of calculus depend on our ability to deduce facts about a function f from information concerning its derivatives. Because $f'(x)$ represents the slope of the curve $y = f(x)$ at the point $(x, f(x))$, it tells us the direction in which the curve proceeds at each point. So it is reasonable to expect that information about $f'(x)$ will provide us with information about $f(x)$.

■ What Does f' Say About f?

To see how the derivative of f can tell us where a function is increasing or decreasing, look at Figure 1. (Increasing functions and decreasing functions were defined in Section 1.1.) Between A and B and between C and D, the tangent lines have positive slope and so $f'(x) > 0$. Between B and C, the tangent lines have negative slope and so $f'(x) < 0$. Thus it appears that f increases when $f'(x)$ is positive and decreases when $f'(x)$ is negative. To prove that this is always the case, we use the Mean Value Theorem.

Increasing/Decreasing Test

(a) If $f'(x) > 0$ on an interval, then f is increasing on that interval.

(b) If $f'(x) < 0$ on an interval, then f is decreasing on that interval.

PROOF

(a) Let x_1 and x_2 be any two numbers in the interval with $x_1 < x_2$. According to the definition of an increasing function (page 19), we have to show that $f(x_1) < f(x_2)$.

Because we are given that $f'(x) > 0$, we know that f is differentiable on $[x_1, x_2]$. So, by the Mean Value Theorem, there is a number c between x_1 and x_2 such that

$$\boxed{1} \qquad f(x_2) - f(x_1) = f'(c)(x_2 - x_1)$$

Now $f'(c) > 0$ by assumption and $x_2 - x_1 > 0$ because $x_1 < x_2$. Thus the right side of Equation 1 is positive, and so

$$f(x_2) - f(x_1) > 0 \qquad \text{or} \qquad f(x_1) < f(x_2)$$

This shows that f is increasing.

Part (b) is proved similarly.   ■

V EXAMPLE 1 Find where the function $f(x) = 3x^4 - 4x^3 - 12x^2 + 5$ is increasing and where it is decreasing.

SOLUTION $$f'(x) = 12x^3 - 12x^2 - 24x = 12x(x - 2)(x + 1)$$

To use the I/D Test we have to know where $f'(x) > 0$ and where $f'(x) < 0$. This depends on the signs of the three factors of $f'(x)$, namely, $12x$, $x - 2$, and $x + 1$. We divide the real line into intervals whose endpoints are the critical numbers -1, 0, and 2 and arrange our work in a chart. A plus sign indicates that the given expression is positive, and a minus sign indicates that it is negative. The last column of the chart gives the conclusion based on the I/D Test. For instance, $f'(x) < 0$ for $0 < x < 2$, so f is decreasing on $(0, 2)$. (It would also be true to say that f is decreasing on the closed interval $[0, 2]$.)

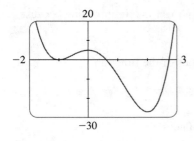

FIGURE 2

Interval	$12x$	$x - 2$	$x + 1$	$f'(x)$	f
$x < -1$	$-$	$-$	$-$	$-$	decreasing on $(-\infty, -1)$
$-1 < x < 0$	$-$	$-$	$+$	$+$	increasing on $(-1, 0)$
$0 < x < 2$	$+$	$-$	$+$	$-$	decreasing on $(0, 2)$
$x > 2$	$+$	$+$	$+$	$+$	increasing on $(2, \infty)$

The graph of f shown in Figure 2 confirms the information in the chart. ∎

Recall from Section 4.1 that if f has a local maximum or minimum at c, then c must be a critical number of f (by Fermat's Theorem), but not every critical number gives rise to a maximum or a minimum. We therefore need a test that will tell us whether or not f has a local maximum or minimum at a critical number.

You can see from Figure 2 that $f(0) = 5$ is a local maximum value of f because f increases on $(-1, 0)$ and decreases on $(0, 2)$. Or, in terms of derivatives, $f'(x) > 0$ for $-1 < x < 0$ and $f'(x) < 0$ for $0 < x < 2$. In other words, the sign of $f'(x)$ changes from positive to negative at 0. This observation is the basis of the following test.

The First Derivative Test Suppose that c is a critical number of a continuous function f.

(a) If f' changes from positive to negative at c, then f has a local maximum at c.

(b) If f' changes from negative to positive at c, then f has a local minimum at c.

(c) If f' does not change sign at c (for example, if f' is positive on both sides of c or negative on both sides), then f has no local maximum or minimum at c.

The First Derivative Test is a consequence of the I/D Test. In part (a), for instance, since the sign of $f'(x)$ changes from positive to negative at c, f is increasing to the left of c and decreasing to the right of c. It follows that f has a local maximum at c.

It is easy to remember the First Derivative Test by visualizing diagrams such as those in Figure 3.

(a) Local maximum

(b) Local minimum

(c) No maximum or minimum

(d) No maximum or minimum

FIGURE 3

V **EXAMPLE 2** Find the local minimum and maximum values of the function f in Example 1.

SOLUTION From the chart in the solution to Example 1 we see that $f'(x)$ changes from negative to positive at -1, so $f(-1) = 0$ is a local minimum value by the First Derivative Test. Similarly, f' changes from negative to positive at 2, so $f(2) = -27$ is also a local minimum value. As previously noted, $f(0) = 5$ is a local maximum value because $f'(x)$ changes from positive to negative at 0. ▬

EXAMPLE 3 Find the local maximum and minimum values of the function

$$g(x) = x + 2 \sin x \qquad 0 \le x \le 2\pi$$

SOLUTION To find the critical numbers of g, we differentiate:

$$g'(x) = 1 + 2 \cos x$$

So $g'(x) = 0$ when $\cos x = -\frac{1}{2}$. The solutions of this equation are $2\pi/3$ and $4\pi/3$. Because g is differentiable everywhere, the only critical numbers are $2\pi/3$ and $4\pi/3$ and so we analyze g in the following table.

The + signs in the table come from the fact that $g'(x) > 0$ when $\cos x > -\frac{1}{2}$. From the graph of $y = \cos x$, this is true in the indicated intervals.

Interval	$g'(x) = 1 + 2 \cos x$	g
$0 < x < 2\pi/3$	$+$	increasing on $(0, 2\pi/3)$
$2\pi/3 < x < 4\pi/3$	$-$	decreasing on $(2\pi/3, 4\pi/3)$
$4\pi/3 < x < 2\pi$	$+$	increasing on $(4\pi/3, 2\pi)$

Because $g'(x)$ changes from positive to negative at $2\pi/3$, the First Derivative Test tells us that there is a local maximum at $2\pi/3$ and the local maximum value is

$$g(2\pi/3) = \frac{2\pi}{3} + 2 \sin \frac{2\pi}{3} = \frac{2\pi}{3} + 2 \left(\frac{\sqrt{3}}{2} \right) = \frac{2\pi}{3} + \sqrt{3} \approx 3.83$$

Likewise, $g'(x)$ changes from negative to positive at $4\pi/3$ and so

$$g(4\pi/3) = \frac{4\pi}{3} + 2 \sin \frac{4\pi}{3} = \frac{4\pi}{3} + 2 \left(-\frac{\sqrt{3}}{2} \right) = \frac{4\pi}{3} - \sqrt{3} \approx 2.46$$

is a local minimum value. The graph of g in Figure 4 supports our conclusion.

FIGURE 4
$g(x) = x + 2 \sin x$

▬ What Does f'' Say About f?

Figure 5 shows the graphs of two increasing functions on (a, b). Both graphs join point A to point B but they look different because they bend in different directions. How can we distinguish between these two types of behavior? In Figure 6 tangents to these curves have been drawn at several points. In (a) the curve lies above the tangents and f is called *concave upward* on (a, b). In (b) the curve lies below the tangents and g is called *concave downward* on (a, b).

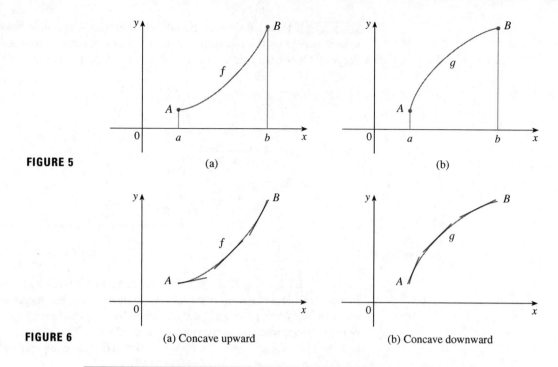

FIGURE 5

(a) (b)

FIGURE 6 (a) Concave upward (b) Concave downward

> **Definition** If the graph of f lies above all of its tangents on an interval I, then it is called **concave upward** on I. If the graph of f lies below all of its tangents on I, it is called **concave downward** on I.

Figure 7 shows the graph of a function that is concave upward (abbreviated CU) on the intervals (b, c), (d, e), and (e, p) and concave downward (CD) on the intervals (a, b), (c, d), and (p, q).

FIGURE 7

Let's see how the second derivative helps determine the intervals of concavity. Looking at Figure 6(a), you can see that, going from left to right, the slope of the tangent increases. This means that the derivative f' is an increasing function and therefore its derivative f'' is positive. Likewise, in Figure 6(b) the slope of the tangent decreases from left to right, so f' decreases and therefore f'' is negative. This reasoning can be reversed and suggests that the following theorem is true. A proof is given in Appendix F with the help of the Mean Value Theorem.

> **Concavity Test**
> (a) If $f''(x) > 0$ for all x in I, then the graph of f is concave upward on I.
> (b) If $f''(x) < 0$ for all x in I, then the graph of f is concave downward on I.

EXAMPLE 4 Figure 8 shows a population graph for Cyprian honeybees raised in an apiary. How does the rate of population increase change over time? When is this rate highest? Over what intervals is P concave upward or concave downward?

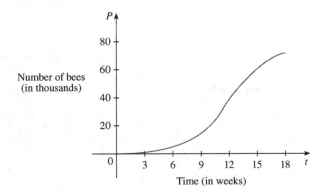

FIGURE 8

SOLUTION By looking at the slope of the curve as t increases, we see that the rate of increase of the population is initially very small, then gets larger until it reaches a maximum at about $t = 12$ weeks, and decreases as the population begins to level off. As the population approaches its maximum value of about 75,000 (called the *carrying capacity*), the rate of increase, $P'(t)$, approaches 0. The curve appears to be concave upward on $(0, 12)$ and concave downward on $(12, 18)$. ∎

In Example 4, the population curve changed from concave upward to concave downward at approximately the point $(12, 38,000)$. This point is called an *inflection point* of the curve. The significance of this point is that the rate of population increase has its maximum value there. In general, an inflection point is a point where a curve changes its direction of concavity.

> **Definition** A point P on a curve $y = f(x)$ is called an **inflection point** if f is continuous there and the curve changes from concave upward to concave downward or from concave downward to concave upward at P.

For instance, in Figure 7, B, C, D, and P are the points of inflection. Notice that if a curve has a tangent at a point of inflection, then the curve crosses its tangent there.

In view of the Concavity Test, there is a point of inflection at any point where the second derivative changes sign.

V **EXAMPLE 5** Sketch a possible graph of a function f that satisfies the following conditions:

    (i) $f'(x) > 0$ on $(-\infty, 1)$, $f'(x) < 0$ on $(1, \infty)$

    (ii) $f''(x) > 0$ on $(-\infty, -2)$ and $(2, \infty)$, $f''(x) < 0$ on $(-2, 2)$

    (iii) $\lim_{x \to -\infty} f(x) = -2$, $\lim_{x \to \infty} f(x) = 0$

SOLUTION Condition (i) tells us that f is increasing on $(-\infty, 1)$ and decreasing on $(1, \infty)$. Condition (ii) says that f is concave upward on $(-\infty, -2)$ and $(2, \infty)$, and concave downward on $(-2, 2)$. From condition (iii) we know that the graph of f has two horizontal asymptotes: $y = -2$ and $y = 0$.

We first draw the horizontal asymptote $y = -2$ as a dashed line (see Figure 9). We then draw the graph of f approaching this asymptote at the far left, increasing to its maximum point at $x = 1$ and decreasing toward the x-axis as at the far right. We also

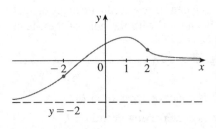

FIGURE 9

make sure that the graph has inflection points when $x = -2$ and 2. Notice that we made the curve bend upward for $x < -2$ and $x > 2$, and bend downward when x is between -2 and 2.

Another application of the second derivative is the following test for maximum and minimum values. It is a consequence of the Concavity Test.

> **The Second Derivative Test** Suppose f'' is continuous near c.
> (a) If $f'(c) = 0$ and $f''(c) > 0$, then f has a local minimum at c.
> (b) If $f'(c) = 0$ and $f''(c) < 0$, then f has a local maximum at c.

For instance, part (a) is true because $f''(x) > 0$ near c and so f is concave upward near c. This means that the graph of f lies *above* its horizontal tangent at c and so f has a local minimum at c. (See Figure 10.)

FIGURE 10
$f''(c) > 0$, f is concave upward

V **EXAMPLE 6** Discuss the curve $y = x^4 - 4x^3$ with respect to concavity, points of inflection, and local maxima and minima. Use this information to sketch the curve.

SOLUTION If $f(x) = x^4 - 4x^3$, then

$$f'(x) = 4x^3 - 12x^2 = 4x^2(x - 3)$$
$$f''(x) = 12x^2 - 24x = 12x(x - 2)$$

To find the critical numbers we set $f'(x) = 0$ and obtain $x = 0$ and $x = 3$. To use the Second Derivative Test we evaluate f'' at these critical numbers:

$$f''(0) = 0 \qquad f''(3) = 36 > 0$$

Since $f'(3) = 0$ and $f''(3) > 0$, $f(3) = -27$ is a local minimum. Since $f''(0) = 0$, the Second Derivative Test gives no information about the critical number 0. But since $f'(x) < 0$ for $x < 0$ and also for $0 < x < 3$, the First Derivative Test tells us that f does not have a local maximum or minimum at 0. [In fact, the expression for $f'(x)$ shows that f decreases to the left of 3 and increases to the right of 3.]

Since $f''(x) = 0$ when $x = 0$ or 2, we divide the real line into intervals with these numbers as endpoints and complete the following chart.

Interval	$f''(x) = 12x(x - 2)$	Concavity
$(-\infty, 0)$	+	upward
$(0, 2)$	−	downward
$(2, \infty)$	+	upward

The point $(0, 0)$ is an inflection point since the curve changes from concave upward to concave downward there. Also $(2, -16)$ is an inflection point since the curve changes from concave downward to concave upward there.

Using the local minimum, the intervals of concavity, and the inflection points, we sketch the curve in Figure 11.

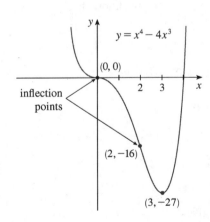

FIGURE 11

NOTE The Second Derivative Test is inconclusive when $f''(c) = 0$. In other words, at such a point there might be a maximum, there might be a minimum, or there might be neither (as in Example 6). This test also fails when $f''(c)$ does not exist. In such cases the First Derivative Test must be used. In fact, even when both tests apply, the First Derivative Test is often the easier one to use.

EXAMPLE 7 Sketch the graph of the function $f(x) = x^{2/3}(6 - x)^{1/3}$.

SOLUTION Calculation of the first two derivatives gives

$$f'(x) = \frac{4 - x}{x^{1/3}(6 - x)^{2/3}} \qquad f''(x) = \frac{-8}{x^{4/3}(6 - x)^{5/3}}$$

Since $f'(x) = 0$ when $x = 4$ and $f'(x)$ does not exist when $x = 0$ or $x = 6$, the critical numbers are 0, 4, and 6.

Interval	$4 - x$	$x^{1/3}$	$(6 - x)^{2/3}$	$f'(x)$	f
$x < 0$	+	−	+	−	decreasing on $(-\infty, 0)$
$0 < x < 4$	+	+	+	+	increasing on $(0, 4)$
$4 < x < 6$	−	+	+	−	decreasing on $(4, 6)$
$x > 6$	−	+	+	−	decreasing on $(6, \infty)$

To find the local extreme values we use the First Derivative Test. Since f' changes from negative to positive at 0, $f(0) = 0$ is a local minimum. Since f' changes from positive to negative at 4, $f(4) = 2^{5/3}$ is a local maximum. The sign of f' does not change at 6, so there is no minimum or maximum there. (The Second Derivative Test could be used at 4 but not at 0 or 6 since f'' does not exist at either of these numbers.)

Looking at the expression for $f''(x)$ and noting that $x^{4/3} \geq 0$ for all x, we have $f''(x) < 0$ for $x < 0$ and for $0 < x < 6$ and $f''(x) > 0$ for $x > 6$. So f is concave downward on $(-\infty, 0)$ and $(0, 6)$ and concave upward on $(6, \infty)$, and the only inflection point is $(6, 0)$. The graph is sketched in Figure 12. Note that the curve has vertical tangents at $(0, 0)$ and $(6, 0)$ because $|f'(x)| \to \infty$ as $x \to 0$ and as $x \to 6$. ▬

EXAMPLE 8 Use the first and second derivatives of $f(x) = e^{1/x}$, together with asymptotes, to sketch its graph.

SOLUTION Notice that the domain of f is $\{x \mid x \neq 0\}$, so we check for vertical asymptotes by computing the left and right limits as $x \to 0$. As $x \to 0^+$, we know that $t = 1/x \to \infty$, so

$$\lim_{x \to 0^+} e^{1/x} = \lim_{t \to \infty} e^t = \infty$$

and this shows that $x = 0$ is a vertical asymptote. As $x \to 0^-$, we have $t = 1/x \to -\infty$, so

$$\lim_{x \to 0^-} e^{1/x} = \lim_{t \to -\infty} e^t = 0$$

As $x \to \pm\infty$, we have $1/x \to 0$ and so

$$\lim_{x \to \pm\infty} e^{1/x} = e^0 = 1$$

This shows that $y = 1$ is a horizontal asymptote.

Now let's compute the derivative. The Chain Rule gives

$$f'(x) = -\frac{e^{1/x}}{x^2}$$

Since $e^{1/x} > 0$ and $x^2 > 0$ for all $x \neq 0$, we have $f'(x) < 0$ for all $x \neq 0$. Thus f is decreasing on $(-\infty, 0)$ and on $(0, \infty)$. There is no critical number, so the function has no

Use the differentiation rules to check these calculations.

Try reproducing the graph in Figure 12 with a graphing calculator or computer. Some machines produce the complete graph, some produce only the portion to the right of the y-axis, and some produce only the portion between $x = 0$ and $x = 6$. For an explanation and cure, see Example 7 in Section 1.4. An equivalent expression that gives the correct graph is

$$y = (x^2)^{1/3} \cdot \frac{6 - x}{|6 - x|} |6 - x|^{1/3}$$

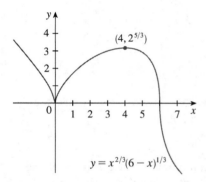

$$y = x^{2/3}(6 - x)^{1/3}$$

FIGURE 12

TEC In Module 4.3 you can practice using information about f', f'', and asymptotes to determine the shape of the graph of f.

local maximum or minimum. The second derivative is

$$f''(x) = -\frac{x^2 e^{1/x}(-1/x^2) - e^{1/x}(2x)}{x^4} = \frac{e^{1/x}(2x + 1)}{x^4}$$

Since $e^{1/x} > 0$ and $x^4 > 0$, we have $f''(x) > 0$ when $x > -\frac{1}{2}$ $(x \neq 0)$ and $f''(x) < 0$ when $x < -\frac{1}{2}$. So the curve is concave downward on $\left(-\infty, -\frac{1}{2}\right)$ and concave upward on $\left(-\frac{1}{2}, 0\right)$ and on $(0, \infty)$. The inflection point is $\left(-\frac{1}{2}, e^{-2}\right)$.

To sketch the graph of f we first draw the horizontal asymptote $y = 1$ (as a dashed line), together with the parts of the curve near the asymptotes in a preliminary sketch [Figure 13(a)]. These parts reflect the information concerning limits and the fact that f is decreasing on both $(-\infty, 0)$ and $(0, \infty)$. Notice that we have indicated that $f(x) \to 0$ as $x \to 0^-$ even though $f(0)$ does not exist. In Figure 13(b) we finish the sketch by incorporating the information concerning concavity and the inflection point. In Figure 13(c) we check our work with a graphing device.

(a) Preliminary sketch

(b) Finished sketch

(c) Computer confirmation

FIGURE 13

4.3 Exercises

1–2 Use the given graph of f to find the following.
(a) The open intervals on which f is increasing.
(b) The open intervals on which f is decreasing.
(c) The open intervals on which f is concave upward.
(d) The open intervals on which f is concave downward.
(e) The coordinates of the points of inflection.

1.

2.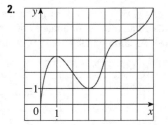

3. Suppose you are given a formula for a function f.
(a) How do you determine where f is increasing or decreasing?

(b) How do you determine where the graph of f is concave upward or concave downward?
(c) How do you locate inflection points?

4. (a) State the First Derivative Test.
(b) State the Second Derivative Test. Under what circumstances is it inconclusive? What do you do if it fails?

5–6 The graph of the *derivative* f' of a function f is shown.
(a) On what intervals is f increasing or decreasing?
(b) At what values of x does f have a local maximum or minimum?

5.

6.

⊞ Graphing calculator or computer required   CAS Computer algebra system required   **1.** Homework Hints available at stewartcalculus.com

7. In each part state the x-coordinates of the inflection points of f. Give reasons for your answers.
   (a) The curve is the graph of f.
   (b) The curve is the graph of f'.
   (c) The curve is the graph of f''.

8. The graph of the first derivative f' of a function f is shown.
   (a) On what intervals is f increasing? Explain.
   (b) At what values of x does f have a local maximum or minimum? Explain.
   (c) On what intervals is f concave upward or concave downward? Explain.
   (d) What are the x-coordinates of the inflection points of f? Why?

9–18
(a) Find the intervals on which f is increasing or decreasing.
(b) Find the local maximum and minimum values of f.
(c) Find the intervals of concavity and the inflection points.

9. $f(x) = 2x^3 + 3x^2 - 36x$

10. $f(x) = 4x^3 + 3x^2 - 6x + 1$

11. $f(x) = x^4 - 2x^2 + 3$ 12. $f(x) = \dfrac{x^2}{x^2 + 3}$

13. $f(x) = \sin x + \cos x, \quad 0 \le x \le 2\pi$

14. $f(x) = \cos^2 x - 2\sin x, \quad 0 \le x \le 2\pi$

15. $f(x) = e^{2x} + e^{-x}$ 16. $f(x) = x^2 \ln x$

17. $f(x) = x^2 - x - \ln x$ 18. $f(x) = \sqrt{x}\, e^{-x}$

19–21 Find the local maximum and minimum values of f using both the First and Second Derivative Tests. Which method do you prefer?

19. $f(x) = x^5 - 5x + 3$ 20. $f(x) = \dfrac{x^2}{x - 1}$

21. $f(x) = \sqrt{x} - \sqrt[4]{x}$

22. (a) Find the critical numbers of $f(x) = x^4(x - 1)^3$.
    (b) What does the Second Derivative Test tell you about the behavior of f at these critical numbers?
    (c) What does the First Derivative Test tell you?

23. Suppose f'' is continuous on $(-\infty, \infty)$.
    (a) If $f'(2) = 0$ and $f''(2) = -5$, what can you say about f?
    (b) If $f'(6) = 0$ and $f''(6) = 0$, what can you say about f?

24–29 Sketch the graph of a function that satisfies all of the given conditions.

24. Vertical asymptote $x = 0$, $\quad f'(x) > 0$ if $x < -2$,
    $f'(x) < 0$ if $x > -2$ $(x \ne 0)$,
    $f''(x) < 0$ if $x < 0$, $\quad f''(x) > 0$ if $x > 0$

25. $f'(0) = f'(2) = f'(4) = 0$,
    $f'(x) > 0$ if $x < 0$ or $2 < x < 4$,
    $f'(x) < 0$ if $0 < x < 2$ or $x > 4$,
    $f''(x) > 0$ if $1 < x < 3$, $\quad f''(x) < 0$ if $x < 1$ or $x > 3$

26. $f'(1) = f'(-1) = 0$, $\quad f'(x) < 0$ if $|x| < 1$,
    $f'(x) > 0$ if $1 < |x| < 2$, $\quad f'(x) = -1$ if $|x| > 2$,
    $f''(x) < 0$ if $-2 < x < 0$, $\quad$ inflection point $(0, 1)$

27. $f'(x) > 0$ if $|x| < 2$, $\quad f'(x) < 0$ if $|x| > 2$,
    $f'(-2) = 0$, $\quad \lim\limits_{x \to 2} |f'(x)| = \infty$, $\quad f''(x) > 0$ if $x \ne 2$

28. $f'(x) > 0$ if $|x| < 2$, $\quad f'(x) < 0$ if $|x| > 2$,
    $f'(2) = 0$, $\quad \lim\limits_{x \to \infty} f(x) = 1$, $\quad f(-x) = -f(x)$,
    $f''(x) < 0$ if $0 < x < 3$, $\quad f''(x) > 0$ if $x > 3$

29. $f'(x) < 0$ and $f''(x) < 0$ for all x

30. Suppose $f(3) = 2$, $f'(3) = \frac{1}{2}$, and $f'(x) > 0$ and $f''(x) < 0$ for all x.
    (a) Sketch a possible graph for f.
    (b) How many solutions does the equation $f(x) = 0$ have? Why?
    (c) Is it possible that $f'(2) = \frac{1}{3}$? Why?

31–32 The graph of the derivative f' of a continuous function f is shown.
(a) On what intervals is f increasing? Decreasing?
(b) At what values of x does f have a local maximum? Local minimum?
(c) On what intervals is f concave upward? Concave downward?
(d) State the x-coordinate(s) of the point(s) of inflection.
(e) Assuming that $f(0) = 0$, sketch a graph of f.

31.

32.

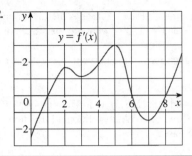

33–44
(a) Find the intervals of increase or decrease.
(b) Find the local maximum and minimum values.
(c) Find the intervals of concavity and the inflection points.
(d) Use the information from parts (a)–(c) to sketch the graph. Check your work with a graphing device if you have one.

33. $f(x) = 2x^3 - 3x^2 - 12x$

34. $f(x) = 2 + 3x - x^3$

35. $f(x) = 2 + 2x^2 - x^4$

36. $g(x) = 200 + 8x^3 + x^4$

37. $h(x) = (x + 1)^5 - 5x - 2$

38. $h(x) = 5x^3 - 3x^5$

39. $F(x) = x\sqrt{6 - x}$

40. $G(x) = 5x^{2/3} - 2x^{5/3}$

41. $C(x) = x^{1/3}(x + 4)$

42. $f(x) = \ln(x^4 + 27)$

43. $f(\theta) = 2\cos\theta + \cos^2\theta, \quad 0 \le \theta \le 2\pi$

44. $S(x) = x - \sin x, \quad 0 \le x \le 4\pi$

45–52
(a) Find the vertical and horizontal asymptotes.
(b) Find the intervals of increase or decrease.
(c) Find the local maximum and minimum values.
(d) Find the intervals of concavity and the inflection points.
(e) Use the information from parts (a)–(d) to sketch the graph of f.

45. $f(x) = 1 + \dfrac{1}{x} - \dfrac{1}{x^2}$

46. $f(x) = \dfrac{x^2 - 4}{x^2 + 4}$

47. $f(x) = \sqrt{x^2 + 1} - x$

48. $f(x) = \dfrac{e^x}{1 - e^x}$

49. $f(x) = e^{-x^2}$

50. $f(x) = x - \frac{1}{6}x^2 - \frac{2}{3}\ln x$

51. $f(x) = \ln(1 - \ln x)$

52. $f(x) = e^{\arctan x}$

53. Suppose the derivative of a function f is
$f'(x) = (x + 1)^2(x - 3)^5(x - 6)^4$. On what interval is f increasing?

54. Use the methods of this section to sketch the curve
$y = x^3 - 3a^2x + 2a^3$, where a is a positive constant. What do the members of this family of curves have in common? How do they differ from each other?

55–56
(a) Use a graph of f to estimate the maximum and minimum values. Then find the exact values.
(b) Estimate the value of x at which f increases most rapidly. Then find the exact value.

55. $f(x) = \dfrac{x + 1}{\sqrt{x^2 + 1}}$

56. $f(x) = x^2 e^{-x}$

57–58
(a) Use a graph of f to give a rough estimate of the intervals of concavity and the coordinates of the points of inflection.
(b) Use a graph of f'' to give better estimates.

57. $f(x) = \cos x + \frac{1}{2}\cos 2x, \quad 0 \le x \le 2\pi$

58. $f(x) = x^3(x - 2)^4$

CAS 59–60 Estimate the intervals of concavity to one decimal place by using a computer algebra system to compute and graph f''.

59. $f(x) = \dfrac{x^4 + x^3 + 1}{\sqrt{x^2 + x + 1}}$

60. $f(x) = \dfrac{x^2 \tan^{-1}x}{1 + x^3}$

61. A graph of a population of yeast cells in a new laboratory culture as a function of time is shown.
(a) Describe how the rate of population increase varies.
(b) When is this rate highest?
(c) On what intervals is the population function concave upward or downward?
(d) Estimate the coordinates of the inflection point.

62. Let $f(t)$ be the temperature at time t where you live and suppose that at time $t = 3$ you feel uncomfortably hot. How do you feel about the given data in each case?
(a) $f'(3) = 2, \quad f''(3) = 4$
(b) $f'(3) = 2, \quad f''(3) = -4$
(c) $f'(3) = -2, \quad f''(3) = 4$
(d) $f'(3) = -2, \quad f''(3) = -4$

63. Let $K(t)$ be a measure of the knowledge you gain by studying for a test for t hours. Which do you think is larger, $K(8) - K(7)$ or $K(3) - K(2)$? Is the graph of K concave upward or concave downward? Why?

64. Coffee is being poured into the mug shown in the figure at a constant rate (measured in volume per unit time). Sketch a rough graph of the depth of the coffee in the mug as a function of time. Account for the shape of the graph in terms of concavity. What is the significance of the inflection point?

65. A *drug response curve* describes the level of medication in the bloodstream after a drug is administered. A surge function $S(t) = At^p e^{-kt}$ is often used to model the response curve, reflecting an initial surge in the drug level and then a more gradual decline. If, for a particular drug, $A = 0.01$, $p = 4$, $k = 0.07$, and t is measured in minutes, estimate the times corresponding to the inflection points and explain their significance. If you have a graphing device, use it to graph the drug response curve.

66. The family of bell-shaped curves

$$y = \frac{1}{\sigma\sqrt{2\pi}} e^{-(x-\mu)^2/(2\sigma^2)}$$

occurs in probability and statistics, where it is called the *normal density function*. The constant μ is called the *mean* and the positive constant σ is called the *standard deviation*. For simplicity, let's scale the function so as to remove the factor $1/(\sigma\sqrt{2\pi})$ and let's analyze the special case where $\mu = 0$. So we study the function

$$f(x) = e^{-x^2/(2\sigma^2)}$$

(a) Find the asymptote, maximum value, and inflection points of f.
(b) What role does σ play in the shape of the curve?
(c) Illustrate by graphing four members of this family on the same screen.

67. Find a cubic function $f(x) = ax^3 + bx^2 + cx + d$ that has a local maximum value of 3 at $x = -2$ and a local minimum value of 0 at $x = 1$.

68. For what values of the numbers a and b does the function

$$f(x) = axe^{bx^2}$$

have the maximum value $f(2) = 1$?

69. (a) If the function $f(x) = x^3 + ax^2 + bx$ has the local minimum value $-\frac{2}{9}\sqrt{3}$ at $x = 1/\sqrt{3}$, what are the values of a and b?
(b) Which of the tangent lines to the curve in part (a) has the smallest slope?

70. For what values of a and b is $(2, 2.5)$ an inflection point of the curve $x^2y + ax + by = 0$? What additional inflection points does the curve have?

71. Show that the curve $y = (1 + x)/(1 + x^2)$ has three points of inflection and they all lie on one straight line.

72. Show that the curves $y = e^{-x}$ and $y = -e^{-x}$ touch the curve $y = e^{-x}\sin x$ at its inflection points.

73. Show that the inflection points of the curve $y = x\sin x$ lie on the curve $y^2(x^2 + 4) = 4x^2$.

74–76 Assume that all of the functions are twice differentiable and the second derivatives are never 0.

74. (a) If f and g are concave upward on I, show that $f + g$ is concave upward on I.
(b) If f is positive and concave upward on I, show that the function $g(x) = [f(x)]^2$ is concave upward on I.

75. (a) If f and g are positive, increasing, concave upward functions on I, show that the product function fg is concave upward on I.
(b) Show that part (a) remains true if f and g are both decreasing.
(c) Suppose f is increasing and g is decreasing. Show, by giving three examples, that fg may be concave upward, concave downward, or linear. Why doesn't the argument in parts (a) and (b) work in this case?

76. Suppose f and g are both concave upward on $(-\infty, \infty)$. Under what condition on f will the composite function $h(x) = f(g(x))$ be concave upward?

77. Show that $\tan x > x$ for $0 < x < \pi/2$. [*Hint:* Show that $f(x) = \tan x - x$ is increasing on $(0, \pi/2)$.]

78. (a) Show that $e^x \geq 1 + x$ for $x \geq 0$.
(b) Deduce that $e^x \geq 1 + x + \frac{1}{2}x^2$ for $x \geq 0$.
(c) Use mathematical induction to prove that for $x \geq 0$ and any positive integer n,

$$e^x \geq 1 + x + \frac{x^2}{2!} + \cdots + \frac{x^n}{n!}$$

79. Show that a cubic function (a third-degree polynomial) always has exactly one point of inflection. If its graph has three x-intercepts x_1, x_2, and x_3, show that the x-coordinate of the inflection point is $(x_1 + x_2 + x_3)/3$.

80. For what values of c does the polynomial
$P(x) = x^4 + cx^3 + x^2$ have two inflection points? One
inflection point? None? Illustrate by graphing P for several
values of c. How does the graph change as c decreases?

81. Prove that if $(c, f(c))$ is a point of inflection of the graph
of f and f'' exists in an open interval that contains c, then
$f''(c) = 0$.   [*Hint:* Apply the First Derivative Test and
Fermat's Theorem to the function $g = f'$.]

82. Show that if $f(x) = x^4$, then $f''(0) = 0$, but $(0, 0)$ is not an
inflection point of the graph of f.

83. Show that the function $g(x) = x|x|$ has an inflection point at
$(0, 0)$ but $g''(0)$ does not exist.

84. Suppose that f''' is continuous and $f'(c) = f''(c) = 0$, but
$f'''(c) > 0$. Does f have a local maximum or minimum at c?
Does f have a point of inflection at c?

85. Suppose f is differentiable on an interval I and $f'(x) > 0$ for
all numbers x in I except for a single number c. Prove that f
is increasing on the entire interval I.

86. For what values of c is the function
$$f(x) = cx + \frac{1}{x^2 + 3}$$
increasing on $(-\infty, \infty)$?

87. The three cases in the First Derivative Test cover the
situations one commonly encounters but do not exhaust all
possibilities. Consider the functions f, g, and h whose values
at 0 are all 0 and, for $x \neq 0$,

$$f(x) = x^4 \sin \frac{1}{x} \qquad g(x) = x^4 \left(2 + \sin \frac{1}{x} \right)$$

$$h(x) = x^4 \left(-2 + \sin \frac{1}{x} \right)$$

(a) Show that 0 is a critical number of all three functions but
their derivatives change sign infinitely often on both sides
of 0.

(b) Show that f has neither a local maximum nor a local minimum at 0, g has a local minimum, and h has a local
maximum.

4.4 Indeterminate Forms and l'Hospital's Rule

Suppose we are trying to analyze the behavior of the function

$$F(x) = \frac{\ln x}{x - 1}$$

Although F is not defined when $x = 1$, we need to know how F behaves *near* 1. In particular, we would like to know the value of the limit

$$\boxed{1} \qquad \lim_{x \to 1} \frac{\ln x}{x - 1}$$

In computing this limit we can't apply Law 5 of limits (the limit of a quotient is the quotient of the limits, see Section 2.3) because the limit of the denominator is 0. In fact,
although the limit in $\boxed{1}$ exists, its value is not obvious because both numerator and
denominator approach 0 and $\frac{0}{0}$ is not defined.

In general, if we have a limit of the form

$$\lim_{x \to a} \frac{f(x)}{g(x)}$$

where both $f(x) \to 0$ and $g(x) \to 0$ as $x \to a$, then this limit may or may not exist and is
called an **indeterminate form of type $\frac{0}{0}$**. We met some limits of this type in Chapter 2. For
rational functions, we can cancel common factors:

$$\lim_{x \to 1} \frac{x^2 - x}{x^2 - 1} = \lim_{x \to 1} \frac{x(x - 1)}{(x + 1)(x - 1)} = \lim_{x \to 1} \frac{x}{x + 1} = \frac{1}{2}$$

We used a geometric argument to show that

$$\lim_{x \to 0} \frac{\sin x}{x} = 1$$

But these methods do not work for limits such as $\boxed{1}$, so in this section we introduce a systematic method, known as *l'Hospital's Rule,* for the evaluation of indeterminate forms.

Another situation in which a limit is not obvious occurs when we look for a horizontal asymptote of F and need to evaluate the limit

$$\boxed{2} \qquad\qquad \lim_{x \to \infty} \frac{\ln x}{x - 1}$$

It isn't obvious how to evaluate this limit because both numerator and denominator become large as $x \to \infty$. There is a struggle between numerator and denominator. If the numerator wins, the limit will be ∞; if the denominator wins, the answer will be 0. Or there may be some compromise, in which case the answer will be some finite positive number.

In general, if we have a limit of the form

$$\lim_{x \to a} \frac{f(x)}{g(x)}$$

where both $f(x) \to \infty$ (or $-\infty$) and $g(x) \to \infty$ (or $-\infty$), then the limit may or may not exist and is called an **indeterminate form of type** ∞/∞. We saw in Section 2.6 that this type of limit can be evaluated for certain functions, including rational functions, by dividing numerator and denominator by the highest power of x that occurs in the denominator. For instance,

$$\lim_{x \to \infty} \frac{x^2 - 1}{2x^2 + 1} = \lim_{x \to \infty} \frac{1 - \dfrac{1}{x^2}}{2 + \dfrac{1}{x^2}} = \frac{1 - 0}{2 + 0} = \frac{1}{2}$$

This method does not work for limits such as $\boxed{2}$, but l'Hospital's Rule also applies to this type of indeterminate form.

FIGURE 1

Figure 1 suggests visually why l'Hospital's Rule might be true. The first graph shows two differentiable functions f and g, each of which approaches 0 as $x \to a$. If we were to zoom in toward the point $(a, 0)$, the graphs would start to look almost linear. But if the functions actually *were* linear, as in the second graph, then their ratio would be

$$\frac{m_1(x - a)}{m_2(x - a)} = \frac{m_1}{m_2}$$

which is the ratio of their derivatives. This suggests that

$$\lim_{x \to a} \frac{f(x)}{g(x)} = \lim_{x \to a} \frac{f'(x)}{g'(x)}$$

L'Hospital's Rule   Suppose f and g are differentiable and $g'(x) \neq 0$ on an open interval I that contains a (except possibly at a). Suppose that

$$\lim_{x \to a} f(x) = 0 \qquad \text{and} \qquad \lim_{x \to a} g(x) = 0$$

or that

$$\lim_{x \to a} f(x) = \pm\infty \qquad \text{and} \qquad \lim_{x \to a} g(x) = \pm\infty$$

(In other words, we have an indeterminate form of type $\frac{0}{0}$ or ∞/∞.) Then

$$\lim_{x \to a} \frac{f(x)}{g(x)} = \lim_{x \to a} \frac{f'(x)}{g'(x)}$$

if the limit on the right side exists (or is ∞ or $-\infty$).

NOTE 1 L'Hospital's Rule says that the limit of a quotient of functions is equal to the limit of the quotient of their derivatives, provided that the given conditions are satisfied. It is especially important to verify the conditions regarding the limits of f and g before using l'Hospital's Rule.

L'Hospital

L'Hospital's Rule is named after a French nobleman, the Marquis de l'Hospital (1661–1704), but was discovered by a Swiss mathematician, John Bernoulli (1667–1748). You might sometimes see l'Hospital spelled as l'Hôpital, but he spelled his own name l'Hospital, as was common in the 17th century. See Exercise 81 for the example that the Marquis used to illustrate his rule. See the project on page 310 for further historical details.

NOTE 2 L'Hospital's Rule is also valid for one-sided limits and for limits at infinity or negative infinity; that is, "$x \to a$" can be replaced by any of the symbols $x \to a^+$, $x \to a^-$, $x \to \infty$, or $x \to -\infty$.

NOTE 3 For the special case in which $f(a) = g(a) = 0$, f' and g' are continuous, and $g'(a) \neq 0$, it is easy to see why l'Hospital's Rule is true. In fact, using the alternative form of the definition of a derivative, we have

$$\lim_{x \to a} \frac{f'(x)}{g'(x)} = \frac{f'(a)}{g'(a)} = \frac{\displaystyle\lim_{x \to a} \frac{f(x) - f(a)}{x - a}}{\displaystyle\lim_{x \to a} \frac{g(x) - g(a)}{x - a}} = \lim_{x \to a} \frac{\dfrac{f(x) - f(a)}{x - a}}{\dfrac{g(x) - g(a)}{x - a}}$$

$$= \lim_{x \to a} \frac{f(x) - f(a)}{g(x) - g(a)} = \lim_{x \to a} \frac{f(x)}{g(x)}$$

It is more difficult to prove the general version of l'Hospital's Rule. See Appendix F.

V EXAMPLE 1 Find $\displaystyle\lim_{x \to 1} \frac{\ln x}{x - 1}$.

SOLUTION Since

$$\lim_{x \to 1} \ln x = \ln 1 = 0 \qquad \text{and} \qquad \lim_{x \to 1} (x - 1) = 0$$

we can apply l'Hospital's Rule:

⊘ Notice that when using l'Hospital's Rule we differentiate the numerator and denominator *separately*. We do *not* use the Quotient Rule.

$$\lim_{x \to 1} \frac{\ln x}{x - 1} = \lim_{x \to 1} \frac{\dfrac{d}{dx} (\ln x)}{\dfrac{d}{dx} (x - 1)} = \lim_{x \to 1} \frac{1/x}{1}$$

$$= \lim_{x \to 1} \frac{1}{x} = 1$$

V EXAMPLE 2 Calculate $\displaystyle\lim_{x \to \infty} \frac{e^x}{x^2}$.

The graph of the function of Example 2 is shown in Figure 2. We have noticed previously that exponential functions grow far more rapidly than power functions, so the result of Example 2 is not unexpected. See also Exercise 71.

SOLUTION We have $\lim_{x \to \infty} e^x = \infty$ and $\lim_{x \to \infty} x^2 = \infty$, so l'Hospital's Rule gives

$$\lim_{x \to \infty} \frac{e^x}{x^2} = \lim_{x \to \infty} \frac{\dfrac{d}{dx} (e^x)}{\dfrac{d}{dx} (x^2)} = \lim_{x \to \infty} \frac{e^x}{2x}$$

Since $e^x \to \infty$ and $2x \to \infty$ as $x \to \infty$, the limit on the right side is also indeterminate, but a second application of l'Hospital's Rule gives

$$\lim_{x \to \infty} \frac{e^x}{x^2} = \lim_{x \to \infty} \frac{e^x}{2x} = \lim_{x \to \infty} \frac{e^x}{2} = \infty$$

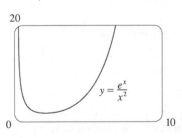

FIGURE 2

The graph of the function of Example 3 is shown in Figure 3. We have discussed previously the slow growth of logarithms, so it isn't surprising that this ratio approaches 0 as $x \to \infty$. See also Exercise 72.

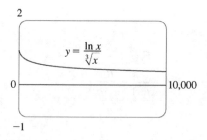

FIGURE 3

The graph in Figure 4 gives visual confirmation of the result of Example 4. If we were to zoom in too far, however, we would get an inaccurate graph because $\tan x$ is close to x when x is small. See Exercise 44(d) in Section 2.2.

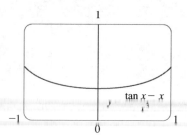

FIGURE 4

V **EXAMPLE 3** Calculate $\lim\limits_{x \to \infty} \dfrac{\ln x}{\sqrt[3]{x}}$.

SOLUTION Since $\ln x \to \infty$ and $\sqrt[3]{x} \to \infty$ as $x \to \infty$, l'Hospital's Rule applies:

$$\lim_{x \to \infty} \frac{\ln x}{\sqrt[3]{x}} = \lim_{x \to \infty} \frac{1/x}{\frac{1}{3}x^{-2/3}}$$

Notice that the limit on the right side is now indeterminate of type $\frac{0}{0}$. But instead of applying l'Hospital's Rule a second time as we did in Example 2, we simplify the expression and see that a second application is unnecessary:

$$\lim_{x \to \infty} \frac{\ln x}{\sqrt[3]{x}} = \lim_{x \to \infty} \frac{1/x}{\frac{1}{3}x^{-2/3}} = \lim_{x \to \infty} \frac{3}{\sqrt[3]{x}} = 0$$

EXAMPLE 4 Find $\lim\limits_{x \to 0} \dfrac{\tan x - x}{x^3}$. (See Exercise 44 in Section 2.2.)

SOLUTION Noting that both $\tan x - x \to 0$ and $x^3 \to 0$ as $x \to 0$, we use l'Hospital's Rule:

$$\lim_{x \to 0} \frac{\tan x - x}{x^3} = \lim_{x \to 0} \frac{\sec^2 x - 1}{3x^2}$$

Since the limit on the right side is still indeterminate of type $\frac{0}{0}$, we apply l'Hospital's Rule again:

$$\lim_{x \to 0} \frac{\sec^2 x - 1}{3x^2} = \lim_{x \to 0} \frac{2\sec^2 x \tan x}{6x}$$

Because $\lim_{x \to 0} \sec^2 x = 1$, we simplify the calculation by writing

$$\lim_{x \to 0} \frac{2\sec^2 x \tan x}{6x} = \frac{1}{3}\lim_{x \to 0} \sec^2 x \cdot \lim_{x \to 0} \frac{\tan x}{x} = \frac{1}{3}\lim_{x \to 0} \frac{\tan x}{x}$$

We can evaluate this last limit either by using l'Hospital's Rule a third time or by writing $\tan x$ as $(\sin x)/(\cos x)$ and making use of our knowledge of trigonometric limits. Putting together all the steps, we get

$$\lim_{x \to 0} \frac{\tan x - x}{x^3} = \lim_{x \to 0} \frac{\sec^2 x - 1}{3x^2} = \lim_{x \to 0} \frac{2\sec^2 x \tan x}{6x}$$

$$= \frac{1}{3}\lim_{x \to 0} \frac{\tan x}{x} = \frac{1}{3}\lim_{x \to 0} \frac{\sec^2 x}{1} = \frac{1}{3}$$

V **EXAMPLE 5** Find $\lim\limits_{x \to \pi^-} \dfrac{\sin x}{1 - \cos x}$.

SOLUTION If we blindly attempted to use l'Hospital's Rule, we would get

$$\lim_{x \to \pi^-} \frac{\sin x}{1 - \cos x} = \lim_{x \to \pi^-} \frac{\cos x}{\sin x} = -\infty$$

This is **wrong**! Although the numerator $\sin x \to 0$ as $x \to \pi^-$, notice that the denominator $(1 - \cos x)$ does not approach 0, so l'Hospital's Rule can't be applied here.

The required limit is, in fact, easy to find because the function is continuous at π and the denominator is nonzero there:

$$\lim_{x \to \pi^-} \frac{\sin x}{1 - \cos x} = \frac{\sin \pi}{1 - \cos \pi} = \frac{0}{1 - (-1)} = 0$$

Example 5 shows what can go wrong if you use l'Hospital's Rule without thinking. Other limits *can* be found using l'Hospital's Rule but are more easily found by other methods. (See Examples 3 and 5 in Section 2.3, Example 3 in Section 2.6, and the discussion at the beginning of this section.) So when evaluating any limit, you should consider other methods before using l'Hospital's Rule.

Indeterminate Products

If $\lim_{x \to a} f(x) = 0$ and $\lim_{x \to a} g(x) = \infty$ (or $-\infty$), then it isn't clear what the value of $\lim_{x \to a} [f(x) g(x)]$, if any, will be. There is a struggle between f and g. If f wins, the answer will be 0; if g wins, the answer will be ∞ (or $-\infty$). Or there may be a compromise where the answer is a finite nonzero number. This kind of limit is called an **indeterminate form of type $0 \cdot \infty$**. We can deal with it by writing the product fg as a quotient:

$$fg = \frac{f}{1/g} \qquad \text{or} \qquad fg = \frac{g}{1/f}$$

This converts the given limit into an indeterminate form of type $\frac{0}{0}$ or ∞/∞ so that we can use l'Hospital's Rule.

V **EXAMPLE 6** Evaluate $\lim_{x \to 0^+} x \ln x$.

SOLUTION The given limit is indeterminate because, as $x \to 0^+$, the first factor (x) approaches 0 while the second factor ($\ln x$) approaches $-\infty$. Writing $x = 1/(1/x)$, we have $1/x \to \infty$ as $x \to 0^+$, so l'Hospital's Rule gives

$$\lim_{x \to 0^+} x \ln x = \lim_{x \to 0^+} \frac{\ln x}{1/x} = \lim_{x \to 0^+} \frac{1/x}{-1/x^2} = \lim_{x \to 0^+} (-x) = 0$$

NOTE In solving Example 6 another possible option would have been to write

$$\lim_{x \to 0^+} x \ln x = \lim_{x \to 0^+} \frac{x}{1/\ln x}$$

This gives an indeterminate form of the type 0/0, but if we apply l'Hospital's Rule we get a more complicated expression than the one we started with. In general, when we rewrite an indeterminate product, we try to choose the option that leads to the simpler limit.

Indeterminate Differences

If $\lim_{x \to a} f(x) = \infty$ and $\lim_{x \to a} g(x) = \infty$, then the limit

$$\lim_{x \to a} [f(x) - g(x)]$$

is called an **indeterminate form of type $\infty - \infty$**. Again there is a contest between f and g. Will the answer be ∞ (f wins) or will it be $-\infty$ (g wins) or will they compromise on a finite

Figure 5 shows the graph of the function in Example 6. Notice that the function is undefined at $x = 0$; the graph approaches the origin but never quite reaches it.

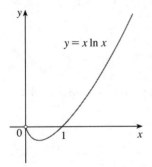

FIGURE 5

number? To find out, we try to convert the difference into a quotient (for instance, by using a common denominator, or rationalization, or factoring out a common factor) so that we have an indeterminate form of type $\frac{0}{0}$ or ∞/∞.

EXAMPLE 7 Compute $\lim_{x \to (\pi/2)^-} (\sec x - \tan x)$.

SOLUTION First notice that $\sec x \to \infty$ and $\tan x \to \infty$ as $x \to (\pi/2)^-$, so the limit is indeterminate. Here we use a common denominator:

$$\lim_{x \to (\pi/2)^-} (\sec x - \tan x) = \lim_{x \to (\pi/2)^-} \left(\frac{1}{\cos x} - \frac{\sin x}{\cos x} \right)$$

$$= \lim_{x \to (\pi/2)^-} \frac{1 - \sin x}{\cos x} = \lim_{x \to (\pi/2)^-} \frac{-\cos x}{-\sin x} = 0$$

Note that the use of l'Hospital's Rule is justified because $1 - \sin x \to 0$ and $\cos x \to 0$ as $x \to (\pi/2)^-$.

Indeterminate Powers

Several indeterminate forms arise from the limit

$$\lim_{x \to a} [f(x)]^{g(x)}$$

1. $\lim_{x \to a} f(x) = 0$ and $\lim_{x \to a} g(x) = 0$ type 0^0

2. $\lim_{x \to a} f(x) = \infty$ and $\lim_{x \to a} g(x) = 0$ type ∞^0

3. $\lim_{x \to a} f(x) = 1$ and $\lim_{x \to a} g(x) = \pm\infty$ type 1^∞

Although forms of the type 0^0, ∞^0, and 1^∞ are indeterminate, the form 0^∞ is not indeterminate. (See Exercise 84.)

Each of these three cases can be treated either by taking the natural logarithm:

$$\text{let} \quad y = [f(x)]^{g(x)}, \quad \text{then} \quad \ln y = g(x) \ln f(x)$$

or by writing the function as an exponential:

$$[f(x)]^{g(x)} = e^{g(x) \ln f(x)}$$

(Recall that both of these methods were used in differentiating such functions.) In either method we are led to the indeterminate product $g(x) \ln f(x)$, which is of type $0 \cdot \infty$.

EXAMPLE 8 Calculate $\lim_{x \to 0^+} (1 + \sin 4x)^{\cot x}$.

SOLUTION First notice that as $x \to 0^+$, we have $1 + \sin 4x \to 1$ and $\cot x \to \infty$, so the given limit is indeterminate. Let

$$y = (1 + \sin 4x)^{\cot x}$$

Then $\ln y = \ln[(1 + \sin 4x)^{\cot x}] = \cot x \ln(1 + \sin 4x)$

so l'Hospital's Rule gives

$$\lim_{x \to 0^+} \ln y = \lim_{x \to 0^+} \frac{\ln(1 + \sin 4x)}{\tan x} = \lim_{x \to 0^+} \frac{\dfrac{4 \cos 4x}{1 + \sin 4x}}{\sec^2 x} = 4$$

So far we have computed the limit of ln y, but what we want is the limit of y. To find this we use the fact that $y = e^{\ln y}$:

$$\lim_{x \to 0^+} (1 + \sin 4x)^{\cot x} = \lim_{x \to 0^+} y = \lim_{x \to 0^+} e^{\ln y} = e^4$$

V **EXAMPLE 9** Find $\lim_{x \to 0^+} x^x$.

SOLUTION Notice that this limit is indeterminate since $0^x = 0$ for any $x > 0$ but $x^0 = 1$ for any $x \neq 0$. We could proceed as in Example 8 or by writing the function as an exponential:

$$x^x = (e^{\ln x})^x = e^{x \ln x}$$

In Example 6 we used l'Hospital's Rule to show that

$$\lim_{x \to 0^+} x \ln x = 0$$

The graph of the function $y = x^x$, $x > 0$, is shown in Figure 6. Notice that although 0^0 is not defined, the values of the function approach 1 as $x \to 0^+$. This confirms the result of Example 9.

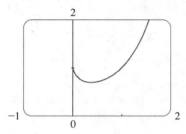

FIGURE 6

Therefore

$$\lim_{x \to 0^+} x^x = \lim_{x \to 0^+} e^{x \ln x} = e^0 = 1$$

4.4 Exercises

1–4 Given that

$$\lim_{x \to a} f(x) = 0 \qquad \lim_{x \to a} g(x) = 0 \qquad \lim_{x \to a} h(x) = 1$$

$$\lim_{x \to a} p(x) = \infty \qquad \lim_{x \to a} q(x) = \infty$$

which of the following limits are indeterminate forms? For those that are not an indeterminate form, evaluate the limit where possible.

1. (a) $\lim_{x \to a} \dfrac{f(x)}{g(x)}$ (b) $\lim_{x \to a} \dfrac{f(x)}{p(x)}$ (c) $\lim_{x \to a} \dfrac{h(x)}{p(x)}$

(d) $\lim_{x \to a} \dfrac{p(x)}{f(x)}$ (e) $\lim_{x \to a} \dfrac{p(x)}{q(x)}$

2. (a) $\lim_{x \to a} [f(x)p(x)]$ (b) $\lim_{x \to a} [h(x)p(x)]$

(c) $\lim_{x \to a} [p(x)q(x)]$

3. (a) $\lim_{x \to a} [f(x) - p(x)]$ (b) $\lim_{x \to a} [p(x) - q(x)]$

(c) $\lim_{x \to a} [p(x) + q(x)]$

4. (a) $\lim_{x \to a} [f(x)]^{g(x)}$ (b) $\lim_{x \to a} [f(x)]^{p(x)}$ (c) $\lim_{x \to a} [h(x)]^{p(x)}$

(d) $\lim_{x \to a} [p(x)]^{f(x)}$ (e) $\lim_{x \to a} [p(x)]^{q(x)}$ (f) $\lim_{x \to a} \sqrt[q(x)]{p(x)}$

5–6 Use the graphs of f and g and their tangent lines at $(2, 0)$ to find $\lim_{x \to 2} \dfrac{f(x)}{g(x)}$.

5.

6.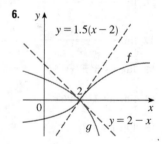

7–66 Find the limit. Use l'Hospital's Rule where appropriate. If there is a more elementary method, consider using it. If l'Hospital's Rule doesn't apply, explain why.

7. $\lim_{x \to -1} \dfrac{x^2 - 1}{x + 1}$

8. $\lim_{x \to 1} \dfrac{x^a - 1}{x^b - 1}$

9. $\lim_{x \to 1} \dfrac{x^3 - 2x^2 + 1}{x^3 - 1}$

10. $\lim_{x \to 1/2} \dfrac{6x^2 + 5x - 4}{4x^2 + 16x - 9}$

11. $\lim_{x \to (\pi/2)^+} \dfrac{\cos x}{1 - \sin x}$

12. $\lim_{x \to 0} \dfrac{\sin 4x}{\tan 5x}$

13. $\lim_{t \to 0} \dfrac{e^{2t} - 1}{\sin t}$

14. $\lim_{x \to 0} \dfrac{x^2}{1 - \cos x}$

15. $\displaystyle\lim_{\theta \to \pi/2} \frac{1 - \sin\theta}{1 + \cos 2\theta}$

16. $\displaystyle\lim_{\theta \to \pi/2} \frac{1 - \sin\theta}{\csc\theta}$

17. $\displaystyle\lim_{r \to \infty} \frac{\ln x}{\sqrt{x}}$

18. $\displaystyle\lim_{x \to 1} \frac{\ln x}{\sin \pi x}$

19. $\displaystyle\lim_{x \to 0^+} \frac{\ln x}{x}$

20. $\displaystyle\lim_{x \to \infty} \frac{\ln \ln x}{x}$

21. $\displaystyle\lim_{t \to 1} \frac{t^8 - 1}{t^5 - 1}$

22. $\displaystyle\lim_{t \to 0} \frac{8^t - 5^t}{t}$

23. $\displaystyle\lim_{x \to 0} \frac{\sqrt{1 + 2x} - \sqrt{1 - 4x}}{x}$

24. $\displaystyle\lim_{u \to \infty} \frac{e^{u/10}}{u^3}$

25. $\displaystyle\lim_{x \to 0} \frac{e^x - 1 - x}{x^2}$

26. $\displaystyle\lim_{x \to 0} \frac{\sinh x - x}{x^3}$

27. $\displaystyle\lim_{x \to 0} \frac{\tanh x}{\tan x}$

28. $\displaystyle\lim_{x \to 0} \frac{x - \sin x}{x - \tan x}$

29. $\displaystyle\lim_{x \to 0} \frac{\sin^{-1}x}{x}$

30. $\displaystyle\lim_{x \to \infty} \frac{(\ln x)^2}{x}$

31. $\displaystyle\lim_{x \to 0} \frac{x3^x}{3^x - 1}$

32. $\displaystyle\lim_{x \to 0} \frac{\cos mx - \cos nx}{x^2}$

33. $\displaystyle\lim_{x \to 0} \frac{x + \sin x}{x + \cos x}$

34. $\displaystyle\lim_{x \to 0} \frac{x}{\tan^{-1}(4x)}$

35. $\displaystyle\lim_{x \to 1} \frac{1 - x + \ln x}{1 + \cos \pi x}$

36. $\displaystyle\lim_{x \to 0^+} \frac{x^x - 1}{\ln x + x - 1}$

37. $\displaystyle\lim_{x \to 1} \frac{x^a - ax + a - 1}{(x - 1)^2}$

38. $\displaystyle\lim_{x \to 0} \frac{e^x - e^{-x} - 2x}{x - \sin x}$

39. $\displaystyle\lim_{x \to 0} \frac{\cos x - 1 + \frac{1}{2}x^2}{x^4}$

40. $\displaystyle\lim_{x \to a^+} \frac{\cos x \ln(x - a)}{\ln(e^x - e^a)}$

41. $\displaystyle\lim_{x \to \infty} x \sin(\pi/x)$

42. $\displaystyle\lim_{x \to \infty} \sqrt{x}\, e^{-x/2}$

43. $\displaystyle\lim_{x \to 0} \cot 2x \sin 6x$

44. $\displaystyle\lim_{x \to 0^+} \sin x \ln x$

45. $\displaystyle\lim_{x \to \infty} x^3 e^{-x^2}$

46. $\displaystyle\lim_{x \to \infty} x \tan(1/x)$

47. $\displaystyle\lim_{x \to 1^+} \ln x \tan(\pi x/2)$

48. $\displaystyle\lim_{x \to (\pi/2)} \cos x \sec 5x$

49. $\displaystyle\lim_{x \to 1} \left(\frac{x}{x - 1} - \frac{1}{\ln x} \right)$

50. $\displaystyle\lim_{x \to 0} (\csc x - \cot x)$

51. $\displaystyle\lim_{x \to 0^+} \left(\frac{1}{x} - \frac{1}{e^x - 1} \right)$

52. $\displaystyle\lim_{x \to 0^+} \left(\cot x - \frac{1}{x} \right)$

53. $\displaystyle\lim_{x \to \infty} (x - \ln x)$

54. $\displaystyle\lim_{x \to 1^+} [\ln(x^7 - 1) - \ln(x^5 - 1)]$

55. $\displaystyle\lim_{x \to 0^+} x^{\sqrt{x}}$

56. $\displaystyle\lim_{x \to 0^+} (\tan 2x)^x$

57. $\displaystyle\lim_{x \to 0} (1 - 2x)^{1/x}$

58. $\displaystyle\lim_{x \to \infty} \left(1 + \frac{a}{x} \right)^{bx}$

59. $\displaystyle\lim_{x \to 1^+} x^{1/(1-x)}$

60. $\displaystyle\lim_{x \to \infty} x^{(\ln 2)/(1 + \ln x)}$

61. $\displaystyle\lim_{x \to \infty} x^{1/x}$

62. $\displaystyle\lim_{x \to \infty} (e^x + x)^{1/x}$

63. $\displaystyle\lim_{x \to 0^+} (4x + 1)^{\cot x}$

64. $\displaystyle\lim_{x \to 1} (2 - x)^{\tan(\pi x/2)}$

65. $\displaystyle\lim_{x \to 0^+} (\cos x)^{1/x^2}$

66. $\displaystyle\lim_{x \to \infty} \left(\frac{2x - 3}{2x + 5} \right)^{2x+1}$

67–68 Use a graph to estimate the value of the limit. Then use l'Hospital's Rule to find the exact value.

67. $\displaystyle\lim_{x \to \infty} \left(1 + \frac{2}{x} \right)^x$

68. $\displaystyle\lim_{x \to 0} \frac{5^x - 4^x}{3^x - 2^x}$

69–70 Illustrate l'Hospital's Rule by graphing both $f(x)/g(x)$ and $f'(x)/g'(x)$ near $x = 0$ to see that these ratios have the same limit as $x \to 0$. Also, calculate the exact value of the limit.

69. $f(x) = e^x - 1, \quad g(x) = x^3 + 4x$

70. $f(x) = 2x \sin x, \quad g(x) = \sec x - 1$

---

71. Prove that
$$\lim_{x \to \infty} \frac{e^x}{x^n} = \infty$$
for any positive integer n. This shows that the exponential function approaches infinity faster than any power of x.

72. Prove that
$$\lim_{x \to \infty} \frac{\ln x}{x^p} = 0$$
for any number $p > 0$. This shows that the logarithmic function approaches ∞ more slowly than any power of x.

73–74 What happens if you try to use l'Hospital's Rule to find the limit? Evaluate the limit using another method.

73. $\displaystyle\lim_{x \to \infty} \frac{x}{\sqrt{x^2 + 1}}$

74. $\displaystyle\lim_{x \to (\pi/2)^-} \frac{\sec x}{\tan x}$

---

75. Investigate the family of curves $f(x) = e^x - cx$. In particular, find the limits as $x \to \pm\infty$ and determine the values of c for which f has an absolute minimum. What happens to the minimum points as c increases?

76. If an object with mass m is dropped from rest, one model for its speed v after t seconds, taking air resistance into account, is
$$v = \frac{mg}{c}(1 - e^{-ct/m})$$
where g is the acceleration due to gravity and c is a positive constant. (In Chapter 9 we will be able to deduce this equation from the assumption that the air resistance is proportional to the speed of the object; c is the proportionality constant.)
(a) Calculate $\lim_{t \to \infty} v$. What is the meaning of this limit?

(b) For fixed t, use l'Hospital's Rule to calculate $\lim_{c \to 0^+} v$. What can you conclude about the velocity of a falling object in a vacuum?

77. If an initial amount A_0 of money is invested at an interest rate r compounded n times a year, the value of the investment after t years is

$$A = A_0 \left(1 + \frac{r}{n} \right)^{nt}$$

If we let $n \to \infty$, we refer to the *continuous compounding* of interest. Use l'Hospital's Rule to show that if interest is compounded continuously, then the amount after t years is

$$A = A_0 e^{rt}$$

78. If a metal ball with mass m is projected in water and the force of resistance is proportional to the square of the velocity, then the distance the ball travels in time t is

$$s(t) = \frac{m}{c} \ln \cosh \sqrt{\frac{gc}{mt}}$$

where c is a positive constant. Find $\lim_{c \to 0^+} s(t)$.

79. If an electrostatic field E acts on a liquid or a gaseous polar dielectric, the net dipole moment P per unit volume is

$$P(E) = \frac{e^E + e^{-E}}{e^E - e^{-E}} - \frac{1}{E}$$

Show that $\lim_{E \to 0^+} P(E) = 0$.

80. A metal cable has radius r and is covered by insulation, so that the distance from the center of the cable to the exterior of the insulation is R. The velocity v of an electrical impulse in the cable is

$$v = -c \left(\frac{r}{R} \right)^2 \ln \left(\frac{r}{R} \right)$$

where c is a positive constant. Find the following limits and interpret your answers.

(a) $\lim\limits_{R \to r^+} v$ (b) $\lim\limits_{r \to 0^+} v$

81. The first appearance in print of l'Hospital's Rule was in the book *Analyse des Infiniment Petits* published by the Marquis de l'Hospital in 1696. This was the first calculus *textbook* ever published and the example that the Marquis used in that book to illustrate his rule was to find the limit of the function

$$y = \frac{\sqrt{2a^3 x - x^4} - a \sqrt[3]{aax}}{a - \sqrt[4]{ax^3}}$$

as x approaches a, where $a > 0$. (At that time it was common to write aa instead of a^2.) Solve this problem.

82. The figure shows a sector of a circle with central angle θ. Let $A(\theta)$ be the area of the segment between the chord PR and the arc PR. Let $B(\theta)$ be the area of the triangle PQR. Find $\lim_{\theta \to 0^+} A(\theta)/B(\theta)$.

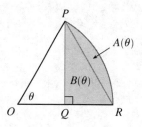

83. Evaluate $\lim\limits_{x \to \infty} \left[x - x^2 \ln \left(\frac{1 + x}{x} \right) \right]$.

84. Suppose f is a positive function. If $\lim_{x \to a} f(x) = 0$ and $\lim_{x \to a} g(x) = \infty$, show that

$$\lim_{x \to a} [f(x)]^{g(x)} = 0$$

This shows that 0^∞ is not an indeterminate form.

85. If f' is continuous, $f(2) = 0$, and $f'(2) = 7$, evaluate

$$\lim_{x \to 0} \frac{f(2 + 3x) + f(2 + 5x)}{x}$$

86. For what values of a and b is the following equation true?

$$\lim_{x \to 0} \left(\frac{\sin 2x}{x^3} + a + \frac{b}{x^2} \right) = 0$$

87. If f' is continuous, use l'Hospital's Rule to show that

$$\lim_{h \to 0} \frac{f(x + h) - f(x - h)}{2h} = f'(x)$$

Explain the meaning of this equation with the aid of a diagram.

88. If f'' is continuous, show that

$$\lim_{h \to 0} \frac{f(x + h) - 2f(x) + f(x - h)}{h^2} = f''(x)$$

89. Let

$$f(x) = \begin{cases} e^{-1/x^2} & \text{if } x \neq 0 \\ 0 & \text{if } x = 0 \end{cases}$$

(a) Use the definition of derivative to compute $f'(0)$.
(b) Show that f has derivatives of all orders that are defined on $\mathbb{R}$. [*Hint:* First show by induction that there is a polynomial $p_n(x)$ and a nonnegative integer k_n such that $f^{(n)}(x) = p_n(x)f(x)/x^{k_n}$ for $x \neq 0$.]

90. Let

$$f(x) = \begin{cases} |x|^x & \text{if } x \neq 0 \\ 1 & \text{if } x = 0 \end{cases}$$

(a) Show that f is continuous at 0.
(b) Investigate graphically whether f is differentiable at 0 by zooming in several times toward the point $(0, 1)$ on the graph of f.
(c) Show that f is not differentiable at 0. How can you reconcile this fact with the appearance of the graphs in part (b)?

WRITING PROJECT   THE ORIGINS OF L'HOSPITAL'S RULE

www.stewartcalculus.com

The Internet is another source of information for this project. Click on *History of Mathematics* for a list of reliable websites.

L'Hospital's Rule was first published in 1696 in the Marquis de l'Hospital's calculus textbook *Analyse des Infiniment Petits,* but the rule was discovered in 1694 by the Swiss mathematician John (Johann) Bernoulli. The explanation is that these two mathematicians had entered into a curious business arrangement whereby the Marquis de l'Hospital bought the rights to Bernoulli's mathematical discoveries. The details, including a translation of l'Hospital's letter to Bernoulli proposing the arrangement, can be found in the book by Eves [1].

Write a report on the historical and mathematical origins of l'Hospital's Rule. Start by providing brief biographical details of both men (the dictionary edited by Gillispie [2] is a good source) and outline the business deal between them. Then give l'Hospital's statement of his rule, which is found in Struik's sourcebook [4] and more briefly in the book of Katz [3]. Notice that l'Hospital and Bernoulli formulated the rule geometrically and gave the answer in terms of differentials. Compare their statement with the version of l'Hospital's Rule given in Section 4.4 and show that the two statements are essentially the same.

1. Howard Eves, *In Mathematical Circles (Volume 2: Quadrants III and IV)* (Boston: Prindle, Weber and Schmidt, 1969), pp. 20–22.

2. C. C. Gillispie, ed., *Dictionary of Scientific Biography* (New York: Scribner's, 1974). See the article on Johann Bernoulli by E. A. Fellmann and J. O. Fleckenstein in Volume II and the article on the Marquis de l'Hospital by Abraham Robinson in Volume VIII.

3. Victor Katz, *A History of Mathematics: An Introduction* (New York: HarperCollins, 1993), p. 484.

4. D. J. Struik, ed., *A Sourcebook in Mathematics, 1200–1800* (Princeton, NJ: Princeton University Press, 1969), pp. 315–316.

4.5 Summary of Curve Sketching

FIGURE 1

FIGURE 2

So far we have been concerned with some particular aspects of curve sketching: domain, range, and symmetry in Chapter 1; limits, continuity, and asymptotes in Chapter 2; derivatives and tangents in Chapters 2 and 3; and extreme values, intervals of increase and decrease, concavity, points of inflection, and l'Hospital's Rule in this chapter. It is now time to put all of this information together to sketch graphs that reveal the important features of functions.

You might ask: Why don't we just use a graphing calculator or computer to graph a curve? Why do we need to use calculus?

It's true that modern technology is capable of producing very accurate graphs. But even the best graphing devices have to be used intelligently. We saw in Section 1.4 that it is extremely important to choose an appropriate viewing rectangle to avoid getting a misleading graph. (See especially Examples 1, 3, 4, and 5 in that section.) The use of calculus enables us to discover the most interesting aspects of graphs and in many cases to calculate maximum and minimum points and inflection points *exactly* instead of approximately.

For instance, Figure 1 shows the graph of $f(x) = 8x^3 - 21x^2 + 18x + 2$. At first glance it seems reasonable: It has the same shape as cubic curves like $y = x^3$, and it appears to have no maximum or minimum point. But if you compute the derivative, you will see that there is a maximum when $x = 0.75$ and a minimum when $x = 1$. Indeed, if we zoom in to this portion of the graph, we see that behavior exhibited in Figure 2. Without calculus, we could easily have overlooked it.

In the next section we will graph functions by using the interaction between calculus and graphing devices. In this section we draw graphs by first considering the following information. We don't assume that you have a graphing device, but if you do have one you should use it as a check on your work.

▮ Guidelines for Sketching a Curve

The following checklist is intended as a guide to sketching a curve $y = f(x)$ by hand. Not every item is relevant to every function. (For instance, a given curve might not have an asymptote or possess symmetry.) But the guidelines provide all the information you need to make a sketch that displays the most important aspects of the function.

A. Domain It's often useful to start by determining the domain D of f, that is, the set of values of x for which $f(x)$ is defined.

B. Intercepts The y-intercept is $f(0)$ and this tells us where the curve intersects the y-axis. To find the x-intercepts, we set $y = 0$ and solve for x. (You can omit this step if the equation is difficult to solve.)

C. Symmetry

(i) If $f(-x) = f(x)$ for all x in D, that is, the equation of the curve is unchanged when x is replaced by $-x$, then f is an **even function** and the curve is symmetric about the y-axis. This means that our work is cut in half. If we know what the curve looks like for $x \geqslant 0$, then we need only reflect about the y-axis to obtain the complete curve [see Figure 3(a)]. Here are some examples: $y = x^2$, $y = x^4$, $y = |x|$, and $y = \cos x$.

(ii) If $f(-x) = -f(x)$ for all x in D, then f is an **odd function** and the curve is symmetric about the origin. Again we can obtain the complete curve if we know what it looks like for $x \geqslant 0$. [Rotate $180°$ about the origin; see Figure 3(b).] Some simple examples of odd functions are $y = x$, $y = x^3$, $y = x^5$, and $y = \sin x$.

(iii) If $f(x + p) = f(x)$ for all x in D, where p is a positive constant, then f is called a **periodic function** and the smallest such number p is called the **period.** For instance, $y = \sin x$ has period 2π and $y = \tan x$ has period π. If we know what the graph looks like in an interval of length p, then we can use translation to sketch the entire graph (see Figure 4).

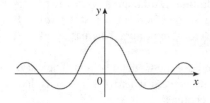

(a) Even function: reflectional symmetry

(b) Odd function: rotational symmetry

FIGURE 3

FIGURE 4
Periodic function:
translational symmetry

D. Asymptotes

(i) *Horizontal Asymptotes.* Recall from Section 2.6 that if either $\lim_{x \to \infty} f(x) = L$ or $\lim_{x \to -\infty} f(x) = L$, then the line $y = L$ is a horizontal asymptote of the curve $y = f(x)$. If it turns out that $\lim_{x \to \infty} f(x) = \infty$ (or $-\infty$), then we do not have an asymptote to the right, but that is still useful information for sketching the curve.

(ii) *Vertical Asymptotes.* Recall from Section 2.2 that the line $x = a$ is a vertical asymptote if at least one of the following statements is true:

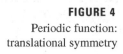

$$\lim_{x \to a^+} f(x) = \infty \qquad \lim_{x \to a^-} f(x) = \infty$$

$$\lim_{x \to a^+} f(x) = -\infty \qquad \lim_{x \to a^-} f(x) = -\infty$$

(For rational functions you can locate the vertical asymptotes by equating the denominator to 0 after canceling any common factors. But for other functions this method does not apply.) Furthermore, in sketching the curve it is very useful to know exactly which of the statements in $\boxed{1}$ is true. If $f(a)$ is not defined but a is an endpoint of the domain of f, then you should compute $\lim_{x \to a^-} f(x)$ or $\lim_{x \to a^+} f(x)$, whether or not this limit is infinite.

(iii) *Slant Asymptotes.*   These are discussed at the end of this section.

E. Intervals of Increase or Decrease   Use the I/D Test. Compute $f'(x)$ and find the intervals on which $f'(x)$ is positive (f is increasing) and the intervals on which $f'(x)$ is negative (f is decreasing).

F. Local Maximum and Minimum Values   Find the critical numbers of f [the numbers c where $f'(c) = 0$ or $f'(c)$ does not exist]. Then use the First Derivative Test. If f' changes from positive to negative at a critical number c, then $f(c)$ is a local maximum. If f' changes from negative to positive at c, then $f(c)$ is a local minimum. Although it is usually preferable to use the First Derivative Test, you can use the Second Derivative Test if $f'(c) = 0$ and $f''(c) \neq 0$. Then $f''(c) > 0$ implies that $f(c)$ is a local minimum, whereas $f''(c) < 0$ implies that $f(c)$ is a local maximum.

G. Concavity and Points of Inflection   Compute $f''(x)$ and use the Concavity Test. The curve is concave upward where $f''(x) > 0$ and concave downward where $f''(x) < 0$. Inflection points occur where the direction of concavity changes.

H. Sketch the Curve   Using the information in items A–G, draw the graph. Sketch the asymptotes as dashed lines. Plot the intercepts, maximum and minimum points, and inflection points. Then make the curve pass through these points, rising and falling according to E, with concavity according to G, and approaching the asymptotes. If additional accuracy is desired near any point, you can compute the value of the derivative there. The tangent indicates the direction in which the curve proceeds.

V $\boxed{\text{EXAMPLE 1}}$ Use the guidelines to sketch the curve $y = \dfrac{2x^2}{x^2 - 1}$.

A. The domain is

$$\{x \mid x^2 - 1 \neq 0\} = \{x \mid x \neq \pm 1\} = (-\infty, -1) \cup (-1, 1) \cup (1, \infty)$$

B. The x- and y-intercepts are both 0.

C. Since $f(-x) = f(x)$, the function f is even. The curve is symmetric about the y-axis.

D.
$$\lim_{x \to \pm\infty} \frac{2x^2}{x^2 - 1} = \lim_{x \to \pm\infty} \frac{2}{1 - 1/x^2} = 2$$

Therefore the line $y = 2$ is a horizontal asymptote.

Since the denominator is 0 when $x = \pm 1$, we compute the following limits:

$$\lim_{x \to 1^+} \frac{2x^2}{x^2 - 1} = \infty \qquad \lim_{x \to 1^-} \frac{2x^2}{x^2 - 1} = -\infty$$

$$\lim_{x \to -1^+} \frac{2x^2}{x^2 - 1} = -\infty \qquad \lim_{x \to -1^-} \frac{2x^2}{x^2 - 1} = \infty$$

Therefore the lines $x = 1$ and $x = -1$ are vertical asymptotes. This information about limits and asymptotes enables us to draw the preliminary sketch in Figure 5, showing the parts of the curve near the asymptotes.

FIGURE 5

Preliminary sketch

We have shown the curve approaching its horizontal asymptote from above in Figure 5. This is confirmed by the intervals of increase and decrease.

E.
$$f'(x) = \frac{(x^2 - 1)(4x) - 2x^2 \cdot 2x}{(x^2 - 1)^2} = \frac{-4x}{(x^2 - 1)^2}$$

Since $f'(x) > 0$ when $x < 0$ $(x \neq -1)$ and $f'(x) < 0$ when $x > 0$ $(x \neq 1)$, f is increasing on $(-\infty, -1)$ and $(-1, 0)$ and decreasing on $(0, 1)$ and $(1, \infty)$.

F. The only critical number is $x = 0$. Since f' changes from positive to negative at 0, $f(0) = 0$ is a local maximum by the First Derivative Test.

G.
$$f''(x) = \frac{(x^2 - 1)^2(-4) + 4x \cdot 2(x^2 - 1)2x}{(x^2 - 1)^4} = \frac{12x^2 + 4}{(x^2 - 1)^3}$$

Since $12x^2 + 4 > 0$ for all x, we have

$$f''(x) > 0 \iff x^2 - 1 > 0 \iff |x| > 1$$

and $f''(x) < 0 \iff |x| < 1$. Thus the curve is concave upward on the intervals $(-\infty, -1)$ and $(1, \infty)$ and concave downward on $(-1, 1)$. It has no point of inflection since 1 and -1 are not in the domain of f.

H. Using the information in E–G, we finish the sketch in Figure 6.

FIGURE 6
Finished sketch of $y = \dfrac{2x^2}{x^2 - 1}$

EXAMPLE 2 Sketch the graph of $f(x) = \dfrac{x^2}{\sqrt{x + 1}}$.

A. Domain $= \{x \mid x + 1 > 0\} = \{x \mid x > -1\} = (-1, \infty)$

B. The x- and y-intercepts are both 0.

C. Symmetry: None

D. Since
$$\lim_{x \to \infty} \frac{x^2}{\sqrt{x + 1}} = \infty$$

there is no horizontal asymptote. Since $\sqrt{x + 1} \to 0$ as $x \to -1^+$ and $f(x)$ is always positive, we have

$$\lim_{x \to -1^+} \frac{x^2}{\sqrt{x + 1}} = \infty$$

and so the line $x = -1$ is a vertical asymptote.

E.
$$f'(x) = \frac{2x\sqrt{x + 1} - x^2 \cdot 1/(2\sqrt{x + 1})}{x + 1} = \frac{x(3x + 4)}{2(x + 1)^{3/2}}$$

We see that $f'(x) = 0$ when $x = 0$ $\left(\text{notice that } -\frac{4}{3} \text{ is not in the domain of } f\right)$, so the only critical number is 0. Since $f'(x) < 0$ when $-1 < x < 0$ and $f'(x) > 0$ when $x > 0$, f is decreasing on $(-1, 0)$ and increasing on $(0, \infty)$.

F. Since $f'(0) = 0$ and f' changes from negative to positive at 0, $f(0) = 0$ is a local (and absolute) minimum by the First Derivative Test.

G.
$$f''(x) = \frac{2(x + 1)^{3/2}(6x + 4) - (3x^2 + 4x)3(x + 1)^{1/2}}{4(x + 1)^3} = \frac{3x^2 + 8x + 8}{4(x + 1)^{5/2}}$$

Note that the denominator is always positive. The numerator is the quadratic $3x^2 + 8x + 8$, which is always positive because its discriminant is $b^2 - 4ac = -32$, which is negative, and the coefficient of x^2 is positive. Thus $f''(x) > 0$ for all x in the domain of f, which means that f is concave upward on $(-1, \infty)$ and there is no point of inflection.

H. The curve is sketched in Figure 7.

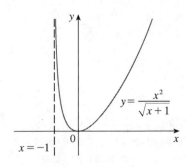

$$y = \frac{x^2}{\sqrt{x + 1}}$$

FIGURE 7

V **EXAMPLE 3** Sketch the graph of $f(x) = xe^x$.

A. The domain is $\mathbb{R}$.

B. The x- and y-intercepts are both 0.

C. Symmetry: None

D. Because both x and e^x become large as $x \to \infty$, we have $\lim_{x\to\infty} xe^x = \infty$. As $x \to -\infty$, however, $e^x \to 0$ and so we have an indeterminate product that requires the use of l'Hospital's Rule:

$$\lim_{x\to-\infty} xe^x = \lim_{x\to-\infty} \frac{x}{e^{-x}} = \lim_{x\to-\infty} \frac{1}{-e^{-x}} = \lim_{x\to-\infty} (-e^x) = 0$$

Thus the x-axis is a horizontal asymptote.

E. $$f'(x) = xe^x + e^x = (x + 1)e^x$$

Since e^x is always positive, we see that $f'(x) > 0$ when $x + 1 > 0$, and $f'(x) < 0$ when $x + 1 < 0$. So f is increasing on $(-1, \infty)$ and decreasing on $(-\infty, -1)$.

F. Because $f'(-1) = 0$ and f' changes from negative to positive at $x = -1$, $f(-1) = -e^{-1}$ is a local (and absolute) minimum.

G. $$f''(x) = (x + 1)e^x + e^x = (x + 2)e^x$$

Since $f''(x) > 0$ if $x > -2$ and $f''(x) < 0$ if $x < -2$, f is concave upward on $(-2, \infty)$ and concave downward on $(-\infty, -2)$. The inflection point is $(-2, -2e^{-2})$.

H. We use this information to sketch the curve in Figure 8.

FIGURE 8

EXAMPLE 4 Sketch the graph of $f(x) = \dfrac{\cos x}{2 + \sin x}$.

A. The domain is $\mathbb{R}$.

B. The y-intercept is $f(0) = \frac{1}{2}$. The x-intercepts occur when $\cos x = 0$, that is, $x = (2n + 1)\pi/2$, where n is an integer.

C. f is neither even nor odd, but $f(x + 2\pi) = f(x)$ for all x and so f is periodic and has period 2π. Thus, in what follows, we need to consider only $0 \le x \le 2\pi$ and then extend the curve by translation in part H.

D. Asymptotes: None

E. $$f'(x) = \frac{(2 + \sin x)(-\sin x) - \cos x\,(\cos x)}{(2 + \sin x)^2} = -\frac{2\sin x + 1}{(2 + \sin x)^2}$$

Thus $f'(x) > 0$ when $2\sin x + 1 < 0 \iff \sin x < -\frac{1}{2} \iff 7\pi/6 < x < 11\pi/6$. So f is increasing on $(7\pi/6, 11\pi/6)$ and decreasing on $(0, 7\pi/6)$ and $(11\pi/6, 2\pi)$.

F. From part E and the First Derivative Test, we see that the local minimum value is $f(7\pi/6) = -1/\sqrt{3}$ and the local maximum value is $f(11\pi/6) = 1/\sqrt{3}$.

G. If we use the Quotient Rule again and simplify, we get

$$f''(x) = -\frac{2\cos x\,(1 - \sin x)}{(2 + \sin x)^3}$$

Because $(2 + \sin x)^3 > 0$ and $1 - \sin x \ge 0$ for all x, we know that $f''(x) > 0$ when $\cos x < 0$, that is, $\pi/2 < x < 3\pi/2$. So f is concave upward on $(\pi/2, 3\pi/2)$ and concave downward on $(0, \pi/2)$ and $(3\pi/2, 2\pi)$. The inflection points are $(\pi/2, 0)$ and $(3\pi/2, 0)$.

H. The graph of the function restricted to $0 \leqslant x \leqslant 2\pi$ is shown in Figure 9. Then we extend it, using periodicity, to the complete graph in Figure 10.

FIGURE 9

FIGURE 10

EXAMPLE 5 Sketch the graph of $y = \ln(4 - x^2)$.

A. The domain is

$$\{x \mid 4 - x^2 > 0\} = \{x \mid x^2 < 4\} = \{x \mid |x| < 2\} = (-2, 2)$$

B. The y-intercept is $f(0) = \ln 4$. To find the x-intercept we set

$$y = \ln(4 - x^2) = 0$$

We know that $\ln 1 = 0$, so we have $4 - x^2 = 1 \Rightarrow x^2 = 3$ and therefore the x-intercepts are $\pm\sqrt{3}$.

C. Since $f(-x) = f(x)$, f is even and the curve is symmetric about the y-axis.

D. We look for vertical asymptotes at the endpoints of the domain. Since $4 - x^2 \to 0^+$ as $x \to 2^-$ and also as $x \to -2^+$, we have

$$\lim_{x \to 2^-} \ln(4 - x^2) = -\infty \qquad \lim_{x \to -2^+} \ln(4 - x^2) = -\infty$$

Thus the lines $x = 2$ and $x = -2$ are vertical asymptotes.

E.
$$f'(x) = \frac{-2x}{4 - x^2}$$

Since $f'(x) > 0$ when $-2 < x < 0$ and $f'(x) < 0$ when $0 < x < 2$, f is increasing on $(-2, 0)$ and decreasing on $(0, 2)$.

F. The only critical number is $x = 0$. Since f' changes from positive to negative at 0, $f(0) = \ln 4$ is a local maximum by the First Derivative Test.

G.
$$f''(x) = \frac{(4 - x^2)(-2) + 2x(-2x)}{(4 - x^2)^2} = \frac{-8 - 2x^2}{(4 - x^2)^2}$$

Since $f''(x) < 0$ for all x, the curve is concave downward on $(-2, 2)$ and has no inflection point.

H. Using this information, we sketch the curve in Figure 11.

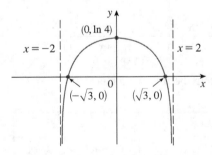

FIGURE 11
$y = \ln(4 - x^2)$

Slant Asymptotes

Some curves have asymptotes that are *oblique*, that is, neither horizontal nor vertical. If

$$\lim_{x \to \infty} [f(x) - (mx + b)] = 0$$

where $m \neq 0$, then the line $y = mx + b$ is called a **slant asymptote** because the vertical

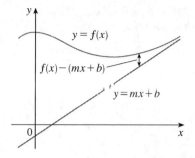

FIGURE 12

distance between the curve $y = f(x)$ and the line $y = mx + b$ approaches 0, as in Figure 12. (A similar situation exists if we let $x \to -\infty$.) For rational functions, slant asymptotes occur when the degree of the numerator is one more than the degree of the denominator. In such a case the equation of the slant asymptote can be found by long division as in the following example.

V **EXAMPLE 6** Sketch the graph of $f(x) = \dfrac{x^3}{x^2 + 1}$.

A. The domain is $\mathbb{R} = (-\infty, \infty)$.

B. The x- and y-intercepts are both 0.

C. Since $f(-x) = -f(x)$, f is odd and its graph is symmetric about the origin.

D. Since $x^2 + 1$ is never 0, there is no vertical asymptote. Since $f(x) \to \infty$ as $x \to \infty$ and $f(x) \to -\infty$ as $x \to -\infty$, there is no horizontal asymptote. But long division gives

$$f(x) = \frac{x^3}{x^2 + 1} = x - \frac{x}{x^2 + 1}$$

$$f(x) - x = -\frac{x}{x^2 + 1} = -\frac{\dfrac{1}{x}}{1 + \dfrac{1}{x^2}} \to 0 \quad \text{as} \quad x \to \pm\infty$$

So the line $y = x$ is a slant asymptote.

E.
$$f'(x) = \frac{3x^2(x^2 + 1) - x^3 \cdot 2x}{(x^2 + 1)^2} = \frac{x^2(x^2 + 3)}{(x^2 + 1)^2}$$

Since $f'(x) > 0$ for all x (except 0), f is increasing on $(-\infty, \infty)$.

F. Although $f'(0) = 0$, f' does not change sign at 0, so there is no local maximum or minimum.

G.
$$f''(x) = \frac{(4x^3 + 6x)(x^2 + 1)^2 - (x^4 + 3x^2) \cdot 2(x^2 + 1)2x}{(x^2 + 1)^4} = \frac{2x(3 - x^2)}{(x^2 + 1)^3}$$

Since $f''(x) = 0$ when $x = 0$ or $x = \pm\sqrt{3}$, we set up the following chart.

Interval	x	$3 - x^2$	$(x^2 + 1)^3$	$f''(x)$	f
$x < -\sqrt{3}$	$-$	$-$	$+$	$+$	CU on $\left(-\infty, -\sqrt{3}\right)$
$-\sqrt{3} < x < 0$	$-$	$+$	$+$	$-$	CD on $\left(-\sqrt{3}, 0\right)$
$0 < x < \sqrt{3}$	$+$	$+$	$+$	$+$	CU on $\left(0, \sqrt{3}\right)$
$x > \sqrt{3}$	$+$	$-$	$+$	$-$	CD on $\left(\sqrt{3}, \infty\right)$

The points of inflection are $\left(-\sqrt{3}, -\frac{3}{4}\sqrt{3}\right)$, $(0, 0)$, and $\left(\sqrt{3}, \frac{3}{4}\sqrt{3}\right)$.

H. The graph of f is sketched in Figure 13.

$y = \dfrac{x^3}{x^2 + 1}$

$\left(\sqrt{3}, \dfrac{3\sqrt{3}}{4}\right)$

$\left(-\sqrt{3}, \dfrac{3\sqrt{3}}{4}\right)$

inflection points

$y = x$

FIGURE 13

4.5 Exercises

1–54 Use the guidelines of this section to sketch the curve.

1. $y = x^3 + x$

2. $y = x^3 + 6x^2 + 9x$

3. $y = 2 - 15x + 9x^2 - x^3$

4. $y = 8x^2 - x^4$

5. $y = x(x - 4)^3$

6. $y = x^5 - 5x$

7. $y = \frac{1}{5}x^5 - \frac{8}{3}x^3 + 16x$

8. $y = (4 - x^2)^5$

9. $y = \dfrac{x}{x - 1}$

10. $y = \dfrac{x^2 - 4}{x^2 - 2x}$

11. $y = \dfrac{x - x^2}{2 - 3x + x^2}$

12. $y = \dfrac{x}{x^2 - 9}$

13. $y = \dfrac{1}{x^2 - 9}$

14. $y = \dfrac{x^2}{x^2 + 9}$

15. $y = \dfrac{x}{x^2 + 9}$

16. $y = 1 + \dfrac{1}{x} + \dfrac{1}{x^2}$

17. $y = \dfrac{x - 1}{x^2}$

18. $y = \dfrac{x}{x^3 - 1}$

19. $y = \dfrac{x^2}{x^2 + 3}$

20. $y = \dfrac{x^3}{x - 2}$

21. $y = (x - 3)\sqrt{x}$

22. $y = 2\sqrt{x} - x$

23. $y = \sqrt{x^2 + x - 2}$

24. $y = \sqrt{x^2 + x} - x$

25. $y = \dfrac{x}{\sqrt{x^2 + 1}}$

26. $y = x\sqrt{2 - x^2}$

27. $y = \dfrac{\sqrt{1 - x^2}}{x}$

28. $y = \dfrac{x}{\sqrt{x^2 - 1}}$

29. $y = x - 3x^{1/3}$

30. $y = x^{5/3} - 5x^{2/3}$

31. $y = \sqrt[3]{x^2 - 1}$

32. $y = \sqrt[3]{x^3 + 1}$

33. $y = \sin^3 x$

34. $y = x + \cos x$

35. $y = x \tan x, \quad -\pi/2 < x < \pi/2$

36. $y = 2x - \tan x, \quad -\pi/2 < x < \pi/2$

37. $y = \frac{1}{2}x - \sin x, \quad 0 < x < 3\pi$

38. $y = \sec x + \tan x, \quad 0 < x < \pi/2$

39. $y = \dfrac{\sin x}{1 + \cos x}$

40. $y = \dfrac{\sin x}{2 + \cos x}$

41. $y = \arctan(e^x)$

42. $y = (1 - x)e^x$

43. $y = 1/(1 + e^{-x})$

44. $y = e^{-x} \sin x, \quad 0 \le x \le 2\pi$

45. $y = x - \ln x$

46. $y = e^{2x} - e^x$

47. $y = (1 + e^x)^{-2}$

48. $y = e^x/x^2$

49. $y = \ln(\sin x)$

50. $y = \ln(x^2 - 3x + 2)$

51. $y = xe^{-1/x}$

52. $y = \dfrac{\ln x}{x^2}$

53. $y = e^{3x} + e^{-2x}$

54. $y = \tan^{-1}\left(\dfrac{x - 1}{x + 1}\right)$

---

55. In the theory of relativity, the mass of a particle is

$$m = \frac{m_0}{\sqrt{1 - v^2/c^2}}$$

where m_0 is the rest mass of the particle, m is the mass when the particle moves with speed v relative to the observer, and c is the speed of light. Sketch the graph of m as a function of v.

56. In the theory of relativity, the energy of a particle is

$$E = \sqrt{m_0^2 c^4 + h^2 c^2/\lambda^2}$$

where m_0 is the rest mass of the particle, λ is its wave length, and h is Planck's constant. Sketch the graph of E as a function of λ. What does the graph say about the energy?

57. A model for the spread of a rumor is given by the equation

$$p(t) = \frac{1}{1 + ae^{-kt}}$$

where $p(t)$ is the proportion of the population that knows the rumor at time t and a and k are positive constants.
(a) When will half the population have heard the rumor?
(b) When is the rate of spread of the rumor greatest?
(c) Sketch the graph of p.

58. A model for the concentration at time t of a drug injected into the bloodstream is

$$C(t) = K(e^{-at} - e^{-bt})$$

where a, b, and K are positive constants and $b > a$. Sketch the graph of the concentration function. What does the graph tell us about how the concentration varies as time passes?

59. The figure shows a beam of length L embedded in concrete walls. If a constant load W is distributed evenly along its length, the beam takes the shape of the deflection curve

$$y = -\frac{W}{24EI}x^4 + \frac{WL}{12EI}x^3 - \frac{WL^2}{24EI}x^2$$

where E and I are positive constants. (E is Young's modulus of elasticity and I is the moment of inertia of a cross-section of the beam.) Sketch the graph of the deflection curve.

---

1. Homework Hints available at stewartcalculus.com

60. Coulomb's Law states that the force of attraction between two charged particles is directly proportional to the product of the charges and inversely proportional to the square of the distance between them. The figure shows particles with charge 1 located at positions 0 and 2 on a coordinate line and a particle with charge -1 at a position x between them. It follows from Coulomb's Law that the net force acting on the middle particle is

$$F(x) = -\frac{k}{x^2} + \frac{k}{(x-2)^2} \qquad 0 < x < 2$$

where k is a positive constant. Sketch the graph of the net force function. What does the graph say about the force?

61–64 Find an equation of the slant asymptote. Do not sketch the curve.

61. $y = \dfrac{x^2 + 1}{x + 1}$

62. $y = \dfrac{2x^3 + x^2 + x + 3}{x^2 + 2x}$

63. $y = \dfrac{4x^3 - 2x^2 + 5}{2x^2 + x - 3}$

64. $y = \dfrac{5x^4 + x^2 + x}{x^3 - x^2 + 2}$

65–70 Use the guidelines of this section to sketch the curve. In guideline D find an equation of the slant asymptote.

65. $y = \dfrac{x^2}{x - 1}$

66. $y = \dfrac{1 + 5x - 2x^2}{x - 2}$

67. $y = \dfrac{x^3 + 4}{x^2}$

68. $y = \dfrac{x^3}{(x + 1)^2}$

69. $y = 1 + \frac{1}{2}x + e^{-x}$

70. $y = 1 - x + e^{1+x/3}$

71. Show that the curve $y = x - \tan^{-1} x$ has two slant asymptotes. $y = x + \pi/2$ and $y = x - \pi/2$. Use this fact to help sketch the curve.

72. Show that the curve $y = \sqrt{x^2 + 4x}$ has two slant asymptotes: $y = x + 2$ and $y = -x - 2$. Use this fact to help sketch the curve.

73. Show that the lines $y = (b/a)x$ and $y = -(b/a)x$ are slant asymptotes of the hyperbola $(x^2/a^2) - (y^2/b^2) = 1$.

74. Let $f(x) = (x^3 + 1)/x$. Show that

$$\lim_{x \to \pm\infty} [f(x) - x^2] = 0$$

This shows that the graph of f approaches the graph of $y = x^2$, and we say that the curve $y = f(x)$ is *asymptotic* to the parabola $y = x^2$. Use this fact to help sketch the graph of f.

75. Discuss the asymptotic behavior of $f(x) = (x^4 + 1)/x$ in the same manner as in Exercise 74. Then use your results to help sketch the graph of f.

76. Use the asymptotic behavior of $f(x) = \cos x + 1/x^2$ to sketch its graph without going through the curve-sketching procedure of this section.

4.6   Graphing with Calculus *and* Calculators

If you have not already read Section 1.4, you should do so now. In particular, it explains how to avoid some of the pitfalls of graphing devices by choosing appropriate viewing rectangles.

The method we used to sketch curves in the preceding section was a culmination of much of our study of differential calculus. The graph was the final object that we produced. In this section our point of view is completely different. Here we *start* with a graph produced by a graphing calculator or computer and then we refine it. We use calculus to make sure that we reveal all the important aspects of the curve. And with the use of graphing devices we can tackle curves that would be far too complicated to consider without technology. The theme is the *interaction* between calculus and calculators.

> **EXAMPLE 1** Graph the polynomial $f(x) = 2x^6 + 3x^5 + 3x^3 - 2x^2$. Use the graphs of f' and f'' to estimate all maximum and minimum points and intervals of concavity.

SOLUTION If we specify a domain but not a range, many graphing devices will deduce a suitable range from the values computed. Figure 1 shows the plot from one such device if we specify that $-5 \le x \le 5$. Although this viewing rectangle is useful for showing that the asymptotic behavior (or end behavior) is the same as for $y = 2x^6$, it is obviously hiding some finer detail. So we change to the viewing rectangle $[-3, 2]$ by $[-50, 100]$ shown in Figure 2.

FIGURE 1

FIGURE 2

From this graph it appears that there is an absolute minimum value of about −15.33 when $x \approx -1.62$ (by using the cursor) and f is decreasing on $(-\infty, -1.62)$ and increasing on $(-1.62, \infty)$. Also there appears to be a horizontal tangent at the origin and inflection points when $x = 0$ and when x is somewhere between −2 and −1.

Now let's try to confirm these impressions using calculus. We differentiate and get

$$f'(x) = 12x^5 + 15x^4 + 9x^2 - 4x$$

$$f''(x) = 60x^4 + 60x^3 + 18x - 4$$

When we graph f' in Figure 3 we see that $f'(x)$ changes from negative to positive when $x \approx -1.62$; this confirms (by the First Derivative Test) the minimum value that we found earlier. But, perhaps to our surprise, we also notice that $f'(x)$ changes from positive to negative when $x = 0$ and from negative to positive when $x \approx 0.35$. This means that f has a local maximum at 0 and a local minimum when $x \approx 0.35$, but these were hidden in Figure 2. Indeed, if we now zoom in toward the origin in Figure 4, we see what we missed before: a local maximum value of 0 when $x = 0$ and a local minimum value of about −0.1 when $x \approx 0.35$.

FIGURE 3

FIGURE 4

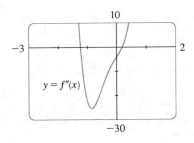

FIGURE 5

What about concavity and inflection points? From Figures 2 and 4 there appear to be inflection points when x is a little to the left of −1 and when x is a little to the right of 0. But it's difficult to determine inflection points from the graph of f, so we graph the second derivative f'' in Figure 5. We see that f'' changes from positive to negative when $x \approx -1.23$ and from negative to positive when $x \approx 0.19$. So, correct to two decimal places, f is concave upward on $(-\infty, -1.23)$ and $(0.19, \infty)$ and concave downward on $(-1.23, 0.19)$. The inflection points are $(-1.23, -10.18)$ and $(0.19, -0.05)$.

We have discovered that no single graph reveals all the important features of this polynomial. But Figures 2 and 4, when taken together, do provide an accurate picture.

V **EXAMPLE 2** Draw the graph of the function

$$f(x) = \frac{x^2 + 7x + 3}{x^2}$$

in a viewing rectangle that contains all the important features of the function. Estimate the maximum and minimum values and the intervals of concavity. Then use calculus to find these quantities exactly.

SOLUTION Figure 6, produced by a computer with automatic scaling, is a disaster. Some graphing calculators use $[-10, 10]$ by $[-10, 10]$ as the default viewing rectangle, so let's try it. We get the graph shown in Figure 7; it's a major improvement.

FIGURE 6

FIGURE 7

FIGURE 8

The y-axis appears to be a vertical asymptote and indeed it is because

$$\lim_{x \to 0} \frac{x^2 + 7x + 3}{x^2} = \infty$$

Figure 7 also allows us to estimate the x-intercepts: about -0.5 and -6.5. The exact values are obtained by using the quadratic formula to solve the equation $x^2 + 7x + 3 = 0$; we get $x = (-7 \pm \sqrt{37})/2$.

To get a better look at horizontal asymptotes, we change to the viewing rectangle $[-20, 20]$ by $[-5, 10]$ in Figure 8. It appears that $y = 1$ is the horizontal asymptote and this is easily confirmed:

$$\lim_{x \to \pm\infty} \frac{x^2 + 7x + 3}{x^2} = \lim_{x \to \pm\infty} \left(1 + \frac{7}{x} + \frac{3}{x^2}\right) = 1$$

To estimate the minimum value we zoom in to the viewing rectangle $[-3, 0]$ by $[-4, 2]$ in Figure 9. The cursor indicates that the absolute minimum value is about -3.1 when $x \approx -0.9$, and we see that the function decreases on $(-\infty, -0.9)$ and $(0, \infty)$ and increases on $(-0.9, 0)$. The exact values are obtained by differentiating:

$$f'(x) = -\frac{7}{x^2} - \frac{6}{x^3} = -\frac{7x + 6}{x^3}$$

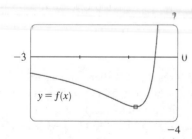

FIGURE 9

This shows that $f'(x) > 0$ when $-\frac{6}{7} < x < 0$ and $f'(x) < 0$ when $x < -\frac{6}{7}$ and when $x > 0$. The exact minimum value is $f\left(-\frac{6}{7}\right) = -\frac{37}{12} \approx -3.08$.

Figure 9 also shows that an inflection point occurs somewhere between $x = -1$ and $x = -2$. We could estimate it much more accurately using the graph of the second derivative, but in this case it's just as easy to find exact values. Since

$$f''(x) = \frac{14}{x^3} + \frac{18}{x^4} = \frac{2(7x + 9)}{x^4}$$

we see that $f''(x) > 0$ when $x > -\frac{9}{7}$ $(x \neq 0)$. So f is concave upward on $\left(-\frac{9}{7}, 0\right)$ and $(0, \infty)$ and concave downward on $\left(-\infty, -\frac{9}{7}\right)$. The inflection point is $\left(-\frac{9}{7}, -\frac{71}{27}\right)$.

The analysis using the first two derivatives shows that Figure 8 displays all the major aspects of the curve.

V **EXAMPLE 3** Graph the function $f(x) = \dfrac{x^2(x+1)^3}{(x-2)^2(x-4)^4}$.

SOLUTION Drawing on our experience with a rational function in Example 2, let's start by graphing f in the viewing rectangle $[-10, 10]$ by $[-10, 10]$. From Figure 10 we have the feeling that we are going to have to zoom in to see some finer detail and also zoom out to see the larger picture. But, as a guide to intelligent zooming, let's first take a close look at the expression for $f(x)$. Because of the factors $(x-2)^2$ and $(x-4)^4$ in the denominator, we expect $x = 2$ and $x = 4$ to be the vertical asymptotes. Indeed

$$\lim_{x \to 2} \frac{x^2(x+1)^3}{(x-2)^2(x-4)^4} = \infty \quad \text{and} \quad \lim_{x \to 4} \frac{x^2(x+1)^3}{(x-2)^2(x-4)^4} = \infty$$

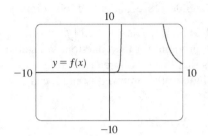

FIGURE 10

To find the horizontal asymptotes, we divide numerator and denominator by x^6:

$$\frac{x^2(x+1)^3}{(x-2)^2(x-4)^4} = \frac{\dfrac{x^2}{x^3} \cdot \dfrac{(x+1)^3}{x^3}}{\dfrac{(x-2)^2}{x^2} \cdot \dfrac{(x-4)^4}{x^4}} = \frac{\dfrac{1}{x}\left(1 + \dfrac{1}{x}\right)^3}{\left(1 - \dfrac{2}{x}\right)^2 \left(1 - \dfrac{4}{x}\right)^4}$$

This shows that $f(x) \to 0$ as $x \to \pm\infty$, so the x-axis is a horizontal asymptote.

It is also very useful to consider the behavior of the graph near the x-intercepts using an analysis like that in Example 12 in Section 2.6. Since x^2 is positive, $f(x)$ does not change sign at 0 and so its graph doesn't cross the x-axis at 0. But, because of the factor $(x+1)^3$, the graph does cross the x-axis at -1 and has a horizontal tangent there. Putting all this information together, but without using derivatives, we see that the curve has to look something like the one in Figure 11.

Now that we know what to look for, we zoom in (several times) to produce the graphs in Figures 12 and 13 and zoom out (several times) to get Figure 14.

FIGURE 11

FIGURE 12

FIGURE 13

FIGURE 14

We can read from these graphs that the absolute minimum is about -0.02 and occurs when $x \approx -20$. There is also a local maximum ≈ 0.00002 when $x \approx -0.3$ and a local minimum ≈ 211 when $x \approx 2.5$. These graphs also show three inflection points near -35, -5, and -1 and two between -1 and 0. To estimate the inflection points closely we would need to graph f'', but to compute f'' by hand is an unreasonable chore. If you have a computer algebra system, then it's easy to do (see Exercise 15).

We have seen that, for this particular function, *three* graphs (Figures 12, 13, and 14) are necessary to convey all the useful information. The only way to display all these features of the function on a single graph is to draw it by hand. Despite the exaggerations and distortions, Figure 11 does manage to summarize the essential nature of the function.

The family of functions

$$f(x) = \sin(x + \sin cx)$$

where c is a constant, occurs in applications to frequency modulation (FM) synthesis. A sine wave is modulated by a wave with a different frequency (sin cx). The case where $c = 2$ is studied in Example 4. Exercise 27 explores another special case.

FIGURE 15

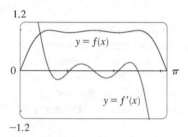

FIGURE 16

EXAMPLE 4 Graph the function $f(x) = \sin(x + \sin 2x)$. For $0 \le x \le \pi$, estimate all maximum and minimum values, intervals of increase and decrease, and inflection points.

SOLUTION We first note that f is periodic with period 2π. Also, f is odd and $|f(x)| \le 1$ for all x. So the choice of a viewing rectangle is not a problem for this function: We start with $[0, \pi]$ by $[-1.1, 1.1]$. (See Figure 15.) It appears that there are three local maximum values and two local minimum values in that window. To confirm this and locate them more accurately, we calculate that

$$f'(x) = \cos(x + \sin 2x) \cdot (1 + 2\cos 2x)$$

and graph both f and f' in Figure 16.

Using zoom-in and the First Derivative Test, we find the following approximate values:

Intervals of increase: $(0, 0.6), (1.0, 1.6), (2.1, 2.5)$

Intervals of decrease: $(0.6, 1.0), (1.6, 2.1), (2.5, \pi)$

Local maximum values: $f(0.6) \approx 1, f(1.6) \approx 1, f(2.5) \approx 1$

Local minimum values: $f(1.0) \approx 0.94, f(2.1) \approx 0.94$

The second derivative is

$$f''(x) = -(1 + 2\cos 2x)^2 \sin(x + \sin 2x) - 4\sin 2x \cos(x + \sin 2x)$$

Graphing both f and f'' in Figure 17, we obtain the following approximate values:

Concave upward on: $(0.8, 1.3), (1.8, 2.3)$

Concave downward on: $(0, 0.8), (1.3, 1.8), (2.3, \pi)$

Inflection points: $(0, 0), (0.8, 0.97), (1.3, 0.97), (1.8, 0.97), (2.3, 0.97)$

FIGURE 17

FIGURE 18

Having checked that Figure 15 does indeed represent f accurately for $0 \le x \le \pi$, we can state that the extended graph in Figure 18 represents f accurately for $-2\pi \le x \le 2\pi$.

Try to solve Equation 1 using the numerical rootfinder on your calculator or computer. Some machines are not able to solve it. Others are successful but require you to specify a starting point for the search.

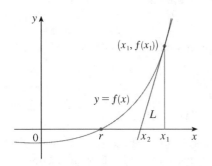

FIGURE 2

we need more accuracy we could zoom in repeatedly, but that becomes tiresome. A faster alternative is to use a numerical rootfinder on a calculator or computer algebra system. If we do so, we find that the root, correct to nine decimal places, is 0.007628603.

How do those numerical rootfinders work? They use a variety of methods, but most of them make some use of **Newton's method**, also called the **Newton-Raphson method**. We will explain how this method works, partly to show what happens inside a calculator or computer, and partly as an application of the idea of linear approximation.

The geometry behind Newton's method is shown in Figure 2, where the root that we are trying to find is labeled r. We start with a first approximation x_1, which is obtained by guessing, or from a rough sketch of the graph of f, or from a computer-generated graph of f. Consider the tangent line L to the curve $y = f(x)$ at the point $(x_1, f(x_1))$ and look at the x-intercept of L, labeled x_2. The idea behind Newton's method is that the tangent line is close to the curve and so its x-intercept, x_2, is close to the x-intercept of the curve (namely, the root r that we are seeking). Because the tangent is a line, we can easily find its x-intercept.

To find a formula for x_2 in terms of x_1 we use the fact that the slope of L is $f'(x_1)$, so its equation is

$$y - f(x_1) = f'(x_1)(x - x_1)$$

Since the x-intercept of L is x_2, we set $y = 0$ and obtain

$$0 - f(x_1) = f'(x_1)(x_2 - x_1)$$

If $f'(x_1) \neq 0$, we can solve this equation for x_2:

$$x_2 = x_1 - \frac{f(x_1)}{f'(x_1)}$$

We use x_2 as a second approximation to r.

Next we repeat this procedure with x_1 replaced by the second approximation x_2, using the tangent line at $(x_2, f(x_2))$. This gives a third approximation:

$$x_3 = x_2 - \frac{f(x_2)}{f'(x_2)}$$

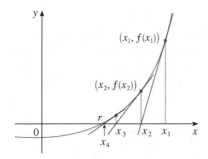

FIGURE 3

If we keep repeating this process, we obtain a sequence of approximations $x_1, x_2, x_3, x_4, \ldots$ as shown in Figure 3. In general, if the nth approximation is x_n and $f'(x_n) \neq 0$, then the next approximation is given by

Sequences were briefly introduced in *A Preview of Calculus* on page 5. A more thorough discussion starts in Section 11.1.

$$\boxed{2} \qquad \boxed{\; x_{n+1} = x_n - \frac{f(x_n)}{f'(x_n)} \;}$$

If the numbers x_n become closer and closer to r as n becomes large, then we say that the sequence *converges* to r and we write

$$\lim_{n \to \infty} x_n = r$$

⊘ Although the sequence of successive approximations converges to the desired root for functions of the type illustrated in Figure 3, in certain circumstances the sequence may not

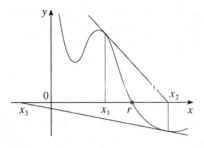

FIGURE 4

TEC In Module 4.8 you can investigate how Newton's Method works for several functions and what happens when you change x_1.

Figure 5 shows the geometry behind the first step in Newton's method in Example 1. Since $f'(2) = 10$, the tangent line to $y = x^3 - 2x - 5$ at $(2, -1)$ has equation $y = 10x - 21$ so its x-intercept is $x_2 = 2.1$.

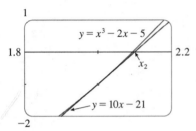

FIGURE 5

converge. For example, consider the situation shown in Figure 4. You can see that x_2 is a worse approximation than x_1. This is likely to be the case when $f'(x_1)$ is close to 0. It might even happen that an approximation (such as x_3 in Figure 4) falls outside the domain of f. Then Newton's method fails and a better initial approximation x_1 should be chosen. See Exercises 31–34 for specific examples in which Newton's method works very slowly or does not work at all.

V **EXAMPLE 1**   Starting with $x_1 = 2$, find the third approximation x_3 to the root of the equation $x^3 - 2x - 5 = 0$.

SOLUTION   We apply Newton's method with

$$f(x) = x^3 - 2x - 5 \quad \text{and} \quad f'(x) = 3x^2 - 2$$

Newton himself used this equation to illustrate his method and he chose $x_1 = 2$ after some experimentation because $f(1) = -6$, $f(2) = -1$, and $f(3) = 16$. Equation 2 becomes

$$x_{n+1} = x_n - \frac{x_n^3 - 2x_n - 5}{3x_n^2 - 2}$$

With $n = 1$ we have

$$x_2 = x_1 - \frac{x_1^3 - 2x_1 - 5}{3x_1^2 - 2}$$

$$= 2 - \frac{2^3 - 2(2) - 5}{3(2)^2 - 2} = 2.1$$

Then with $n = 2$ we obtain

$$x_3 = x_2 - \frac{x_2^3 - 2x_2 - 5}{3x_2^2 - 2} = 2.1 - \frac{(2.1)^3 - 2(2.1) - 5}{3(2.1)^2 - 2} \approx 2.0946$$

It turns out that this third approximation $x_3 \approx 2.0946$ is accurate to four decimal places.

Suppose that we want to achieve a given accuracy, say to eight decimal places, using Newton's method. How do we know when to stop? The rule of thumb that is generally used is that we can stop when successive approximations x_n and x_{n+1} agree to eight decimal places. (A precise statement concerning accuracy in Newton's method will be given in Exercise 39 in Section 11.11.)

Notice that the procedure in going from n to $n + 1$ is the same for all values of n. (It is called an *iterative* process.) This means that Newton's method is particularly convenient for use with a programmable calculator or a computer.

V **EXAMPLE 2**   Use Newton's method to find $\sqrt[6]{2}$ correct to eight decimal places.

SOLUTION   First we observe that finding $\sqrt[6]{2}$ is equivalent to finding the positive root of the equation

$$x^6 - 2 = 0$$

so we take $f(x) = x^6 - 2$. Then $f'(x) = 6x^5$ and Formula 2 (Newton's method) becomes

$$x_{n+1} = x_n - \frac{x_n^6 - 2}{6x_n^5}$$

If we choose $x_1 = 1$ as the initial approximation, then we obtain

$$x_2 \approx 1.16666667$$
$$x_3 \approx 1.12644368$$
$$x_4 \approx 1.12249707$$
$$x_5 \approx 1.12246205$$
$$x_6 \approx 1.12246205$$

Since x_5 and x_6 agree to eight decimal places, we conclude that

$$\sqrt[6]{2} \approx 1.12246205$$

to eight decimal places.

V **EXAMPLE 3** Find, correct to six decimal places, the root of the equation $\cos x = x$.

SOLUTION   We first rewrite the equation in standard form:

$$\cos x - x = 0$$

Therefore we let $f(x) = \cos x - x$. Then $f'(x) = -\sin x - 1$, so Formula 2 becomes

$$x_{n+1} = x_n - \frac{\cos x_n - x_n}{-\sin x_n - 1} = x_n + \frac{\cos x_n - x_n}{\sin x_n + 1}$$

In order to guess a suitable value for x_1 we sketch the graphs of $y = \cos x$ and $y = x$ in Figure 6. It appears that they intersect at a point whose x-coordinate is somewhat less than 1, so let's take $x_1 = 1$ as a convenient first approximation. Then, remembering to put our calculator in radian mode, we get

$$x_2 \approx 0.75036387$$
$$x_3 \approx 0.73911289$$
$$x_4 \approx 0.73908513$$
$$x_5 \approx 0.73908513$$

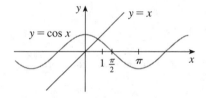

$y = \cos x$ $y = x$

FIGURE 6

Since x_4 and x_5 agree to six decimal places (eight, in fact), we conclude that the root of the equation, correct to six decimal places, is 0.739085.

Instead of using the rough sketch in Figure 6 to get a starting approximation for Newton's method in Example 3, we could have used the more accurate graph that a calculator or computer provides. Figure 7 suggests that we use $x_1 = 0.75$ as the initial approximation. Then Newton's method gives

$$x_2 \approx 0.73911114 \qquad x_3 \approx 0.73908513 \qquad x_4 \approx 0.73908513$$

and so we obtain the same answer as before, but with one fewer step.

You might wonder why we bother at all with Newton's method if a graphing device is available. Isn't it easier to zoom in repeatedly and find the roots as we did in Section 1.4? If only one or two decimal places of accuracy are required, then indeed Newton's method is inappropriate and a graphing device suffices. But if six or eight decimal places are required, then repeated zooming becomes tiresome. It is usually faster and more efficient to use a computer and Newton's method in tandem—the graphing device to get started and Newton's method to finish.

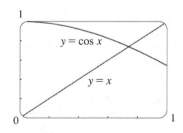

$y = \cos x$

$y = x$

FIGURE 7

4.8 **Exercises**

1. The figure shows the graph of a function f. Suppose that Newton's method is used to approximate the root r of the equation $f(x) = 0$ with initial approximation $x_1 = 1$.
   (a) Draw the tangent lines that are used to find x_2 and x_3, and estimate the numerical values of x_2 and x_3.
   (b) Would $x_1 = 5$ be a better first approximation? Explain.

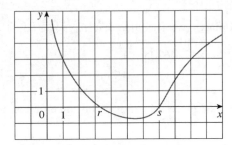

2. Follow the instructions for Exercise 1(a) but use $x_1 = 9$ as the starting approximation for finding the root s.

3. Suppose the tangent line to the curve $y = f(x)$ at the point $(2, 5)$ has the equation $y = 9 - 2x$. If Newton's method is used to locate a root of the equation $f(x) = 0$ and the initial approximation is $x_1 = 2$, find the second approximation x_2.

4. For each initial approximation, determine graphically what happens if Newton's method is used for the function whose graph is shown.
   (a) $x_1 = 0$ (b) $x_1 = 1$ (c) $x_1 = 3$
   (d) $x_1 = 4$ (e) $x_1 = 5$

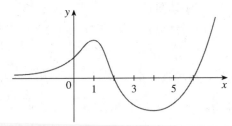

5. For which of the initial approximations $x_1 = a, b, c$, and d do you think Newton's method will work and lead to the root of the equation $f(x) = 0$?

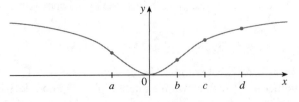

6–8 Use Newton's method with the specified initial approximation x_1 to find x_3, the third approximation to the root of the given equation. (Give your answer to four decimal places.)

6. $\frac{1}{3}x^3 + \frac{1}{2}x^2 + 3 = 0$, $x_1 = -3$

7. $x^5 - x - 1 = 0$, $x_1 = 1$ 8. $x^7 + 4 = 0$, $x_1 = -1$

 9. Use Newton's method with initial approximation $x_1 = -1$ to find x_2, the second approximation to the root of the equation $x^3 + x + 3 = 0$. Explain how the method works by first graphing the function and its tangent line at $(-1, 1)$.

10. Use Newton's method with initial approximation $x_1 = 1$ to find x_2, the second approximation to the root of the equation $x^4 - x - 1 = 0$. Explain how the method works by first graphing the function and its tangent line at $(1, -1)$.

11–12 Use Newton's method to approximate the given number correct to eight decimal places.

11. $\sqrt[5]{20}$ 12. $\sqrt[100]{100}$

13–16 Use Newton's method to approximate the indicated root of the equation correct to six decimal places.

13. The root of $x^4 - 2x^3 + 5x^2 - 6 = 0$ in the interval $[1, 2]$

14. The root of $2.2x^5 - 4.4x^3 + 1.3x^2 - 0.9x - 4.0 = 0$ in the interval $[-2, -1]$

15. The positive root of $\sin x = x^2$

16. The positive root of $2 \cos x = x^4$

17–22 Use Newton's method to find all roots of the equation correct to six decimal places.

17. $3 \cos x = x + 1$ 18. $\sqrt{x + 1} = x^2 - x$

19. $(x - 2)^2 = \ln x$ 20. $\frac{1}{x} = 1 + x^3$

21. $\cos x = \sqrt{x}$ 22. $\tan x = \sqrt{1 - x^2}$

 23–28 Use Newton's method to find all the roots of the equation correct to eight decimal places. Start by drawing a graph to find initial approximations.

23. $x^6 - x^5 - 6x^4 - x^2 + x + 10 = 0$

24. $x^5 - 3x^4 + x^3 - x^2 - x + 6 = 0$

25. $\frac{x}{x^2 + 1} = \sqrt{1 - x}$ 26. $\cos(x^2 - x) = x^4$

27. $4e^{-x^2} \sin x = x^2 - x + 1$ 28. $e^{\arctan x} = \sqrt{x^3 + 1}$

29. (a) Apply Newton's method to the equation $x^2 - a = 0$ to derive the following square-root algorithm (used by the ancient Babylonians to compute $\sqrt{a}$):
$$x_{n+1} = \frac{1}{2}\left(x_n + \frac{a}{x_n}\right)$$

(b) Use part (a) to compute $\sqrt{1000}$ correct to six decimal places.

30. (a) Apply Newton's method to the equation $1/x - a = 0$ to derive the following reciprocal algorithm:

$$x_{n+1} = 2x_n - ax_n^2$$

(This algorithm enables a computer to find reciprocals without actually dividing.)

(b) Use part (a) to compute $1/1.6984$ correct to six decimal places.

31. Explain why Newton's method doesn't work for finding the root of the equation $x^3 - 3x + 6 = 0$ if the initial approximation is chosen to be $x_1 = 1$.

32. (a) Use Newton's method with $x_1 = 1$ to find the root of the equation $x^3 - x = 1$ correct to six decimal places.

(b) Solve the equation in part (a) using $x_1 = 0.6$ as the initial approximation.

(c) Solve the equation in part (a) using $x_1 = 0.57$. (You definitely need a programmable calculator for this part.)

(d) Graph $f(x) = x^3 - x - 1$ and its tangent lines at $x_1 = 1$, 0.6, and 0.57 to explain why Newton's method is so sensitive to the value of the initial approximation.

33. Explain why Newton's method fails when applied to the equation $\sqrt[3]{x} = 0$ with any initial approximation $x_1 \neq 0$. Illustrate your explanation with a sketch.

34. If

$$f(x) = \begin{cases} \sqrt{x} & \text{if } x \geq 0 \\ -\sqrt{-x} & \text{if } x < 0 \end{cases}$$

then the root of the equation $f(x) = 0$ is $x = 0$. Explain why Newton's method fails to find the root no matter which initial approximation $x_1 \neq 0$ is used. Illustrate your explanation with a sketch.

35. (a) Use Newton's method to find the critical numbers of the function $f(x) = x^6 - x^4 + 3x^3 - 2x$ correct to six decimal places.

(b) Find the absolute minimum value of f correct to four decimal places.

36. Use Newton's method to find the absolute maximum value of the function $f(x) = x \cos x$, $0 \leq x \leq \pi$, correct to six decimal places.

37. Use Newton's method to find the coordinates of the inflection point of the curve $y = x^2 \sin x$, $0 \leq x \leq \pi$, correct to six decimal places.

38. Of the infinitely many lines that are tangent to the curve $y = -\sin x$ and pass through the origin, there is one that has the largest slope. Use Newton's method to find the slope of that line correct to six decimal places.

39. Use Newton's method to find the coordinates, correct to six decimal places, of the point on the parabola $y = (x - 1)^2$ that is closest to the origin.

40. In the figure, the length of the chord AB is 4 cm and the length of the arc AB is 5 cm. Find the central angle θ, in radians, correct to four decimal places. Then give the answer to the nearest degree.

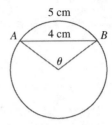

41. A car dealer sells a new car for $18,000. He also offers to sell the same car for payments of $375 per month for five years. What monthly interest rate is this dealer charging?

To solve this problem you will need to use the formula for the present value A of an annuity consisting of n equal payments of size R with interest rate i per time period:

$$A = \frac{R}{i}[1 - (1 + i)^{-n}]$$

Replacing i by x, show that

$$48x(1 + x)^{60} - (1 + x)^{60} + 1 = 0$$

Use Newton's method to solve this equation.

42. The figure shows the sun located at the origin and the earth at the point $(1, 0)$. (The unit here is the distance between the centers of the earth and the sun, called an *astronomical unit:* 1 AU $\approx 1.496 \times 10^8$ km.) There are five locations L_1, L_2, L_3, L_4, and L_5 in this plane of rotation of the earth about the sun where a satellite remains motionless with respect to the earth because the forces acting on the satellite (including the gravitational attractions of the earth and the sun) balance each other. These locations are called *libration points.* (A solar research satellite has been placed at one of these libration points.) If m_1 is the mass of the sun, m_2 is the mass of the earth, and $r = m_2/(m_1 + m_2)$, it turns out that the x-coordinate of L_1 is the unique root of the fifth-degree equation

$$p(x) = x^5 - (2 + r)x^4 + (1 + 2r)x^3 - (1 - r)x^2$$
$$+ 2(1 - r)x + r - 1 = 0$$

and the x-coordinate of L_2 is the root of the equation

$$p(x) - 2rx^2 = 0$$

Using the value $r \approx 3.04042 \times 10^{-6}$, find the locations of the libration points (a) L_1 and (b) L_2.

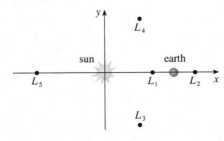

4.9   Antiderivatives

A physicist who knows the velocity of a particle might wish to know its position at a given time. An engineer who can measure the variable rate at which water is leaking from a tank wants to know the amount leaked over a certain time period. A biologist who knows the rate at which a bacteria population is increasing might want to deduce what the size of the population will be at some future time. In each case, the problem is to find a function F whose derivative is a known function f. If such a function F exists, it is called an *antiderivative* of f.

> **Definition**   A function F is called an **antiderivative** of f on an interval I if $F'(x) = f(x)$ for all x in I.

For instance, let $f(x) = x^2$. It isn't difficult to discover an antiderivative of f if we keep the Power Rule in mind. In fact, if $F(x) = \frac{1}{3}x^3$, then $F'(x) = x^2 = f(x)$. But the function $G(x) = \frac{1}{3}x^3 + 100$ also satisfies $G'(x) = x^2$. Therefore both F and G are antiderivatives of f. Indeed, any function of the form $H(x) = \frac{1}{3}x^3 + C$, where C is a constant, is an antiderivative of f. The question arises: Are there any others?

To answer this question, recall that in Section 4.2 we used the Mean Value Theorem to prove that if two functions have identical derivatives on an interval, then they must differ by a constant (Corollary 4.2.7). Thus if F and G are any two antiderivatives of f, then

$$F'(x) = f(x) = G'(x)$$

so $G(x) - F(x) = C$, where C is a constant. We can write this as $G(x) = F(x) + C$, so we have the following result.

> **1**   **Theorem**   If F is an antiderivative of f on an interval I, then the most general antiderivative of f on I is
> $$F(x) + C$$
> where C is an arbitrary constant.

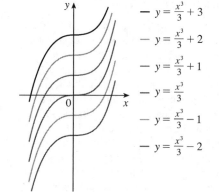

$$- \ y = \frac{x^3}{3} + 3$$

$$- \ y = \frac{x^3}{3} + 2$$

$$- \ y = \frac{x^3}{3} + 1$$

$$- \ y = \frac{x^3}{3}$$

$$- \ y = \frac{x^3}{3} - 1$$

$$- \ y = \frac{x^3}{3} - 2$$

FIGURE 1
Members of the family of
antiderivatives of $f(x) = x^2$

Going back to the function $f(x) = x^2$, we see that the general antiderivative of f is $\frac{1}{3}x^3 + C$. By assigning specific values to the constant C, we obtain a family of functions whose graphs are vertical translates of one another (see Figure 1). This makes sense because each curve must have the same slope at any given value of x.

EXAMPLE 1   Find the most general antiderivative of each of the following functions.
(a) $f(x) = \sin x$ (b) $f(x) = 1/x$ (c) $f(x) = x^n$, $n \neq -1$

SOLUTION
(a) If $F(x) = -\cos x$, then $F'(x) = \sin x$, so an antiderivative of $\sin x$ is $-\cos x$. By Theorem 1, the most general antiderivative is $G(x) = -\cos x + C$.

(b) Recall from Section 3.6 that

$$\frac{d}{dx}(\ln x) = \frac{1}{x}$$

So on the interval $(0, \infty)$ the general antiderivative of $1/x$ is $\ln x + C$. We also learned that

$$\frac{d}{dx}(\ln |x|) = \frac{1}{x}$$

for all $x \neq 0$. Theorem 1 then tells us that the general antiderivative of $f(x) = 1/x$ is $\ln |x| + C$ on any interval that doesn't contain 0. In particular, this is true on each of the intervals $(-\infty, 0)$ and $(0, \infty)$. So the general antiderivative of f is

$$F(x) = \begin{cases} \ln x + C_1 & \text{if } x > 0 \\ \ln(-x) + C_2 & \text{if } x < 0 \end{cases}$$

(c) We use the Power Rule to discover an antiderivative of x^n. In fact, if $n \neq -1$, then

$$\frac{d}{dx}\left(\frac{x^{n+1}}{n+1}\right) = \frac{(n+1)x^n}{n+1} = x^n$$

Thus the general antiderivative of $f(x) = x^n$ is

$$F(x) = \frac{x^{n+1}}{n+1} + C$$

This is valid for $n \geq 0$ since then $f(x) = x^n$ is defined on an interval. If n is negative (but $n \neq -1$), it is valid on any interval that doesn't contain 0. ■

As in Example 1, every differentiation formula, when read from right to left, gives rise to an antidifferentiation formula. In Table 2 we list some particular antiderivatives. Each formula in the table is true because the derivative of the function in the right column appears in the left column. In particular, the first formula says that the antiderivative of a constant times a function is the constant times the antiderivative of the function. The second formula says that the antiderivative of a sum is the sum of the antiderivatives. (We use the notation $F' = f, G' = g$.)

2 | **Table of Antidifferentiation Formulas**

To obtain the most general antiderivative from the particular ones in Table 2, we have to add a constant (or constants), as in Example 1.

Function	Particular antiderivative	Function	Particular antiderivative
$cf(x)$	$cF(x)$	$\sec^2 x$	$\tan x$
$f(x) + g(x)$	$F(x) + G(x)$	$\sec x \tan x$	$\sec x$
$x^n \ (n \neq -1)$	$\dfrac{x^{n+1}}{n+1}$	$\dfrac{1}{\sqrt{1-x^2}}$	$\sin^{-1} x$
$\dfrac{1}{x}$	$\ln|x|$	$\dfrac{1}{1+x^2}$	$\tan^{-1} x$
e^x	e^x	$\cosh x$	$\sinh x$
$\cos x$	$\sin x$	$\sinh x$	$\cosh x$
$\sin x$	$-\cos x$		

EXAMPLE 2 Find all functions g such that

$$g'(x) = 4 \sin x + \frac{2x^5 - \sqrt{x}}{x}$$

SOLUTION We first rewrite the given function as follows:

$$g'(x) = 4 \sin x + \frac{2x^5}{x} - \frac{\sqrt{x}}{x} = 4 \sin x + 2x^4 - \frac{1}{\sqrt{x}}$$

Thus we want to find an antiderivative of

$$g'(x) = 4 \sin x + 2x^4 - x^{-1/2}$$

Using the formulas in Table 2 together with Theorem 1, we obtain

$$g(x) = 4(-\cos x) + 2\,\frac{x^5}{5} - \frac{x^{1/2}}{\frac{1}{2}} + C$$

$$= -4\cos x + \tfrac{2}{5}x^5 - 2\sqrt{x} + C$$

In applications of calculus it is very common to have a situation as in Example 2, where it is required to find a function, given knowledge about its derivatives. An equation that involves the derivatives of a function is called a **differential equation**. These will be studied in some detail in Chapter 9, but for the present we can solve some elementary differential equations. The general solution of a differential equation involves an arbitrary constant (or constants) as in Example 2. However, there may be some extra conditions given that will determine the constants and therefore uniquely specify the solution.

Figure 2 shows the graphs of the function f' in Example 3 and its antiderivative f. Notice that $f'(x) > 0$, so f is always increasing. Also notice that when f' has a maximum or minimum, f appears to have an inflection point. So the graph serves as a check on our calculation.

FIGURE 2

EXAMPLE 3   Find f if $f'(x) = e^x + 20(1 + x^2)^{-1}$ and $f(0) = -2$.

SOLUTION   The general antiderivative of

$$f'(x) = e^x + \frac{20}{1 + x^2}$$

is

$$f(x) = e^x + 20\tan^{-1}x + C$$

To determine C we use the fact that $f(0) = -2$:

$$f(0) = e^0 + 20\tan^{-1}0 + C = -2$$

Thus we have $C = -2 - 1 = -3$, so the particular solution is

$$f(x) = e^x + 20\tan^{-1}x - 3$$

V   EXAMPLE 4   Find f if $f''(x) = 12x^2 + 6x - 4$, $f(0) = 4$, and $f(1) = 1$.

SOLUTION   The general antiderivative of $f''(x) = 12x^2 + 6x - 4$ is

$$f'(x) = 12\,\frac{x^3}{3} + 6\,\frac{x^2}{2} - 4x + C = 4x^3 + 3x^2 - 4x + C$$

Using the antidifferentiation rules once more, we find that

$$f(x) = 4\,\frac{x^4}{4} + 3\,\frac{x^3}{3} - 4\,\frac{x^2}{2} + Cx + D = x^4 + x^3 - 2x^2 + Cx + D$$

To determine C and D we use the given conditions that $f(0) = 4$ and $f(1) = 1$. Since $f(0) = 0 + D = 4$, we have $D = 4$. Since

$$f(1) = 1 + 1 - 2 + C + 4 = 1$$

we have $C = -3$. Therefore the required function is

$$f(x) = x^4 + x^3 - 2x^2 - 3x + 4$$

If we are given the graph of a function f, it seems reasonable that we should be able to sketch the graph of an antiderivative F. Suppose, for instance, that we are given that $F(0) = 1$. Then we have a place to start, the point $(0, 1)$, and the direction in which we move our pencil is given at each stage by the derivative $F'(x) = f(x)$. In the next example we use the principles of this chapter to show how to graph F even when we don't have a formula for f. This would be the case, for instance, when $f(x)$ is determined by experimental data.

FIGURE 3

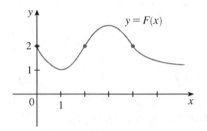

FIGURE 4

V EXAMPLE 5 The graph of a function f is given in Figure 3. Make a rough sketch of an antiderivative F, given that $F(0) = 2$.

SOLUTION We are guided by the fact that the slope of $y = F(x)$ is $f(x)$. We start at the point $(0, 2)$ and draw F as an initially decreasing function since $f(x)$ is negative when $0 < x < 1$. Notice that $f(1) = f(3) = 0$, so F has horizontal tangents when $x = 1$ and $x = 3$. For $1 < x < 3$, $f(x)$ is positive and so F is increasing. We see that F has a local minimum when $x = 1$ and a local maximum when $x = 3$. For $x > 3$, $f(x)$ is negative and so F is decreasing on $(3, \infty)$. Since $f(x) \rightarrow 0$ as $x \rightarrow \infty$, the graph of F becomes flatter as $x \rightarrow \infty$. Also notice that $F''(x) = f'(x)$ changes from positive to negative at $x = 2$ and from negative to positive at $x = 4$, so F has inflection points when $x = 2$ and $x = 4$. We use this information to sketch the graph of the antiderivative in Figure 4. ▪

Rectilinear Motion

Antidifferentiation is particularly useful in analyzing the motion of an object moving in a straight line. Recall that if the object has position function $s = f(t)$, then the velocity function is $v(t) = s'(t)$. This means that the position function is an antiderivative of the velocity function. Likewise, the acceleration function is $a(t) = v'(t)$, so the velocity function is an antiderivative of the acceleration. If the acceleration and the initial values $s(0)$ and $v(0)$ are known, then the position function can be found by antidifferentiating twice.

V EXAMPLE 6 A particle moves in a straight line and has acceleration given by $a(t) = 6t + 4$. Its initial velocity is $v(0) = -6$ cm/s and its initial displacement is $s(0) = 9$ cm. Find its position function $s(t)$.

SOLUTION Since $v'(t) = a(t) = 6t + 4$, antidifferentiation gives

$$v(t) = 6\frac{t^2}{2} + 4t + C = 3t^2 + 4t + C$$

Note that $v(0) = C$. But we are given that $v(0) = -6$, so $C = -6$ and

$$v(t) = 3t^2 + 4t - 6$$

Since $v(t) = s'(t)$, s is the antiderivative of v:

$$s(t) = 3\frac{t^3}{3} + 4\frac{t^2}{2} - 6t + D = t^3 + 2t^2 - 6t + D$$

This gives $s(0) = D$. We are given that $s(0) = 9$, so $D = 9$ and the required position function is

$$s(t) = t^3 + 2t^2 - 6t + 9$$ ▪

An object near the surface of the earth is subject to a gravitational force that produces a downward acceleration denoted by g. For motion close to the ground we may assume that g is constant, its value being about 9.8 m/s² (or 32 ft/s²).

EXAMPLE 7 A ball is thrown upward with a speed of 15 m/s from the edge of a cliff 140 m above the ground. Find its height above the ground t seconds later. When does it reach its maximum height? When does it hit the ground?

SOLUTION The motion is vertical and we choose the positive direction to be upward. At time t the distance above the ground is $s(t)$ and the velocity $v(t)$ is decreasing. Therefore the acceleration must be negative and we have

$$a(t) = \frac{dv}{dt} = -9.8$$

Taking antiderivatives, we have

$$v(t) = -9.8t + C$$

To determine C we use the given information that $v(0) = 15$. This gives $15 = 0 + C$, so

$$v(t) = -9.8t + 15$$

The maximum height is reached when $v(t) = 0$, that is, after $15/9.8 \approx 1.53$ s. Since $s'(t) = v(t)$, we antidifferentiate again and obtain

$$s(t) = -4.9t^2 + 15t + D$$

Using the fact that $s(0) = 140$, we have $140 = 0 + D$ and so

$$s(t) = -4.9t^2 + 15t + 140$$

The expression for $s(t)$ is valid until the ball hits the ground. This happens when $s(t) = 0$, that is, when

$$-4.9t^2 - 15t - 140 = 0$$

Using the quadratic formula to solve this equation, we get

$$t = \frac{15 \pm \sqrt{2969}}{9.8}$$

We reject the solution with the minus sign since it gives a negative value for t. Therefore the ball hits the ground after

$$\frac{15 + \sqrt{2969}}{9.8} \approx 7.1 \text{ s}$$

Figure 5 shows the position function of the ball in Example 7. The graph corroborates the conclusions we reached: The ball reaches its maximum height after 1.5 s and hits the ground after 7.1 s.

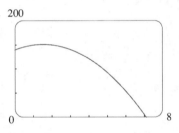

FIGURE 5

4.9   Exercises

1–22 Find the most general antiderivative of the function. (Check your answer by differentiation.)

1. $f(x) = x - 3$

2. $f(x) = \frac{1}{2}x^2 - 2x + 6$

3. $f(x) = \frac{1}{2} + \frac{3}{4}x^2 - \frac{4}{5}x^3$

4. $f(x) = 8x^9 - 3x^6 + 12x^3$

5. $f(x) = (x + 1)(2x - 1)$

6. $f(x) = x(2 - x)^2$

7. $f(x) = 7x^{2/5} + 8x^{-4/5}$

8. $f(x) = x^{3.4} - 2x^{\sqrt{2}-1}$

9. $f(x) = \sqrt{2}$

10. $f(x) = e^2$

11. $f(x) = 3\sqrt{x} - 2\sqrt[3]{x}$

12. $f(x) = \sqrt[3]{x^2} + x\sqrt{x}$

13. $f(x) = \dfrac{1}{5} - \dfrac{2}{x}$

14. $f(t) = \dfrac{3t^4 - t^3 + 6t^2}{t^4}$

15. $g(t) = \dfrac{1 + t + t^2}{\sqrt{t}}$

16. $r(\theta) = \sec\theta\tan\theta - 2e^\theta$

17. $h(\theta) = 2\sin\theta - \sec^2\theta$

18. $f(t) = \sin t + 2\sinh t$

19. $f(x) = 5e^x - 3\cosh x$

20. $f(x) = 2\sqrt{x} + 6\cos x$

21. $f(x) = \dfrac{x^3 - x^2 + 2x}{x^4}$

22. $f(x) = \dfrac{2 + x^2}{1 + x^2}$

23–24 Find the antiderivative F of f that satisfies the given condition. Check your answer by comparing the graphs of f and F.

23. $f(x) = 5x^4 - 2x^5$, $F(0) = 4$

24. $f(x) = 4 - 3(1 + x^2)^{-1}$, $F(1) = 0$

25–48 Find f.

25. $f''(x) = 20x^3 - 12x^2 + 6x$

26. $f''(x) = x^6 - 4x^4 + x + 1$

27. $f''(x) = \frac{2}{3}x^{2/3}$

28. $f''(x) = 6x + \sin x$

29. $f'''(t) = \cos t$

30. $f'''(t) = e^t + t^{-4}$

31. $f'(x) = 1 + 3\sqrt{x}, \quad f(4) = 25$

32. $f'(x) = 5x^4 - 3x^2 + 4, \quad f(-1) = 2$

33. $f'(t) = 4/(1 + t^2), \quad f(1) = 0$

34. $f'(t) = t + 1/t^3, \quad t > 0, \quad f(1) = 6$

35. $f'(t) = 2\cos t + \sec^2 t, \quad -\pi/2 < t < \pi/2, \quad f(\pi/3) = 4$

36. $f'(x) = (x^2 - 1)/x, \quad f(1) = \frac{1}{2}, \quad f(-1) = 0$

37. $f'(x) = x^{-1/3}, \quad f(1) = 1, \quad f(-1) = -1$

38. $f'(x) = 4/\sqrt{1 - x^2}, \quad f(\frac{1}{2}) = 1$

39. $f''(x) = -2 + 12x - 12x^2, \quad f(0) = 4, \quad f'(0) = 12$

40. $f''(x) = 8x^3 + 5, \quad f(1) = 0, \quad f'(1) = 8$

41. $f''(\theta) = \sin\theta + \cos\theta, \quad f(0) = 3, \quad f'(0) = 4$

42. $f''(t) = 3/\sqrt{t}, \quad f(4) = 20, \quad f'(4) = 7$

43. $f''(x) = 4 + 6x + 24x^2, \quad f(0) = 3, \quad f(1) = 10$

44. $f''(x) = x^3 + \sinh x, \quad f(0) = 1, \quad f(2) = 2.6$

45. $f''(x) = 2 + \cos x, \quad f(0) = -1, \quad f(\pi/2) = 0$

46. $f''(t) = 2e^t + 3\sin t, \quad f(0) = 0, \quad f(\pi) = 0$

47. $f''(x) = x^{-2}, \quad x > 0, \quad f(1) = 0, \quad f(2) = 0$

48. $f'''(x) = \cos x, \quad f(0) = 1, \quad f'(0) = 2, \quad f''(0) = 3$

49. Given that the graph of f passes through the point $(1, 6)$ and that the slope of its tangent line at $(x, f(x))$ is $2x + 1$, find $f(2)$.

50. Find a function f such that $f'(x) = x^3$ and the line $x + y = 0$ is tangent to the graph of f.

51–52 The graph of a function f is shown. Which graph is an anti-derivative of f and why?

51.

52.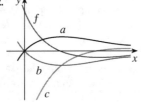

53. The graph of a function is shown in the figure. Make a rough sketch of an antiderivative F, given that $F(0) = 1$.

54. The graph of the velocity function of a particle is shown in the figure. Sketch the graph of a position function.

55. The graph of f' is shown in the figure. Sketch the graph of f if f is continuous and $f(0) = -1$.

56. (a) Use a graphing device to graph $f(x) = 2x - 3\sqrt{x}$.
   (b) Starting with the graph in part (a), sketch a rough graph of the antiderivative F that satisfies $F(0) = 1$.
   (c) Use the rules of this section to find an expression for $F(x)$.
   (d) Graph F using the expression in part (c). Compare with your sketch in part (b).

57–58 Draw a graph of f and use it to make a rough sketch of the antiderivative that passes through the origin.

57. $f(x) = \dfrac{\sin x}{1 + x^2}, \quad -2\pi \le x \le 2\pi$

58. $f(x) = \sqrt{x^4 - 2x^2 + 2} - 2, \quad -3 \le x \le 3$

59–64 A particle is moving with the given data. Find the position of the particle.

59. $v(t) = \sin t - \cos t, \quad s(0) = 0$

60. $v(t) = 1.5\sqrt{t}, \quad s(4) = 10$

61. $a(t) = 2t + 1, \quad s(0) = 3, \quad v(0) = -2$

62. $a(t) = 3\cos t - 2\sin t, \quad s(0) = 0, \quad v(0) = 4$

63. $a(t) = 10\sin t + 3\cos t, \quad s(0) = 0, \quad s(2\pi) = 12$

64. $a(t) = t^2 - 4t + 6, \quad s(0) = 0, \quad s(1) = 20$

65. A stone is dropped from the upper observation deck (the Space Deck) of the CN Tower, 450 m above the ground.
   (a) Find the distance of the stone above ground level at time t.
   (b) How long does it take the stone to reach the ground?
   (c) With what velocity does it strike the ground?
   (d) If the stone is thrown downward with a speed of 5 m/s, how long does it take to reach the ground?

66. Show that for motion in a straight line with constant acceleration a, initial velocity v_0, and initial displacement s_0, the displacement after time t is

$$s = \tfrac{1}{2}at^2 + v_0t + s_0$$

67. An object is projected upward with initial velocity v_0 meters per second from a point s_0 meters above the ground. Show that

$$[v(t)]^2 = v_0^2 - 19.6[s(t) - s_0]$$

68. Two balls are thrown upward from the edge of the cliff in Example 7. The first is thrown with a speed of 15 m/s and the other is thrown a second later with a speed of 8 m/s. Do the balls ever pass each other?

69. A stone was dropped off a cliff and hit the ground with a speed of 40 m/s. What is the height of the cliff?

70. If a diver of mass m stands at the end of a diving board with length L and linear density ρ, then the board takes on the shape of a curve $y = f(x)$, where

$$EIy'' = mg(L - x) + \tfrac{1}{2}\rho g(L - x)^2$$

E and I are positive constants that depend on the material of the board and g (< 0) is the acceleration due to gravity.
(a) Find an expression for the shape of the curve.
(b) Use $f(L)$ to estimate the distance below the horizontal at the end of the board.

71. A company estimates that the marginal cost (in dollars per item) of producing x items is $1.92 - 0.002x$. If the cost of producing one item is $562, find the cost of producing 100 items.

72. The linear density of a rod of length 1 m is given by $\rho(x) = 1/\sqrt{x}$, in grams per centimeter, where x is measured in centimeters from one end of the rod. Find the mass of the rod.

73. Since raindrops grow as they fall, their surface area increases and therefore the resistance to their falling increases. A raindrop has an initial downward velocity of 10 m/s and its

downward acceleration is

$$a = \begin{cases} 9 - 0.9t & \text{if } 0 \le t \le 10 \\ 0 & \text{if } t > 10 \end{cases}$$

If the raindrop is initially 500 m above the ground, how long does it take to fall?

74. A car is traveling at 80 km/h when the brakes are fully applied, producing a constant deceleration of 7 m/s^2. What is the distance traveled before the car comes to a stop?

75. What constant acceleration is required to increase the speed of a car from 50 km/h to 80 km/h in 5 s?

76. A car braked with a constant deceleration of 5 m/s^2, producing skid marks measuring 60 m before coming to a stop. How fast was the car traveling when the brakes were first applied?

77. A car is traveling at 100 km/h when the driver sees an accident 80 m ahead and slams on the brakes. What constant deceleration is required to stop the car in time to avoid a pileup?

78. A model rocket is fired vertically upward from rest. Its acceleration for the first three seconds is $a(t) = 18t$, at which time the fuel is exhausted and it becomes a freely "falling" body. Fourteen seconds later, the rocket's parachute opens, and the (downward) velocity slows linearly to -5.5 m/s in five seconds. The rocket then "floats" to the ground at that rate.
(a) Determine the position function s and the velocity function v (for all times t). Sketch the graphs of s and v.
(b) At what time does the rocket reach its maximum height, and what is that height?
(c) At what time does the rocket land?

79. A high-speed bullet train accelerates and decelerates at the rate of 1.2 m/s^2. Its maximum cruising speed is 145 km/h.
(a) What is the maximum distance the train can travel if it accelerates from rest until it reaches its cruising speed and then runs at that speed for 15 minutes?
(b) Suppose that the train starts from rest and must come to a complete stop in 15 minutes. What is the maximum distance it can travel under those conditions?
(c) Find the minimum time that the train takes to travel between two consecutive stations that are 72 km apart.
(d) The trip from one station to the next takes 37.5 minutes. How far apart are the stations?

4   Review

Concept Check

1. Explain the difference between an absolute maximum and a local maximum. Illustrate with a sketch.

2. (a) What does the Extreme Value Theorem say?
   (b) Explain how the Closed Interval Method works.

3. (a) State Fermat's Theorem.
   (b) Define a critical number of f.

4. (a) State Rolle's Theorem.
   (b) State the Mean Value Theorem and give a geometric interpretation.

5. (a) State the Increasing/Decreasing Test.
   (b) What does it mean to say that f is concave upward on an interval I?
   (c) State the Concavity Test.
   (d) What are inflection points? How do you find them?

6. (a) State the First Derivative Test.
   (b) State the Second Derivative Test.
   (c) What are the relative advantages and disadvantages of these tests?

7. (a) What does l'Hospital's Rule say?
   (b) How can you use l'Hospital's Rule if you have a product $f(x)\,g(x)$ where $f(x) \to 0$ and $g(x) \to \infty$ as $x \to a$?

(c) How can you use l'Hospital's Rule if you have a differ-ence $f(x) - g(x)$ where $f(x) \to \infty$ and $g(x) \to \infty$ as $x \to a$?

(d) How can you use l'Hospital's Rule if you have a power $[f(x)]^{g(x)}$ where $f(x) \to 0$ and $g(x) \to 0$ as $x \to a$?

8. If you have a graphing calculator or computer, why do you need calculus to graph a function?

9. (a) Given an initial approximation x_1 to a root of the equation $f(x) = 0$, explain geometrically, with a diagram, how the second approximation x_2 in Newton's method is obtained.
   (b) Write an expression for x_2 in terms of x_1, $f(x_1)$, and $f'(x_1)$.
   (c) Write an expression for x_{n+1} in terms of x_n, $f(x_n)$, and $f'(x_n)$.
   (d) Under what circumstances is Newton's method likely to fail or to work very slowly?

10. (a) What is an antiderivative of a function f?
    (b) Suppose F_1 and F_2 are both antiderivatives of f on an interval I. How are F_1 and F_2 related?

True-False Quiz

Determine whether the statement is true or false. If it is true, explain why. If it is false, explain why or give an example that disproves the statement.

1. If $f'(c) = 0$, then f has a local maximum or minimum at c.

2. If f has an absolute minimum value at c, then $f'(c) = 0$.

3. If f is continuous on (a, b), then f attains an absolute maximum value $f(c)$ and an absolute minimum value $f(d)$ at some numbers c and d in (a, b).

4. If f is differentiable and $f(-1) = f(1)$, then there is a number c such that $|c| < 1$ and $f'(c) = 0$.

5. If $f'(x) < 0$ for $1 < x < 6$, then f is decreasing on $(1, 6)$.

6. If $f''(2) = 0$, then $(2, f(2))$ is an inflection point of the curve $y = f(x)$.

7. If $f'(x) = g'(x)$ for $0 < x < 1$, then $f(x) = g(x)$ for $0 < x < 1$.

8. There exists a function f such that $f(1) = -2$, $f(3) = 0$, and $f'(x) > 1$ for all x.

9. There exists a function f such that $f(x) > 0$, $f'(x) < 0$, and $f''(x) > 0$ for all x.

10. There exists a function f such that $f(x) < 0$, $f'(x) < 0$, and $f''(x) > 0$ for all x.

11. If f and g are increasing on an interval I, then $f + g$ is increasing on I.

12. If f and g are increasing on an interval I, then $f - g$ is increasing on I.

13. If f and g are increasing on an interval I, then fg is increasing on I.

14. If f and g are positive increasing functions on an interval I, then fg is increasing on I.

15. If f is increasing and $f(x) > 0$ on I, then $g(x) = 1/f(x)$ is decreasing on I.

16. If f is even, then f' is even.

17. If f is periodic, then f' is periodic.

18. The most general antiderivative of $f(x) = x^{-2}$ is

$$F(x) = -\frac{1}{x} + C$$

19. If $f'(x)$ exists and is nonzero for all x, then $f(1) \neq f(0)$.

20. $\displaystyle\lim_{x \to 0} \frac{x}{e^x} = 1$

Exercises

1–6 Find the local and absolute extreme values of the function on the given interval.

1. $f(x) = x^3 - 6x^2 + 9x + 1$, $[2, 4]$

2. $f(x) = x\sqrt{1 - x}$, $[-1, 1]$

3. $f(x) = \dfrac{3x - 4}{x^2 + 1}$, $[-2, 2]$

4. $f(x) = \sqrt{x^2 + x + 1}$, $[-2, 1]$

5. $f(x) = x + 2\cos x$, $[-\pi, \pi]$

6. $f(x) = x^2 e^{-x}$, $[-1, 3]$

7–14 Evaluate the limit.

7. $\displaystyle\lim_{x \to 0} \frac{e^x - 1}{\tan x}$

8. $\displaystyle\lim_{x \to 0} \frac{\tan 4x}{x + \sin 2x}$

9. $\displaystyle\lim_{x \to 0} \frac{e^{4x} - 1 - 4x}{x^2}$

10. $\displaystyle\lim_{x \to \infty} \frac{e^{4x} - 1 - 4x}{x^2}$

11. $\displaystyle\lim_{x \to -\infty} (x^2 - x^3)e^{2x}$

12. $\displaystyle\lim_{x \to \pi^-} (x - \pi)\csc x$

13. $\displaystyle\lim_{x \to 1^+} \left(\frac{x}{x - 1} - \frac{1}{\ln x} \right)$

14. $\displaystyle\lim_{x \to (\pi/2)^-} (\tan x)^{\cos x}$

15–17 Sketch the graph of a function that satisfies the given conditions.

15. $f(0) = 0$, $f'(-2) = f'(1) = f'(9) = 0$,
$\displaystyle\lim_{x \to \infty} f(x) = 0$, $\displaystyle\lim_{x \to 6} f(x) = -\infty$,
$f'(x) < 0$ on $(-\infty, -2)$, $(1, 6)$, and $(9, \infty)$,
$f'(x) > 0$ on $(-2, 1)$ and $(6, 9)$,
$f''(x) > 0$ on $(-\infty, 0)$ and $(12, \infty)$,
$f''(x) < 0$ on $(0, 6)$ and $(6, 12)$

16. $f(0) = 0$, f is continuous and even,
$f'(x) = 2x$ if $0 < x < 1$, $f'(x) = -1$ if $1 < x < 3$,
$f'(x) = 1$ if $x > 3$

17. f is odd, $f'(x) < 0$ for $0 < x < 2$,
$f'(x) > 0$ for $x > 2$, $f''(x) > 0$ for $0 < x < 3$,
$f''(x) < 0$ for $x > 3$, $\displaystyle\lim_{x \to \infty} f(x) = -2$

18. The figure shows the graph of the *derivative* f' of a function f.
(a) On what intervals is f increasing or decreasing?
(b) For what values of x does f have a local maximum or minimum?

(c) Sketch the graph of f''.
(d) Sketch a possible graph of f.

19–34 Use the guidelines of Section 4.5 to sketch the curve.

19. $y = 2 - 2x - x^3$

20. $y = x^3 - 6x^2 - 15x + 4$

21. $y = x^4 - 3x^3 + 3x^2 - x$

22. $y = \dfrac{x}{1 - x^2}$

23. $y = \dfrac{1}{x(x - 3)^2}$

24. $y = \dfrac{1}{x^2} - \dfrac{1}{(x - 2)^2}$

25. $y = x^2/(x + 8)$

26. $y = \sqrt{1 - x} + \sqrt{1 + x}$

27. $y = x\sqrt{2 + x}$

28. $y = \sqrt[3]{x^2 + 1}$

29. $y = e^x \sin x$, $-\pi \le x \le \pi$

30. $y = 4x - \tan x$, $-\pi/2 < x < \pi/2$

31. $y = \sin^{-1}(1/x)$

32. $y = e^{2x - x^2}$

33. $y = (x - 2)e^{-x}$

34. $y = x + \ln(x^2 + 1)$

35–38 Produce graphs of f that reveal all the important aspects of the curve. Use graphs of f' and f'' to estimate the intervals of increase and decrease, extreme values, intervals of concavity, and inflection points. In Exercise 35 use calculus to find these quantities exactly.

35. $f(x) = \dfrac{x^2 - 1}{x^3}$

36. $f(x) = \dfrac{x^3 - x}{x^2 + x + 3}$

37. $f(x) = 3x^6 - 5x^5 + x^4 - 5x^3 - 2x^2 + 2$

38. $f(x) = x^2 + 6.5 \sin x$, $-5 \le x \le 5$

39. Graph $f(x) = e^{-1/x^2}$ in a viewing rectangle that shows all the main aspects of this function. Estimate the inflection points. Then use calculus to find them exactly.

CAS 40. (a) Graph the function $f(x) = 1/(1 + e^{1/x})$.
(b) Explain the shape of the graph by computing the limits of $f(x)$ as x approaches ∞, $-\infty$, 0^+, and 0^-.
(c) Use the graph of f to estimate the coordinates of the inflection points.
(d) Use your CAS to compute and graph f''.
(e) Use the graph in part (d) to estimate the inflection points more accurately.

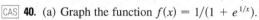

Graphing calculator or computer required   CAS Computer algebra system required

CAS **41–42** Use the graphs of f, f', and f'' to estimate the x-coordinates of the maximum and minimum points and inflection points of f.

41. $f(x) = \dfrac{\cos^2 x}{\sqrt{x^2 + x + 1}}$, $-\pi \leqslant x \leqslant \pi$

42. $f(x) = e^{-0.1x} \ln(x^2 - 1)$

43. Investigate the family of functions $f(x) = \ln(\sin x + C)$. What features do the members of this family have in common? How do they differ? For which values of C is f continuous on $(-\infty, \infty)$? For which values of C does f have no graph at all? What happens as $C \to \infty$?

44. Investigate the family of functions $f(x) = cxe^{-cx^2}$. What happens to the maximum and minimum points and the inflection points as c changes? Illustrate your conclusions by graphing several members of the family.

45. Show that the equation $3x + 2\cos x + 5 = 0$ has exactly one real root.

46. Suppose that f is continuous on $[0, 4]$, $f(0) = 1$, and $2 \leqslant f'(x) \leqslant 5$ for all x in $(0, 4)$. Show that $9 \leqslant f(4) \leqslant 21$.

47. By applying the Mean Value Theorem to the function $f(x) = x^{1/5}$ on the interval $[32, 33]$, show that

$$2 < \sqrt[5]{33} < 2.0125$$

48. For what values of the constants a and b is $(1, 3)$ a point of inflection of the curve $y = ax^3 + bx^2$?

49. Let $g(x) = f(x^2)$, where f is twice differentiable for all x, $f'(x) > 0$ for all $x \neq 0$, and f is concave downward on $(-\infty, 0)$ and concave upward on $(0, \infty)$.
 (a) At what numbers does g have an extreme value?
 (b) Discuss the concavity of g.

50. Find two positive integers such that the sum of the first number and four times the second number is 1000 and the product of the numbers is as large as possible.

51. Show that the shortest distance from the point (x_1, y_1) to the straight line $Ax + By + C = 0$ is

$$\frac{|Ax_1 + By_1 + C|}{\sqrt{A^2 + B^2}}$$

52. Find the point on the hyperbola $xy = 8$ that is closest to the point $(3, 0)$.

53. Find the smallest possible area of an isosceles triangle that is circumscribed about a circle of radius r.

54. Find the volume of the largest circular cone that can be inscribed in a sphere of radius r.

55. In $\triangle ABC$, D lies on AB, $CD \perp AB$, $|AD| = |BD| = 4$ cm, and $|CD| = 5$ cm. Where should a point P be chosen on CD so that the sum $|PA| + |PB| + |PC|$ is a minimum?

56. Solve Exercise 55 when $|CD| = 2$ cm.

57. The velocity of a wave of length L in deep water is

$$v = K\sqrt{\frac{L}{C} + \frac{C}{L}}$$

where K and C are known positive constants. What is the length of the wave that gives the minimum velocity?

58. A metal storage tank with volume V is to be constructed in the shape of a right circular cylinder surmounted by a hemisphere. What dimensions will require the least amount of metal?

59. A hockey team plays in an arena with a seating capacity of 15,000 spectators. With the ticket price set at \$12, average attendance at a game has been 11,000. A market survey indicates that for each dollar the ticket price is lowered, average attendance will increase by 1000. How should the owners of the team set the ticket price to maximize their revenue from ticket sales?

60. A manufacturer determines that the cost of making x units of a commodity is $C(x) = 1800 + 25x - 0.2x^2 + 0.001x^3$ and the demand function is $p(x) = 48.2 - 0.03x$.
 (a) Graph the cost and revenue functions and use the graphs to estimate the production level for maximum profit.
 (b) Use calculus to find the production level for maximum profit.
 (c) Estimate the production level that minimizes the average cost.

61. Use Newton's method to find the root of the equation $x^5 - x^4 + 3x^2 - 3x - 2 = 0$ in the interval $[1, 2]$ correct to six decimal places.

62. Use Newton's method to find all roots of the equation $\sin x = x^2 - 3x + 1$ correct to six decimal places.

63. Use Newton's method to find the absolute maximum value of the function $f(t) = \cos t + t - t^2$ correct to eight decimal places.

64. Use the guidelines in Section 4.5 to sketch the curve $y = x \sin x$, $0 \leqslant x \leqslant 2\pi$. Use Newton's method when necessary.

65–72 Find f.

65. $f'(x) = \cos x - (1 - x^2)^{-1/2}$

66. $f'(x) = 2e^x + \sec x \tan x$

67. $f'(x) = \sqrt{x^3} + \sqrt[3]{x^2}$

68. $f'(x) = \sinh x + 2\cosh x$, $f(0) = 2$

69. $f'(t) = 2t - 3\sin t$, $f(0) = 5$

70. $f'(u) = \dfrac{u^2 + \sqrt{u}}{u}$, $f(1) = 3$

71. $f''(x) = 1 - 6x + 48x^2$, $f(0) = 1$, $f'(0) = 2$

72. $f''(x) = 2x^3 + 3x^2 - 4x + 5$, $f(0) = 2$, $f(1) = 0$

73–74 A particle is moving with the given data. Find the position of the particle.

73. $v(t) = 2t - 1/(1 + t^2)$, $s(0) = 1$

74. $a(t) = \sin t + 3 \cos t$, $s(0) = 0$, $v(0) = 2$

75. (a) If $f(x) = 0.1e^x + \sin x$, $-4 \le x \le 4$, use a graph of f to sketch a rough graph of the antiderivative F of f that satisfies $F(0) = 0$.
   (b) Find an expression for $F(x)$.
   (c) Graph F using the expression in part (b). Compare with your sketch in part (a).

76. Investigate the family of curves given by

$$f(x) = x^4 + x^3 + cx^2$$

In particular you should determine the transitional value of c at which the number of critical numbers changes and the transitional value at which the number of inflection points changes. Illustrate the various possible shapes with graphs.

77. A canister is dropped from a helicopter 500 m above the ground. Its parachute does not open, but the canister has been designed to withstand an impact velocity of 100 m/s. Will it burst?

78. In an automobile race along a straight road, car A passed car B twice. Prove that at some time during the race their accelerations were equal. State the assumptions that you make.

79. A rectangular beam will be cut from a cylindrical log of radius 30 cm.
   (a) Show that the beam of maximal cross-sectional area is a square.
   (b) Four rectangular planks will be cut from the four sections of the log that remain after cutting the square beam. Determine the dimensions of the planks that will have maximal cross-sectional area.
   (c) Suppose that the strength of a rectangular beam is proportional to the product of its width and the square of its depth. Find the dimensions of the strongest beam that can be cut from the cylindrical log.

80. If a projectile is fired with an initial velocity v at an angle of inclination θ from the horizontal, then its trajectory, neglecting air resistance, is the parabola

$$y = (\tan \theta)x - \frac{g}{2v^2 \cos^2\theta}x^2 \qquad 0 < \theta < \frac{\pi}{2}$$

   (a) Suppose the projectile is fired from the base of a plane that is inclined at an angle α, $\alpha > 0$, from the horizontal, as shown in the figure. Show that the range of the projectile, measured up the slope, is given by

$$R(\theta) = \frac{2v^2 \cos \theta \, \sin(\theta - \alpha)}{g \cos^2\alpha}$$

   (b) Determine θ so that R is a maximum.
   (c) Suppose the plane is at an angle α *below* the horizontal. Determine the range R in this case, and determine the angle at which the projectile should be fired to maximize R.

81. Show that, for $x > 0$,

$$\frac{x}{1 + x^2} < \tan^{-1}x < x$$

82. Sketch the graph of a function f such that $f'(x) < 0$ for all x, $f''(x) > 0$ for $|x| > 1$, $f''(x) < 0$ for $|x| < 1$, and $\lim_{x \to \pm\infty}[f(x) + x] = 0$.

83. A light is to be placed atop a pole of height h meters to illuminate a busy traffic circle, which has a radius of 20 m. The intensity of illumination I at any point P on the circle is directly proportional to the cosine of the angle θ (see the figure) and inversely proportional to the square of the distance d from the source.
   (a) How tall should the light pole be to maximize I?
   (b) Suppose that the light pole is h meters tall and that a woman is walking away from the base of the pole at the rate of 1 m/s. At what rate is the intensity of the light at the point on her back 1 m above the ground decreasing when she reaches the outer edge of the traffic circle?

84. Water is flowing at a constant rate into a spherical tank. Let $V(t)$ be the volume of water in the tank and $H(t)$ be the height of the water in the tank at time t.
   (a) What are the meanings of $V'(t)$ and $H'(t)$? Are these derivatives positive, negative, or zero?
   (b) Is $V''(t)$ positive, negative, or zero? Explain.
   (c) Let t_1, t_2, and t_3 be the times when the tank is one-quarter full, half full, and three-quarters full, respectively. Are the values $H''(t_1)$, $H''(t_2)$, and $H''(t_3)$ positive, negative, or zero? Why?

Problems Plus

One of the most important principles of problem solving is *analogy* (see page 75). If you are having trouble getting started on a problem, it is sometimes helpful to start by solving a similar, but simpler, problem. The following example illustrates the principle. Cover up the solution and try solving it yourself first.

EXAMPLE 1 If x, y, and z are positive numbers, prove that

$$\frac{(x^2 + 1)(y^2 + 1)(z^2 + 1)}{xyz} \geqslant 8$$

SOLUTION It may be difficult to get started on this problem. (Some students have tackled it by multiplying out the numerator, but that just creates a mess.) Let's try to think of a similar, simpler problem. When several variables are involved, it's often helpful to think of an analogous problem with fewer variables. In the present case we can reduce the number of variables from three to one and prove the analogous inequality

$$\boxed{1} \qquad \frac{x^2 + 1}{x} \geqslant 2 \qquad \text{for } x > 0$$

In fact, if we are able to prove $\boxed{1}$, then the desired inequality follows because

$$\frac{(x^2 + 1)(y^2 + 1)(z^2 + 1)}{xyz} = \left(\frac{x^2 + 1}{x}\right)\left(\frac{y^2 + 1}{y}\right)\left(\frac{z^2 + 1}{z}\right) \geqslant 2 \cdot 2 \cdot 2 = 8$$

The key to proving $\boxed{1}$ is to recognize that it is a disguised version of a minimum problem. If we let

$$f(x) = \frac{x^2 + 1}{x} = x + \frac{1}{x} \qquad x > 0$$

then $f'(x) = 1 - (1/x^2)$, so $f'(x) = 0$ when $x = 1$. Also, $f'(x) < 0$ for $0 < x < 1$ and $f'(x) > 0$ for $x > 1$. Therefore the absolute minimum value of f is $f(1) = 2$. This means that

$$\frac{x^2 + 1}{x} \geqslant 2 \qquad \text{for all positive values of } x$$

and, as previously mentioned, the given inequality follows by multiplication.

The inequality in $\boxed{1}$ could also be proved without calculus. In fact, if $x > 0$, we have

$$\frac{x^2 + 1}{x} \geqslant 2 \iff x^2 + 1 \geqslant 2x \iff x^2 - 2x + 1 \geqslant 0$$

$$\iff (x - 1)^2 \geqslant 0$$

Because the last inequality is obviously true, the first one is true too. ▬

PS **LOOK BACK**
What have we learned from the solution to this example?

■ To solve a problem involving several variables, it might help to solve a similar problem with just one variable.

■ When trying to prove an inequality, it might help to think of it as a maximum or minimum problem.

1. If a rectangle has its base on the x-axis and two vertices on the curve $y = e^{-x^2}$, show that the rectangle has the largest possible area when the two vertices are at the points of inflection of the curve.

2. Show that $|\sin x - \cos x| \leq \sqrt{2}$ for all x.

3. Does the function $f(x) = e^{10|x-2|-x^2}$ have an absolute maximum? If so, find it. What about an absolute minimum?

4. Show that $x^2 y^2 (4 - x^2)(4 - y^2) \leq 16$ for all numbers x and y such that $|x| \leq 2$ and $|y| \leq 2$.

5. Show that the inflection points of the curve $y = (\sin x)/x$ lie on the curve $y^2(x^4 + 4) = 4$.

6. Find the point on the parabola $y = 1 - x^2$ at which the tangent line cuts from the first quadrant the triangle with the smallest area.

7. If a, b, c, and d are constants such that

$$\lim_{x \to 0} \frac{ax^2 + \sin bx + \sin cx + \sin dx}{3x^2 + 5x^4 + 7x^6} = 8$$

find the value of the sum $a + b + c + d$.

8. Sketch the set of all points (x, y) such that $|x + y| \leq e^x$.

9. Find the highest and lowest points on the curve $x^2 + xy + y^2 = 12$.

10. For what values of c does the curve $y = cx^3 + e^x$ have inflection points?

11. If $P(a, a^2)$ is any point on the parabola $y = x^2$, except for the origin, let Q be the point where the normal line intersects the parabola again (see the figure). Show that the line segment PQ has the shortest possible length when $a = 1/\sqrt{2}$.

12. Sketch the region in the plane consisting of all points (x, y) such that

$$2xy \leq |x - y| \leq x^2 + y^2$$

13. The line $y = mx + b$ intersects the parabola $y = x^2$ in points A and B. (See the figure.) Find the point P on the arc AOB of the parabola that maximizes the area of the triangle PAB.

FIGURE FOR PROBLEM 11

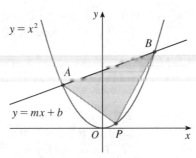

14. $ABCD$ is a square piece of paper with sides of length 1 m. A quarter-circle is drawn from B to D with center A. The piece of paper is folded along EF, with E on AB and F on AD, so that A falls on the quarter-circle. Determine the maximum and minimum areas that the triangle AEF can have.

15. For which positive numbers a does the curve $y = a^x$ intersect the line $y = x$?

16. For what value of a is the following equation true?

$$\lim_{x \to \infty} \left(\frac{x+a}{x-a} \right)^x = e$$

17. Let $f(x) = a_1 \sin x + a_2 \sin 2x + \cdots + a_n \sin nx$, where $a_1, a_2, \ldots, a_n$ are real numbers and n is a positive integer. If it is given that $|f(x)| \le |\sin x|$ for all x, show that

$$|a_1 + 2a_2 + \cdots + na_n| \le 1$$

18. An arc PQ of a circle subtends a central angle θ as in the figure. Let $A(\theta)$ be the area between the chord PQ and the arc PQ. Let $B(\theta)$ be the area between the tangent lines PR, QR, and the arc. Find

$$\lim_{\theta \to 0^+} \frac{A(\theta)}{B(\theta)}$$

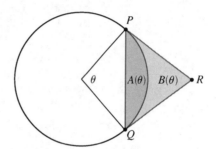

19. The speeds of sound c_1 in an upper layer and c_2 in a lower layer of rock and the thickness h of the upper layer can be determined by seismic exploration if the speed of sound in the lower layer is greater than the speed in the upper layer. A dynamite charge is detonated at a point P and the transmitted signals are recorded at a point Q, which is a distance D from P. The first signal to arrive at Q travels along the surface and takes T_1 seconds. The next signal travels from P to a point R, from R to S in the lower layer, and then to Q, taking T_2 seconds. The third signal is reflected off the lower layer at the midpoint O of RS and takes T_3 seconds to reach Q.

(a) Express T_1, T_2, and T_3 in terms of D, h, c_1, c_2, and θ.
(b) Show that T_2 is a minimum when $\sin \theta = c_1/c_2$.
(c) Suppose that $D = 1$ km, $T_1 = 0.26$ s, $T_2 = 0.32$ s, and $T_3 = 0.34$ s. Find c_1, c_2, and h.

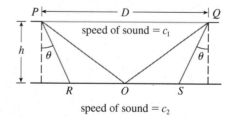

Note: Geophysicists use this technique when studying the structure of the earth's crust, whether searching for oil or examining fault lines.

20. For what values of c is there a straight line that intersects the curve

$$y = x^4 + cx^3 + 12x^2 - 5x + 2$$

in four distinct points?

FIGURE FOR PROBLEM 21

21. One of the problems posed by the Marquis de l'Hospital in his calculus textbook *Analyse des Infiniment Petits* concerns a pulley that is attached to the ceiling of a room at a point C by a rope of length r. At another point B on the ceiling, at a distance d from C (where $d > r$), a rope of length ℓ is attached and passed through the pulley at F and connected to a weight W. The weight is released and comes to rest at its equilibrium position D. As l'Hospital argued, this happens when the distance $|ED|$ is maximized. Show that when the system reaches equilibrium, the value of x is

$$\frac{r}{4d}\left(r + \sqrt{r^2 + 8d^2}\right)$$

Notice that this expression is independent of both W and ℓ.

22. Given a sphere with radius r, find the height of a pyramid of minimum volume whose base is a square and whose base and triangular faces are all tangent to the sphere. What if the base of the pyramid is a regular n-gon? (A regular n-gon is a polygon with n equal sides and angles.) (Use the fact that the volume of a pyramid is $\frac{1}{3}Ah$, where A is the area of the base.)

23. Assume that a snowball melts so that its volume decreases at a rate proportional to its surface area. If it takes three hours for the snowball to decrease to half its original volume, how much longer will it take for the snowball to melt completely?

24. A hemispherical bubble is placed on a spherical bubble of radius 1. A smaller hemispherical bubble is then placed on the first one. This process is continued until n chambers, including the sphere, are formed. (The figure shows the case $n = 4$.) Use mathematical induction to prove that the maximum height of any bubble tower with n chambers is $1 + \sqrt{n}$.

5 Integrals

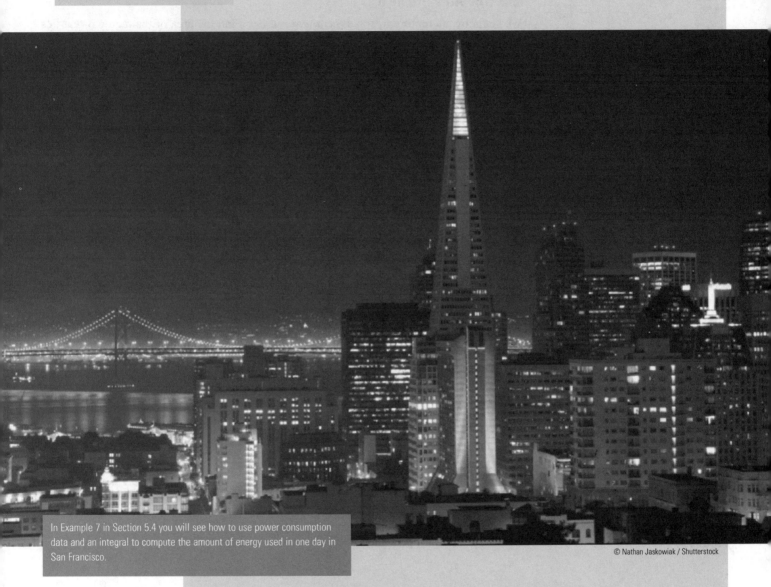

In Example 7 in Section 5.4 you will see how to use power consumption data and an integral to compute the amount of energy used in one day in San Francisco.

© Nathan Jaskowiak / Shutterstock

In Chapter 2 we used the tangent and velocity problems to introduce the derivative, which is the central idea in differential calculus. In much the same way, this chapter starts with the area and distance problems and uses them to formulate the idea of a definite integral, which is the basic concept of integral calculus. We will see in Chapters 6 and 8 how to use the integral to solve problems concerning volumes, lengths of curves, population predictions, cardiac output, forces on a dam, work, consumer surplus, and baseball, among many others.

There is a connection between integral calculus and differential calculus. The Fundamental Theorem of Calculus relates the integral to the derivative, and we will see in this chapter that it greatly simplifies the solution of many problems.

Now is a good time to read (or reread)
A Preview of Calculus (see page 1). It discusses
the unifying ideas of calculus and helps put in
perspective where we have been and where
we are going.

FIGURE 1

$S = \{(x, y) \mid a \leq x \leq b, 0 \leq y \leq f(x)\}$

5.1   Areas and Distances

In this section we discover that in trying to find the area under a curve or the distance traveled by a car, we end up with the same special type of limit.

The Area Problem

We begin by attempting to solve the *area problem:* Find the area of the region S that lies under the curve $y = f(x)$ from a to b. This means that S, illustrated in Figure 1, is bounded by the graph of a continuous function f [where $f(x) \geq 0$], the vertical lines $x = a$ and $x = b$, and the x-axis.

In trying to solve the area problem we have to ask ourselves: What is the meaning of the word *area*? This question is easy to answer for regions with straight sides. For a rectangle, the area is defined as the product of the length and the width. The area of a triangle is half the base times the height. The area of a polygon is found by dividing it into triangles (as in Figure 2) and adding the areas of the triangles.

FIGURE 2

$A = lw$ $A = \frac{1}{2}bh$ $A = A_1 + A_2 + A_3 + A_4$

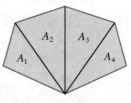

However, it isn't so easy to find the area of a region with curved sides. We all have an intuitive idea of what the area of a region is. But part of the area problem is to make this intuitive idea precise by giving an exact definition of area.

Recall that in defining a tangent we first approximated the slope of the tangent line by slopes of secant lines and then we took the limit of these approximations. We pursue a similar idea for areas. We first approximate the region S by rectangles and then we take the limit of the areas of these rectangles as we increase the number of rectangles. The following example illustrates the procedure.

FIGURE 3

V **EXAMPLE 1** Use rectangles to estimate the area under the parabola $y = x^2$ from 0 to 1 (the parabolic region S illustrated in Figure 3).

SOLUTION We first notice that the area of S must be somewhere between 0 and 1 because S is contained in a square with side length 1, but we can certainly do better than that. Suppose we divide S into four strips S_1, S_2, S_3, and S_4 by drawing the vertical lines $x = \frac{1}{4}$, $x = \frac{1}{2}$, and $x = \frac{3}{4}$ as in Figure 4(a).

FIGURE 4   (a)   (b)

We can approximate each strip by a rectangle that has the same base as the strip and whose height is the same as the right edge of the strip [see Figure 4(b)]. In other words, the heights of these rectangles are the values of the function $f(x) = x^2$ at the *right* endpoints of the subintervals $\left[0, \frac{1}{4}\right]$, $\left[\frac{1}{4}, \frac{1}{2}\right]$, $\left[\frac{1}{2}, \frac{3}{4}\right]$, and $\left[\frac{3}{4}, 1\right]$.

Each rectangle has width $\frac{1}{4}$ and the heights are $\left(\frac{1}{4}\right)^2$, $\left(\frac{1}{2}\right)^2$, $\left(\frac{3}{4}\right)^2$, and 1^2. If we let R_4 be the sum of the areas of these approximating rectangles, we get

$$R_4 = \frac{1}{4} \cdot \left(\frac{1}{4}\right)^2 + \frac{1}{4} \cdot \left(\frac{1}{2}\right)^2 + \frac{1}{4} \cdot \left(\frac{3}{4}\right)^2 + \frac{1}{4} \cdot 1^2 = \frac{15}{32} = 0.46875$$

From Figure 4(b) we see that the area A of S is less than R_4, so

$$A < 0.46875$$

Instead of using the rectangles in Figure 4(b) we could use the smaller rectangles in Figure 5 whose heights are the values of f at the *left* endpoints of the subintervals. (The leftmost rectangle has collapsed because its height is 0.) The sum of the areas of these approximating rectangles is

$$L_4 = \frac{1}{4} \cdot 0^2 + \frac{1}{4} \cdot \left(\frac{1}{4}\right)^2 + \frac{1}{4} \cdot \left(\frac{1}{2}\right)^2 + \frac{1}{4} \cdot \left(\frac{3}{4}\right)^2 = \frac{7}{32} = 0.21875$$

We see that the area of S is larger than L_4, so we have lower and upper estimates for A:

$$0.21875 < A < 0.46875$$

FIGURE 5

We can repeat this procedure with a larger number of strips. Figure 6 shows what happens when we divide the region S into eight strips of equal width.

   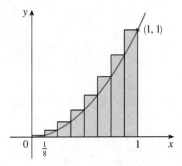

FIGURE 6

Approximating S with eight rectangles

(a) Using left endpoints   (b) Using right endpoints

By computing the sum of the areas of the smaller rectangles (L_8) and the sum of the areas of the larger rectangles (R_8), we obtain better lower and upper estimates for A:

$$0.2734375 < A < 0.3984375$$

n	L_n	R_n
10	0.2850000	0.3850000
20	0.3087500	0.3587500
30	0.3168519	0.3501852
50	0.3234000	0.3434000
100	0.3283500	0.3383500
1000	0.3328335	0.3338335

So one possible answer to the question is to say that the true area of S lies somewhere between 0.2734375 and 0.3984375.

We could obtain better estimates by increasing the number of strips. The table at the left shows the results of similar calculations (with a computer) using n rectangles whose heights are found with left endpoints (L_n) or right endpoints (R_n). In particular, we see by using 50 strips that the area lies between 0.3234 and 0.3434. With 1000 strips we narrow it down even more: A lies between 0.3328335 and 0.3338335. A good estimate is obtained by averaging these numbers: $A \approx 0.3333335$.

From the values in the table in Example 1, it looks as if R_n is approaching $\frac{1}{3}$ as n increases. We confirm this in the next example.

V **EXAMPLE 2** For the region S in Example 1, show that the sum of the areas of the upper approximating rectangles approaches $\frac{1}{3}$, that is,

$$\lim_{n \to \infty} R_n = \frac{1}{3}$$

SOLUTION R_n is the sum of the areas of the n rectangles in Figure 7. Each rectangle has width $1/n$ and the heights are the values of the function $f(x) = x^2$ at the points $1/n, 2/n, 3/n, \ldots, n/n$; that is, the heights are $(1/n)^2, (2/n)^2, (3/n)^2, \ldots, (n/n)^2$. Thus

$$R_n = \frac{1}{n}\left(\frac{1}{n}\right)^2 + \frac{1}{n}\left(\frac{2}{n}\right)^2 + \frac{1}{n}\left(\frac{3}{n}\right)^2 + \cdots + \frac{1}{n}\left(\frac{n}{n}\right)^2$$

$$= \frac{1}{n} \cdot \frac{1}{n^2}(1^2 + 2^2 + 3^2 + \cdots + n^2)$$

$$= \frac{1}{n^3}(1^2 + 2^2 + 3^2 + \cdots + n^2)$$

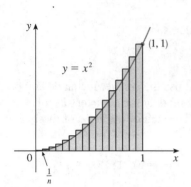

$y = x^2$

(1, 1)

$\frac{1}{n}$

FIGURE 7

Here we need the formula for the sum of the squares of the first n positive integers:

1 $$1^2 + 2^2 + 3^2 + \cdots + n^2 = \frac{n(n + 1)(2n + 1)}{6}$$

Perhaps you have seen this formula before. It is proved in Example 5 in Appendix E. Putting Formula 1 into our expression for R_n, we get

$$R_n = \frac{1}{n^3} \cdot \frac{n(n + 1)(2n + 1)}{6} = \frac{(n + 1)(2n + 1)}{6n^2}$$

Here we are computing the limit of the sequence $\{R_n\}$. Sequences and their limits were discussed in *A Preview of Calculus* and will be studied in detail in Section 11.1. The idea is very similar to a limit at infinity (Section 2.6) except that in writing $\lim_{n \to \infty}$ we restrict n to be a positive integer. In particular, we know that

$$\lim_{n \to \infty} \frac{1}{n} = 0$$

When we write $\lim_{n \to \infty} R_n = \frac{1}{3}$ we mean that we can make R_n as close to $\frac{1}{3}$ as we like by taking n sufficiently large.

Thus we have

$$\lim_{n \to \infty} R_n = \lim_{n \to \infty} \frac{(n + 1)(2n + 1)}{6n^2}$$

$$= \lim_{n \to \infty} \frac{1}{6}\left(\frac{n + 1}{n}\right)\left(\frac{2n + 1}{n}\right)$$

$$= \lim_{n \to \infty} \frac{1}{6}\left(1 + \frac{1}{n}\right)\left(2 + \frac{1}{n}\right)$$

$$= \frac{1}{6} \cdot 1 \cdot 2 = \frac{1}{3}$$

It can be shown that the lower approximating sums also approach $\frac{1}{3}$, that is,

$$\lim_{n \to \infty} L_n = \frac{1}{3}$$

From Figures 8 and 9 it appears that, as n increases, both L_n and R_n become better and better approximations to the area of S. Therefore we *define* the area A to be the limit of the sums of the areas of the approximating rectangles, that is,

TEC In Visual 5.1 you can create pictures like those in Figures 8 and 9 for other values of n.

$$A = \lim_{n \to \infty} R_n = \lim_{n \to \infty} L_n = \tfrac{1}{3}$$

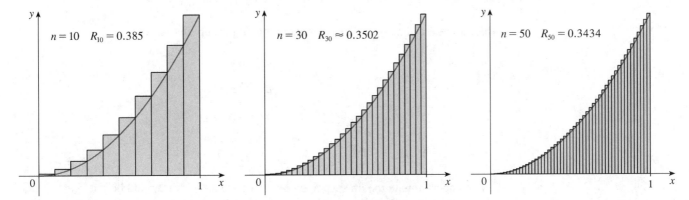

FIGURE 8 Right endpoints produce upper sums because $f(x) = x^2$ is increasing

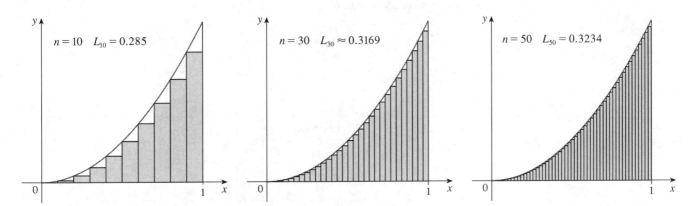

FIGURE 9 Left endpoints produce lower sums because $f(x) = x^2$ is increasing

Let's apply the idea of Examples 1 and 2 to the more general region S of Figure 1. We start by subdividing S into n strips $S_1, S_2, \ldots, S_n$ of equal width as in Figure 10.

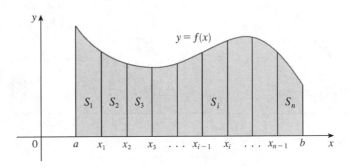

FIGURE 10

The width of the interval $[a, b]$ is $b - a$, so the width of each of the n strips is

$$\Delta x = \frac{b - a}{n}$$

These strips divide the interval $[a, b]$ into n subintervals

$$[x_0, x_1], \quad [x_1, x_2], \quad [x_2, x_3], \quad \ldots, \quad [x_{n-1}, x_n]$$

where $x_0 = a$ and $x_n = b$. The right endpoints of the subintervals are

$$x_1 = a + \Delta x,$$

$$x_2 = a + 2\,\Delta x,$$

$$x_3 = a + 3\,\Delta x,$$

$$\vdots$$

Let's approximate the ith strip S_i by a rectangle with width Δx and height $f(x_i)$, which is the value of f at the right endpoint (see Figure 11). Then the area of the ith rectangle is $f(x_i)\,\Delta x$. What we think of intuitively as the area of S is approximated by the sum of the areas of these rectangles, which is

$$R_n = f(x_1)\,\Delta x + f(x_2)\,\Delta x + \cdots + f(x_n)\,\Delta x$$

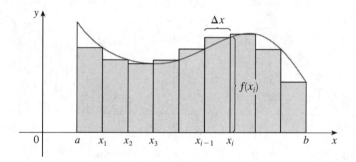

FIGURE 11

Figure 12 shows this approximation for $n = 2, 4, 8,$ and 12. Notice that this approximation appears to become better and better as the number of strips increases, that is, as $n \to \infty$. Therefore we define the area A of the region S in the following way.

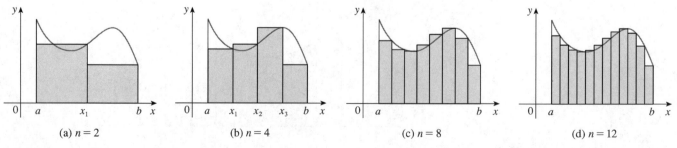

(a) $n = 2$ (b) $n = 4$ (c) $n = 8$ (d) $n = 12$

FIGURE 12

> **2** **Definition** The **area** A of the region S that lies under the graph of the continu-ous function f is the limit of the sum of the areas of approximating rectangles:
>
> $$A = \lim_{n \to \infty} R_n = \lim_{n \to \infty} \left[f(x_1)\,\Delta x + f(x_2)\,\Delta x + \cdots + f(x_n)\,\Delta x \right]$$

It can be proved that the limit in Definition 2 always exists, since we are assuming that f is continuous. It can also be shown that we get the same value if we use left endpoints:

$$\boxed{3} \qquad A = \lim_{n \to \infty} L_n = \lim_{n \to \infty} \left[f(x_0)\,\Delta x + f(x_1)\,\Delta x + \cdots + f(x_{n-1})\,\Delta x \right]$$

In fact, instead of using left endpoints or right endpoints, we could take the height of the ith rectangle to be the value of f at *any* number x_i^* in the ith subinterval $[x_{i-1}, x_i]$. We call the numbers $x_1^*, x_2^*, \ldots, x_n^*$ the **sample points**. Figure 13 shows approximating rectangles when the sample points are not chosen to be endpoints. So a more general expression for the area of S is

$$\boxed{4} \qquad A = \lim_{n \to \infty} \left[f(x_1^*)\,\Delta x + f(x_2^*)\,\Delta x + \cdots + f(x_n^*)\,\Delta x \right]$$

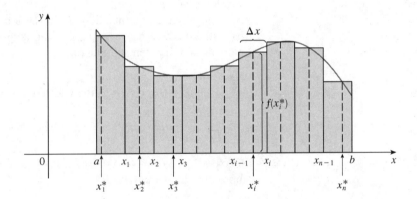

FIGURE 13

NOTE It can be shown that an equivalent definition of area is the following: *A is the unique number that is smaller than all the upper sums and bigger than all the lower sums.* We saw in Examples 1 and 2, for instance, that the area $\left(A = \frac{1}{3} \right)$ is trapped between all the left approximating sums L_n and all the right approximating sums R_n. The function in those examples, $f(x) = x^2$, happens to be increasing on $[0, 1]$ and so the lower sums arise from left endpoints and the upper sums from right endpoints. (See Figures 8 and 9.) In gen-eral, we form **lower** (and **upper**) **sums** by choosing the sample points x_i^* so that $f(x_i^*)$ is the minimum (and maximum) value of f on the ith subinterval. (See Figure 14 and Exercises 7–8).

FIGURE 14
Lower sums (short rectangles)
and upper sums (tall rectangles)

This tells us to end with $i = n$.

This tells us to add. $\longrightarrow \displaystyle\sum_{i=m}^{n} f(x_i)\, \Delta x$

This tells us to start with $i = m$.

If you need practice with sigma notation, look at the examples and try some of the exercises in Appendix E.

We often use **sigma notation** to write sums with many terms more compactly. For instance,

$$\sum_{i=1}^{n} f(x_i)\, \Delta x = f(x_1)\, \Delta x + f(x_2)\, \Delta x + \cdots + f(x_n)\, \Delta x$$

So the expressions for area in Equations 2, 3, and 4 can be written as follows:

$$A = \lim_{n \to \infty} \sum_{i=1}^{n} f(x_i)\, \Delta x$$

$$A = \lim_{n \to \infty} \sum_{i=1}^{n} f(x_{i-1})\, \Delta x$$

$$A = \lim_{n \to \infty} \sum_{i=1}^{n} f(x_i^*)\, \Delta x$$

We can also rewrite Formula 1 in the following way:

$$\sum_{i=1}^{n} i^2 = \frac{n(n + 1)(2n + 1)}{6}$$

EXAMPLE 3 Let A be the area of the region that lies under the graph of $f(x) = e^{-x}$ between $x = 0$ and $x = 2$.
(a) Using right endpoints, find an expression for A as a limit. Do not evaluate the limit.
(b) Estimate the area by taking the sample points to be midpoints and using four subintervals and then ten subintervals.

SOLUTION
(a) Since $a = 0$ and $b = 2$, the width of a subinterval is

$$\Delta x = \frac{2 - 0}{n} = \frac{2}{n}$$

So $x_1 = 2/n$, $x_2 = 4/n$, $x_3 = 6/n$, $x_i = 2i/n$, and $x_n = 2n/n$. The sum of the areas of the approximating rectangles is

$$R_n = f(x_1)\, \Delta x + f(x_2)\, \Delta x + \cdots + f(x_n)\, \Delta x$$

$$= e^{-x_1}\, \Delta x + e^{-x_2}\, \Delta x + \cdots + e^{-x_n}\, \Delta x$$

$$= e^{-2/n}\left(\frac{2}{n}\right) + e^{-4/n}\left(\frac{2}{n}\right) + \cdots + e^{-2n/n}\left(\frac{2}{n}\right)$$

According to Definition 2, the area is

$$A = \lim_{n \to \infty} R_n = \lim_{n \to \infty} \frac{2}{n}\left(e^{-2/n} + e^{-4/n} + e^{-6/n} + \cdots + e^{-2n/n}\right)$$

Using sigma notation we could write

$$A = \lim_{n \to \infty} \frac{2}{n} \sum_{i=1}^{n} e^{-2i/n}$$

It is difficult to evaluate this limit directly by hand, but with the aid of a computer algebra system it isn't hard (see Exercise 28). In Section 5.3 we will be able to find A more easily using a different method.

FIGURE 15

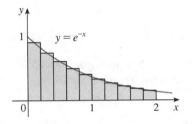

FIGURE 16

(b) With $n = 4$ the subintervals of equal width $\Delta x = 0.5$ are $[0, 0.5]$, $[0.5, 1]$, $[1, 1.5]$, and $[1.5, 2]$. The midpoints of these subintervals are $x_1^* = 0.25$, $x_2^* = 0.75$, $x_3^* = 1.25$, and $x_4^* = 1.75$, and the sum of the areas of the four approximating rectangles (see Figure 15) is

$$M_4 = \sum_{i=1}^{4} f(x_i^*)\, \Delta x$$

$$= f(0.25)\, \Delta x + f(0.75)\, \Delta x + f(1.25)\, \Delta x + f(1.75)\, \Delta x$$

$$= e^{-0.25}(0.5) + e^{-0.75}(0.5) + e^{-1.25}(0.5) + e^{-1.75}(0.5)$$

$$= \tfrac{1}{2}(e^{-0.25} + e^{-0.75} + e^{-1.25} + e^{-1.75}) \approx 0.8557$$

So an estimate for the area is

$$A \approx 0.8557$$

With $n = 10$ the subintervals are $[0, 0.2]$, $[0.2, 0.4]$, $\ldots$, $[1.8, 2]$ and the midpoints are $x_1^* = 0.1$, $x_2^* = 0.3$, $x_3^* = 0.5$, $\ldots$, $x_{10}^* = 1.9$. Thus

$$A \approx M_{10} = f(0.1)\, \Delta x + f(0.3)\, \Delta x + f(0.5)\, \Delta x + \cdots + f(1.9)\, \Delta x$$

$$= 0.2(e^{-0.1} + e^{-0.3} + e^{-0.5} + \cdots + e^{-1.9}) \approx 0.8632$$

From Figure 16 it appears that this estimate is better than the estimate with $n = 4$. ■

■ The Distance Problem

Now let's consider the *distance problem:* Find the distance traveled by an object during a certain time period if the velocity of the object is known at all times. (In a sense this is the inverse problem of the velocity problem that we discussed in Section 2.1.) If the velocity remains constant, then the distance problem is easy to solve by means of the formula

$$\text{distance} = \text{velocity} \times \text{time}$$

But if the velocity varies, it's not so easy to find the distance traveled. We investigate the problem in the following example.

▼ EXAMPLE 4 Suppose the odometer on our car is broken and we want to estimate the distance driven over a 30-second time interval. We take speedometer readings every five seconds and record them in the following table:

Time (s)	0	5	10	15	20	25	30
Velocity (km/h)	27	34	38	46	51	50	45

In order to have the time and the velocity in consistent units, let's convert the velocity readings to meters per second (1 km/h = 1000/3600 m/s):

Time (s)	0	5	10	15	20	25	30
Velocity (m/s)	7.5	9.4	10.6	12.8	14.2	13.9	12.5

During the first five seconds the velocity doesn't change very much, so we can estimate the distance traveled during that time by assuming that the velocity is constant. If we take the velocity during that time interval to be the initial velocity (7.5 m/s), then we obtain the approximate distance traveled during the first five seconds:

$$7.5 \text{ m/s} \times 5 \text{ s} = 37.5 \text{ m}$$

Similarly, during the second time interval the velocity is approximately constant and we take it to be the velocity when $t = 5$ s. So our estimate for the distance traveled from $t = 5$ s to $t = 10$ s is

$$9.4 \text{ m/s} \times 5 \text{ s} = 47 \text{ m}$$

If we add similar estimates for the other time intervals, we obtain an estimate for the total distance traveled:

$$(7.5 \times 5) + (9.4 \times 5) + (10.6 \times 5) + (12.8 \times 5) + (14.2 \times 5) + (13.9 \times 5) = 342 \text{ m}$$

We could just as well have used the velocity at the *end* of each time period instead of the velocity at the beginning as our assumed constant velocity. Then our estimate becomes

$$(9.4 \times 5) + (10.6 \times 5) + (12.8 \times 5) + (14.2 \times 5) + (13.9 \times 5) + (12.5 \times 5) = 367 \text{ m}$$

If we had wanted a more accurate estimate, we could have taken velocity readings every two seconds, or even every second. ∎

Perhaps the calculations in Example 4 remind you of the sums we used earlier to estimate areas. The similarity is explained when we sketch a graph of the velocity function of the car in Figure 17 and draw rectangles whose heights are the initial velocities for each time interval. The area of the first rectangle is $7.5 \times 5 = 37.5$, which is also our estimate for the distance traveled in the first five seconds. In fact, the area of each rectangle can be interpreted as a distance because the height represents velocity and the width represents time. The sum of the areas of the rectangles in Figure 17 is $L_6 = 342$, which is our initial estimate for the total distance traveled.

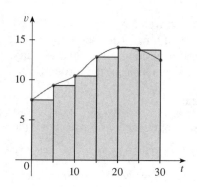

FIGURE 17

In general, suppose an object moves with velocity $v = f(t)$, where $a \leq t \leq b$ and $f(t) \geq 0$ (so the object always moves in the positive direction). We take velocity readings at times $t_0 \, (= a), t_1, t_2, \ldots, t_n \, (= b)$ so that the velocity is approximately constant on each subinterval. If these times are equally spaced, then the time between consecutive readings is $\Delta t = (b - a)/n$. During the first time interval the velocity is approximately $f(t_0)$ and so the distance traveled is approximately $f(t_0) \, \Delta t$. Similarly, the distance traveled during the second time interval is about $f(t_1) \, \Delta t$ and the total distance traveled during the time interval $[a, b]$ is approximately

$$f(t_0) \, \Delta t + f(t_1) \, \Delta t + \cdots + f(t_{n-1}) \, \Delta t = \sum_{i=1}^{n} f(t_{i-1}) \, \Delta t$$

If we use the velocity at right endpoints instead of left endpoints, our estimate for the total distance becomes

$$f(t_1) \, \Delta t + f(t_2) \, \Delta t + \cdots + f(t_n) \, \Delta t = \sum_{i=1}^{n} f(t_i) \, \Delta t$$

The more frequently we measure the velocity, the more accurate our estimates become, so it seems plausible that the *exact* distance d traveled is the *limit* of such expressions:

$$\boxed{5} \qquad d = \lim_{n \to \infty} \sum_{i=1}^{n} f(t_{i-1})\, \Delta t = \lim_{n \to \infty} \sum_{i=1}^{n} f(t_i)\, \Delta t$$

We will see in Section 5.4 that this is indeed true.

Because Equation 5 has the same form as our expressions for area in Equations 2 and 3, it follows that the distance traveled is equal to the area under the graph of the velocity function. In Chapter 6 we will see that other quantities of interest in the natural and social sciences—such as the work done by a variable force or the cardiac output of the heart—can also be interpreted as the area under a curve. So when we compute areas in this chapter, bear in mind that they can be interpreted in a variety of practical ways.

5.1   Exercises

1. (a) By reading values from the given graph of f, use four rectangles to find a lower estimate and an upper estimate for the area under the given graph of f from $x = 0$ to $x = 8$. In each case sketch the rectangles that you use.
   (b) Find new estimates using eight rectangles in each case.

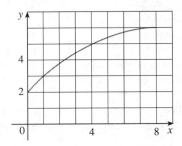

2. (a) Use six rectangles to find estimates of each type for the area under the given graph of f from $x = 0$ to $x = 12$.
   (i) L_6 (sample points are left endpoints)
   (ii) R_6 (sample points are right endpoints)
   (iii) M_6 (sample points are midpoints)
   (b) Is L_6 an underestimate or overestimate of the true area?
   (c) Is R_6 an underestimate or overestimate of the true area?
   (d) Which of the numbers L_6, R_6, or M_6 gives the best estimate? Explain.

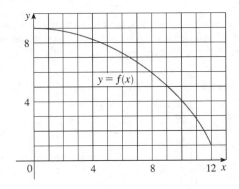

3. (a) Estimate the area under the graph of $f(x) = \cos x$ from $x = 0$ to $x = \pi/2$ using four approximating rectangles and right endpoints. Sketch the graph and the rectangles. Is your estimate an underestimate or an overestimate?
   (b) Repeat part (a) using left endpoints.

4. (a) Estimate the area under the graph of $f(x) = \sqrt{x}$ from $x = 0$ to $x = 4$ using four approximating rectangles and right endpoints. Sketch the graph and the rectangles. Is your estimate an underestimate or an overestimate?
   (b) Repeat part (a) using left endpoints.

5. (a) Estimate the area under the graph of $f(x) = 1 + x^2$ from $x = -1$ to $x = 2$ using three rectangles and right endpoints. Then improve your estimate by using six rectangles. Sketch the curve and the approximating rectangles.
   (b) Repeat part (a) using left endpoints.
   (c) Repeat part (a) using midpoints.
   (d) From your sketches in parts (a)–(c), which appears to be the best estimate?

6. (a) Graph the function

$$f(x) = x - 2 \ln x, \quad 1 \leqslant x \leqslant 5$$

   (b) Estimate the area under the graph of f using four approximating rectangles and taking the sample points to be
   (i) right endpoints and (ii) midpoints. In each case sketch the curve and the rectangles.
   (c) Improve your estimates in part (b) by using eight rectangles.

7. Evaluate the upper and lower sums for $f(x) = 2 + \sin x$, $0 \leqslant x \leqslant \pi$, with $n = 2, 4$, and 8. Illustrate with diagrams like Figure 14.

8. Evaluate the upper and lower sums for $f(x) = 1 + x^2$, $-1 \leqslant x \leqslant 1$, with $n = 3$ and 4. Illustrate with diagrams like Figure 14.

9–10 With a programmable calculator (or a computer), it is possible to evaluate the expressions for the sums of areas of approximating rectangles, even for large values of n, using looping. (On a TI use the Is> command or a For-EndFor loop, on a Casio use Isz, on an HP or in BASIC use a FOR-NEXT loop.) Compute the sum of the areas of approximating rectangles using equal subintervals and right endpoints for $n = 10, 30, 50$, and 100. Then guess the value of the exact area.

9. The region under $y = x^4$ from 0 to 1

10. The region under $y = \cos x$ from 0 to $\pi/2$

---

11. Some computer algebra systems have commands that will draw approximating rectangles and evaluate the sums of their areas, at least if x_i^* is a left or right endpoint. (For instance, in Maple use `leftbox`, `rightbox`, `leftsum`, and `rightsum`.)
  (a) If $f(x) = 1/(x^2 + 1)$, $0 \le x \le 1$, find the left and right sums for $n = 10, 30$, and 50.
  (b) Illustrate by graphing the rectangles in part (a).
  (c) Show that the exact area under f lies between 0.780 and 0.791.

12. (a) If $f(x) = \ln x$, $1 \le x \le 4$, use the commands discussed in Exercise 11 to find the left and right sums for $n = 10, 30$, and 50.
  (b) Illustrate by graphing the rectangles in part (a).
  (c) Show that the exact area under f lies between 2.50 and 2.59.

13. The speed of a runner increased steadily during the first three seconds of a race. Her speed at half-second intervals is given in the table. Find lower and upper estimates for the distance that she traveled during these three seconds.

t (s)	0	0.5	1.0	1.5	2.0	2.5	3.0
v (m/s)	0	1.9	3.3	4.5	5.5	5.9	6.2

14. Speedometer readings for a motorcycle at 12-second intervals are given in the table.
  (a) Estimate the distance traveled by the motorcycle during this time period using the velocities at the beginning of the time intervals.
  (b) Give another estimate using the velocities at the end of the time periods.
  (c) Are your estimates in parts (a) and (b) upper and lower estimates? Explain.

t (s)	0	12	24	36	48	60
v (m/s)	9.1	8.5	7.6	6.7	7.3	8.2

15. Oil leaked from a tank at a rate of $r(t)$ liters per hour. The rate decreased as time passed and values of the rate at two-hour time intervals are shown in the table. Find lower and upper estimates for the total amount of oil that leaked out.

t (h)	0	2	4	6	8	10
$r(t)$ (L/h)	8.7	7.6	6.8	6.2	5.7	5.3

16. When we estimate distances from velocity data, it is sometimes necessary to use times $t_0, t_1, t_2, t_3, \ldots$ that are not equally spaced. We can still estimate distances using the time periods $\Delta t_i = t_i - t_{i-1}$. For example, on May 7, 1992, the space shuttle *Endeavour* was launched on mission STS-49, the purpose of which was to install a new perigee kick motor in an Intelsat communications satellite. The table, provided by NASA, gives the velocity data for the shuttle between liftoff and the jettisoning of the solid rocket boosters. Use these data to estimate the height above the earth's surface of the *Endeavour*, 62 seconds after liftoff.

Event	Time (s)	Velocity (m/s)
Launch	0	0
Begin roll maneuver	10	56
End roll maneuver	15	97
Throttle to 89%	20	136
Throttle to 67%	32	226
Throttle to 104%	59	404
Maximum dynamic pressure	62	440
Solid rocket booster separation	125	1265

17. The velocity graph of a braking car is shown. Use it to estimate the distance traveled by the car while the brakes are applied.

18. The velocity graph of a car accelerating from rest to a speed of 120 km/h over a period of 30 seconds is shown. Estimate the distance traveled during this period.

19–21 Use Definition 2 to find an expression for the area under the graph of f as a limit. Do not evaluate the limit.

19. $f(x) = \dfrac{2x}{x^2 + 1}, \quad 1 \le x \le 3$

20. $f(x) = x^2 + \sqrt{1 + 2x}, \quad 4 \le x \le 7$

21. $f(x) = \sqrt{\sin x}, \quad 0 \le x \le \pi$

22–23 Determine a region whose area is equal to the given limit. Do not evaluate the limit.

22. $\displaystyle\lim_{n \to \infty} \sum_{i=1}^{n} \frac{2}{n}\left(5 + \frac{2i}{n}\right)^{10}$

23. $\displaystyle\lim_{n \to \infty} \sum_{i=1}^{n} \frac{\pi}{4n} \tan \frac{i\pi}{4n}$

24. (a) Use Definition 2 to find an expression for the area under the curve $y = x^3$ from 0 to 1 as a limit.
   (b) The following formula for the sum of the cubes of the first n integers is proved in Appendix E. Use it to evaluate the limit in part (a).

$$1^3 + 2^3 + 3^3 + \cdots + n^3 = \left[\frac{n(n+1)}{2}\right]^2$$

25. Let A be the area under the graph of an increasing continuous function f from a to b, and let L_n and R_n be the approximations to A with n subintervals using left and right endpoints, respectively.
   (a) How are A, L_n, and R_n related?
   (b) Show that

$$R_n - L_n = \frac{b-a}{n}[f(b) - f(a)]$$

   Then draw a diagram to illustrate this equation by showing

that the n rectangles representing $R_n - L_n$ can be reassembled to form a single rectangle whose area is the right side of the equation.
   (c) Deduce that

$$R_n - A < \frac{b-a}{n}[f(b) - f(a)]$$

26. If A is the area under the curve $y = e^x$ from 1 to 3, use Exercise 25 to find a value of n such that $R_n - A < 0.0001$.

CAS **27.** (a) Express the area under the curve $y = x^5$ from 0 to 2 as a limit.
   (b) Use a computer algebra system to find the sum in your expression from part (a).
   (c) Evaluate the limit in part (a).

CAS **28.** Find the exact area of the region under the graph of $y = e^{-x}$ from 0 to 2 by using a computer algebra system to evaluate the sum and then the limit in Example 3(a). Compare your answer with the estimate obtained in Example 3(b).

CAS **29.** Find the exact area under the cosine curve $y = \cos x$ from $x = 0$ to $x = b$, where $0 \le b \le \pi/2$. (Use a computer algebra system both to evaluate the sum and compute the limit.) In particular, what is the area if $b = \pi/2$?

30. (a) Let A_n be the area of a polygon with n equal sides inscribed in a circle with radius r. By dividing the polygon into n congruent triangles with central angle $2\pi/n$, show that

$$A_n = \tfrac{1}{2}nr^2 \sin\left(\frac{2\pi}{n}\right)$$

   (b) Show that $\lim_{n \to \infty} A_n = \pi r^2$. [*Hint:* Use Equation 3.3.2 on page 192.]

5.2 The Definite Integral

We saw in Section 5.1 that a limit of the form

$$\boxed{1} \qquad \lim_{n \to \infty} \sum_{i=1}^{n} f(x_i^*)\,\Delta x = \lim_{n \to \infty} \left[f(x_1^*)\,\Delta x + f(x_2^*)\,\Delta x + \cdots + f(x_n^*)\,\Delta x\right]$$

arises when we compute an area. We also saw that it arises when we try to find the distance traveled by an object. It turns out that this same type of limit occurs in a wide variety of situations even when f is not necessarily a positive function. In Chapters 6 and 8 we will see that limits of the form $\boxed{1}$ also arise in finding lengths of curves, volumes of solids, centers of mass, force due to water pressure, and work, as well as other quantities. We therefore give this type of limit a special name and notation.

---

2 **Definition of a Definite Integral** If f is a function defined for $a \leqslant x \leqslant b$, we divide the interval $[a, b]$ into n subintervals of equal width $\Delta x = (b - a)/n$. We let $x_0 (= a)$, $x_1, x_2, \ldots, x_n (= b)$ be the endpoints of these subintervals and we let $x_1^*, x_2^*, \ldots, x_n^*$ be any **sample points** in these subintervals, so x_i^* lies in the ith subinterval $[x_{i-1}, x_i]$. Then the **definite integral of f from a to b is**

$$\int_a^b f(x)\, dx = \lim_{n \to \infty} \sum_{i=1}^n f(x_i^*)\, \Delta x$$

provided that this limit exists and gives the same value for all possible choices of sample points. If it does exist, we say that f is **integrable** on $[a, b]$.

The precise meaning of the limit that defines the integral is as follows:

For every number $\varepsilon > 0$ there is an integer N such that

$$\left| \int_a^b f(x)\, dx - \sum_{i=1}^n f(x_i^*)\, \Delta x \right| < \varepsilon$$

for every integer $n > N$ and for every choice of x_i^* in $[x_{i-1}, x_i]$.

NOTE 1 The symbol $\int$ was introduced by Leibniz and is called an **integral sign**. It is an elongated S and was chosen because an integral is a limit of sums. In the notation $\int_a^b f(x)\, dx$, $f(x)$ is called the **integrand** and a and b are called the **limits of integration**; a is the **lower limit** and b is the **upper limit**. For now, the symbol dx has no meaning by itself; $\int_a^b f(x)\, dx$ is all one symbol. The dx simply indicates that the independent variable is x. The procedure of calculating an integral is called **integration**.

NOTE 2 The definite integral $\int_a^b f(x)\, dx$ is a number; it does not depend on x. In fact, we could use any letter in place of x without changing the value of the integral:

$$\int_a^b f(x)\, dx = \int_a^b f(t)\, dt = \int_a^b f(r)\, dr$$

NOTE 3 The sum

$$\sum_{i=1}^n f(x_i^*)\, \Delta x$$

Riemann

Bernhard Riemann received his Ph.D. under the direction of the legendary Gauss at the University of Göttingen and remained there to teach. Gauss, who was not in the habit of praising other mathematicians, spoke of Riemann's "creative, active, truly mathematical mind and gloriously fertile originality." The definition 2 of an integral that we use is due to Riemann. He also made major contributions to the theory of functions of a complex variable, mathematical physics, number theory, and the foundations of geometry. Riemann's broad concept of space and geometry turned out to be the right setting, 50 years later, for Einstein's general relativity theory. Riemann's health was poor throughout his life, and he died of tuberculosis at the age of 39.

that occurs in Definition 2 is called a **Riemann sum** after the German mathematician Bernhard Riemann (1826–1866). So Definition 2 says that the definite integral of an integrable function can be approximated to within any desired degree of accuracy by a Riemann sum.

We know that if f happens to be positive, then the Riemann sum can be interpreted as a sum of areas of approximating rectangles (see Figure 1). By comparing Definition 2 with the definition of area in Section 5.1, we see that the definite integral $\int_a^b f(x)\, dx$ can be interpreted as the area under the curve $y = f(x)$ from a to b. (See Figure 2.)

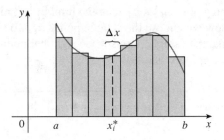

FIGURE 1

If $f(x) \geq 0$, the Riemann sum $\Sigma f(x_i^*) \, \Delta x$ is the sum of areas of rectangles.

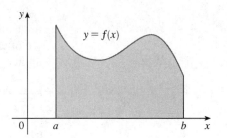

FIGURE 2

If $f(x) \geq 0$, the integral $\int_a^b f(x) \, dx$ is the area under the curve $y = f(x)$ from a to b.

FIGURE 3

$\Sigma f(x_i^*) \, \Delta x$ is an approximation to the net area.

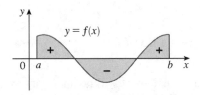

FIGURE 4

$\int_a^b f(x) \, dx$ is the net area.

If f takes on both positive and negative values, as in Figure 3, then the Riemann sum is the sum of the areas of the rectangles that lie above the x-axis and the *negatives* of the areas of the rectangles that lie below the x-axis (the areas of the blue rectangles *minus* the areas of the gold rectangles). When we take the limit of such Riemann sums, we get the situation illustrated in Figure 4. A definite integral can be interpreted as a **net area**, that is, a difference of areas:

$$\int_a^b f(x) \, dx = A_1 - A_2$$

where A_1 is the area of the region above the x-axis and below the graph of f, and A_2 is the area of the region below the x-axis and above the graph of f.

NOTE 4 Although we have defined $\int_a^b f(x) \, dx$ by dividing $[a, b]$ into subintervals of equal width, there are situations in which it is advantageous to work with subintervals of unequal width. For instance, in Exercise 16 in Section 5.1 NASA provided velocity data at times that were not equally spaced, but we were still able to estimate the distance traveled. And there are methods for numerical integration that take advantage of unequal subintervals.

If the subinterval widths are $\Delta x_1, \Delta x_2, \ldots, \Delta x_n$, we have to ensure that all these widths approach 0 in the limiting process. This happens if the largest width, $\max \Delta x_i$, approaches 0. So in this case the definition of a definite integral becomes

$$\int_a^b f(x) \, dx = \lim_{\max \Delta x_i \to 0} \sum_{i=1}^n f(x_i^*) \, \Delta x_i$$

NOTE 5 We have defined the definite integral for an integrable function, but not all functions are integrable (see Exercises 69–70). The following theorem shows that the most commonly occurring functions are in fact integrable. The theorem is proved in more advanced courses.

---

3 **Theorem** If f is continuous on $[a, b]$, or if f has only a finite number of jump discontinuities, then f is integrable on $[a, b]$; that is, the definite integral $\int_a^b f(x) \, dx$ exists.

If f is integrable on $[a, b]$, then the limit in Definition 2 exists and gives the same value no matter how we choose the sample points x_i^*. To simplify the calculation of the integral we often take the sample points to be right endpoints. Then $x_i^* = x_i$ and the definition of an integral simplifies as follows.

---

4 **Theorem** If f is integrable on $[a, b]$, then

$$\int_a^b f(x)\, dx = \lim_{n \to \infty} \sum_{i=1}^n f(x_i)\, \Delta x$$

where

$$\Delta x = \frac{b - a}{n} \qquad \text{and} \qquad x_i = a + i\, \Delta x$$

EXAMPLE 1 Express

$$\lim_{n \to \infty} \sum_{i=1}^n (x_i^3 + x_i \sin x_i)\, \Delta x$$

as an integral on the interval $[0, \pi]$.

SOLUTION Comparing the given limit with the limit in Theorem 4, we see that they will be identical if we choose $f(x) = x^3 + x \sin x$. We are given that $a = 0$ and $b = \pi$. Therefore, by Theorem 4, we have

$$\lim_{n \to \infty} \sum_{i=1}^n (x_i^3 + x_i \sin x_i)\, \Delta x = \int_0^\pi (x^3 + x \sin x)\, dx \qquad \blacksquare$$

Later, when we apply the definite integral to physical situations, it will be important to recognize limits of sums as integrals, as we did in Example 1. When Leibniz chose the notation for an integral, he chose the ingredients as reminders of the limiting process. In general, when we write

$$\lim_{n \to \infty} \sum_{i=1}^n f(x_i^*)\, \Delta x = \int_a^b f(x)\, dx$$

we replace $\lim \Sigma$ by $\int$, x_i^* by x, and Δx by dx.

� Evaluating Integrals

When we use a limit to evaluate a definite integral, we need to know how to work with sums. The following three equations give formulas for sums of powers of positive integers. Equation 5 may be familiar to you from a course in algebra. Equations 6 and 7 were discussed in Section 5.1 and are proved in Appendix E.

5
$$\sum_{i=1}^n i = \frac{n(n + 1)}{2}$$

6
$$\sum_{i=1}^n i^2 = \frac{n(n + 1)(2n + 1)}{6}$$

7
$$\sum_{i=1}^n i^3 = \left[\frac{n(n + 1)}{2} \right]^2$$

The remaining formulas are simple rules for working with sigma notation:

Formulas 8–11 are proved by writing out
each side in expanded form. The left side of
Equation 9 is

$$ca_1 + ca_2 + \cdots + ca_n$$

The right side is

$$c(a_1 + a_2 + \cdots + a_n)$$

These are equal by the distributive property.
The other formulas are discussed in Appendix E.

$$\boxed{8} \qquad \sum_{i=1}^{n} c = nc$$

$$\boxed{9} \qquad \sum_{i=1}^{n} ca_i = c \sum_{i=1}^{n} a_i$$

$$\boxed{10} \qquad \sum_{i=1}^{n} (a_i + b_i) = \sum_{i=1}^{n} a_i + \sum_{i=1}^{n} b_i$$

$$\boxed{11} \qquad \sum_{i=1}^{n} (a_i - b_i) = \sum_{i=1}^{n} a_i - \sum_{i=1}^{n} b_i$$

EXAMPLE 2

(a) Evaluate the Riemann sum for $f(x) = x^3 - 6x$, taking the sample points to be right endpoints and $a = 0$, $b = 3$, and $n = 6$.

(b) Evaluate $\int_0^3 (x^3 - 6x)\, dx$.

SOLUTION

(a) With $n = 6$ the interval width is

$$\Delta x = \frac{b - a}{n} = \frac{3 - 0}{6} = \frac{1}{2}$$

and the right endpoints are $x_1 = 0.5$, $x_2 = 1.0$, $x_3 = 1.5$, $x_4 = 2.0$, $x_5 = 2.5$, and $x_6 = 3.0$. So the Riemann sum is

$$R_6 = \sum_{i=1}^{6} f(x_i)\, \Delta x$$

$$= f(0.5)\, \Delta x + f(1.0)\, \Delta x + f(1.5)\, \Delta x + f(2.0)\, \Delta x + f(2.5)\, \Delta x + f(3.0)\, \Delta x$$

$$= \tfrac{1}{2}(-2.875 - 5 - 5.625 - 4 + 0.625 + 9)$$

$$= -3.9375$$

Notice that f is not a positive function and so the Riemann sum does not represent a sum of areas of rectangles. But it does represent the sum of the areas of the blue rectangles (above the x-axis) minus the sum of the areas of the gold rectangles (below the x-axis) in Figure 5.

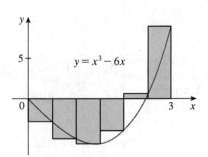

FIGURE 5

(b) With n subintervals we have

$$\Delta x = \frac{b - a}{n} = \frac{3}{n}$$

Thus $x_0 = 0$, $x_1 = 3/n$, $x_2 = 6/n$, $x_3 = 9/n$, and, in general, $x_i = 3i/n$. Since we are using right endpoints, we can use Theorem 4:

$$\int_0^3 (x^3 - 6x)\, dx = \lim_{n \to \infty} \sum_{i=1}^n f(x_i)\,\Delta x = \lim_{n \to \infty} \sum_{i=1}^n f\left(\frac{3i}{n}\right)\frac{3}{n}$$

In the sum, n is a constant (unlike i), so we can move $3/n$ in front of the Σ sign.

$$= \lim_{n \to \infty} \frac{3}{n} \sum_{i=1}^n \left[\left(\frac{3i}{n}\right)^3 - 6\left(\frac{3i}{n}\right)\right] \qquad \text{(Equation 9 with } c = 3/n)$$

$$= \lim_{n \to \infty} \frac{3}{n} \sum_{i=1}^n \left[\frac{27}{n^3} i^3 - \frac{18}{n} i\right]$$

$$= \lim_{n \to \infty} \left[\frac{81}{n^4} \sum_{i=1}^n i^3 - \frac{54}{n^2} \sum_{i=1}^n i\right] \qquad \text{(Equations 11 and 9)}$$

$$= \lim_{n \to \infty} \left\{\frac{81}{n^4}\left[\frac{n(n+1)}{2}\right]^2 - \frac{54}{n^2}\frac{n(n+1)}{2}\right\} \qquad \text{(Equations 7 and 5)}$$

$$= \lim_{n \to \infty} \left[\frac{81}{4}\left(1 + \frac{1}{n}\right)^2 - 27\left(1 + \frac{1}{n}\right)\right]$$

$$= \frac{81}{4} - 27 = -\frac{27}{4} = -6.75$$

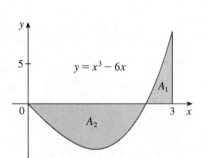

FIGURE 6
$$\int_0^3 (x^3 - 6x)\, dx = A_1 - A_2 = -6.75$$

This integral can't be interpreted as an area because f takes on both positive and negative values. But it can be interpreted as the difference of areas $A_1 - A_2$, where A_1 and A_2 are shown in Figure 6.

Figure 7 illustrates the calculation by showing the positive and negative terms in the right Riemann sum R_n for $n = 40$. The values in the table show the Riemann sums approaching the exact value of the integral, -6.75, as $n \to \infty$.

FIGURE 7
$R_{40} \approx -6.3998$

n	R_n
40	-6.3998
100	-6.6130
500	-6.7229
1000	-6.7365
5000	-6.7473

A much simpler method for evaluating the integral in Example 2 will be given in Section 5.4.

Because $f(x) = e^x$ is positive, the integral in Example 3 represents the area shown in Figure 8.

FIGURE 8

EXAMPLE 3
(a) Set up an expression for $\int_1^3 e^x \, dx$ as a limit of sums.
(b) Use a computer algebra system to evaluate the expression.

SOLUTION
(a) Here we have $f(x) = e^x$, $a = 1$, $b = 3$, and

$$\Delta x = \frac{b - a}{n} = \frac{2}{n}$$

So $x_0 = 1$, $x_1 = 1 + 2/n$, $x_2 = 1 + 4/n$, $x_3 = 1 + 6/n$, and

$$x_i = 1 + \frac{2i}{n}$$

From Theorem 4, we get

$$\int_1^3 e^x \, dx = \lim_{n \to \infty} \sum_{i=1}^n f(x_i) \, \Delta x$$

$$= \lim_{n \to \infty} \sum_{i=1}^n f\left(1 + \frac{2i}{n}\right) \frac{2}{n}$$

$$= \lim_{n \to \infty} \frac{2}{n} \sum_{i=1}^n e^{1 + 2i/n}$$

A computer algebra system is able to find an explicit expression for this sum because it is a geometric series. The limit could be found using l'Hospital's Rule.

(b) If we ask a computer algebra system to evaluate the sum and simplify, we obtain

$$\sum_{i=1}^n e^{1 + 2i/n} = \frac{e^{(3n+2)/n} - e^{(n+2)/n}}{e^{2/n} - 1}$$

Now we ask the computer algebra system to evaluate the limit:

$$\int_1^3 e^x \, dx = \lim_{n \to \infty} \frac{2}{n} \cdot \frac{e^{(3n+2)/n} - e^{(n+2)/n}}{e^{2/n} - 1} = e^3 - e$$

We will learn a much easier method for the evaluation of integrals in the next section.

V   EXAMPLE 4 Evaluate the following integrals by interpreting each in terms of areas.

(a) $\displaystyle\int_0^1 \sqrt{1 - x^2} \, dx$ (b) $\displaystyle\int_0^3 (x - 1) \, dx$

SOLUTION
(a) Since $f(x) = \sqrt{1 - x^2} \geq 0$, we can interpret this integral as the area under the curve $y = \sqrt{1 - x^2}$ from 0 to 1. But, since $y^2 = 1 - x^2$, we get $x^2 + y^2 = 1$, which shows that the graph of f is the quarter-circle with radius 1 in Figure 9. Therefore

$$\int_0^1 \sqrt{1 - x^2} \, dx = \tfrac{1}{4} \pi (1)^2 = \frac{\pi}{4}$$

(In Section 7.3 we will be able to *prove* that the area of a circle of radius r is πr^2.)

FIGURE 9

(b) The graph of $y = x - 1$ is the line with slope 1 shown in Figure 10. We compute the integral as the difference of the areas of the two triangles:

$$\int_0^3 (x - 1)\, dx = A_1 - A_2 = \tfrac{1}{2}(2 \cdot 2) - \tfrac{1}{2}(1 \cdot 1) = 1.5$$

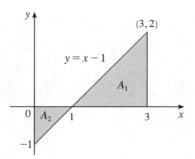

FIGURE 10

The Midpoint Rule

We often choose the sample point x_i^* to be the right endpoint of the ith subinterval because it is convenient for computing the limit. But if the purpose is to find an *approximation* to an integral, it is usually better to choose x_i^* to be the midpoint of the interval, which we denote by $\bar{x}_i$. Any Riemann sum is an approximation to an integral, but if we use midpoints we get the following approximation.

TEC Module 5.2/7.7 shows how the Midpoint Rule estimates improve as n increases.

Midpoint Rule

$$\int_a^b f(x)\, dx \approx \sum_{i=1}^n f(\bar{x}_i)\, \Delta x = \Delta x\, [\, f(\bar{x}_1) + \cdots + f(\bar{x}_n)\,]$$

where
$$\Delta x = \frac{b - a}{n}$$

and
$$\bar{x}_i = \tfrac{1}{2}(x_{i-1} + x_i) = \text{midpoint of } [x_{i-1}, x_i]$$

V **EXAMPLE 5** Use the Midpoint Rule with $n = 5$ to approximate $\int_1^2 \dfrac{1}{x}\, dx$.

SOLUTION The endpoints of the five subintervals are 1, 1.2, 1.4, 1.6, 1.8, and 2.0, so the midpoints are 1.1, 1.3, 1.5, 1.7, and 1.9. The width of the subintervals is $\Delta x = (2 - 1)/5 = \tfrac{1}{5}$, so the Midpoint Rule gives

$$\int_1^2 \frac{1}{x}\, dx \approx \Delta x\, [\, f(1.1) + f(1.3) + f(1.5) + f(1.7) + f(1.9)\,]$$

$$= \frac{1}{5}\left(\frac{1}{1.1} + \frac{1}{1.3} + \frac{1}{1.5} + \frac{1}{1.7} + \frac{1}{1.9} \right)$$

$$\approx 0.691908$$

FIGURE 11

Since $f(x) = 1/x > 0$ for $1 \leqslant x \leqslant 2$, the integral represents an area, and the approximation given by the Midpoint Rule is the sum of the areas of the rectangles shown in Figure 11.

At the moment we don't know how accurate the approximation in Example 5 is, but in Section 7.7 we will learn a method for estimating the error involved in using the Midpoint Rule. At that time we will discuss other methods for approximating definite integrals.

If we apply the Midpoint Rule to the integral in Example 2, we get the picture in Figure 12. The approximation $M_{40} \approx -6.7563$ is much closer to the true value -6.75 than the right endpoint approximation, $R_{40} \approx -6.3998$, shown in Figure 7.

TEC In Visual 5.2 you can compare left, right, and midpoint approximations to the integral in Example 2 for different values of n.

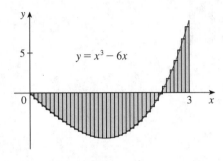

FIGURE 12

$M_{40} \approx -6.7563$

Properties of the Definite Integral

When we defined the definite integral $\int_a^b f(x)\,dx$, we implicitly assumed that $a < b$. But the definition as a limit of Riemann sums makes sense even if $a > b$. Notice that if we reverse a and b, then Δx changes from $(b - a)/n$ to $(a - b)/n$. Therefore

$$\int_b^a f(x)\,dx = -\int_a^b f(x)\,dx$$

If $a = b$, then $\Delta x = 0$ and so

$$\int_a^a f(x)\,dx = 0$$

We now develop some basic properties of integrals that will help us to evaluate integrals in a simple manner. We assume that f and g are continuous functions.

Properties of the Integral

1. $\displaystyle\int_a^b c\,dx = c(b - a),$ where c is any constant

2. $\displaystyle\int_a^b [f(x) + g(x)]\,dx = \int_a^b f(x)\,dx + \int_a^b g(x)\,dx$

3. $\displaystyle\int_a^b cf(x)\,dx = c\int_a^b f(x)\,dx,$ where c is any constant

4. $\displaystyle\int_a^b [f(x) - g(x)]\,dx = \int_a^b f(x)\,dx - \int_a^b g(x)\,dx$

FIGURE 13

$\int_a^b c\,dx = c(b - a)$

Property 1 says that the integral of a constant function $f(x) = c$ is the constant times the length of the interval. If $c > 0$ and $a < b$, this is to be expected because $c(b - a)$ is the area of the shaded rectangle in Figure 13.

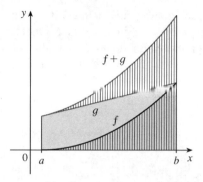

FIGURE 14

$$\int_a^b [f(x) + g(x)]\,dx =$$
$$\int_a^b f(x)\,dx + \int_a^b g(x)\,dx$$

Property 3 seems intuitively reasonable because we know that multiplying a function by a positive number c stretches or shrinks its graph vertically by a factor of c. So it stretches or shrinks each approximating rectangle by a factor c and therefore it has the effect of multiplying the area by c.

Property 2 says that the integral of a sum is the sum of the integrals. For positive functions it says that the area under $f + g$ is the area under f plus the area under g. Figure 14 helps us understand why this is true: In view of how graphical addition works, the corresponding vertical line segments have equal height.

In general, Property 2 follows from Theorem 4 and the fact that the limit of a sum is the sum of the limits:

$$\int_a^b [f(x) + g(x)]\,dx = \lim_{n \to \infty} \sum_{i=1}^n [f(x_i) + g(x_i)]\,\Delta x$$

$$= \lim_{n \to \infty} \left[\sum_{i=1}^n f(x_i)\,\Delta x + \sum_{i=1}^n g(x_i)\,\Delta x \right]$$

$$= \lim_{n \to \infty} \sum_{i=1}^n f(x_i)\,\Delta x + \lim_{n \to \infty} \sum_{i=1}^n g(x_i)\,\Delta x$$

$$= \int_a^b f(x)\,dx + \int_a^b g(x)\,dx$$

Property 3 can be proved in a similar manner and says that the integral of a constant times a function is the constant times the integral of the function. In other words, a constant (but *only* a constant) can be taken in front of an integral sign. Property 4 is proved by writing $f - g = f + (-g)$ and using Properties 2 and 3 with $c = -1$.

EXAMPLE 6   Use the properties of integrals to evaluate $\int_0^1 (4 + 3x^2)\,dx$.

SOLUTION   Using Properties 2 and 3 of integrals, we have

$$\int_0^1 (4 + 3x^2)\,dx = \int_0^1 4\,dx + \int_0^1 3x^2\,dx = \int_0^1 4\,dx + 3\int_0^1 x^2\,dx$$

We know from Property 1 that

$$\int_0^1 4\,dx = 4(1 - 0) = 4$$

and we found in Example 2 in Section 5.1 that $\int_0^1 x^2\,dx = \frac{1}{3}$. So

$$\int_0^1 (4 + 3x^2)\,dx = \int_0^1 4\,dx + 3\int_0^1 x^2\,dx$$

$$= 4 + 3 \cdot \tfrac{1}{3} = 5$$

The next property tells us how to combine integrals of the same function over adjacent intervals:

5.
$$\int_a^c f(x)\,dx + \int_c^b f(x)\,dx = \int_a^b f(x)\,dx$$

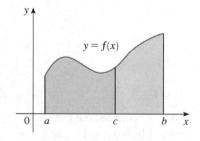

FIGURE 15

This is not easy to prove in general, but for the case where $f(x) \geqslant 0$ and $a < c < b$ Property 5 can be seen from the geometric interpretation in Figure 15: The area under $y = f(x)$ from a to c plus the area from c to b is equal to the total area from a to b.

V **EXAMPLE 7** If it is known that $\int_0^{10} f(x)\,dx = 17$ and $\int_0^8 f(x)\,dx = 12$, find $\int_8^{10} f(x)\,dx$.

SOLUTION By Property 5, we have

$$\int_0^8 f(x)\,dx + \int_8^{10} f(x)\,dx = \int_0^{10} f(x)\,dx$$

so $$\int_8^{10} f(x)\,dx = \int_0^{10} f(x)\,dx - \int_0^8 f(x)\,dx = 17 - 12 = 5 \qquad \blacksquare$$

Properties 1–5 are true whether $a < b$, $a = b$, or $a > b$. The following properties, in which we compare sizes of functions and sizes of integrals, are true only if $a \leqslant b$.

Comparison Properties of the Integral

6. If $f(x) \geqslant 0$ for $a \leqslant x \leqslant b$, then $\int_a^b f(x)\,dx \geqslant 0$.

7. If $f(x) \geqslant g(x)$ for $a \leqslant x \leqslant b$, then $\int_a^b f(x)\,dx \geqslant \int_a^b g(x)\,dx$.

8. If $m \leqslant f(x) \leqslant M$ for $a \leqslant x \leqslant b$, then

$$m(b - a) \leqslant \int_a^b f(x)\,dx \leqslant M(b - a)$$

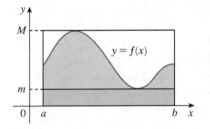

FIGURE 16

If $f(x) \geqslant 0$, then $\int_a^b f(x)\,dx$ represents the area under the graph of f, so the geometric interpretation of Property 6 is simply that areas are positive. (It also follows directly from the definition because all the quantities involved are positive.) Property 7 says that a bigger function has a bigger integral. It follows from Properties 6 and 4 because $f - g \geqslant 0$.

Property 8 is illustrated by Figure 16 for the case where $f(x) \geqslant 0$. If f is continuous we could take m and M to be the absolute minimum and maximum values of f on the interval $[a, b]$. In this case Property 8 says that the area under the graph of f is greater than the area of the rectangle with height m and less than the area of the rectangle with height M.

PROOF OF PROPERTY 8 Since $m \leqslant f(x) \leqslant M$, Property 7 gives

$$\int_a^b m\,dx \leqslant \int_a^b f(x)\,dx \leqslant \int_a^b M\,dx$$

Using Property 1 to evaluate the integrals on the left and right sides, we obtain

$$m(b - a) \leqslant \int_a^b f(x)\,dx \leqslant M(b - a) \qquad \blacksquare$$

Property 8 is useful when all we want is a rough estimate of the size of an integral without going to the bother of using the Midpoint Rule.

EXAMPLE 8 Use Property 8 to estimate $\int_0^1 e^{-x^2}\,dx$.

SOLUTION Because $f(x) = e^{-x^2}$ is a decreasing function on $[0, 1]$, its absolute maximum value is $M = f(0) = 1$ and its absolute minimum value is $m = f(1) = e^{-1}$. Thus, by

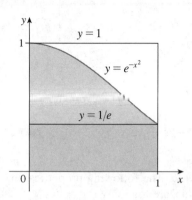

FIGURE 17

Property 8,

$$e^{-1}(1 - 0) \le \int_0^1 e^{-x^2} dx \le 1(1 - 0)$$

$$e^{-1} \le \int_0^1 e^{-x^2} dx \le 1$$

Since $e^{-1} \approx 0.3679$, we can write

$$0.367 \le \int_0^1 e^{-x^2} dx \le 1$$

The result of Example 8 is illustrated in Figure 17. The integral is greater than the area of the lower rectangle and less than the area of the square.

5.2 Exercises

1. Evaluate the Riemann sum for $f(x) = 3 - \frac{1}{2}x$, $2 \le x \le 14$, with six subintervals, taking the sample points to be left endpoints. Explain, with the aid of a diagram, what the Riemann sum represents.

2. If $f(x) = x^2 - 2x$, $0 \le x \le 3$, evaluate the Riemann sum with $n = 6$, taking the sample points to be right endpoints. What does the Riemann sum represent? Illustrate with a diagram.

3. If $f(x) = e^x - 2$, $0 \le x \le 2$, find the Riemann sum with $n = 4$ correct to six decimal places, taking the sample points to be midpoints. What does the Riemann sum represent? Illustrate with a diagram.

4. (a) Find the Riemann sum for $f(x) = \sin x$, $0 \le x \le 3\pi/2$, with six terms, taking the sample points to be right endpoints. (Give your answer correct to six decimal places.) Explain what the Riemann sum represents with the aid of a sketch.
   (b) Repeat part (a) with midpoints as the sample points.

5. The graph of a function f is given. Estimate $\int_0^{10} f(x)\,dx$ using five subintervals with (a) right endpoints, (b) left endpoints, and (c) midpoints.

6. The graph of g is shown. Estimate $\int_{-2}^4 g(x)\,dx$ with six subintervals using (a) right endpoints, (b) left endpoints, and (c) midpoints.

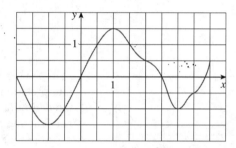

7. A table of values of an increasing function f is shown. Use the table to find lower and upper estimates for $\int_0^{25} f(x)\,dx$.

x	0	5	10	15	20	25
$f(x)$	-42	-37	-25	-6	15	36

8. The table gives the values of a function obtained from an experiment. Use them to estimate $\int_3^9 f(x)\,dx$ using three equal subintervals with (a) right endpoints, (b) left endpoints, and (c) midpoints. If the function is known to be an increasing function, can you say whether your estimates are less than or greater than the exact value of the integral?

x	3	4	5	6	7	8	9
$f(x)$	-3.4	-2.1	-0.6	0.3	0.9	1.4	1.8

EXAMPLE 4 Find $\int \dfrac{x}{\sqrt{x^2+4}}\,dx$.

SOLUTION It would be possible to use the trigonometric substitution $x = 2\tan\theta$ here (as in Example 3). But the direct substitution $u = x^2 + 4$ is simpler, because then $du = 2x\,dx$ and

$$\int \frac{x}{\sqrt{x^2+4}}\,dx = \frac{1}{2}\int \frac{du}{\sqrt{u}} = \sqrt{u} + C = \sqrt{x^2+4} + C$$

NOTE Example 4 illustrates the fact that even when trigonometric substitutions are possible, they may not give the easiest solution. You should look for a simpler method first.

EXAMPLE 5 Evaluate $\int \dfrac{dx}{\sqrt{x^2-a^2}}$, where $a > 0$.

SOLUTION 1 We let $x = a\sec\theta$, where $0 < \theta < \pi/2$ or $\pi < \theta < 3\pi/2$. Then $dx = a\sec\theta\tan\theta\,d\theta$ and

$$\sqrt{x^2-a^2} = \sqrt{a^2(\sec^2\theta - 1)} = \sqrt{a^2\tan^2\theta} = a\,|\tan\theta| = a\tan\theta$$

Therefore

$$\int \frac{dx}{\sqrt{x^2-a^2}} = \int \frac{a\sec\theta\tan\theta}{a\tan\theta}\,d\theta = \int \sec\theta\,d\theta = \ln|\sec\theta + \tan\theta| + C$$

The triangle in Figure 4 gives $\tan\theta = \sqrt{x^2-a^2}/a$, so we have

$$\int \frac{dx}{\sqrt{x^2-a^2}} = \ln\left| \frac{x}{a} + \frac{\sqrt{x^2-a^2}}{a} \right| + C$$

$$= \ln\left| x + \sqrt{x^2-a^2} \right| - \ln a + C$$

Writing $C_1 = C - \ln a$, we have

$$\boxed{1} \qquad\qquad \int \frac{dx}{\sqrt{x^2-a^2}} = \ln\left| x + \sqrt{x^2-a^2} \right| + C_1$$

FIGURE 4

$\sec\theta = \dfrac{x}{a}$

SOLUTION 2 For $x > 0$ the hyperbolic substitution $x = a\cosh t$ can also be used. Using the identity $\cosh^2 y - \sinh^2 y = 1$, we have

$$\sqrt{x^2-a^2} = \sqrt{a^2(\cosh^2 t - 1)} = \sqrt{a^2\sinh^2 t} = a\sinh t$$

Since $dx = a\sinh t\,dt$, we obtain

$$\int \frac{dx}{\sqrt{x^2-a^2}} = \int \frac{a\sinh t\,dt}{a\sinh t} = \int dt = t + C$$

Since $\cosh t = x/a$, we have $t = \cosh^{-1}(x/a)$ and

$$\boxed{2} \qquad\qquad \int \frac{dx}{\sqrt{x^2-a^2}} = \cosh^{-1}\left(\frac{x}{a}\right) + C$$

Although Formulas 1 and 2 look quite different, they are actually equivalent by Formula 3.11.4.

NOTE As Example 5 illustrates, hyperbolic substitutions can be used in place of trigonometric substitutions and sometimes they lead to simpler answers. But we usually use trigonometric substitutions because trigonometric identities are more familiar than hyperbolic identities.

As Example 6 shows, trigonometric substitution is sometimes a good idea when $(x^2 + a^2)^{n/2}$ occurs in an integral, where n is any integer. The same is true when $(a^2 - x^2)^{n/2}$ or $(x^2 - a^2)^{n/2}$ occur.

EXAMPLE 6 Find $\displaystyle\int_0^{3\sqrt{3}/2} \frac{x^3}{(4x^2 + 9)^{3/2}}\, dx$.

SOLUTION First we note that $(4x^2 + 9)^{3/2} = (\sqrt{4x^2 + 9})^3$ so trigonometric substitution is appropriate. Although $\sqrt{4x^2 + 9}$ is not quite one of the expressions in the table of trigonometric substitutions, it becomes one of them if we make the preliminary substitution $u = 2x$. When we combine this with the tangent substitution, we have $x = \frac{3}{2}\tan\theta$, which gives $dx = \frac{3}{2}\sec^2\theta\, d\theta$ and

$$\sqrt{4x^2 + 9} = \sqrt{9\tan^2\theta + 9} = 3\sec\theta$$

When $x = 0$, $\tan\theta = 0$, so $\theta = 0$; when $x = 3\sqrt{3}/2$, $\tan\theta = \sqrt{3}$, so $\theta = \pi/3$.

$$\int_0^{3\sqrt{3}/2} \frac{x^3}{(4x^2 + 9)^{3/2}}\, dx = \int_0^{\pi/3} \frac{\frac{27}{8}\tan^3\theta}{27\sec^3\theta}\, \frac{3}{2}\sec^2\theta\, d\theta$$

$$= \frac{3}{16}\int_0^{\pi/3} \frac{\tan^3\theta}{\sec\theta}\, d\theta = \frac{3}{16}\int_0^{\pi/3} \frac{\sin^3\theta}{\cos^2\theta}\, d\theta$$

$$= \frac{3}{16}\int_0^{\pi/3} \frac{1 - \cos^2\theta}{\cos^2\theta}\, \sin\theta\, d\theta$$

Now we substitute $u = \cos\theta$ so that $du = -\sin\theta\, d\theta$. When $\theta = 0$, $u = 1$; when $\theta = \pi/3$, $u = \frac{1}{2}$. Therefore

$$\int_0^{3\sqrt{3}/2} \frac{x^3}{(4x^2 + 9)^{3/2}}\, dx = -\frac{3}{16}\int_1^{1/2} \frac{1 - u^2}{u^2}\, du$$

$$= \frac{3}{16}\int_1^{1/2} (1 - u^{-2})\, du = \frac{3}{16}\left[u + \frac{1}{u}\right]_1^{1/2}$$

$$= \frac{3}{16}\left[\left(\tfrac{1}{2} + 2\right) - (1 + 1)\right] = \frac{3}{32}$$

EXAMPLE 7 Evaluate $\displaystyle\int \frac{x}{\sqrt{3 - 2x - x^2}}\, dx$.

SOLUTION We can transform the integrand into a function for which trigonometric substitution is appropriate by first completing the square under the root sign:

$$3 - 2x - x^2 = 3 - (x^2 + 2x) = 3 + 1 - (x^2 + 2x + 1)$$

$$= 4 - (x + 1)^2$$

This suggests that we make the substitution $u = x + 1$. Then $du = dx$ and $x = u - 1$, so

$$\int \frac{x}{\sqrt{3 - 2x - x^2}}\, dx = \int \frac{u - 1}{\sqrt{4 - u^2}}\, du$$

Figure 5 shows the graphs of the integrand in Example 7 and its indefinite integral (with $C = 0$). Which is which?

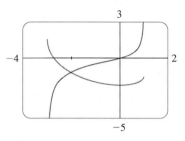

FIGURE 5

We now substitute $u = 2 \sin \theta$, giving $du = 2 \cos \theta \, d\theta$ and $\sqrt{4 - u^2} = 2 \cos \theta$, so

$$\int \frac{x}{\sqrt{3 - 2x - x^2}} \, dx = \int \frac{2 \sin \theta - 1}{2 \cos \theta} \, 2 \cos \theta \, d\theta$$

$$= \int (2 \sin \theta - 1) \, d\theta$$

$$= -2 \cos \theta - \theta + C$$

$$= -\sqrt{4 - u^2} - \sin^{-1}\left(\frac{u}{2}\right) + C$$

$$= -\sqrt{3 - 2x - x^2} - \sin^{-1}\left(\frac{x + 1}{2}\right) + C$$

7.3   Exercises

1–3 Evaluate the integral using the indicated trigonometric substitution. Sketch and label the associated right triangle.

1. $\displaystyle\int \frac{1}{x^2 \sqrt{x^2 - 9}} \, dx; \quad x = 3 \sec \theta$

2. $\displaystyle\int x^3 \sqrt{9 - x^2} \, dx; \quad x = 3 \sin \theta$

3. $\displaystyle\int \frac{x^3}{\sqrt{x^2 + 9}} \, dx; \quad x = 3 \tan \theta$

4–30 Evaluate the integral.

4. $\displaystyle\int_0^1 x^3 \sqrt{1 - x^2} \, dx$

5. $\displaystyle\int_{\sqrt{2}}^2 \frac{1}{t^3 \sqrt{t^2 - 1}} \, dt$

6. $\displaystyle\int_0^3 \frac{x}{\sqrt{36 - x^2}} \, dx$

7. $\displaystyle\int_0^a \frac{dx}{(a^2 + x^2)^{3/2}}, \quad a > 0$

8. $\displaystyle\int \frac{dt}{t^2 \sqrt{t^2 - 16}}$

9. $\displaystyle\int \frac{dx}{\sqrt{x^2 + 16}}$

10. $\displaystyle\int \frac{t^5}{\sqrt{t^2 + 2}} \, dt$

11. $\displaystyle\int \sqrt{1 - 4x^2} \, dx$

12. $\displaystyle\int \frac{du}{u \sqrt{5 - u^2}}$

13. $\displaystyle\int \frac{\sqrt{x^2 - 9}}{x^3} \, dx$

14. $\displaystyle\int_0^1 \frac{dx}{(x^2 + 1)^2}$

15. $\displaystyle\int_0^a x^2 \sqrt{a^2 - x^2} \, dx$

16. $\displaystyle\int_{\sqrt{2}/3}^{2/3} \frac{dx}{x^5 \sqrt{9x^2 - 1}}$

17. $\displaystyle\int \frac{x}{\sqrt{x^2 - 7}} \, dx$

18. $\displaystyle\int \frac{dx}{[(ax)^2 - b^2]^{3/2}}$

19. $\displaystyle\int \frac{\sqrt{1 + x^2}}{x} \, dx$

20. $\displaystyle\int \frac{x}{\sqrt{1 + x^2}} \, dx$

21. $\displaystyle\int_0^{0.6} \frac{x^2}{\sqrt{9 - 25x^2}} \, dx$

22. $\displaystyle\int_0^1 \sqrt{x^2 + 1} \, dx$

23. $\displaystyle\int \sqrt{5 + 4x - x^2} \, dx$

24. $\displaystyle\int \frac{dt}{\sqrt{t^2 - 6t + 13}}$

25. $\displaystyle\int \frac{x}{\sqrt{x^2 + x + 1}} \, dx$

26. $\displaystyle\int \frac{x^2}{(3 + 4x - 4x^2)^{3/2}} \, dx$

27. $\displaystyle\int \sqrt{x^2 + 2x} \, dx$

28. $\displaystyle\int \frac{x^2 + 1}{(x^2 - 2x + 2)^2} \, dx$

29. $\displaystyle\int x \sqrt{1 - x^4} \, dx$

30. $\displaystyle\int_0^{\pi/2} \frac{\cos t}{\sqrt{1 + \sin^2 t}} \, dt$

---

31. (a) Use trigonometric substitution to show that

$$\int \frac{dx}{\sqrt{x^2 + a^2}} = \ln\left(x + \sqrt{x^2 + a^2}\right) + C$$

(b) Use the hyperbolic substitution $x = a \sinh t$ to show that

$$\int \frac{dx}{\sqrt{x^2 + a^2}} = \sinh^{-1}\left(\frac{x}{a}\right) + C$$

These formulas are connected by Formula 3.11.3.

32. Evaluate

$$\int \frac{x^2}{(x^2 + a^2)^{3/2}} \, dx$$

(a) by trigonometric substitution.
(b) by the hyperbolic substitution $x = a \sinh t$.

33. Find the average value of $f(x) = \sqrt{x^2 - 1}/x$, $1 \le x \le 7$.

34. Find the area of the region bounded by the hyperbola $9x^2 - 4y^2 = 36$ and the line $x = 3$.

---

35. Prove the formula $A = \frac{1}{2}r^2\theta$ for the area of a sector of a circle with radius r and central angle θ. [*Hint:* Assume $0 < \theta < \pi/2$ and place the center of the circle at the origin so it has the equation $x^2 + y^2 = r^2$. Then A is the sum of the area of the triangle POQ and the area of the region PQR in the figure.]

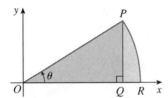

36. Evaluate the integral

$$\int \frac{dx}{x^4\sqrt{x^2 - 2}}$$

Graph the integrand and its indefinite integral on the same screen and check that your answer is reasonable.

37. Find the volume of the solid obtained by rotating about the x-axis the region enclosed by the curves $y = 9/(x^2 + 9)$, $y = 0$, $x = 0$, and $x = 3$.

38. Find the volume of the solid obtained by rotating about the line $x = 1$ the region under the curve $y = x\sqrt{1 - x^2}$, $0 \le x \le 1$.

39. (a) Use trigonometric substitution to verify that

$$\int_0^x \sqrt{a^2 - t^2}\, dt = \frac{1}{2}a^2 \sin^{-1}(x/a) + \frac{1}{2}x\sqrt{a^2 - x^2}$$

(b) Use the figure to give trigonometric interpretations of both terms on the right side of the equation in part (a).

40. The parabola $y = \frac{1}{2}x^2$ divides the disk $x^2 + y^2 \le 8$ into two parts. Find the areas of both parts.

41. A torus is generated by rotating the circle $x^2 + (y - R)^2 = r^2$ about the x-axis. Find the volume enclosed by the torus.

42. A charged rod of length L produces an electric field at point $P(a, b)$ given by

$$E(P) = \int_{-a}^{L-a} \frac{\lambda b}{4\pi\varepsilon_0(x^2 + b^2)^{3/2}}\, dx$$

where λ is the charge density per unit length on the rod and ε_0 is the free space permittivity (see the figure). Evaluate the integral to determine an expression for the electric field $E(P)$.

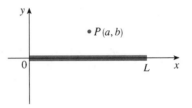

43. Find the area of the crescent-shaped region (called a *lune*) bounded by arcs of circles with radii r and R. (See the figure.)

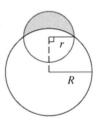

44. A water storage tank has the shape of a cylinder with diameter 10 m. It is mounted so that the circular cross-sections are vertical. If the depth of the water is 7 m, what percentage of the total capacity is being used?

7.4   **Integration of Rational Functions by Partial Fractions**

In this section we show how to integrate any rational function (a ratio of polynomials) by expressing it as a sum of simpler fractions, called *partial fractions,* that we already know how to integrate. To illustrate the method, observe that by taking the fractions $2/(x - 1)$ and $1/(x + 2)$ to a common denominator we obtain

$$\frac{2}{x - 1} - \frac{1}{x + 2} = \frac{2(x + 2) - (x - 1)}{(x - 1)(x + 2)} = \frac{x + 5}{x^2 + x - 2}$$

If we now reverse the procedure, we see how to integrate the function on the right side of this equation:

$$\int \frac{x+5}{x^2+x-2}\, dx = \int \left(\frac{2}{x-1} - \frac{1}{x+2} \right) dx$$

$$= 2 \ln|x-1| - \ln|x+2| + C$$

To see how the method of partial fractions works in general, let's consider a rational function

$$f(x) = \frac{P(x)}{Q(x)}$$

where P and Q are polynomials. It's possible to express f as a sum of simpler fractions provided that the degree of P is less than the degree of Q. Such a rational function is called *proper*. Recall that if

$$P(x) = a_n x^n + a_{n-1} x^{n-1} + \cdots + a_1 x + a_0$$

where $a_n \neq 0$, then the degree of P is n and we write $\deg(P) = n$.

If f is *improper*, that is, $\deg(P) \geqslant \deg(Q)$, then we must take the preliminary step of dividing Q into P (by long division) until a remainder $R(x)$ is obtained such that $\deg(R) < \deg(Q)$. The division statement is

$$\boxed{1} \qquad f(x) = \frac{P(x)}{Q(x)} = S(x) + \frac{R(x)}{Q(x)}$$

where S and R are also polynomials.

As the following example illustrates, sometimes this preliminary step is all that is required.

V **EXAMPLE 1** Find $\displaystyle\int \frac{x^3+x}{x-1}\, dx$.

SOLUTION Since the degree of the numerator is greater than the degree of the denominator, we first perform the long division. This enables us to write

$$\int \frac{x^3+x}{x-1}\, dx = \int \left(x^2 + x + 2 + \frac{2}{x-1} \right) dx$$

$$= \frac{x^3}{3} + \frac{x^2}{2} + 2x + 2 \ln|x-1| + C \qquad \blacksquare$$

$$
\begin{array}{r}
x^2 + x\ + 2 \\
x-1 \overline{\smash{)}\, x^3\qquad\ + x} \\
\underline{x^3 - x^2} \\
x^2 + x \\
\underline{x^2 - x} \\
2x \\
\underline{2x - 2} \\
2
\end{array}
$$

The next step is to factor the denominator $Q(x)$ as far as possible. It can be shown that any polynomial Q can be factored as a product of linear factors (of the form $ax + b$) and irreducible quadratic factors (of the form $ax^2 + bx + c$, where $b^2 - 4ac < 0$). For instance, if $Q(x) = x^4 - 16$, we could factor it as

$$Q(x) = (x^2 - 4)(x^2 + 4) = (x - 2)(x + 2)(x^2 + 4)$$

The third step is to express the proper rational function $R(x)/Q(x)$ (from Equation 1) as a sum of **partial fractions** of the form

$$\frac{A}{(ax+b)^i} \qquad \text{or} \qquad \frac{Ax+B}{(ax^2+bx+c)^j}$$

A theorem in algebra guarantees that it is always possible to do this. We explain the details for the four cases that occur.

CASE I The denominator $Q(x)$ is a product of distinct linear factors.
This means that we can write

$$Q(x) = (a_1x + b_1)(a_2x + b_2) \cdots (a_kx + b_k)$$

where no factor is repeated (and no factor is a constant multiple of another). In this case the partial fraction theorem states that there exist constants $A_1, A_2, \ldots, A_k$ such that

$$\boxed{2} \qquad \frac{R(x)}{Q(x)} = \frac{A_1}{a_1x + b_1} + \frac{A_2}{a_2x + b_2} + \cdots + \frac{A_k}{a_kx + b_k}$$

These constants can be determined as in the following example.

V EXAMPLE 2 Evaluate $\displaystyle\int \frac{x^2 + 2x - 1}{2x^3 + 3x^2 - 2x}\, dx$.

SOLUTION Since the degree of the numerator is less than the degree of the denominator, we don't need to divide. We factor the denominator as

$$2x^3 + 3x^2 - 2x = x(2x^2 + 3x - 2) = x(2x - 1)(x + 2)$$

Since the denominator has three distinct linear factors, the partial fraction decomposition of the integrand $\boxed{2}$ has the form

$$\boxed{3} \qquad \frac{x^2 + 2x - 1}{x(2x - 1)(x + 2)} = \frac{A}{x} + \frac{B}{2x - 1} + \frac{C}{x + 2}$$

Another method for finding A, B, and C is given in the note after this example.

To determine the values of A, B, and C, we multiply both sides of this equation by the product of the denominators, $x(2x - 1)(x + 2)$, obtaining

$$\boxed{4} \qquad x^2 + 2x - 1 = A(2x - 1)(x + 2) + Bx(x + 2) + Cx(2x - 1)$$

Expanding the right side of Equation 4 and writing it in the standard form for polynomials, we get

$$\boxed{5} \qquad x^2 + 2x - 1 = (2A + B + 2C)x^2 + (3A + 2B - C)x - 2A$$

The polynomials in Equation 5 are identical, so their coefficients must be equal. The coefficient of x^2 on the right side, $2A + B + 2C$, must equal the coefficient of x^2 on the left side—namely, 1. Likewise, the coefficients of x are equal and the constant terms are equal. This gives the following system of equations for A, B, and C:

$$2A + B + 2C = 1$$
$$3A + 2B - C = 2$$
$$-2A \qquad\qquad = -1$$

Solving, we get $A = \frac{1}{2}$, $B = \frac{1}{5}$, and $C = -\frac{1}{10}$, and so

$$\int \frac{x^2 + 2x - 1}{2x^3 + 3x^2 - 2x}\, dx = \int \left[\frac{1}{2}\frac{1}{x} + \frac{1}{5}\frac{1}{2x - 1} - \frac{1}{10}\frac{1}{x + 2} \right] dx$$

$$= \tfrac{1}{2}\ln|x| + \tfrac{1}{10}\ln|2x - 1| - \tfrac{1}{10}\ln|x + 2| + K$$

We could check our work by taking the terms to a common denominator and adding them.

Figure 1 shows the graphs of the integrand in Example 2 and its indefinite integral (with $K = 0$). Which is which?

FIGURE 1

In integrating the middle term we have made the mental substitution $u = 2x - 1$, which gives $du = 2\, dx$ and $dx = \frac{1}{2}\, du$. ◼

NOTE We can use an alternative method to find the coefficients A, B, and C in Example 2. Equation 4 is an identity; it is true for every value of x. Let's choose values of x that simplify the equation. If we put $x = 0$ in Equation 4, then the second and third terms on the right side vanish and the equation then becomes $-2A = -1$, or $A = \frac{1}{2}$. Likewise, $x = \frac{1}{2}$ gives $5B/4 = \frac{1}{4}$ and $x = -2$ gives $10C = -1$, so $B = \frac{1}{5}$ and $C = -\frac{1}{10}$. (You may object that Equation 3 is not valid for $x = 0, \frac{1}{2}$, or -2, so why should Equation 4 be valid for those values? In fact, Equation 4 is true for all values of x, even $x = 0, \frac{1}{2}$, and -2. See Exercise 71 for the reason.)

EXAMPLE 3 Find $\int \dfrac{dx}{x^2 - a^2}$, where $a \neq 0$.

SOLUTION The method of partial fractions gives

$$\frac{1}{x^2 - a^2} = \frac{1}{(x - a)(x + a)} = \frac{A}{x - a} + \frac{B}{x + a}$$

and therefore

$$A(x + a) + B(x - a) = 1$$

Using the method of the preceding note, we put $x = a$ in this equation and get $A(2a) = 1$, so $A = 1/(2a)$. If we put $x = -a$, we get $B(-2a) = 1$, so $B = -1/(2a)$. Thus

$$\int \frac{dx}{x^2 - a^2} = \frac{1}{2a} \int \left(\frac{1}{x - a} - \frac{1}{x + a} \right) dx$$

$$= \frac{1}{2a} \left(\ln|x - a| - \ln|x + a| \right) + C$$

Since $\ln x - \ln y = \ln(x/y)$, we can write the integral as

$$\boxed{6} \qquad \int \frac{dx}{x^2 - a^2} = \frac{1}{2a} \ln\left| \frac{x - a}{x + a} \right| + C$$

See Exercises 57–58 for ways of using Formula 6. ◼

CASE II $Q(x)$ **is a product of linear factors, some of which are repeated.**
Suppose the first linear factor $(a_1x + b_1)$ is repeated r times; that is, $(a_1x + b_1)^r$ occurs in the factorization of $Q(x)$. Then instead of the single term $A_1/(a_1x + b_1)$ in Equation 2, we

would use

$$\boxed{7} \qquad \frac{A_1}{a_1x + b_1} + \frac{A_2}{(a_1x + b_1)^2} + \cdots + \frac{A_r}{(a_1x + b_1)^r}$$

By way of illustration, we could write

$$\frac{x^3 - x + 1}{x^2(x - 1)^3} = \frac{A}{x} + \frac{B}{x^2} + \frac{C}{x - 1} + \frac{D}{(x - 1)^2} + \frac{E}{(x - 1)^3}$$

but we prefer to work out in detail a simpler example.

EXAMPLE 4 Find $\displaystyle\int \frac{x^4 - 2x^2 + 4x + 1}{x^3 - x^2 - x + 1}\,dx$.

SOLUTION The first step is to divide. The result of long division is

$$\frac{x^4 - 2x^2 + 4x + 1}{x^3 - x^2 - x + 1} = x + 1 + \frac{4x}{x^3 - x^2 - x + 1}$$

The second step is to factor the denominator $Q(x) = x^3 - x^2 - x + 1$. Since $Q(1) = 0$, we know that $x - 1$ is a factor and we obtain

$$x^3 - x^2 - x + 1 = (x - 1)(x^2 - 1) = (x - 1)(x - 1)(x + 1)$$
$$= (x - 1)^2(x + 1)$$

Since the linear factor $x - 1$ occurs twice, the partial fraction decomposition is

$$\frac{4x}{(x - 1)^2(x + 1)} = \frac{A}{x - 1} + \frac{B}{(x - 1)^2} + \frac{C}{x + 1}$$

Multiplying by the least common denominator, $(x - 1)^2(x + 1)$, we get

$$\boxed{8} \qquad 4x = A(x - 1)(x + 1) + B(x + 1) + C(x - 1)^2$$
$$= (A + C)x^2 + (B - 2C)x + (-A + B + C)$$

Another method for finding the coefficients:
Put $x = 1$ in $\boxed{8}$: $B = 2$.
Put $x = -1$: $C = -1$.
Put $x = 0$: $A = B + C = 1$.

Now we equate coefficients:

$$A \qquad + C = 0$$
$$B - 2C = 4$$
$$-A + B + C = 0$$

Solving, we obtain $A = 1$, $B = 2$, and $C = -1$, so

$$\int \frac{x^4 - 2x^2 + 4x + 1}{x^3 - x^2 - x + 1}\,dx = \int \left[x + 1 + \frac{1}{x - 1} + \frac{2}{(x - 1)^2} - \frac{1}{x + 1} \right] dx$$

$$= \frac{x^2}{2} + x + \ln|x - 1| - \frac{2}{x - 1} - \ln|x + 1| + K$$

$$= \frac{x^2}{2} + x - \frac{2}{x - 1} + \ln\left|\frac{x - 1}{x + 1}\right| + K \qquad \blacksquare$$

CASE III $Q(x)$ **contains irreducible quadratic factors, none of which is repeated.**

If $Q(x)$ has the factor $ax^2 + bx + c$, where $b^2 - 4ac < 0$, then, in addition to the partial fractions in Equations 2 and 7, the expression for $R(x)/Q(x)$ will have a term of the form

$$\boxed{9} \qquad \frac{Ax + B}{ax^2 + bx + c}$$

where A and B are constants to be determined. For instance, the function given by $f(x) = x/[(x - 2)(x^2 + 1)(x^2 + 4)]$ has a partial fraction decomposition of the form

$$\frac{x}{(x - 2)(x^2 + 1)(x^2 + 4)} = \frac{A}{x - 2} + \frac{Bx + C}{x^2 + 1} + \frac{Dx + E}{x^2 + 4}$$

The term given in $\boxed{9}$ can be integrated by completing the square (if necessary) and using the formula

$$\boxed{10} \qquad \boxed{\int \frac{dx}{x^2 + a^2} = \frac{1}{a} \tan^{-1}\left(\frac{x}{a}\right) + C}$$

V EXAMPLE 5 Evaluate $\displaystyle\int \frac{2x^2 - x + 4}{x^3 + 4x}\, dx$.

SOLUTION Since $x^3 + 4x = x(x^2 + 4)$ can't be factored further, we write

$$\frac{2x^2 - x + 4}{x(x^2 + 4)} = \frac{A}{x} + \frac{Bx + C}{x^2 + 4}$$

Multiplying by $x(x^2 + 4)$, we have

$$2x^2 - x + 4 = A(x^2 + 4) + (Bx + C)x$$
$$= (A + B)x^2 + Cx + 4A$$

Equating coefficients, we obtain

$$A + B = 2 \qquad C = -1 \qquad 4A = 4$$

Thus $A = 1$, $B = 1$, and $C = -1$ and so

$$\int \frac{2x^2 - x + 4}{x^3 + 4x}\, dx = \int \left(\frac{1}{x} + \frac{x - 1}{x^2 + 4} \right) dx$$

In order to integrate the second term we split it into two parts:

$$\int \frac{x - 1}{x^2 + 4}\, dx = \int \frac{x}{x^2 + 4}\, dx - \int \frac{1}{x^2 + 4}\, dx$$

We make the substitution $u = x^2 + 4$ in the first of these integrals so that $du = 2x\, dx$. We evaluate the second integral by means of Formula 10 with $a = 2$:

$$\int \frac{2x^2 - x + 4}{x(x^2 + 4)}\, dx = \int \frac{1}{x}\, dx + \int \frac{x}{x^2 + 4}\, dx - \int \frac{1}{x^2 + 4}\, dx$$

$$= \ln|x| + \tfrac{1}{2}\ln(x^2 + 4) - \tfrac{1}{2}\tan^{-1}(x/2) + K \qquad \blacksquare$$

EXAMPLE 6 Evaluate $\displaystyle\int \frac{4x^2 - 3x + 2}{4x^2 - 4x + 3}\, dx$.

SOLUTION Since the degree of the numerator is *not less than* the degree of the denominator, we first divide and obtain

$$\frac{4x^2 - 3x + 2}{4x^2 - 4x + 3} = 1 + \frac{x - 1}{4x^2 - 4x + 3}$$

Notice that the quadratic $4x^2 - 4x + 3$ is irreducible because its discriminant is $b^2 - 4ac = -32 < 0$. This means it can't be factored, so we don't need to use the partial fraction technique.

To integrate the given function we complete the square in the denominator:

$$4x^2 - 4x + 3 = (2x - 1)^2 + 2$$

This suggests that we make the substitution $u = 2x - 1$. Then $du = 2\, dx$ and $x = \frac{1}{2}(u + 1)$, so

$$\int \frac{4x^2 - 3x + 2}{4x^2 - 4x + 3}\, dx = \int \left(1 + \frac{x - 1}{4x^2 - 4x + 3} \right) dx$$

$$= x + \frac{1}{2}\int \frac{\frac{1}{2}(u + 1) - 1}{u^2 + 2}\, du = x + \frac{1}{4}\int \frac{u - 1}{u^2 + 2}\, du$$

$$= x + \frac{1}{4}\int \frac{u}{u^2 + 2}\, du - \frac{1}{4}\int \frac{1}{u^2 + 2}\, du$$

$$= x + \frac{1}{8}\ln(u^2 + 2) - \frac{1}{4}\cdot\frac{1}{\sqrt{2}}\tan^{-1}\left(\frac{u}{\sqrt{2}} \right) + C$$

$$= x + \frac{1}{8}\ln(4x^2 - 4x + 3) - \frac{1}{4\sqrt{2}}\tan^{-1}\left(\frac{2x - 1}{\sqrt{2}} \right) + C$$

NOTE Example 6 illustrates the general procedure for integrating a partial fraction of the form

$$\frac{Ax + B}{ax^2 + bx + c} \qquad \text{where } b^2 - 4ac < 0$$

We complete the square in the denominator and then make a substitution that brings the integral into the form

$$\int \frac{Cu + D}{u^2 + a^2}\, du = C\int \frac{u}{u^2 + a^2}\, du + D\int \frac{1}{u^2 + a^2}\, du$$

Then the first integral is a logarithm and the second is expressed in terms of $\tan^{-1}$.

CASE IV $Q(x)$ **contains a repeated irreducible quadratic factor.**
If $Q(x)$ has the factor $(ax^2 + bx + c)^r$, where $b^2 - 4ac < 0$, then instead of the single partial fraction $\boxed{9}$, the sum

$$\boxed{11} \qquad \frac{A_1x + B_1}{ax^2 + bx + c} + \frac{A_2x + B_2}{(ax^2 + bx + c)^2} + \cdots + \frac{A_rx + B_r}{(ax^2 + bx + c)^r}$$

occurs in the partial fraction decomposition of $R(x)/Q(x)$. Each of the terms in $\boxed{11}$ can be integrated by using a substitution or by first completing the square if necessary.

EXAMPLE 7 Write out the form of the partial fraction decomposition of the function

$$\frac{x^3 + x^2 + 1}{x(x - 1)(x^2 + x + 1)(x^2 + 1)^3}$$

SOLUTION

$$\frac{x^3 + x^2 + 1}{x(x - 1)(x^2 + x + 1)(x^2 + 1)^3}$$

$$= \frac{A}{x} + \frac{B}{x - 1} + \frac{Cx + D}{x^2 + x + 1} + \frac{Ex + F}{x^2 + 1} + \frac{Gx + H}{(x^2 + 1)^2} + \frac{Ix + J}{(x^2 + 1)^3}$$

■

It would be extremely tedious to work out by hand the numerical values of the coefficients in Example 7. Most computer algebra systems, however, can find the numerical values very quickly. For instance, the Maple command

```
convert(f, parfrac, x)
```

or the Mathematica command

```
           Apart[f]
```

gives the following values:

$A = -1$, $B = \frac{1}{8}$, $C = D = -1$,

$E = \frac{15}{8}$, $F = -\frac{1}{8}$, $G = H = \frac{3}{4}$,

$I = -\frac{1}{2}$, $J = \frac{1}{2}$

EXAMPLE 8 Evaluate $\displaystyle\int \frac{1 - x + 2x^2 - x^3}{x(x^2 + 1)^2}\,dx$.

SOLUTION The form of the partial fraction decomposition is

$$\frac{1 - x + 2x^2 - x^3}{x(x^2 + 1)^2} = \frac{A}{x} + \frac{Bx + C}{x^2 + 1} + \frac{Dx + E}{(x^2 + 1)^2}$$

Multiplying by $x(x^2 + 1)^2$, we have

$$-x^3 + 2x^2 - x + 1 = A(x^2 + 1)^2 + (Bx + C)x(x^2 + 1) + (Dx + E)x$$

$$= A(x^4 + 2x^2 + 1) + B(x^4 + x^2) + C(x^3 + x) + Dx^2 + Ex$$

$$= (A + B)x^4 + Cx^3 + (2A + B + D)x^2 + (C + E)x + A$$

If we equate coefficients, we get the system

$$A + B = 0 \qquad C = -1 \qquad 2A + B + D = 2 \qquad C + E = -1 \qquad A = 1$$

which has the solution $A = 1$, $B = -1$, $C = -1$, $D = 1$, and $E = 0$. Thus

$$\int \frac{1 - x + 2x^2 - x^3}{x(x^2 + 1)^2}\,dx = \int \left(\frac{1}{x} - \frac{x + 1}{x^2 + 1} + \frac{x}{(x^2 + 1)^2} \right) dx$$

$$= \int \frac{dx}{x} - \int \frac{x}{x^2 + 1}\,dx - \int \frac{dx}{x^2 + 1} + \int \frac{x\,dx}{(x^2 + 1)^2}$$

In the second and fourth terms we made the mental substitution $u = x^2 + 1$.

$$= \ln|x| - \tfrac{1}{2}\ln(x^2 + 1) - \tan^{-1}x - \frac{1}{2(x^2 + 1)} + K$$

■

We note that sometimes partial fractions can be avoided when integrating a rational function. For instance, although the integral

$$\int \frac{x^2 + 1}{x(x^2 + 3)}\,dx$$

could be evaluated by the method of Case III, it's much easier to observe that if $u = x(x^2 + 3) = x^3 + 3x$, then $du = (3x^2 + 3)\, dx$ and so

$$\int \frac{x^2 + 1}{x(x^2 + 3)}\, dx = \tfrac{1}{3} \ln |x^3 + 3x| + C$$

▬ Rationalizing Substitutions

Some nonrational functions can be changed into rational functions by means of appropriate substitutions. In particular, when an integrand contains an expression of the form $\sqrt[n]{g(x)}$, then the substitution $u = \sqrt[n]{g(x)}$ may be effective. Other instances appear in the exercises.

EXAMPLE 9 Evaluate $\displaystyle\int \frac{\sqrt{x + 4}}{x}\, dx$.

SOLUTION Let $u = \sqrt{x + 4}$. Then $u^2 = x + 4$, so $x = u^2 - 4$ and $dx = 2u\, du$. Therefore

$$\int \frac{\sqrt{x + 4}}{x}\, dx = \int \frac{u}{u^2 - 4}\, 2u\, du = 2 \int \frac{u^2}{u^2 - 4}\, du$$

$$= 2 \int \left(1 + \frac{4}{u^2 - 4} \right) du$$

We can evaluate this integral either by factoring $u^2 - 4$ as $(u - 2)(u + 2)$ and using partial fractions or by using Formula 6 with $a = 2$:

$$\int \frac{\sqrt{x + 4}}{x}\, dx = 2 \int du + 8 \int \frac{du}{u^2 - 4} = 2u + 8 \cdot \frac{1}{2 \cdot 2} \ln \left| \frac{u - 2}{u + 2} \right| + C$$

$$= 2\sqrt{x + 4} + 2 \ln \left| \frac{\sqrt{x + 4} - 2}{\sqrt{x + 4} + 2} \right| + C \qquad ▬$$

7.4 Exercises

1–6 Write out the form of the partial fraction decomposition of the function (as in Example 7). Do not determine the numerical values of the coefficients.

1. (a) $\dfrac{1 + 6x}{(4x - 3)(2x + 5)}$ (b) $\dfrac{10}{5x^2 - 2x^3}$

2. (a) $\dfrac{x}{x^2 + x - 2}$ (b) $\dfrac{x^2}{x^2 + x + 2}$

3. (a) $\dfrac{x^4 + 1}{x^5 + 4x^3}$ (b) $\dfrac{1}{(x^2 - 9)^2}$

4. (a) $\dfrac{x^4 - 2x^3 + x^2 + 2x - 1}{x^2 - 2x + 1}$ (b) $\dfrac{x^2 - 1}{x^3 + x^2 + x}$

5. (a) $\dfrac{x^6}{x^2 - 4}$ (b) $\dfrac{x^4}{(x^2 - x + 1)(x^2 + 2)^2}$

6. (a) $\dfrac{t^6 + 1}{t^6 + t^3}$ (b) $\dfrac{x^5 + 1}{(x^2 - x)(x^4 + 2x^2 + 1)}$

7–38 Evaluate the integral.

7. $\displaystyle\int \frac{x}{x - 6}\, dx$ **8.** $\displaystyle\int \frac{r^2}{r + 4}\, dr$

9. $\displaystyle\int \frac{x - 9}{(x + 5)(x - 2)}\, dx$ **10.** $\displaystyle\int \frac{1}{(t + 4)(t - 1)}\, dt$

11. $\int_0^1 \dfrac{2}{2x^2 + 3x + 1}\, dx$

12. $\int_0^1 \dfrac{x - 4}{x^2 - 5x + 6}\, dx$

13. $\int \dfrac{ax}{x^2 - bx}\, dx$

14. $\int \dfrac{1}{(x + a)(x + b)}\, dx$

15. $\int_3^4 \dfrac{x^3 - 2x^2 - 4}{x^3 - 2x^2}\, dx$

16. $\int_0^1 \dfrac{x^3 - 4x - 10}{x^2 - x - 6}\, dx$

17. $\int_1^2 \dfrac{4y^2 - 7y - 12}{y(y + 2)(y - 3)}\, dy$

18. $\int \dfrac{x^2 + 2x - 1}{x^3 - x}\, dx$

19. $\int \dfrac{x^2 + 1}{(x - 3)(x - 2)^2}\, dx$

20. $\int \dfrac{x^2 - 5x + 16}{(2x + 1)(x - 2)^2}\, dx$

21. $\int \dfrac{x^3 + 4}{x^2 + 4}\, dx$

22. $\int \dfrac{ds}{s^2(s - 1)^2}$

23. $\int \dfrac{10}{(x - 1)(x^2 + 9)}\, dx$

24. $\int \dfrac{x^2 - x + 6}{x^3 + 3x}\, dx$

25. $\int \dfrac{4x}{x^3 + x^2 + x + 1}\, dx$

26. $\int \dfrac{x^2 + x + 1}{(x^2 + 1)^2}\, dx$

27. $\int \dfrac{x^3 + x^2 + 2x + 1}{(x^2 + 1)(x^2 + 2)}\, dx$

28. $\int \dfrac{x^2 - 2x - 1}{(x - 1)^2(x^2 + 1)}\, dx$

29. $\int \dfrac{x + 4}{x^2 + 2x + 5}\, dx$

30. $\int \dfrac{3x^2 + x + 4}{x^4 + 3x^2 + 2}\, dx$

31. $\int \dfrac{1}{x^3 - 1}\, dx$

32. $\int_0^1 \dfrac{x}{x^2 + 4x + 13}\, dx$

33. $\int_0^1 \dfrac{x^3 + 2x}{x^4 + 4x^2 + 3}\, dx$

34. $\int \dfrac{x^5 + x - 1}{x^3 + 1}\, dx$

35. $\int \dfrac{dx}{x(x^2 + 4)^2}$

36. $\int \dfrac{x^4 + 3x^2 + 1}{x^5 + 5x^3 + 5x}\, dx$

37. $\int \dfrac{x^2 - 3x + 7}{(x^2 - 4x + 6)^2}\, dx$

38. $\int \dfrac{x^3 + 2x^2 + 3x - 2}{(x^2 + 2x + 2)^2}\, dx$

39–52 Make a substitution to express the integrand as a rational function and then evaluate the integral.

39. $\int \dfrac{\sqrt{x + 1}}{x}\, dx$

40. $\int \dfrac{dx}{2\sqrt{x + 3} + x}$

41. $\int \dfrac{dx}{x^2 + x\sqrt{x}}$

42. $\int_0^1 \dfrac{1}{1 + \sqrt[3]{x}}\, dx$

43. $\int \dfrac{x^3}{\sqrt[3]{x^2 + 1}}\, dx$

44. $\int_{1/3}^3 \dfrac{\sqrt{x}}{x^2 + x}\, dx$

45. $\int \dfrac{1}{\sqrt{x} - \sqrt[3]{x}}\, dx$ $\bigl[$*Hint:* Substitute $u = \sqrt[6]{x}\,.\bigr]$

46. $\int \dfrac{\sqrt{1 + \sqrt{x}}}{x}\, dx$

47. $\int \dfrac{e^{2x}}{e^{2x} + 3e^x + 2}\, dx$

48. $\int \dfrac{\sin x}{\cos^2 x - 3\cos x}\, dx$

49. $\int \dfrac{\sec^2 t}{\tan^2 t + 3\tan t + 2}\, dt$

50. $\int \dfrac{e^x}{(e^x - 2)(e^{2x} + 1)}\, dx$

51. $\int \dfrac{dx}{1 + e^x}$

52. $\int \dfrac{\cosh t}{\sinh^2 t + \sinh^4 t}\, dt$

53–54 Use integration by parts, together with the techniques of this section, to evaluate the integral.

53. $\int \ln(x^2 - x + 2)\, dx$

54. $\int x \tan^{-1}x\, dx$

---

55. Use a graph of $f(x) = 1/(x^2 - 2x - 3)$ to decide whether $\int_0^2 f(x)\, dx$ is positive or negative. Use the graph to give a rough estimate of the value of the integral and then use partial fractions to find the exact value.

56. Evaluate

$$\int \frac{1}{x^2 + k}\, dx$$

by considering several cases for the constant k.

57–58 Evaluate the integral by completing the square and using Formula 6.

57. $\int \dfrac{dx}{x^2 - 2x}$

58. $\int \dfrac{2x + 1}{4x^2 + 12x - 7}\, dx$

---

59. The German mathematician Karl Weierstrass (1815–1897) noticed that the substitution $t = \tan(x/2)$ will convert any rational function of $\sin x$ and $\cos x$ into an ordinary rational function of t.

(a) If $t = \tan(x/2)$, $-\pi < x < \pi$, sketch a right triangle or use trigonometric identities to show that

$$\cos\left(\frac{x}{2}\right) = \frac{1}{\sqrt{1 + t^2}} \quad \text{and} \quad \sin\left(\frac{x}{2}\right) = \frac{t}{\sqrt{1 + t^2}}$$

(b) Show that

$$\cos x = \frac{1 - t^2}{1 + t^2} \quad \text{and} \quad \sin x = \frac{2t}{1 + t^2}$$

(c) Show that

$$dx = \frac{2}{1 + t^2}\, dt$$

60–63 Use the substitution in Exercise 59 to transform the integrand into a rational function of t and then evaluate the integral.

60. $\int \dfrac{dx}{1 - \cos x}$

61. $\int \dfrac{1}{3\sin x - 4\cos x}\, dx$

62. $\int_{\pi/3}^{\pi/2} \dfrac{1}{1 + \sin x - \cos x}\, dx$

63. $\displaystyle\int_0^{\pi/2} \frac{\sin 2x}{2 + \cos x}\, dx$

64–65 Find the area of the region under the given curve from 1 to 2.

64. $y = \dfrac{1}{x^3 + x}$

65. $y = \dfrac{x^2 + 1}{3x - x^2}$

---

66. Find the volume of the resulting solid if the region under the curve $y = 1/(x^2 + 3x + 2)$ from $x = 0$ to $x = 1$ is rotated about (a) the x-axis and (b) the y-axis.

67. One method of slowing the growth of an insect population without using pesticides is to introduce into the population a number of sterile males that mate with fertile females but produce no offspring. If P represents the number of female insects in a population, S the number of sterile males introduced each generation, and r the population's natural growth rate, then the female population is related to time t by

$$t = \int \frac{P + S}{P[(r - 1)P - S]}\, dP$$

Suppose an insect population with 10,000 females grows at a rate of $r = 0.10$ and 900 sterile males are added. Evaluate the integral to give an equation relating the female population to time. (Note that the resulting equation can't be solved explicitly for P.)

68. Factor $x^4 + 1$ as a difference of squares by first adding and subtracting the same quantity. Use this factorization to evaluate $\int 1/(x^4 + 1)\, dx$.

CAS **69.** (a) Use a computer algebra system to find the partial fraction decomposition of the function

$$f(x) = \frac{4x^3 - 27x^2 + 5x - 32}{30x^5 - 13x^4 + 50x^3 - 286x^2 - 299x - 70}$$

(b) Use part (a) to find $\int f(x)\, dx$ (by hand) and compare with the result of using the CAS to integrate f directly. Comment on any discrepancy.

CAS **70.** (a) Find the partial fraction decomposition of the function

$$f(x) = \frac{12x^5 - 7x^3 - 13x^2 + 8}{100x^6 - 80x^5 + 116x^4 - 80x^3 + 41x^2 - 20x + 4}$$

(b) Use part (a) to find $\int f(x)\, dx$ and graph f and its indefinite integral on the same screen.

(c) Use the graph of f to discover the main features of the graph of $\int f(x)\, dx$.

71. Suppose that F, G, and Q are polynomials and

$$\frac{F(x)}{Q(x)} = \frac{G(x)}{Q(x)}$$

for all x except when $Q(x) = 0$. Prove that $F(x) = G(x)$ for all x. [*Hint:* Use continuity.]

72. If f is a quadratic function such that $f(0) = 1$ and

$$\int \frac{f(x)}{x^2(x + 1)^3}\, dx$$

is a rational function, find the value of $f'(0)$.

73. If $a \neq 0$ and n is a positive integer, find the partial fraction decomposition of

$$f(x) = \frac{1}{x^n(x - a)}$$

Hint: First find the coefficient of $1/(x - a)$. Then subtract the resulting term and simplify what is left.

7.5 Strategy for Integration

As we have seen, integration is more challenging than differentiation. In finding the derivative of a function it is obvious which differentiation formula we should apply. But it may not be obvious which technique we should use to integrate a given function.

Until now individual techniques have been applied in each section. For instance, we usually used substitution in Exercises 5.5, integration by parts in Exercises 7.1, and partial fractions in Exercises 7.4. But in this section we present a collection of miscellaneous integrals in random order and the main challenge is to recognize which technique or formula to use. No hard and fast rules can be given as to which method applies in a given situation, but we give some advice on strategy that you may find useful.

A prerequisite for applying a strategy is a knowledge of the basic integration formulas. In the following table we have collected the integrals from our previous list together with several additional formulas that we have learned in this chapter. Most of them should be memorized. It is useful to know them all, but the ones marked with an asterisk need not be memorized since they are easily derived. Formula 19 can be avoided by using partial fractions, and trigonometric substitutions can be used in place of Formula 20.

Table of Integration Formulas Constants of integration have been omitted.

1. $\displaystyle\int x^n\,dx = \frac{x^{n+1}}{n+1} \quad (n \neq -1)$ **2.** $\displaystyle\int \frac{1}{x}\,dx = \ln|x|$

3. $\displaystyle\int e^x\,dx = e^x$ **4.** $\displaystyle\int a^x\,dx = \frac{a^x}{\ln a}$

5. $\displaystyle\int \sin x\,dx = -\cos x$ **6.** $\displaystyle\int \cos x\,dx = \sin x$

7. $\displaystyle\int \sec^2 x\,dx = \tan x$ **8.** $\displaystyle\int \csc^2 x\,dx = -\cot x$

9. $\displaystyle\int \sec x \tan x\,dx = \sec x$ **10.** $\displaystyle\int \csc x \cot x\,dx = -\csc x$

11. $\displaystyle\int \sec x\,dx = \ln|\sec x + \tan x|$ **12.** $\displaystyle\int \csc x\,dx = \ln|\csc x - \cot x|$

13. $\displaystyle\int \tan x\,dx = \ln|\sec x|$ **14.** $\displaystyle\int \cot x\,dx = \ln|\sin x|$

15. $\displaystyle\int \sinh x\,dx = \cosh x$ **16.** $\displaystyle\int \cosh x\,dx = \sinh x$

17. $\displaystyle\int \frac{dx}{x^2 + a^2} = \frac{1}{a}\tan^{-1}\left(\frac{x}{a}\right)$ **18.** $\displaystyle\int \frac{dx}{\sqrt{a^2 - x^2}} = \sin^{-1}\left(\frac{x}{a}\right), \quad a > 0$

*19. $\displaystyle\int \frac{dx}{x^2 - a^2} = \frac{1}{2a}\ln\left|\frac{x-a}{x+a}\right|$ ***20.** $\displaystyle\int \frac{dx}{\sqrt{x^2 \pm a^2}} = \ln\left|x + \sqrt{x^2 \pm a^2}\right|$

Once you are armed with these basic integration formulas, if you don't immediately see how to attack a given integral, you might try the following four-step strategy.

1. Simplify the Integrand if Possible Sometimes the use of algebraic manipulation or trigonometric identities will simplify the integrand and make the method of integration obvious. Here are some examples:

$$\int \sqrt{x}\,(1 + \sqrt{x})\,dx = \int (\sqrt{x} + x)\,dx$$

$$\int \frac{\tan\theta}{\sec^2\theta}\,d\theta = \int \frac{\sin\theta}{\cos\theta}\cos^2\theta\,d\theta$$

$$= \int \sin\theta\cos\theta\,d\theta = \tfrac{1}{2}\int \sin 2\theta\,d\theta$$

$$\int (\sin x + \cos x)^2\,dx = \int (\sin^2 x + 2\sin x\cos x + \cos^2 x)\,dx$$

$$= \int (1 + 2\sin x\cos x)\,dx$$

2. Look for an Obvious Substitution   Try to find some function $u = g(x)$ in the integrand whose differential $du = g'(x)\,dx$ also occurs, apart from a constant factor. For instance, in the integral

$$\int \frac{x}{x^2 - 1}\,dx$$

we notice that if $u = x^2 - 1$, then $du = 2x\,dx$. Therefore we use the substitution $u = x^2 - 1$ instead of the method of partial fractions.

3. Classify the Integrand According to Its Form   If Steps 1 and 2 have not led to the solution, then we take a look at the form of the integrand $f(x)$.

(a) *Trigonometric functions.*   If $f(x)$ is a product of powers of $\sin x$ and $\cos x$, of $\tan x$ and $\sec x$, or of $\cot x$ and $\csc x$, then we use the substitutions recommended in Section 7.2.

(b) *Rational functions.*   If f is a rational function, we use the procedure of Section 7.4 involving partial fractions.

(c) *Integration by parts.*   If $f(x)$ is a product of a power of x (or a polynomial) and a transcendental function (such as a trigonometric, exponential, or logarithmic function), then we try integration by parts, choosing u and dv according to the advice given in Section 7.1. If you look at the functions in Exercises 7.1, you will see that most of them are the type just described.

(d) *Radicals.*   Particular kinds of substitutions are recommended when certain radicals appear.

  (i) If $\sqrt{\pm x^2 \pm a^2}$ occurs, we use a trigonometric substitution according to the table in Section 7.3.
  (ii) If $\sqrt[n]{ax + b}$ occurs, we use the rationalizing substitution $u = \sqrt[n]{ax + b}$. More generally, this sometimes works for $\sqrt[n]{g(x)}$.

4. Try Again   If the first three steps have not produced the answer, remember that there are basically only two methods of integration: substitution and parts.

(a) *Try substitution.*   Even if no substitution is obvious (Step 2), some inspiration or ingenuity (or even desperation) may suggest an appropriate substitution.

(b) *Try parts.*   Although integration by parts is used most of the time on products of the form described in Step 3(c), it is sometimes effective on single functions. Looking at Section 7.1, we see that it works on $\tan^{-1}x$, $\sin^{-1}x$, and $\ln x$, and these are all inverse functions.

(c) *Manipulate the integrand.*   Algebraic manipulations (perhaps rationalizing the denominator or using trigonometric identities) may be useful in transforming the integral into an easier form. These manipulations may be more substantial than in Step 1 and may involve some ingenuity. Here is an example:

$$\int \frac{dx}{1 - \cos x} = \int \frac{1}{1 - \cos x} \cdot \frac{1 + \cos x}{1 + \cos x}\,dx = \int \frac{1 + \cos x}{1 - \cos^2 x}\,dx$$

$$= \int \frac{1 + \cos x}{\sin^2 x}\,dx = \int \left(\csc^2 x + \frac{\cos x}{\sin^2 x} \right) dx$$

(d) *Relate the problem to previous problems.*   When you have built up some experience in integration, you may be able to use a method on a given integral that is similar to a method you have already used on a previous integral. Or you may even be able to express the given integral in terms of a previous one. For instance, $\int \tan^2 x \sec x \, dx$ is a challenging integral, but if we make use of the identity $\tan^2 x = \sec^2 x - 1$, we can write

$$\int \tan^2 x \sec x \, dx = \int \sec^3 x \, dx - \int \sec x \, dx$$

and if $\int \sec^3 x \, dx$ has previously been evaluated (see Example 8 in Section 7.2), then that calculation can be used in the present problem.

(e) *Use several methods.* Sometimes two or three methods are required to evaluate an integral. The evaluation could involve several successive substitutions of different types, or it might combine integration by parts with one or more substitutions.

In the following examples we indicate a method of attack but do not fully work out the integral.

EXAMPLE 1 $\int \dfrac{\tan^3 x}{\cos^3 x} \, dx$

In Step 1 we rewrite the integral:

$$\int \frac{\tan^3 x}{\cos^3 x} \, dx = \int \tan^3 x \sec^3 x \, dx$$

The integral is now of the form $\int \tan^m x \sec^n x \, dx$ with m odd, so we can use the advice in Section 7.2.

Alternatively, if in Step 1 we had written

$$\int \frac{\tan^3 x}{\cos^3 x} \, dx = \int \frac{\sin^3 x}{\cos^3 x} \frac{1}{\cos^3 x} \, dx = \int \frac{\sin^3 x}{\cos^6 x} \, dx$$

then we could have continued as follows with the substitution $u = \cos x$:

$$\int \frac{\sin^3 x}{\cos^6 x} \, dx = \int \frac{1 - \cos^2 x}{\cos^6 x} \sin x \, dx = \int \frac{1 - u^2}{u^6} (-du)$$

$$= \int \frac{u^2 - 1}{u^6} \, du = \int (u^{-4} - u^{-6}) \, du$$
▬

V EXAMPLE 2 $\int e^{\sqrt{x}} \, dx$

According to (ii) in Step 3(d), we substitute $u = \sqrt{x}$. Then $x = u^2$, so $dx = 2u \, du$ and

$$\int e^{\sqrt{x}} \, dx = 2 \int u e^u \, du$$

The integrand is now a product of u and the transcendental function e^u so it can be integrated by parts.
▬

EXAMPLE 3 $\displaystyle\int \frac{x^5 + 1}{x^3 - 3x^2 - 10x}\, dx$

No algebraic simplification or substitution is obvious, so Steps 1 and 2 don't apply here. The integrand is a rational function so we apply the procedure of Section 7.4, remembering that the first step is to divide.

V EXAMPLE 4 $\displaystyle\int \frac{dx}{x\sqrt{\ln x}}$

Here Step 2 is all that is needed. We substitute $u = \ln x$ because its differential is $du = dx/x$, which occurs in the integral.

V EXAMPLE 5 $\displaystyle\int \sqrt{\frac{1 - x}{1 + x}}\, dx$

Although the rationalizing substitution

$$u = \sqrt{\frac{1 - x}{1 + x}}$$

works here [(ii) in Step 3(d)], it leads to a very complicated rational function. An easier method is to do some algebraic manipulation [either as Step 1 or as Step 4(c)]. Multiplying numerator and denominator by $\sqrt{1 - x}$, we have

$$\int \sqrt{\frac{1 - x}{1 + x}}\, dx = \int \frac{1 - x}{\sqrt{1 - x^2}}\, dx$$

$$= \int \frac{1}{\sqrt{1 - x^2}}\, dx - \int \frac{x}{\sqrt{1 - x^2}}\, dx$$

$$= \sin^{-1}x + \sqrt{1 - x^2} + C$$

Can We Integrate All Continuous Functions?

The question arises: Will our strategy for integration enable us to find the integral of every continuous function? For example, can we use it to evaluate $\int e^{x^2}\, dx$? The answer is No, at least not in terms of the functions that we are familiar with.

The functions that we have been dealing with in this book are called **elementary functions**. These are the polynomials, rational functions, power functions (x^a), exponential functions (a^x), logarithmic functions, trigonometric and inverse trigonometric functions, hyperbolic and inverse hyperbolic functions, and all functions that can be obtained from these by the five operations of addition, subtraction, multiplication, division, and composition. For instance, the function

$$f(x) = \sqrt{\frac{x^2 - 1}{x^3 + 2x - 1}} + \ln(\cosh x) - xe^{\sin 2x}$$

is an elementary function.

If f is an elementary function, then f' is an elementary function but $\int f(x)\, dx$ need not be an elementary function. Consider $f(x) = e^{x^2}$. Since f is continuous, its integral exists, and if we define the function F by

$$F(x) = \int_0^x e^{t^2}\, dt$$

then we know from Part 1 of the Fundamental Theorem of Calculus that

$$F'(x) = e^{x^2}$$

Thus $f(x) = e^{x^2}$ has an antiderivative F, but it has been proved that F is not an elementary function. This means that no matter how hard we try, we will never succeed in evaluating $\int e^{x^2}\,dx$ in terms of the functions we know. (In Chapter 11, however, we will see how to express $\int e^{x^2}\,dx$ as an infinite series.) The same can be said of the following integrals:

$$\int \frac{e^x}{x}\,dx \qquad\qquad \int \sin(x^2)\,dx \qquad\qquad \int \cos(e^x)\,dx$$

$$\int \sqrt{x^3+1}\,dx \qquad\qquad \int \frac{1}{\ln x}\,dx \qquad\qquad \int \frac{\sin x}{x}\,dx$$

In fact, the majority of elementary functions don't have elementary antiderivatives. You may be assured, though, that the integrals in the following exercises are all elementary functions.

7.5 Exercises

1–82 Evaluate the integral.

1. $\int \cos x\,(1 + \sin^2 x)\,dx$

2. $\int_0^1 (3x+1)^{\sqrt{2}}\,dx$

3. $\int \dfrac{\sin x + \sec x}{\tan x}\,dx$

4. $\int \tan^3\theta\,d\theta$

5. $\int_0^2 \dfrac{2t}{(t-3)^2}\,dt$

6. $\int \dfrac{x}{\sqrt{3-x^4}}\,dx$

7. $\int_{-1}^1 \dfrac{e^{\arctan y}}{1+y^2}\,dy$

8. $\int t\sin t\,\cos t\,dt$

9. $\int_1^3 r^4 \ln r\,dr$

10. $\int_0^4 \dfrac{x-1}{x^2-4x-5}\,dx$

11. $\int \dfrac{x-1}{x^2-4x+5}\,dx$

12. $\int \dfrac{x}{x^4+x^2+1}\,dx$

13. $\int \sin^5 t\,\cos^4 t\,dt$

14. $\int \dfrac{x^3}{\sqrt{1+x^2}}\,dx$

15. $\int \dfrac{dx}{(1-x^2)^{3/2}}$

16. $\int_0^{\sqrt{2}/2} \dfrac{x^2}{\sqrt{1-x^2}}\,dx$

17. $\int_0^\pi t\cos^2 t\,dt$

18. $\int_1^4 \dfrac{e^{\sqrt{t}}}{\sqrt{t}}\,dt$

19. $\int e^{x+e^x}\,dx$

20. $\int e^2\,dx$

21. $\int \arctan\sqrt{x}\,dx$

22. $\int \dfrac{\ln x}{x\sqrt{1+(\ln x)^2}}\,dx$

23. $\int_0^1 (1+\sqrt{x})^8\,dx$

24. $\int_0^4 \dfrac{6z+5}{2z+1}\,dz$

25. $\int \dfrac{3x^2-2}{x^2-2x-8}\,dx$

26. $\int \dfrac{3x^2-2}{x^3-2x-8}\,dx$

27. $\int \dfrac{dx}{1+e^x}$

28. $\int \sin\sqrt{at}\,dt$

29. $\int \ln\!\left(x+\sqrt{x^2-1}\right)dx$

30. $\int_{-1}^2 |e^x-1|\,dx$

31. $\int \sqrt{\dfrac{1+x}{1-x}}\,dx$

32. $\int \dfrac{\sqrt{2x-1}}{2x+3}\,dx$

33. $\int \sqrt{3-2x-x^2}\,dx$

34. $\int_{\pi/4}^{\pi/2} \dfrac{1+4\cot x}{4-\cot x}\,dx$

35. $\int \cos 2x\,\cos 6x\,dx$

36. $\int_{-\pi/4}^{\pi/4} \dfrac{x^2\tan x}{1+\cos^4 x}\,dx$

37. $\int_0^{\pi/4} \tan^3\theta\,\sec^2\theta\,d\theta$

38. $\int_{\pi/6}^{\pi/3} \dfrac{\sin\theta\cot\theta}{\sec\theta}\,d\theta$

39. $\int \dfrac{\sec\theta\tan\theta}{\sec^2\theta-\sec\theta}\,d\theta$

40. $\int \dfrac{1}{\sqrt{4y^2-4y-3}}\,dy$

41. $\int \theta\tan^2\theta\,d\theta$

42. $\int \dfrac{\tan^{-1}x}{x^2}\,dx$

43. $\int \dfrac{\sqrt{x}}{1+x^3}\,dx$

44. $\int \sqrt{1+e^x}\,dx$

45. $\int x^5 e^{-x^3}\,dx$

46. $\int \dfrac{(x-1)e^x}{x^2}\,dx$

47. $\int x^3(x-1)^{-4}\,dx$

48. $\int_0^1 x\sqrt{2-\sqrt{1-x^2}}\,dx$

49. $\int \dfrac{1}{x\sqrt{4x+1}}\,dx$

50. $\int \dfrac{1}{x^2\sqrt{4x+1}}\,dx$

51. $\int \dfrac{1}{x\sqrt{4x^2+1}}\,dx$

52. $\int \dfrac{dx}{x(x^4+1)}$

1. Homework Hints available at stewartcalculus.com

53. $\int x^2 \sinh mx \, dx$

54. $\int (x + \sin x)^2 \, dx$

55. $\int \dfrac{dx}{x + x\sqrt{x}}$

56. $\int \dfrac{dx}{\sqrt{x} + x\sqrt{x}}$

57. $\int x\sqrt[3]{x + c} \, dx$

58. $\int \dfrac{x \ln x}{\sqrt{x^2 - 1}} \, dx$

59. $\int \cos x \cos^3(\sin x) \, dx$

60. $\int \dfrac{dx}{x^2\sqrt{4x^2 - 1}}$

61. $\int \dfrac{d\theta}{1 + \cos \theta}$

62. $\int \dfrac{d\theta}{1 + \cos^2\theta}$

63. $\int \sqrt{x}\, e^{\sqrt{x}} \, dx$

64. $\int \dfrac{1}{\sqrt{\sqrt{x} + 1}} \, dx$

65. $\int \dfrac{\sin 2x}{1 + \cos^4 x} \, dx$

66. $\int_{\pi/4}^{\pi/3} \dfrac{\ln(\tan x)}{\sin x \cos x} \, dx$

67. $\int \dfrac{1}{\sqrt{x + 1} + \sqrt{x}} \, dx$

68. $\int \dfrac{x^2}{x^6 + 3x^3 + 2} \, dx$

69. $\int_1^{\sqrt{3}} \dfrac{\sqrt{1 + x^2}}{x^2} \, dx$

70. $\int \dfrac{1}{1 + 2e^x - e^{-x}} \, dx$

71. $\int \dfrac{e^{2x}}{1 + e^x} \, dx$

72. $\int \dfrac{\ln(x + 1)}{x^2} \, dx$

73. $\int \dfrac{x + \arcsin x}{\sqrt{1 - x^2}} \, dx$

74. $\int \dfrac{4^x + 10^x}{2^x} \, dx$

75. $\int \dfrac{1}{(x - 2)(x^2 + 4)} \, dx$

76. $\int \dfrac{dx}{\sqrt{x}\,(2 + \sqrt{x}\,)^4}$

77. $\int \dfrac{xe^x}{\sqrt{1 + e^x}} \, dx$

78. $\int \dfrac{1 + \sin x}{1 - \sin x} \, dx$

79. $\int x \sin^2 x \cos x \, dx$

80. $\int \dfrac{\sec x \cos 2x}{\sin x + \sec x} \, dx$

81. $\int \sqrt{1 - \sin x} \, dx$

82. $\int \dfrac{\sin x \cos x}{\sin^4 x + \cos^4 x} \, dx$

83. The functions $y = e^{x^2}$ and $y = x^2 e^{x^2}$ don't have elementary antiderivatives, but $y = (2x^2 + 1)e^{x^2}$ does. Evaluate $\int (2x^2 + 1)e^{x^2} dx$.

84. We know that $F(x) = \int_0^x e^{e^t} \, dt$ is a continuous function by FTC1, though it is not an elementary function. The functions

$$\int \dfrac{e^x}{x} \, dx \qquad \text{and} \qquad \int \dfrac{1}{\ln x} \, dx$$

are not elementary either, but they can be expressed in terms of F. Evaluate the following integrals in terms of F.

(a) $\int_1^2 \dfrac{e^x}{x} \, dx$ (b) $\int_2^3 \dfrac{1}{\ln x} \, dx$

7.6 Integration Using Tables and Computer Algebra Systems

In this section we describe how to use tables and computer algebra systems to integrate functions that have elementary antiderivatives. You should bear in mind, though, that even the most powerful computer algebra systems can't find explicit formulas for the antiderivatives of functions like e^{x^2} or the other functions described at the end of Section 7.5.

Tables of Integrals

Tables of indefinite integrals are very useful when we are confronted by an integral that is difficult to evaluate by hand and we don't have access to a computer algebra system. A relatively brief table of 120 integrals, categorized by form, is provided on the Reference Pages at the back of the book. More extensive tables are available in the *CRC Standard Mathematical Tables and Formulae*, 31st ed. by Daniel Zwillinger (Boca Raton, FL, 2002) (709 entries) or in Gradshteyn and Ryzhik's *Table of Integrals, Series, and Products*, 7e (San Diego, 2007), which contains hundreds of pages of integrals. It should be remembered, however, that integrals do not often occur in exactly the form listed in a table. Usually we need to use the Substitution Rule or algebraic manipulation to transform a given integral into one of the forms in the table.

EXAMPLE 1 The region bounded by the curves $y = \arctan x$, $y = 0$, and $x = 1$ is rotated about the y-axis. Find the volume of the resulting solid.

SOLUTION Using the method of cylindrical shells, we see that the volume is

$$V = \int_0^1 2\pi x \arctan x \, dx$$

The Table of Integrals appears on Reference Pages 6–10 at the back of the book.

In the section of the Table of Integrals titled *Inverse Trigonometric Forms* we locate Formula 92:

$$\int u \tan^{-1}u \, du = \frac{u^2 + 1}{2} \tan^{-1}u - \frac{u}{2} + C$$

Thus the volume is

$$V = 2\pi \int_0^1 x \tan^{-1}x \, dx = 2\pi \left[\frac{x^2 + 1}{2} \tan^{-1}x - \frac{x}{2} \right]_0^1$$

$$= \pi \left[(x^2 + 1) \tan^{-1}x - x \right]_0^1 = \pi(2 \tan^{-1}1 - 1)$$

$$= \pi[2(\pi/4) - 1] = \tfrac{1}{2}\pi^2 - \pi$$

V **EXAMPLE 2** Use the Table of Integrals to find $\displaystyle\int \frac{x^2}{\sqrt{5 - 4x^2}} \, dx$.

SOLUTION If we look at the section of the table titled *Forms Involving* $\sqrt{a^2 - u^2}$, we see that the closest entry is number 34:

$$\int \frac{u^2}{\sqrt{a^2 - u^2}} \, du = -\frac{u}{2} \sqrt{a^2 - u^2} + \frac{a^2}{2} \sin^{-1}\left(\frac{u}{a}\right) + C$$

This is not exactly what we have, but we will be able to use it if we first make the substitution $u = 2x$:

$$\int \frac{x^2}{\sqrt{5 - 4x^2}} \, dx = \int \frac{(u/2)^2}{\sqrt{5 - u^2}} \frac{du}{2} = \frac{1}{8} \int \frac{u^2}{\sqrt{5 - u^2}} \, du$$

Then we use Formula 34 with $a^2 = 5$ (so $a = \sqrt{5}$):

$$\int \frac{x^2}{\sqrt{5 - 4x^2}} \, dx = \frac{1}{8} \int \frac{u^2}{\sqrt{5 - u^2}} \, du = \frac{1}{8} \left(-\frac{u}{2} \sqrt{5 - u^2} + \frac{5}{2} \sin^{-1}\frac{u}{\sqrt{5}} \right) + C$$

$$= -\frac{x}{8} \sqrt{5 - 4x^2} + \frac{5}{16} \sin^{-1}\left(\frac{2x}{\sqrt{5}}\right) + C$$

EXAMPLE 3 Use the Table of Integrals to evaluate $\displaystyle\int x^3 \sin x \, dx$.

SOLUTION If we look in the section called *Trigonometric Forms,* we see that none of the entries explicitly includes a u^3 factor. However, we can use the reduction formula in entry 84 with $n = 3$:

$$\int x^3 \sin x \, dx = -x^3 \cos x + 3 \int x^2 \cos x \, dx$$

85. $\displaystyle\int u^n \cos u \, du$

$\displaystyle = u^n \sin u - n \int u^{n-1} \sin u \, du$

We now need to evaluate $\int x^2 \cos x \, dx$. We can use the reduction formula in entry 85 with $n = 2$, followed by entry 82:

$$\int x^2 \cos x \, dx = x^2 \sin x - 2 \int x \sin x \, dx$$

$$= x^2 \sin x - 2(\sin x - x \cos x) + K$$

Combining these calculations, we get

$$\int x^3 \sin x \, dx = -x^3 \cos x + 3x^2 \sin x + 6x \cos x - 6 \sin x + C$$

where $C = 3K$.

V EXAMPLE 4 Use the Table of Integrals to find $\int x\sqrt{x^2 + 2x + 4} \, dx$.

SOLUTION Since the table gives forms involving $\sqrt{a^2 + x^2}$, $\sqrt{a^2 - x^2}$, and $\sqrt{x^2 - a^2}$, but not $\sqrt{ax^2 + bx + c}$, we first complete the square:

$$x^2 + 2x + 4 = (x + 1)^2 + 3$$

If we make the substitution $u = x + 1$ (so $x = u - 1$), the integrand will involve the pattern $\sqrt{a^2 + u^2}$:

$$\int x\sqrt{x^2 + 2x + 4} \, dx = \int (u - 1) \sqrt{u^2 + 3} \, du$$

$$= \int u\sqrt{u^2 + 3} \, du - \int \sqrt{u^2 + 3} \, du$$

The first integral is evaluated using the substitution $t = u^2 + 3$:

$$\int u\sqrt{u^2 + 3} \, du = \tfrac{1}{2}\int \sqrt{t} \, dt = \tfrac{1}{2} \cdot \tfrac{2}{3} t^{3/2} = \tfrac{1}{3}(u^2 + 3)^{3/2}$$

21. $\int \sqrt{a^2 + u^2} \, du = \dfrac{u}{2}\sqrt{a^2 + u^2}$

$\quad + \dfrac{a^2}{2}\ln\left(u + \sqrt{a^2 + u^2}\right) + C$

For the second integral we use Formula 21 with $a = \sqrt{3}$:

$$\int \sqrt{u^2 + 3} \, du = \frac{u}{2}\sqrt{u^2 + 3} + \tfrac{3}{2}\ln\left(u + \sqrt{u^2 + 3}\right)$$

Thus

$$\int x\sqrt{x^2 + 2x + 4} \, dx$$

$$= \tfrac{1}{3}(x^2 + 2x + 4)^{3/2} - \frac{x + 1}{2}\sqrt{x^2 + 2x + 4} - \tfrac{3}{2}\ln\left(x + 1 + \sqrt{x^2 + 2x + 4}\right) + C$$

Computer Algebra Systems

We have seen that the use of tables involves matching the form of the given integrand with the forms of the integrands in the tables. Computers are particularly good at matching patterns. And just as we used substitutions in conjunction with tables, a CAS can perform substitutions that transform a given integral into one that occurs in its stored formulas. So it isn't surprising that computer algebra systems excel at integration. That doesn't mean that integration by hand is an obsolete skill. We will see that a hand computation sometimes produces an indefinite integral in a form that is more convenient than a machine answer.

To begin, let's see what happens when we ask a machine to integrate the relatively simple function $y = 1/(3x - 2)$. Using the substitution $u = 3x - 2$, an easy calculation by hand gives

$$\int \frac{1}{3x - 2} \, dx = \tfrac{1}{3}\ln|3x - 2| + C$$

whereas Derive, Mathematica, and Maple all return the answer

$$\tfrac{1}{3}\ln(3x - 2)$$

The first thing to notice is that computer algebra systems omit the constant of integration. In other words, they produce a *particular* antiderivative, not the most general one. Therefore, when making use of a machine integration, we might have to add a constant. Second, the absolute value signs are omitted in the machine answer. That is fine if our problem is concerned only with values of x greater than $\tfrac{2}{3}$. But if we are interested in other values of x, then we need to insert the absolute value symbol.

In the next example we reconsider the integral of Example 4, but this time we ask a machine for the answer.

EXAMPLE 5 Use a computer algebra system to find $\displaystyle\int x\sqrt{x^2 + 2x + 4}\, dx$.

SOLUTION Maple responds with the answer

$$\tfrac{1}{3}(x^2 + 2x + 4)^{3/2} - \tfrac{1}{4}(2x + 2)\sqrt{x^2 + 2x + 4} - \frac{3}{2}\,\text{arcsinh}\,\frac{\sqrt{3}}{3}(1 + x)$$

This looks different from the answer we found in Example 4, but it is equivalent because the third term can be rewritten using the identity

This is Equation 3.11.3.

$$\text{arcsinh}\, x = \ln\!\left(x + \sqrt{x^2 + 1}\right)$$

Thus

$$\text{arcsinh}\,\frac{\sqrt{3}}{3}(1 + x) = \ln\!\left[\frac{\sqrt{3}}{3}(1 + x) + \sqrt{\tfrac{1}{3}(1 + x)^2 + 1}\,\right]$$

$$= \ln\frac{1}{\sqrt{3}}\left[1 + x + \sqrt{(1 + x)^2 + 3}\,\right]$$

$$= \ln\frac{1}{\sqrt{3}} + \ln\!\left(x + 1 + \sqrt{x^2 + 2x + 4}\,\right)$$

The resulting extra term $-\tfrac{3}{2}\ln\!\left(1/\sqrt{3}\,\right)$ can be absorbed into the constant of integration.

Mathematica gives the answer

$$\left(\frac{5}{6} + \frac{x}{6} + \frac{x^2}{3}\right)\sqrt{x^2 + 2x + 4} - \frac{3}{2}\,\text{arcsinh}\!\left(\frac{1 + x}{\sqrt{3}}\right)$$

Mathematica combined the first two terms of Example 4 (and the Maple result) into a single term by factoring.

Derive gives the answer

$$\tfrac{1}{6}\sqrt{x^2 + 2x + 4}\,(2x^2 + x + 5) - \tfrac{3}{2}\ln\!\left(\sqrt{x^2 + 2x + 4} + x + 1\right)$$

The first term is like the first term in the Mathematica answer, and the second term is identical to the last term in Example 4. ◼

EXAMPLE 6 Use a CAS to evaluate $\displaystyle\int x(x^2 + 5)^8\, dx$.

SOLUTION Maple and Mathematica give the same answer:

$$\tfrac{1}{18}x^{18} + \tfrac{5}{2}x^{16} + 50x^{14} + \tfrac{1750}{3}x^{12} + 4375x^{10} + 21875x^8 + \tfrac{218750}{3}x^6 + 156250x^4 + \tfrac{390625}{2}x^2$$

It's clear that both systems must have expanded $(x^2 + 5)^8$ by the Binomial Theorem and then integrated each term.

If we integrate by hand instead, using the substitution $u = x^2 + 5$, we get

Derive and the TI-89 and TI-92 also give this answer

$$\int x(x^2 + 5)^8 \, dx \quad \tfrac{1}{18}(x^2 + 5)^9 + C$$

For most purposes, this is a more convenient form of the answer.

EXAMPLE 7 Use a CAS to find $\int \sin^5 x \cos^2 x \, dx$.

SOLUTION In Example 2 in Section 7.2 we found that

$$\boxed{1} \qquad \int \sin^5 x \cos^2 x \, dx = -\tfrac{1}{3}\cos^3 x + \tfrac{2}{5}\cos^5 x - \tfrac{1}{7}\cos^7 x + C$$

Derive and Maple report the answer

$$-\tfrac{1}{7}\sin^4 x \cos^3 x - \tfrac{4}{35}\sin^2 x \cos^3 x - \tfrac{8}{105}\cos^3 x$$

whereas Mathematica produces

$$-\tfrac{5}{64}\cos x - \tfrac{1}{192}\cos 3x + \tfrac{3}{320}\cos 5x - \tfrac{1}{448}\cos 7x$$

• We suspect that there are trigonometric identities which show that these three answers are equivalent. Indeed, if we ask Derive, Maple, and Mathematica to simplify their expressions using trigonometric identities, they ultimately produce the same form of the answer as in Equation 1.

7.6 Exercises

1–4 Use the indicated entry in the Table of Integrals on the Reference Pages to evaluate the integral.

1. $\displaystyle\int_0^{\pi/2} \cos 5x \cos 2x \, dx$;   entry 80

2. $\displaystyle\int_0^1 \sqrt{x - x^2} \, dx$;   entry 113

3. $\displaystyle\int_1^2 \sqrt{4x^2 - 3} \, dx$;   entry 39

4. $\displaystyle\int_0^1 \tan^3(\pi x/6) \, dx$;   entry 69

5–32 Use the Table of Integrals on Reference Pages 6–10 to evaluate the integral.

5. $\displaystyle\int_0^1 2x \cos^{-1} x \, dx$

6. $\displaystyle\int_2^3 \frac{1}{x^2\sqrt{4x^2 - 7}} \, dx$

7. $\displaystyle\int \frac{\cos x}{\sin^2 x - 9} \, dx$

8. $\displaystyle\int \frac{\ln(1 + \sqrt{x})}{\sqrt{x}} \, dx$

9. $\displaystyle\int \frac{dx}{x^2\sqrt{4x^2 + 9}}$

10. $\displaystyle\int \frac{\sqrt{2y^2 - 3}}{y^2} \, dy$

11. $\displaystyle\int_{-1}^0 t^2 e^{-t} \, dt$

12. $\displaystyle\int x^2 \operatorname{csch}(x^3 + 1) \, dx$

13. $\displaystyle\int \frac{\tan^3(1/z)}{z^2} \, dz$

14. $\displaystyle\int \sin^{-1}\sqrt{x} \, dx$

15. $\displaystyle\int e^{2x} \arctan(e^x) \, dx$

16. $\displaystyle\int x \sin(x^2) \cos(3x^2) \, dx$

17. $\displaystyle\int y\sqrt{6 + 4y - 4y^2} \, dy$

18. $\displaystyle\int \frac{dx}{2x^3 - 3x^2}$

19. $\displaystyle\int \sin^2 x \cos x \ln(\sin x) \, dx$

20. $\displaystyle\int \frac{\sin 2\theta}{\sqrt{5 - \sin \theta}} \, d\theta$

21. $\displaystyle\int \frac{e^x}{3 - e^{2x}} \, dx$

22. $\displaystyle\int_0^2 x^3\sqrt{4x^2 - x^4} \, dx$

23. $\displaystyle\int \sec^5 x \, dx$

24. $\displaystyle\int \sin^6 2x \, dx$

CAS Computer algebra system required   **1.** Homework Hints available at stewartcalculus.com

25. $\displaystyle\int \frac{\sqrt{4 + (\ln x)^2}}{x}\, dx$

26. $\displaystyle\int_0^1 x^4 e^{-x}\, dx$

27. $\displaystyle\int \frac{\cos^{-1}(x^{-2})}{x^3}\, dx$

28. $\displaystyle\int (t + 1)\sqrt{t^2 - 2t - 1}\, dt$

29. $\displaystyle\int \sqrt{e^{2x} - 1}\, dx$

30. $\displaystyle\int e^t \sin(\alpha t - 3)\, dt$

31. $\displaystyle\int \frac{x^4\, dx}{\sqrt{x^{10} - 2}}$

32. $\displaystyle\int \frac{\sec^2\theta\, \tan^2\theta}{\sqrt{9 - \tan^2\theta}}\, d\theta$

33. The region under the curve $y = \sin^2 x$ from 0 to π is rotated about the x-axis. Find the volume of the resulting solid.

34. Find the volume of the solid obtained when the region under the curve $y = \arcsin x$, $x \geqslant 0$, is rotated about the y-axis.

35. Verify Formula 53 in the Table of Integrals (a) by differentiation and (b) by using the substitution $t = a + bu$.

36. Verify Formula 31 (a) by differentiation and (b) by substituting $u = a \sin \theta$.

[CAS] **37–44** Use a computer algebra system to evaluate the integral. Compare the answer with the result of using tables. If the answers are not the same, show that they are equivalent.

37. $\displaystyle\int \sec^4 x\, dx$

38. $\displaystyle\int \csc^5 x\, dx$

39. $\displaystyle\int x^2\sqrt{x^2 + 4}\, dx$

40. $\displaystyle\int \frac{dx}{e^x(3e^x + 2)}$

41. $\displaystyle\int \cos^4 x\, dx$

42. $\displaystyle\int x^2\sqrt{1 - x^2}\, dx$

43. $\displaystyle\int \tan^5 x\, dx$

44. $\displaystyle\int \frac{1}{\sqrt{1 + \sqrt[3]{x}}}\, dx$

[CAS] **45.** (a) Use the table of integrals to evaluate $F(x) = \int f(x)\, dx$, where

$$f(x) = \frac{1}{x\sqrt{1 - x^2}}$$

What is the domain of f and F?

(b) Use a CAS to evaluate $F(x)$. What is the domain of the function F that the CAS produces? Is there a discrepancy between this domain and the domain of the function F that you found in part (a)?

[CAS] **46.** Computer algebra systems sometimes need a helping hand from human beings. Try to evaluate

$$\int (1 + \ln x)\sqrt{1 + (x \ln x)^2}\, dx$$

with a computer algebra system. If it doesn't return an answer, make a substitution that changes the integral into one that the CAS *can* evaluate.

DISCOVERY PROJECT   **PATTERNS IN INTEGRALS**

In this project a computer algebra system is used to investigate indefinite integrals of families of functions. By observing the patterns that occur in the integrals of several members of the family, you will first guess, and then prove, a general formula for the integral of any member of the family.

1. (a) Use a computer algebra system to evaluate the following integrals.

(i) $\displaystyle\int \frac{1}{(x + 2)(x + 3)}\, dx$

(ii) $\displaystyle\int \frac{1}{(x + 1)(x + 5)}\, dx$

(iii) $\displaystyle\int \frac{1}{(x + 2)(x - 5)}\, dx$

(iv) $\displaystyle\int \frac{1}{(x + 2)^2}\, dx$

(b) Based on the pattern of your responses in part (a), guess the value of the integral

$$\int \frac{1}{(x + a)(x + b)}\, dx$$

if $a \neq b$. What if $a = b$?

(c) Check your guess by asking your CAS to evaluate the integral in part (b). Then prove it using partial fractions.

[CAS] Computer algebra system required

2. (a) Use a computer algebra system to evaluate the following integrals.

(i) $\int \sin x \cos 2x \, dx$ (ii) $\int \sin 3x \cos 7x \, dx$ (iii) $\int \sin 8x \cos 3x \, dx$

(b) Based on the pattern of your responses in part (a), guess the value of the integral

$$\int \sin ax \cos bx \, dx$$

(c) Check your guess with a CAS. Then prove it using the techniques of Section 7.2. For what values of a and b is it valid?

3. (a) Use a computer algebra system to evaluate the following integrals.

(i) $\int \ln x \, dx$ (ii) $\int x \ln x \, dx$ (iii) $\int x^2 \ln x \, dx$

(iv) $\int x^3 \ln x \, dx$ (v) $\int x^7 \ln x \, dx$

(b) Based on the pattern of your responses in part (a), guess the value of

$$\int x^n \ln x \, dx$$

(c) Use integration by parts to prove the conjecture that you made in part (b). For what values of n is it valid?

4. (a) Use a computer algebra system to evaluate the following integrals.

(i) $\int xe^x \, dx$ (ii) $\int x^2 e^x \, dx$ (iii) $\int x^3 e^x \, dx$

(iv) $\int x^4 e^x \, dx$ (v) $\int x^5 e^x \, dx$

(b) Based on the pattern of your responses in part (a), guess the value of $\int x^6 e^x \, dx$. Then use your CAS to check your guess.

(c) Based on the patterns in parts (a) and (b), make a conjecture as to the value of the integral

$$\int x^n e^x \, dx$$

when n is a positive integer.

(d) Use mathematical induction to prove the conjecture you made in part (c).

7.7   Approximate Integration

There are two situations in which it is impossible to find the exact value of a definite integral.

The first situation arises from the fact that in order to evaluate $\int_a^b f(x) \, dx$ using the Fundamental Theorem of Calculus we need to know an antiderivative of f. Sometimes, however, it is difficult, or even impossible, to find an antiderivative (see Section 7.5). For example, it is impossible to evaluate the following integrals exactly:

$$\int_0^1 e^{x^2} dx \qquad \int_{-1}^1 \sqrt{1 + x^3} \, dx$$

(a) Left endpoint approximation

(b) Right endpoint approximation

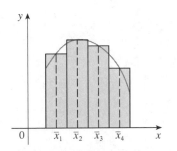

(c) Midpoint approximation

FIGURE 1

The second situation arises when the function is determined from a scientific experiment through instrument readings or collected data. There may be no formula for the function (see Example 5).

In both cases we need to find approximate values of definite integrals. We already know one such method. Recall that the definite integral is defined as a limit of Riemann sums, so any Riemann sum could be used as an approximation to the integral: If we divide $[a, b]$ into n subintervals of equal length $\Delta x = (b - a)/n$, then we have

$$\int_a^b f(x)\, dx \approx \sum_{i=1}^n f(x_i^*)\, \Delta x$$

where x_i^* is any point in the ith subinterval $[x_{i-1}, x_i]$. If x_i^* is chosen to be the left endpoint of the interval, then $x_i^* = x_{i-1}$ and we have

$$\boxed{1} \qquad \int_a^b f(x)\, dx \approx L_n = \sum_{i=1}^n f(x_{i-1})\, \Delta x$$

If $f(x) \geq 0$, then the integral represents an area and $\boxed{1}$ represents an approximation of this area by the rectangles shown in Figure 1(a). If we choose x_i^* to be the right endpoint, then $x_i^* = x_i$ and we have

$$\boxed{2} \qquad \int_a^b f(x)\, dx \approx R_n = \sum_{i=1}^n f(x_i)\, \Delta x$$

[See Figure 1(b).] The approximations L_n and R_n defined by Equations 1 and 2 are called the **left endpoint approximation** and **right endpoint approximation**, respectively.

In Section 5.2 we also considered the case where x_i^* is chosen to be the midpoint $\bar{x}_i$ of the subinterval $[x_{i-1}, x_i]$. Figure 1(c) shows the midpoint approximation M_n, which appears to be better than either L_n or R_n.

Midpoint Rule

$$\int_a^b f(x)\, dx \approx M_n = \Delta x \left[f(\bar{x}_1) + f(\bar{x}_2) + \cdots + f(\bar{x}_n) \right]$$

where

$$\Delta x = \frac{b - a}{n}$$

and

$$\bar{x}_i = \tfrac{1}{2}(x_{i-1} + x_i) = \text{midpoint of } [x_{i-1}, x_i]$$

Another approximation, called the Trapezoidal Rule, results from averaging the approximations in Equations 1 and 2:

$$\int_a^b f(x)\, dx \approx \frac{1}{2} \left[\sum_{i=1}^n f(x_{i-1})\, \Delta x + \sum_{i=1}^n f(x_i)\, \Delta x \right] = \frac{\Delta x}{2} \left[\sum_{i=1}^n \left(f(x_{i-1}) + f(x_i) \right) \right]$$

$$= \frac{\Delta x}{2} \left[\left(f(x_0) + f(x_1) \right) + \left(f(x_1) + f(x_2) \right) + \cdots + \left(f(x_{n-1}) + f(x_n) \right) \right]$$

$$= \frac{\Delta x}{2} \left[f(x_0) + 2f(x_1) + 2f(x_2) + \cdots + 2f(x_{n-1}) + f(x_n) \right]$$

FIGURE 2
Trapezoidal approximation

FIGURE 3

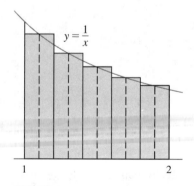

FIGURE 4

Trapezoidal Rule

$$\int_a^b f(x)\,dx \approx T_n = \frac{\Delta x}{2}\left[f(x_0) + 2f(x_1) + 2f(x_2) + \cdots + 2f(x_{n-1}) + f(x_n)\right]$$

where $\Delta x = (b - a)/n$ and $x_i = a + i\,\Delta x$.

The reason for the name Trapezoidal Rule can be seen from Figure 2, which illustrates the case with $f(x) \geqslant 0$ and $n = 4$. The area of the trapezoid that lies above the ith sub-interval is

$$\Delta x\left(\frac{f(x_{i-1}) + f(x_i)}{2}\right) = \frac{\Delta x}{2}\left[f(x_{i-1}) + f(x_i)\right]$$

and if we add the areas of all these trapezoids, we get the right side of the Trapezoidal Rule.

EXAMPLE 1 Use (a) the Trapezoidal Rule and (b) the Midpoint Rule with $n = 5$ to approximate the integral $\int_1^2 (1/x)\,dx$.

SOLUTION
(a) With $n = 5$, $a = 1$, and $b = 2$, we have $\Delta x = (2 - 1)/5 = 0.2$, and so the Trapezoidal Rule gives

$$\int_1^2 \frac{1}{x}\,dx \approx T_5 = \frac{0.2}{2}\left[f(1) + 2f(1.2) + 2f(1.4) + 2f(1.6) + 2f(1.8) + f(2)\right]$$

$$= 0.1\left(\frac{1}{1} + \frac{2}{1.2} + \frac{2}{1.4} + \frac{2}{1.6} + \frac{2}{1.8} + \frac{1}{2}\right)$$

$$\approx 0.695635$$

This approximation is illustrated in Figure 3.

(b) The midpoints of the five subintervals are 1.1, 1.3, 1.5, 1.7, and 1.9, so the Midpoint Rule gives

$$\int_1^2 \frac{1}{x}\,dx \approx \Delta x\left[f(1.1) + f(1.3) + f(1.5) + f(1.7) + f(1.9)\right]$$

$$= \frac{1}{5}\left(\frac{1}{1.1} + \frac{1}{1.3} + \frac{1}{1.5} + \frac{1}{1.7} + \frac{1}{1.9}\right)$$

$$\approx 0.691908$$

This approximation is illustrated in Figure 4.

In Example 1 we deliberately chose an integral whose value can be computed explicitly so that we can see how accurate the Trapezoidal and Midpoint Rules are. By the Fundamental Theorem of Calculus,

$$\int_1^2 \frac{1}{x}\,dx = \ln x\Big]_1^2 = \ln 2 = 0.693147\ldots$$

$$\int_a^b f(x)\,dx = \text{approximation} + \text{error}$$

The **error** in using an approximation is defined to be the amount that needs to be added to the approximation to make it exact. From the values in Example 1 we see that the errors in the Trapezoidal and Midpoint Rule approximations for $n = 5$ are

$$E_T \approx -0.002488 \qquad \text{and} \qquad E_M \approx 0.001239$$

In general, we have

$$E_T = \int_a^b f(x)\, dx - T_n \qquad \text{and} \qquad E_M = \int_a^b f(x)\, dx - M_n$$

TEC Module 5.2/7.7 allows you to compare approximation methods.

The following tables show the results of calculations similar to those in Example 1, but for $n = 5$, 10, and 20 and for the left and right endpoint approximations as well as the Trapezoidal and Midpoint Rules.

Approximations to $\int_1^2 \dfrac{1}{x}\, dx$

n	L_n	R_n	T_n	M_n
5	0.745635	0.645635	0.695635	0.691908
10	0.718771	0.668771	0.693771	0.692835
20	0.705803	0.680803	0.693303	0.693069

Corresponding errors

n	E_L	E_R	E_T	E_M
5	-0.052488	0.047512	-0.002488	0.001239
10	-0.025624	0.024376	-0.000624	0.000312
20	-0.012656	0.012344	-0.000156	0.000078

We can make several observations from these tables:

1. In all of the methods we get more accurate approximations when we increase the value of n. (But very large values of n result in so many arithmetic operations that we have to beware of accumulated round-off error.)

2. The errors in the left and right endpoint approximations are opposite in sign and appear to decrease by a factor of about 2 when we double the value of n.

3. The Trapezoidal and Midpoint Rules are much more accurate than the endpoint approximations.

It turns out that these observations are true in most cases.

4. The errors in the Trapezoidal and Midpoint Rules are opposite in sign and appear to decrease by a factor of about 4 when we double the value of n.

5. The size of the error in the Midpoint Rule is about half the size of the error in the Trapezoidal Rule.

Figure 5 shows why we can usually expect the Midpoint Rule to be more accurate than the Trapezoidal Rule. The area of a typical rectangle in the Midpoint Rule is the same as the area of the trapezoid $ABCD$ whose upper side is tangent to the graph at P. The area of this trapezoid is closer to the area under the graph than is the area of the trapezoid $AQRD$ used in the Trapezoidal Rule. [The midpoint error (shaded red) is smaller than the trapezoidal error (shaded blue).]

FIGURE 5

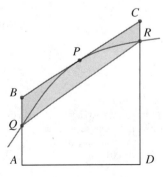

These observations are corroborated in the following error estimates, which are proved in books on numerical analysis. Notice that Observation 4 corresponds to the n^2 in each denominator because $(2n)^2 = 4n^2$. The fact that the estimates depend on the size of the second derivative is not surprising if you look at Figure 5, because $f''(x)$ measures how much the graph is curved. [Recall that $f''(x)$ measures how fast the slope of $y = f(x)$ changes.]

---

3 **Error Bounds** Suppose $|f''(x)| \leqslant K$ for $a \leqslant x \leqslant b$. If E_T and E_M are the errors in the Trapezoidal and Midpoint Rules, then

$$|E_T| \leqslant \frac{K(b-a)^3}{12n^2} \quad \text{and} \quad |E_M| \leqslant \frac{K(b-a)^3}{24n^2}$$

Let's apply this error estimate to the Trapezoidal Rule approximation in Example 1. If $f(x) = 1/x$, then $f'(x) = -1/x^2$ and $f''(x) = 2/x^3$. Since $1 \leqslant x \leqslant 2$, we have $1/x \leqslant 1$, so

$$|f''(x)| = \left|\frac{2}{x^3}\right| \leqslant \frac{2}{1^3} = 2$$

Therefore, taking $K = 2$, $a = 1$, $b = 2$, and $n = 5$ in the error estimate $\boxed{3}$, we see that

K can be any number larger than all the values of $|f''(x)|$, but smaller values of K give better error bounds.

$$|E_T| \leqslant \frac{2(2-1)^3}{12(5)^2} = \frac{1}{150} \approx 0.006667$$

Comparing this error estimate of 0.006667 with the actual error of about 0.002488, we see that it can happen that the actual error is substantially less than the upper bound for the error given by $\boxed{3}$.

V **EXAMPLE 2** How large should we take n in order to guarantee that the Trapezoidal and Midpoint Rule approximations for $\int_1^2 (1/x)\, dx$ are accurate to within 0.0001?

SOLUTION We saw in the preceding calculation that $|f''(x)| \leqslant 2$ for $1 \leqslant x \leqslant 2$, so we can take $K = 2$, $a = 1$, and $b = 2$ in $\boxed{3}$. Accuracy to within 0.0001 means that the size of the error should be less than 0.0001. Therefore we choose n so that

$$\frac{2(1)^3}{12n^2} < 0.0001$$

Solving the inequality for n, we get

$$n^2 > \frac{2}{12(0.0001)}$$

It's quite possible that a lower value for n would suffice, but 41 is the smallest value for which the error bound formula can *guarantee* us accuracy to within 0.0001.

or

$$n > \frac{1}{\sqrt{0.0006}} \approx 40.8$$

Thus $n = 41$ will ensure the desired accuracy.

For the same accuracy with the Midpoint Rule we choose n so that

$$\frac{2(1)^3}{24n^2} < 0.0001 \qquad \text{and so} \qquad n > \frac{1}{\sqrt{0.0012}} \approx 29$$

▼ EXAMPLE 3

(a) Use the Midpoint Rule with $n = 10$ to approximate the integral $\int_0^1 e^{x^2}\,dx$.
(b) Give an upper bound for the error involved in this approximation.

SOLUTION
(a) Since $a = 0$, $b = 1$, and $n = 10$, the Midpoint Rule gives

$$\int_0^1 e^{x^2}\,dx \approx \Delta x\,[f(0.05) + f(0.15) + \cdots + f(0.85) + f(0.95)]$$

$$= 0.1[e^{0.0025} + e^{0.0225} + e^{0.0625} + e^{0.1225} + e^{0.2025} + e^{0.3025}$$

$$+ e^{0.4225} + e^{0.5625} + e^{0.7225} + e^{0.9025}]$$

$$\approx 1.460393$$

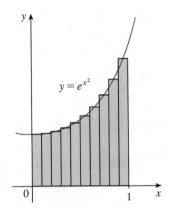

FIGURE 6

Figure 6 illustrates this approximation.

(b) Since $f(x) = e^{x^2}$, we have $f'(x) = 2xe^{x^2}$ and $f''(x) = (2 + 4x^2)e^{x^2}$. Also, since $0 \le x \le 1$, we have $x^2 \le 1$ and so

$$0 \le f''(x) = (2 + 4x^2)e^{x^2} \le 6e$$

Error estimates give upper bounds for the error. They are theoretical, worst-case scenarios. The actual error in this case turns out to be about 0.0023.

Taking $K = 6e$, $a = 0$, $b = 1$, and $n = 10$ in the error estimate ③, we see that an upper bound for the error is

$$\frac{6e(1)^3}{24(10)^2} = \frac{e}{400} \approx 0.007$$

■ Simpson's Rule

Another rule for approximate integration results from using parabolas instead of straight line segments to approximate a curve. As before, we divide $[a, b]$ into n subintervals of equal length $h = \Delta x = (b - a)/n$, but this time we assume that n is an *even* number. Then on each consecutive pair of intervals we approximate the curve $y = f(x) \ge 0$ by a parabola as shown in Figure 7. If $y_i = f(x_i)$, then $P_i(x_i, y_i)$ is the point on the curve lying above x_i. A typical parabola passes through three consecutive points P_i, P_{i+1}, and P_{i+2}.

FIGURE 7

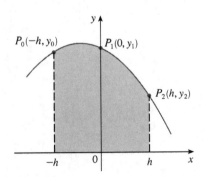

FIGURE 8

To simplify our calculations, we first consider the case where $x_0 = -h$, $x_1 = 0$, and $x_2 = h$. (See Figure 8.) We know that the equation of the parabola through P_0, P_1, and P_2 is of the form $y = Ax^2 + Bx + C$ and so the area under the parabola from $x = -h$ to $x = h$ is

$$\int_{-h}^{h} (Ax^2 + Bx + C)\, dx = 2 \int_{0}^{h} (Ax^2 + C)\, dx$$

Here we have used Theorem 6.6.7.
Notice that $Ax^2 + C$ is even and Bx is odd.

$$= 2\left[A\frac{x^3}{3} + Cx \right]_0^h$$

$$= 2\left(A\frac{h^3}{3} + Ch \right) = \frac{h}{3}(2Ah^2 + 6C)$$

But, since the parabola passes through $P_0(-h, y_0)$, $P_1(0, y_1)$, and $P_2(h, y_2)$, we have

$$y_0 = A(-h)^2 + B(-h) + C = Ah^2 - Bh + C$$

$$y_1 = C$$

$$y_2 = Ah^2 + Bh + C$$

and therefore

$$y_0 + 4y_1 + y_2 = 2Ah^2 + 6C$$

Thus we can rewrite the area under the parabola as

$$\frac{h}{3}(y_0 + 4y_1 + y_2)$$

Now by shifting this parabola horizontally we do not change the area under it. This means that the area under the parabola through P_0, P_1, and P_2 from $x = x_0$ to $x = x_2$ in Figure 7 is still

$$\frac{h}{3}(y_0 + 4y_1 + y_2)$$

Similarly, the area under the parabola through P_2, P_3, and P_4 from $x = x_2$ to $x = x_4$ is

$$\frac{h}{3}(y_2 + 4y_3 + y_4)$$

If we compute the areas under all the parabolas in this manner and add the results, we get

$$\int_a^b f(x)\, dx \approx \frac{h}{3}(y_0 + 4y_1 + y_2) + \frac{h}{3}(y_2 + 4y_3 + y_4)$$

$$+ \cdots + \frac{h}{3}(y_{n-2} + 4y_{n-1} + y_n)$$

$$= \frac{h}{3}(y_0 + 4y_1 + 2y_2 + 4y_3 + 2y_4 + \cdots + 2y_{n-2} + 4y_{n-1} + y_n)$$

Although we have derived this approximation for the case in which $f(x) \geq 0$, it is a reasonable approximation for any continuous function f and is called Simpson's Rule after the English mathematician Thomas Simpson (1710–1761). Note the pattern of coefficients: $1, 4, 2, 4, 2, 4, 2, \ldots, 4, 2, 4, 1$.

Simpson

Thomas Simpson was a weaver who taught himself mathematics and went on to become one of the best English mathematicians of the 18th century. What we call Simpson's Rule was actually known to Cavalieri and Gregory in the 17th century, but Simpson popularized it in his book *Mathematical Dissertations* (1743).

Simpson's Rule

$$\int_a^b f(x)\,dx \approx S_n = \frac{\Delta x}{3}\left[f(x_0) + 4f(x_1) + 2f(x_2) + 4f(x_3) + \cdots \right.$$

$$\left. + 2f(x_{n-2}) + 4f(x_{n-1}) + f(x_n) \right]$$

where n is even and $\Delta x = (b - a)/n$.

EXAMPLE 4   Use Simpson's Rule with $n = 10$ to approximate $\int_1^2 (1/x)\,dx$.

SOLUTION   Putting $f(x) = 1/x$, $n = 10$, and $\Delta x = 0.1$ in Simpson's Rule, we obtain

$$\int_1^2 \frac{1}{x}\,dx \approx S_{10}$$

$$= \frac{\Delta x}{3}\left[f(1) + 4f(1.1) + 2f(1.2) + 4f(1.3) + \cdots + 2f(1.8) + 4f(1.9) + f(2) \right]$$

$$= \frac{0.1}{3}\left(\frac{1}{1} + \frac{4}{1.1} + \frac{2}{1.2} + \frac{4}{1.3} + \frac{2}{1.4} + \frac{4}{1.5} + \frac{2}{1.6} + \frac{4}{1.7} + \frac{2}{1.8} + \frac{4}{1.9} + \frac{1}{2} \right)$$

$$\approx 0.693150$$

Notice that, in Example 4, Simpson's Rule gives us a *much* better approximation ($S_{10} \approx 0.693150$) to the true value of the integral ($\ln 2 \approx 0.693147\ldots$) than does the Trapezoidal Rule ($T_{10} \approx 0.693771$) or the Midpoint Rule ($M_{10} \approx 0.692835$). It turns out (see Exercise 50) that the approximations in Simpson's Rule are weighted averages of those in the Trapezoidal and Midpoint Rules:

$$S_{2n} = \tfrac{1}{3}T_n + \tfrac{2}{3}M_n$$

(Recall that E_T and E_M usually have opposite signs and $|E_M|$ is about half the size of $|E_T|$.)

In many applications of calculus we need to evaluate an integral even if no explicit formula is known for y as a function of x. A function may be given graphically or as a table of values of collected data. If there is evidence that the values are not changing rapidly, then the Trapezoidal Rule or Simpson's Rule can still be used to find an approximate value for $\int_a^b y\,dx$, the integral of y with respect to x.

V   EXAMPLE 5   Figure 9 shows data traffic on the link from the United States to SWITCH, the Swiss academic and research network, on February 10, 1998. $D(t)$ is the data throughput, measured in megabits per second (Mb/s). Use Simpson's Rule to estimate the total amount of data transmitted on the link from midnight to noon on that day.

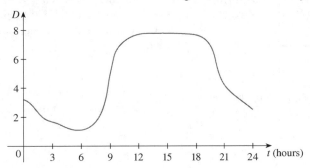

FIGURE 9

SOLUTION Because we want the units to be consistent and $D(t)$ is measured in megabits per second, we convert the units for t from hours to seconds. If we let $A(t)$ be the amount of data (in megabits) transmitted by time t, where t is measured in seconds, then $A'(t) = D(t)$. So, by the Net Change Theorem (see Section 5.4), the total amount of data transmitted by noon (when $t = 12 \times 60^2 = 43{,}200$) is

$$A(43{,}200) = \int_0^{43{,}200} D(t)\, dt$$

We estimate the values of $D(t)$ at hourly intervals from the graph and compile them in the table.

t (hours)	t (seconds)	$D(t)$	t (hours)	t (seconds)	$D(t)$
0	0	3.2	7	25,200	1.3
1	3,600	2.7	8	28,800	2.8
2	7,200	1.9	9	32,400	5.7
3	10,800	1.7	10	36,000	7.1
4	14,400	1.3	11	39,600	7.7
5	18,000	1.0	12	43,200	7.9
6	21,600	1.1			

Then we use Simpson's Rule with $n = 12$ and $\Delta t = 3600$ to estimate the integral:

$$\int_0^{43{,}200} A(t)\, dt \approx \frac{\Delta t}{3} [D(0) + 4D(3600) + 2D(7200) + \cdots + 4D(39{,}600) + D(43{,}200)]$$

$$\approx \frac{3600}{3} [3.2 + 4(2.7) + 2(1.9) + 4(1.7) + 2(1.3) + 4(1.0)$$

$$+ 2(1.1) + 4(1.3) + 2(2.8) + 4(5.7) + 2(7.1) + 4(7.7) + 7.9]$$

$$= 143{,}880$$

Thus the total amount of data transmitted from midnight to noon is about 144,000 megabits, or 144 gigabits. ▬

The table in the margin shows how Simpson's Rule compares with the Midpoint Rule for the integral $\int_1^2 (1/x)\, dx$, whose value is about 0.69314718. The second table shows how the error E_s in Simpson's Rule decreases by a factor of about 16 when n is doubled. (In Exercises 27 and 28 you are asked to verify this for two additional integrals.) That is consistent with the appearance of n^4 in the denominator of the following error estimate for Simpson's Rule. It is similar to the estimates given in ③ for the Trapezoidal and Midpoint Rules, but it uses the fourth derivative of f.

n	M_n	S_n
4	0.69121989	0.69315453
8	0.69266055	0.69314765
16	0.69302521	0.69314721

n	E_M	E_S
4	0.00192729	−0.00000735
8	0.00048663	−0.00000047
16	0.00012197	−0.00000003

④ **Error Bound for Simpson's Rule** Suppose that $|f^{(4)}(x)| \leq K$ for $a \leq x \leq b$. If E_s is the error involved in using Simpson's Rule, then

$$|E_S| \leq \frac{K(b-a)^5}{180n^4}$$

EXAMPLE 6 How large should we take n in order to guarantee that the Simpson's Rule approximation for $\int_1^2 (1/x)\, dx$ is accurate to within 0.0001?

SOLUTION If $f(x) = 1/x$, then $f^{(4)}(x) = 24/x^5$. Since $x \geqslant 1$, we have $1/x \leqslant 1$ and so

$$\left| f^{(4)}(x) \right| = \left| \frac{24}{x^5} \right| \leqslant 24$$

Therefore we can take $K = 24$ in $\boxed{4}$. Thus, for an error less than 0.0001, we should choose n so that

$$\frac{24(1)^5}{180 n^4} < 0.0001$$

This gives

$$n^4 > \frac{24}{180(0.0001)}$$

or

$$n > \frac{1}{\sqrt[4]{0.00075}} \approx 6.04$$

Therefore $n = 8$ (n must be even) gives the desired accuracy. (Compare this with Example 2, where we obtained $n = 41$ for the Trapezoidal Rule and $n = 29$ for the Midpoint Rule.)

EXAMPLE 7
(a) Use Simpson's Rule with $n = 10$ to approximate the integral $\int_0^1 e^{x^2}\, dx$.
(b) Estimate the error involved in this approximation.

SOLUTION
(a) If $n = 10$, then $\Delta x = 0.1$ and Simpson's Rule gives

$$\int_0^1 e^{x^2}\, dx \approx \frac{\Delta x}{3} [f(0) + 4f(0.1) + 2f(0.2) + \cdots + 2f(0.8) + 4f(0.9) + f(1)]$$

$$= \frac{0.1}{3} [e^0 + 4e^{0.01} + 2e^{0.04} + 4e^{0.09} + 2e^{0.16} + 4e^{0.25} + 2e^{0.36}$$

$$+ 4e^{0.49} + 2e^{0.64} + 4e^{0.81} + e^1]$$

$$\approx 1.462681$$

(b) The fourth derivative of $f(x) = e^{x^2}$ is

$$f^{(4)}(x) = (12 + 48x^2 + 16x^4)e^{x^2}$$

and so, since $0 \leqslant x \leqslant 1$, we have

$$0 \leqslant f^{(4)}(x) \leqslant (12 + 48 + 16)e^1 = 76e$$

Therefore, putting $K = 76e$, $a = 0$, $b = 1$, and $n = 10$ in $\boxed{4}$, we see that the error is at most

$$\frac{76e(1)^5}{180(10)^4} \approx 0.000115$$

(Compare this with Example 3.) Thus, correct to three decimal places, we have

$$\int_0^1 e^{x^2}\, dx \approx 1.463$$

Many calculators and computer algebra systems have a built-in algorithm that computes an approximation of a definite integral. Some of these machines use Simpson's Rule; others use more sophisticated techniques such as *adaptive* numerical integration. This means that if a function fluctuates much more on a certain part of the interval than it does elsewhere, then that part gets divided into more subintervals. This strategy reduces the number of calculations required to achieve a prescribed accuracy.

Figure 10 illustrates the calculation in Example 7. Notice that the parabolic arcs are so close to the graph of $y = e^{x^2}$ that they are practically indistinguishable from it.

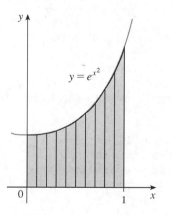

FIGURE 10

7.7   **Exercises**

1. Let $I = \int_0^4 f(x)\, dx$, where f is the function whose graph is shown.
   (a) Use the graph to find L_2, R_2, and M_2.
   (b) Are these underestimates or overestimates of I?
   (c) Use the graph to find T_2. How does it compare with I?
   (d) For any value of n, list the numbers L_n, R_n, M_n, T_n, and I in increasing order.

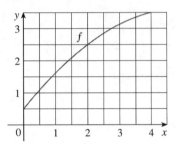

2. The left, right, Trapezoidal, and Midpoint Rule approximations were used to estimate $\int_0^2 f(x)\, dx$, where f is the function whose graph is shown. The estimates were 0.7811, 0.8675, 0.8632, and 0.9540, and the same number of subintervals were used in each case.
   (a) Which rule produced which estimate?
   (b) Between which two approximations does the true value of $\int_0^2 f(x)\, dx$ lie?

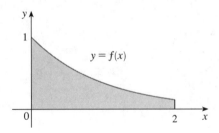

3. Estimate $\int_0^1 \cos(x^2)\, dx$ using (a) the Trapezoidal Rule and (b) the Midpoint Rule, each with $n = 4$. From a graph of the integrand, decide whether your answers are underestimates or overestimates. What can you conclude about the true value of the integral?

4. Draw the graph of $f(x) = \sin\left(\frac{1}{2}x^2\right)$ in the viewing rectangle [0, 1] by [0, 0.5] and let $I = \int_0^1 f(x)\, dx$.
   (a) Use the graph to decide whether L_2, R_2, M_2, and T_2 underestimate or overestimate I.
   (b) For any value of n, list the numbers L_n, R_n, M_n, T_n, and I in increasing order.

(c) Compute L_5, R_5, M_5, and T_5. From the graph, which do you think gives the best estimate of I?

5–6 Use (a) the Midpoint Rule and (b) Simpson's Rule to approximate the given integral with the specified value of n. (Round your answers to six decimal places.) Compare your results to the actual value to determine the error in each approximation.

5. $\int_0^\pi x^2 \sin x\, dx$, $n = 8$ 6. $\int_0^1 e^{-\sqrt{x}}\, dx$, $n = 6$

7–18 Use (a) the Trapezoidal Rule, (b) the Midpoint Rule, and (c) Simpson's Rule to approximate the given integral with the specified value of n. (Round your answers to six decimal places.)

7. $\int_1^2 \sqrt{x^3 - 1}\, dx$, $n = 10$ 8. $\int_0^2 \frac{1}{1 + x^6}\, dx$, $n = 8$

9. $\int_0^2 \frac{e^x}{1 + x^2}\, dx$, $n = 10$ 10. $\int_0^{\pi/2} \sqrt[3]{1 + \cos x}$, $n = 4$

11. $\int_1^4 \sqrt{\ln x}\, dx$, $n = 6$ 12. $\int_0^1 \sin(x^3)\, dx$, $n = 10$

13. $\int_0^4 e^{\sqrt{t}} \sin t\, dt$, $n = 8$ 14. $\int_0^1 \sqrt{z}\, e^{-z}\, dz$, $n = 10$

15. $\int_1^5 \frac{\cos x}{x}\, dx$, $n = 8$ 16. $\int_4^6 \ln(x^3 + 2)\, dx$, $n = 10$

17. $\int_{-1}^1 e^{e^x}\, dx$, $n = 10$ 18. $\int_0^4 \cos \sqrt{x}\, dx$, $n = 10$

19. (a) Find the approximations T_8 and M_8 for the integral $\int_0^1 \cos(x^2)\, dx$.
    (b) Estimate the errors in the approximations of part (a).
    (c) How large do we have to choose n so that the approximations T_n and M_n to the integral in part (a) are accurate to within 0.0001?

20. (a) Find the approximations T_{10} and M_{10} for $\int_1^2 e^{1/x}\, dx$.
    (b) Estimate the errors in the approximations of part (a).
    (c) How large do we have to choose n so that the approximations T_n and M_n to the integral in part (a) are accurate to within 0.0001?

21. (a) Find the approximations T_{10}, M_{10}, and S_{10} for $\int_0^\pi \sin x\, dx$ and the corresponding errors E_T, E_M, and E_S.

(b) Compare the actual errors in part (a) with the error estimates given by ③ and ④.

(c) How large do we have to choose n so that the approximations T_n, M_n, and S_n to the integral in part (a) are accurate to within 0.00001?

22. How large should n be to guarantee that the Simpson's Rule approximation to $\int_0^1 e^{x^2} dx$ is accurate to within 0.00001?

CAS **23.** The trouble with the error estimates is that it is often very difficult to compute four derivatives and obtain a good upper bound K for $|f^{(4)}(x)|$ by hand. But computer algebra systems have no problem computing $f^{(4)}$ and graphing it, so we can easily find a value for K from a machine graph. This exercise deals with approximations to the integral $I = \int_0^{2\pi} f(x)\, dx$, where $f(x) = e^{\cos x}$.

(a) Use a graph to get a good upper bound for $|f''(x)|$.

(b) Use M_{10} to approximate I.

(c) Use part (a) to estimate the error in part (b).

(d) Use the built-in numerical integration capability of your CAS to approximate I.

(e) How does the actual error compare with the error estimate in part (c)?

(f) Use a graph to get a good upper bound for $|f^{(4)}(x)|$.

(g) Use S_{10} to approximate I.

(h) Use part (f) to estimate the error in part (g).

(i) How does the actual error compare with the error estimate in part (h)?

(j) How large should n be to guarantee that the size of the error in using S_n is less than 0.0001?

CAS **24.** Repeat Exercise 23 for the integral $\int_{-1}^1 \sqrt{4 - x^3}\, dx$.

25–26 Find the approximations L_n, R_n, T_n, and M_n for $n = 5, 10$, and 20. Then compute the corresponding errors E_L, E_R, E_T, and E_M. (Round your answers to six decimal places. You may wish to use the sum command on a computer algebra system.) What observations can you make? In particular, what happens to the errors when n is doubled?

25. $\displaystyle\int_0^1 xe^x\, dx$ **26.** $\displaystyle\int_1^2 \frac{1}{x^2}\, dx$

27–28 Find the approximations T_n, M_n, and S_n for $n = 6$ and 12. Then compute the corresponding errors E_T, E_M, and E_S. (Round your answers to six decimal places. You may wish to use the sum command on a computer algebra system.) What observations can you make? In particular, what happens to the errors when n is doubled?

27. $\displaystyle\int_0^2 x^4\, dx$ **28.** $\displaystyle\int_1^4 \frac{1}{\sqrt{x}}\, dx$

29. Estimate the area under the graph in the figure by using (a) the Trapezoidal Rule, (b) the Midpoint Rule, and (c) Simpson's Rule, each with $n = 6$.

30. The widths (in meters) of a kidney-shaped swimming pool were measured at 2-meter intervals as indicated in the figure. Use Simpson's Rule to estimate the area of the pool.

31. (a) Use the Midpoint Rule and the given data to estimate the value of the integral $\int_1^5 f(x)\, dx$.

x	$f(x)$	x	$f(x)$
1.0	2.4	3.5	4.0
1.5	2.9	4.0	4.1
2.0	3.3	4.5	3.9
2.5	3.6	5.0	3.5
3.0	3.8		

(b) If it is known that $-2 \leqslant f''(x) \leqslant 3$ for all x, estimate the error involved in the approximation in part (a).

32. (a) A table of values of a function g is given. Use Simpson's Rule to estimate $\int_0^{1.6} g(x)\, dx$.

x	$g(x)$	x	$g(x)$
0.0	12.1	1.0	12.2
0.2	11.6	1.2	12.6
0.4	11.3	1.4	13.0
0.6	11.1	1.6	13.2
0.8	11.7		

(b) If $-5 \leqslant g^{(4)}(x) \leqslant 2$ for $0 \leqslant x \leqslant 1.6$, estimate the error involved in the approximation in part (a).

33. A graph of the temperature in New York City on September 19, 2009 is shown. Use Simpson's Rule with $n = 12$ to estimate the average temperature on that day.

34. A radar gun was used to record the speed of a runner during the first 5 seconds of a race (see the table). Use Simpson's Rule to estimate the distance the runner covered during those 5 seconds.

t (s)	v (m/s)	t (s)	v (m/s)
0	0	3.0	10.51
0.5	4.67	3.5	10.67
1.0	7.34	4.0	10.76
1.5	8.86	4.5	10.81
2.0	9.73	5.0	10.81
2.5	10.22		

35. The graph of the acceleration $a(t)$ of a car measured in m/s^2 is shown. Use Simpson's Rule to estimate the increase in the velocity of the car during the 6-second time interval.

36. Water leaked from a tank at a rate of $r(t)$ liters per hour, where the graph of r is as shown. Use Simpson's Rule to estimate the total amount of water that leaked out during the first 6 hours.

37. The table gives the power consumption in megawatts in Ontario from midnight to 6:00 AM on December 10, 2004. Use Simpson's Rule to estimate the energy used during that time period. (Use the fact that power is the derivative of energy.)

t	P	t	P
0:00	17,888	3:30	16,835
0:30	17,398	4:00	17,065
1:00	17,110	4:30	17,264
1:30	16,881	5:00	17,577
2:00	16,832	5:30	17,992
2:30	16,950	6:00	18,216
3:00	16,833		

38. Shown is the graph of traffic on an Internet service provider's T1 data line from midnight to 8:00 AM. D is the data throughput, measured in megabits per second. Use Simpson's Rule to estimate the total amount of data transmitted during that time period.

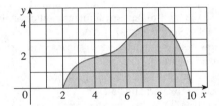

39. Use Simpson's Rule with $n = 8$ to estimate the volume of the solid obtained by rotating the region shown in the figure about (a) the x-axis and (b) the y-axis.

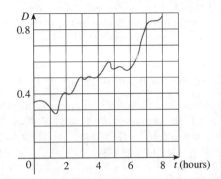

40. The table shows values of a force function $f(x)$, where x is measured in meters and $f(x)$ in newtons. Use Simpson's Rule to estimate the work done by the force in moving an object a distance of 18 m.

x	0	3	6	9	12	15	18
$f(x)$	9.8	9.1	8.5	8.0	7.7	7.5	7.4

41. The region bounded by the curves $y = e^{-1/x}$, $y = 0$, $x = 1$, and $x = 5$ is rotated about the x-axis. Use Simpson's Rule with $n = 8$ to estimate the volume of the resulting solid.

CAS **42.** The figure shows a pendulum with length L that makes a maximum angle θ_0 with the vertical. Using Newton's Second Law, it can be shown that the period T (the time for one complete swing) is given by

$$T = 4\sqrt{\frac{L}{g}} \int_0^{\pi/2} \frac{dx}{\sqrt{1 - k^2 \sin^2 x}}$$

where $k = \sin\left(\frac{1}{2}\theta_0\right)$ and g is the acceleration due to gravity. If $L = 1$ m and $\theta_0 = 42°$, use Simpson's Rule with $n = 10$ to find the period.

43. The intensity of light with wavelength λ traveling through a diffraction grating with N slits at an angle θ is given by $I(\theta) = N^2 \sin^2 k/k^2$, where $k = (\pi N d \sin \theta)/\lambda$ and d is the distance between adjacent slits. A helium-neon laser with wavelength $\lambda = 632.8 \times 10^{-9}$ m is emitting a narrow band of light, given by $-10^{-6} < \theta < 10^{-6}$, through a grating with 10,000 slits spaced 10^{-4} m apart. Use the Midpoint Rule with $n = 10$ to estimate the total light intensity $\int_{-10^{-6}}^{10^{-6}} I(\theta) \, d\theta$ emerging from the grating.

44. Use the Trapezoidal Rule with $n = 10$ to approximate $\int_0^{20} \cos(\pi x) \, dx$. Compare your result to the actual value. Can you explain the discrepancy?

45. Sketch the graph of a continuous function on $[0, 2]$ for which the Trapezoidal Rule with $n = 2$ is more accurate than the Midpoint Rule.

46. Sketch the graph of a continuous function on $[0, 2]$ for which the right endpoint approximation with $n = 2$ is more accurate than Simpson's Rule.

47. If f is a positive function and $f''(x) < 0$ for $a \le x \le b$, show that

$$T_n < \int_a^b f(x) \, dx < M_n$$

48. Show that if f is a polynomial of degree 3 or lower, then Simpson's Rule gives the exact value of $\int_a^b f(x) \, dx$.

49. Show that $\frac{1}{2}(T_n + M_n) = T_{2n}$.

50. Show that $\frac{1}{3}T_n + \frac{2}{3}M_n = S_{2n}$.

7.8 Improper Integrals

In defining a definite integral $\int_a^b f(x) \, dx$ we dealt with a function f defined on a finite interval $[a, b]$ and we assumed that f does not have an infinite discontinuity (see Section 5.2). In this section we extend the concept of a definite integral to the case where the interval is infinite and also to the case where f has an infinite discontinuity in $[a, b]$. In either case the integral is called an *improper* integral. One of the most important applications of this idea, probability distributions, will be studied in Section 8.5.

Type 1: Infinite Intervals

Consider the infinite region S that lies under the curve $y = 1/x^2$, above the x-axis, and to the right of the line $x = 1$. You might think that, since S is infinite in extent, its area must be infinite, but let's take a closer look. The area of the part of S that lies to the left of the line $x = t$ (shaded in Figure 1) is

$$A(t) = \int_1^t \frac{1}{x^2} \, dx = -\frac{1}{x} \Big]_1^t = 1 - \frac{1}{t}$$

Notice that $A(t) < 1$ no matter how large t is chosen.

We also observe that

$$\lim_{t \to \infty} A(t) = \lim_{t \to \infty} \left(1 - \frac{1}{t} \right) = 1$$

The area of the shaded region approaches 1 as $t \to \infty$ (see Figure 2), so we say that the area of the infinite region S is equal to 1 and we write

$$\int_1^\infty \frac{1}{x^2} \, dx = \lim_{t \to \infty} \int_1^t \frac{1}{x^2} \, dx = 1$$

FIGURE 1

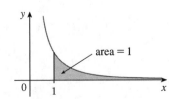

FIGURE 2

Using this example as a guide, we define the integral of f (not necessarily a positive function) over an infinite interval as the limit of integrals over finite intervals.

---

1   **Definition of an Improper Integral of Type 1**

(a) If $\int_a^t f(x)\,dx$ exists for every number $t \geq a$, then

$$\int_a^\infty f(x)\,dx = \lim_{t \to \infty} \int_a^t f(x)\,dx$$

provided this limit exists (as a finite number).

(b) If $\int_t^b f(x)\,dx$ exists for every number $t \leq b$, then

$$\int_{-\infty}^b f(x)\,dx = \lim_{t \to -\infty} \int_t^b f(x)\,dx$$

provided this limit exists (as a finite number).

The improper integrals $\int_a^\infty f(x)\,dx$ and $\int_{-\infty}^b f(x)\,dx$ are called **convergent** if the corresponding limit exists and **divergent** if the limit does not exist.

(c) If both $\int_a^\infty f(x)\,dx$ and $\int_{-\infty}^a f(x)\,dx$ are convergent, then we define

$$\int_{-\infty}^\infty f(x)\,dx = \int_{-\infty}^a f(x)\,dx + \int_a^\infty f(x)\,dx$$

In part (c) any real number a can be used (see Exercise 74).

Any of the improper integrals in Definition 1 can be interpreted as an area provided that f is a positive function. For instance, in case (a) if $f(x) \geq 0$ and the integral $\int_a^\infty f(x)\,dx$ is convergent, then we define the area of the region $S = \{(x, y) \mid x \geq a, 0 \leq y \leq f(x)\}$ in Figure 3 to be

$$A(S) = \int_a^\infty f(x)\,dx$$

This is appropriate because $\int_a^\infty f(x)\,dx$ is the limit as $t \to \infty$ of the area under the graph of f from a to t.

FIGURE 3

V EXAMPLE 1   Determine whether the integral $\int_1^\infty (1/x)\,dx$ is convergent or divergent.

SOLUTION   According to part (a) of Definition 1, we have

$$\int_1^\infty \frac{1}{x}\,dx = \lim_{t \to \infty} \int_1^t \frac{1}{x}\,dx = \lim_{t \to \infty} \ln|x|\,\Big]_1^t$$

$$= \lim_{t \to \infty} (\ln t - \ln 1) = \lim_{t \to \infty} \ln t = \infty$$

The limit does not exist as a finite number and so the improper integral $\int_1^\infty (1/x)\,dx$ is divergent.

Let's compare the result of Example 1 with the example given at the beginning of this section:

$$\int_1^\infty \frac{1}{x^2}\,dx \text{ converges} \qquad \int_1^\infty \frac{1}{x}\,dx \text{ diverges}$$

Geometrically, this says that although the curves $y = 1/x^2$ and $y = 1/x$ look very similar for $x > 0$, the region under $y = 1/x^2$ to the right of $x = 1$ (the shaded region in Figure 4) has finite area whereas the corresponding region under $y = 1/x$ (in Figure 5) has infinite area. Note that both $1/x^2$ and $1/x$ approach 0 as $x \to \infty$ but $1/x^2$ approaches 0 faster than $1/x$. The values of $1/x$ don't decrease fast enough for its integral to have a finite value.

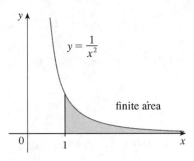

FIGURE 4 $\int_1^\infty (1/x^2)\,dx$ converges

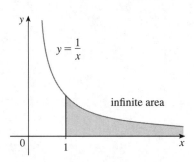

FIGURE 5 $\int_1^\infty (1/x)\,dx$ diverges

EXAMPLE 2 Evaluate $\int_{-\infty}^0 xe^x\,dx$.

SOLUTION Using part (b) of Definition 1, we have

$$\int_{-\infty}^0 xe^x\,dx = \lim_{t \to -\infty} \int_t^0 xe^x\,dx$$

We integrate by parts with $u = x$, $dv = e^x\,dx$ so that $du = dx$, $v = e^x$:

$$\int_t^0 xe^x\,dx = xe^x\Big]_t^0 - \int_t^0 e^x\,dx$$

$$= -te^t - 1 + e^t$$

We know that $e^t \to 0$ as $t \to -\infty$, and by l'Hospital's Rule we have

$$\lim_{t \to -\infty} te^t = \lim_{t \to -\infty} \frac{t}{e^{-t}} = \lim_{t \to -\infty} \frac{1}{-e^{-t}}$$

$$= \lim_{t \to -\infty} (-e^t) = 0$$

Therefore

$$\int_{-\infty}^0 xe^x\,dx = \lim_{t \to -\infty} (-te^t - 1 + e^t)$$

$$= -0 - 1 + 0 = -1$$

TEC In Module 7.8 you can investigate visually and numerically whether several improper integrals are convergent or divergent.

EXAMPLE 3 Evaluate $\int_{-\infty}^{\infty} \dfrac{1}{1+x^2}\,dx$.

SOLUTION It's convenient to choose $a = 0$ in Definition 1(c):

$$\int_{-\infty}^{\infty} \frac{1}{1+x^2}\,dx = \int_{-\infty}^{0} \frac{1}{1+x^2}\,dx + \int_{0}^{\infty} \frac{1}{1+x^2}\,dx$$

We must now evaluate the integrals on the right side separately:

$$\int_{0}^{\infty} \frac{1}{1+x^2}\,dx = \lim_{t \to \infty} \int_{0}^{t} \frac{dx}{1+x^2} = \lim_{t \to \infty} \tan^{-1}x\,\Big]_{0}^{t}$$

$$= \lim_{t \to \infty} (\tan^{-1}t - \tan^{-1}0) = \lim_{t \to \infty} \tan^{-1}t = \frac{\pi}{2}$$

$$\int_{-\infty}^{0} \frac{1}{1+x^2}\,dx = \lim_{t \to -\infty} \int_{t}^{0} \frac{dx}{1+x^2} = \lim_{t \to -\infty} \tan^{-1}x\,\Big]_{t}^{0}$$

$$= \lim_{t \to -\infty} (\tan^{-1}0 - \tan^{-1}t)$$

$$= 0 - \left(-\frac{\pi}{2}\right) = \frac{\pi}{2}$$

Since both of these integrals are convergent, the given integral is convergent and

$$\int_{-\infty}^{\infty} \frac{1}{1+x^2}\,dx = \frac{\pi}{2} + \frac{\pi}{2} = \pi$$

Since $1/(1+x^2) > 0$, the given improper integral can be interpreted as the area of the infinite region that lies under the curve $y = 1/(1+x^2)$ and above the x-axis (see Figure 6).

$y = \dfrac{1}{1+x^2}$ area $= \pi$

FIGURE 6

EXAMPLE 4 For what values of p is the integral

$$\int_{1}^{\infty} \frac{1}{x^p}\,dx$$

convergent?

SOLUTION We know from Example 1 that if $p = 1$, then the integral is divergent, so let's assume that $p \neq 1$. Then

$$\int_{1}^{\infty} \frac{1}{x^p}\,dx = \lim_{t \to \infty} \int_{1}^{t} x^{-p}\,dx$$

$$= \lim_{t \to \infty} \frac{x^{-p+1}}{-p+1}\,\Bigg]_{x=1}^{x=t}$$

$$= \lim_{t \to \infty} \frac{1}{1-p}\left[\frac{1}{t^{p-1}} - 1\right]$$

If $p > 1$, then $p - 1 > 0$, so as $t \to \infty$, $t^{p-1} \to \infty$ and $1/t^{p-1} \to 0$. Therefore

$$\int_{1}^{\infty} \frac{1}{x^p}\,dx = \frac{1}{p-1} \qquad \text{if } p > 1$$

and so the integral converges. But if $p < 1$, then $p - 1 < 0$ and so

$$\frac{1}{t^{p-1}} = t^{1-p} \to \infty \qquad \text{as } t \to \infty$$

and the integral diverges.

We summarize the result of Example 4 for future reference:

$$\boxed{2} \qquad \int_1^\infty \frac{1}{x^p}\, dx \quad \text{is convergent if } p > 1 \text{ and divergent if } p \leqslant 1.$$

◼ Type 2: Discontinuous Integrands

Suppose that f is a positive continuous function defined on a finite interval $[a, b)$ but has a vertical asymptote at b. Let S be the unbounded region under the graph of f and above the x-axis between a and b. (For Type 1 integrals, the regions extended indefinitely in a horizontal direction. Here the region is infinite in a vertical direction.) The area of the part of S between a and t (the shaded region in Figure 7) is

$$A(t) = \int_a^t f(x)\, dx$$

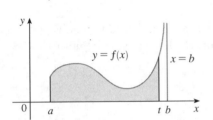

FIGURE 7

If it happens that $A(t)$ approaches a definite number A as $t \to b^-$, then we say that the area of the region S is A and we write

$$\int_a^b f(x)\, dx = \lim_{t \to b^-} \int_a^t f(x)\, dx$$

Parts (b) and (c) of Definition 3 are illustrated in Figures 8 and 9 for the case where $f(x) \geqslant 0$ and f has vertical asymptotes at a and c, respectively.

We use this equation to define an improper integral of Type 2 even when f is not a positive function, no matter what type of discontinuity f has at b.

FIGURE 8

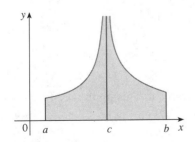

FIGURE 9

3   **Definition of an Improper Integral of Type 2**

    (a) If f is continuous on $[a, b)$ and is discontinuous at b, then

$$\int_a^b f(x)\, dx = \lim_{t \to b^-} \int_a^t f(x)\, dx$$

    if this limit exists (as a finite number).

    (b) If f is continuous on $(a, b]$ and is discontinuous at a, then

$$\int_a^b f(x)\, dx = \lim_{t \to a^+} \int_t^b f(x)\, dx$$

    if this limit exists (as a finite number).

The improper integral $\int_a^b f(x)\, dx$ is called **convergent** if the corresponding limit exists and **divergent** if the limit does not exist.

    (c) If f has a discontinuity at c, where $a < c < b$, and both $\int_a^c f(x)\, dx$ and $\int_c^b f(x)\, dx$ are convergent, then we define

$$\int_a^b f(x)\, dx = \int_a^c f(x)\, dx + \int_c^b f(x)\, dx$$

EXAMPLE 5 Find $\int_{2}^{5} \dfrac{1}{\sqrt{x-2}}\,dx$.

SOLUTION We note first that the given integral is improper because $f(x) = 1/\sqrt{x-2}$ has the vertical asymptote $x = 2$. Since the infinite discontinuity occurs at the left endpoint of $[2, 5]$, we use part (b) of Definition 3:

$$\int_{2}^{5} \frac{dx}{\sqrt{x-2}} = \lim_{t \to 2^{+}} \int_{t}^{5} \frac{dx}{\sqrt{x-2}}$$

$$= \lim_{t \to 2^{+}} 2\sqrt{x-2}\,\Big]_{t}^{5}$$

$$= \lim_{t \to 2^{+}} 2\left(\sqrt{3} - \sqrt{t-2}\right)$$

$$= 2\sqrt{3}$$

$$y = \frac{1}{\sqrt{x-2}}$$

area $= 2\sqrt{3}$

FIGURE 10

Thus the given improper integral is convergent and, since the integrand is positive, we can interpret the value of the integral as the area of the shaded region in Figure 10. ▬

V EXAMPLE 6 Determine whether $\int_{0}^{\pi/2} \sec x\,dx$ converges or diverges.

SOLUTION Note that the given integral is improper because $\lim_{x \to (\pi/2)^{-}} \sec x = \infty$. Using part (a) of Definition 3 and Formula 14 from the Table of Integrals, we have

$$\int_{0}^{\pi/2} \sec x\,dx = \lim_{t \to (\pi/2)^{-}} \int_{0}^{t} \sec x\,dx = \lim_{t \to (\pi/2)^{-}} \ln\left|\sec x + \tan x\right|\,\Big]_{0}^{t}$$

$$= \lim_{t \to (\pi/2)^{-}} \left[\ln(\sec t + \tan t) - \ln 1\right] = \infty$$

because $\sec t \to \infty$ and $\tan t \to \infty$ as $t \to (\pi/2)^{-}$. Thus the given improper integral is divergent. ▬

EXAMPLE 7 Evaluate $\int_{0}^{3} \dfrac{dx}{x-1}$ if possible.

SOLUTION Observe that the line $x = 1$ is a vertical asymptote of the integrand. Since it occurs in the middle of the interval $[0, 3]$, we must use part (c) of Definition 3 with $c = 1$:

$$\int_{0}^{3} \frac{dx}{x-1} = \int_{0}^{1} \frac{dx}{x-1} + \int_{1}^{3} \frac{dx}{x-1}$$

where

$$\int_{0}^{1} \frac{dx}{x-1} = \lim_{t \to 1^{-}} \int_{0}^{t} \frac{dx}{x-1} = \lim_{t \to 1^{-}} \ln\left|x-1\right|\,\Big]_{0}^{t}$$

$$= \lim_{t \to 1^{-}} \left(\ln\left|t-1\right| - \ln\left|-1\right|\right)$$

$$= \lim_{t \to 1^{-}} \ln(1-t) = -\infty$$

because $1 - t \to 0^{+}$ as $t \to 1^{-}$. Thus $\int_{0}^{1} dx/(x-1)$ is divergent. This implies that $\int_{0}^{3} dx/(x-1)$ is divergent. [We do not need to evaluate $\int_{1}^{3} dx/(x-1)$.] ▬

⊘   **WARNING** If we had not noticed the asymptote $x = 1$ in Example 7 and had instead confused the integral with an ordinary integral, then we might have made the following erroneous calculation:

$$\int_0^3 \frac{dx}{x-1} = \ln|x-1|\,\Big]_0^3 = \ln 2 - \ln 1 = \ln 2$$

This is wrong because the integral is improper and must be calculated in terms of limits.

From now on, whenever you meet the symbol $\int_a^b f(x)\,dx$ you must decide, by looking at the function f on $[a, b]$, whether it is an ordinary definite integral or an improper integral.

EXAMPLE 8 Evaluate $\int_0^1 \ln x\,dx$.

SOLUTION We know that the function $f(x) = \ln x$ has a vertical asymptote at 0 since $\lim_{x\to0^+} \ln x = -\infty$. Thus the given integral is improper and we have

$$\int_0^1 \ln x\,dx = \lim_{t\to0^+} \int_t^1 \ln x\,dx$$

Now we integrate by parts with $u = \ln x$, $dv = dx$, $du = dx/x$, and $v = x$:

$$\int_t^1 \ln x\,dx = x \ln x\,\Big]_t^1 - \int_t^1 dx$$

$$= 1\ln 1 - t\ln t - (1 - t)$$

$$= -t\ln t - 1 + t$$

To find the limit of the first term we use l'Hospital's Rule:

$$\lim_{t\to0^+} t\ln t = \lim_{t\to0^+} \frac{\ln t}{1/t} = \lim_{t\to0^+} \frac{1/t}{-1/t^2} = \lim_{t\to0^+}(-t) = 0$$

Therefore $\displaystyle\int_0^1 \ln x\,dx = \lim_{t\to0^+}(-t\ln t - 1 + t) = -0 - 1 + 0 = -1$

Figure 11 shows the geometric interpretation of this result. The area of the shaded region above $y = \ln x$ and below the x-axis is 1.

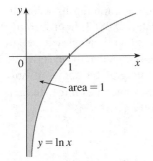

FIGURE 11

A Comparison Test for Improper Integrals

Sometimes it is impossible to find the exact value of an improper integral and yet it is important to know whether it is convergent or divergent. In such cases the following theorem is useful. Although we state it for Type 1 integrals, a similar theorem is true for Type 2 integrals.

Comparison Theorem Suppose that f and g are continuous functions with $f(x) \geq g(x) \geq 0$ for $x \geq a$.

(a) If $\int_a^\infty f(x)\,dx$ is convergent, then $\int_a^\infty g(x)\,dx$ is convergent.

(b) If $\int_a^\infty g(x)\,dx$ is divergent, then $\int_a^\infty f(x)\,dx$ is divergent.

We omit the proof of the Comparison Theorem, but Figure 12 makes it seem plausible. If the area under the top curve $y = f(x)$ is finite, then so is the area under the bottom curve $y = g(x)$. And if the area under $y = g(x)$ is infinite, then so is the area under $y = f(x)$. [Note

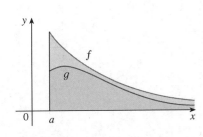

FIGURE 12

that the reverse is not necessarily true: If $\int_a^\infty g(x)\,dx$ is convergent, $\int_a^\infty f(x)\,dx$ may or may not be convergent, and if $\int_a^\infty f(x)\,dx$ is divergent, $\int_a^\infty g(x)\,dx$ may or may not be divergent.]

V **EXAMPLE 9** Show that $\int_0^\infty e^{-x^2}dx$ is convergent.

SOLUTION We can't evaluate the integral directly because the antiderivative of e^{-x^2} is not an elementary function (as explained in Section 7.5). We write

$$\int_0^\infty e^{-x^2}dx = \int_0^1 e^{-x^2}dx + \int_1^\infty e^{-x^2}dx$$

and observe that the first integral on the right-hand side is just an ordinary definite integral. In the second integral we use the fact that for $x \geqslant 1$ we have $x^2 \geqslant x$, so $-x^2 \leqslant -x$ and therefore $e^{-x^2} \leqslant e^{-x}$. (See Figure 13.) The integral of e^{-x} is easy to evaluate:

$$\int_1^\infty e^{-x}dx = \lim_{t\to\infty}\int_1^t e^{-x}dx = \lim_{t\to\infty}(e^{-1} - e^{-t}) = e^{-1}$$

Thus, taking $f(x) = e^{-x}$ and $g(x) = e^{-x^2}$ in the Comparison Theorem, we see that $\int_1^\infty e^{-x^2}dx$ is convergent. It follows that $\int_0^\infty e^{-x^2}dx$ is convergent.

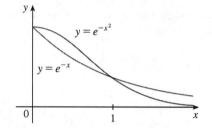

$y = e^{-x^2}$

$y = e^{-x}$

FIGURE 13

In Example 9 we showed that $\int_0^\infty e^{-x^2}dx$ is convergent without computing its value. In Exercise 70 we indicate how to show that its value is approximately 0.8862. In probability theory it is important to know the exact value of this improper integral, as we will see in Section 8.5; using the methods of multivariable calculus it can be shown that the exact value is $\sqrt{\pi}/2$. Table 1 illustrates the definition of an improper integral by showing how the (computer-generated) values of $\int_0^t e^{-x^2}dx$ approach $\sqrt{\pi}/2$ as t becomes large. In fact, these values converge quite quickly because $e^{-x^2} \to 0$ very rapidly as $x \to \infty$.

TABLE 1

t	$\int_0^t e^{-x^2}\,dx$
1	0.7468241328
2	0.8820813908
3	0.8862073483
4	0.8862269118
5	0.8862269255
6	0.8862269255

EXAMPLE 10 The integral $\int_1^\infty \dfrac{1 + e^{-x}}{x}\,dx$ is divergent by the Comparison Theorem because

$$\frac{1 + e^{-x}}{x} > \frac{1}{x}$$

and $\int_1^\infty (1/x)\,dx$ is divergent by Example 1 [or by $\boxed{2}$ with $p = 1$].

Table 2 illustrates the divergence of the integral in Example 10. It appears that the values are not approaching any fixed number.

TABLE 2

t	$\int_1^t [(1 + e^{-x})/x]\,dx$
2	0.8636306042
5	1.8276735512
10	2.5219648704
100	4.8245541204
1000	7.1271392134
10000	9.4297243064

7.8 Exercises

1. Explain why each of the following integrals is improper.

   (a) $\int_1^2 \dfrac{x}{x-1}\, dx$ (b) $\int_0^\infty \dfrac{1}{1+x^3}\, dx$

   (c) $\int_{-\infty}^\infty x^2 e^{-x^2}\, dx$ (d) $\int_0^{\pi/4} \cot x\, dx$

2. Which of the following integrals are improper? Why?

   (a) $\int_0^{\pi/4} \tan x\, dx$ (b) $\int_0^\pi \tan x\, dx$

   (c) $\int_{-1}^1 \dfrac{dx}{x^2 - x - 2}$ (d) $\int_0^\infty e^{-x^3}\, dx$

3. Find the area under the curve $y = 1/x^3$ from $x = 1$ to $x = t$ and evaluate it for $t = 10$, 100, and 1000. Then find the total area under this curve for $x \geqslant 1$.

 4. (a) Graph the functions $f(x) = 1/x^{1.1}$ and $g(x) = 1/x^{0.9}$ in the viewing rectangles $[0, 10]$ by $[0, 1]$ and $[0, 100]$ by $[0, 1]$.
   (b) Find the areas under the graphs of f and g from $x = 1$ to $x = t$ and evaluate for $t = 10$, 100, 10^4, 10^6, 10^{10}, and 10^{20}.
   (c) Find the total area under each curve for $x \geqslant 1$, if it exists.

5–40 Determine whether each integral is convergent or divergent. Evaluate those that are convergent.

5. $\int_3^\infty \dfrac{1}{(x-2)^{3/2}}\, dx$ 6. $\int_0^\infty \dfrac{1}{\sqrt[4]{1+x}}\, dx$

7. $\int_{-\infty}^0 \dfrac{1}{3 - 4x}\, dx$ 8. $\int_1^\infty \dfrac{1}{(2x+1)^3}\, dx$

9. $\int_2^\infty e^{-5p}\, dp$ 10. $\int_{-\infty}^0 2^r\, dr$

11. $\int_0^\infty \dfrac{x^2}{\sqrt{1+x^3}}\, dx$ 12. $\int_{-\infty}^\infty (y^3 - 3y^2)\, dy$

13. $\int_{-\infty}^\infty x e^{-x^2}\, dx$ 14. $\int_1^\infty \dfrac{e^{-\sqrt{x}}}{\sqrt{x}}\, dx$

15. $\int_0^\infty \sin^2\alpha\, d\alpha$ 16. $\int_{-\infty}^\infty \cos \pi t\, dt$

17. $\int_1^\infty \dfrac{x+1}{x^2 + 2x}\, dx$ 18. $\int_0^\infty \dfrac{dz}{z^2 + 3z + 2}$

19. $\int_{-\infty}^0 z e^{2z}\, dz$ 20. $\int_2^\infty y e^{-3y}\, dy$

21. $\int_1^\infty \dfrac{\ln x}{x}\, dx$ 22. $\int_{-\infty}^\infty x^3 e^{-x^4}\, dx$

23. $\int_{-\infty}^\infty \dfrac{x^2}{9 + x^6}\, dx$ 24. $\int_0^\infty \dfrac{e^x}{e^{2x} + 3}\, dx$

25. $\int_e^\infty \dfrac{1}{x(\ln x)^3}\, dx$ 26. $\int_0^\infty \dfrac{x \arctan x}{(1 + x^2)^2}\, dx$

27. $\int_0^1 \dfrac{3}{x^5}\, dx$ 28. $\int_2^3 \dfrac{1}{\sqrt{3 - x}}\, dx$

29. $\int_{-2}^{14} \dfrac{dx}{\sqrt[4]{x + 2}}$ 30. $\int_6^8 \dfrac{4}{(x - 6)^3}\, dx$

31. $\int_{-2}^3 \dfrac{1}{x^4}\, dx$ 32. $\int_0^1 \dfrac{dx}{\sqrt{1 - x^2}}$

33. $\int_0^9 \dfrac{1}{\sqrt[3]{x - 1}}\, dx$ 34. $\int_0^5 \dfrac{w}{w - 2}\, dw$

35. $\int_0^3 \dfrac{dx}{x^2 - 6x + 5}$ 36. $\int_{\pi/2}^\pi \csc x\, dx$

37. $\int_{-1}^0 \dfrac{e^{1/x}}{x^3}\, dx$ 38. $\int_0^1 \dfrac{e^{1/x}}{x^3}\, dx$

39. $\int_0^2 z^2 \ln z\, dz$ 40. $\int_0^1 \dfrac{\ln x}{\sqrt{x}}\, dx$

41–46 Sketch the region and find its area (if the area is finite).

41. $S = \{(x, y) \mid x \geqslant 1,\ 0 \leqslant y \leqslant e^{-x}\}$

42. $S = \{(x, y) \mid x \leqslant 0,\ 0 \leqslant y \leqslant e^x\}$

43. $S = \{(x, y) \mid x \geqslant 1,\ 0 \leqslant y \leqslant 1/(x^3 + x)\}$

44. $S = \{(x, y) \mid x \geqslant 0,\ 0 \leqslant y \leqslant xe^{-x}\}$

45. $S = \{(x, y) \mid 0 \leqslant x < \pi/2,\ 0 \leqslant y \leqslant \sec^2 x\}$

46. $S = \{(x, y) \mid -2 < x \leqslant 0,\ 0 \leqslant y \leqslant 1/\sqrt{x + 2}\}$

47. (a) If $g(x) = (\sin^2 x)/x^2$, use your calculator or computer to make a table of approximate values of $\int_1^t g(x)\, dx$ for $t = 2$, 5, 10, 100, 1000, and 10,000. Does it appear that $\int_1^\infty g(x)\, dx$ is convergent?
    (b) Use the Comparison Theorem with $f(x) = 1/x^2$ to show that $\int_1^\infty g(x)\, dx$ is convergent.
    (c) Illustrate part (b) by graphing f and g on the same screen for $1 \leqslant x \leqslant 10$. Use your graph to explain intuitively why $\int_1^\infty g(x)\, dx$ is convergent.

48. (a) If $g(x) = 1/(\sqrt{x} - 1)$, use your calculator or computer to make a table of approximate values of $\int_2^t g(x)\, dx$ for $t = 5$, 10, 100, 1000, and 10,000. Does it appear that $\int_2^\infty g(x)\, dx$ is convergent or divergent?

Graphing calculator or computer required   **1.** Homework Hints available at stewartcalculus.com

(b) Use the Comparison Theorem with $f(x) = 1/\sqrt{x}$ to show that $\int_2^\infty g(x)\, dx$ is divergent.

(c) Illustrate part (b) by graphing f and g on the same screen for $2 \le x \le 20$. Use your graph to explain intuitively why $\int_2^\infty g(x)\, dx$ is divergent.

49–54 Use the Comparison Theorem to determine whether the integral is convergent or divergent.

49. $\displaystyle\int_0^\infty \frac{x}{x^3 + 1}\, dx$

50. $\displaystyle\int_1^\infty \frac{2 + e^{-x}}{x}\, dx$

51. $\displaystyle\int_1^\infty \frac{x + 1}{\sqrt{x^4 - x}}\, dx$

52. $\displaystyle\int_0^\infty \frac{\arctan x}{2 + e^x}\, dx$

53. $\displaystyle\int_0^1 \frac{\sec^2 x}{x\sqrt{x}}\, dx$

54. $\displaystyle\int_0^\pi \frac{\sin^2 x}{\sqrt{x}}\, dx$

55. The integral

$$\int_0^\infty \frac{1}{\sqrt{x}\,(1 + x)}\, dx$$

is improper for two reasons: The interval $[0, \infty)$ is infinite and the integrand has an infinite discontinuity at 0. Evaluate it by expressing it as a sum of improper integrals of Type 2 and Type 1 as follows:

$$\int_0^\infty \frac{1}{\sqrt{x}\,(1 + x)}\, dx = \int_0^1 \frac{1}{\sqrt{x}\,(1 + x)}\, dx + \int_1^\infty \frac{1}{\sqrt{x}\,(1 + x)}\, dx$$

56. Evaluate

$$\int_2^\infty \frac{1}{x\sqrt{x^2 - 4}}\, dx$$

by the same method as in Exercise 55.

57–59 Find the values of p for which the integral converges and evaluate the integral for those values of p.

57. $\displaystyle\int_0^1 \frac{1}{x^p}\, dx$

58. $\displaystyle\int_e^\infty \frac{1}{x(\ln x)^p}\, dx$

59. $\displaystyle\int_0^1 x^p \ln x\, dx$

60. (a) Evaluate the integral $\int_0^\infty x^n e^{-x}\, dx$ for $n = 0, 1, 2,$ and 3.

(b) Guess the value of $\int_0^\infty x^n e^{-x}\, dx$ when n is an arbitrary positive integer.

(c) Prove your guess using mathematical induction.

61. (a) Show that $\int_{-\infty}^\infty x\, dx$ is divergent.

(b) Show that

$$\lim_{t \to \infty} \int_{-t}^t x\, dx = 0$$

This shows that we can't define

$$\int_{-\infty}^\infty f(x)\, dx = \lim_{t \to \infty} \int_{-t}^t f(x)\, dx$$

62. The *average speed* of molecules in an ideal gas is

$$\bar{v} = \frac{4}{\sqrt{\pi}} \left(\frac{M}{2RT}\right)^{3/2} \int_0^\infty v^3 e^{-Mv^2/(2RT)}\, dv$$

where M is the molecular weight of the gas, R is the gas constant, T is the gas temperature, and v is the molecular speed. Show that

$$\bar{v} = \sqrt{\frac{8RT}{\pi M}}$$

63. We know from Example 1 that the region $\mathcal{R} = \{(x, y) \mid x \ge 1,\ 0 \le y \le 1/x\}$ has infinite area. Show that by rotating $\mathcal{R}$ about the x-axis we obtain a solid with finite volume.

64. Use the information and data in Exercise 29 of Section 6.4 to find the work required to propel a 1000-kg space vehicle out of the earth's gravitational field.

65. Find the *escape velocity* v_0 that is needed to propel a rocket of mass m out of the gravitational field of a planet with mass M and radius R. Use Newton's Law of Gravitation (see Exercise 29 in Section 6.4) and the fact that the initial kinetic energy of $\frac{1}{2}mv_0^2$ supplies the needed work.

66. Astronomers use a technique called *stellar stereography* to determine the density of stars in a star cluster from the observed (two-dimensional) density that can be analyzed from a photograph. Suppose that in a spherical cluster of radius R the density of stars depends only on the distance r from the center of the cluster. If the perceived star density is given by $y(s)$, where s is the observed planar distance from the center of the cluster, and $x(r)$ is the actual density, it can be shown that

$$y(s) = \int_s^R \frac{2r}{\sqrt{r^2 - s^2}}\, x(r)\, dr$$

If the actual density of stars in a cluster is $x(r) = \frac{1}{2}(R - r)^2$, find the perceived density $y(s)$.

67. A manufacturer of lightbulbs wants to produce bulbs that last about 700 hours but, of course, some bulbs burn out faster than others. Let $F(t)$ be the fraction of the company's bulbs that burn out before t hours, so $F(t)$ always lies between 0 and 1.

(a) Make a rough sketch of what you think the graph of F might look like.

(b) What is the meaning of the derivative $r(t) = F'(t)$?

(c) What is the value of $\int_0^\infty r(t)\, dt$? Why?

68. As we saw in Section 3.8, a radioactive substance decays exponentially: The mass at time t is $m(t) = m(0)e^{kt}$, where $m(0)$ is the initial mass and k is a negative constant. The *mean life* M of an atom in the substance is

$$M = -k \int_0^\infty t e^{kt}\, dt$$

For the radioactive carbon isotope, ^{14}C, used in radiocarbon dating, the value of k is -0.000121. Find the mean life of a ^{14}C atom.

69. Determine how large the number a has to be so that

$$\int_a^\infty \frac{1}{x^2 + 1}\, dx < 0.001$$

70. Estimate the numerical value of $\int_0^\infty e^{-x^2}\, dx$ by writing it as the sum of $\int_0^4 e^{-x^2}\, dx$ and $\int_4^\infty e^{-x^2}\, dx$. Approximate the first integral by using Simpson's Rule with $n = 8$ and show that the second integral is smaller than $\int_4^\infty e^{-4x}\, dx$, which is less than 0.0000001.

71. If $f(t)$ is continuous for $t \ge 0$, the *Laplace transform* of f is the function F defined by

$$F(s) = \int_0^\infty f(t)e^{-st}\, dt$$

and the domain of F is the set consisting of all numbers s for which the integral converges. Find the Laplace transforms of the following functions.
(a) $f(t) = 1$ (b) $f(t) = e^t$ (c) $f(t) = t$

72. Show that if $0 \le f(t) \le Me^{at}$ for $t \ge 0$, where M and a are constants, then the Laplace transform $F(s)$ exists for $s > a$.

73. Suppose that $0 \le f(t) \le Me^{at}$ and $0 \le f'(t) \le Ke^{at}$ for $t \ge 0$, where f' is continuous. If the Laplace transform of $f(t)$ is $F(s)$ and the Laplace transform of $f'(t)$ is $G(s)$, show that

$$G(s) = sF(s) - f(0) \qquad s > a$$

74. If $\int_{-\infty}^\infty f(x)\, dx$ is convergent and a and b are real numbers, show that

$$\int_{-\infty}^a f(x)\, dx + \int_a^\infty f(x)\, dx = \int_{-\infty}^b f(x)\, dx + \int_b^\infty f(x)\, dx$$

75. Show that $\int_0^\infty x^2 e^{-x^2}\, dx = \frac{1}{2} \int_0^\infty e^{-x^2}\, dx$.

76. Show that $\int_0^\infty e^{-x^2}\, dx = \int_0^1 \sqrt{-\ln y}\, dy$ by interpreting the integrals as areas.

77. Find the value of the constant C for which the integral

$$\int_0^\infty \left(\frac{1}{\sqrt{x^2 + 4}} - \frac{C}{x + 2} \right) dx$$

converges. Evaluate the integral for this value of C.

78. Find the value of the constant C for which the integral

$$\int_0^\infty \left(\frac{x}{x^2 + 1} - \frac{C}{3x + 1} \right) dx$$

converges. Evaluate the integral for this value of C.

79. Suppose f is continuous on $[0, \infty)$ and $\lim_{x \to \infty} f(x) = 1$. Is it possible that $\int_0^\infty f(x)\, dx$ is convergent?

80. Show that if $a > -1$ and $b > a + 1$, then the following integral is convergent.

$$\int_0^\infty \frac{x^a}{1 + x^b}\, dx$$

7   Review

Concept Check

1. State the rule for integration by parts. In practice, how do you use it?

2. How do you evaluate $\int \sin^m x \cos^n x\, dx$ if m is odd? What if n is odd? What if m and n are both even?

3. If the expression $\sqrt{a^2 - x^2}$ occurs in an integral, what substitution might you try? What if $\sqrt{a^2 + x^2}$ occurs? What if $\sqrt{x^2 - a^2}$ occurs?

4. What is the form of the partial fraction decomposition of a rational function $P(x)/Q(x)$ if the degree of P is less than the degree of Q and $Q(x)$ has only distinct linear factors? What if a linear factor is repeated? What if $Q(x)$ has an irreducible quadratic factor (not repeated)? What if the quadratic factor is repeated?

5. State the rules for approximating the definite integral $\int_a^b f(x)\, dx$ with the Midpoint Rule, the Trapezoidal Rule, and Simpson's Rule. Which would you expect to give the best estimate? How do you approximate the error for each rule?

6. Define the following improper integrals.
(a) $\int_a^\infty f(x)\, dx$ (b) $\int_{-\infty}^b f(x)\, dx$ (c) $\int_{-\infty}^\infty f(x)\, dx$

7. Define the improper integral $\int_a^b f(x)\, dx$ for each of the following cases.
(a) f has an infinite discontinuity at a.
(b) f has an infinite discontinuity at b.
(c) f has an infinite discontinuity at c, where $a < c < b$.

8. State the Comparison Theorem for improper integrals.

True-False Quiz

Determine whether the statement is true or false. If it is true, explain why. If it is false, explain why or give an example that disproves the statement.

1. $\dfrac{x(x^2+4)}{x^2-4}$ can be put in the form $\dfrac{A}{x+2} + \dfrac{B}{x-2}$.

2. $\dfrac{x^2+4}{x(x^2-4)}$ can be put in the form $\dfrac{A}{x} + \dfrac{B}{x+2} + \dfrac{C}{x-2}$.

3. $\dfrac{x^2+4}{x^2(x-4)}$ can be put in the form $\dfrac{A}{x^2} + \dfrac{B}{x-4}$.

4. $\dfrac{x^2-4}{x(x^2+4)}$ can be put in the form $\dfrac{A}{x} + \dfrac{B}{x^2+4}$.

5. $\displaystyle\int_0^4 \dfrac{x}{x^2-1}\,dx = \tfrac{1}{2}\ln 15$

6. $\displaystyle\int_1^\infty \dfrac{1}{x^{\sqrt{2}}}\,dx$ is convergent.

7. If f is continuous, then $\displaystyle\int_{-\infty}^\infty f(x)\,dx = \lim_{t\to\infty}\int_{-t}^t f(x)\,dx$.

8. The Midpoint Rule is always more accurate than the Trapezoidal Rule.

9. (a) Every elementary function has an elementary derivative.
   (b) Every elementary function has an elementary anti-derivative.

10. If f is continuous on $[0,\infty)$ and $\int_1^\infty f(x)\,dx$ is convergent, then $\int_0^\infty f(x)\,dx$ is convergent.

11. If f is a continuous, decreasing function on $[1,\infty)$ and $\lim_{x\to\infty} f(x) = 0$, then $\int_1^\infty f(x)\,dx$ is convergent.

12. If $\int_a^\infty f(x)\,dx$ and $\int_a^\infty g(x)\,dx$ are both convergent, then $\int_a^\infty [f(x)+g(x)]\,dx$ is convergent.

13. If $\int_a^\infty f(x)\,dx$ and $\int_a^\infty g(x)\,dx$ are both divergent, then $\int_a^\infty [f(x)+g(x)]\,dx$ is divergent.

14. If $f(x) \le g(x)$ and $\int_0^\infty g(x)\,dx$ diverges, then $\int_0^\infty f(x)\,dx$ also diverges.

Exercises

Note: Additional practice in techniques of integration is provided in Exercises 7.5.

1–40 Evaluate the integral.

1. $\displaystyle\int_1^2 \dfrac{(x+1)^2}{x}\,dx$

2. $\displaystyle\int_1^2 \dfrac{x}{(x+1)^2}\,dx$

3. $\displaystyle\int_0^{\pi/2} \sin\theta\, e^{\cos\theta}\,d\theta$

4. $\displaystyle\int_0^{\pi/6} t\sin 2t\,dt$

5. $\displaystyle\int \dfrac{dt}{2t^2+3t+1}$

6. $\displaystyle\int_1^2 x^5 \ln x\,dx$

7. $\displaystyle\int_0^{\pi/2} \sin^3\theta\cos^2\theta\,d\theta$

8. $\displaystyle\int \dfrac{dx}{\sqrt{e^x-1}}$

9. $\displaystyle\int \dfrac{\sin(\ln t)}{t}\,dt$

10. $\displaystyle\int_0^1 \dfrac{\sqrt{\arctan x}}{1+x^2}\,dx$

11. $\displaystyle\int_1^2 \dfrac{\sqrt{x^2-1}}{x}\,dx$

12. $\displaystyle\int \dfrac{e^{2x}}{1+e^{4x}}\,dx$

13. $\displaystyle\int e^{\sqrt[3]{x}}\,dx$

14. $\displaystyle\int \dfrac{x^2+2}{x+2}\,dx$

15. $\displaystyle\int \dfrac{x-1}{x^2+2x}\,dx$

16. $\displaystyle\int \dfrac{\sec^6\theta}{\tan^2\theta}\,d\theta$

17. $\displaystyle\int x\sec x\tan x\,dx$

18. $\displaystyle\int \dfrac{x^2+8x-3}{x^3+3x^2}\,dx$

19. $\displaystyle\int \dfrac{x+1}{9x^2+6x+5}\,dx$

20. $\displaystyle\int \tan^5\theta\sec^3\theta\,d\theta$

21. $\displaystyle\int \dfrac{dx}{\sqrt{x^2-4x}}$

22. $\displaystyle\int te^{\sqrt{t}}\,dt$

23. $\displaystyle\int \dfrac{dx}{x\sqrt{x^2+1}}$

24. $\displaystyle\int e^x\cos x\,dx$

25. $\displaystyle\int \dfrac{3x^3-x^2+6x-4}{(x^2+1)(x^2+2)}\,dx$

26. $\displaystyle\int x\sin x\cos x\,dx$

27. $\displaystyle\int_0^{\pi/2} \cos^3 x\sin 2x\,dx$

28. $\displaystyle\int \dfrac{\sqrt[3]{x}+1}{\sqrt[3]{x}-1}\,dx$

29. $\displaystyle\int_{-3}^3 \dfrac{x}{1+|x|}\,dx$

30. $\displaystyle\int \dfrac{dx}{e^x\sqrt{1-e^{-2x}}}$

31. $\displaystyle\int_0^{\ln 10} \dfrac{e^x\sqrt{e^x-1}}{e^x+8}\,dx$

32. $\displaystyle\int_0^{\pi/4} \dfrac{x\sin x}{\cos^3 x}\,dx$

33. $\displaystyle\int \dfrac{x^2}{(4-x^2)^{3/2}}\,dx$

34. $\displaystyle\int (\arcsin x)^2\,dx$

35. $\displaystyle\int \dfrac{1}{\sqrt{x+x^{3/2}}}\,dx$

36. $\displaystyle\int \dfrac{1-\tan\theta}{1+\tan\theta}\,d\theta$

37. $\displaystyle\int (\cos x+\sin x)^2\cos 2x\,dx$

38. $\displaystyle\int \dfrac{2^{\sqrt{x}}}{\sqrt{x}}\,dx$

39. $\displaystyle\int_0^{1/2} \dfrac{xe^{2x}}{(1+2x)^2}\,dx$

40. $\displaystyle\int_{\pi/4}^{\pi/3} \dfrac{\sqrt{\tan\theta}}{\sin 2\theta}\,d\theta$

41–50 Evaluate the integral or show that it is divergent.

41. $\int_1^\infty \dfrac{1}{(2x+1)^3}\,dx$

42. $\int_1^\infty \dfrac{\ln x}{x^4}\,dx$

43. $\int_2^\infty \dfrac{dx}{x\ln x}$

44. $\int_2^6 \dfrac{y}{\sqrt{y-2}}\,dy$

45. $\int_0^4 \dfrac{\ln x}{\sqrt{x}}\,dx$

46. $\int_0^1 \dfrac{1}{2-3x}\,dx$

47. $\int_0^1 \dfrac{x-1}{\sqrt{x}}\,dx$

48. $\int_{-1}^1 \dfrac{dx}{x^2-2x}$

49. $\int_{-\infty}^\infty \dfrac{dx}{4x^2+4x+5}$

50. $\int_1^\infty \dfrac{\tan^{-1}x}{x^2}\,dx$

51–52 Evaluate the indefinite integral. Illustrate and check that your answer is reasonable by graphing both the function and its antiderivative (take $C=0$).

51. $\int \ln(x^2+2x+2)\,dx$

52. $\int \dfrac{x^3}{\sqrt{x^2+1}}\,dx$

---

53. Graph the function $f(x) = \cos^2 x\,\sin^3 x$ and use the graph to guess the value of the integral $\int_0^{2\pi} f(x)\,dx$. Then evaluate the integral to confirm your guess.

54. (a) How would you evaluate $\int x^5 e^{-2x}\,dx$ by hand? (Don't actually carry out the integration.)
(b) How would you evaluate $\int x^5 e^{-2x}\,dx$ using tables? (Don't actually do it.)
(c) Use a CAS to evaluate $\int x^5 e^{-2x}\,dx$.
(d) Graph the integrand and the indefinite integral on the same screen.

55–58 Use the Table of Integrals on the Reference Pages to evaluate the integral.

55. $\int \sqrt{4x^2-4x-3}\,dx$

56. $\int \csc^5 t\,dt$

57. $\int \cos x\,\sqrt{4+\sin^2 x}\,dx$

58. $\int \dfrac{\cot x}{\sqrt{1+2\sin x}}\,dx$

---

59. Verify Formula 33 in the Table of Integrals (a) by differentiation and (b) by using a trigonometric substitution.

60. Verify Formula 62 in the Table of Integrals.

61. Is it possible to find a number n such that $\int_0^\infty x^n\,dx$ is convergent?

62. For what values of a is $\int_0^\infty e^{ax}\cos x\,dx$ convergent? Evaluate the integral for those values of a.

63–64 Use (a) the Trapezoidal Rule, (b) the Midpoint Rule, and (c) Simpson's Rule with $n=10$ to approximate the given integral. Round your answers to six decimal places.

63. $\int_2^4 \dfrac{1}{\ln x}\,dx$

64. $\int_1^4 \sqrt{x}\,\cos x\,dx$

---

65. Estimate the errors involved in Exercise 63, parts (a) and (b). How large should n be in each case to guarantee an error of less than 0.00001?

66. Use Simpson's Rule with $n=6$ to estimate the area under the curve $y = e^x/x$ from $x=1$ to $x=4$.

67. The speedometer reading (v) on a car was observed at 1-minute intervals and recorded in the chart. Use Simpson's Rule to estimate the distance traveled by the car.

t (min)	v (km/h)	t (min)	v (km/h)
0	64	6	90
1	67	7	91
2	72	8	91
3	78	9	88
4	83	10	90
5	86		

68. A population of honeybees increased at a rate of $r(t)$ bees per week, where the graph of r is as shown. Use Simpson's Rule with six subintervals to estimate the increase in the bee population during the first 24 weeks.

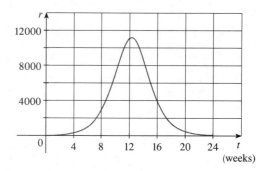

69. (a) If $f(x) = \sin(\sin x)$, use a graph to find an upper bound for $|f^{(4)}(x)|$.
(b) Use Simpson's Rule with $n=10$ to approximate $\int_0^\pi f(x)\,dx$ and use part (a) to estimate the error.
(c) How large should n be to guarantee that the size of the error in using S_n is less than 0.00001?

70. Suppose you are asked to estimate the volume of a football. You measure and find that a football is 28 cm long. You use a piece of string and measure the circumference at its widest point to be 53 cm. The circumference 7 cm from each end is 45 cm. Use Simpson's Rule to make your estimate.

|← —— 28 cm —— →|

71. Use the Comparison Theorem to determine whether the integral is convergent or divergent.

(a) $\displaystyle\int_1^\infty \frac{2 + \sin x}{\sqrt{x}}\, dx$ (b) $\displaystyle\int_1^\infty \frac{1}{\sqrt{1 + x^4}}\, dx$

72. Find the area of the region bounded by the hyperbola $y^2 - x^2 = 1$ and the line $y = 3$.

73. Find the area bounded by the curves $y = \cos x$ and $y = \cos^2 x$ between $x = 0$ and $x = \pi$.

74. Find the area of the region bounded by the curves $y = 1/(2 + \sqrt{x}\,)$, $y = 1/(2 - \sqrt{x}\,)$, and $x = 1$.

75. The region under the curve $y = \cos^2 x$, $0 \le x \le \pi/2$, is rotated about the x-axis. Find the volume of the resulting solid.

76. The region in Exercise 75 is rotated about the y-axis. Find the volume of the resulting solid.

77. If f' is continuous on $[0, \infty)$ and $\lim_{x\to\infty} f(x) = 0$, show that

$$\int_0^\infty f'(x)\, dx = -f(0)$$

78. We can extend our definition of average value of a continuous function to an infinite interval by defining the average value of f on the interval $[a, \infty)$ to be

$$\lim_{t\to\infty} \frac{1}{t - a} \int_a^t f(x)\, dx$$

(a) Find the average value of $y = \tan^{-1}x$ on the interval $[0, \infty)$.

(b) If $f(x) \ge 0$ and $\int_a^\infty f(x)\, dx$ is divergent, show that the average value of f on the interval $[a, \infty)$ is $\lim_{x\to\infty} f(x)$, if this limit exists.

(c) If $\int_a^\infty f(x)\, dx$ is convergent, what is the average value of f on the interval $[a, \infty)$?

(d) Find the average value of $y = \sin x$ on the interval $[0, \infty)$.

79. Use the substitution $u = 1/x$ to show that

$$\int_0^\infty \frac{\ln x}{1 + x^2}\, dx = 0$$

80. The magnitude of the repulsive force between two point charges with the same sign, one of size 1 and the other of size q, is

$$F = \frac{q}{4\pi\varepsilon_0 r^2}$$

where r is the distance between the charges and ε_0 is a constant. The *potential* V at a point P due to the charge q is defined to be the work expended in bringing a unit charge to P from infinity along the straight line that joins q and P. Find a formula for V.

Problems Plus

Cover up the solution to the example and try it yourself first.

EXAMPLE 1

(a) Prove that if f is a continuous function, then

$$\int_0^a f(x)\, dx = \int_0^a f(a - x)\, dx$$

(b) Use part (a) to show that

$$\int_0^{\pi/2} \frac{\sin^n x}{\sin^n x + \cos^n x}\, dx = \frac{\pi}{4}$$

for all positive numbers n.

SOLUTION

PS The principles of problem solving are discussed on page 75.

(a) At first sight, the given equation may appear somewhat baffling. How is it possible to connect the left side to the right side? Connections can often be made through one of the principles of problem solving: *introduce something extra*. Here the extra ingredient is a new variable. We often think of introducing a new variable when we use the Substitution Rule to integrate a specific function. But that technique is still useful in the present circumstance in which we have a general function f.

Once we think of making a substitution, the form of the right side suggests that it should be $u = a - x$. Then $du = -dx$. When $x = 0$, $u = a$; when $x = a$, $u = 0$. So

$$\int_0^a f(a - x)\, dx = -\int_a^0 f(u)\, du = \int_0^a f(u)\, du$$

But this integral on the right side is just another way of writing $\int_0^a f(x)\, dx$. So the given equation is proved.

(b) If we let the given integral be I and apply part (a) with $a = \pi/2$, we get

$$I = \int_0^{\pi/2} \frac{\sin^n x}{\sin^n x + \cos^n x}\, dx = \int_0^{\pi/2} \frac{\sin^n(\pi/2 - x)}{\sin^n(\pi/2 - x) + \cos^n(\pi/2 - x)}\, dx$$

The computer graphs in Figure 1 make it seem plausible that all of the integrals in the example have the same value. The graph of each integrand is labeled with the corresponding value of n.

A well-known trigonometric identity tells us that $\sin(\pi/2 - x) = \cos x$ and $\cos(\pi/2 - x) = \sin x$, so we get

$$I = \int_0^{\pi/2} \frac{\cos^n x}{\cos^n x + \sin^n x}\, dx$$

Notice that the two expressions for I are very similar. In fact, the integrands have the same denominator. This suggests that we should add the two expressions. If we do so, we get

$$2I = \int_0^{\pi/2} \frac{\sin^n x + \cos^n x}{\sin^n x + \cos^n x}\, dx = \int_0^{\pi/2} 1\, dx = \frac{\pi}{2}$$

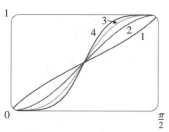

FIGURE 1

Therefore $I = \pi/4$.

|← 14 in →|

FIGURE FOR PROBLEM 1

FIGURE FOR PROBLEM 6

 1. Three mathematics students have ordered a 14-inch pizza. Instead of slicing it in the traditional way, they decide to slice it by parallel cuts, as shown in the figure. Being mathematics majors, they are able to determine where to slice so that each gets the same amount of pizza. Where are the cuts made?

2. Evaluate

$$\int \frac{1}{x^7 - x}\,dx$$

The straightforward approach would be to start with partial fractions, but that would be brutal. Try a substitution.

3. Evaluate $\int_0^1 \left(\sqrt[3]{1 - x^7} - \sqrt[7]{1 - x^3}\right) dx$.

4. The centers of two disks with radius 1 are one unit apart. Find the area of the union of the two disks.

5. An ellipse is cut out of a circle with radius a. The major axis of the ellipse coincides with a diameter of the circle and the minor axis has length $2b$. Prove that the area of the remaining part of the circle is the same as the area of an ellipse with semiaxes a and $a - b$.

6. A man initially standing at the point O walks along a pier pulling a rowboat by a rope of length L. The man keeps the rope straight and taut. The path followed by the boat is a curve called a *tractrix* and it has the property that the rope is always tangent to the curve (see the figure).
(a) Show that if the path followed by the boat is the graph of the function $y = f(x)$, then

$$f'(x) = \frac{dy}{dx} = \frac{-\sqrt{L^2 - x^2}}{x}$$

(b) Determine the function $y = f(x)$.

7. A function f is defined by

$$f(x) = \int_0^\pi \cos t \, \cos(x - t)\,dt \qquad 0 \leqslant x \leqslant 2\pi$$

Find the minimum value of f.

8. If n is a positive integer, prove that

$$\int_0^1 (\ln x)^n \, dx = (-1)^n n!$$

9. Show that

$$\int_0^1 (1 - x^2)^n \, dx = \frac{2^{2n}(n!)^2}{(2n + 1)!}$$

Hint: Start by showing that if I_n denotes the integral, then

$$I_{k+1} = \frac{2k + 2}{2k + 3}\,I_k$$

 Graphing calculator or computer required

10. Suppose that f is a positive function such that f' is continuous.
  (a) How is the graph of $y = f(x) \sin nx$ related to the graph of $y = f(x)$? What happens as $n \to \infty$?
  (b) Make a guess as to the value of the limit

$$\lim_{n \to \infty} \int_0^1 f(x) \sin nx \, dx$$

  based on graphs of the integrand.
  (c) Using integration by parts, confirm the guess that you made in part (b). [Use the fact that, since f' is continuous, there is a constant M such that $|f'(x)| \le M$ for $0 \le x \le 1$.]

11. If $0 < a < b$, find $\displaystyle\lim_{t \to 0} \left\{ \int_0^1 [bx + a(1-x)]^t \, dx \right\}^{1/t}$.

 12. Graph $f(x) = \sin(e^x)$ and use the graph to estimate the value of t such that $\int_t^{t+1} f(x) \, dx$ is a maximum. Then find the exact value of t that maximizes this integral.

13. Evaluate $\displaystyle\int_{-1}^{\infty} \left(\frac{x^4}{1 + x^6} \right)^2 dx$.

14. Evaluate $\displaystyle\int \sqrt{\tan x} \, dx$.

15. The circle with radius 1 shown in the figure touches the curve $y = |2x|$ twice. Find the area of the region that lies between the two curves.

16. A rocket is fired straight up, burning fuel at the constant rate of b kilograms per second. Let $v = v(t)$ be the velocity of the rocket at time t and suppose that the velocity u of the exhaust gas is constant. Let $M = M(t)$ be the mass of the rocket at time t and note that M decreases as the fuel burns. If we neglect air resistance, it follows from Newton's Second Law that

$$F = M \frac{dv}{dt} - ub$$

where the force $F = -Mg$. Thus

$$\boxed{1} \qquad M \frac{dv}{dt} - ub = -Mg$$

Let M_1 be the mass of the rocket without fuel, M_2 the initial mass of the fuel, and $M_0 = M_1 + M_2$. Then, until the fuel runs out at time $t = M_2/b$, the mass is $M = M_0 - bt$.
  (a) Substitute $M = M_0 - bt$ into Equation 1 and solve the resulting equation for v. Use the initial condition $v(0) = 0$ to evaluate the constant.
  (b) Determine the velocity of the rocket at time $t = M_2/b$. This is called the *burnout velocity*.
  (c) Determine the height of the rocket $y = y(t)$ at the burnout time.
  (d) Find the height of the rocket at any time t.

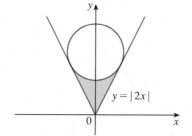

FIGURE FOR PROBLEM 15

8 Further Applications of Integration

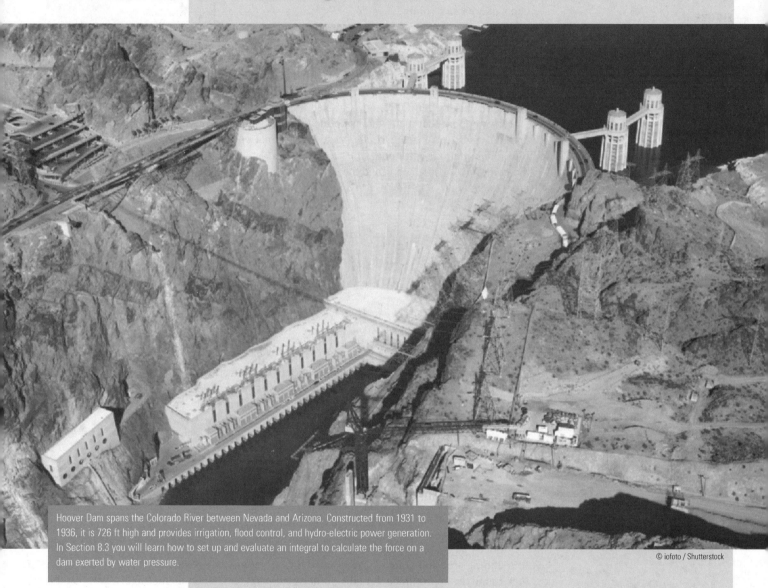

Hoover Dam spans the Colorado River between Nevada and Arizona. Constructed from 1931 to 1936, it is 726 ft high and provides irrigation, flood control, and hydro-electric power generation. In Section 8.3 you will learn how to set up and evaluate an integral to calculate the force on a dam exerted by water pressure.

© iofoto / Shutterstock

We looked at some applications of integrals in Chapter 6: areas, volumes, work, and average values. Here we explore some of the many other geometric applications of integration—the length of a curve, the area of a surface—as well as quantities of interest in physics, engineering, biology, economics, and statistics. For instance, we will investigate the center of gravity of a plate, the force exerted by water pressure on a dam, the flow of blood from the human heart, and the average time spent on hold during a customer support telephone call.

8.1 Arc Length

FIGURE 1

TEC Visual 8.1 shows an animation of Figure 2.

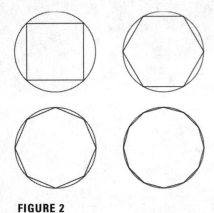

FIGURE 2

What do we mean by the length of a curve? We might think of fitting a piece of string to the curve in Figure 1 and then measuring the string against a ruler. But that might be difficult to do with much accuracy if we have a complicated curve. We need a precise definition for the length of an arc of a curve, in the same spirit as the definitions we developed for the concepts of area and volume.

If the curve is a polygon, we can easily find its length; we just add the lengths of the line segments that form the polygon. (We can use the distance formula to find the distance between the endpoints of each segment.) We are going to define the length of a general curve by first approximating it by a polygon and then taking a limit as the number of segments of the polygon is increased. This process is familiar for the case of a circle, where the circumference is the limit of lengths of inscribed polygons (see Figure 2).

Now suppose that a curve C is defined by the equation $y = f(x)$, where f is continuous and $a \leq x \leq b$. We obtain a polygonal approximation to C by dividing the interval $[a, b]$ into n subintervals with endpoints $x_0, x_1, \ldots, x_n$ and equal width Δx. If $y_i = f(x_i)$, then the point $P_i(x_i, y_i)$ lies on C and the polygon with vertices $P_0, P_1, \ldots, P_n$, illustrated in Figure 3, is an approximation to C.

FIGURE 3

FIGURE 4

The length L of C is approximately the length of this polygon and the approximation gets better as we let n increase. (See Figure 4, where the arc of the curve between P_{i-1} and P_i has been magnified and approximations with successively smaller values of Δx are shown.) Therefore we define the **length** L of the curve C with equation $y = f(x)$, $a \leq x \leq b$, as the limit of the lengths of these inscribed polygons (if the limit exists):

$$\boxed{1} \qquad L = \lim_{n \to \infty} \sum_{i=1}^{n} |P_{i-1}P_i|$$

Notice that the procedure for defining arc length is very similar to the procedure we used for defining area and volume: We divided the curve into a large number of small parts. We then found the approximate lengths of the small parts and added them. Finally, we took the limit as $n \to \infty$.

The definition of arc length given by Equation 1 is not very convenient for computational purposes, but we can derive an integral formula for L in the case where f has a continuous derivative. [Such a function f is called **smooth** because a small change in x produces a small change in $f'(x)$.]

If we let $\Delta y_i = y_i - y_{i-1}$, then

$$|P_{i-1}P_i| = \sqrt{(x_i - x_{i-1})^2 + (y_i - y_{i-1})^2} = \sqrt{(\Delta x)^2 + (\Delta y_i)^2}$$

By applying the Mean Value Theorem to f on the interval $[x_{i-1}, x_i]$, we find that there is a number x_i^* between x_{i-1} and x_i such that

$$f(x_i) - f(x_{i-1}) = f'(x_i^*)(x_i - x_{i-1})$$

that is,
$$\Delta y_i = f'(x_i^*)\,\Delta x$$

Thus we have

$$|P_{i-1}P_i| = \sqrt{(\Delta x)^2 + (\Delta y_i)^2} = \sqrt{(\Delta x)^2 + [f'(x_i^*)\,\Delta x]^2}$$

$$= \sqrt{1 + [f'(x_i^*)]^2}\,\sqrt{(\Delta x)^2} = \sqrt{1 + [f'(x_i^*)]^2}\,\Delta x \qquad \text{(since } \Delta x > 0\text{)}$$

Therefore, by Definition 1,

$$L = \lim_{n\to\infty} \sum_{i=1}^{n} |P_{i-1}P_i| = \lim_{n\to\infty} \sum_{i=1}^{n} \sqrt{1 + [f'(x_i^*)]^2}\,\Delta x$$

We recognize this expression as being equal to

$$\int_a^b \sqrt{1 + [f'(x)]^2}\,dx$$

by the definition of a definite integral. This integral exists because the function $g(x) = \sqrt{1 + [f'(x)]^2}$ is continuous. Thus we have proved the following theorem:

---

2 The Arc Length Formula If f' is continuous on $[a, b]$, then the length of the curve $y = f(x)$, $a \leq x \leq b$, is

$$L = \int_a^b \sqrt{1 + [f'(x)]^2}\,dx$$

If we use Leibniz notation for derivatives, we can write the arc length formula as follows:

3
$$L = \int_a^b \sqrt{1 + \left(\frac{dy}{dx}\right)^2}\,dx$$

EXAMPLE 1 Find the length of the arc of the semicubical parabola $y^2 = x^3$ between the points $(1, 1)$ and $(4, 8)$. (See Figure 5.)

SOLUTION For the top half of the curve we have

$$y = x^{3/2} \qquad \frac{dy}{dx} = \tfrac{3}{2}x^{1/2}$$

and so the arc length formula gives

$$L = \int_1^4 \sqrt{1 + \left(\frac{dy}{dx}\right)^2}\,dx = \int_1^4 \sqrt{1 + \tfrac{9}{4}x}\,dx$$

If we substitute $u = 1 + \tfrac{9}{4}x$, then $du = \tfrac{9}{4}\,dx$. When $x = 1$, $u = \tfrac{13}{4}$; when $x = 4$, $u = 10$.

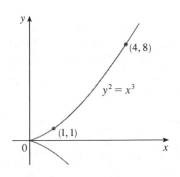

FIGURE 5

As a check on our answer to Example 1, notice from Figure 5 that the arc length ought to be slightly larger than the distance from $(1, 1)$ to $(4, 8)$, which is

$$\sqrt{58} \approx 7.615773$$

According to our calculation in Example 1, we have

$$L = \tfrac{1}{27}\left(80\sqrt{10} - 13\sqrt{13}\right) \approx 7.633705$$

Sure enough, this is a bit greater than the length of the line segment.

Therefore

$$L = \tfrac{4}{9}\int_{13/4}^{10} \sqrt{u}\ du = \tfrac{4}{9} \cdot \tfrac{2}{3}u^{3/2}\Big]_{13/4}^{10}$$

$$= \tfrac{8}{27}\left[10^{3/2} - \left(\tfrac{13}{4}\right)^{3/2}\right] = \tfrac{1}{27}\left(80\sqrt{10} - 13\sqrt{13}\right)$$

If a curve has the equation $x = g(y)$, $c \le y \le d$, and $g'(y)$ is continuous, then by interchanging the roles of x and y in Formula 2 or Equation 3, we obtain the following formula for its length:

$$\boxed{4} \qquad \boxed{\quad L = \int_c^d \sqrt{1 + [g'(y)]^2}\ dy = \int_c^d \sqrt{1 + \left(\frac{dx}{dy}\right)^2}\ dy \quad}$$

▽ EXAMPLE 2 Find the length of the arc of the parabola $y^2 = x$ from $(0, 0)$ to $(1, 1)$.

SOLUTION Since $x = y^2$, we have $dx/dy = 2y$, and Formula 4 gives

$$L = \int_0^1 \sqrt{1 + \left(\frac{dx}{dy}\right)^2}\ dy = \int_0^1 \sqrt{1 + 4y^2}\ dy$$

We make the trigonometric substitution $y = \tfrac{1}{2}\tan\theta$, which gives $dy = \tfrac{1}{2}\sec^2\theta\ d\theta$ and $\sqrt{1 + 4y^2} = \sqrt{1 + \tan^2\theta} = \sec\theta$. When $y = 0$, $\tan\theta = 0$, so $\theta = 0$; when $y = 1$, $\tan\theta = 2$, so $\theta = \tan^{-1}2 = \alpha$, say. Thus

$$L = \int_0^\alpha \sec\theta \cdot \tfrac{1}{2}\sec^2\theta\ d\theta = \tfrac{1}{2}\int_0^\alpha \sec^3\theta\ d\theta$$

$$= \tfrac{1}{2} \cdot \tfrac{1}{2}\Big[\sec\theta\tan\theta + \ln|\sec\theta + \tan\theta|\Big]_0^\alpha \qquad \text{(from Example 8 in Section 7.2)}$$

$$= \tfrac{1}{4}\Big(\sec\alpha\tan\alpha + \ln|\sec\alpha + \tan\alpha|\Big)$$

(We could have used Formula 21 in the Table of Integrals.) Since $\tan\alpha = 2$, we have $\sec^2\alpha = 1 + \tan^2\alpha = 5$, so $\sec\alpha = \sqrt{5}$ and

$$L = \frac{\sqrt{5}}{2} + \frac{\ln(\sqrt{5} + 2)}{4}$$

Figure 6 shows the arc of the parabola whose length is computed in Example 2, together with polygonal approximations having $n = 1$ and $n = 2$ line segments, respectively. For $n = 1$ the approximate length is $L_1 = \sqrt{2}$, the diagonal of a square. The table shows the approximations L_n that we get by dividing $[0, 1]$ into n equal subintervals. Notice that each time we double the number of sides of the polygon, we get closer to the exact length, which is

$$L = \frac{\sqrt{5}}{2} + \frac{\ln(\sqrt{5} + 2)}{4} \approx 1.478943$$

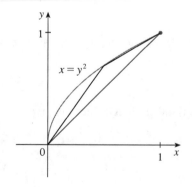

FIGURE 6

n	L_n
1	1.414
2	1.445
4	1.464
8	1.472
16	1.476
32	1.478
64	1.479

Because of the presence of the square root sign in Formulas 2 and 4, the calculation of an arc length often leads to an integral that is very difficult or even impossible to evaluate explicitly. Thus we sometimes have to be content with finding an approximation to the length of a curve, as in the following example.

V EXAMPLE 3

(a) Set up an integral for the length of the arc of the hyperbola $xy = 1$ from the point $(1, 1)$ to the point $(2, \frac{1}{2})$.

(b) Use Simpson's Rule with $n = 10$ to estimate the arc length.

SOLUTION

(a) We have

$$y = \frac{1}{x} \qquad \frac{dy}{dx} = -\frac{1}{x^2}$$

and so the arc length is

$$L = \int_1^2 \sqrt{1 + \left(\frac{dy}{dx}\right)^2}\, dx = \int_1^2 \sqrt{1 + \frac{1}{x^4}}\, dx = \int_1^2 \frac{\sqrt{x^4 + 1}}{x^2}\, dx$$

(b) Using Simpson's Rule (see Section 7.7) with $a = 1$, $b = 2$, $n = 10$, $\Delta x = 0.1$, and $f(x) = \sqrt{1 + 1/x^4}$, we have

$$L = \int_1^2 \sqrt{1 + \frac{1}{x^4}}\, dx$$

Checking the value of the definite integral with a more accurate approximation produced by a computer algebra system, we see that the approximation using Simpson's Rule is accurate to four decimal places.

$$\approx \frac{\Delta x}{3}[f(1) + 4f(1.1) + 2f(1.2) + 4f(1.3) + \cdots + 2f(1.8) + 4f(1.9) + f(2)]$$

$$\approx 1.1321$$

■

The Arc Length Function

We will find it useful to have a function that measures the arc length of a curve from a particular starting point to any other point on the curve. Thus if a smooth curve C has the equation $y = f(x)$, $a \le x \le b$, let $s(x)$ be the distance along C from the initial point $P_0(a, f(a))$ to the point $Q(x, f(x))$. Then s is a function, called the **arc length function**, and, by Formula 2,

$$\boxed{5} \qquad\qquad s(x) = \int_a^x \sqrt{1 + [f'(t)]^2}\, dt$$

(We have replaced the variable of integration by t so that x does not have two meanings.) We can use Part 1 of the Fundamental Theorem of Calculus to differentiate Equation 5 (since the integrand is continuous):

$$\boxed{6} \qquad\qquad \frac{ds}{dx} = \sqrt{1 + [f'(x)]^2} = \sqrt{1 + \left(\frac{dy}{dx}\right)^2}$$

Equation 6 shows that the rate of change of s with respect to x is always at least 1 and is equal to 1 when $f'(x)$, the slope of the curve, is 0. The differential of arc length is

$$\boxed{7} \qquad ds = \sqrt{1 + \left(\frac{dy}{dx}\right)^2}\, dx$$

and this equation is sometimes written in the symmetric form

$$\boxed{8} \qquad (ds)^2 = (dx)^2 + (dy)^2$$

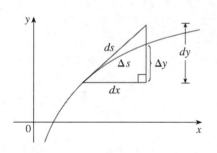

FIGURE 7

The geometric interpretation of Equation 8 is shown in Figure 7. It can be used as a mnemonic device for remembering both of the Formulas 3 and 4. If we write $L = \int ds$, then from Equation 8 either we can solve to get $\boxed{7}$, which gives $\boxed{3}$, or we can solve to get

$$ds = \sqrt{1 + \left(\frac{dx}{dy}\right)^2}\, dy$$

which gives $\boxed{4}$.

▼ EXAMPLE 4 Find the arc length function for the curve $y = x^2 - \frac{1}{8}\ln x$ taking $P_0(1, 1)$ as the starting point.

SOLUTION If $f(x) = x^2 - \frac{1}{8}\ln x$, then

$$f'(x) = 2x - \frac{1}{8x}$$

$$1 + [f'(x)]^2 = 1 + \left(2x - \frac{1}{8x}\right)^2 = 1 + 4x^2 - \frac{1}{2} + \frac{1}{64x^2}$$

$$= 4x^2 + \frac{1}{2} + \frac{1}{64x^2} = \left(2x + \frac{1}{8x}\right)^2$$

$$\sqrt{1 + [f'(x)]^2} = 2x + \frac{1}{8x}$$

Thus the arc length function is given by

$$s(x) = \int_1^x \sqrt{1 + [f'(t)]^2}\, dt$$

$$= \int_1^x \left(2t + \frac{1}{8t}\right) dt = t^2 + \tfrac{1}{8}\ln t\Big]_1^x$$

$$= x^2 + \tfrac{1}{8}\ln x - 1$$

For instance, the arc length along the curve from $(1, 1)$ to $(3, f(3))$ is

$$s(3) = 3^2 + \tfrac{1}{8}\ln 3 - 1 = 8 + \frac{\ln 3}{8} \approx 8.1373$$

Figure 8 shows the interpretation of the arc length function in Example 4. Figure 9 shows the graph of this arc length function. Why is $s(x)$ negative when x is less than 1?

$y = x^2 - \frac{1}{8}\ln x$

FIGURE 8

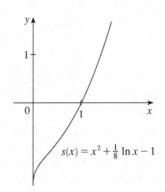

$s(x) = x^2 + \frac{1}{8}\ln x - 1$

FIGURE 9

8.1 Exercises

1. Use the arc length formula $\boxed{3}$ to find the length of the curve $y = 2x - 5$, $-1 \leqslant x \leqslant 3$. Check your answer by noting that the curve is a line segment and calculating its length by the distance formula.

2. Use the arc length formula to find the length of the curve $y = \sqrt{2 - x^2}$, $0 \leqslant x \leqslant 1$. Check your answer by noting that the curve is part of a circle.

3–6 Set up an integral that represents the length of the curve. Then use your calculator to find the length correct to four decimal places.

3. $y = \sin x$, $0 \leqslant x \leqslant \pi$

4. $y = xe^{-x}$, $0 \leqslant x \leqslant 2$

5. $x = \sqrt{y} - y$, $1 \leqslant y \leqslant 4$

6. $x = y^2 - 2y$, $0 \leqslant y \leqslant 2$

7–18 Find the exact length of the curve.

7. $y = 1 + 6x^{3/2}$, $0 \leqslant x \leqslant 1$

8. $y^2 = 4(x + 4)^3$, $0 \leqslant x \leqslant 2$, $y > 0$

9. $y = \dfrac{x^5}{6} + \dfrac{1}{10x^3}$, $1 \leqslant x \leqslant 2$

10. $x = \dfrac{y^4}{8} + \dfrac{1}{4y^2}$, $1 \leqslant y \leqslant 2$

11. $x = \frac{1}{3}\sqrt{y}\,(y - 3)$, $1 \leqslant y \leqslant 9$

12. $y = \ln(\cos x)$, $0 \leqslant x \leqslant \pi/3$

13. $y = \ln(\sec x)$, $0 \leqslant x \leqslant \pi/4$

14. $y = 3 + \frac{1}{2}\cosh 2x$, $0 \leqslant x \leqslant 1$

15. $y = \frac{1}{4}x^2 - \frac{1}{2}\ln x$, $1 \leqslant x \leqslant 2$

16. $y = \sqrt{x - x^2} + \sin^{-1}(\sqrt{x}\,)$

17. $y = \ln(1 - x^2)$, $0 \leqslant x \leqslant \frac{1}{2}$

18. $y = 1 - e^{-x}$, $0 \leqslant x \leqslant 2$

19–20 Find the length of the arc of the curve from point P to point Q.

19. $y = \frac{1}{2}x^2$, $P\left(-1, \frac{1}{2}\right)$, $Q\left(1, \frac{1}{2}\right)$

20. $x^2 = (y - 4)^3$, $P(1, 5)$, $Q(8, 8)$

21–22 Graph the curve and visually estimate its length. Then use your calculator to find the length correct to four decimal places.

21. $y = x^2 + x^3$, $1 \leqslant x \leqslant 2$

22. $y = x + \cos x$, $0 \leqslant x \leqslant \pi/2$

23–26 Use Simpson's Rule with $n = 10$ to estimate the arc length of the curve. Compare your answer with the value of the integral produced by your calculator.

23. $y = x \sin x$, $0 \leqslant x \leqslant 2\pi$

24. $y = \sqrt[3]{x}$, $1 \leqslant x \leqslant 6$

25. $y = \ln(1 + x^3)$, $0 \leqslant x \leqslant 5$

26. $y = e^{-x^2}$, $0 \leqslant x \leqslant 2$

27. (a) Graph the curve $y = x\sqrt[3]{4 - x}$, $0 \leqslant x \leqslant 4$.
　　(b) Compute the lengths of inscribed polygons with $n = 1, 2$, and 4 sides. (Divide the interval into equal subintervals.) Illustrate by sketching these polygons (as in Figure 6).
　　(c) Set up an integral for the length of the curve.
　　(d) Use your calculator to find the length of the curve to four decimal places. Compare with the approximations in part (b).

28. Repeat Exercise 27 for the curve

$$y = x + \sin x \qquad 0 \leqslant x \leqslant 2\pi$$

29. Use either a computer algebra system or a table of integrals to find the *exact* length of the arc of the curve $y = \ln x$ that lies between the points $(1, 0)$ and $(2, \ln 2)$.

30. Use either a computer algebra system or a table of integrals to find the *exact* length of the arc of the curve $y = x^{4/3}$ that lies between the points $(0, 0)$ and $(1, 1)$. If your CAS has trouble evaluating the integral, make a substitution that changes the integral into one that the CAS can evaluate.

31. Sketch the curve with equation $x^{2/3} + y^{2/3} = 1$ and use symmetry to find its length.

32. (a) Sketch the curve $y^3 = x^2$.
   (b) Use Formulas 3 and 4 to set up two integrals for the arc length from $(0, 0)$ to $(1, 1)$. Observe that one of these is an improper integral and evaluate both of them.
   (c) Find the length of the arc of this curve from $(-1, 1)$ to $(8, 4)$.

33. Find the arc length function for the curve $y = 2x^{3/2}$ with starting point $P_0(1, 2)$.

34. (a) Find the arc length function for the curve $y = \ln(\sin x)$, $0 < x < \pi$, with starting point $(\pi/2, 0)$.
   (b) Graph both the curve and its arc length function on the same screen.

35. Find the arc length function for the curve $y = \sin^{-1}x + \sqrt{1 - x^2}$ with starting point $(0, 1)$.

36. A steady wind blows a kite due west. The kite's height above ground from horizontal position $x = 0$ to $x = 25$ m is given by $y = 50 - 0.1(x - 15)^2$. Find the distance traveled by the kite.

37. A hawk flying at 15 m/s at an altitude of 180 m accidentally drops its prey. The parabolic trajectory of the falling prey is described by the equation

$$y = 180 - \frac{x^2}{45}$$

until it hits the ground, where y is its height above the ground and x is the horizontal distance traveled in meters. Calculate the distance traveled by the prey from the time it is dropped until the time it hits the ground. Express your answer correct to the nearest tenth of a meter.

38. The Gateway Arch in St. Louis (see the photo on page 259) was constructed using the equation

$$y = 211.49 - 20.96 \cosh 0.03291765x$$

for the central curve of the arch, where x and y are measured in meters and $|x| \leqslant 91.20$. Set up an integral for the length of the arch and use your calculator to estimate the length correct to the nearest meter.

39. A manufacturer of corrugated metal roofing wants to produce panels that are 60 cm wide and 4 cm thick by processing flat sheets of metal as shown in the figure. The profile of the roofing takes the shape of a sine wave. Verify that the sine curve has equation $y = 2 \sin(\pi x/15)$ and find the width w of a flat metal sheet that is needed to make a 60-cm panel. (Use your calculator to evaluate the integral correct to four significant digits.)

40. (a) The figure shows a telephone wire hanging between two poles at $x = -b$ and $x = b$. It takes the shape of a catenary with equation $y = c + a \cosh(x/a)$. Find the length of the wire.
   (b) Suppose two telephone poles are 20 m apart and the length of the wire between the poles is 20.4 m. If the lowest point of the wire must be 9 m above the ground, how high up on each pole should the wire be attached?

41. Find the length of the curve

$$y = \int_1^x \sqrt{t^3 - 1}\, dt \qquad 1 \leqslant x \leqslant 4$$

42. The curves with equations $x^n + y^n = 1$, $n = 4, 6, 8, \ldots$, are called **fat circles**. Graph the curves with $n = 2, 4, 6, 8,$ and 10 to see why. Set up an integral for the length L_{2k} of the fat circle with $n = 2k$. Without attempting to evaluate this integral, state the value of $\lim_{k \to \infty} L_{2k}$.

ARC LENGTH CONTEST

The curves shown are all examples of graphs of continuous functions f that have the following properties.

1. $f(0) = 0$ and $f(1) = 0$

2. $f(x) \geqslant 0$ for $0 \leqslant x \leqslant 1$

3. The area under the graph of f from 0 to 1 is equal to 1.

The lengths L of these curves, however, are different.

$$L \approx 3.249 \qquad L \approx 2.919 \qquad L \approx 3.152 \qquad L \approx 3.213$$

Try to discover formulas for two functions that satisfy the given conditions 1, 2, and 3. (Your graphs might be similar to the ones shown or could look quite different.) Then calculate the arc length of each graph. The winning entry will be the one with the smallest arc length.

8.2 Area of a Surface of Revolution

A surface of revolution is formed when a curve is rotated about a line. Such a surface is the lateral boundary of a solid of revolution of the type discussed in Sections 6.2 and 6.3.

We want to define the area of a surface of revolution in such a way that it corresponds to our intuition. If the surface area is A, we can imagine that painting the surface would require the same amount of paint as does a flat region with area A.

Let's start with some simple surfaces. The lateral surface area of a circular cylinder with radius r and height h is taken to be $A = 2\pi rh$ because we can imagine cutting the cylinder and unrolling it (as in Figure 1) to obtain a rectangle with dimensions $2\pi r$ and h.

Likewise, we can take a circular cone with base radius r and slant height l, cut it along the dashed line in Figure 2, and flatten it to form a sector of a circle with radius l and central

FIGURE 1

FIGURE 2

angle $\theta = 2\pi r/l$. We know that, in general, the area of a sector of a circle with radius l and angle θ is $\frac{1}{2}l^2\theta$ (see Exercise 35 in Section 7.3) and so in this case the area is

$$A = \tfrac{1}{2}l^2\theta = \tfrac{1}{2}l^2\left(\frac{2\pi r}{l}\right) = \pi r l$$

Therefore we define the lateral surface area of a cone to be $A = \pi r l$.

What about more complicated surfaces of revolution? If we follow the strategy we used with arc length, we can approximate the original curve by a polygon. When this polygon is rotated about an axis, it creates a simpler surface whose surface area approximates the actual surface area. By taking a limit, we can determine the exact surface area.

The approximating surface, then, consists of a number of *bands*, each formed by rotating a line segment about an axis. To find the surface area, each of these bands can be considered a portion of a circular cone, as shown in Figure 3. The area of the band (or frustum of a cone) with slant height l and upper and lower radii r_1 and r_2 is found by subtracting the areas of two cones:

FIGURE 3

$$\boxed{1} \qquad A = \pi r_2(l_1 + l) - \pi r_1 l_1 = \pi[(r_2 - r_1)l_1 + r_2 l]$$

From similar triangles we have

$$\frac{l_1}{r_1} = \frac{l_1 + l}{r_2}$$

which gives

$$r_2 l_1 = r_1 l_1 + r_1 l \qquad \text{or} \qquad (r_2 - r_1)l_1 = r_1 l$$

Putting this in Equation 1, we get

$$A = \pi(r_1 l + r_2 l)$$

or

$$\boxed{2} \qquad \boxed{A = 2\pi r l}$$

where $r = \frac{1}{2}(r_1 + r_2)$ is the average radius of the band.

Now we apply this formula to our strategy. Consider the surface shown in Figure 4, which is obtained by rotating the curve $y = f(x)$, $a \le x \le b$, about the x-axis, where f is positive and has a continuous derivative. In order to define its surface area, we divide the interval $[a, b]$ into n subintervals with endpoints $x_0, x_1, \ldots, x_n$ and equal width Δx, as we did in determining arc length. If $y_i = f(x_i)$, then the point $P_i(x_i, y_i)$ lies on the curve. The part of the surface between x_{i-1} and x_i is approximated by taking the line segment $P_{i-1}P_i$ and rotating it about the x-axis. The result is a band with slant height $l = |P_{i-1}P_i|$ and average radius $r = \frac{1}{2}(y_{i-1} + y_i)$ so, by Formula 2, its surface area is

$$2\pi \frac{y_{i-1} + y_i}{2}|P_{i-1}P_i|$$

As in the proof of Theorem 8.1.2, we have

$$|P_{i-1}P_i| = \sqrt{1 + [f'(x_i^*)]^2}\,\Delta x$$

(a) Surface of revolution

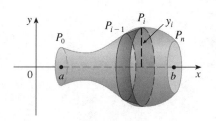

(b) Approximating band

FIGURE 4

where x_i^* is some number in $[x_{i-1}, x_i]$. When Δx is small, we have $y_i = f(x_i) \approx f(x_i^*)$ and also $y_{i-1} = f(x_{i-1}) \approx f(x_i^*)$, since f is continuous. Therefore

$$2\pi \frac{y_{i-1} + y_i}{2} \left| P_{i-1}P_i \right| \approx 2\pi f(x_i^*) \sqrt{1 + [f'(x_i^*)]^2}\, \Delta x$$

and so an approximation to what we think of as the area of the complete surface of revolution is

$$\boxed{3} \qquad \sum_{i=1}^{n} 2\pi f(x_i^*) \sqrt{1 + [f'(x_i^*)]^2}\, \Delta x$$

This approximation appears to become better as $n \to \infty$ and, recognizing $\boxed{3}$ as a Riemann sum for the function $g(x) = 2\pi f(x) \sqrt{1 + [f'(x)]^2}$, we have

$$\lim_{n \to \infty} \sum_{i=1}^{n} 2\pi f(x_i^*) \sqrt{1 + [f'(x_i^*)]^2}\, \Delta x = \int_a^b 2\pi f(x) \sqrt{1 + [f'(x)]^2}\, dx$$

Therefore, in the case where f is positive and has a continuous derivative, we define the **surface area** of the surface obtained by rotating the curve $y = f(x)$, $a \leq x \leq b$, about the x-axis as

$$\boxed{4} \qquad S = \int_a^b 2\pi f(x) \sqrt{1 + [f'(x)]^2}\, dx$$

With the Leibniz notation for derivatives, this formula becomes

$$\boxed{5} \qquad S = \int_a^b 2\pi y \sqrt{1 + \left(\frac{dy}{dx}\right)^2}\, dx$$

If the curve is described as $x = g(y)$, $c \leq y \leq d$, then the formula for surface area becomes

$$\boxed{6} \qquad S = \int_c^d 2\pi y \sqrt{1 + \left(\frac{dx}{dy}\right)^2}\, dy$$

and both Formulas 5 and 6 can be summarized symbolically, using the notation for arc length given in Section 8.1, as

$$\boxed{7} \qquad S = \int 2\pi y\, ds$$

For rotation about the y-axis, the surface area formula becomes

$$\boxed{8} \qquad S = \int 2\pi x \, ds$$

where, as before, we can use either

$$ds = \sqrt{1 + \left(\frac{dy}{dx}\right)^2} \, dx \qquad \text{or} \qquad ds = \sqrt{1 + \left(\frac{dx}{dy}\right)^2} \, dy$$

These formulas can be remembered by thinking of $2\pi y$ or $2\pi x$ as the circumference of a circle traced out by the point (x, y) on the curve as it is rotated about the x-axis or y-axis, respectively (see Figure 5).

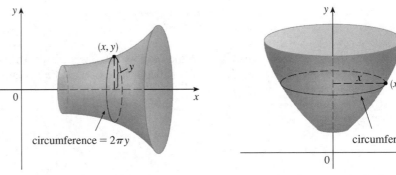

FIGURE 5   (a) Rotation about x-axis: $S = \int 2\pi y \, ds$ (b) Rotation about y-axis: $S = \int 2\pi x \, ds$

V **EXAMPLE 1** The curve $y = \sqrt{4 - x^2}$, $-1 \leqslant x \leqslant 1$, is an arc of the circle $x^2 + y^2 = 4$. Find the area of the surface obtained by rotating this arc about the x-axis. (The surface is a portion of a sphere of radius 2. See Figure 6.)

SOLUTION We have

$$\frac{dy}{dx} = \tfrac{1}{2}(4 - x^2)^{-1/2}(-2x) = \frac{-x}{\sqrt{4 - x^2}}$$

and so, by Formula 5, the surface area is

$$S = \int_{-1}^{1} 2\pi y \sqrt{1 + \left(\frac{dy}{dx}\right)^2} \, dx$$

$$= 2\pi \int_{-1}^{1} \sqrt{4 - x^2} \sqrt{1 + \frac{x^2}{4 - x^2}} \, dx$$

$$= 2\pi \int_{-1}^{1} \sqrt{4 - x^2} \frac{2}{\sqrt{4 - x^2}} \, dx$$

$$= 4\pi \int_{-1}^{1} 1 \, dx = 4\pi(2) = 8\pi$$

FIGURE 6

Figure 6 shows the portion of the sphere whose surface area is computed in Example 1.

Figure 7 shows the surface of revolution whose area is computed in Example 2.

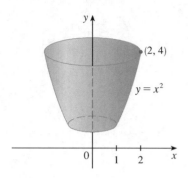

FIGURE 7

V **EXAMPLE 2** The arc of the parabola $y = x^2$ from $(1, 1)$ to $(2, 4)$ is rotated about the y-axis. Find the area of the resulting surface.

SOLUTION 1 Using

$$y = x^2 \quad \text{and} \quad \frac{dy}{dx} = 2x$$

we have, from Formula 8,

$$S = \int 2\pi x \, ds$$

$$= \int_1^2 2\pi x \sqrt{1 + \left(\frac{dy}{dx}\right)^2} \, dx$$

$$= 2\pi \int_1^2 x \sqrt{1 + 4x^2} \, dx$$

Substituting $u = 1 + 4x^2$, we have $du = 8x \, dx$. Remembering to change the limits of integration, we have

$$S = \frac{\pi}{4} \int_5^{17} \sqrt{u} \, du = \frac{\pi}{4} \left[\tfrac{2}{3} u^{3/2} \right]_5^{17}$$

$$= \frac{\pi}{6} \left(17\sqrt{17} - 5\sqrt{5} \right)$$

As a check on our answer to Example 2, notice from Figure 7 that the surface area should be close to that of a circular cylinder with the same height and radius halfway between the upper and lower radius of the surface: $2\pi(1.5)(3) \approx 28.27$. We computed that the surface area was

$$\frac{\pi}{6} \left(17\sqrt{17} - 5\sqrt{5} \right) \approx 30.85$$

which seems reasonable. Alternatively, the surface area should be slightly larger than the area of a frustum of a cone with the same top and bottom edges. From Equation 2, this is $2\pi(1.5)(\sqrt{10}) \approx 29.80$.

SOLUTION 2 Using

$$x = \sqrt{y} \quad \text{and} \quad \frac{dx}{dy} = \frac{1}{2\sqrt{y}}$$

we have

$$S = \int 2\pi x \, ds = \int_1^4 2\pi x \sqrt{1 + \left(\frac{dx}{dy}\right)^2} \, dy$$

$$= 2\pi \int_1^4 \sqrt{y} \sqrt{1 + \frac{1}{4y}} \, dy = \pi \int_1^4 \sqrt{4y + 1} \, dy$$

$$= \frac{\pi}{4} \int_5^{17} \sqrt{u} \, du \quad \text{(where } u = 1 + 4y\text{)}$$

$$= \frac{\pi}{6} \left(17\sqrt{17} - 5\sqrt{5} \right) \quad \text{(as in Solution 1)}$$

Another method: Use Formula 6 with $x = \ln y$.

V **EXAMPLE 3** Find the area of the surface generated by rotating the curve $y = e^x$, $0 \le x \le 1$, about the x-axis.

SOLUTION Using Formula 5 with

$$y = e^x \quad \text{and} \quad \frac{dy}{dx} = e^x$$

we have

$$S = \int_0^1 2\pi y \sqrt{1 + \left(\frac{dy}{dx}\right)^2}\, dx = 2\pi \int_0^1 e^x \sqrt{1 + e^{2x}}\, dx$$

$$= 2\pi \int_1^e \sqrt{1 + u^2}\, du \qquad \text{(where } u = e^x)$$

$$= 2\pi \int_{\pi/4}^{\alpha} \sec^3\theta\, d\theta \qquad \text{(where } u = \tan\theta \text{ and } \alpha = \tan^{-1}e)$$

Or use Formula 21 in the Table of Integrals.

$$= 2\pi \cdot \tfrac{1}{2}\big[\sec\theta \tan\theta + \ln|\sec\theta + \tan\theta|\big]_{\pi/4}^{\alpha} \qquad \text{(by Example 8 in Section 7.2)}$$

$$= \pi\big[\sec\alpha \tan\alpha + \ln(\sec\alpha + \tan\alpha) - \sqrt{2} - \ln(\sqrt{2} + 1)\big]$$

Since $\tan\alpha = e$, we have $\sec^2\alpha = 1 + \tan^2\alpha = 1 + e^2$ and

$$S = \pi\big[e\sqrt{1 + e^2} + \ln(e + \sqrt{1 + e^2}) - \sqrt{2} - \ln(\sqrt{2} + 1)\big]$$

8.2 Exercises

1–4
(a) Set up an integral for the area of the surface obtained by rotating the curve about (i) the x-axis and (ii) the y-axis.
(b) Use the numerical integration capability of your calculator to evaluate the surface areas correct to four decimal places.

1. $y = \tan x, \quad 0 \le x \le \pi/3$ **2.** $y = x^{-2}, \quad 1 \le x \le 2$

3. $y = e^{-x^2}, \quad -1 \le x \le 1$ **4.** $x = \ln(2y + 1), \quad 0 \le y \le 1$

5–12 Find the exact area of the surface obtained by rotating the curve about the x-axis.

5. $y = x^3, \quad 0 \le x \le 2$

6. $9x = y^2 + 18, \quad 2 \le x \le 6$

7. $y = \sqrt{1 + 4x}, \quad 1 \le x \le 5$

8. $y = \sqrt{1 + e^x}, \quad 0 \le x \le 1$

9. $y = \sin \pi x, \quad 0 \le x \le 1$

10. $y = \dfrac{x^3}{6} + \dfrac{1}{2x}, \quad \tfrac{1}{2} \le x \le 1$

11. $x = \tfrac{1}{3}(y^2 + 2)^{3/2}, \quad 1 \le y \le 2$

12. $x = 1 + 2y^2, \quad 1 \le y \le 2$

13–16 The given curve is rotated about the y-axis. Find the area of the resulting surface.

13. $y = \sqrt[3]{x}, \quad 1 \le y \le 2$

14. $y = 1 - x^2, \quad 0 \le x \le 1$

15. $x = \sqrt{a^2 - y^2}, \quad 0 \le y \le a/2$

16. $y = \tfrac{1}{4}x^2 - \tfrac{1}{2}\ln x, \quad 1 \le x \le 2$

17–20 Use Simpson's Rule with $n = 10$ to approximate the area of the surface obtained by rotating the curve about the x-axis. Compare your answer with the value of the integral produced by your calculator.

17. $y = \ln x, \quad 1 \le x \le 3$ **18.** $y = x + \sqrt{x}, \quad 1 \le x \le 2$

19. $y = xe^x, \quad 0 \le x \le 1$ **20.** $y = x \ln x, \quad 1 \le x \le 2$

CAS **21–22** Use either a CAS or a table of integrals to find the exact area of the surface obtained by rotating the given curve about the x-axis.

21. $y = 1/x, \quad 1 \le x \le 2$ **22.** $y = \sqrt{x^2 + 1}, \quad 0 \le x \le 3$

CAS **23–24** Use a CAS to find the exact area of the surface obtained by rotating the curve about the y-axis. If your CAS has trouble evaluating the integral, express the surface area as an integral in the other variable.

23. $y = x^3, \quad 0 \le y \le 1$ **24.** $y = \ln(x + 1), \quad 0 \le x \le 1$

---

25. If the region $\mathcal{R} = \{(x, y) \mid x \ge 1, \ 0 \le y \le 1/x\}$ is rotated about the x-axis, the volume of the resulting solid is finite (see Exercise 63 in Section 7.8). Show that the surface area is infinite. (The surface is shown in the figure and is known as **Gabriel's horn**.)

---

26. If the infinite curve $y = e^{-x}$, $x \geqslant 0$, is rotated about the x-axis, find the area of the resulting surface.

27. (a) If $a > 0$, find the area of the surface generated by rotating the loop of the curve $3ay^2 = x(a - x)^2$ about the x-axis.
(b) Find the surface area if the loop is rotated about the y-axis.

28. A group of engineers is building a parabolic satellite dish whose shape will be formed by rotating the curve $y = ax^2$ about the y-axis. If the dish is to have a 10-ft diameter and a maximum depth of 2 ft, find the value of a and the surface area of the dish.

29. (a) The ellipse

$$\frac{x^2}{a^2} + \frac{y^2}{b^2} = 1 \qquad a > b$$

is rotated about the x-axis to form a surface called an *ellipsoid, or prolate spheroid*. Find the surface area of this ellipsoid.
(b) If the ellipse in part (a) is rotated about its minor axis (the y-axis), the resulting ellipsoid is called an *oblate spheroid*. Find the surface area of this ellipsoid.

30. Find the surface area of the torus in Exercise 61 in Section 6.2.

31. If the curve $y = f(x)$, $a \leqslant x \leqslant b$, is rotated about the horizontal line $y = c$, where $f(x) \leqslant c$, find a formula for the area of the resulting surface.

32. Use the result of Exercise 31 to set up an integral to find the area of the surface generated by rotating the curve $y = \sqrt{x}$, $0 \leqslant x \leqslant 4$, about the line $y = 4$. Then use a CAS to evaluate the integral.

33. Find the area of the surface obtained by rotating the circle $x^2 + y^2 = r^2$ about the line $y = r$.

34. (a) Show that the surface area of a zone of a sphere that lies between two parallel planes is $S = 2\pi R h$, where R is the radius of the sphere and h is the distance between the planes. (Notice that S depends only on the distance between the planes and not on their location, provided that both planes intersect the sphere.)
(b) Show that the surface area of a zone of a *cylinder* with radius R and height h is the same as the surface area of the zone of a *sphere* in part (a).

35. Formula 4 is valid only when $f(x) \geqslant 0$. Show that when $f(x)$ is not necessarily positive, the formula for surface area becomes

$$S = \int_a^b 2\pi \, |f(x)| \sqrt{1 + [f'(x)]^2} \; dx$$

36. Let L be the length of the curve $y = f(x)$, $a \leqslant x \leqslant b$, where f is positive and has a continuous derivative. Let S_f be the surface area generated by rotating the curve about the x-axis. If c is a positive constant, define $g(x) = f(x) + c$ and let S_g be the corresponding surface area generated by the curve $y = g(x)$, $a \leqslant x \leqslant b$. Express S_g in terms of S_f and L.

DISCOVERY PROJECT   ROTATING ON A SLANT

We know how to find the volume of a solid of revolution obtained by rotating a region about a horizontal or vertical line (see Section 6.2). We also know how to find the surface area of a surface of revolution if we rotate a curve about a horizontal or vertical line (see Section 8.2). But what if we rotate about a slanted line, that is, a line that is neither horizontal nor vertical? In this project you are asked to discover formulas for the volume of a solid of revolution and for the area of a surface of revolution when the axis of rotation is a slanted line.

Let C be the arc of the curve $y = f(x)$ between the points $P(p, f(p))$ and $Q(q, f(q))$ and let $\mathcal{R}$ be the region bounded by C, by the line $y = mx + b$ (which lies entirely below C), and by the perpendiculars to the line from P and Q.

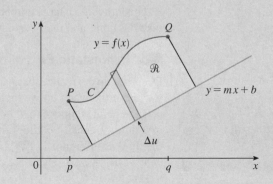

1. Show that the area of $\mathcal{R}$ is

$$\frac{1}{1+m^2} \int_p^q [f(x) - mx - b][1 + mf'(x)]\,dx$$

[*Hint:* This formula can be verified by subtracting areas, but it will be helpful throughout the project to derive it by first approximating the area using rectangles perpendicular to the line, as shown in the following figure. Use the figure to help express Δu in terms of Δx.]

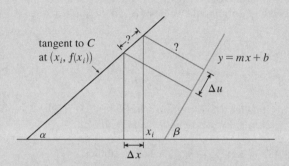

2. Find the area of the region shown in the figure at the left.

3. Find a formula (similar to the one in Problem 1) for the volume of the solid obtained by rotating $\mathcal{R}$ about the line $y = mx + b$.

4. Find the volume of the solid obtained by rotating the region of Problem 2 about the line $y = x - 2$.

5. Find a formula for the area of the surface obtained by rotating C about the line $y = mx + b$.

CAS 6. Use a computer algebra system to find the exact area of the surface obtained by rotating the curve $y = \sqrt{x}$, $0 \le x \le 4$, about the line $y = \frac{1}{2}x$. Then approximate your result to three decimal places.

CAS Computer algebra system required

8.3   Applications to Physics and Engineering

Among the many applications of integral calculus to physics and engineering, we consider two here: force due to water pressure and centers of mass. As with our previous applications to geometry (areas, volumes, and lengths) and to work, our strategy is to break up the physical quantity into a large number of small parts, approximate each small part, add the results, take the limit, and then evaluate the resulting integral.

Hydrostatic Pressure and Force

Deep-sea divers realize that water pressure increases as they dive deeper. This is because the weight of the water above them increases.

In general, suppose that a thin horizontal plate with area A square meters is submerged in a fluid of density ρ kilograms per cubic meter at a depth d meters below the surface of the fluid as in Figure 1. The fluid directly above the plate has volume $V = Ad$, so its mass is $m = \rho V = \rho Ad$. The force exerted by the fluid on the plate is therefore

$$F = mg = \rho g A d$$

FIGURE 1

where g is the acceleration due to gravity. The **pressure** P on the plate is defined to be the force per unit area:

$$P = \frac{F}{A} = \rho g d$$

When using US Customary units, we write $P = \rho g d = \delta d$, where $\delta = \rho g$ is the *weight density* (as opposed to ρ, which is the *mass density*). For instance, the weight density of water is $\delta = 62.5 \text{ lb/ft}^3$.

The SI unit for measuring pressure is newtons per square meter, which is called a pascal (abbreviation: $1 \text{ N/m}^2 = 1 \text{ Pa}$). Since this is a small unit, the kilopascal (kPa) is often used. For instance, because the density of water is $\rho = 1000 \text{ kg/m}^3$, the pressure at the bottom of a swimming pool 2 m deep is

$$P = \rho g d = 1000 \text{ kg/m}^3 \times 9.8 \text{ m/s}^2 \times 2 \text{ m}$$

$$= 19{,}600 \text{ Pa} = 19.6 \text{ kPa}$$

An important principle of fluid pressure is the experimentally verified fact that *at any point in a liquid the pressure is the same in all directions*. (A diver feels the same pressure on nose and both ears.) Thus the pressure in *any* direction at a depth d in a fluid with mass density ρ is given by

$$\boxed{1} \qquad\qquad P = \rho g d = \delta d$$

This helps us determine the hydrostatic force against a *vertical* plate or wall or dam in a fluid. This is not a straightforward problem because the pressure is not constant but increases as the depth increases.

V EXAMPLE 1 A dam has the shape of the trapezoid shown in Figure 2. The height is 20 m and the width is 50 m at the top and 30 m at the bottom. Find the force on the dam due to hydrostatic pressure if the water level is 4 m from the top of the dam.

SOLUTION We choose a vertical x-axis with origin at the surface of the water and directed downward as in Figure 3(a). The depth of the water is 16 m, so we divide the interval $[0, 16]$ into subintervals of equal length with endpoints x_i and we choose $x_i^* \in [x_{i-1}, x_i]$. The ith horizontal strip of the dam is approximated by a rectangle with height Δx and width w_i, where, from similar triangles in Figure 3(b),

$$\frac{a}{16 - x_i^*} = \frac{10}{20} \qquad \text{or} \qquad a = \frac{16 - x_i^*}{2} = 8 - \frac{x_i^*}{2}$$

and so

$$w_i = 2(15 + a) = 2\left(15 + 8 - \tfrac{1}{2}x_i^*\right) = 46 - x_i^*$$

If A_i is the area of the ith strip, then

$$A_i \approx w_i \,\Delta x = (46 - x_i^*)\,\Delta x$$

If Δx is small, then the pressure P_i on the ith strip is almost constant and we can use Equation 1 to write

$$P_i \approx 1000 g x_i^*$$

The hydrostatic force F_i acting on the ith strip is the product of the pressure and the area:

$$F_i = P_i A_i \approx 1000 g x_i^* (46 - x_i^*)\,\Delta x$$

FIGURE 2

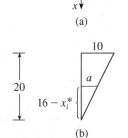

FIGURE 3

Adding these forces and taking the limit as $n \to \infty$, we obtain the total hydrostatic force on the dam:

$$F = \lim_{n \to \infty} \sum_{i=1}^{n} 1000gx_i^*(46 - x_i^*) \, \Delta x = \int_0^{16} 1000gx(46 - x) \, dx$$

$$= 1000(9.8) \int_0^{16} (46x - x^2) \, dx = 9800 \left[23x^2 - \frac{x^3}{3} \right]_0^{16}$$

$$\approx 4.43 \times 10^7 \, \text{N}$$

EXAMPLE 2 Find the hydrostatic force on one end of a cylindrical drum with radius 3 ft if the drum is submerged in water 10 ft deep.

SOLUTION In this example it is convenient to choose the axes as in Figure 4 so that the origin is placed at the center of the drum. Then the circle has a simple equation, $x^2 + y^2 = 9$. As in Example 1 we divide the circular region into horizontal strips of equal width. From the equation of the circle, we see that the length of the ith strip is $2\sqrt{9 - (y_i^*)^2}$ and so its area is

$$A_i = 2\sqrt{9 - (y_i^*)^2} \, \Delta y$$

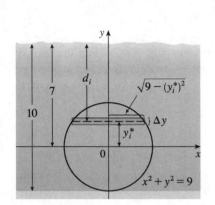

FIGURE 4

The pressure on this strip is approximately

$$\delta d_i = 62.5(7 - y_i^*)$$

and so the force on the strip is approximately

$$\delta d_i A_i = 62.5(7 - y_i^*) 2\sqrt{9 - (y_i^*)^2} \, \Delta y$$

The total force is obtained by adding the forces on all the strips and taking the limit:

$$F = \lim_{n \to \infty} \sum_{i=1}^{n} 62.5(7 - y_i^*) 2\sqrt{9 - (y_i^*)^2} \, \Delta y$$

$$= 125 \int_{-3}^{3} (7 - y) \sqrt{9 - y^2} \, dy$$

$$= 125 \cdot 7 \int_{-3}^{3} \sqrt{9 - y^2} \, dy - 125 \int_{-3}^{3} y\sqrt{9 - y^2} \, dy$$

The second integral is 0 because the integrand is an odd function (see Theorem 5.5.7). The first integral can be evaluated using the trigonometric substitution $y = 3 \sin \theta$, but it's simpler to observe that it is the area of a semicircular disk with radius 3. Thus

$$F = 875 \int_{-3}^{3} \sqrt{9 - y^2} \, dy = 875 \cdot \tfrac{1}{2} \pi (3)^2$$

$$= \frac{7875\pi}{2} \approx 12{,}370 \, \text{lb}$$

FIGURE 5

Moments and Centers of Mass

Our main objective here is to find the point P on which a thin plate of any given shape balances horizontally as in Figure 5. This point is called the **center of mass** (or center of gravity) of the plate.

FIGURE 6

We first consider the simpler situation illustrated in Figure 6, where two masses m_1 and m_2 are attached to a rod of negligible mass on opposite sides of a fulcrum and at distances d_1 and d_2 from the fulcrum. The rod will balance if

$$\boxed{2} \qquad m_1 d_1 = m_2 d_2$$

This is an experimental fact discovered by Archimedes and called the Law of the Lever. (Think of a lighter person balancing a heavier one on a seesaw by sitting farther away from the center.)

Now suppose that the rod lies along the x-axis with m_1 at x_1 and m_2 at x_2 and the center of mass at $\bar{x}$. If we compare Figures 6 and 7, we see that $d_1 = \bar{x} - x_1$ and $d_2 = x_2 - \bar{x}$ and so Equation 2 gives

$$m_1(\bar{x} - x_1) = m_2(x_2 - \bar{x})$$

$$m_1\bar{x} + m_2\bar{x} = m_1 x_1 + m_2 x_2$$

$$\boxed{3} \qquad \bar{x} = \frac{m_1 x_1 + m_2 x_2}{m_1 + m_2}$$

The numbers $m_1 x_1$ and $m_2 x_2$ are called the **moments** of the masses m_1 and m_2 (with respect to the origin), and Equation 3 says that the center of mass $\bar{x}$ is obtained by adding the moments of the masses and dividing by the total mass $m = m_1 + m_2$.

FIGURE 7

In general, if we have a system of n particles with masses $m_1, m_2, \ldots, m_n$ located at the points $x_1, x_2, \ldots, x_n$ on the x-axis, it can be shown similarly that the center of mass of the system is located at

$$\boxed{4} \qquad \bar{x} = \frac{\displaystyle\sum_{i=1}^{n} m_i x_i}{\displaystyle\sum_{i=1}^{n} m_i} = \frac{\displaystyle\sum_{i=1}^{n} m_i x_i}{m}$$

where $m = \Sigma\, m_i$ is the total mass of the system, and the sum of the individual moments

$$M = \sum_{i=1}^{n} m_i x_i$$

is called the **moment of the system about the origin**. Then Equation 4 could be rewritten as $m\bar{x} = M$, which says that if the total mass were considered as being concentrated at the center of mass $\bar{x}$, then its moment would be the same as the moment of the system.

Now we consider a system of n particles with masses $m_1, m_2, \ldots, m_n$ located at the points $(x_1, y_1), (x_2, y_2), \ldots, (x_n, y_n)$ in the xy-plane as shown in Figure 8. By analogy with the one-dimensional case, we define the **moment of the system about the y-axis** to be

$$\boxed{5} \qquad M_y = \sum_{i=1}^{n} m_i x_i$$

FIGURE 8

and the **moment of the system about the x-axis** as

$$\boxed{6} \qquad M_x = \sum_{i=1}^{n} m_i y_i$$

Then M_y measures the tendency of the system to rotate about the y-axis and M_x measures the tendency to rotate about the x-axis.

As in the one-dimensional case, the coordinates $(\bar{x}, \bar{y})$ of the center of mass are given in terms of the moments by the formulas

$$\boxed{7} \qquad \bar{x} = \frac{M_y}{m} \qquad \bar{y} = \frac{M_x}{m}$$

where $m = \sum m_i$ is the total mass. Since $m\bar{x} = M_y$ and $m\bar{y} = M_x$, the center of mass $(\bar{x}, \bar{y})$ is the point where a single particle of mass m would have the same moments as the system.

V EXAMPLE 3 Find the moments and center of mass of the system of objects that have masses 3, 4, and 8 at the points $(-1, 1)$, $(2, -1)$, and $(3, 2)$, respectively.

SOLUTION We use Equations 5 and 6 to compute the moments:

$$M_y = 3(-1) + 4(2) + 8(3) = 29$$

$$M_x = 3(1) + 4(-1) + 8(2) = 15$$

Since $m = 3 + 4 + 8 = 15$, we use Equations 7 to obtain

$$\bar{x} = \frac{M_y}{m} = \frac{29}{15} \qquad \bar{y} = \frac{M_x}{m} = \frac{15}{15} = 1$$

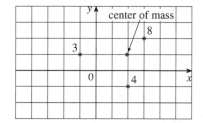

FIGURE 9

Thus the center of mass is $\left(1\frac{14}{15}, 1\right)$. (See Figure 9.)

Next we consider a flat plate (called a *lamina*) with uniform density ρ that occupies a region $\mathcal{R}$ of the plane. We wish to locate the center of mass of the plate, which is called the **centroid** of $\mathcal{R}$. In doing so we use the following physical principles: The **symmetry principle** says that if $\mathcal{R}$ is symmetric about a line l, then the centroid of $\mathcal{R}$ lies on l. (If $\mathcal{R}$ is reflected about l, then $\mathcal{R}$ remains the same so its centroid remains fixed. But the only fixed points lie on l.) Thus the centroid of a rectangle is its center. Moments should be defined so that if the entire mass of a region is concentrated at the center of mass, then its moments remain unchanged. Also, the moment of the union of two nonoverlapping regions should be the sum of the moments of the individual regions.

Suppose that the region $\mathcal{R}$ is of the type shown in Figure 10(a); that is, $\mathcal{R}$ lies between the lines $x = a$ and $x = b$, above the x-axis, and beneath the graph of f, where f is a continuous function. We divide the interval $[a, b]$ into n subintervals with endpoints x_0, $x_1, \ldots, x_n$ and equal width Δx. We choose the sample point x_i^* to be the midpoint $\bar{x}_i$ of the ith subinterval, that is, $\bar{x}_i = (x_{i-1} + x_i)/2$. This determines the polygonal approximation to $\mathcal{R}$ shown in Figure 10(b). The centroid of the ith approximating rectangle R_i is its center $C_i\left(\bar{x}_i, \frac{1}{2} f(\bar{x}_i)\right)$. Its area is $f(\bar{x}_i) \Delta x$, so its mass is

$$\rho f(\bar{x}_i) \Delta x$$

The moment of R_i about the y-axis is the product of its mass and the distance from C_i to the

(a)

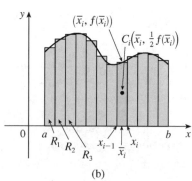

(b)

FIGURE 10

y-axis, which is $\overline{x}_i$. Thus

$$M_y(R_i) = [\rho f(\overline{x}_i)\,\Delta x]\,\overline{x}_i = \rho \overline{x}_i f(\overline{x}_i)\,\Delta x$$

Adding these moments, we obtain the moment of the polygonal approximation to $\mathcal{R}$, and then by taking the limit as $n \to \infty$ we obtain the moment of $\mathcal{R}$ itself about the y-axis:

$$M_y = \lim_{n \to \infty} \sum_{i=1}^{n} \rho \overline{x}_i f(\overline{x}_i)\,\Delta x = \rho \int_a^b x f(x)\,dx$$

In a similar fashion we compute the moment of R_i about the x-axis as the product of its mass and the distance from C_i to the x-axis:

$$M_x(R_i) = [\rho f(\overline{x}_i)\,\Delta x]\tfrac{1}{2} f(\overline{x}_i) = \rho \cdot \tfrac{1}{2}[f(\overline{x}_i)]^2\,\Delta x$$

Again we add these moments and take the limit to obtain the moment of $\mathcal{R}$ about the x-axis:

$$M_x = \lim_{n \to \infty} \sum_{i=1}^{n} \rho \cdot \tfrac{1}{2}[f(\overline{x}_i)]^2\,\Delta x = \rho \int_a^b \tfrac{1}{2}[f(x)]^2\,dx$$

Just as for systems of particles, the center of mass of the plate is defined so that $m\overline{x} = M_y$ and $m\overline{y} = M_x$. But the mass of the plate is the product of its density and its area:

$$m = \rho A = \rho \int_a^b f(x)\,dx$$

and so

$$\overline{x} = \frac{M_y}{m} = \frac{\rho \int_a^b x f(x)\,dx}{\rho \int_a^b f(x)\,dx} = \frac{\int_a^b x f(x)\,dx}{\int_a^b f(x)\,dx}$$

$$\overline{y} = \frac{M_x}{m} = \frac{\rho \int_a^b \tfrac{1}{2}[f(x)]^2\,dx}{\rho \int_a^b f(x)\,dx} = \frac{\int_a^b \tfrac{1}{2}[f(x)]^2\,dx}{\int_a^b f(x)\,dx}$$

Notice the cancellation of the ρ's. The location of the center of mass is independent of the density.

In summary, the center of mass of the plate (or the centroid of $\mathcal{R}$) is located at the point $(\overline{x}, \overline{y})$, where

$$\boxed{8} \qquad \overline{x} = \frac{1}{A} \int_a^b x f(x)\,dx \qquad \overline{y} = \frac{1}{A} \int_a^b \tfrac{1}{2}[f(x)]^2\,dx$$

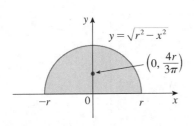

$y = \sqrt{r^2 - x^2}$

$\left(0, \dfrac{4r}{3\pi}\right)$

FIGURE 11

EXAMPLE 4 Find the center of mass of a semicircular plate of radius r.

SOLUTION In order to use $\boxed{8}$ we place the semicircle as in Figure 11 so that $f(x) = \sqrt{r^2 - x^2}$ and $a = -r$, $b = r$. Here there is no need to use the formula to calculate $\overline{x}$ because, by the symmetry principle, the center of mass must lie on the y-axis, so $\bar{x} = 0$. The area of the semicircle is $A = \frac{1}{2}\pi r^2$, so

$$\bar{y} = \frac{1}{A}\int_{-r}^{r}\frac{1}{2}[f(x)]^2\,dx$$

$$= \frac{1}{\frac{1}{2}\pi r^2}\cdot\frac{1}{2}\int_{r}^{r}\left(\sqrt{r^2 - x^2}\right)^2\,dx$$

$$= \frac{2}{\pi r^2}\int_0^r (r^2 - x^2)\,dx = \frac{2}{\pi r^2}\left[r^2 x - \frac{x^3}{3}\right]_0^r$$

$$= \frac{2}{\pi r^2}\frac{2r^3}{3} = \frac{4r}{3\pi}$$

The center of mass is located at the point $(0, 4r/(3\pi))$.

EXAMPLE 5   Find the centroid of the region bounded by the curves $y = \cos x$, $y = 0$, $x = 0$, and $x = \pi/2$.

SOLUTION   The area of the region is

$$A = \int_0^{\pi/2}\cos x\,dx = \sin x\Big]_0^{\pi/2} = 1$$

so Formulas 8 give

$$\bar{x} = \frac{1}{A}\int_0^{\pi/2} xf(x)\,dx = \int_0^{\pi/2} x\cos x\,dx$$

$$= x\sin x\Big]_0^{\pi/2} - \int_0^{\pi/2}\sin x\,dx \qquad \text{(by integration by parts)}$$

$$= \frac{\pi}{2} - 1$$

$$\bar{y} = \frac{1}{A}\int_0^{\pi/2}\frac{1}{2}[f(x)]^2\,dx = \frac{1}{2}\int_0^{\pi/2}\cos^2 x\,dx$$

$$= \frac{1}{4}\int_0^{\pi/2}(1 + \cos 2x)\,dx = \frac{1}{4}\left[x + \frac{1}{2}\sin 2x\right]_0^{\pi/2}$$

$$= \frac{\pi}{8}$$

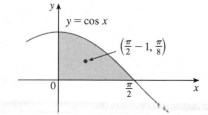

FIGURE 12

The centroid is $\left(\frac{1}{2}\pi - 1, \frac{1}{8}\pi\right)$ and is shown in Figure 12.

If the region $\mathcal{R}$ lies between two curves $y = f(x)$ and $y = g(x)$, where $f(x) \geq g(x)$, as illustrated in Figure 13, then the same sort of argument that led to Formulas 8 can be used to show that the centroid of $\mathcal{R}$ is $(\bar{x}, \bar{y})$, where

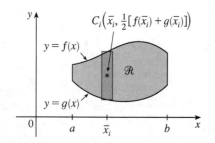

FIGURE 13

9

$$\bar{x} = \frac{1}{A}\int_a^b x[f(x) - g(x)]\,dx$$

$$\bar{y} = \frac{1}{A}\int_a^b \frac{1}{2}\{[f(x)]^2 - [g(x)]^2\}\,dx$$

(See Exercise 47.)

EXAMPLE 6 Find the centroid of the region bounded by the line $y = x$ and the parabola $y = x^2$.

SOLUTION The region is sketched in Figure 14. We take $f(x) = x$, $g(x) = x^2$, $a = 0$, and $b = 1$ in Formulas 9. First we note that the area of the region is

$$A = \int_0^1 (x - x^2)\, dx = \frac{x^2}{2} - \frac{x^3}{3} \bigg]_0^1 = \frac{1}{6}$$

Therefore

$$\bar{x} = \frac{1}{A} \int_0^1 x[f(x) - g(x)]\, dx = \frac{1}{\frac{1}{6}} \int_0^1 x(x - x^2)\, dx$$

$$= 6 \int_0^1 (x^2 - x^3)\, dx = 6 \left[\frac{x^3}{3} - \frac{x^4}{4} \right]_0^1 = \frac{1}{2}$$

$$\bar{y} = \frac{1}{A} \int_0^1 \tfrac{1}{2} \{ [f(x)]^2 - [g(x)]^2 \}\, dx = \frac{1}{\frac{1}{6}} \int_0^1 \tfrac{1}{2}(x^2 - x^4)\, dx$$

$$= 3 \left[\frac{x^3}{3} - \frac{x^5}{5} \right]_0^1 = \frac{2}{5}$$

The centroid is $\left(\frac{1}{2}, \frac{2}{5} \right)$.

We end this section by showing a surprising connection between centroids and volumes of revolution.

FIGURE 14

This theorem is named after the Greek mathematician Pappus of Alexandria, who lived in the fourth century AD.

> **Theorem of Pappus** Let $\mathcal{R}$ be a plane region that lies entirely on one side of a line l in the plane. If $\mathcal{R}$ is rotated about l, then the volume of the resulting solid is the product of the area A of $\mathcal{R}$ and the distance d traveled by the centroid of $\mathcal{R}$.

PROOF We give the proof for the special case in which the region lies between $y = f(x)$ and $y = g(x)$ as in Figure 13 and the line l is the y-axis. Using the method of cylindrical shells (see Section 6.3), we have

$$V = \int_a^b 2\pi x[f(x) - g(x)]\, dx$$

$$= 2\pi \int_a^b x[f(x) - g(x)]\, dx$$

$$= 2\pi(\bar{x}A) \qquad \text{(by Formulas 9)}$$

$$= (2\pi\bar{x})A = Ad$$

where $d = 2\pi\bar{x}$ is the distance traveled by the centroid during one rotation about the y-axis.

V EXAMPLE 7 A torus is formed by rotating a circle of radius r about a line in the plane of the circle that is a distance R $(> r)$ from the center of the circle. Find the volume of the torus.

SOLUTION The circle has area $A = \pi r^2$. By the symmetry principle, its centroid is its center and so the distance traveled by the centroid during a rotation is $d = 2\pi R$. Therefore, by the Theorem of Pappus, the volume of the torus is

$$V = Ad = (2\pi R)(\pi r^2) = 2\pi^2 r^2 R$$

The method of Example 7 should be compared with the method of Exercise 61 in Section 6.2.

8.3 Exercises

1. An aquarium 5 ft long, 2 ft wide, and 3 ft deep is full of water. Find (a) the hydrostatic pressure on the bottom of the aquarium, (b) the hydrostatic force on the bottom, and (c) the hydrostatic force on one end of the aquarium.

2. A tank is 8 m long, 4 m wide, 2 m high, and contains kerosene with density 820 kg/m^3 to a depth of 1.5 m. Find (a) the hydrostatic pressure on the bottom of the tank, (b) the hydrostatic force on the bottom, and (c) the hydrostatic force on one end of the tank.

3–11 A vertical plate is submerged (or partially submerged) in water and has the indicated shape. Explain how to approximate the hydrostatic force against one side of the plate by a Riemann sum. Then express the force as an integral and evaluate it.

3.

4.

5.

6.

7.

8.

9.

10.

11.

12. A milk truck carries milk with density 64.6 lb/ft^3 in a horizontal cylindrical tank with diameter 6 ft.
(a) Find the force exerted by the milk on one end of the tank when the tank is full.
(b) What if the tank is half full?

13. A trough is filled with a liquid of density 840 kg/m^3. The ends of the trough are equilateral triangles with sides 8 m long and vertex at the bottom. Find the hydrostatic force on one end of the trough.

14. A vertical dam has a semicircular gate as shown in the figure. Find the hydrostatic force against the gate.

15. A cube with 20-cm-long sides is sitting on the bottom of an aquarium in which the water is one meter deep. Estimate the hydrostatic force on (a) the top of the cube and (b) one of the sides of the cube.

16. A dam is inclined at an angle of 30° from the vertical and has the shape of an isosceles trapezoid 100 ft wide at the top and 50 ft wide at the bottom and with a slant height of 70 ft. Find the hydrostatic force on the dam when it is full of water.

17. A swimming pool is 10 m wide and 20 m long and its bottom is an inclined plane, the shallow end having a depth of 1 m and the deep end, 3 m. If the pool is full of water, find the hydrostatic force on (a) the shallow end, (b) the deep end, (c) one of the sides, and (d) the bottom of the pool.

18. Suppose that a plate is immersed vertically in a fluid with density ρ and the width of the plate is $w(x)$ at a depth of x meters beneath the surface of the fluid. If the top of the plate is at depth a and the bottom is at depth b, show that the hydrostatic force on one side of the plate is

$$F = \int_a^b \rho g x w(x)\, dx$$

19. A metal plate was found submerged vertically in sea water, which has density 64 lb/ft^3. Measurements of the width of the plate were taken at the indicated depths. Use Simpson's Rule to estimate the force of the water against the plate.

Depth (m)	7.0	7.4	7.8	8.2	8.6	9.0	9.4
Plate width (m)	1.2	1.8	2.9	3.8	3.6	4.2	4.4

20. (a) Use the formula of Exercise 18 to show that

$$F = (\rho g \bar{x}) A$$

where $\bar{x}$ is the x-coordinate of the centroid of the plate and A is its area. This equation shows that the hydrostatic force against a vertical plane region is the same as if the region were horizontal at the depth of the centroid of the region.

(b) Use the result of part (a) to give another solution to Exercise 10.

21–22 Point-masses m_i are located on the x-axis as shown. Find the moment M of the system about the origin and the center of mass $\bar{x}$.

21.
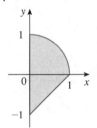

22.

23–24 The masses m_i are located at the points P_i. Find the moments M_x and M_y and the center of mass of the system.

23. $m_1 = 6$, $m_2 = 5$, $m_3 = 10$;
   $P_1(1, 5)$, $P_2(3, -2)$, $P_3(-2, -1)$

24. $m_1 = 6$, $m_2 = 5$, $m_3 = 1$, $m_4 = 4$;
   $P_1(1, -2)$, $P_2(3, 4)$, $P_3(-3, -7)$, $P_4(6, -1)$

25–28 Sketch the region bounded by the curves, and visually estimate the location of the centroid. Then find the exact coordinates of the centroid.

25. $y = 2x$, $y = 0$, $x = 1$

26. $y = \sqrt{x}$, $y = 0$, $x = 4$

27. $y = e^x$, $y = 0$, $x = 0$, $x = 1$

28. $y = \sin x$, $y = 0$, $0 \le x \le \pi$

29–33 Find the centroid of the region bounded by the given curves.

29. $y = x^2$, $x = y^2$

30. $y = 2 - x^2$, $y = x$

31. $y = \sin x$, $y = \cos x$, $x = 0$, $x = \pi/4$

32. $y = x^3$, $x + y = 2$, $y = 0$

33. $x + y = 2$, $x = y^2$

34–35 Calculate the moments M_x and M_y and the center of mass of a lamina with the given density and shape.

34. $\rho = 3$ **35.** $\rho = 10$

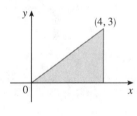

36. Use Simpson's Rule to estimate the centroid of the region shown.

37. Find the centroid of the region bounded by the curves
$y = x^3 - x$ and $y = x^2 - 1$. Sketch the region and plot the
centroid to see if your answer is reasonable.

38. Use a graph to find approximate x-coordinates of the points
of intersection of the curves $y = e^x$ and $y = 2 - x^2$. Then
find (approximately) the centroid of the region bounded by
these curves.

39. Prove that the centroid of any triangle is located at the point
of intersection of the medians. [*Hints:* Place the axes so that
the vertices are $(a, 0)$, $(0, b)$, and $(c, 0)$. Recall that a median
is a line segment from a vertex to the midpoint of the opposite side. Recall also that the medians intersect at a point two-
thirds of the way from each vertex (along the median) to the
opposite side.]

40–41 Find the centroid of the region shown, not by integration,
but by locating the centroids of the rectangles and triangles (from
Exercise 39) and using additivity of moments.

40.

41.

42. A rectangle R with sides a and b is divided into two parts
R_1 and R_2 by an arc of a parabola that has its vertex at one

corner of R and passes through the opposite corner. Find the
centroids of both R_1 and R_2.

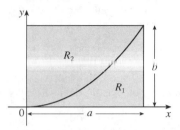

43. If $\bar{x}$ is the x-coordinate of the centroid of the region that lies
under the graph of a continuous function f, where $a \leqslant x \leqslant b$,
show that

$$\int_a^b (cx + d)f(x)\, dx = (c\bar{x} + d)\int_a^b f(x)\, dx$$

44–46 Use the Theorem of Pappus to find the volume of the
given solid.

44. A sphere of radius r (Use Example 4.)

45. A cone with height h and base radius r

46. The solid obtained by rotating the triangle with vertices
$(2, 3)$, $(2, 5)$, and $(5, 4)$ about the x-axis

47. Prove Formulas 9.

48. Let $\mathcal{R}$ be the region that lies between the curves $y = x^m$
and $y = x^n$, $0 \leqslant x \leqslant 1$, where m and n are integers with
$0 \leqslant n < m$.
  (a) Sketch the region $\mathcal{R}$.
  (b) Find the coordinates of the centroid of $\mathcal{R}$.
  (c) Try to find values of m and n such that the centroid lies
      outside $\mathcal{R}$.

DISCOVERY PROJECT   COMPLEMENTARY COFFEE CUPS

Suppose you have a choice of two coffee cups of the type shown, one that bends outward and one
inward, and you notice that they have the same height and their shapes fit together snugly. You
wonder which cup holds more coffee. Of course you could fill one cup with water and pour it
into the other one but, being a calculus student, you decide on a more mathematical approach.
Ignoring the handles, you observe that both cups are surfaces of revolution, so you can think of the
coffee as a volume of revolution.

Cup A   Cup B

1. Suppose the cups have height h, cup A is formed by rotating the curve $x = f(y)$ about the y-axis, and cup B is formed by rotating the same curve about the line $x = k$. Find the value of k such that the two cups hold the same amount of coffee.

2. What does your result from Problem 1 say about the areas A_1 and A_2 shown in the figure?

3. Use Pappus's Theorem to explain your result in Problems 1 and 2.

4. Based on your own measurements and observations, suggest a value for h and an equation for $x = f(y)$ and calculate the amount of coffee that each cup holds.

8.4 Applications to Economics and Biology

In this section we consider some applications of integration to economics (consumer surplus) and biology (blood flow, cardiac output). Others are described in the exercises.

Consumer Surplus

Recall from Section 4.7 that the demand function $p(x)$ is the price that a company has to charge in order to sell x units of a commodity. Usually, selling larger quantities requires lowering prices, so the demand function is a decreasing function. The graph of a typical demand function, called a **demand curve**, is shown in Figure 1. If X is the amount of the commodity that is currently available, then $P = p(X)$ is the current selling price.

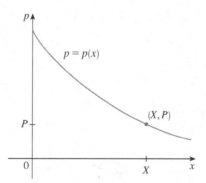

FIGURE 1

A typical demand curve

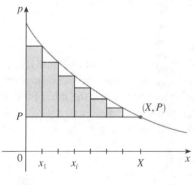

FIGURE 2

We divide the interval $[0, X]$ into n subintervals, each of length $\Delta x = X/n$, and let $x_i^* = x_i$ be the right endpoint of the ith subinterval, as in Figure 2. If, after the first x_{i-1} units were sold, a total of only x_i units had been available and the price per unit had been set at $p(x_i)$ dollars, then the additional Δx units could have been sold (but no more). The consumers who would have paid $p(x_i)$ dollars placed a high value on the product; they would have paid what it was worth to them. So in paying only P dollars they have saved an amount of

$$(\text{savings per unit})(\text{number of units}) = [p(x_i) - P]\,\Delta x$$

Considering similar groups of willing consumers for each of the subintervals and adding the savings, we get the total savings:

$$\sum_{i=1}^{n} [p(x_i) - P]\,\Delta x$$

(This sum corresponds to the area enclosed by the rectangles in Figure 2.) If we let $n \to \infty$,

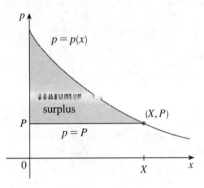

FIGURE 3

this Riemann sum approaches the integral

$$\boxed{1} \qquad \int_0^X [p(x) - P]\, dx$$

which economists call the **consumer surplus** for the commodity.

The consumer surplus represents the amount of money saved by consumers in purchasing the commodity at price P, corresponding to an amount demanded of X. Figure 3 shows the interpretation of the consumer surplus as the area under the demand curve and above the line $p = P$.

V   EXAMPLE 1 The demand for a product, in dollars, is

$$p = 1200 - 0.2x - 0.0001x^2$$

Find the consumer surplus when the sales level is 500.

SOLUTION Since the number of products sold is $X = 500$, the corresponding price is

$$P = 1200 - (0.2)(500) - (0.0001)(500)^2 = 1075$$

Therefore, from Definition 1, the consumer surplus is

$$\int_0^{500} [p(x) - P]\, dx = \int_0^{500} (1200 - 0.2x - 0.0001x^2 - 1075)\, dx$$

$$= \int_0^{500} (125 - 0.2x - 0.0001x^2)\, dx$$

$$= 125x - 0.1x^2 - (0.0001)\left(\frac{x^3}{3}\right) \Bigg]_0^{500}$$

$$= (125)(500) - (0.1)(500)^2 - \frac{(0.0001)(500)^3}{3}$$

$$= \$33{,}333.33$$

Blood Flow

In Example 7 in Section 3.7 we discussed the law of laminar flow:

$$v(r) = \frac{P}{4\eta l}(R^2 - r^2)$$

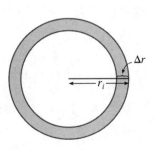

FIGURE 4

which gives the velocity v of blood that flows along a blood vessel with radius R and length l at a distance r from the central axis, where P is the pressure difference between the ends of the vessel and η is the viscosity of the blood. Now, in order to compute the rate of blood flow, or *flux* (volume per unit time), we consider smaller, equally spaced radii $r_1, r_2, \ldots$. The approximate area of the ring (or washer) with inner radius r_{i-1} and outer radius r_i is

$$2\pi r_i\, \Delta r \qquad \text{where} \quad \Delta r = r_i - r_{i-1}$$

(See Figure 4.) If Δr is small, then the velocity is almost constant throughout this ring and can be approximated by $v(r_i)$. Thus the volume of blood per unit time that flows across the ring is approximately

$$(2\pi r_i\, \Delta r)\, v(r_i) = 2\pi r_i\, v(r_i)\, \Delta r$$

and the total volume of blood that flows across a cross-section per unit time is about

$$\sum_{i=1}^{n} 2\pi r_i \, v(r_i) \, \Delta r$$

FIGURE 5

This approximation is illustrated in Figure 5. Notice that the velocity (and hence the volume per unit time) increases toward the center of the blood vessel. The approximation gets better as n increases. When we take the limit we get the exact value of the **flux** (or *discharge*), which is the volume of blood that passes a cross-section per unit time:

$$F = \lim_{n \to \infty} \sum_{i=1}^{n} 2\pi r_i \, v(r_i) \, \Delta r = \int_0^R 2\pi r \, v(r) \, dr$$

$$= \int_0^R 2\pi r \, \frac{P}{4\eta l} \, (R^2 - r^2) \, dr$$

$$= \frac{\pi P}{2\eta l} \int_0^R (R^2 r - r^3) \, dr = \frac{\pi P}{2\eta l} \left[R^2 \frac{r^2}{2} - \frac{r^4}{4} \right]_{r=0}^{r=R}$$

$$= \frac{\pi P}{2\eta l} \left[\frac{R^4}{2} - \frac{R^4}{4} \right] = \frac{\pi P R^4}{8\eta l}$$

The resulting equation

$$\boxed{2} \qquad\qquad F = \frac{\pi P R^4}{8\eta l}$$

is called **Poiseuille's Law**; it shows that the flux is proportional to the fourth power of the radius of the blood vessel.

▮▮ Cardiac Output

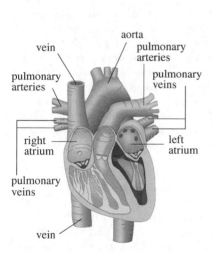

FIGURE 6

Figure 6 shows the human cardiovascular system. Blood returns from the body through the veins, enters the right atrium of the heart, and is pumped to the lungs through the pulmonary arteries for oxygenation. It then flows back into the left atrium through the pulmonary veins and then out to the rest of the body through the aorta. The **cardiac output** of the heart is the volume of blood pumped by the heart per unit time, that is, the rate of flow into the aorta.

The *dye dilution method* is used to measure the cardiac output. Dye is injected into the right atrium and flows through the heart into the aorta. A probe inserted into the aorta measures the concentration of the dye leaving the heart at equally spaced times over a time interval $[0, T]$ until the dye has cleared. Let $c(t)$ be the concentration of the dye at time t. If we divide $[0, T]$ into subintervals of equal length Δt, then the amount of dye that flows past the measuring point during the subinterval from $t = t_{i-1}$ to $t = t_i$ is approximately

$$(\text{concentration})(\text{volume}) = c(t_i)(F \, \Delta t)$$

where F is the rate of flow that we are trying to determine. Thus the total amount of dye is approximately

$$\sum_{i=1}^{n} c(t_i) F \, \Delta t = F \sum_{i=1}^{n} c(t_i) \, \Delta t$$

and, letting $n \to \infty$, we find that the amount of dye is

$$A = F \int_0^T c(t) \, dt$$

Thus the cardiac output is given by

$$\boxed{3} \qquad F = \frac{A}{\displaystyle\int_0^T c(t)\,dt}$$

where the amount of dye A is known and the integral can be approximated from the concentration readings.

t	$c(t)$	t	$c(t)$
0	0	6	6.1
1	0.4	7	4.0
2	2.8	8	2.3
3	6.5	9	1.1
4	9.8	10	0
5	8.9		

▼ **EXAMPLE 2**   A 5-mg bolus of dye is injected into a right atrium. The concentration of the dye (in milligrams per liter) is measured in the aorta at one-second intervals as shown in the chart. Estimate the cardiac output.

SOLUTION   Here $A = 5$, $\Delta t = 1$, and $T = 10$. We use Simpson's Rule to approximate the integral of the concentration:

$$\int_0^{10} c(t)\,dt \approx \tfrac{1}{3}[0 + 4(0.4) + 2(2.8) + 4(6.5) + 2(9.8) + 4(8.9)$$

$$+ 2(6.1) + 4(4.0) + 2(2.3) + 4(1.1) + 0]$$

$$\approx 41.87$$

Thus Formula 3 gives the cardiac output to be

$$F = \frac{A}{\displaystyle\int_0^{10} c(t)\,dt} \approx \frac{5}{41.87} \approx 0.12 \text{ L/s} = 7.2 \text{ L/min}$$

8.4   Exercises

1. The marginal cost function $C'(x)$ was defined to be the derivative of the cost function. (See Sections 3.7 and 4.7.) If the marginal cost of maufacturing x meters of a fabric is $C'(x) = 5 - 0.008x + 0.000009x^2$ (measured in dollars per meter) and the fixed start-up cost is $C(0) = \$20,000$, use the Net Change Theorem to find the cost of producing the first 2000 units.

2. A company estimates that the marginal revenue (in dollars per unit) realized by selling x units of a product is $48 - 0.0012x$. Assuming the estimate is accurate, find the increase in revenue if sales increase from 5000 units to 10,000 units.

3. A mining company estimates that the marginal cost of extracting x tons of copper ore from a mine is $0.6 + 0.008x$, measured in thousands of dollars per ton. Start-up costs are $\$100,000$. What is the cost of extracting the first 50 tons of copper? What about the next 50 tons?

4. The demand function for a certain commodity is $p = 20 - 0.05x$. Find the consumer surplus when the sales level is 300. Illustrate by drawing the demand curve and identifying the consumer surplus as an area.

5. A demand curve is given by $p = 450/(x + 8)$. Find the consumer surplus when the selling price is $\$10$.

6. The **supply function** $p_S(x)$ for a commodity gives the relation between the selling price and the number of units that manufacturers will produce at that price. For a higher price, manufacturers will produce more units, so p_S is an increasing function of x. Let X be the amount of the commodity currently produced and let $P = p_S(X)$ be the current price. Some producers would be willing to make and sell the commodity for a lower selling price and are therefore receiving more than their minimal price. The excess is called the **producer surplus**. An argument similar to that for consumer surplus shows that the surplus is given by the integral

$$\int_0^X [P - p_S(x)]\,dx$$

Calculate the producer surplus for the supply function $p_S(x) = 3 + 0.01x^2$ at the sales level $X = 10$. Illustrate by drawing the supply curve and identifying the producer surplus as an area.

7. If a supply curve is modeled by the equation $p = 200 + 0.2x^{3/2}$, find the producer surplus when the selling price is $\$400$.

8. For a given commodity and pure competition, the number of units produced and the price per unit are determined as the coordinates of the point of intersection of the supply and

demand curves. Given the demand curve $p = 50 - \frac{1}{20}x$ and the supply curve $p = 20 + \frac{1}{10}x$, find the consumer surplus and the producer surplus. Illustrate by sketching the supply and demand curves and identifying the surpluses as areas.

 9. A company modeled the demand curve for its product (in dollars) by the equation

$$p = \frac{800{,}000e^{-x/5000}}{x + 20{,}000}$$

Use a graph to estimate the sales level when the selling price is \$16. Then find (approximately) the consumer surplus for this sales level.

10. A movie theater has been charging \$10.00 per person and selling about 500 tickets on a typical weeknight. After surveying their customers, the theater management estimates that for every 50 cents that they lower the price, the number of moviegoers will increase by 50 per night. Find the demand function and calculate the consumer surplus when the tickets are priced at \$8.00.

11. If the amount of capital that a company has at time t is $f(t)$, then the derivative, $f'(t)$, is called the *net investment flow*. Suppose that the net investment flow is $\sqrt{t}$ million dollars per year (where t is measured in years). Find the increase in capital (the *capital formation*) from the fourth year to the eighth year.

12. If revenue flows into a company at a rate of $f(t) = 9000\sqrt{1 + 2t}$, where t is measured in years and $f(t)$ is measured in dollars per year, find the total revenue obtained in the first four years.

13. *Pareto's Law of Income* states that the number of people with incomes between $x = a$ and $x = b$ is $N = \int_a^b Ax^{-k}\, dx$, where A and k are constants with $A > 0$ and $k > 1$. The average income of these people is

$$\bar{x} = \frac{1}{N}\int_a^b Ax^{1-k}\, dx$$

Calculate $\bar{x}$.

14. A hot, wet summer is causing a mosquito population explosion in a lake resort area. The number of mosquitos is increasing at an estimated rate of $2200 + 10e^{0.8t}$ per week (where t is measured in weeks). By how much does the mosquito population increase between the fifth and ninth weeks of summer?

15. Use Poiseuille's Law to calculate the rate of flow in a small human artery where we can take $\eta = 0.027$, $R = 0.008$ cm, $l = 2$ cm, and $P = 4000$ dynes/cm^2.

16. High blood pressure results from constriction of the arteries. To maintain a normal flow rate (flux), the heart has to pump harder, thus increasing the blood pressure. Use Poiseuille's Law to show that if R_0 and P_0 are normal values of the radius and pressure in an artery and the constricted values are R and P, then for the flux to remain constant, P and R are related by the equation

$$\frac{P}{P_0} = \left(\frac{R_0}{R}\right)^4$$

Deduce that if the radius of an artery is reduced to three-fourths of its former value, then the pressure is more than tripled.

17. The dye dilution method is used to measure cardiac output with 6 mg of dye. The dye concentrations, in mg/L, are modeled by $c(t) = 20te^{-0.6t}$, $0 \le t \le 10$, where t is measured in seconds. Find the cardiac output.

18. After a 5.5-mg injection of dye, the readings of dye concentration, in mg/L, at two-second intervals are as shown in the table. Use Simpson's Rule to estimate the cardiac output.

t	$c(t)$	t	$c(t)$
0	0.0	10	4.3
2	4.1	12	2.5
4	8.9	14	1.2
6	8.5	16	0.2
8	6.7		

19. The graph of the concentration function $c(t)$ is shown after a 7-mg injection of dye into a heart. Use Simpson's Rule to estimate the cardiac output.

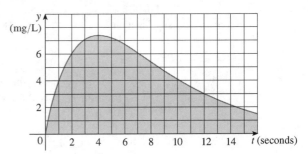

8.5 | Probability

Calculus plays a role in the analysis of random behavior. Suppose we consider the cholesterol level of a person chosen at random from a certain age group, or the height of an adult female chosen at random, or the lifetime of a randomly chosen battery of a certain type. Such quantities are called **continuous random variables** because their values actually range over an interval of real numbers, although they might be measured or recorded only to the nearest integer. We might want to know the probability that a blood cholesterol level is greater than 250, or the probability that the height of an adult female is between 60 and 70 inches, or the probability that the battery we are buying lasts between 100 and 200 hours. If X represents the lifetime of that type of battery, we denote this last probability as follows:

$$P(100 \leq X \leq 200)$$

According to the frequency interpretation of probability, this number is the long-run proportion of all batteries of the specified type whose lifetimes are between 100 and 200 hours. Since it represents a proportion, the probability naturally falls between 0 and 1.

Every continuous random variable X has a **probability density function** f. This means that the probability that X lies between a and b is found by integrating f from a to b:

$$\boxed{1} \qquad\qquad P(a \leq X \leq b) = \int_a^b f(x)\, dx$$

For example, Figure 1 shows the graph of a model for the probability density function f for a random variable X defined to be the height in inches of an adult female in the United States (according to data from the National Health Survey). The probability that the height of a woman chosen at random from this population is between 60 and 70 inches is equal to the area under the graph of f from 60 to 70.

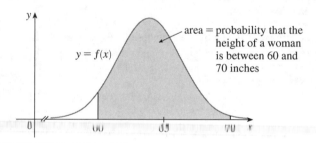

FIGURE 1
Probability density function
for the height of an adult female

In general, the probability density function f of a random variable X satisfies the condition $f(x) \geq 0$ for all x. Because probabilities are measured on a scale from 0 to 1, it follows that

$$\boxed{2} \qquad\qquad \int_{-\infty}^{\infty} f(x)\, dx = 1$$

EXAMPLE 1   Let $f(x) = 0.006x(10 - x)$ for $0 \leq x \leq 10$ and $f(x) = 0$ for all other values of x.
(a) Verify that f is a probability density function.
(b) Find $P(4 \leq X \leq 8)$.

SOLUTION

(a) For $0 \leqslant x \leqslant 10$ we have $0.006x(10 - x) \geqslant 0$, so $f(x) \geqslant 0$ for all x. We also need to check that Equation 2 is satisfied:

$$\int_{-\infty}^{\infty} f(x) \, dx = \int_0^{10} 0.006x(10 - x) \, dx = 0.006 \int_0^{10} (10x - x^2) \, dx$$

$$= 0.006 \left[5x^2 - \tfrac{1}{3}x^3 \right]_0^{10} = 0.006(500 - \tfrac{1000}{3}) = 1$$

Therefore f is a probability density function.

(b) The probability that X lies between 4 and 8 is

$$P(4 \leqslant X \leqslant 8) = \int_4^8 f(x) \, dx = 0.006 \int_4^8 (10x - x^2) \, dx$$

$$= 0.006 \left[5x^2 - \tfrac{1}{3}x^3 \right]_4^8 = 0.544$$

V **EXAMPLE 2** Phenomena such as waiting times and equipment failure times are commonly modeled by exponentially decreasing probability density functions. Find the exact form of such a function.

SOLUTION Think of the random variable as being the time you wait on hold before an agent of a company you're telephoning answers your call. So instead of x, let's use t to represent time, in minutes. If f is the probability density function and you call at time $t = 0$, then, from Definition 1, $\int_0^2 f(t) \, dt$ represents the probability that an agent answers within the first two minutes and $\int_4^5 f(t) \, dt$ is the probability that your call is answered during the fifth minute.

It's clear that $f(t) = 0$ for $t < 0$ (the agent can't answer before you place the call). For $t > 0$ we are told to use an exponentially decreasing function, that is, a function of the form $f(t) = Ae^{-ct}$, where A and c are positive constants. Thus

$$f(t) = \begin{cases} 0 & \text{if } t < 0 \\ Ae^{-ct} & \text{if } t \geqslant 0 \end{cases}$$

We use Equation 2 to determine the value of A:

$$1 = \int_{-\infty}^{\infty} f(t) \, dt = \int_{-\infty}^0 f(t) \, dt + \int_0^{\infty} f(t) \, dt$$

$$= \int_0^{\infty} Ae^{-ct} \, dt = \lim_{x \to \infty} \int_0^x Ae^{-ct} \, dt$$

$$= \lim_{x \to \infty} \left[-\frac{A}{c} e^{-ct} \right]_0^x = \lim_{x \to \infty} \frac{A}{c} (1 - e^{-cx})$$

$$= \frac{A}{c}$$

Therefore $A/c = 1$ and so $A = c$. Thus every exponential density function has the form

$$f(t) = \begin{cases} 0 & \text{if } t < 0 \\ ce^{-ct} & \text{if } t \geqslant 0 \end{cases}$$

A typical graph is shown in Figure 2.

$$f(t) = \begin{cases} 0 & \text{if } t < 0 \\ ce^{-ct} & \text{if } t \geqslant 0 \end{cases}$$

FIGURE 2
An exponential density function

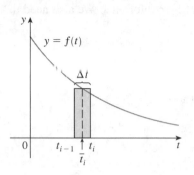

FIGURE 3

Average Values

Suppose you're waiting for a company to answer your phone call and you wonder how long, on average, you can expect to wait. Let $f(t)$ be the corresponding density function, where t is measured in minutes, and think of a sample of N people who have called this company. Most likely, none of them had to wait more than an hour, so let's restrict our attention to the interval $0 \leq t \leq 60$. Let's divide that interval into n intervals of length Δt and endpoints $0, t_1, t_2, \ldots, t_n = 60$. (Think of Δt as lasting a minute, or half a minute, or 10 seconds, or even a second.) The probability that somebody's call gets answered during the time period from t_{i-1} to t_i is the area under the curve $y = f(t)$ from t_{i-1} to t_i, which is approximately equal to $f(\bar{t}_i)\,\Delta t$. (This is the area of the approximating rectangle in Figure 3, where $\bar{t}_i$ is the midpoint of the interval.)

Since the long-run proportion of calls that get answered in the time period from t_{i-1} to t_i is $f(\bar{t}_i)\,\Delta t$, we expect that, out of our sample of N callers, the number whose call was answered in that time period is approximately $Nf(\bar{t}_i)\,\Delta t$ and the time that each waited is about $\bar{t}_i$. Therefore the total time they waited is the product of these numbers: approximately $\bar{t}_i[Nf(\bar{t}_i)\,\Delta t]$. Adding over all such intervals, we get the approximate total of everybody's waiting times:

$$\sum_{i=1}^{n} N\bar{t}_i\, f(\bar{t}_i)\, \Delta t$$

If we now divide by the number of callers N, we get the approximate *average* waiting time:

$$\sum_{i=1}^{n} \bar{t}_i\, f(\bar{t}_i)\, \Delta t$$

We recognize this as a Riemann sum for the function $t\,f(t)$. As the time interval shrinks (that is, $\Delta t \to 0$ and $n \to \infty$), this Riemann sum approaches the integral

$$\int_0^{60} t\,f(t)\, dt$$

This integral is called the *mean waiting time*.

In general, the **mean** of any probability density function f is defined to be

It is traditional to denote the mean by the Greek letter μ (mu).

$$\mu = \int_{-\infty}^{\infty} x\, f(x)\, dx$$

The mean can be interpreted as the long-run average value of the random variable X. It can also be interpreted as a measure of centrality of the probability density function.

The expression for the mean resembles an integral we have seen before. If $\mathcal{R}$ is the region that lies under the graph of f, we know from Formula 8.3.8 that the x-coordinate of the centroid of $\mathcal{R}$ is

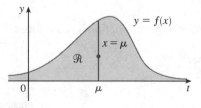

FIGURE 4
$\mathcal{R}$ balances at a point on the line $x = \mu$

$$\bar{x} = \frac{\displaystyle\int_{-\infty}^{\infty} x\, f(x)\, dx}{\displaystyle\int_{-\infty}^{\infty} f(x)\, dx} = \int_{-\infty}^{\infty} x\, f(x)\, dx = \mu$$

because of Equation 2. So a thin plate in the shape of $\mathcal{R}$ balances at a point on the vertical line $x = \mu$. (See Figure 4.)

EXAMPLE 3 Find the mean of the exponential distribution of Example 2:

$$f(t) = \begin{cases} 0 & \text{if } t < 0 \\ ce^{-ct} & \text{if } t \geqslant 0 \end{cases}$$

SOLUTION According to the definition of a mean, we have

$$\mu = \int_{-\infty}^{\infty} tf(t)\, dt = \int_{0}^{\infty} tce^{-ct}\, dt$$

To evaluate this integral we use integration by parts, with $u = t$ and $dv = ce^{-ct}\, dt$:

$$\int_{0}^{\infty} tce^{-ct}\, dt = \lim_{x \to \infty} \int_{0}^{x} tce^{-ct}\, dt = \lim_{x \to \infty} \left(-te^{-ct} \Big]_{0}^{x} + \int_{0}^{x} e^{-ct}\, dt \right)$$

The limit of the first term is 0 by l'Hospital's Rule.

$$= \lim_{x \to \infty} \left(-xe^{-cx} + \frac{1}{c} - \frac{e^{-cx}}{c} \right) = \frac{1}{c}$$

The mean is $\mu = 1/c$, so we can rewrite the probability density function as

$$f(t) = \begin{cases} 0 & \text{if } t < 0 \\ \mu^{-1}e^{-t/\mu} & \text{if } t \geqslant 0 \end{cases}$$

V **EXAMPLE 4** Suppose the average waiting time for a customer's call to be answered by a company representative is five minutes.
(a) Find the probability that a call is answered during the first minute.
(b) Find the probability that a customer waits more than five minutes to be answered.

SOLUTION
(a) We are given that the mean of the exponential distribution is $\mu = 5$ min and so, from the result of Example 3, we know that the probability density function is

$$f(t) = \begin{cases} 0 & \text{if } t < 0 \\ 0.2e^{-t/5} & \text{if } t \geqslant 0 \end{cases}$$

Thus the probability that a call is answered during the first minute is

$$P(0 \leqslant T \leqslant 1) = \int_{0}^{1} f(t)\, dt$$

$$= \int_{0}^{1} 0.2e^{-t/5}\, dt = 0.2(-5)e^{-t/5} \Big]_{0}^{1}$$

$$= 1 - e^{-1/5} \approx 0.1813$$

So about 18% of customers' calls are answered during the first minute.

(b) The probability that a customer waits more than five minutes is

$$P(T > 5) = \int_{5}^{\infty} f(t)\, dt = \int_{5}^{\infty} 0.2e^{-t/5}\, dt$$

$$= \lim_{x \to \infty} \int_{5}^{x} 0.2e^{-t/5}\, dt = \lim_{x \to \infty} (e^{-1} - e^{-x/5})$$

$$= \frac{1}{e} \approx 0.368$$

About 37% of customers wait more than five minutes before their calls are answered.

Notice the result of Example 4(b): Even though the mean waiting time is 5 minutes, only 37% of callers wait more than 5 minutes. The reason is that some callers have to wait much longer (maybe 10 or 15 minutes), and this brings up the average.

Another measure of centrality of a probability density function is the *median*. That is a number m such that half the callers have a waiting time less than m and the other callers have a waiting time longer than m. In general, the *median* of a probability density function is the number m such that

$$\int_m^\infty f(x)\, dx = \tfrac{1}{2}$$

This means that half the area under the graph of f lies to the right of m. In Exercise 9 you are asked to show that the median waiting time for the company described in Example 4 is approximately 3.5 minutes.

▮ Normal Distributions

Many important random phenomena—such as test scores on aptitude tests, heights and weights of individuals from a homogeneous population, annual rainfall in a given location—are modeled by a **normal distribution**. This means that the probability density function of the random variable X is a member of the family of functions

3         $f(x) = \dfrac{1}{\sigma\sqrt{2\pi}}\, e^{-(x-\mu)^2/(2\sigma^2)}$

The standard deviation is denoted by the lowercase Greek letter σ (sigma).

You can verify that the mean for this function is μ. The positive constant σ is called the **standard deviation**; it measures how spread out the values of X are. From the bell-shaped graphs of members of the family in Figure 5, we see that for small values of σ the values of X are clustered about the mean, whereas for larger values of σ the values of X are more spread out. Statisticians have methods for using sets of data to estimate μ and σ.

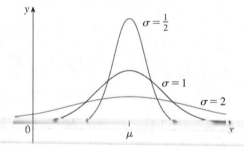

FIGURE 5
Normal distributions

The factor $1/(\sigma\sqrt{2\pi})$ is needed to make f a probability density function. In fact, it can be verified using the methods of multivariable calculus that

$$\int_{-\infty}^{\infty} \frac{1}{\sigma\sqrt{2\pi}}\, e^{-(x-\mu)^2/(2\sigma^2)}\, dx = 1$$

FIGURE 6
Distribution of IQ scores

V EXAMPLE 5 Intelligence Quotient (IQ) scores are distributed normally with mean 100 and standard deviation 15. (Figure 6 shows the corresponding probability density function.)
(a) What percentage of the population has an IQ score between 85 and 115?
(b) What percentage of the population has an IQ above 140?

SOLUTION

(a) Since IQ scores are normally distributed, we use the probability density function given by Equation 3 with $\mu = 100$ and $\sigma = 15$:

$$P(85 \le X \le 115) = \int_{85}^{115} \frac{1}{15\sqrt{2\pi}} e^{-(x-100)^2/(2 \cdot 15^2)} dx$$

Recall from Section 7.5 that the function $y = e^{-x^2}$ doesn't have an elementary antiderivative, so we can't evaluate the integral exactly. But we can use the numerical integration capability of a calculator or computer (or the Midpoint Rule or Simpson's Rule) to estimate the integral. Doing so, we find that

$$P(85 \le X \le 115) \approx 0.68$$

So about 68% of the population has an IQ between 85 and 115, that is, within one standard deviation of the mean.

(b) The probability that the IQ score of a person chosen at random is more than 140 is

$$P(X > 140) = \int_{140}^{\infty} \frac{1}{15\sqrt{2\pi}} e^{-(x-100)^2/450} dx$$

To avoid the improper integral we could approximate it by the integral from 140 to 200. (It's quite safe to say that people with an IQ over 200 are extremely rare.) Then

$$P(X > 140) \approx \int_{140}^{200} \frac{1}{15\sqrt{2\pi}} e^{-(x-100)^2/450} dx \approx 0.0038$$

Therefore about 0.4% of the population has an IQ over 140.

8.5 Exercises

1. Let $f(x)$ be the probability density function for the lifetime of a manufacturer's highest quality car tire, where x is measured in miles. Explain the meaning of each integral.

(a) $\int_{30,000}^{40,000} f(x) \, dx$ (b) $\int_{25,000}^{\infty} f(x) \, dx$

2. Let $f(t)$ be the probability density function for the time it takes you to drive to school in the morning, where t is measured in minutes. Express the following probabilities as integrals.
(a) The probability that you drive to school in less than 15 minutes
(b) The probability that it takes you more than half an hour to get to school

3. Let $f(x) = 30x^2(1-x)^2$ for $0 \le x \le 1$ and $f(x) = 0$ for all other values of x.
(a) Verify that f is a probability density function.
(b) Find $P(X \le \frac{1}{3})$.

4. Let $f(x) = xe^{-x}$ if $x \ge 0$ and $f(x) = 0$ if $x < 0$.
(a) Verify that f is a probability density function.
(b) Find $P(1 \le X \le 2)$.

5. Let $f(x) = c/(1 + x^2)$.
(a) For what value of c is f a probability density function?
(b) For that value of c, find $P(-1 < X < 1)$.

6. Let $f(x) = k(3x - x^2)$ if $0 \le x \le 3$ and $f(x) = 0$ if $x < 0$ or $x > 3$.
(a) For what value of k is f a probability density function?
(b) For that value of k, find $P(X > 1)$.
(c) Find the mean.

7. A spinner from a board game randomly indicates a real number between 0 and 10. The spinner is fair in the sense that it indicates a number in a given interval with the same probability as it indicates a number in any other interval of the same length.
(a) Explain why the function

$$f(x) = \begin{cases} 0.1 & \text{if } 0 \le x \le 10 \\ 0 & \text{if } x < 0 \text{ or } x > 10 \end{cases}$$

is a probability density function for the spinner's values.
(b) What does your intuition tell you about the value of the mean? Check your guess by evaluating an integral.

⚏ Graphing calculator or computer required   **1.** Homework Hints available at stewartcalculus.com

8. (a) Explain why the function whose graph is shown is a probability density function.
   (b) Use the graph to find the following probabilities:
      (i) $P(X < 3)$ (ii) $P(3 \le X \le 8)$
   (c) Calculate the mean.

9. Show that the median waiting time for a phone call to the company described in Example 4 is about 3.5 minutes.

10. (a) A type of lightbulb is labeled as having an average lifetime of 1000 hours. It's reasonable to model the probability of failure of these bulbs by an exponential density function with mean $\mu = 1000$. Use this model to find the probability that a bulb
      (i) fails within the first 200 hours,
      (ii) burns for more than 800 hours.
   (b) What is the median lifetime of these lightbulbs?

11. The manager of a fast-food restaurant determines that the average time that her customers wait for service is 2.5 minutes.
   (a) Find the probability that a customer has to wait more than 4 minutes.
   (b) Find the probability that a customer is served within the first 2 minutes.
   (c) The manager wants to advertise that anybody who isn't served within a certain number of minutes gets a free hamburger. But she doesn't want to give away free hamburgers to more than 2% of her customers. What should the advertisement say?

12. According to the National Health Survey, the heights of adult males in the United States are normally distributed with mean 69.0 inches and standard deviation 2.8 inches.
   (a) What is the probability that an adult male chosen at random is between 65 inches and 73 inches tall?
   (b) What percentage of the adult male population is more than 6 feet tall?

13. The "Garbage Project" at the University of Arizona reports that the amount of paper discarded by households per week is normally distributed with mean 4.3 kg and standard deviation 1.9 kg. What percentage of households throw out at least 5 kg of paper a week?

14. Boxes are labeled as containing 500 g of cereal. The machine filling the boxes produces weights that are normally distributed with standard deviation 12 g.
   (a) If the target weight is 500 g, what is the probability that the machine produces a box with less than 480 g of cereal?
   (b) Suppose a law states that no more than 5% of a manufacturer's cereal boxes can contain less than the stated weight

of 500 g. At what target weight should the manufacturer set its filling machine?

15. The speeds of vehicles on a highway with speed limit 100 km/h are normally distributed with mean 112 km/h and standard deviation 8 km/h.
   (a) What is the probability that a randomly chosen vehicle is traveling at a legal speed?
   (b) If police are instructed to ticket motorists driving 125 km/h or more, what percentage of motorists are targeted?

16. Show that the probability density function for a normally distributed random variable has inflection points at $x = \mu \pm \sigma$.

17. For any normal distribution, find the probability that the random variable lies within two standard deviations of the mean.

18. The standard deviation for a random variable with probability density function f and mean μ is defined by

$$\sigma = \left[\int_{-\infty}^{\infty} (x - \mu)^2 f(x)\, dx \right]^{1/2}$$

Find the standard deviation for an exponential density function with mean μ.

19. The hydrogen atom is composed of one proton in the nucleus and one electron, which moves about the nucleus. In the quantum theory of atomic structure, it is assumed that the electron does not move in a well-defined orbit. Instead, it occupies a state known as an *orbital,* which may be thought of as a "cloud" of negative charge surrounding the nucleus. At the state of lowest energy, called the *ground state,* or *1s-orbital,* the shape of this cloud is assumed to be a sphere centered at the nucleus. This sphere is described in terms of the probability density function

$$p(r) = \frac{4}{a_0^3}\, r^2 e^{-2r/a_0} \qquad r \ge 0$$

where a_0 is the Bohr radius ($a_0 \approx 5.59 \times 10^{-11}$ m). The integral

$$P(r) = \int_0^r \frac{4}{a_0^3}\, s^2 e^{-2s/a_0}\, ds$$

gives the probability that the electron will be found within the sphere of radius r meters centered at the nucleus.
   (a) Verify that $p(r)$ is a probability density function.
   (b) Find $\lim_{r \to \infty} p(r)$. For what value of r does $p(r)$ have its maximum value?
   (c) Graph the density function.
   (d) Find the probability that the electron will be within the sphere of radius $4a_0$ centered at the nucleus.
   (e) Calculate the mean distance of the electron from the nucleus in the ground state of the hydrogen atom.

8 Review

Concept Check

1. (a) How is the length of a curve defined?
   (b) Write an expression for the length of a smooth curve given by $y = f(x)$, $a \leq x \leq b$.
   (c) What if x is given as a function of y?

2. (a) Write an expression for the surface area of the surface obtained by rotating the curve $y = f(x)$, $a \leq x \leq b$, about the x-axis.
   (b) What if x is given as a function of y?
   (c) What if the curve is rotated about the y-axis?

3. Describe how we can find the hydrostatic force against a vertical wall submersed in a fluid.

4. (a) What is the physical significance of the center of mass of a thin plate?
   (b) If the plate lies between $y = f(x)$ and $y = 0$, where $a \leq x \leq b$, write expressions for the coordinates of the center of mass.

5. What does the Theorem of Pappus say?

6. Given a demand function $p(x)$, explain what is meant by the consumer surplus when the amount of a commodity currently available is X and the current selling price is P. Illustrate with a sketch.

7. (a) What is the cardiac output of the heart?
   (b) Explain how the cardiac output can be measured by the dye dilution method.

8. What is a probability density function? What properties does such a function have?

9. Suppose $f(x)$ is the probability density function for the weight of a female college student, where x is measured in kilograms.
   (a) What is the meaning of the integral $\int_0^{60} f(x)\, dx$?
   (b) Write an expression for the mean of this density function.
   (c) How can we find the median of this density function?

10. What is a normal distribution? What is the significance of the standard deviation?

Exercises

1–2 Find the length of the curve.

1. $y = \frac{1}{6}(x^2 + 4)^{3/2}$, $0 \leq x \leq 3$

2. $y = 2 \ln\left(\sin \frac{1}{2}x\right)$, $\pi/3 \leq x \leq \pi$

3. (a) Find the length of the curve
$$y = \frac{x^4}{16} + \frac{1}{2x^2} \qquad 1 \leq x \leq 2$$
   (b) Find the area of the surface obtained by rotating the curve in part (a) about the y-axis.

4. (a) The curve $y = x^2$, $0 \leq x \leq 1$, is rotated about the y-axis. Find the area of the resulting surface.
   (b) Find the area of the surface obtained by rotating the curve in part (a) about the x-axis.

5. Use Simpson's Rule with $n = 10$ to estimate the length of the sine curve $y = \sin x$, $0 \leq x \leq \pi$.

6. Use Simpson's Rule with $n = 10$ to estimate the area of the surface obtained by rotating the sine curve in Exercise 5 about the x-axis.

7. Find the length of the curve
$$y = \int_1^x \sqrt{\sqrt{t} - 1}\; dt \qquad 1 \leq x \leq 16$$

8. Find the area of the surface obtained by rotating the curve in Exercise 7 about the y-axis.

9. A gate in an irrigation canal is constructed in the form of a trapezoid 1 m wide at the bottom, 2 m wide at the top, and 1 m high. It is placed vertically in the canal, with the water extending to its top. Find the hydrostatic force on one side of the gate.

10. A trough is filled with water and its vertical ends have the shape of the parabolic region in the figure. Find the hydrostatic force on one end of the trough.

11–12 Find the centroid of the region bounded by the given curves.

11. $y = \frac{1}{2}x$, $y = \sqrt{x}$

12. $y = \sin x$, $y = 0$, $x = \pi/4$, $x = 3\pi/4$

13–14 Find the centroid of the region shown

13.

14.

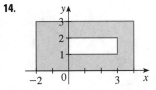

15. Find the volume obtained when the circle of radius 1 with center $(1, 0)$ is rotated about the y-axis.

16. Use the Theorem of Pappus and the fact that the volume of a sphere of radius r is $\frac{4}{3}\pi r^3$ to find the centroid of the semicircular region bounded by the curve $y = \sqrt{r^2 - x^2}$ and the x-axis.

17. The demand function for a commodity is given by

$$p = 2000 - 0.1x - 0.01x^2$$

Find the consumer surplus when the sales level is 100.

18. After a 6-mg injection of dye into a heart, the readings of dye concentration at two-second intervals are as shown in the table. Use Simpson's Rule to estimate the cardiac output.

t	$c(t)$	t	$c(t)$
0	0	14	4.7
2	1.9	16	3.3
4	3.3	18	2.1
6	5.1	20	1.1
8	7.6	22	0.5
10	7.1	24	0
12	5.8		

19. (a) Explain why the function

$$f(x) = \begin{cases} \dfrac{\pi}{20}\sin\left(\dfrac{\pi x}{10}\right) & \text{if } 0 \leqslant x \leqslant 10 \\ 0 & \text{if } x < 0 \text{ or } x > 10 \end{cases}$$

   is a probability density function.
   (b) Find $P(X < 4)$.
   (c) Calculate the mean. Is the value what you would expect?

20. Lengths of human pregnancies are normally distributed with mean 268 days and standard deviation 15 days. What percentage of pregnancies last between 250 days and 280 days?

21. The length of time spent waiting in line at a certain bank is modeled by an exponential density function with mean 8 minutes.
   (a) What is the probability that a customer is served in the first 3 minutes?
   (b) What is the probability that a customer has to wait more than 10 minutes?
   (c) What is the median waiting time?

1. Find the area of the region $S = \{(x, y) \mid x \geq 0, \ y \leq 1, \ x^2 + y^2 \leq 4y\}$.

2. Find the centroid of the region enclosed by the loop of the curve $y^2 = x^3 - x^4$.

3. If a sphere of radius r is sliced by a plane whose distance from the center of the sphere is d, then the sphere is divided into two pieces called *segments of one base*. The corresponding surfaces are called *spherical zones of one base*.
   (a) Determine the surface areas of the two spherical zones indicated in the figure.
   (b) Determine the approximate area of the Arctic Ocean by assuming that it is approximately circular in shape, with center at the North Pole and "circumference" at 75° north latitude. Use $r = 6370$ km for the radius of the earth.
   (c) A sphere of radius r is inscribed in a right circular cylinder of radius r. Two planes perpendicular to the central axis of the cylinder and a distance h apart cut off a *spherical zone of two bases* on the sphere. Show that the surface area of the spherical zone equals the surface area of the region that the two planes cut off on the cylinder.
   (d) The *Torrid Zone* is the region on the surface of the earth that is between the Tropic of Cancer (23.45° north latitude) and the Tropic of Capricorn (23.45° south latitude). What is the area of the Torrid Zone?

4. (a) Show that an observer at height H above the north pole of a sphere of radius r can see a part of the sphere that has area

$$\frac{2\pi r^2 H}{r + H}$$

   (b) Two spheres with radii r and R are placed so that the distance between their centers is d, where $d > r + R$. Where should a light be placed on the line joining the centers of the spheres in order to illuminate the largest total surface?

5. Suppose that the density of seawater, $\rho = \rho(z)$, varies with the depth z below the surface.
   (a) Show that the hydrostatic pressure is governed by the differential equation

$$\frac{dP}{dz} = \rho(z)g$$

   where g is the acceleration due to gravity. Let P_0 and ρ_0 be the pressure and density at $z = 0$. Express the pressure at depth z as an integral.
   (b) Suppose the density of seawater at depth z is given by $\rho = \rho_0 e^{z/H}$, where H is a positive constant. Find the total force, expressed as an integral, exerted on a vertical circular porthole of radius r whose center is located at a distance $L > r$ below the surface.

6. The figure shows a semicircle with radius 1, horizontal diameter PQ, and tangent lines at P and Q. At what height above the diameter should the horizontal line be placed so as to minimize the shaded area?

7. Let P be a pyramid with a square base of side $2b$ and suppose that S is a sphere with its center on the base of P and S is tangent to all eight edges of P. Find the height of P. Then find the volume of the intersection of S and P.

P Q

FIGURE FOR PROBLEM 6

8. Consider a flat metal plate to be placed vertically under water with its top 2 m below the surface of the water. Determine a shape for the plate so that if the plate is divided into any number of horizontal strips of equal height, the hydrostatic force on each strip is the same.

9. A uniform disk with radius 1 m is to be cut by a line so that the center of mass of the smaller piece lies halfway along a radius. How close to the center of the disk should the cut be made? (Express your answer correct to two decimal places.)

10. A triangle with area 30 cm^2 is cut from a corner of a square with side 10 cm, as shown in the figure. If the centroid of the remaining region is 4 cm from the right side of the square, how far is it from the bottom of the square?

10 cm

11. In a famous 18th-century problem, known as *Buffon's needle problem*, a needle of length h is dropped onto a flat surface (for example, a table) on which parallel lines L units apart, $L \geq h$, have been drawn. The problem is to determine the probability that the needle will come to rest intersecting one of the lines. Assume that the lines run east-west, parallel to the x-axis in a rectangular coordinate system (as in the figure). Let y be the distance from the "southern" end of the needle to the nearest line to the north. (If the needle's southern end lies on a line, let $y = 0$. If the needle happens to lie east-west, let the "western" end be the "southern" end.) Let θ be the angle that the needle makes with a ray extending eastward from the "southern" end. Then $0 \leq y \leq L$ and $0 \leq \theta \leq \pi$. Note that the needle intersects one of the lines only when $y < h \sin \theta$. The total set of possibilities for the needle can be identified with the rectangular region $0 \leq y \leq L$, $0 \leq \theta \leq \pi$, and the proportion of times that the needle intersects a line is the ratio

$$\frac{\text{area under } y = h \sin \theta}{\text{area of rectangle}}$$

This ratio is the probability that the needle intersects a line. Find the probability that the needle will intersect a line if $h = L$. What if $h = \frac{1}{2}L$?

12. If the needle in Problem 11 has length $h > L$, it's possible for the needle to intersect more than one line.
    (a) If $L = 4$, find the probability that a needle of length 7 will intersect at least one line. [*Hint:* Proceed as in Problem 11. Define y as before, then the total set of possibilities for the needle can be identified with the same rectangular region $0 \leq y \leq L$, $0 \leq \theta \leq \pi$. What portion of the rectangle corresponds to the needle intersecting a line?]
    (b) If $L = 4$, find the probability that a needle of length 7 will intersect *two* lines.
    (c) If $2L < h \leq 3L$, find a general formula for the probability that the needle intersects three lines.

13. Find the centroid of the region enclosed by the ellipse $x^2 + (x + y + 1)^2 = 1$.

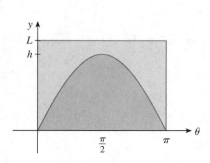

FIGURE FOR PROBLEM 11

9 Differential Equations

The relationship between populations of predators and prey (sharks and food fish, ladybugs and aphids, wolves and rabbits) is explored using pairs of differential equations in the last section of this chapter.

© Ciurzynski / Shutterstock

Perhaps the most important of all the applications of calculus is to differential equations. When physical scientists or social scientists use calculus, more often than not it is to analyze a differential equation that has arisen in the process of modeling some phenomenon that they are studying. Although it is often impossible to find an explicit formula for the solution of a differential equation, we will see that graphical and numerical approaches provide the needed information.

9.1   Modeling with Differential Equations

Now is a good time to read (or reread) the discussion of mathematical modeling on page 23.

In describing the process of modeling in Section 1.2, we talked about formulating a mathematical model of a real-world problem either through intuitive reasoning about the phenomenon or from a physical law based on evidence from experiments. The mathematical model often takes the form of a *differential equation,* that is, an equation that contains an unknown function and some of its derivatives. This is not surprising because in a real-world problem we often notice that changes occur and we want to predict future behavior on the basis of how current values change. Let's begin by examining several examples of how differential equations arise when we model physical phenomena.

Models of Population Growth

One model for the growth of a population is based on the assumption that the population grows at a rate proportional to the size of the population. That is a reasonable assumption for a population of bacteria or animals under ideal conditions (unlimited environment, adequate nutrition, absence of predators, immunity from disease).

Let's identify and name the variables in this model:

$$t = \text{time} \quad \text{(the independent variable)}$$

$$P = \text{the number of individuals in the population} \quad \text{(the dependent variable)}$$

The rate of growth of the population is the derivative dP/dt. So our assumption that the rate of growth of the population is proportional to the population size is written as the equation

$$\boxed{1} \qquad\qquad\qquad \frac{dP}{dt} = kP$$

where k is the proportionality constant. Equation 1 is our first model for population growth; it is a differential equation because it contains an unknown function P and its derivative dP/dt.

Having formulated a model, let's look at its consequences. If we rule out a population of 0, then $P(t) > 0$ for all t. So, if $k > 0$, then Equation 1 shows that $P'(t) > 0$ for all t. This means that the population is always increasing. In fact, as $P(t)$ increases, Equation 1 shows that dP/dt becomes larger. In other words, the growth rate increases as the population increases.

Let's try to think of a solution of Equation 1. This equation asks us to find a function whose derivative is a constant multiple of itself. We know from Chapter 3 that exponential functions have that property. In fact, if we let $P(t) = Ce^{kt}$, then

$$P'(t) = C(ke^{kt}) = k(Ce^{kt}) = kP(t)$$

Thus any exponential function of the form $P(t) = Ce^{kt}$ is a solution of Equation 1. In Section 9.4, we will see that there is no other solution.

Allowing C to vary through all the real numbers, we get the *family* of solutions $P(t) = Ce^{kt}$ whose graphs are shown in Figure 1. But populations have only positive values and so we are interested only in the solutions with $C > 0$. And we are probably con-

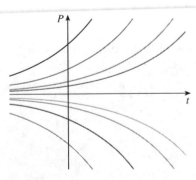

FIGURE 1
The family of solutions of $dP/dt = kP$

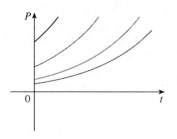

FIGURE 2

The family of solutions $P(t) = Ce^{kt}$ with $C > 0$ and $t \geqslant 0$

cerned only with values of t greater than the initial time $t = 0$. Figure 2 shows the physically meaningful solutions. Putting $t = 0$, we get $P(0) = Ce^{k(0)} = C$, so the constant C turns out to be the initial population, $P(0)$.

Equation 1 is appropriate for modeling population growth under ideal conditions, but we have to recognize that a more realistic model must reflect the fact that a given environment has limited resources. Many populations start by increasing in an exponential manner, but the population levels off when it approaches its *carrying capacity M* (or decreases toward M if it ever exceeds M). For a model to take into account both trends, we make two assumptions:

- $\dfrac{dP}{dt} \approx kP$ if P is small   (Initially, the growth rate is proportional to P.)

- $\dfrac{dP}{dt} < 0$ if $P > M$ (P decreases if it ever exceeds M.)

A simple expression that incorporates both assumptions is given by the equation

$$\boxed{2} \qquad \frac{dP}{dt} = kP\left(1 - \frac{P}{M}\right)$$

Notice that if P is small compared with M, then P/M is close to 0 and so $dP/dt \approx kP$. If $P > M$, then $1 - P/M$ is negative and so $dP/dt < 0$.

Equation 2 is called the *logistic differential equation* and was proposed by the Dutch mathematical biologist Pierre-François Verhulst in the 1840s as a model for world population growth. We will develop techniques that enable us to find explicit solutions of the logistic equation in Section 9.4, but for now we can deduce qualitative characteristics of the solutions directly from Equation 2. We first observe that the constant functions $P(t) = 0$ and $P(t) = M$ are solutions because, in either case, one of the factors on the right side of Equation 2 is zero. (This certainly makes physical sense: If the population is ever either 0 or at the carrying capacity, it stays that way.) These two constant solutions are called *equilibrium solutions*.

If the initial population $P(0)$ lies between 0 and M, then the right side of Equation 2 is positive, so $dP/dt > 0$ and the population increases. But if the population exceeds the carrying capacity ($P > M$), then $1 - P/M$ is negative, so $dP/dt < 0$ and the population decreases. Notice that, in either case, if the population approaches the carrying capacity ($P \to M$), then $dP/dt \to 0$, which means the population levels off. So we expect that the solutions of the logistic differential equation have graphs that look something like the ones in Figure 3. Notice that the graphs move away from the equilibrium solution $P = 0$ and move toward the equilibrium solution $P = M$.

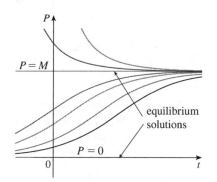

FIGURE 3

Solutions of the logistic equation

A Model for the Motion of a Spring

Let's now look at an example of a model from the physical sciences. We consider the motion of an object with mass m at the end of a vertical spring (as in Figure 4). In Section 6.4 we discussed Hooke's Law, which says that if the spring is stretched (or compressed) x units from its natural length, then it exerts a force that is proportional to x:

$$\text{restoring force} = -kx$$

where k is a positive constant (called the *spring constant*). If we ignore any external resisting forces (due to air resistance or friction) then, by Newton's Second Law (force equals mass times acceleration), we have

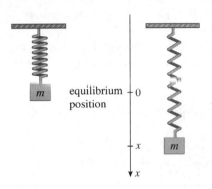

FIGURE 4

$$\boxed{3} \qquad m\frac{d^2x}{dt^2} = -kx$$

This is an example of what is called a *second-order differential equation* because it involves second derivatives. Let's see what we can guess about the form of the solution directly from the equation. We can rewrite Equation 3 in the form

$$\frac{d^2x}{dt^2} = -\frac{k}{m}x$$

which says that the second derivative of x is proportional to x but has the opposite sign. We know two functions with this property, the sine and cosine functions. In fact, it turns out that all solutions of Equation 3 can be written as combinations of certain sine and cosine functions (see Exercise 4). This is not surprising; we expect the spring to oscillate about its equilibrium position and so it is natural to think that trigonometric functions are involved.

General Differential Equations

In general, a **differential equation** is an equation that contains an unknown function and one or more of its derivatives. The **order** of a differential equation is the order of the highest derivative that occurs in the equation. Thus Equations 1 and 2 are first-order equations and Equation 3 is a second-order equation. In all three of those equations the independent variable is called t and represents time, but in general the independent variable doesn't have to represent time. For example, when we consider the differential equation

$$\boxed{4} \qquad y' = xy$$

it is understood that y is an unknown function of x.

A function f is called a **solution** of a differential equation if the equation is satisfied when $y = f(x)$ and its derivatives are substituted into the equation. Thus f is a solution of Equation 4 if

$$f'(x) = xf(x)$$

for all values of x in some interval.

When we are asked to *solve* a differential equation we are expected to find all possible solutions of the equation. We have already solved some particularly simple differential equations, namely, those of the form

$$y' = f(x)$$

For instance, we know that the general solution of the differential equation

$$y' = x^3$$

is given by

$$y = \frac{x^4}{4} + C$$

where C is an arbitrary constant.

But, in general, solving a differential equation is not an easy matter. There is no systematic technique that enables us to solve all differential equations. In Section 9.2, however, we will see how to draw rough graphs of solutions even when we have no explicit formula. We will also learn how to find numerical approximations to solutions.

V **EXAMPLE 1** Show that every member of the family of functions

$$y = \frac{1 + ce^t}{1 - ce^t}$$

is a solution of the differential equation $y' = \frac{1}{2}(y^2 - 1)$.

SOLUTION We use the Quotient Rule to differentiate the expression for y:

$$y' = \frac{(1 - ce^t)(ce^t) - (1 + ce^t)(-ce^t)}{(1 - ce^t)^2}$$

$$= \frac{ce^t - c^2e^{2t} + ce^t + c^2e^{2t}}{(1 - ce^t)^2} = \frac{2ce^t}{(1 - ce^t)^2}$$

The right side of the differential equation becomes

$$\tfrac{1}{2}(y^2 - 1) = \frac{1}{2}\left[\left(\frac{1 + ce^t}{1 - ce^t}\right)^2 - 1\right]$$

$$= \frac{1}{2}\left[\frac{(1 + ce^t)^2 - (1 - ce^t)^2}{(1 - ce^t)^2}\right]$$

$$= \frac{1}{2}\frac{4ce^t}{(1 - ce^t)^2} = \frac{2ce^t}{(1 - ce^t)^2}$$

Figure 5 shows graphs of seven members of the family in Example 1. The differential equation shows that if $y \approx \pm 1$, then $y' \approx 0$. That is borne out by the flatness of the graphs near $y = 1$ and $y = -1$.

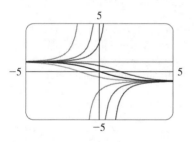

FIGURE 5

Therefore, for every value of c, the given function is a solution of the differential equation.

When applying differential equations, we are usually not as interested in finding a family of solutions (the *general solution*) as we are in finding a solution that satisfies some additional requirement. In many physical problems we need to find the particular solution that satisfies a condition of the form $y(t_0) = y_0$. This is called an **initial condition**, and the problem of finding a solution of the differential equation that satisfies the initial condition is called an **initial-value problem**.

Geometrically, when we impose an initial condition, we look at the family of solution curves and pick the one that passes through the point (t_0, y_0). Physically, this corresponds to measuring the state of a system at time t_0 and using the solution of the initial-value problem to predict the future behavior of the system.

V EXAMPLE 2 Find a solution of the differential equation $y' = \frac{1}{2}(y^2 - 1)$ that satisfies the initial condition $y(0) = 2$.

SOLUTION Substituting the values $t = 0$ and $y = 2$ into the formula

$$y = \frac{1 + ce^t}{1 - ce^t}$$

from Example 1, we get

$$2 = \frac{1 + ce^0}{1 - ce^0} = \frac{1 + c}{1 - c}$$

Solving this equation for c, we get $2 - 2c = 1 + c$, which gives $c = \frac{1}{3}$. So the solution of the initial-value problem is

$$y = \frac{1 + \frac{1}{3}e^t}{1 - \frac{1}{3}e^t} = \frac{3 + e^t}{3 - e^t}$$

9.1 Exercises

1. Show that $y = x - x^{-1}$ is a solution of the differential equation $xy' + y = 2x$.

2. Verify that $y = \sin x \cos x - \cos x$ is a solution of the initial-value problem

$$y' + (\tan x)y = \cos^2 x \qquad y(0) = -1$$

on the interval $-\pi/2 < x < \pi/2$.

3. (a) For what values of r does the function $y = e^{rx}$ satisfy the differential equation $2y'' + y' - y = 0$?
   (b) If r_1 and r_2 are the values of r that you found in part (a), show that every member of the family of functions $y = ae^{r_1 x} + be^{r_2 x}$ is also a solution.

4. (a) For what values of k does the function $y = \cos kt$ satisfy the differential equation $4y'' = -25y$?
   (b) For those values of k, verify that every member of the family of functions $y = A \sin kt + B \cos kt$ is also a solution.

5. Which of the following functions are solutions of the differential equation $y'' + y = \sin x$?
   (a) $y = \sin x$ (b) $y = \cos x$
   (c) $y = \frac{1}{2}x \sin x$ (d) $y = -\frac{1}{2}x \cos x$

6. (a) Show that every member of the family of functions $y = (\ln x + C)/x$ is a solution of the differential equation $x^2 y' + xy = 1$.
   (b) Illustrate part (a) by graphing several members of the family of solutions on a common screen.
   (c) Find a solution of the differential equation that satisfies the initial condition $y(1) = 2$.
   (d) Find a solution of the differential equation that satisfies the initial condition $y(2) = 1$.

7. (a) What can you say about a solution of the equation $y' = -y^2$ just by looking at the differential equation?
   (b) Verify that all members of the family $y = 1/(x + C)$ are solutions of the equation in part (a).
   (c) Can you think of a solution of the differential equation $y' = -y^2$ that is not a member of the family in part (b)?
   (d) Find a solution of the initial-value problem

$$y' = -y^2 \qquad y(0) = 0.5$$

8. (a) What can you say about the graph of a solution of the equation $y' = xy^3$ when x is close to 0? What if x is large?
   (b) Verify that all members of the family $y = (c - x^2)^{-1/2}$ are solutions of the differential equation $y' = xy^3$.
   (c) Graph several members of the family of solutions on a common screen. Do the graphs confirm what you predicted in part (a)?
   (d) Find a solution of the initial-value problem

$$y' = xy^3 \qquad y(0) = 2$$

9. A population is modeled by the differential equation

$$\frac{dP}{dt} = 1.2P\left(1 - \frac{P}{4200}\right)$$

   (a) For what values of P is the population increasing?
   (b) For what values of P is the population decreasing?
   (c) What are the equilibrium solutions?

10. A function $y(t)$ satisfies the differential equation

$$\frac{dy}{dt} = y^4 - 6y^3 + 5y^2$$

   (a) What are the constant solutions of the equation?

(b) For what values of y is y increasing?

(c) For what values of y is y decreasing?

11. Explain why the functions with the given graphs *can't* be solutions of the differential equation

$$\frac{dy}{dt} = e^t(y - 1)^2$$

(a)

(b)

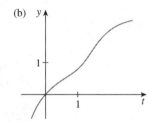

12. The function with the given graph is a solution of one of the following differential equations. Decide which is the correct equation and justify your answer.

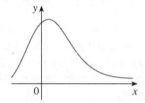

A. $y' = 1 + xy$ **B.** $y' = -2xy$ **C.** $y' = 1 - 2xy$

13. Match the differential equations with the solution graphs labeled I–IV. Give reasons for your choices.

(a) $y' = 1 + x^2 + y^2$ (b) $y' = xe^{-x^2-y^2}$

(c) $y' = \dfrac{1}{1 + e^{x^2+y^2}}$ (d) $y' = \sin(xy)\cos(xy)$

I

II

III   IV

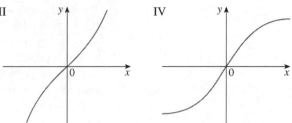

14. Suppose you have just poured a cup of freshly brewed coffee with temperature 95°C in a room where the temperature is 20°C.

(a) When do you think the coffee cools most quickly? What happens to the rate of cooling as time goes by? Explain.

(b) Newton's Law of Cooling states that the rate of cooling of an object is proportional to the temperature difference between the object and its surroundings, provided that this difference is not too large. Write a differential equation that expresses Newton's Law of Cooling for this particular situation. What is the initial condition? In view of your answer to part (a), do you think this differential equation is an appropriate model for cooling?

(c) Make a rough sketch of the graph of the solution of the initial-value problem in part (b).

15. Psychologists interested in learning theory study **learning curves**. A learning curve is the graph of a function $P(t)$, the performance of someone learning a skill as a function of the training time t. The derivative dP/dt represents the rate at which performance improves.

(a) When do you think P increases most rapidly? What happens to dP/dt as t increases? Explain.

(b) If M is the maximum level of performance of which the learner is capable, explain why the differential equation

$$\frac{dP}{dt} = k(M - P) \qquad k \text{ a positive constant}$$

is a reasonable model for learning.

(c) Make a rough sketch of a possible solution of this differential equation.

9.2   Direction Fields and Euler's Method

Unfortunately, it's impossible to solve most differential equations in the sense of obtaining an explicit formula for the solution. In this section we show that, despite the absence of an explicit solution, we can still learn a lot about the solution through a graphical approach (direction fields) or a numerical approach (Euler's method).

▇ Direction Fields

Suppose we are asked to sketch the graph of the solution of the initial-value problem

$$y' = x + y \qquad y(0) = 1$$

We don't know a formula for the solution, so how can we possibly sketch its graph? Let's think about what the differential equation means. The equation $y' = x + y$ tells us that the slope at any point (x, y) on the graph (called the *solution curve*) is equal to the sum of the x- and y-coordinates of the point (see Figure 1). In particular, because the curve passes through the point $(0, 1)$, its slope there must be $0 + 1 = 1$. So a small portion of the solution curve near the point $(0, 1)$ looks like a short line segment through $(0, 1)$ with slope 1. (See Figure 2.)

FIGURE 1

A solution of $y' = x + y$

FIGURE 2

Beginning of the solution curve through $(0, 1)$

As a guide to sketching the rest of the curve, let's draw short line segments at a number of points (x, y) with slope $x + y$. The result is called a *direction field* and is shown in Figure 3. For instance, the line segment at the point $(1, 2)$ has slope $1 + 2 = 3$. The direction field allows us to visualize the general shape of the solution curves by indicating the direction in which the curves proceed at each point.

FIGURE 3

Direction field for $y' = x + y$

FIGURE 4

The solution curve through $(0, 1)$

Now we can sketch the solution curve through the point $(0, 1)$ by following the direction field as in Figure 4. Notice that we have drawn the curve so that it is parallel to nearby line segments.

In general, suppose we have a first-order differential equation of the form

$$y' = F(x, y)$$

where $F(x, y)$ is some expression in x and y. The differential equation says that the slope of a solution curve at a point (x, y) on the curve is $F(x, y)$. If we draw short line segments with slope $F(x, y)$ at several points (x, y), the result is called a **direction field** (or **slope field**). These line segments indicate the direction in which a solution curve is heading, so the direction field helps us visualize the general shape of these curves.

FIGURE 5

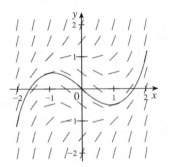

FIGURE 6

TEC Module 9.2A shows direction fields and solution curves for a variety of differential equations.

V   EXAMPLE 1

(a) Sketch the direction field for the differential equation $y' = x^2 + y^2 - 1$.

(b) Use part (a) to sketch the solution curve that passes through the origin.

SOLUTION

(a) We start by computing the slope at several points in the following chart:

x	-2	-1	0	1	2	-2	-1	0	1	2	$\ldots$
y	0	0	0	0	0	1	1	1	1	1	$\ldots$
$y' = x^2 + y^2 - 1$	3	0	-1	0	3	4	1	0	1	4	$\ldots$

Now we draw short line segments with these slopes at these points. The result is the direction field shown in Figure 5.

(b) We start at the origin and move to the right in the direction of the line segment (which has slope -1). We continue to draw the solution curve so that it moves parallel to the nearby line segments. The resulting solution curve is shown in Figure 6. Returning to the origin, we draw the solution curve to the left as well.   ▬

The more line segments we draw in a direction field, the clearer the picture becomes. Of course, it's tedious to compute slopes and draw line segments for a huge number of points by hand, but computers are well suited for this task. Figure 7 shows a more detailed, computer-drawn direction field for the differential equation in Example 1. It enables us to draw, with reasonable accuracy, the solution curves shown in Figure 8 with y-intercepts $-2, -1, 0, 1,$ and 2.

FIGURE 7

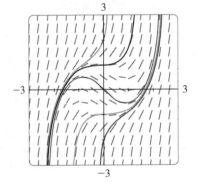

FIGURE 8

Now let's see how direction fields give insight into physical situations. The simple electric circuit shown in Figure 9 contains an electromotive force (usually a battery or generator) that produces a voltage of $E(t)$ volts (V) and a current of $I(t)$ amperes (A) at time t. The circuit also contains a resistor with a resistance of R ohms (Ω) and an inductor with an inductance of L henries (H).

Ohm's Law gives the drop in voltage due to the resistor as RI. The voltage drop due to the inductor is $L(dI/dt)$. One of Kirchhoff's laws says that the sum of the voltage drops is equal to the supplied voltage $E(t)$. Thus we have

FIGURE 9

$$\boxed{1} \qquad L\frac{dI}{dt} + RI = E(t)$$

which is a first-order differential equation that models the current I at time t.

V EXAMPLE 2 Suppose that in the simple circuit of Figure 9 the resistance is 12 Ω, the inductance is 4 H, and a battery gives a constant voltage of 60 V.

(a) Draw a direction field for Equation 1 with these values.

(b) What can you say about the limiting value of the current?

(c) Identify any equilibrium solutions

(d) If the switch is closed when $t = 0$ so the current starts with $I(0) = 0$, use the direction field to sketch the solution curve.

SOLUTION

(a) If we put $L = 4$, $R = 12$, and $E(t) = 60$ in Equation 1, we get

$$4\frac{dI}{dt} + 12I = 60 \qquad \text{or} \qquad \frac{dI}{dt} = 15 - 3I$$

The direction field for this differential equation is shown in Figure 10.

FIGURE 10

(b) It appears from the direction field that all solutions approach the value 5 A, that is,

$$\lim_{t \to \infty} I(t) = 5$$

(c) It appears that the constant function $I(t) = 5$ is an equilibrium solution. Indeed, we can verify this directly from the differential equation $dI/dt = 15 - 3I$. If $I(t) = 5$, then the left side is $dI/dt = 0$ and the right side is $15 - 3(5) = 0$.

(d) We use the direction field to sketch the solution curve that passes through $(0, 0)$, as shown in red in Figure 11.

FIGURE 11

Notice from Figure 10 that the line segments along any horizontal line are parallel. That is because the independent variable t does not occur on the right side of the equation

$I' = 15 - 3I$. In general, a differential equation of the form

$$y' = f(y)$$

in which the independent variable is missing from the right side, is called **autonomous**. For such an equation, the slopes corresponding to two different points with the same y-coordinate must be equal. This means that if we know one solution to an autonomous differential equation, then we can obtain infinitely many others just by shifting the graph of the known solution to the right or left. In Figure 11 we have shown the solutions that result from shifting the solution curve of Example 2 one and two time units (namely, seconds) to the right. They correspond to closing the switch when $t = 1$ or $t = 2$.

■ Euler's Method

The basic idea behind direction fields can be used to find numerical approximations to solutions of differential equations. We illustrate the method on the initial-value problem that we used to introduce direction fields:

$$y' = x + y \qquad y(0) = 1$$

The differential equation tells us that $y'(0) = 0 + 1 = 1$, so the solution curve has slope 1 at the point $(0, 1)$. As a first approximation to the solution we could use the linear approximation $L(x) = x + 1$. In other words, we could use the tangent line at $(0, 1)$ as a rough approximation to the solution curve (see Figure 12).

Euler's idea was to improve on this approximation by proceeding only a short distance along this tangent line and then making a midcourse correction by changing direction as indicated by the direction field. Figure 13 shows what happens if we start out along the tangent line but stop when $x = 0.5$. (This horizontal distance traveled is called the *step size*.) Since $L(0.5) = 1.5$, we have $y(0.5) \approx 1.5$ and we take $(0.5, 1.5)$ as the starting point for a new line segment. The differential equation tells us that $y'(0.5) = 0.5 + 1.5 = 2$, so we use the linear function

$$y = 1.5 + 2(x - 0.5) = 2x + 0.5$$

as an approximation to the solution for $x > 0.5$ (the green segment in Figure 13). If we decrease the step size from 0.5 to 0.25, we get the better Euler approximation shown in Figure 14.

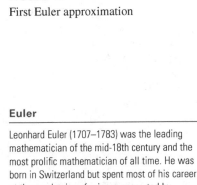

FIGURE 12

First Euler approximation

Euler

Leonhard Euler (1707–1783) was the leading mathematician of the mid-18th century and the most prolific mathematician of all time. He was born in Switzerland but spent most of his career at the academies of science supported by Catherine the Great in St. Petersburg and Frederick the Great in Berlin. The collected works of Euler (pronounced *Oiler*) fill about 100 large volumes. As the French physicist Arago said, "Euler calculated without apparent effort, as men breathe or as eagles sustain themselves in the air." Euler's calculations and writings were not diminished by raising 13 children or being totally blind for the last 17 years of his life. In fact, when blind, he dictated his discoveries to his helpers from his prodigious memory and imagination. His treatises on calculus and most other mathematical subjects became the standard for mathematics instruction and the equation $e^{i\pi} + 1 = 0$ that he discovered brings together the five most famous numbers in all of mathematics.

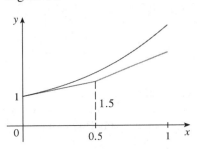

FIGURE 13

Euler approximation with step size 0.5

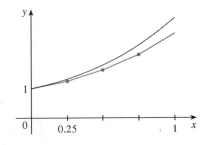

FIGURE 14

Euler approximation with step size 0.25

In general, Euler's method says to start at the point given by the initial value and proceed in the direction indicated by the direction field. Stop after a short time, look at the slope at the new location, and proceed in that direction. Keep stopping and changing direction according to the direction field. Euler's method does not produce the exact solution to an initial-value problem—it gives approximations. But by decreasing the step size (and therefore increasing the number of midcourse corrections), we obtain successively better approximations to the exact solution. (Compare Figures 12, 13, and 14.)

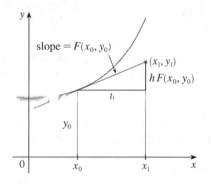

FIGURE 15

For the general first-order initial-value problem $y' = F(x, y)$, $y(x_0) = y_0$, our aim is to find approximate values for the solution at equally spaced numbers x_0, $x_1 = x_0 + h$, $x_2 = x_1 + h, \ldots$, where h is the step size. The differential equation tells us that the slope at (x_0, y_0) is $y' = F(x_0, y_0)$, so Figure 15 shows that the approximate value of the solution when $x = x_1$ is

$$y_1 = y_0 + hF(x_0, y_0)$$

Similarly,

$$y_2 = y_1 + hF(x_1, y_1)$$

In general,

$$y_n = y_{n-1} + hF(x_{n-1}, y_{n-1})$$

> **Euler's Method** Approximate values for the solution of the initial-value problem $y' = F(x, y)$, $y(x_0) = y_0$, with step size h, at $x_n = x_{n-1} + h$, are
>
> $$y_n = y_{n-1} + hF(x_{n-1}, y_{n-1}) \qquad n = 1, 2, 3, \ldots$$

EXAMPLE 3   Use Euler's method with step size 0.1 to construct a table of approximate values for the solution of the initial-value problem

$$y' = x + y \qquad y(0) = 1$$

SOLUTION   We are given that $h = 0.1$, $x_0 = 0$, $y_0 = 1$, and $F(x, y) = x + y$. So we have

$$y_1 = y_0 + hF(x_0, y_0) = 1 + 0.1(0 + 1) = 1.1$$

$$y_2 = y_1 + hF(x_1, y_1) = 1.1 + 0.1(0.1 + 1.1) = 1.22$$

$$y_3 = y_2 + hF(x_2, y_2) = 1.22 + 0.1(0.2 + 1.22) = 1.362$$

This means that if $y(x)$ is the exact solution, then $y(0.3) \approx 1.362$.

Proceeding with similar calculations, we get the values in the table:

TEC Module 9.2B shows how Euler's method works numerically and visually for a variety of differential equations and step sizes.

n	x_n	y_n	n	x_n	y_n
1	0.1	1.100000	6	0.6	1.943122
2	0.2	1.220000	7	0.7	2.197434
3	0.3	1.362000	8	0.8	2.487178
4	0.4	1.528200	9	0.9	2.815895
5	0.5	1.721020	10	1.0	3.187485

For a more accurate table of values in Example 3 we could decrease the step size. But for a large number of small steps the amount of computation is considerable and so we need to program a calculator or computer to carry out these calculations. The following table shows the results of applying Euler's method with decreasing step size to the initial-value problem of Example 3.

Computer software packages that produce numerical approximations to solutions of differential equations use methods that are refinements of Euler's method. Although Euler's method is simple and not as accurate, it is the basic idea on which the more accurate methods are based.

Step size	Euler estimate of $y(0.5)$	Euler estimate of $y(1)$
0.500	1.500000	2.500000
0.250	1.625000	2.882813
0.100	1.721020	3.187485
0.050	1.757789	3.306595
0.020	1.781212	3.383176
0.010	1.789264	3.409628
0.005	1.793337	3.423034
0.001	1.796619	3.433848

Notice that the Euler estimates in the table seem to be approaching limits, namely, the true values of $y(0.5)$ and $y(1)$. Figure 16 shows graphs of the Euler approximations with step sizes 0.5, 0.25, 0.1, 0.05, 0.02, 0.01, and 0.005. They are approaching the exact solution curve as the step size h approaches 0.

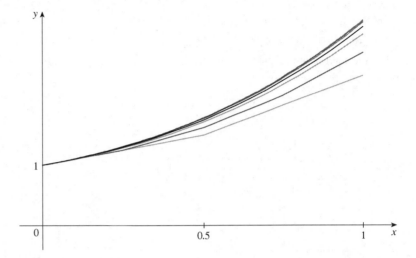

FIGURE 16

Euler approximations
approaching the exact solution

V **EXAMPLE 4** In Example 2 we discussed a simple electric circuit with resistance 12 Ω, inductance 4 H, and a battery with voltage 60 V. If the switch is closed when $t = 0$, we modeled the current I at time t by the initial-value problem

$$\frac{dI}{dt} = 15 - 3I \qquad I(0) = 0$$

Estimate the current in the circuit half a second after the switch is closed.

SOLUTION We use Euler's method with $F(t, I) = 15 - 3I$, $t_0 = 0$, $I_0 = 0$, and step size $h = 0.1$ second:

$$I_1 = 0 + 0.1(15 - 3 \cdot 0) = 1.5$$

$$I_2 = 1.5 + 0.1(15 - 3 \cdot 1.5) = 2.55$$

$$I_3 = 2.55 + 0.1(15 - 3 \cdot 2.55) = 3.285$$

$$I_4 = 3.285 + 0.1(15 - 3 \cdot 3.285) = 3.7995$$

$$I_5 = 3.7995 + 0.1(15 - 3 \cdot 3.7995) = 4.15965$$

So the current after 0.5 s is

$$I(0.5) \approx 4.16 \text{ A}$$

9.2 Exercises

1. A direction field for the differential equation $y' = x \cos \pi y$ is shown.

   (a) Sketch the graphs of the solutions that satisfy the given initial conditions.

      (i) $y(0) = 0$ (ii) $y(0) = 0.5$

      (iii) $y(0) = 1$ (iv) $y(0) = 1.6$

   (b) Find all the equilibrium solutions.

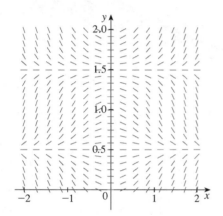

2. A direction field for the differential equation $y' = \tan\left(\frac{1}{2}\pi y\right)$ is shown.

   (a) Sketch the graphs of the solutions that satisfy the given initial conditions.

      (i) $y(0) = 1$ (ii) $y(0) = 0.2$

      (iii) $y(0) = 2$ (iv) $y(1) = 3$

   (b) Find all the equilibrium solutions.

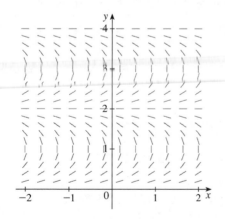

3–6 Match the differential equation with its direction field (labeled I–IV). Give reasons for your answer.

3. $y' = 2 - y$ **4.** $y' = x(2 - y)$

5. $y' = x + y - 1$ **6.** $y' = \sin x \sin y$

I

II

III

IV

7. Use the direction field labeled II (above) to sketch the graphs of the solutions that satisfy the given initial conditions.

   (a) $y(0) = 1$ (b) $y(0) = 2$ (c) $y(0) = -1$

8. Use the direction field labeled IV (above) to sketch the graphs of the solutions that satisfy the given initial conditions.

   (a) $y(0) = -1$ (b) $y(0) = 0$ (c) $y(0) = 1$

9–10 Sketch a direction field for the differential equation. Then use it to sketch three solution curves.

9. $y' = \frac{1}{2}y$ **10.** $y' = x - y + 1$

11–14 Sketch the direction field of the differential equation. Then use it to sketch a solution curve that passes through the given point.

11. $y' = y - 2x$, $(1, 0)$ **12.** $y' = xy - x^2$, $(0, 1)$

13. $y' = y + xy$, $(0, 1)$ **14.** $y' = x + y^2$, $(0, 0)$

[CAS] **15–16** Use a computer algebra system to draw a direction field for the given differential equation. Get a printout and sketch on it the solution curve that passes through $(0, 1)$. Then use the CAS to draw the solution curve and compare it with your sketch.

15. $y' = x^2 \sin y$ **16.** $y' = x(y^2 - 4)$

Graphing calculator or computer required   [CAS] Computer algebra system required   **1.** Homework Hints available at stewartcalculus.com

CAS **17.** Use a computer algebra system to draw a direction field for the differential equation $y' = y^3 - 4y$. Get a printout and sketch on it solutions that satisfy the initial condition $y(0) = c$ for various values of c. For what values of c does $\lim_{t \to \infty} y(t)$ exist? What are the possible values for this limit?

18. Make a rough sketch of a direction field for the autonomous differential equation $y' = f(y)$, where the graph of f is as shown. How does the limiting behavior of solutions depend on the value of $y(0)$?

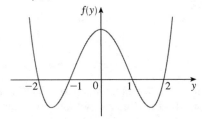

19. (a) Use Euler's method with each of the following step sizes to estimate the value of $y(0.4)$, where y is the solution of the initial-value problem $y' = y$, $y(0) = 1$.
   (i) $h = 0.4$ (ii) $h = 0.2$ (iii) $h = 0.1$
   (b) We know that the exact solution of the initial-value problem in part (a) is $y = e^x$. Draw, as accurately as you can, the graph of $y = e^x$, $0 \le x \le 0.4$, together with the Euler approximations using the step sizes in part (a). (Your sketches should resemble Figures 12, 13, and 14.) Use your sketches to decide whether your estimates in part (a) are underestimates or overestimates.
   (c) The error in Euler's method is the difference between the exact value and the approximate value. Find the errors made in part (a) in using Euler's method to estimate the true value of $y(0.4)$, namely $e^{0.4}$. What happens to the error each time the step size is halved?

20. A direction field for a differential equation is shown. Draw, with a ruler, the graphs of the Euler approximations to the solution curve that passes through the origin. Use step sizes $h = 1$ and $h = 0.5$. Will the Euler estimates be underestimates or overestimates? Explain.

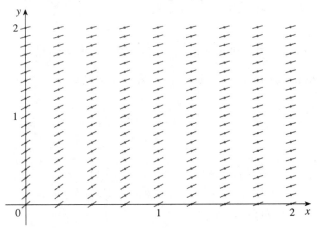

21. Use Euler's method with step size 0.5 to compute the approximate y-values y_1, y_2, y_3, and y_4 of the solution of the initial-value problem $y' = y - 2x$, $y(1) = 0$.

22. Use Euler's method with step size 0.2 to estimate $y(1)$, where $y(x)$ is the solution of the initial-value problem $y' = 1 - xy$, $y(0) = 0$.

23. Use Euler's method with step size 0.1 to estimate $y(0.5)$, where $y(x)$ is the solution of the initial-value problem $y' = y + xy$, $y(0) = 1$.

24. (a) Use Euler's method with step size 0.2 to estimate $y(0.4)$, where $y(x)$ is the solution of the initial-value problem $y' = x + y^2$, $y(0) = 0$.
   (b) Repeat part (a) with step size 0.1.

25. (a) Program a calculator or computer to use Euler's method to compute $y(1)$, where $y(x)$ is the solution of the initial-value problem

$$\frac{dy}{dx} + 3x^2 y = 6x^2 \qquad y(0) = 3$$

   (i) $h = 1$ (ii) $h = 0.1$
   (iii) $h = 0.01$ (iv) $h = 0.001$
   (b) Verify that $y = 2 + e^{-x^3}$ is the exact solution of the differential equation.
   (c) Find the errors in using Euler's method to compute $y(1)$ with the step sizes in part (a). What happens to the error when the step size is divided by 10?

CAS **26.** (a) Program your computer algebra system, using Euler's method with step size 0.01, to calculate $y(2)$, where y is the solution of the initial-value problem

$$y' = x^3 - y^3 \qquad y(0) = 1$$

   (b) Check your work by using the CAS to draw the solution curve.

27. The figure shows a circuit containing an electromotive force, a capacitor with a capacitance of C farads (F), and a resistor with a resistance of R ohms (Ω). The voltage drop across the capacitor is Q/C, where Q is the charge (in coulombs, C), so in this case Kirchhoff's Law gives

$$RI + \frac{Q}{C} = E(t)$$

But $I = dQ/dt$, so we have

$$R\frac{dQ}{dt} + \frac{1}{C}Q = E(t)$$

Suppose the resistance is 5 Ω, the capacitance is 0.05 F, and a battery gives a constant voltage of 60 V.
   (a) Draw a direction field for this differential equation.
   (b) What is the limiting value of the charge?
   (c) Is there an equilibrium solution?
   (d) If the initial charge is $Q(0) = 0$ C, use the direction field to sketch the solution curve.

(e) If the initial charge is $Q(0) = 0$ C, use Euler's method with step size 0.1 to estimate the charge after half a second.

28. In Exercise 14 in Section 9.1 we considered a 95°C cup of coffee in a 20°C room. Suppose it is known that the coffee cools at a rate of 1°C per minute when its temperature is 70°C.
   (a) What does the differential equation become in this case?
   (b) Sketch a direction field and use it to sketch the solution curve for the initial-value problem. What is the limiting value of the temperature?
   (c) Use Euler's method with step size $h = 2$ minutes to estimate the temperature of the coffee after 10 minutes.

9.3 Separable Equations

We have looked at first-order differential equations from a geometric point of view (direction fields) and from a numerical point of view (Euler's method). What about the symbolic point of view? It would be nice to have an explicit formula for a solution of a differential equation. Unfortunately, that is not always possible. But in this section we examine a certain type of differential equation that *can* be solved explicitly.

A **separable equation** is a first-order differential equation in which the expression for dy/dx can be factored as a function of x times a function of y. In other words, it can be written in the form

$$\frac{dy}{dx} = g(x)f(y)$$

The name *separable* comes from the fact that the expression on the right side can be "separated" into a function of x and a function of y. Equivalently, if $f(y) \neq 0$, we could write

$$\boxed{1} \qquad \frac{dy}{dx} = \frac{g(x)}{h(y)}$$

where $h(y) = 1/f(y)$. To solve this equation we rewrite it in the differential form

$$h(y)\, dy = g(x)\, dx$$

so that all y's are on one side of the equation and all x's are on the other side. Then we integrate both sides of the equation:

$$\boxed{2} \qquad \int h(y)\, dy = \int g(x)\, dx$$

The technique for solving separable differential equations was first used by James Bernoulli (in 1690) in solving a problem about pendulums and by Leibniz (in a letter to Huygens in 1691). John Bernoulli explained the general method in a paper published in 1694

Equation 2 defines y implicitly as a function of x. In some cases we may be able to solve for y in terms of x.

We use the Chain Rule to justify this procedure: If h and g satisfy $\boxed{2}$, then

$$\frac{d}{dx}\left(\int h(y)\, dy\right) = \frac{d}{dx}\left(\int g(x)\, dx\right)$$

so

$$\frac{d}{dy}\left(\int h(y)\, dy\right)\frac{dy}{dx} = g(x)$$

and

$$h(y)\frac{dy}{dx} = g(x)$$

Thus Equation 1 is satisfied.

EXAMPLE 1

(a) Solve the differential equation $\dfrac{dy}{dx} = \dfrac{x^2}{y^2}$.

(b) Find the solution of this equation that satisfies the initial condition $y(0) = 2$.

SOLUTION

(a) We write the equation in terms of differentials and integrate both sides:

$$y^2\,dy = x^2\,dx$$

$$\int y^2\,dy = \int x^2\,dx$$

$$\tfrac{1}{3}y^3 = \tfrac{1}{3}x^3 + C$$

Figure 1 shows graphs of several members of the family of solutions of the differential equation in Example 1. The solution of the initial-value problem in part (b) is shown in red.

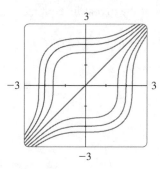

FIGURE 1

where C is an arbitrary constant. (We could have used a constant C_1 on the left side and another constant C_2 on the right side. But then we could combine these constants by writing $C = C_2 - C_1$.)

Solving for y, we get

$$y = \sqrt[3]{x^3 + 3C}$$

We could leave the solution like this or we could write it in the form

$$y = \sqrt[3]{x^3 + K}$$

where $K = 3C$. (Since C is an arbitrary constant, so is K.)

(b) If we put $x = 0$ in the general solution in part (a), we get $y(0) = \sqrt[3]{K}$. To satisfy the initial condition $y(0) = 2$, we must have $\sqrt[3]{K} = 2$ and so $K = 8$. Thus the solution of the initial-value problem is

$$y = \sqrt[3]{x^3 + 8}$$

Some computer algebra systems can plot curves defined by implicit equations. Figure 2 shows the graphs of several members of the family of solutions of the differential equation in Example 2. As we look at the curves from left to right, the values of C are 3, 2, 1, 0, -1, -2, and -3.

FIGURE 2

V EXAMPLE 2 Solve the differential equation $\dfrac{dy}{dx} = \dfrac{6x^2}{2y + \cos y}$.

SOLUTION Writing the equation in differential form and integrating both sides, we have

$$(2y + \cos y)\,dy = 6x^2\,dx$$

$$\int (2y + \cos y)\,dy = \int 6x^2\,dx$$

3
$$y^2 + \sin y = 2x^3 + C$$

where C is a constant. Equation 3 gives the general solution implicitly. In this case it's impossible to solve the equation to express y explicitly as a function of x.

EXAMPLE 3 Solve the equation $y' = x^2 y$.

SOLUTION First we rewrite the equation using Leibniz notation:

$$\frac{dy}{dx} = x^2 y$$

If a solution y is a function that satisfies $y(x) \neq 0$ for some x, it follows from a uniqueness theorem for solutions of differential equations that $y(x) \neq 0$ for all x.

If $y \neq 0$, we can rewrite it in differential notation and integrate:

$$\frac{dy}{y} = x^2 \, dx \qquad y \neq 0$$

$$\int \frac{dy}{y} = \int x^2 \, dx$$

$$\ln |y| = \frac{x^3}{3} + C$$

This equation defines y implicitly as a function of x. But in this case we can solve explicitly for y as follows:

$$|y| = e^{\ln |y|} = e^{(x^3/3)+C} = e^C e^{x^3/3}$$

so

$$y = \pm e^C e^{x^3/3}$$

We can easily verify that the function $y = 0$ is also a solution of the given differential equation. So we can write the general solution in the form

$$y = A e^{x^3/3}$$

where A is an arbitrary constant ($A = e^C$, or $A = -e^C$, or $A = 0$).

Figure 3 shows a direction field for the differential equation in Example 3. Compare it with Figure 4, in which we use the equation $y = A e^{x^3/3}$ to graph solutions for several values of A. If you use the direction field to sketch solution curves with y-intercepts 5, 2, 1, −1, and −2, they will resemble the curves in Figure 4.

FIGURE 3

FIGURE 4

FIGURE 5

V EXAMPLE 4 In Section 9.2 we modeled the current $I(t)$ in the electric circuit shown in Figure 5 by the differential equation

$$L\frac{dI}{dt} + RI = E(t)$$

Find an expression for the current in a circuit where the resistance is 12 Ω, the inductance is 4 H, a battery gives a constant voltage of 60 V, and the switch is turned on when $t = 0$. What is the limiting value of the current?

SOLUTION With $L = 4$, $R = 12$, and $E(t) = 60$, the equation becomes

$$4\frac{dI}{dt} + 12I = 60 \qquad \text{or} \qquad \frac{dI}{dt} = 15 - 3I$$

and the initial-value problem is

$$\frac{dI}{dt} = 15 - 3I \qquad I(0) = 0$$

We recognize this equation as being separable, and we solve it as follows:

$$\int \frac{dI}{15 - 3I} = \int dt \qquad (15 - 3I \neq 0)$$

$$-\tfrac{1}{3} \ln |15 - 3I| = t + C$$

$$|15 - 3I| = e^{-3(t+C)}$$

$$15 - 3I = \pm e^{-3C} e^{-3t} = A e^{-3t}$$

$$I = 5 - \tfrac{1}{3} A e^{-3t}$$

Figure 6 shows how the solution in Example 4 (the current) approaches its limiting value. Comparison with Figure 11 in Section 9.2 shows that we were able to draw a fairly accurate solution curve from the direction field.

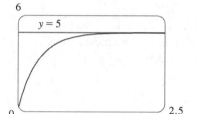

FIGURE 6

Since $I(0) = 0$, we have $5 - \tfrac{1}{3} A = 0$, so $A = 15$ and the solution is

$$I(t) = 5 - 5 e^{-3t}$$

The limiting current, in amperes, is

$$\lim_{t \to \infty} I(t) = \lim_{t \to \infty} (5 - 5 e^{-3t}) = 5 - 5 \lim_{t \to \infty} e^{-3t} = 5 - 0 = 5$$

Orthogonal Trajectories

An **orthogonal trajectory** of a family of curves is a curve that intersects each curve of the family orthogonally, that is, at right angles (see Figure 7). For instance, each member of the family $y = mx$ of straight lines through the origin is an orthogonal trajectory of the family $x^2 + y^2 = r^2$ of concentric circles with center the origin (see Figure 8). We say that the two families are orthogonal trajectories of each other.

orthogonal
trajectory

FIGURE 7

FIGURE 8

V EXAMPLE 5 Find the orthogonal trajectories of the family of curves $x = ky^2$, where k is an arbitrary constant.

SOLUTION The curves $x = ky^2$ form a family of parabolas whose axis of symmetry is the x-axis. The first step is to find a single differential equation that is satisfied by all members of the family. If we differentiate $x = ky^2$, we get

$$1 = 2ky \frac{dy}{dx} \qquad \text{or} \qquad \frac{dy}{dx} = \frac{1}{2ky}$$

This differential equation depends on k, but we need an equation that is valid for all values of k simultaneously. To eliminate k we note that, from the equation of the given general parabola $x = ky^2$, we have $k = x/y^2$ and so the differential equation can be written as

$$\frac{dy}{dx} = \frac{1}{2ky} = \frac{1}{2 \dfrac{x}{y^2} y}$$

or

$$\frac{dy}{dx} = \frac{y}{2x}$$

This means that the slope of the tangent line at any point (x, y) on one of the parabolas is $y' = y/(2x)$. On an orthogonal trajectory the slope of the tangent line must be the negative reciprocal of this slope. Therefore the orthogonal trajectories must satisfy the differential equation

$$\frac{dy}{dx} = -\frac{2x}{y}$$

This differential equation is separable, and we solve it as follows:

$$\int y \, dy = -\int 2x \, dx$$

$$\frac{y^2}{2} = -x^2 + C$$

4 $$x^2 + \frac{y^2}{2} = C$$

where C is an arbitrary positive constant. Thus the orthogonal trajectories are the family of ellipses given by Equation 4 and sketched in Figure 9. ∎

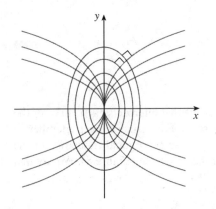

FIGURE 9

Orthogonal trajectories occur in various branches of physics. For example, in an electrostatic field the lines of force are orthogonal to the lines of constant potential. Also, the streamlines in aerodynamics are orthogonal trajectories of the velocity-equipotential curves.

Mixing Problems

A typical mixing problem involves a tank of fixed capacity filled with a thoroughly mixed solution of some substance, such as salt. A solution of a given concentration enters the tank at a fixed rate and the mixture, thoroughly stirred, leaves at a fixed rate, which may differ from the entering rate. If $y(t)$ denotes the amount of substance in the tank at time t, then $y'(t)$ is the rate at which the substance is being added minus the rate at which it is being removed. The mathematical description of this situation often leads to a first-order separable differential equation. We can use the same type of reasoning to model a variety of phenomena: chemical reactions, discharge of pollutants into a lake, injection of a drug into the bloodstream.

EXAMPLE 6 A tank contains 20 kg of salt dissolved in 5000 L of water. Brine that contains 0.03 kg of salt per liter of water enters the tank at a rate of 25 L/min. The solution is kept thoroughly mixed and drains from the tank at the same rate. How much salt remains in the tank after half an hour?

SOLUTION Let $y(t)$ be the amount of salt (in kilograms) after t minutes. We are given that $y(0) = 20$ and we want to find $y(30)$. We do this by finding a differential equation satisfied by $y(t)$. Note that dy/dt is the rate of change of the amount of salt, so

$$\boxed{5} \qquad \frac{dy}{dt} = (\text{rate in}) - (\text{rate out})$$

where (rate in) is the rate at which salt enters the tank and (rate out) is the rate at which salt leaves the tank. We have

$$\text{rate in} = \left(0.03\,\frac{\text{kg}}{\text{L}}\right)\left(25\,\frac{\text{L}}{\text{min}}\right) = 0.75\,\frac{\text{kg}}{\text{min}}$$

The tank always contains 5000 L of liquid, so the concentration at time t is $y(t)/5000$ (measured in kilograms per liter). Since the brine flows out at a rate of 25 L/min, we have

$$\text{rate out} = \left(\frac{y(t)}{5000}\,\frac{\text{kg}}{\text{L}}\right)\left(25\,\frac{\text{L}}{\text{min}}\right) = \frac{y(t)}{200}\,\frac{\text{kg}}{\text{min}}$$

Thus, from Equation 5, we get

$$\frac{dy}{dt} = 0.75 - \frac{y(t)}{200} = \frac{150 - y(t)}{200}$$

Solving this separable differential equation, we obtain

$$\int \frac{dy}{150 - y} = \int \frac{dt}{200}$$

$$-\ln|150 - y| = \frac{t}{200} + C$$

Since $y(0) = 20$, we have $-\ln 130 = C$, so

$$-\ln|150 - y| = \frac{t}{200} - \ln 130$$

Therefore $\qquad |150 - y| = 130e^{-t/200}$

Since $y(t)$ is continuous and $y(0) = 20$ and the right side is never 0, we deduce that $150 - y(t)$ is always positive. Thus $|150 - y| = 150 - y$ and so

$$y(t) = 150 - 130e^{-t/200}$$

The amount of salt after 30 min is

$$y(30) = 150 - 130e^{-30/200} \approx 38.1\text{ kg}$$

Figure 10 shows the graph of the function $y(t)$ of Example 6. Notice that, as time goes by, the amount of salt approaches 150 kg.

FIGURE 10

9.3 Exercises

1–10 Solve the differential equation.

1. $\dfrac{dy}{dx} = \dfrac{y}{x}$

2. $\dfrac{dy}{dx} = \dfrac{\sqrt{x}}{e^y}$

3. $xy^2 y' = x + 1$

4. $(y^2 + xy^2)y' = 1$

5. $(y + \sin y)y' = x + x^3$

6. $\dfrac{dv}{ds} = \dfrac{s + 1}{sv + s}$

7. $\dfrac{dy}{dt} = \dfrac{t}{ye^{y + t^2}}$

8. $\dfrac{dy}{d\theta} = \dfrac{e^y \sin^2\theta}{y \sec \theta}$

9. $\dfrac{dp}{dt} = t^2 p - p + t^2 - 1$

10. $\dfrac{dz}{dt} + e^{t+z} = 0$

11–18 Find the solution of the differential equation that satisfies the given initial condition.

11. $\dfrac{dy}{dx} = \dfrac{x}{y}, \quad y(0) = -3$

12. $\dfrac{dy}{dx} = \dfrac{\ln x}{xy}, \quad y(1) = 2$

13. $\dfrac{du}{dt} = \dfrac{2t + \sec^2 t}{2u}, \quad u(0) = -5$

14. $y' = \dfrac{xy \sin x}{y + 1}, \quad y(0) = 1$

15. $x \ln x = y\left(1 + \sqrt{3 + y^2}\,\right)y', \quad y(1) = 1$

16. $\dfrac{dP}{dt} = \sqrt{Pt}, \quad P(1) = 2$

17. $y' \tan x = a + y, \quad y(\pi/3) = a, \quad 0 < x < \pi/2$

18. $\dfrac{dL}{dt} = kL^2 \ln t, \quad L(1) = -1$

19. Find an equation of the curve that passes through the point $(0, 1)$ and whose slope at (x, y) is xy.

20. Find the function f such that $f'(x) = f(x)(1 - f(x))$ and $f(0) = \frac{1}{2}$.

21. Solve the differential equation $y' = x + y$ by making the change of variable $u = x + y$.

22. Solve the differential equation $xy' = y + xe^{y/x}$ by making the change of variable $v = y/x$.

23. (a) Solve the differential equation $y' = 2x\sqrt{1 - y^2}$.
  (b) Solve the initial-value problem $y' = 2x\sqrt{1 - y^2}$, $y(0) = 0$ and graph the solution.
  (c) Does the initial-value problem $y' = 2x\sqrt{1 - y^2}$, $y(0) = 2$, have a solution? Explain.

24. Solve the equation $e^{-y}y' + \cos x = 0$ and graph several members of the family of solutions. How does the solution curve change as the constant C varies?

CAS 25. Solve the initial-value problem $y' = (\sin x)/\sin y$, $y(0) = \pi/2$, and graph the solution (if your CAS does implicit plots).

CAS 26. Solve the equation $y' = x\sqrt{x^2 + 1}/(ye^y)$ and graph several members of the family of solutions (if your CAS does implicit plots). How does the solution curve change as the constant C varies?

CAS 27–28
  (a) Use a computer algebra system to draw a direction field for the differential equation. Get a printout and use it to sketch some solution curves without solving the differential equation.
  (b) Solve the differential equation.
  (c) Use the CAS to draw several members of the family of solutions obtained in part (b). Compare with the curves from part (a).

27. $y' = y^2$

28. $y' = xy$

29–32 Find the orthogonal trajectories of the family of curves. Use a graphing device to draw several members of each family on a common screen.

29. $x^2 + 2y^2 = k^2$

30. $y^2 = kx^3$

31. $y = \dfrac{k}{x}$

32. $y = \dfrac{x}{1 + kx}$

33–35 An **integral equation** is an equation that contains an unknown function $y(x)$ and an integral that involves $y(x)$. Solve the given integral equation. [*Hint:* Use an initial condition obtained from the integral equation.]

33. $y(x) = 2 + \displaystyle\int_2^x [t - ty(t)]\, dt$

34. $y(x) = 2 + \displaystyle\int_1^x \dfrac{dt}{ty(t)}, \quad x > 0$

35. $y(x) = 4 + \displaystyle\int_0^x 2t\sqrt{y(t)}\, dt$

Graphing calculator or computer required | **CAS** Computer algebra system required | **1.** Homework Hints available at stewartcalculus.com

36. Find a function f such that $f(3) = 2$ and

$$(t^2 + 1)f'(t) + [f(t)]^2 + 1 = 0 \qquad t \neq 1$$

[*Hint*: Use the addition formula for $\tan(x + y)$ on Reference Page 2.]

37. Solve the initial-value problem in Exercise 27 in Section 9.2 to find an expression for the charge at time t. Find the limiting value of the charge.

38. In Exercise 28 in Section 9.2 we discussed a differential equation that models the temperature of a 95°C cup of coffee in a 20°C room. Solve the differential equation to find an expression for the temperature of the coffee at time t.

39. In Exercise 15 in Section 9.1 we formulated a model for learning in the form of the differential equation

$$\frac{dP}{dt} = k(M - P)$$

where $P(t)$ measures the performance of someone learning a skill after a training time t, M is the maximum level of performance, and k is a positive constant. Solve this differential equation to find an expression for $P(t)$. What is the limit of this expression?

40. In an elementary chemical reaction, single molecules of two reactants A and B form a molecule of the product C: A + B → C. The law of mass action states that the rate of reaction is proportional to the product of the concentrations of A and B:

$$\frac{d[C]}{dt} = k[A][B]$$

(See Example 4 in Section 3.7.) Thus, if the initial concentrations are $[A] = a$ moles/L and $[B] = b$ moles/L and we write $x = [C]$, then we have

$$\frac{dx}{dt} = k(a - x)(b - x)$$

(a) Assuming that $a \neq b$, find x as a function of t. Use the fact that the initial concentration of C is 0.
(b) Find $x(t)$ assuming that $a = b$. How does this expression for $x(t)$ simplify if it is known that $[C] = \frac{1}{2}a$ after 20 seconds?

41. In contrast to the situation of Exercise 40, experiments show that the reaction $H_2 + Br_2 \rightarrow 2HBr$ satisfies the rate law

$$\frac{d[HBr]}{dt} = k[H_2][Br_2]^{1/2}$$

and so for this reaction the differential equation becomes

$$\frac{dx}{dt} = k(a - x)(b - x)^{1/2}$$

where $x = [HBr]$ and a and b are the initial concentrations of hydrogen and bromine.
(a) Find x as a function of t in the case where $a = b$. Use the fact that $x(0) = 0$.

(b) If $a > b$, find t as a function of x. [*Hint*: In performing the integration, make the substitution $u = \sqrt{b - x}$.]

42. A sphere with radius 1 m has temperature 15°C. It lies inside a concentric sphere with radius 2 m and temperature 25°C. The temperature $T(r)$ at a distance r from the common center of the spheres satisfies the differential equation

$$\frac{d^2T}{dr^2} + \frac{2}{r}\frac{dT}{dr} = 0$$

If we let $S = dT/dr$, then S satisfies a first-order differential equation. Solve it to find an expression for the temperature $T(r)$ between the spheres.

43. A glucose solution is administered intravenously into the bloodstream at a constant rate r. As the glucose is added, it is converted into other substances and removed from the bloodstream at a rate that is proportional to the concentration at that time. Thus a model for the concentration $C = C(t)$ of the glucose solution in the bloodstream is

$$\frac{dC}{dt} = r - kC$$

where k is a positive constant.
(a) Suppose that the concentration at time $t = 0$ is C_0. Determine the concentration at any time t by solving the differential equation.
(b) Assuming that $C_0 < r/k$, find $\lim_{t \to \infty} C(t)$ and interpret your answer.

44. A certain small country has $10 billion in paper currency in circulation, and each day $50 million comes into the country's banks. The government decides to introduce new currency by having the banks replace old bills with new ones whenever old currency comes into the banks. Let $x = x(t)$ denote the amount of new currency in circulation at time t, with $x(0) = 0$.
(a) Formulate a mathematical model in the form of an initial-value problem that represents the "flow" of the new currency into circulation.
(b) Solve the initial-value problem found in part (a).
(c) How long will it take for the new bills to account for 90% of the currency in circulation?

45. A tank contains 1000 L of brine with 15 kg of dissolved salt. Pure water enters the tank at a rate of 10 L/min. The solution is kept thoroughly mixed and drains from the tank at the same rate. How much salt is in the tank (a) after t minutes and (b) after 20 minutes?

46. The air in a room with volume 180 m³ contains 0.15% carbon dioxide initially. Fresher air with only 0.05% carbon dioxide flows into the room at a rate of 2 m³/min and the mixed air flows out at the same rate. Find the percentage of carbon dioxide in the room as a function of time. What happens in the long run?

47. A vat with 2000 L of beer contains 4% alcohol (by volume). Beer with 6% alcohol is pumped into the vat at a rate of 20 L/min and the mixture is pumped out at the same rate. What is the percentage of alcohol after an hour?

48. A tank contains 1000 L of pure water. Brine that contains 0.05 kg of salt per liter of water enters the tank at a rate of 5 L/min. Brine that contains 0.04 kg of salt per liter of water enters the tank at a rate of 10 L/min. The solution is kept thoroughly mixed and drains from the tank at a rate of 15 L/min. How much salt is in the tank (a) after t minutes and (b) after one hour?

49. When a raindrop falls, it increases in size and so its mass at time t is a function of t, namely $m(t)$. The rate of growth of the mass is $km(t)$ for some positive constant k. When we apply Newton's Law of Motion to the raindrop, we get $(mv)' = gm$, where v is the velocity of the raindrop (directed downward) and g is the acceleration due to gravity. The *terminal velocity* of the raindrop is $\lim_{t \to \infty} v(t)$. Find an expression for the terminal velocity in terms of g and k.

50. An object of mass m is moving horizontally through a medium which resists the motion with a force that is a function of the velocity; that is,

$$m \frac{d^2 s}{dt^2} = m \frac{dv}{dt} = f(v)$$

where $v = v(t)$ and $s = s(t)$ represent the velocity and position of the object at time t, respectively. For example, think of a boat moving through the water.

(a) Suppose that the resisting force is proportional to the velocity, that is, $f(v) = -kv$, k a positive constant. (This model is appropriate for small values of v.) Let $v(0) = v_0$ and $s(0) = s_0$ be the initial values of v and s. Determine v and s at any time t. What is the total distance that the object travels from time $t = 0$?

(b) For larger values of v a better model is obtained by supposing that the resisting force is proportional to the square of the velocity, that is, $f(v) = -kv^2$, $k > 0$. (This model was first proposed by Newton.) Let v_0 and s_0 be the initial values of v and s. Determine v and s at any time t. What is the total distance that the object travels in this case?

51. *Allometric growth* in biology refers to relationships between sizes of parts of an organism (skull length and body length, for instance). If $L_1(t)$ and $L_2(t)$ are the sizes of two organs in an organism of age t, then L_1 and L_2 satisfy an allometric law if their specific growth rates are proportional:

$$\frac{1}{L_1} \frac{dL_1}{dt} = k \frac{1}{L_2} \frac{dL_2}{dt}$$

where k is a constant.

(a) Use the allometric law to write a differential equation relating L_1 and L_2 and solve it to express L_1 as a function of L_2.

(b) In a study of several species of unicellular algae, the proportionality constant in the allometric law relating B (cell biomass) and V (cell volume) was found to be $k = 0.0794$. Write B as a function of V.

52. *Homeostasis* refers to a state in which the nutrient content of a consumer is independent of the nutrient content of its food. In the absence of homeostasis, a model proposed by Sterner and Elser is given by

$$\frac{dy}{dx} = \frac{1}{\theta} \frac{y}{x}$$

where x and y represent the nutrient content of the food and the consumer, respectively, and θ is a constant with $\theta \geq 1$.

(a) Solve the differential equation.

(b) What happens when $\theta = 1$? What happens when $\theta \to \infty$?

53. Let $A(t)$ be the area of a tissue culture at time t and let M be the final area of the tissue when growth is complete. Most cell divisions occur on the periphery of the tissue and the number of cells on the periphery is proportional to $\sqrt{A(t)}$. So a reasonable model for the growth of tissue is obtained by assuming that the rate of growth of the area is jointly proportional to $\sqrt{A(t)}$ and $M - A(t)$.

(a) Formulate a differential equation and use it to show that the tissue grows fastest when $A(t) = \frac{1}{3} M$.

CAS (b) Solve the differential equation to find an expression for $A(t)$. Use a computer algebra system to perform the integration.

54. According to Newton's Law of Universal Gravitation, the gravitational force on an object of mass m that has been projected vertically upward from the earth's surface is

$$F = \frac{mgR^2}{(x + R)^2}$$

where $x = x(t)$ is the object's distance above the surface at time t, R is the earth's radius, and g is the acceleration due to gravity. Also, by Newton's Second Law, $F = ma = m(dv/dt)$ and so

$$m \frac{dv}{dt} = -\frac{mgR^2}{(x + R)^2}$$

(a) Suppose a rocket is fired vertically upward with an initial velocity v_0. Let h be the maximum height above the surface reached by the object. Show that

$$v_0 = \sqrt{\frac{2gRh}{R + h}}$$

[*Hint:* By the Chain Rule, $m(dv/dt) = mv(dv/dx)$.]

(b) Calculate $v_e = \lim_{h \to \infty} v_0$. This limit is called the *escape velocity* for the earth.

(c) Use $R = 6370$ km and $g = 9.8$ m/s^2 to calculate v_e in kilometers per second.

HOW FAST DOES A TANK DRAIN?

If water (or other liquid) drains from a tank, we expect that the flow will be greatest at first (when the water depth is greatest) and will gradually decrease as the water level decreases. But we need a more precise mathematical description of how the flow decreases in order to answer the kinds of questions that engineers ask: How long does it take for a tank to drain completely? How much water should a tank hold in order to guarantee a certain minimum water pressure for a sprinkler system?

Let $h(t)$ and $V(t)$ be the height and volume of water in a tank at time t. If water drains through a hole with area a at the bottom of the tank, then Torricelli's Law says that

$$\boxed{1} \qquad \frac{dV}{dt} = -a\sqrt{2gh}$$

where g is the acceleration due to gravity. So the rate at which water flows from the tank is proportional to the square root of the water height.

1. (a) Suppose the tank is cylindrical with height 2 m and radius 1 m and the hole is circular with radius 2 cm. If we take $g = 10$ m/s^2, show that h satisfies the differential equation

$$\frac{dh}{dt} = -0.0004\sqrt{20h}$$

   (b) Solve this equation to find the height of the water at time t, assuming the tank is full at time $t = 0$.

   (c) How long will it take for the water to drain completely?

2. Because of the rotation and viscosity of the liquid, the theoretical model given by Equation 1 isn't quite accurate. Instead, the model

$$\boxed{2} \qquad \frac{dh}{dt} = k\sqrt{h}$$

is often used and the constant k (which depends on the physical properties of the liquid) is determined from data concerning the draining of the tank.

   (a) Suppose that a hole is drilled in the side of a cylindrical bottle and the height h of the water (above the hole) decreases from 10 cm to 3 cm in 68 seconds. Use Equation 2 to find an expression for $h(t)$. Evaluate $h(t)$ for $t = 10, 20, 30, 40, 50, 60$.

   (b) Drill a 4-mm hole near the bottom of the cylindrical part of a two-liter plastic soft-drink bottle. Attach a strip of masking tape marked in centimeters from 0 to 10, with 0 corresponding to the top of the hole. With one finger over the hole, fill the bottle with water to the 10-cm mark. Then take your finger off the hole and record the values of $h(t)$ for $t = 10, 20, 30, 40, 50, 60$ seconds. (You will probably find that it takes 68 seconds for the level to decrease to $h = 3$ cm.) Compare your data with the values of $h(t)$ from part (a). How well did the model predict the actual values?

3. In many parts of the world, the water for sprinkler systems in large hotels and hospitals is supplied by gravity from cylindrical tanks on or near the roofs of the buildings. Suppose such a tank has radius 3 m and the diameter of the outlet is 6 cm. An engineer has to guarantee that the water pressure will be at least 104 kPa for a period of 10 minutes. (When a fire happens, the electrical system might fail and it could take up to 10 minutes for the emergency generator and fire pump to be activated.) What height should the engineer specify for the tank in order to make such a guarantee? (Use the fact that the water pressure at a depth of d meters is $P = 10d$ kilopascals. See Section 8.3.)

Problem 2(b) is best done as a classroom demonstration or as a group project with three students in each group: a timekeeper to call out seconds, a bottle keeper to estimate the height every 10 seconds, and a record keeper to record these values.

© Richard Le Borne, Dept. Mathematics, Tennessee Technological University

4. Not all water tanks are shaped like cylinders. Suppose a tank has cross-sectional area $A(h)$ at height h. Then the volume of water up to height h is $V = \int_0^h A(u)\,du$ and so the Fundamental Theorem of Calculus gives $dV/dh = A(h)$. It follows that

$$\frac{dV}{dt} = \frac{dV}{dh}\frac{dh}{dt} = A(h)\frac{dh}{dt}$$

and so Torricelli's Law becomes

$$A(h)\frac{dh}{dt} = -a\sqrt{2gh}$$

(a) Suppose the tank has the shape of a sphere with radius 2 m and is initially half full of water. If the radius of the circular hole is 1 cm and we take $g = 10$ m/s^2, show that h satisfies the differential equation

$$(4h - h^2)\frac{dh}{dt} = -0.0001\sqrt{20h}$$

(b) How long will it take for the water to drain completely?

APPLIED PROJECT

WHICH IS FASTER, GOING UP OR COMING DOWN?

Suppose you throw a ball into the air. Do you think it takes longer to reach its maximum height or to fall back to earth from its maximum height? We will solve the problem in this project but, before getting started, think about that situation and make a guess based on your physical intuition.

In modeling force due to air resistance, various functions have been used, depending on the physical characteristics and speed of the ball. Here we use a linear model, $-pv$, but a quadratic model ($-pv^2$ on the way up and pv^2 on the way down) is another possibility for higher speeds (see Exercise 50 in Section 9.3). For a golf ball, experiments have shown that a good model is $-pv^{1.3}$ going up and $p|v|^{1.3}$ coming down. But no matter which force function $-f(v)$ is used [where $f(v) > 0$ for $v > 0$ and $f(v) < 0$ for $v < 0$], the answer to the question remains the same. See F. Brauer, "What Goes Up Must Come Down, Eventually," *Amer. Math. Monthly* 108 (2001), pp. 437–440.

1. A ball with mass m is projected vertically upward from the earth's surface with a positive initial velocity v_0. We assume the forces acting on the ball are the force of gravity and a retarding force of air resistance with direction opposite to the direction of motion and with magnitude $p|v(t)|$, where p is a positive constant and $v(t)$ is the velocity of the ball at time t. In both the ascent and the descent, the total force acting on the ball is $-pv - mg$. [During ascent, $v(t)$ is positive and the resistance acts downward; during descent, $v(t)$ is negative and the resistance acts upward.] So, by Newton's Second Law, the equation of motion is

$$mv' = -pv - mg$$

Solve this differential equation to show that the velocity is

$$v(t) = \left(v_0 + \frac{mg}{p}\right)e^{-pt/m} - \frac{mg}{p}$$

2. Show that the height of the ball, until it hits the ground, is

$$y(t) = \left(v_0 + \frac{mg}{p}\right)\frac{m}{p}\left(1 - e^{-pt/m}\right) - \frac{mgt}{p}$$

Graphing calculator or computer required

3. Let t_1 be the time that the ball takes to reach its maximum height. Show that

$$t_1 = \frac{m}{p} \ln\left(\frac{mg + pv_0}{mg}\right)$$

Find this time for a ball with mass 1 kg and initial velocity 20 m/s. Assume the air resistance is $\frac{1}{10}$ of the speed.

4. Let t_2 be the time at which the ball falls back to earth. For the particular ball in Problem 3, estimate t_2 by using a graph of the height function $y(t)$. Which is faster, going up or coming down?

5. In general, it's not easy to find t_2 because it's impossible to solve the equation $y(t) = 0$ explicitly. We can, however, use an indirect method to determine whether ascent or descent is faster: we determine whether $y(2t_1)$ is positive or negative. Show that

$$y(2t_1) = \frac{m^2 g}{p^2}\left(x - \frac{1}{x} - 2\ln x\right)$$

where $x = e^{pt_1/m}$. Then show that $x > 1$ and the function

$$f(x) = x - \frac{1}{x} - 2\ln x$$

is increasing for $x > 1$. Use this result to decide whether $y(2t_1)$ is positive or negative. What can you conclude? Is ascent or descent faster?

9.4 **Models for Population Growth**

In this section we investigate differential equations that are used to model population growth: the law of natural growth, the logistic equation, and several others.

■ The Law of Natural Growth

One of the models for population growth that we considered in Section 9.1 was based on the assumption that the population grows at a rate proportional to the size of the population:

$$\frac{dP}{dt} = kP$$

Is that a reasonable assumption? Suppose we have a population (of bacteria, for instance) with size $P = 1000$ and at a certain time it is growing at a rate of $P' = 300$ bacteria per hour. Now let's take another 1000 bacteria of the same type and put them with the first population. Each half of the combined population was previously growing at a rate of 300 bacteria per hour. We would expect the total population of 2000 to increase at a rate of 600 bacteria per hour initially (provided there's enough room and nutrition). So if we double the size, we double the growth rate. It seems reasonable that the growth rate should be proportional to the size.

In general, if $P(t)$ is the value of a quantity y at time t and if the rate of change of P with respect to t is proportional to its size $P(t)$ at any time, then

1
$$\frac{dP}{dt} = kP$$

where k is a constant. Equation 1 is sometimes called the **law of natural growth**. If k is positive, then the population increases; if k is negative, it decreases.

Because Equation 1 is a separable differential equation, we can solve it by the methods of Section 9.3:

$$\int \frac{dP}{P} = \int k \, dt$$

$$\ln |P| = kt + C$$

$$|P| = e^{kt+C} = e^C e^{kt}$$

$$P = Ae^{kt}$$

where $A \, (= \pm e^C \text{ or } 0)$ is an arbitrary constant. To see the significance of the constant A, we observe that

$$P(0) = Ae^{k \cdot 0} = A$$

Therefore A is the initial value of the function.

Examples and exercises on the use of $\boxed{2}$ are given in Section 3.8.

> $\boxed{2}$ The solution of the initial-value problem
>
> $$\frac{dP}{dt} = kP \qquad P(0) = P_0$$
>
> is
> $$P(t) = P_0 e^{kt}$$

Another way of writing Equation 1 is

$$\frac{1}{P} \frac{dP}{dt} = k$$

which says that the **relative growth rate** (the growth rate divided by the population size) is constant. Then $\boxed{2}$ says that a population with constant relative growth rate must grow exponentially.

We can account for emigration (or "harvesting") from a population by modifying Equation 1: If the rate of emigration is a constant m, then the rate of change of the population is modeled by the differential equation

$$\boxed{3} \qquad\qquad \frac{dP}{dt} = kP - m$$

See Exercise 15 for the solution and consequences of Equation 3.

▮ The Logistic Model

As we discussed in Section 9.1, a population often increases exponentially in its early stages but levels off eventually and approaches its carrying capacity because of limited resources. If $P(t)$ is the size of the population at time t, we assume that

$$\frac{dP}{dt} \approx kP \qquad \text{if } P \text{ is small}$$

This says that the growth rate is initially close to being proportional to size. In other words, the relative growth rate is almost constant when the population is small. But we also want to reflect the fact that the relative growth rate decreases as the population P increases and becomes negative if P ever exceeds its **carrying capacity** M, the maximum population that the environment is capable of sustaining in the long run. The simplest expression for the relative growth rate that incorporates these assumptions is

$$\frac{1}{P}\frac{dP}{dt} = k\left(1 - \frac{P}{M}\right)$$

Multiplying by P, we obtain the model for population growth known as the **logistic differential equation**:

4
$$\frac{dP}{dt} = kP\left(1 - \frac{P}{M}\right)$$

Notice from Equation 4 that if P is small compared with M, then P/M is close to 0 and so $dP/dt \approx kP$. However, if $P \to M$ (the population approaches its carrying capacity), then $P/M \to 1$, so $dP/dt \to 0$. We can deduce information about whether solutions increase or decrease directly from Equation 4. If the population P lies between 0 and M, then the right side of the equation is positive, so $dP/dt > 0$ and the population increases. But if the population exceeds the carrying capacity ($P > M$), then $1 - P/M$ is negative, so $dP/dt < 0$ and the population decreases.

Let's start our more detailed analysis of the logistic differential equation by looking at a direction field.

V **EXAMPLE 1** Draw a direction field for the logistic equation with $k = 0.08$ and carrying capacity $M = 1000$. What can you deduce about the solutions?

SOLUTION In this case the logistic differential equation is

$$\frac{dP}{dt} = 0.08P\left(1 - \frac{P}{1000}\right)$$

A direction field for this equation is shown in Figure 1. We show only the first quadrant because negative populations aren't meaningful and we are interested only in what happens after $t = 0$.

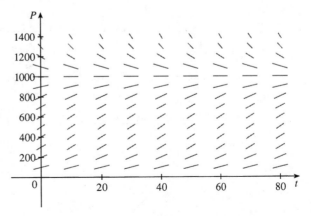

FIGURE 1
Direction field for the logistic equation in Example 1

The logistic equation is autonomous (dP/dt depends only on P, not on t), so the slopes are the same along any horizontal line. As expected, the slopes are positive for $0 < P < 1000$ and negative for $P > 1000$.

The slopes are small when P is close to 0 or 1000 (the carrying capacity). Notice that the solutions move away from the equilibrium solution $P = 0$ and move toward the equilibrium solution $P = 1000$.

In Figure 2 we use the direction field to sketch solution curves with initial populations $P(0) = 100$, $P(0) = 400$, and $P(0) = 1300$. Notice that solution curves that start below $P = 1000$ are increasing and those that start above $P = 1000$ are decreasing. The slopes are greatest when $P \approx 500$ and therefore the solution curves that start below $P = 1000$ have inflection points when $P \approx 500$. In fact we can prove that all solution curves that start below $P = 500$ have an inflection point when P is exactly 500. (See Exercise 11.)

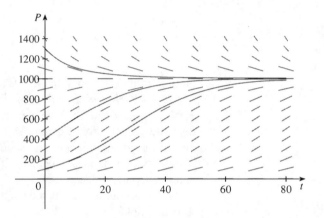

FIGURE 2

Solution curves for the logistic equation in Example 1

The logistic equation ④ is separable and so we can solve it explicitly using the method of Section 9.3. Since

$$\frac{dP}{dt} = kP\left(1 - \frac{P}{M}\right)$$

we have

⑤
$$\int \frac{dP}{P(1 - P/M)} = \int k\, dt$$

To evaluate the integral on the left side, we write

$$\frac{1}{P(1 - P/M)} = \frac{M}{P(M - P)}$$

Using partial fractions (see Section 7.4), we get

$$\frac{M}{P(M - P)} = \frac{1}{P} + \frac{1}{M - P}$$

This enables us to rewrite Equation 5:

$$\int \left(\frac{1}{P} + \frac{1}{M - P} \right) dP = \int k \, dt$$

$$\ln |P| - \ln |M - P| = kt + C$$

$$\ln \left| \frac{M - P}{P} \right| = -kt - C$$

$$\left| \frac{M - P}{P} \right| = e^{-kt - C} = e^{-C} e^{-kt}$$

6
$$\frac{M - P}{P} = Ae^{-kt}$$

where $A = \pm e^{-C}$. Solving Equation 6 for P, we get

$$\frac{M}{P} - 1 = Ae^{-kt} \qquad \Rightarrow \qquad \frac{P}{M} = \frac{1}{1 + Ae^{-kt}}$$

so
$$P = \frac{M}{1 + Ae^{-kt}}$$

We find the value of A by putting $t = 0$ in Equation 6. If $t = 0$, then $P = P_0$ (the initial population), so

$$\frac{M - P_0}{P_0} = Ae^0 = A$$

Thus the solution to the logistic equation is

7
$$P(t) = \frac{M}{1 + Ae^{-kt}} \qquad \text{where} \quad A = \frac{M - P_0}{P_0}$$

Using the expression for $P(t)$ in Equation 7, we see that

$$\lim_{t \to \infty} P(t) = M$$

which is to be expected.

EXAMPLE 2 Write the solution of the initial-value problem

$$\frac{dP}{dt} = 0.08P \left(1 - \frac{P}{1000} \right) \qquad P(0) = 100$$

and use it to find the population sizes $P(40)$ and $P(80)$. At what time does the population reach 900?

SOLUTION The differential equation is a logistic equation with $k = 0.08$, carrying capacity $M = 1000$, and initial population $P_0 = 100$. So Equation 7 gives the

population at time t as

$$P(t) = \frac{1000}{1 + Ae^{-0.08t}} \qquad \text{where } A = \frac{1000 - 100}{100} = 9$$

Thus

$$P(t) = \frac{1000}{1 + 9e^{-0.08t}}$$

So the population sizes when $t = 40$ and 80 are

$$P(40) = \frac{1000}{1 + 9e^{-3.2}} \approx 731.6 \qquad P(80) = \frac{1000}{1 + 9e^{-6.4}} \approx 985.3$$

The population reaches 900 when

$$\frac{1000}{1 + 9e^{-0.08t}} = 900$$

Solving this equation for t, we get

$$1 + 9e^{-0.08t} = \tfrac{10}{9}$$

$$e^{-0.08t} = \tfrac{1}{81}$$

$$-0.08t = \ln\tfrac{1}{81} = -\ln 81$$

$$t = \frac{\ln 81}{0.08} \approx 54.9$$

So the population reaches 900 when t is approximately 55. As a check on our work, we graph the population curve in Figure 3 and observe where it intersects the line $P = 900$. The cursor indicates that $t \approx 55$.

Compare the solution curve in Figure 3 with the lowest solution curve we drew from the direction field in Figure 2.

FIGURE 3

▪ Comparison of the Natural Growth and Logistic Models

In the 1930s the biologist G. F. Gause conducted an experiment with the protozoan *Paramecium* and used a logistic equation to model his data. The table gives his daily count of the population of protozoa. He estimated the initial relative growth rate to be 0.7944 and the carrying capacity to be 64.

t (days)	0	1	2	3	4	5	6	7	8	9	10	11	12	13	14	15	16
P (observed)	2	3	22	16	39	52	54	47	50	76	69	51	57	70	53	59	57

V EXAMPLE 3 Find the exponential and logistic models for Gause's data. Compare the predicted values with the observed values and comment on the fit.

SOLUTION Given the relative growth rate $k = 0.7944$ and the initial population $P_0 = 2$, the exponential model is

$$P(t) = P_0 e^{kt} = 2e^{0.7944t}$$

Gause used the same value of k for his logistic model. [This is reasonable because $P_0 = 2$ is small compared with the carrying capacity ($M = 64$). The equation

$$\frac{1}{P_0} \frac{dP}{dt}\bigg|_{t=0} = k\left(1 - \frac{2}{64}\right) \approx k$$

shows that the value of k for the logistic model is very close to the value for the exponential model.]

Then the solution of the logistic equation in Equation 7 gives

$$P(t) = \frac{M}{1 + Ae^{-kt}} = \frac{64}{1 + Ae^{-0.7944t}}$$

where

$$A = \frac{M - P_0}{P_0} = \frac{64 - 2}{2} = 31$$

So

$$P(t) = \frac{64}{1 + 31e^{-0.7944t}}$$

We use these equations to calculate the predicted values (rounded to the nearest integer) and compare them in the following table.

t (days)	0	1	2	3	4	5	6	7	8	9	10	11	12	13	14	15	16
P (observed)	2	3	22	16	39	52	54	47	50	76	69	51	57	70	53	59	57
P (logistic model)	2	4	9	17	28	40	51	57	61	62	63	64	64	64	64	64	64
P (exponential model)	2	4	10	22	48	106	$\cdots$										

We notice from the table and from the graph in Figure 4 that for the first three or four days the exponential model gives results comparable to those of the more sophisticated logistic model. For $t \geq 5$, however, the exponential model is hopelessly inaccurate, but the logistic model fits the observations reasonably well.

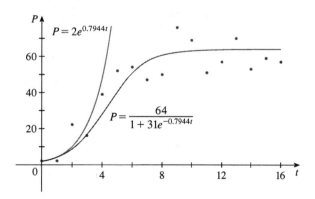

FIGURE 4

The exponential and logistic models for the *Paramecium* data

Many countries that formerly experienced exponential growth are now finding that their rates of population growth are declining and the logistic model provides a better model.

t	$B(t)$	t	$B(t)$
1980	9,847	1992	10,036
1982	9,856	1994	10,109
1984	9,855	1996	10,152
1986	9,862	1998	10,175
1988	9,884	2000	10,186
1990	9,962		

The table in the margin shows midyear values of $B(t)$, the population of Belgium, in thousands, at time t, from 1980 to 2000. Figure 5 shows these data points together with a shifted logistic function obtained from a calculator with the ability to fit a logistic function to these points by regression. We see that the logistic model provides a very good fit.

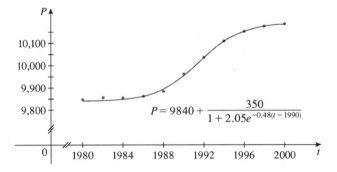

FIGURE 5

Logistic model for
the population of Belgium

Other Models for Population Growth

The Law of Natural Growth and the logistic differential equation are not the only equations that have been proposed to model population growth. In Exercise 20 we look at the Gompertz growth function and in Exercises 21 and 22 we investigate seasonal-growth models.

Two of the other models are modifications of the logistic model. The differential equation

$$\frac{dP}{dt} = kP\left(1 - \frac{P}{M}\right) - c$$

has been used to model populations that are subject to harvesting of one sort or another. (Think of a population of fish being caught at a constant rate.) This equation is explored in Exercises 17 and 18.

For some species there is a minimum population level m below which the species tends to become extinct. (Adults may not be able to find suitable mates.) Such populations have been modeled by the differential equation

$$\frac{dP}{dt} = kP\left(1 - \frac{P}{M}\right)\left(1 - \frac{m}{P}\right)$$

where the extra factor, $1 - m/P$, takes into account the consequences of a sparse population (see Exercise 19).

9.4 Exercises

1. Suppose that a population develops according to the logistic equation

$$\frac{dP}{dt} = 0.05P - 0.0005P^2$$

where t is measured in weeks.
(a) What is the carrying capacity? What is the value of k?
(b) A direction field for this equation is shown. Where are the slopes close to 0? Where are they largest? Which solutions are increasing? Which solutions are decreasing?

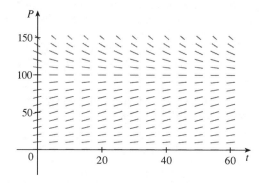

(c) Use the direction field to sketch solutions for initial populations of 20, 40, 60, 80, 120, and 140. What do these solutions have in common? How do they differ? Which solutions have inflection points? At what population levels do they occur?
(d) What are the equilibrium solutions? How are the other solutions related to these solutions?

 2. Suppose that a population grows according to a logistic model with carrying capacity 6000 and $k = 0.0015$ per year.
(a) Write the logistic differential equation for these data.
(b) Draw a direction field (either by hand or with a computer algebra system). What does it tell you about the solution curves?
(c) Use the direction field to sketch the solution curves for initial populations of 1000, 2000, 4000, and 8000. What can you say about the concavity of these curves? What is the significance of the inflection points?
(d) Program a calculator or computer to use Euler's method with step size $h = 1$ to estimate the population after 50 years if the initial population is 1000.
(e) If the initial population is 1000, write a formula for the population after t years. Use it to find the population after 50 years and compare with your estimate in part (d).
(f) Graph the solution in part (e) and compare with the solution curve you sketched in part (c).

3. The Pacific halibut fishery has been modeled by the differential equation

$$\frac{dy}{dt} = ky\left(1 - \frac{y}{M}\right)$$

where $y(t)$ is the biomass (the total mass of the members of the population) in kilograms at time t (measured in years), the carrying capacity is estimated to be $M = 8 \times 10^7$ kg, and $k = 0.71$ per year.
(a) If $y(0) = 2 \times 10^7$ kg, find the biomass a year later.
(b) How long will it take for the biomass to reach 4×10^7 kg?

4. Suppose a population $P(t)$ satisfies

$$\frac{dP}{dt} = 0.4P - 0.001P^2 \qquad P(0) = 50$$

where t is measured in years.
(a) What is the carrying capacity?
(b) What is $P'(0)$?
(c) When will the population reach 50% of the carrying capacity?

5. Suppose a population grows according to a logistic model with initial population 1000 and carrying capacity 10,000. If the population grows to 2500 after one year, what will the population be after another three years?

6. The table gives the number of yeast cells in a new laboratory culture.

Time (hours)	Yeast cells	Time (hours)	Yeast cells
0	18	10	509
2	39	12	597
4	80	14	640
6	171	16	664
8	336	18	672

(a) Plot the data and use the plot to estimate the carrying capacity for the yeast population.
(b) Use the data to estimate the initial relative growth rate.
(c) Find both an exponential model and a logistic model for these data.
(d) Compare the predicted values with the observed values, both in a table and with graphs. Comment on how well your models fit the data.
(e) Use your logistic model to estimate the number of yeast cells after 7 hours.

7. The population of the world was about 5.3 billion in 1990. Birth rates in the 1990s ranged from 35 to 40 million per year and death rates ranged from 15 to 20 million per year. Let's assume that the carrying capacity for world population is 100 billion.
(a) Write the logistic differential equation for these data. (Because the initial population is small compared to the

carrying capacity, you can take k to be an estimate of the initial relative growth rate.)

(b) Use the logistic model to estimate the world population in the year 2000 and compare with the actual population of 6.1 billion.

(c) Use the logistic model to predict the world population in the years 2100 and 2500.

(d) What are your predictions if the carrying capacity is 50 billion?

8. (a) Make a guess as to the carrying capacity for the US population. Use it and the fact that the population was 250 million in 1990 to formulate a logistic model for the US population.

(b) Determine the value of k in your model by using the fact that the population in 2000 was 275 million.

(c) Use your model to predict the US population in the years 2100 and 2200.

(d) Use your model to predict the year in which the US population will exceed 350 million.

9. One model for the spread of a rumor is that the rate of spread is proportional to the product of the fraction y of the population who have heard the rumor and the fraction who have not heard the rumor.

(a) Write a differential equation that is satisfied by y.

(b) Solve the differential equation.

(c) A small town has 1000 inhabitants. At 8 AM, 80 people have heard a rumor. By noon half the town has heard it. At what time will 90% of the population have heard the rumor?

10. Biologists stocked a lake with 400 fish and estimated the carrying capacity (the maximal population for the fish of that species in that lake) to be 10,000. The number of fish tripled in the first year.

(a) Assuming that the size of the fish population satisfies the logistic equation, find an expression for the size of the population after t years.

(b) How long will it take for the population to increase to 5000?

11. (a) Show that if P satisfies the logistic equation $\boxed{4}$, then

$$\frac{d^2P}{dt^2} = k^2P\left(1 - \frac{P}{M}\right)\left(1 - \frac{2P}{M}\right)$$

(b) Deduce that a population grows fastest when it reaches half its carrying capacity.

12. For a fixed value of M (say $M = 10$), the family of logistic functions given by Equation 7 depends on the initial value P_0 and the proportionality constant k. Graph several members of this family. How does the graph change when P_0 varies? How does it change when k varies?

13. The table gives the midyear population of Japan, in thousands, from 1960 to 2005.

Year	Population	Year	Population
1960	94,092	1985	120,754
1965	98,883	1990	123,537
1970	104,345	1995	125,341
1975	111,573	2000	126,700
1980	116,807	2005	127,417

Use a graphing calculator to fit both an exponential function and a logistic function to these data. Graph the data points and both functions, and comment on the accuracy of the models. [*Hint:* Subtract 94,000 from each of the population figures. Then, after obtaining a model from your calculator, add 94,000 to get your final model. It might be helpful to choose $t = 0$ to correspond to 1960 or 1980.]

14. The table gives the midyear population of Spain, in thousands, from 1955 to 2000.

Year	Population	Year	Population
1955	29,319	1980	37,488
1960	30,641	1985	38,535
1965	32,085	1990	39,351
1970	33,876	1995	39,750
1975	35,564	2000	40,016

Use a graphing calculator to fit both an exponential function and a logistic function to these data. Graph the data points and both functions, and comment on the accuracy of the models. [*Hint:* Subtract 29,000 from each of the population figures. Then, after obtaining a model from your calculator, add 29,000 to get your final model. It might be helpful to choose $t = 0$ to correspond to 1955 or 1975.]

15. Consider a population $P = P(t)$ with constant relative birth and death rates α and β, respectively, and a constant emigration rate m, where α, β, and m are positive constants. Assume that $\alpha > \beta$. Then the rate of change of the population at time t is modeled by the differential equation

$$\frac{dP}{dt} = kP - m \qquad \text{where } k = \alpha - \beta$$

(a) Find the solution of this equation that satisfies the initial condition $P(0) = P_0$.

(b) What condition on m will lead to an exponential expansion of the population?

(c) What condition on m will result in a constant population? A population decline?

(d) In 1847, the population of Ireland was about 8 million and the difference between the relative birth and death rates was 1.6% of the population. Because of the potato famine in the 1840s and 1850s, about 210,000 inhabitants per year emigrated from Ireland. Was the population expanding or declining at that time?

16. Let c be a positive number. A differential equation of the form

$$\frac{dy}{dt} = ky^{1+c}$$

where k is a positive constant, is called a *doomsday equation* because the exponent in the expression ky^{1+c} is larger than the exponent 1 for natural growth.
    (a) Determine the solution that satisfies the initial condition $y(0) = y_0$.
    (b) Show that there is a finite time $t = T$ (doomsday) such that $\lim_{t \to T^-} y(t) = \infty$.
    (c) An especially prolific breed of rabbits has the growth term $ky^{1.01}$. If 2 such rabbits breed initially and the warren has 16 rabbits after three months, then when is doomsday?

17. Let's modify the logistic differential equation of Example 1 as follows:

$$\frac{dP}{dt} = 0.08P\left(1 - \frac{P}{1000}\right) - 15$$

    (a) Suppose $P(t)$ represents a fish population at time t, where t is measured in weeks. Explain the meaning of the final term in the equation (-15).
    (b) Draw a direction field for this differential equation.
    (c) What are the equilibrium solutions?
    (d) Use the direction field to sketch several solution curves. Describe what happens to the fish population for various initial populations.
     (e) Solve this differential equation explicitly, either by using partial fractions or with a computer algebra system. Use the initial populations 200 and 300. Graph the solutions and compare with your sketches in part (d).

 18. Consider the differential equation

$$\frac{dP}{dt} = 0.08P\left(1 - \frac{P}{1000}\right) - c$$

as a model for a fish population, where t is measured in weeks and c is a constant.
    (a) Use a CAS to draw direction fields for various values of c.
    (b) From your direction fields in part (a), determine the values of c for which there is at least one equilibrium solution. For what values of c does the fish population always die out?
    (c) Use the differential equation to prove what you discovered graphically in part (b).
    (d) What would you recommend for a limit to the weekly catch of this fish population?

19. There is considerable evidence to support the theory that for some species there is a minimum population m such that the species will become extinct if the size of the population falls below m. This condition can be incorporated into the logistic equation by introducing the factor $(1 - m/P)$. Thus the modified logistic model is given by the differential equation

$$\frac{dP}{dt} = kP\left(1 - \frac{P}{M}\right)\left(1 - \frac{m}{P}\right)$$

    (a) Use the differential equation to show that any solution is increasing if $m < P < M$ and decreasing if $0 < P < m$.
    (b) For the case where $k = 0.08$, $M = 1000$, and $m = 200$, draw a direction field and use it to sketch several solution curves. Describe what happens to the population for various initial populations. What are the equilibrium solutions?
    (c) Solve the differential equation explicitly, either by using partial fractions or with a computer algebra system. Use the initial population P_0.
    (d) Use the solution in part (c) to show that if $P_0 < m$, then the species will become extinct. [*Hint:* Show that the numerator in your expression for $P(t)$ is 0 for some value of t.]

20. Another model for a growth function for a limited population is given by the **Gompertz function**, which is a solution of the differential equation

$$\frac{dP}{dt} = c \ln\left(\frac{M}{P}\right)P$$

where c is a constant and M is the carrying capacity.
    (a) Solve this differential equation.
    (b) Compute $\lim_{t \to \infty} P(t)$.
    (c) Graph the Gompertz growth function for $M = 1000$, $P_0 = 100$, and $c = 0.05$, and compare it with the logistic function in Example 2. What are the similarities? What are the differences?
    (d) We know from Exercise 11 that the logistic function grows fastest when $P = M/2$. Use the Gompertz differential equation to show that the Gompertz function grows fastest when $P = M/e$.

21. In a **seasonal-growth model**, a periodic function of time is introduced to account for seasonal variations in the rate of growth. Such variations could, for example, be caused by seasonal changes in the availability of food.
    (a) Find the solution of the seasonal-growth model

$$\frac{dP}{dt} = kP \cos(rt - \phi) \qquad P(0) = P_0$$

where k, r, and ϕ are positive constants.
    (b) By graphing the solution for several values of k, r, and ϕ, explain how the values of k, r, and ϕ affect the solution. What can you say about $\lim_{t \to \infty} P(t)$?

22. Suppose we alter the differential equation in Exercise 21 as follows:

$$\frac{dP}{dt} = kP \cos^2(rt - \phi) \qquad P(0) = P_0$$

(a) Solve this differential equation with the help of a table of integrals or a CAS.

(b) Graph the solution for several values of k, r, and ϕ. How do the values of k, r, and ϕ affect the solution? What can you say about $\lim_{t \to \infty} P(t)$ in this case?

23. Graphs of logistic functions (Figures 2 and 3) look suspiciously similar to the graph of the hyperbolic tangent function (Figure 3 in Section 3.11). Explain the similarity by showing that the logistic function given by Equation 7 can be written as

$$P(t) = \tfrac{1}{2}M\left[1 + \tanh\left(\tfrac{1}{2}k(t - c)\right)\right]$$

where $c = (\ln A)/k$. Thus the logistic function is really just a shifted hyperbolic tangent.

9.5   Linear Equations

A first-order **linear** differential equation is one that can be put into the form

$$\boxed{1} \qquad \frac{dy}{dx} + P(x)y = Q(x)$$

where P and Q are continuous functions on a given interval. This type of equation occurs frequently in various sciences, as we will see.

An example of a linear equation is $xy' + y = 2x$ because, for $x \neq 0$, it can be written in the form

$$\boxed{2} \qquad y' + \frac{1}{x}y = 2$$

Notice that this differential equation is not separable because it's impossible to factor the expression for y' as a function of x times a function of y. But we can still solve the equation by noticing, by the Product Rule, that

$$xy' + y = (xy)'$$

and so we can rewrite the equation as

$$(xy)' = 2x$$

If we now integrate both sides of this equation, we get

$$xy = x^2 + C \qquad \text{or} \qquad y = x + \frac{C}{x}$$

If we had been given the differential equation in the form of Equation 2, we would have had to take the preliminary step of multiplying each side of the equation by x.

It turns out that every first-order linear differential equation can be solved in a similar fashion by multiplying both sides of Equation 1 by a suitable function $I(x)$ called an *integrating factor*. We try to find I so that the left side of Equation 1, when multiplied by $I(x)$, becomes the derivative of the product $I(x)y$:

$$\boxed{3} \qquad I(x)\big(y' + P(x)y\big) = \big(I(x)y\big)'$$

If we can find such a function I, then Equation 1 becomes

$$\big(I(x)y\big)' = I(x)\,Q(x)$$

Integrating both sides, we would have

$$I(x)y = \int I(x)\,Q(x)\,dx + C$$

so the solution would be

$$\boxed{4} \qquad y(x) = \frac{1}{I(x)} \left[\int I(x)\,Q(x)\,dx + C \right]$$

To find such an I, we expand Equation 3 and cancel terms:

$$I(x)y' + I(x)\,P(x)y = \big(I(x)y\big)' = I'(x)y + I(x)y'$$

$$I(x)\,P(x) = I'(x)$$

This is a separable differential equation for I, which we solve as follows:

$$\int \frac{dI}{I} = \int P(x)\,dx$$

$$\ln |I| = \int P(x)\,dx$$

$$I = A e^{\int P(x)\,dx}$$

where $A = \pm e^{C}$. We are looking for a particular integrating factor, not the most general one, so we take $A = 1$ and use

$$\boxed{5} \qquad I(x) = e^{\int P(x)\,dx}$$

Thus a formula for the general solution to Equation 1 is provided by Equation 4, where I is given by Equation 5. Instead of memorizing this formula, however, we just remember the form of the integrating factor.

> To solve the linear differential equation $y' + P(x)y = Q(x)$, multiply both sides by the **integrating factor** $I(x) = e^{\int P(x)\,dx}$ and integrate both sides.

V **EXAMPLE 1** Solve the differential equation $\dfrac{dy}{dx} + 3x^2 y = 6x^2$.

SOLUTION The given equation is linear since it has the form of Equation 1 with $P(x) = 3x^2$ and $Q(x) = 6x^2$. An integrating factor is

$$I(x) = e^{\int 3x^2\,dx} = e^{x^3}$$

Multiplying both sides of the differential equation by e^{x^3}, we get

$$e^{x^3}\frac{dy}{dx} + 3x^2 e^{x^3}y = 6x^2 e^{x^3}$$

or

$$\frac{d}{dx}\left(e^{x^3}y\right) = 6x^2 e^{x^3}$$

Figure 1 shows the graphs of several members of the family of solutions in Example 1. Notice that they all approach 2 as $x \to \infty$.

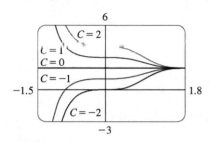

FIGURE 1

Integrating both sides, we have

$$e^{x^3}y = \int 6x^2 e^{x^3}\, dx = 2e^{x^3} + C$$

$$y = 2 + Ce^{-x^3}$$

V **EXAMPLE 2** Find the solution of the initial-value problem

$$x^2 y' + xy = 1 \qquad x > 0 \qquad y(1) = 2$$

SOLUTION We must first divide both sides by the coefficient of y' to put the differential equation into standard form:

6
$$y' + \frac{1}{x}y = \frac{1}{x^2} \qquad x > 0$$

The integrating factor is

$$I(x) = e^{\int (1/x)\, dx} = e^{\ln x} = x$$

Multiplication of Equation 6 by x gives

$$xy' + y = \frac{1}{x} \qquad \text{or} \qquad (xy)' = \frac{1}{x}$$

Then
$$xy = \int \frac{1}{x}\, dx = \ln x + C$$

and so
$$y = \frac{\ln x + C}{x}$$

Since $y(1) = 2$, we have

$$2 = \frac{\ln 1 + C}{1} = C$$

Therefore the solution to the initial-value problem is

$$y = \frac{\ln x + 2}{x}$$

The solution of the initial-value problem in Example 2 is shown in Figure 2.

FIGURE 2

EXAMPLE 3 Solve $y' + 2xy = 1$.

SOLUTION The given equation is in the standard form for a linear equation. Multiplying by the integrating factor

$$e^{\int 2x\, dx} = e^{x^2}$$

we get
$$e^{x^2}y' + 2xe^{x^2}y = e^{x^2}$$

or
$$\left(e^{x^2}y\right)' = e^{x^2}$$

Therefore
$$e^{x^2}y = \int e^{x^2}\, dx + C$$

Even though the solutions of the differential equation in Example 3 are expressed in terms of an integral, they can still be graphed by a computer algebra system (Figure 3).

FIGURE 3

FIGURE 4

Recall from Section 7.5 that $\int e^{x^2}\, dx$ can't be expressed in terms of elementary functions. Nonetheless, it's a perfectly good function and we can leave the answer as

$$y = e^{-x^2} \int e^{x^2}\, dx + Ce^{-x^2}$$

Another way of writing the solution is

$$y = e^{-x^2} \int_0^x e^{t^2}\, dt + Ce^{-x^2}$$

(Any number can be chosen for the lower limit of integration.)

▪ Application to Electric Circuits

In Section 9.2 we considered the simple electric circuit shown in Figure 4: An electromotive force (usually a battery or generator) produces a voltage of $E(t)$ volts (V) and a current of $I(t)$ amperes (A) at time t. The circuit also contains a resistor with a resistance of R ohms (Ω) and an inductor with an inductance of L henries (H).

Ohm's Law gives the drop in voltage due to the resistor as RI. The voltage drop due to the inductor is $L(dI/dt)$. One of Kirchhoff's laws says that the sum of the voltage drops is equal to the supplied voltage $E(t)$. Thus we have

$$\boxed{7} \qquad L\frac{dI}{dt} + RI = E(t)$$

which is a first-order linear differential equation. The solution gives the current I at time t.

V EXAMPLE 4 Suppose that in the simple circuit of Figure 4 the resistance is 12 Ω and the inductance is 4 H. If a battery gives a constant voltage of 60 V and the switch is closed when $t = 0$ so the current starts with $I(0) = 0$, find (a) $I(t)$, (b) the current after 1 s, and (c) the limiting value of the current.

SOLUTION

The differential equation in Example 4 is both linear and separable, so an alternative method is to solve it as a separable equation (Example 4 in Section 9.3). If we replace the battery by a generator, however, we get an equation that is linear but not separable (Example 5).

(a) If we put $L = 4$, $R = 12$, and $E(t) = 60$ in Equation 7, we obtain the initial-value problem

$$4\frac{dI}{dt} + 12I = 60 \qquad I(0) = 0$$

or

$$\frac{dI}{dt} + 3I = 15 \qquad I(0) = 0$$

Multiplying by the integrating factor $e^{\int 3\, dt} = e^{3t}$, we get

$$e^{3t}\frac{dI}{dt} + 3e^{3t}I = 15e^{3t}$$

$$\frac{d}{dt}(e^{3t}I) = 15e^{3t}$$

$$e^{3t}I = \int 15e^{3t}\, dt = 5e^{3t} + C$$

$$I(t) = 5 + Ce^{-3t}$$

Figure 5 shows how the current in Example 4 approaches its limiting value.

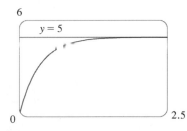

FIGURE 5

Since $I(0) = 0$, we have $5 + C = 0$, so $C = -5$ and

$$I(t) = 5(1 - e^{-3t})$$

(b) After 1 second the current is

$$I(1) = 5(1 - e^{0}) \approx 4.75 \text{ A}$$

(c) The limiting value of the current is given by

$$\lim_{t \to \infty} I(t) = \lim_{t \to \infty} 5(1 - e^{-3t}) = 5 - 5 \lim_{t \to \infty} e^{-3t} = 5 - 0 = 5$$

EXAMPLE 5 Suppose that the resistance and inductance remain as in Example 4 but, instead of the battery, we use a generator that produces a variable voltage of $E(t) = 60 \sin 30t$ volts. Find $I(t)$.

SOLUTION This time the differential equation becomes

$$4 \frac{dI}{dt} + 12I = 60 \sin 30t \qquad \text{or} \qquad \frac{dI}{dt} + 3I = 15 \sin 30t$$

The same integrating factor e^{3t} gives

$$\frac{d}{dt}(e^{3t}I) = e^{3t}\frac{dI}{dt} + 3e^{3t}I = 15e^{3t}\sin 30t$$

Figure 6 shows the graph of the current when the battery is replaced by a generator.

FIGURE 6

Using Formula 98 in the Table of Integrals, we have

$$e^{3t}I = \int 15e^{3t}\sin 30t \, dt = 15 \frac{e^{3t}}{909}(3 \sin 30t - 30 \cos 30t) + C$$

$$I = \tfrac{5}{101}(\sin 30t - 10 \cos 30t) + Ce^{-3t}$$

Since $I(0) = 0$, we get

$$-\tfrac{50}{101} + C = 0$$

so

$$I(t) = \tfrac{5}{101}(\sin 30t - 10 \cos 30t) + \tfrac{50}{101}e^{-3t}$$

9.5 Exercises

1–4 Determine whether the differential equation is linear.

1. $x - y' = xy$

2. $y' + xy^2 = \sqrt{x}$

3. $y' = \dfrac{1}{x} + \dfrac{1}{y}$

4. $y \sin x = x^2 y' - x$

11. $\sin x \dfrac{dy}{dx} + (\cos x)y = \sin(x^2)$

12. $x \dfrac{dy}{dx} - 4y = x^4 e^x$

13. $(1 + t)\dfrac{du}{dt} + u = 1 + t, \quad t > 0$

14. $t \ln t \dfrac{dr}{dt} + r = te^t$

5–14 Solve the differential equation.

5. $xy' - 2y = x^2$

6. $y' = x + 5y$

7. $y' = x - y$

8. $4x^3y + x^4y' = \sin^3 x$

9. $xy' + y = \sqrt{x}$

10. $y' + y = \sin(e^x)$

15–20 Solve the initial-value problem.

15. $x^2y' + 2xy = \ln x, \quad y(1) = 2$

⌨ Graphing calculator or computer required   **1.** Homework Hints available at stewartcalculus.com

16. $t^3 \dfrac{dy}{dt} + 3t^2 y = \cos t, \quad y(\pi) = 0$

17. $t \dfrac{du}{dt} = t^2 + 3u, \quad t > 0, \quad u(2) = 4$

18. $2xy' + y = 6x, \quad x > 0, \quad y(4) = 20$

19. $xy' = y + x^2 \sin x, \quad y(\pi) = 0$

20. $(x^2 + 1) \dfrac{dy}{dx} + 3x(y - 1) = 0, \quad y(0) = 2$

21–22 Solve the differential equation and use a graphing calculator or computer to graph several members of the family of solutions. How does the solution curve change as C varies?

21. $xy' + 2y = e^x$ **22.** $xy' = x^2 + 2y$

---

23. A **Bernoulli differential equation** (named after James Bernoulli) is of the form

$$\frac{dy}{dx} + P(x)y = Q(x)y^n$$

Observe that, if $n = 0$ or 1, the Bernoulli equation is linear. For other values of n, show that the substitution $u = y^{1-n}$ transforms the Bernoulli equation into the linear equation

$$\frac{du}{dx} + (1 - n)P(x)u = (1 - n)Q(x)$$

24–25 Use the method of Exercise 23 to solve the differential equation.

24. $xy' + y = -xy^2$ **25.** $y' + \dfrac{2}{x}y = \dfrac{y^3}{x^2}$

---

26. Solve the second-order equation $xy'' + 2y' = 12x^2$ by making the substitution $u = y'$.

27. In the circuit shown in Figure 4, a battery supplies a constant voltage of 40 V, the inductance is 2 H, the resistance is 10 Ω, and $I(0) = 0$.
(a) Find $I(t)$.
(b) Find the current after 0.1 s.

28. In the circuit shown in Figure 4, a generator supplies a voltage of $E(t) = 40 \sin 60t$ volts, the inductance is 1 H, the resistance is 20 Ω, and $I(0) = 1$ A.
(a) Find $I(t)$.
(b) Find the current after 0.1 s.
(c) Use a graphing device to draw the graph of the current function.

29. The figure shows a circuit containing an electromotive force, a capacitor with a capacitance of C farads (F), and a resistor with a resistance of R ohms (Ω). The voltage drop across the capacitor is Q/C, where Q is the charge (in coulombs), so in

this case Kirchhoff's Law gives

$$RI + \frac{Q}{C} = E(t)$$

But $I = dQ/dt$ (see Example 3 in Section 3.7), so we have

$$R \frac{dQ}{dt} + \frac{1}{C} Q = E(t)$$

Suppose the resistance is 5 Ω, the capacitance is 0.05 F, a battery gives a constant voltage of 60 V, and the initial charge is $Q(0) = 0$ C. Find the charge and the current at time t.

30. In the circuit of Exercise 29, $R = 2\ \Omega$, $C = 0.01$ F, $Q(0) = 0$, and $E(t) = 10 \sin 60t$. Find the charge and the current at time t.

31. Let $P(t)$ be the performance level of someone learning a skill as a function of the training time t. The graph of P is called a *learning curve*. In Exercise 15 in Section 9.1 we proposed the differential equation

$$\frac{dP}{dt} = k[M - P(t)]$$

as a reasonable model for learning, where k is a positive constant. Solve it as a linear differential equation and use your solution to graph the learning curve.

32. Two new workers were hired for an assembly line. Jim processed 25 units during the first hour and 45 units during the second hour. Mark processed 35 units during the first hour and 50 units the second hour. Using the model of Exercise 31 and assuming that $P(0) = 0$, estimate the maximum number of units per hour that each worker is capable of processing.

33. In Section 9.3 we looked at mixing problems in which the volume of fluid remained constant and saw that such problems give rise to separable equations. (See Example 6 in that section.) If the rates of flow into and out of the system are different, then the volume is not constant and the resulting differential equation is linear but not separable.

A tank contains 100 L of water. A solution with a salt concentration of 0.4 kg/L is added at a rate of 5 L/min. The solution is kept mixed and is drained from the tank at a rate of 3 L/min. If $y(t)$ is the amount of salt (in kilograms) after t minutes, show that y satisfies the differential equation

$$\frac{dy}{dt} = 2 - \frac{3y}{100 + 2t}$$

Solve this equation and find the concentration after 20 minutes.

34. A tank with a capacity of 400 L is full of a mixture of water and chlorine with a concentration of 0.05 g of chlorine per liter. In order to reduce the concentration of chlorine, fresh water is pumped into the tank at a rate of 4 L/s. The mixture is kept stirred and is pumped out at a rate of 10 L/s. Find the amount of chlorine in the tank as a function of time.

35. An object with mass m is dropped from rest and we assume that the air resistance is proportional to the speed of the object. If $s(t)$ is the distance dropped after t seconds, then the speed is $v = s'(t)$ and the acceleration is $a = v'(t)$. If g is the acceleration due to gravity, then the downward force on the object is $mg - cv$, where c is a positive constant, and Newton's Second Law gives

$$m\frac{dv}{dt} = mg - cv$$

(a) Solve this as a linear equation to show that

$$v = \frac{mg}{c}\left(1 - e^{-ct/m}\right)$$

(b) What is the limiting velocity?
(c) Find the distance the object has fallen after t seconds.

36. If we ignore air resistance, we can conclude that heavier objects fall no faster than lighter objects. But if we take air resistance into account, our conclusion changes. Use the expression for the velocity of a falling object in Exercise 35(a) to find dv/dm and show that heavier objects *do* fall faster than lighter ones.

37. (a) Show that the substitution $z = 1/P$ transforms the logistic differential equation $P' = kP(1 - P/M)$ into the linear differential equation

$$z' + kz = \frac{k}{M}$$

(b) Solve the linear differential equation in part (a) and thus obtain an expression for $P(t)$. Compare with Equation 9.4.7.

38. To account for seasonal variation in the logistic differential equation we could allow k and M to be functions of t:

$$\frac{dP}{dt} = k(t)P\left(1 - \frac{P}{M(t)}\right)$$

(a) Verify that the substitution $z = 1/P$ transforms this equation into the linear equation

$$\frac{dz}{dt} + k(t)z = \frac{k(t)}{M(t)}$$

(b) Write an expression for the solution of the linear equation in part (a) and use it to show that if the carrying capacity M is constant, then

$$P(t) = \frac{M}{1 + CMe^{-\int k(t)\,dt}}$$

Deduce that if $\int_0^\infty k(t)\,dt = \infty$, then $\lim_{t\to\infty} P(t) = M$. [This will be true if $k(t) = k_0 + a\cos bt$ with $k_0 > 0$, which describes a positive intrinsic growth rate with a periodic seasonal variation.]

(c) If k is constant but M varies, show that

$$z(t) = e^{-kt}\int_0^t \frac{ke^{ks}}{M(s)}\,ds + Ce^{-kt}$$

and use l'Hospital's Rule to deduce that if $M(t)$ has a limit as $t\to\infty$, then $P(t)$ has the same limit.

9.6 Predator-Prey Systems

We have looked at a variety of models for the growth of a single species that lives alone in an environment. In this section we consider more realistic models that take into account the interaction of two species in the same habitat. We will see that these models take the form of a pair of linked differential equations.

We first consider the situation in which one species, called the *prey*, has an ample food supply and the second species, called the *predators*, feeds on the prey. Examples of prey and predators include rabbits and wolves in an isolated forest, food fish and sharks, aphids and ladybugs, and bacteria and amoebas. Our model will have two dependent variables and both are functions of time. We let $R(t)$ be the number of prey (using R for rabbits) and $W(t)$ be the number of predators (with W for wolves) at time t.

In the absence of predators, the ample food supply would support exponential growth of the prey, that is,

$$\frac{dR}{dt} = kR \qquad \text{where } k \text{ is a positive constant}$$

In the absence of prey, we assume that the predator population would decline at a rate proportional to itself, that is,

$$\frac{dW}{dt} = -rW \qquad \text{where } r \text{ is a positive constant}$$

With both species present, however, we assume that the principal cause of death among the prey is being eaten by a predator, and the birth and survival rates of the predators depend on their available food supply, namely, the prey. We also assume that the two species encounter each other at a rate that is proportional to both populations and is therefore proportional to the product RW. (The more there are of either population, the more encounters there are likely to be.) A system of two differential equations that incorporates these assumptions is as follows:

W represents the predator.

R represents the prey.

$$\boxed{1} \qquad \frac{dR}{dt} = kR - aRW \qquad \frac{dW}{dt} = -rW + bRW$$

where k, r, a, and b are positive constants. Notice that the term $-aRW$ decreases the natural growth rate of the prey and the term bRW increases the natural growth rate of the predators.

The Lotka-Volterra equations were proposed as a model to explain the variations in the shark and food-fish populations in the Adriatic Sea by the Italian mathematician Vito Volterra (1860–1940).

The equations in $\boxed{1}$ are known as the **predator-prey equations**, or the **Lotka-Volterra equations**. A **solution** of this system of equations is a pair of functions $R(t)$ and $W(t)$ that describe the populations of prey and predator as functions of time. Because the system is coupled (R and W occur in both equations), we can't solve one equation and then the other; we have to solve them simultaneously. Unfortunately, it is usually impossible to find explicit formulas for R and W as functions of t. We can, however, use graphical methods to analyze the equations.

V **EXAMPLE 1** Suppose that populations of rabbits and wolves are described by the Lotka-Volterra equations $\boxed{1}$ with $k = 0.08$, $a = 0.001$, $r = 0.02$, and $b = 0.00002$. The time t is measured in months.
(a) Find the constant solutions (called the **equilibrium solutions**) and interpret the answer.
(b) Use the system of differential equations to find an expression for dW/dR.
(c) Draw a direction field for the resulting differential equation in the RW-plane. Then use that direction field to sketch some solution curves.
(d) Suppose that, at some point in time, there are 1000 rabbits and 40 wolves. Draw the corresponding solution curve and use it to describe the changes in both population levels.
(e) Use part (d) to make sketches of R and W as functions of t.

SOLUTION
(a) With the given values of k, a, r, and b, the Lotka-Volterra equations become

$$\frac{dR}{dt} = 0.08R - 0.001RW$$

$$\frac{dW}{dt} = -0.02W + 0.00002RW$$

Both R and W will be constant if both derivatives are 0, that is,

$$R' = R(0.08 - 0.001W) = 0$$

$$W' = W(-0.02 + 0.00002R) = 0$$

One solution is given by $R = 0$ and $W = 0$. (This makes sense: If there are no rabbits or wolves, the populations are certainly not going to increase.) The other constant solution is

$$W = \frac{0.08}{0.001} = 80 \qquad R = \frac{0.02}{0.00002} = 1000$$

So the equilibrium populations consist of 80 wolves and 1000 rabbits. This means that 1000 rabbits are just enough to support a constant wolf population of 80. There are neither too many wolves (which would result in fewer rabbits) nor too few wolves (which would result in more rabbits).

(b) We use the Chain Rule to eliminate t:

$$\frac{dW}{dt} = \frac{dW}{dR} \frac{dR}{dt}$$

so

$$\frac{dW}{dR} = \frac{\dfrac{dW}{dt}}{\dfrac{dR}{dt}} = \frac{-0.02W + 0.00002RW}{0.08R - 0.001RW}$$

(c) If we think of W as a function of R, we have the differential equation

$$\frac{dW}{dR} = \frac{-0.02W + 0.00002RW}{0.08R - 0.001RW}$$

We draw the direction field for this differential equation in Figure 1 and we use it to sketch several solution curves in Figure 2. If we move along a solution curve, we observe how the relationship between R and W changes as time passes. Notice that the curves appear to be closed in the sense that if we travel along a curve, we always return to the same point. Notice also that the point (1000, 80) is inside all the solution curves. That point is called an *equilibrium point* because it corresponds to the equilibrium solution $R = 1000$, $W = 80$.

FIGURE 1 Direction field for the predator-prey system   **FIGURE 2** Phase portrait of the system

When we represent solutions of a system of differential equations as in Figure 2, we refer to the RW-plane as the **phase plane**, and we call the solution curves **phase trajectories**. So a phase trajectory is a path traced out by solutions (R, W) as time goes by. A **phase portrait** consists of equilibrium points and typical phase trajectories, as shown in Figure 2.

(d) Starting with 1000 rabbits and 40 wolves corresponds to drawing the solution curve through the point $P_0(1000, 40)$. Figure 3 shows this phase trajectory with the direction field removed. Starting at the point P_0 at time $t = 0$ and letting t increase, do we move clockwise or counterclockwise around the phase trajectory? If we put $R = 1000$ and $W = 40$ in the first differential equation, we get

$$\frac{dR}{dt} = 0.08(1000) - 0.001(1000)(40) = 80 - 40 = 40$$

Since $dR/dt > 0$, we conclude that R is increasing at P_0 and so we move counterclockwise around the phase trajectory.

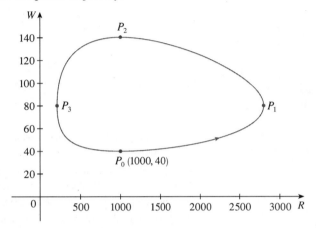

FIGURE 3
Phase trajectory through (1000, 40)

We see that at P_0 there aren't enough wolves to maintain a balance between the populations, so the rabbit population increases. That results in more wolves and eventually there are so many wolves that the rabbits have a hard time avoiding them. So the number of rabbits begins to decline (at P_1, where we estimate that R reaches its maximum population of about 2800). This means that at some later time the wolf population starts to fall (at P_2, where $R = 1000$ and $W \approx 140$). But this benefits the rabbits, so their population later starts to increase (at P_3, where $W = 80$ and $R \approx 210$). As a consequence, the wolf population eventually starts to increase as well. This happens when the populations return to their initial values of $R = 1000$ and $W = 40$, and the entire cycle begins again.

(e) From the description in part (d) of how the rabbit and wolf populations rise and fall, we can sketch the graphs of $R(t)$ and $W(t)$. Suppose the points P_1, P_2, and P_3 in Figure 3 are reached at times t_1, t_2, and t_3. Then we can sketch graphs of R and W as in Figure 4.

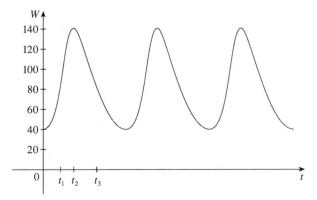

FIGURE 4 Graphs of the rabbit and wolf populations as functions of time

TEC In Module 9.6 you can change the coefficients in the Lotka-Volterra equations and observe the resulting changes in the phase trajectory and graphs of the rabbit and wolf populations.

To make the graphs easier to compare, we draw the graphs on the same axes but with different scales for R and W, as in Figure 5. Notice that the rabbits reach their maximum populations about a quarter of a cycle before the wolves.

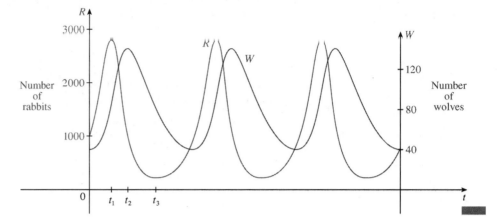

FIGURE 5

Comparison of the rabbit and wolf populations

An important part of the modeling process, as we discussed in Section 1.2, is to interpret our mathematical conclusions as real-world predictions and to test the predictions against real data. The Hudson's Bay Company, which started trading in animal furs in Canada in 1670, has kept records that date back to the 1840s. Figure 6 shows graphs of the number of pelts of the snowshoe hare and its predator, the Canada lynx, traded by the company over a 90-year period. You can see that the coupled oscillations in the hare and lynx populations predicted by the Lotka-Volterra model do actually occur and the period of these cycles is roughly 10 years.

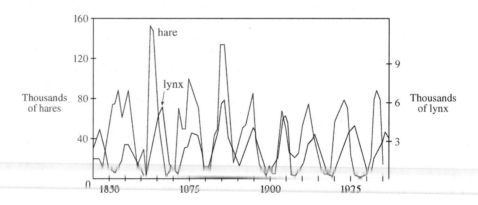

FIGURE 6

Relative abundance of hare and lynx from Hudson's Bay Company records

Although the relatively simple Lotka-Volterra model has had some success in explaining and predicting coupled populations, more sophisticated models have also been proposed. One way to modify the Lotka-Volterra equations is to assume that, in the absence of predators, the prey grow according to a logistic model with carrying capacity M. Then the Lotka-Volterra equations $\boxed{1}$ are replaced by the system of differential equations

$$\frac{dR}{dt} = kR\left(1 - \frac{R}{M}\right) - aRW \qquad \frac{dW}{dt} = -rW + bRW$$

This model is investigated in Exercises 11 and 12.

Models have also been proposed to describe and predict population levels of two or more species that compete for the same resources or cooperate for mutual benefit. Such models are explored in Exercises 2–4.

Exercises

1. For each predator-prey system, determine which of the variables, x or y, represents the prey population and which represents the predator population. Is the growth of the prey restricted just by the predators or by other factors as well? Do the predators feed only on the prey or do they have additional food sources? Explain.

   (a) $\dfrac{dx}{dt} = -0.05x + 0.0001xy$

   $\dfrac{dy}{dt} = 0.1y - 0.005xy$

   (b) $\dfrac{dx}{dt} = 0.2x - 0.0002x^2 - 0.006xy$

   $\dfrac{dy}{dt} = -0.015y + 0.00008xy$

2. Each system of differential equations is a model for two species that either compete for the same resources or cooperate for mutual benefit (flowering plants and insect pollinators, for instance). Decide whether each system describes competition or cooperation and explain why it is a reasonable model. (Ask yourself what effect an increase in one species has on the growth rate of the other.)

   (a) $\dfrac{dx}{dt} = 0.12x - 0.0006x^2 + 0.00001xy$

   $\dfrac{dy}{dt} = 0.08x + 0.00004xy$

   (b) $\dfrac{dx}{dt} = 0.15x - 0.0002x^2 - 0.0006xy$

   $\dfrac{dy}{dt} = 0.2y - 0.00008y^2 - 0.0002xy$

3. The system of differential equations

   $$\frac{dx}{dt} = 0.5x - 0.004x^2 - 0.001xy$$

   $$\frac{dy}{dt} = 0.4y - 0.001y^2 - 0.002xy$$

   is a model for the populations of two species.
   (a) Does the model describe cooperation, or competition, or a predator-prey relationship?
   (b) Find the equilibrium solutions and explain their significance.

4. Flies, frogs, and crocodiles coexist in an environment. To survive, frogs need to eat flies and crocodiles need to eat frogs. In the absence of frogs, the fly population will grow exponentially and the crocodile population will decay exponentially. In the absence of crocodiles and flies, the frog population will decay exponentially. If $P(t)$, $Q(t)$, and $R(t)$ represent the populations of these three species at time t, write a system of differential equations as a model for their evolution. If the constants in your equation are all positive, explain why you have used plus or minus signs.

5–6 A phase trajectory is shown for populations of rabbits (R) and foxes (F).
(a) Describe how each population changes as time goes by.
(b) Use your description to make a rough sketch of the graphs of R and F as functions of time.

5.

6.

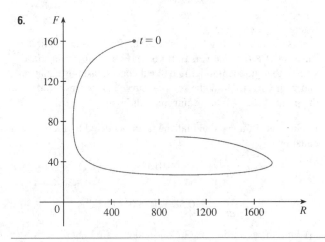

7–8 Graphs of populations of two species are shown. Use them to sketch the corresponding phase trajectory.

7.

8.

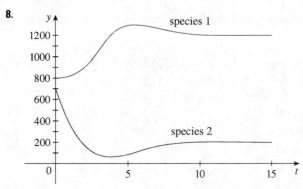

9. In Example 1(b) we showed that the rabbit and wolf populations satisfy the differential equation

$$\frac{dW}{dR} = \frac{-0.02W + 0.00002RW}{0.08R - 0.001RW}$$

By solving this separable differential equation, show that

$$\frac{R^{0.02}W^{0.08}}{e^{0.00002R}e^{0.001W}} = C$$

where C is a constant.

It is impossible to solve this equation for W as an explicit function of R (or vice versa). If you have a computer algebra system that graphs implicitly defined curves, use this equation and your CAS to draw the solution curve that passes through the point (1000, 40) and compare with Figure 3.

10. Populations of aphids and ladybugs are modeled by the equations

$$\frac{dA}{dt} = 2A - 0.01AL$$

$$\frac{dL}{dt} = -0.5L + 0.0001AL$$

(a) Find the equilibrium solutions and explain their significance.
(b) Find an expression for dL/dA.

(c) The direction field for the differential equation in part (b) is shown. Use it to sketch a phase portrait. What do the phase trajectories have in common?

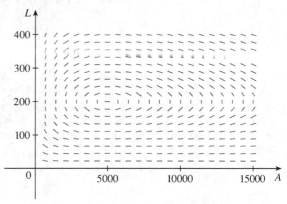

(d) Suppose that at time $t = 0$ there are 1000 aphids and 200 ladybugs. Draw the corresponding phase trajectory and use it to describe how both populations change.
(e) Use part (d) to make rough sketches of the aphid and ladybug populations as functions of t. How are the graphs related to each other?

11. In Example 1 we used Lotka-Volterra equations to model populations of rabbits and wolves. Let's modify those equations as follows:

$$\frac{dR}{dt} = 0.08R(1 - 0.0002R) - 0.001RW$$

$$\frac{dW}{dt} = -0.02W + 0.00002RW$$

(a) According to these equations, what happens to the rabbit population in the absence of wolves?
(b) Find all the equilibrium solutions and explain their significance.
(c) The figure shows the phase trajectory that starts at the point (1000, 40). Describe what eventually happens to the rabbit and wolf populations.

(d) Sketch graphs of the rabbit and wolf populations as functions of time.

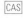 **12.** In Exercise 10 we modeled populations of aphids and lady-bugs with a Lotka-Volterra system. Suppose we modify those equations as follows:

$$\frac{dA}{dt} = 2A(1 - 0.0001A) - 0.01AL$$

$$\frac{dL}{dt} = -0.5L + 0.0001AL$$

(a) In the absence of ladybugs, what does the model predict about the aphids?

(b) Find the equilibrium solutions.
(c) Find an expression for dL/dA.
(d) Use a computer algebra system to draw a direction field for the differential equation in part (c). Then use the direction field to sketch a phase portrait. What do the phase trajectories have in common?
(e) Suppose that at time $t = 0$ there are 1000 aphids and 200 ladybugs. Draw the corresponding phase trajectory and use it to describe how both populations change.
(f) Use part (e) to make rough sketches of the aphid and ladybug populations as functions of t. How are the graphs related to each other?

---

9   Review

Concept Check

1. (a) What is a differential equation?
    (b) What is the order of a differential equation?
    (c) What is an initial condition?

2. What can you say about the solutions of the equation $y' = x^2 + y^2$ just by looking at the differential equation?

3. What is a direction field for the differential equation $y' = F(x, y)$?

4. Explain how Euler's method works.

5. What is a separable differential equation? How do you solve it?

6. What is a first-order linear differential equation? How do you solve it?

7. (a) Write a differential equation that expresses the law of natural growth. What does it say in terms of relative growth rate?
    (b) Under what circumstances is this an appropriate model for population growth?
    (c) What are the solutions of this equation?

8. (a) Write the logistic equation.
    (b) Under what circumstances is this an appropriate model for population growth?

9. (a) Write Lotka-Volterra equations to model populations of food fish (F) and sharks (S).
    (b) What do these equations say about each population in the absence of the other?

True-False Quiz

Determine whether the statement is true or false. If it is true, explain why. If it is false, explain why or give an example that disproves the statement.

1. All solutions of the differential equation $y' = -1 - y^4$ are decreasing functions.

2. The function $f(x) = (\ln x)/x$ is a solution of the differential equation $x^2 y' + xy = 1$.

3. The equation $y' = x + y$ is separable.

4. The equation $y' = 3y - 2x + 6xy - 1$ is separable.

5. The equation $e^x y' = y$ is linear.

6. The equation $y' + xy = e^y$ is linear.

7. If y is the solution of the initial-value problem

$$\frac{dy}{dt} = 2y\left(1 - \frac{y}{5}\right) \qquad y(0) = 1$$

then $\lim_{t \to \infty} y = 5$.

Exercises

1. (a) A direction field for the differential equation
$y' = y(y - 2)(y - 4)$ is shown. Sketch the graphs of the
solutions that satisfy the given initial conditions.

   (i) $y(0) = -0.3$ (ii) $y(0) = 1$
   (iii) $y(0) = 3$ (iv) $y(0) = 4.3$

   (b) If the initial condition is $y(0) = c$, for what values of
   c is $\lim_{t \to \infty} y(t)$ finite? What are the equilibrium solutions?

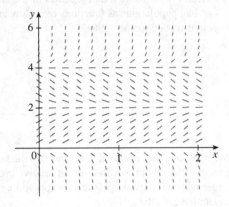

2. (a) Sketch a direction field for the differential equation
$y' = x/y$. Then use it to sketch the four solutions that
satisfy the initial conditions $y(0) = 1$, $y(0) = -1$,
$y(2) = 1$, and $y(-2) = 1$.

   (b) Check your work in part (a) by solving the differential
   equation explicitly. What type of curve is each solution
   curve?

3. (a) A direction field for the differential equation
$y' = x^2 - y^2$ is shown. Sketch the solution of the
initial-value problem

$$y' = x^2 - y^2 \qquad y(0) = 1$$

Use your graph to estimate the value of $y(0.3)$.

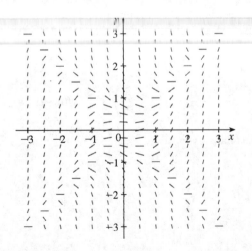

   (b) Use Euler's method with step size 0.1 to estimate $y(0.3)$,
   where $y(x)$ is the solution of the initial-value problem in
   part (a). Compare with your estimate from part (a).

   (c) On what lines are the centers of the horizontal line
   segments of the direction field in part (a) located? What
   happens when a solution curve crosses these lines?

4. (a) Use Euler's method with step size 0.2 to estimate $y(0.4)$,
where $y(x)$ is the solution of the initial-value problem

$$y' = 2xy^2 \qquad y(0) = 1$$

   (b) Repeat part (a) with step size 0.1.

   (c) Find the exact solution of the differential equation and
   compare the value at 0.4 with the approximations in
   parts (a) and (b).

5–8 Solve the differential equation.

5. $y' = xe^{-\sin x} - y \cos x$

6. $\dfrac{dx}{dt} = 1 - t + x - tx$

7. $2ye^{y^2}y' = 2x + 3\sqrt{x}$

8. $x^2y' - y = 2x^3e^{-1/x}$

9–11 Solve the initial-value problem.

9. $\dfrac{dr}{dt} + 2tr = r, \quad r(0) = 5$

10. $(1 + \cos x)y' = (1 + e^{-y})\sin x, \quad y(0) = 0$

11. $xy' - y = x \ln x, \quad y(1) = 2$

12. Solve the initial-value problem $y' = 3x^2e^y$, $y(0) = 1$, and
graph the solution.

13–14 Find the orthogonal trajectories of the family of curves.

13. $y = ke^x$

14. $y = e^{kx}$

15. (a) Write the solution of the initial-value problem

$$\frac{dP}{dt} = 0.1P\left(1 - \frac{P}{2000}\right) \qquad P(0) = 100$$

   and use it to find the population when $t = 20$.

   (b) When does the population reach 1200?

16. (a) The population of the world was 5.28 billion in 1990 and
6.07 billion in 2000. Find an exponential model for these
data and use the model to predict the world population in
the year 2020.

   (b) According to the model in part (a), when will the world
   population exceed 10 billion?

   (c) Use the data in part (a) to find a logistic model for the population. Assume a carrying capacity of 100 billion. Then

use the logistic model to predict the population in 2020. Compare with your prediction from the exponential model.

(d) According to the logistic model, when will the world population exceed 10 billion? Compare with your prediction in part (b).

17. The von Bertalanffy growth model is used to predict the length $L(t)$ of a fish over a period of time. If L_∞ is the largest length for a species, then the hypothesis is that the rate of growth in length is proportional to $L_\infty - L$, the length yet to be achieved.
(a) Formulate and solve a differential equation to find an expression for $L(t)$.
(b) For the North Sea haddock it has been determined that $L_\infty = 53$ cm, $L(0) = 10$ cm, and the constant of proportionality is 0.2. What does the expression for $L(t)$ become with these data?

18. A tank contains 100 L of pure water. Brine that contains 0.1 kg of salt per liter enters the tank at a rate of 10 L/min. The solution is kept thoroughly mixed and drains from the tank at the same rate. How much salt is in the tank after 6 minutes?

19. One model for the spread of an epidemic is that the rate of spread is jointly proportional to the number of infected people and the number of uninfected people. In an isolated town of 5000 inhabitants, 160 people have a disease at the beginning of the week and 1200 have it at the end of the week. How long does it take for 80% of the population to become infected?

20. The Brentano-Stevens Law in psychology models the way that a subject reacts to a stimulus. It states that if R represents the reaction to an amount S of stimulus, then the relative rates of increase are proportional:

$$\frac{1}{R}\frac{dR}{dt} = \frac{k}{S}\frac{dS}{dt}$$

where k is a positive constant. Find R as a function of S.

21. The transport of a substance across a capillary wall in lung physiology has been modeled by the differential equation

$$\frac{dh}{dt} = -\frac{R}{V}\left(\frac{h}{k+h}\right)$$

where h is the hormone concentration in the bloodstream, t is time, R is the maximum transport rate, V is the volume of the capillary, and k is a positive constant that measures the affinity between the hormones and the enzymes that assist the process. Solve this differential equation to find a relationship between h and t.

22. Populations of birds and insects are modeled by the equations

$$\frac{dx}{dt} = 0.4x - 0.002xy$$

$$\frac{dy}{dt} = -0.2y + 0.000008xy$$

(a) Which of the variables, x or y, represents the bird population and which represents the insect population? Explain.

(b) Find the equilibrium solutions and explain their significance.
(c) Find an expression for dy/dx.
(d) The direction field for the differential equation in part (c) is shown. Use it to sketch the phase trajectory corresponding to initial populations of 100 birds and 40,000 insects. Then use the phase trajectory to describe how both populations change.

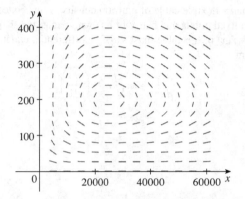

(e) Use part (d) to make rough sketches of the bird and insect populations as functions of time. How are these graphs related to each other?

23. Suppose the model of Exercise 22 is replaced by the equations

$$\frac{dx}{dt} = 0.4x(1 - 0.000005x) - 0.002xy$$

$$\frac{dy}{dt} = -0.2y + 0.000008xy$$

(a) According to these equations, what happens to the insect population in the absence of birds?
(b) Find the equilibrium solutions and explain their significance.
(c) The figure shows the phase trajectory that starts with 100 birds and 40,000 insects. Describe what eventually happens to the bird and insect populations.

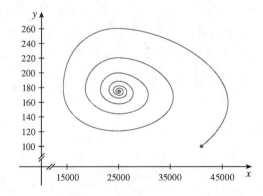

(d) Sketch graphs of the bird and insect populations as functions of time.

24. Barbara weighs 60 kg and is on a diet of 1600 calories per day, of which 850 are used automatically by basal metabolism. She spends about 15 cal/kg/day times her weight doing exercise. If 1 kg of fat contains 10,000 cal and we assume that the storage of calories in the form of fat is 100% efficient, formulate a differential equation and solve it to find her weight as a function of time. Does her weight ultimately approach an equilibrium weight?

25. When a flexible cable of uniform density is suspended between two fixed points and hangs of its own weight, the shape $y = f(x)$ of the cable must satisfy a differential equation of the form

$$\frac{d^2y}{dx^2} = k \sqrt{1 + \left(\frac{dy}{dx}\right)^2}$$

where k is a positive constant. Consider the cable shown in the figure.

(a) Let $z = dy/dx$ in the differential equation. Solve the resulting first-order differential equation (in z), and then integrate to find y.

(b) Determine the length of the cable.

Problems Plus

1. Find all functions f such that f' is continuous and

$$[f(x)]^2 = 100 + \int_0^x \{[f(t)]^2 + [f'(t)]^2\}\, dt \qquad \text{for all real } x$$

2. A student forgot the Product Rule for differentiation and made the mistake of thinking that $(fg)' = f'g'$. However, he was lucky and got the correct answer. The function f that he used was $f(x) = e^{x^2}$ and the domain of his problem was the interval $(\frac{1}{2}, \infty)$. What was the function g?

3. Let f be a function with the property that $f(0) = 1$, $f'(0) = 1$, and $f(a + b) = f(a)f(b)$ for all real numbers a and b. Show that $f'(x) = f(x)$ for all x and deduce that $f(x) = e^x$.

4. Find all functions f that satisfy the equation

$$\left(\int f(x)\, dx \right)\left(\int \frac{1}{f(x)}\, dx \right) = -1$$

5. Find the curve $y = f(x)$ such that $f(x) \geqslant 0$, $f(0) = 0$, $f(1) = 1$, and the area under the graph of f from 0 to x is proportional to the $(n + 1)$st power of $f(x)$.

6. A *subtangent* is a portion of the x-axis that lies directly beneath the segment of a tangent line from the point of contact to the x-axis. Find the curves that pass through the point $(c, 1)$ and whose subtangents all have length c.

7. A peach pie is taken out of the oven at 5:00 PM. At that time it is piping hot, 100°C. At 5:10 PM its temperature is 80°C; at 5:20 PM it is 65°C. What is the temperature of the room?

8. Snow began to fall during the morning of February 2 and continued steadily into the afternoon. At noon a snowplow began removing snow from a road at a constant rate. The plow traveled 6 km from noon to 1 PM but only 3 km from 1 PM to 2 PM. When did the snow begin to fall? [*Hints:* To get started, let t be the time measured in hours after noon; let $x(t)$ be the distance traveled by the plow at time t; then the speed of the plow is dx/dt. Let b be the number of hours before noon that it began to snow. Find an expression for the height of the snow at time t. Then use the given information that the rate of removal R (in m³/h) is constant.]

9. A dog sees a rabbit running in a straight line across an open field and gives chase. In a rectangular coordinate system (as shown in the figure), assume:
   (i) The rabbit is at the origin and the dog is at the point $(L, 0)$ at the instant the dog first sees the rabbit.
   (ii) The rabbit runs up the y-axis and the dog always runs straight for the rabbit.
   (iii) The dog runs at the same speed as the rabbit.
   (a) Show that the dog's path is the graph of the function $y = f(x)$, where y satisfies the differential equation

$$x\frac{d^2y}{dx^2} = \sqrt{1 + \left(\frac{dy}{dx}\right)^2}$$

FIGURE FOR PROBLEM 9

   (b) Determine the solution of the equation in part (a) that satisfies the initial conditions $y = y' = 0$ when $x = L$. [*Hint:* Let $z = dy/dx$ in the differential equation and solve the resulting first-order equation to find z; then integrate z to find y.]
   (c) Does the dog ever catch the rabbit?

633

10. (a) Suppose that the dog in Problem 9 runs twice as fast as the rabbit. Find a differential equation for the path of the dog. Then solve it to find the point where the dog catches the rabbit.
    (b) Suppose the dog runs half as fast as the rabbit. How close does the dog get to the rabbit? What are their positions when they are closest?

11. A planning engineer for a new alum plant must present some estimates to his company regarding the capacity of a silo designed to contain bauxite ore until it is processed into alum. The ore resembles pink talcum powder and is poured from a conveyor at the top of the silo. The silo is a cylinder 30 m high with a radius of 60 m. The conveyor carries $1500\pi \, m^3/h$ and the ore maintains a conical shape whose radius is 1.5 times its height.
    (a) If, at a certain time t, the pile is 20 m high, how long will it take for the pile to reach the top of the silo?
    (b) Management wants to know how much room will be left in the floor area of the silo when the pile is 20 m high. How fast is the floor area of the pile growing at that height?
    (c) Suppose a loader starts removing the ore at the rate of $500\pi \, m^3/h$ when the height of the pile reaches 27 m. Suppose, also, that the pile continues to maintain its shape. How long will it take for the pile to reach the top of the silo under these conditions?

12. Find the curve that passes through the point $(3, 2)$ and has the property that if the tangent line is drawn at any point P on the curve, then the part of the tangent line that lies in the first quadrant is bisected at P.

13. Recall that the normal line to a curve at a point P on the curve is the line that passes through P and is perpendicular to the tangent line at P. Find the curve that passes through the point $(3, 2)$ and has the property that if the normal line is drawn at any point on the curve, then the y-intercept of the normal line is always 6.

14. Find all curves with the property that if the normal line is drawn at any point P on the curve, then the part of the normal line between P and the x-axis is bisected by the y-axis.

15. Find all curves with the property that if a line is drawn from the origin to any point (x, y) on the curve, and then a tangent is drawn to the curve at that point and extended to meet the x-axis, the result is an isosceles triangle with equal sides meeting at (x, y).

Parametric Equations and Polar Coordinates

The Hale-Bopp comet, with its blue ion tail and white dust tail, appeared in the sky in March 1997. In Section 10.6 you will see how polar coordinates provide a convenient equation for the path of this comet.

© Dean Ketelsen

So far we have described plane curves by giving y as a function of x $[y = f(x)]$ or x as a function of y $[x = g(y)]$ or by giving a relation between x and y that defines y implicitly as a function of x $[f(x, y) = 0]$. In this chapter we discuss two new methods for describing curves.

Some curves, such as the cycloid, are best handled when both x and y are given in terms of a third variable t called a parameter $[x = f(t), y = g(t)]$. Other curves, such as the cardioid, have their most convenient description when we use a new coordinate system, called the polar coordinate system.

10.1   Curves Defined by Parametric Equations

FIGURE 1

Imagine that a particle moves along the curve C shown in Figure 1. It is impossible to describe C by an equation of the form $y = f(x)$ because C fails the Vertical Line Test. But the x- and y-coordinates of the particle are functions of time and so we can write $x = f(t)$ and $y = g(t)$. Such a pair of equations is often a convenient way of describing a curve and gives rise to the following definition.

Suppose that x and y are both given as functions of a third variable t (called a **parameter**) by the equations

$$x = f(t) \qquad y = g(t)$$

(called **parametric equations**). Each value of t determines a point (x, y), which we can plot in a coordinate plane. As t varies, the point $(x, y) = (f(t), g(t))$ varies and traces out a curve C, which we call a **parametric curve**. The parameter t does not necessarily represent time and, in fact, we could use a letter other than t for the parameter. But in many applications of parametric curves, t does denote time and therefore we can interpret $(x, y) = (f(t), g(t))$ as the position of a particle at time t.

EXAMPLE 1   Sketch and identify the curve defined by the parametric equations

$$x = t^2 - 2t \qquad y = t + 1$$

SOLUTION   Each value of t gives a point on the curve, as shown in the table. For instance, if $t = 0$, then $x = 0$, $y = 1$ and so the corresponding point is $(0, 1)$. In Figure 2 we plot the points (x, y) determined by several values of the parameter and we join them to produce a curve.

t	x	y
-2	8	-1
-1	3	0
0	0	1
1	-1	2
2	0	3
3	3	4
4	8	5

FIGURE 2

A particle whose position is given by the parametric equations moves along the curve in the direction of the arrows as t increases. Notice that the consecutive points marked on the curve appear at equal time intervals but not at equal distances. That is because the particle slows down and then speeds up as t increases.

It appears from Figure 2 that the curve traced out by the particle may be a parabola. This can be confirmed by eliminating the parameter t as follows. We obtain $t = y - 1$ from the second equation and substitute into the first equation. This gives

$$x = t^2 - 2t = (y - 1)^2 - 2(y - 1) = y^2 - 4y + 3$$

This equation in x and y describes *where* the particle has been, but it doesn't tell us *when* the particle was at a particular point. The parametric equations have an advantage—they tell us *when* the particle was at a point. They also indicate the *direction* of the motion.

and so the curve represented by the given parametric equations is the parabola $x = y^2 - 4y + 3$.   ▬

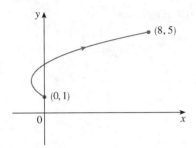

FIGURE 3

No restriction was placed on the parameter t in Example 1, so we assumed that t could be any real number. But sometimes we restrict t to lie in a finite interval. For instance, the parametric curve

$$x = t^2 - 2t \qquad y = t + 1 \qquad 0 \leqslant t \leqslant 4$$

shown in Figure 3 is the part of the parabola in Example 1 that starts at the point $(0, 1)$ and ends at the point $(8, 5)$. The arrowhead indicates the direction in which the curve is traced as t increases from 0 to 4.

In general, the curve with parametric equations

$$x = f(t) \qquad y = g(t) \qquad a \leqslant t \leqslant b$$

has **initial point** $(f(a), g(a))$ and **terminal point** $(f(b), g(b))$.

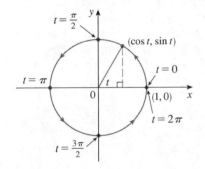

FIGURE 4

V EXAMPLE 2 What curve is represented by the following parametric equations?

$$x = \cos t \qquad y = \sin t \qquad 0 \leqslant t \leqslant 2\pi$$

SOLUTION If we plot points, it appears that the curve is a circle. We can confirm this impression by eliminating t. Observe that

$$x^2 + y^2 = \cos^2 t + \sin^2 t = 1$$

Thus the point (x, y) moves on the unit circle $x^2 + y^2 = 1$. Notice that in this example the parameter t can be interpreted as the angle (in radians) shown in Figure 4. As t increases from 0 to 2π, the point $(x, y) = (\cos t, \sin t)$ moves once around the circle in the counterclockwise direction starting from the point $(1, 0)$. ▬

EXAMPLE 3 What curve is represented by the given parametric equations?

$$x = \sin 2t \qquad y = \cos 2t \qquad 0 \leqslant t \leqslant 2\pi$$

SOLUTION Again we have

$$x^2 + y^2 = \sin^2 2t + \cos^2 2t = 1$$

so the parametric equations again represent the unit circle $x^2 + y^2 = 1$. But as t increases from 0 to 2π, the point $(x, y) = (\sin 2t, \cos 2t)$ starts at $(0, 1)$ and moves *twice* around the circle in the clockwise direction as indicated in Figure 5. ▬

FIGURE 5

Examples 2 and 3 show that different sets of parametric equations can represent the same curve. Thus we distinguish between a *curve*, which is a set of points, and a *parametric curve*, in which the points are traced in a particular way.

EXAMPLE 4 Find parametric equations for the circle with center (h, k) and radius r.

SOLUTION If we take the equations of the unit circle in Example 2 and multiply the expressions for x and y by r, we get $x = r \cos t$, $y = r \sin t$. You can verify that these equations represent a circle with radius r and center the origin traced counterclockwise. We now shift h units in the x-direction and k units in the y-direction and obtain parametric equations of the circle (Figure 6) with center (h, k) and radius r:

$$x = h + r\cos t \qquad y = k + r\sin t \qquad 0 \leqslant t \leqslant 2\pi$$

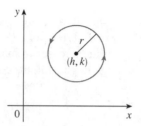

FIGURE 6
$x = h + r\cos t,\ y = k + r\sin t$

FIGURE 7

V **EXAMPLE 5** Sketch the curve with parametric equations $x = \sin t$, $y = \sin^2 t$.

SOLUTION Observe that $y = (\sin t)^2 = x^2$ and so the point (x, y) moves on the parabola $y = x^2$. But note also that, since $-1 \leqslant \sin t \leqslant 1$, we have $-1 \leqslant x \leqslant 1$, so the parametric equations represent only the part of the parabola for which $-1 \leqslant x \leqslant 1$. Since $\sin t$ is periodic, the point $(x, y) = (\sin t, \sin^2 t)$ moves back and forth infinitely often along the parabola from $(-1, 1)$ to $(1, 1)$. (See Figure 7.)

TEC Module 10.1A gives an animation of the relationship between motion along a parametric curve $x = f(t)$, $y = g(t)$ and motion along the graphs of f and g as functions of t. Clicking on TRIG gives you the family of parametric curves

$$x = a\cos bt \qquad y = c\sin dt$$

If you choose $a = b = c = d = 1$ and click on animate, you will see how the graphs of $x = \cos t$ and $y = \sin t$ relate to the circle in Example 2. If you choose $a = b = c = 1$, $d = 2$, you will see graphs as in Figure 8. By clicking on animate or moving the t-slider to the right, you can see from the color coding how motion along the graphs of $x = \cos t$ and $y = \sin 2t$ corresponds to motion along the parametric curve, which is called a **Lissajous figure**.

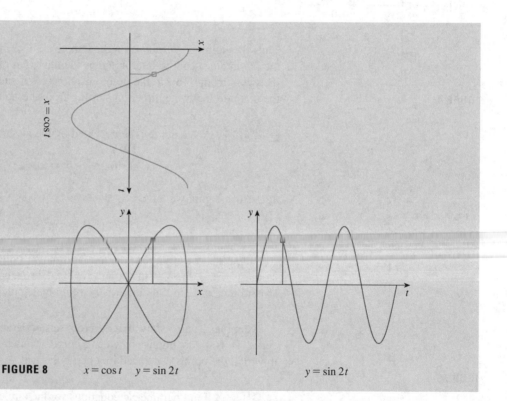

FIGURE 8 $x = \cos t$ $y = \sin 2t$ $y = \sin 2t$

Graphing Devices

Most graphing calculators and computer graphing programs can be used to graph curves defined by parametric equations. In fact, it's instructive to watch a parametric curve being drawn by a graphing calculator because the points are plotted in order as the corresponding parameter values increase.

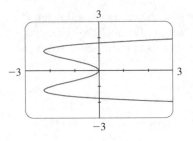

FIGURE 9

EXAMPLE 6 Use a graphing device to graph the curve $x = y^4 - 3y^2$.

SOLUTION If we let the parameter be $t = y$, then we have the equations

$$x = t^4 - 3t^2 \qquad y = t$$

Using these parametric equations to graph the curve, we obtain Figure 9. It would be possible to solve the given equation ($x = y^4 - 3y^2$) for y as four functions of x and graph them individually, but the parametric equations provide a much easier method.

In general, if we need to graph an equation of the form $x = g(y)$, we can use the parametric equations

$$x = g(t) \qquad y = t$$

Notice also that curves with equations $y = f(x)$ (the ones we are most familiar with—graphs of functions) can also be regarded as curves with parametric equations

$$x = t \qquad y = f(t)$$

Graphing devices are particularly useful for sketching complicated curves. For instance, the curves shown in Figures 10, 11, and 12 would be virtually impossible to produce by hand.

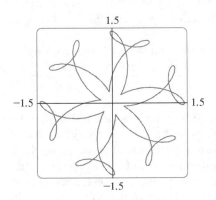

FIGURE 10
$x = \sin t + \frac{1}{2} \cos 5t + \frac{1}{4} \sin 13t$
$y = \cos t + \frac{1}{2} \sin 5t + \frac{1}{4} \cos 13t$

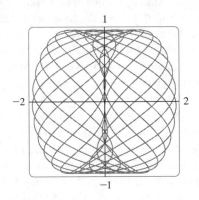

FIGURE 11
$x = \sin t - \sin 2.3t$
$y = \cos t$

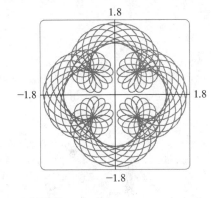

FIGURE 12
$x = \sin t + \frac{1}{2} \sin 5t + \frac{1}{4} \cos 2.3t$
$y = \cos t + \frac{1}{2} \cos 5t + \frac{1}{4} \sin 2.3t$

One of the most important uses of parametric curves is in computer-aided design (CAD). In the Laboratory Project after Section 10.2 we will investigate special parametric curves, called **Bézier curves**, that are used extensively in manufacturing, especially in the automotive industry. These curves are also employed in specifying the shapes of letters and other symbols in laser printers.

The Cycloid

TEC An animation in Module 10.1B shows how the cycloid is formed as the circle moves.

EXAMPLE 7 The curve traced out by a point P on the circumference of a circle as the circle rolls along a straight line is called a **cycloid** (see Figure 13). If the circle has radius r and rolls along the x-axis and if one position of P is the origin, find parametric equations for the cycloid.

FIGURE 13

FIGURE 14

cycloid

FIGURE 15

FIGURE 16

SOLUTION We choose as parameter the angle of rotation θ of the circle ($\theta = 0$ when P is at the origin). Suppose the circle has rotated through θ radians. Because the circle has been in contact with the line, we see from Figure 14 that the distance it has rolled from the origin is

$$|OT| = \text{arc } PT = r\theta$$

Therefore the center of the circle is $C(r\theta, r)$. Let the coordinates of P be (x, y). Then from Figure 14 we see that

$$x = |OT| - |PQ| = r\theta - r\sin\theta = r(\theta - \sin\theta)$$

$$y = |TC| - |QC| = r - r\cos\theta = r(1 - \cos\theta)$$

Therefore parametric equations of the cycloid are

$$\boxed{1} \qquad x = r(\theta - \sin\theta) \qquad y = r(1 - \cos\theta) \qquad \theta \in \mathbb{R}$$

One arch of the cycloid comes from one rotation of the circle and so is described by $0 \leq \theta \leq 2\pi$. Although Equations 1 were derived from Figure 14, which illustrates the case where $0 < \theta < \pi/2$, it can be seen that these equations are still valid for other values of θ (see Exercise 39).

Although it is possible to eliminate the parameter θ from Equations 1, the resulting Cartesian equation in x and y is very complicated and not as convenient to work with as the parametric equations. ▬

One of the first people to study the cycloid was Galileo, who proposed that bridges be built in the shape of cycloids and who tried to find the area under one arch of a cycloid. Later this curve arose in connection with the **brachistochrone problem**: Find the curve along which a particle will slide in the shortest time (under the influence of gravity) from a point A to a lower point B not directly beneath A. The Swiss mathematician John Bernoulli, who posed this problem in 1696, showed that among all possible curves that join A to B, as in Figure 15, the particle will take the least time sliding from A to B if the curve is part of an inverted arch of a cycloid.

The Dutch physicist Huygens had already shown that the cycloid is also the solution to the **tautochrone problem**; that is, no matter where a particle P is placed on an inverted cycloid, it takes the same time to slide to the bottom (see Figure 16). Huygens proposed that pendulum clocks (which he invented) should swing in cycloidal arcs because then the pendulum would take the same time to make a complete oscillation whether it swings through a wide or a small arc.

▬ Families of Parametric Curves

V **EXAMPLE 8** Investigate the family of curves with parametric equations

$$x = a + \cos t \qquad y = a\tan t + \sin t$$

What do these curves have in common? How does the shape change as a increases?

SOLUTION We use a graphing device to produce the graphs for the cases $a = -2, -1, -0.5, -0.2, 0, 0.5, 1,$ and 2 shown in Figure 17. Notice that all of these curves (except the case $a = 0$) have two branches, and both branches approach the vertical asymptote $x = a$ as x approaches a from the left or right.

$a = -2$

$a = -1$

$a = -0.5$

$a = -0.2$

$a = 0$

$a = 0.5$

$a = 1$

$a = 2$

FIGURE 17 Members of the family $x = a + \cos t$, $y = a \tan t + \sin t$, all graphed in the viewing rectangle $[-4, 4]$ by $[-4, 4]$

When $a < -1$, both branches are smooth; but when a reaches -1, the right branch acquires a sharp point, called a *cusp*. For a between -1 and 0 the cusp turns into a loop, which becomes larger as a approaches 0. When $a = 0$, both branches come together and form a circle (see Example 2). For a between 0 and 1, the left branch has a loop, which shrinks to become a cusp when $a = 1$. For $a > 1$, the branches become smooth again, and as a increases further, they become less curved. Notice that the curves with a positive are reflections about the y-axis of the corresponding curves with a negative.

These curves are called **conchoids of Nicomedes** after the ancient Greek scholar Nicomedes. He called them conchoids because the shape of their outer branches resembles that of a conch shell or mussel shell.

10.1 Exercises

1–4 Sketch the curve by using the parametric equations to plot points. Indicate with an arrow the direction in which the curve is traced as t increases.

1. $x = 1 + \sqrt{t}$, $\quad y = t^2 - 4t$, $\quad 0 \le t \le 5$

2. $x = 2 \cos t$, $\quad y = t - \cos t$, $\quad 0 \le t \le 2\pi$

3. $x = \cos^2 t$, $\quad y = 1 - \sin t$, $\quad 0 \le t \le \pi/2$

4. $x = e^{-t} + t$, $\quad y = e^t - t$, $\quad -2 \le t \le 2$

5–10
(a) Sketch the curve by using the parametric equations to plot points. Indicate with an arrow the direction in which the curve is traced as t increases.
(b) Eliminate the parameter to find a Cartesian equation of the curve.

5. $x = 3 - 4t$, $\quad y = 2 - 3t$

6. $x = 1 - 2t$, $\quad y = \frac{1}{2}t - 1$, $\quad -2 \le t \le 4$

7. $x = 1 - t^2$, $\quad y = t - 2$, $\quad -2 \le t \le 2$

8. $x = t - 1$, $\quad y = t^3 + 1$, $\quad -2 \le t \le 2$

9. $x = \sqrt{t}$, $\quad y = 1 - t$

10. $x = t^2$, $\quad y = t^3$

11–18
(a) Eliminate the parameter to find a Cartesian equation of the curve.
(b) Sketch the curve and indicate with an arrow the direction in which the curve is traced as the parameter increases.

11. $x = \sin \frac{1}{2}\theta$, $\quad y = \cos \frac{1}{2}\theta$, $\quad -\pi \le \theta \le \pi$

12. $x = \frac{1}{2}\cos \theta$, $\quad y = 2 \sin \theta$, $\quad 0 \le \theta \le \pi$

13. $x = \sin t$, $\quad y = \csc t$, $\quad 0 < t < \pi/2$

14. $x = e^t - 1$, $\quad y = e^{2t}$

15. $x = e^{2t}$, $\quad y = t + 1$

16. $x = \sqrt{t + 1}$, $\quad y = \sqrt{t - 1}$

17. $x = \sinh t$, $\quad y = \cosh t$

18. $x = \tan^2 \theta$, $\quad y = \sec \theta$, $\quad -\pi/2 < \theta < \pi/2$

⊞ Graphing calculator or computer required   **1.** Homework Hints available at stewartcalculus.com

19–22 Describe the motion of a particle with position (x, y) as t varies in the given interval.

19. $x = 3 + 2\cos t$, $y = 1 + 2\sin t$, $\pi/2 \leqslant t \leqslant 3\pi/2$

20. $x = 2\sin t$, $y = 4 + \cos t$, $0 \leqslant t \leqslant 3\pi/2$

21. $x = 5\sin t$, $y = 2\cos t$, $-\pi \leqslant t \leqslant 5\pi$

22. $x = \sin t$, $y = \cos^2 t$, $-2\pi \leqslant t \leqslant 2\pi$

23. Suppose a curve is given by the parametric equations $x = f(t)$, $y = g(t)$, where the range of f is $[1, 4]$ and the range of g is $[2, 3]$. What can you say about the curve?

24. Match the graphs of the parametric equations $x = f(t)$ and $y = g(t)$ in (a)–(d) with the parametric curves labeled I–IV. Give reasons for your choices.

(a)

I

(b)

II

(c)

III

(d)

IV

25–27 Use the graphs of $x = f(t)$ and $y = g(t)$ to sketch the parametric curve $x = f(t)$, $y = g(t)$. Indicate with arrows the direction in which the curve is traced as t increases.

25.

26.

27.

28. Match the parametric equations with the graphs labeled I-VI. Give reasons for your choices. (Do not use a graphing device.)

(a) $x = t^4 - t + 1$, $y = t^2$

(b) $x = t^2 - 2t$, $y = \sqrt{t}$

(c) $x = \sin 2t$, $y = \sin(t + \sin 2t)$

(d) $x = \cos 5t$, $y = \sin 2t$

(e) $x = t + \sin 4t$, $y = t^2 + \cos 3t$

(f) $x = \dfrac{\sin 2t}{4 + t^2}$, $y = \dfrac{\cos 2t}{4 + t^2}$

I   II   III

IV   V   VI

29. Graph the curve $x = y - 2 \sin \pi y$.

30. Graph the curves $y = x^3 - 4x$ and $x = y^3 - 4y$ and find their points of intersection correct to one decimal place.

31. (a) Show that the parametric equations

$$x = x_1 + (x_2 - x_1)t \qquad y = y_1 + (y_2 - y_1)t$$

where $0 \leq t \leq 1$, describe the line segment that joins the points $P_1(x_1, y_1)$ and $P_2(x_2, y_2)$.

(b) Find parametric equations to represent the line segment from $(-2, 7)$ to $(3, -1)$.

32. Use a graphing device and the result of Exercise 31(a) to draw the triangle with vertices $A(1, 1)$, $B(4, 2)$, and $C(1, 5)$.

33. Find parametric equations for the path of a particle that moves along the circle $x^2 + (y - 1)^2 = 4$ in the manner described.

(a) Once around clockwise, starting at $(2, 1)$

(b) Three times around counterclockwise, starting at $(2, 1)$

(c) Halfway around counterclockwise, starting at $(0, 3)$

34. (a) Find parametric equations for the ellipse $x^2/a^2 + y^2/b^2 = 1$. [*Hint:* Modify the equations of the circle in Example 2.]

(b) Use these parametric equations to graph the ellipse when $a = 3$ and $b = 1, 2, 4$, and 8.

(c) How does the shape of the ellipse change as b varies?

35–36 Use a graphing calculator or computer to reproduce the picture.

35.

36.

37–38 Compare the curves represented by the parametric equations. How do they differ?

37. (a) $x = t^3$, $y = t^2$ (b) $x = t^6$, $y = t^4$

    (c) $x = e^{-3t}$, $y = e^{-2t}$

38. (a) $x = t$, $y = t^{-2}$ (b) $x = \cos t$, $y = \sec^2 t$

    (c) $x = e^t$, $y = e^{-2t}$

39. Derive Equations 1 for the case $\pi/2 < \theta < \pi$.

40. Let P be a point at a distance d from the center of a circle of radius r. The curve traced out by P as the circle rolls along a straight line is called a **trochoid**. (Think of the motion of a point on a spoke of a bicycle wheel.) The cycloid is the special case of a trochoid with $d = r$. Using the same parameter θ as for the cycloid and, assuming the line is the x-axis and

$\theta = 0$ when P is at one of its lowest points, show that parametric equations of the trochoid are

$$x = r\theta - d \sin \theta \qquad y = r - d \cos \theta$$

Sketch the trochoid for the cases $d < r$ and $d > r$.

41. If a and b are fixed numbers, find parametric equations for the curve that consists of all possible positions of the point P in the figure, using the angle θ as the parameter. Then eliminate the parameter and identify the curve.

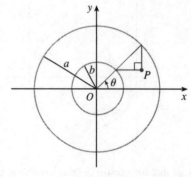

42. If a and b are fixed numbers, find parametric equations for the curve that consists of all possible positions of the point P in the figure, using the angle θ as the parameter. The line segment AB is tangent to the larger circle.

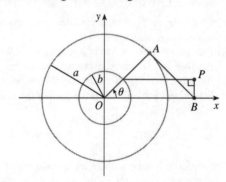

43. A curve, called a **witch of Maria Agnesi**, consists of all possible positions of the point P in the figure. Show that parametric equations for this curve can be written as

$$x = 2a \cot \theta \qquad y = 2a \sin^2 \theta$$

Sketch the curve.

44. (a) Find parametric equations for the set of all points P as shown in the figure such that $|OP| = |AB|$. (This curve is called the **cissoid of Diocles** after the Greek scholar Diocles, who introduced the cissoid as a graphical method for constructing the edge of a cube whose volume is twice that of a given cube.)

(b) Use the geometric description of the curve to draw a rough sketch of the curve by hand. Check your work by using the parametric equations to graph the curve.

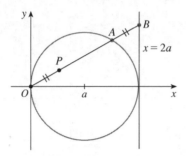

45. Suppose that the position of one particle at time t is given by

$$x_1 = 3 \sin t \qquad y_1 = 2 \cos t \qquad 0 \leqslant t \leqslant 2\pi$$

and the position of a second particle is given by

$$x_2 = -3 + \cos t \qquad y_2 = 1 + \sin t \qquad 0 \leqslant t \leqslant 2\pi$$

(a) Graph the paths of both particles. How many points of intersection are there?

(b) Are any of these points of intersection *collision points*? In other words, are the particles ever at the same place at the same time? If so, find the collision points.

(c) Describe what happens if the path of the second particle is given by

$$x_2 = 3 + \cos t \qquad y_2 = 1 + \sin t \qquad 0 \leqslant t \leqslant 2\pi$$

46. If a projectile is fired with an initial velocity of v_0 meters per second at an angle α above the horizontal and air resistance is assumed to be negligible, then its position after t seconds

is given by the parametric equations

$$x = (v_0 \cos \alpha)t \qquad y = (v_0 \sin \alpha)t - \tfrac{1}{2}gt^2$$

where g is the acceleration due to gravity (9.8 m/s^2).

(a) If a gun is fired with $\alpha = 30°$ and $v_0 = 500$ m/s, when will the bullet hit the ground? How far from the gun will it hit the ground? What is the maximum height reached by the bullet?

(b) Use a graphing device to check your answers to part (a). Then graph the path of the projectile for several other values of the angle α to see where it hits the ground. Summarize your findings.

(c) Show that the path is parabolic by eliminating the parameter.

47. Investigate the family of curves defined by the parametric equations $x = t^2$, $y = t^3 - ct$. How does the shape change as c increases? Illustrate by graphing several members of the family.

48. The **swallowtail catastrophe curves** are defined by the parametric equations $x = 2ct - 4t^3$, $y = -ct^2 + 3t^4$. Graph several of these curves. What features do the curves have in common? How do they change when c increases?

49. Graph several members of the family of curves with parametric equations $x = t + a \cos t$, $y = t + a \sin t$, where $a > 0$. How does the shape change as a increases? For what values of a does the curve have a loop?

50. Graph several members of the family of curves $x = \sin t + \sin nt$, $y = \cos t + \cos nt$ where n is a positive integer. What features do the curves have in common? What happens as n increases?

51. The curves with equations $x = a \sin nt$, $y = b \cos t$ are called **Lissajous figures**. Investigate how these curves vary when a, b, and n vary. (Take n to be a positive integer.)

52. Investigate the family of curves defined by the parametric equations $x = \cos t$, $y = \sin t - \sin ct$, where $c > 0$. Start by letting c be a positive integer and see what happens to the shape as c increases. Then explore some of the possibilities that occur when c is a fraction.

LABORATORY PROJECT RUNNING CIRCLES AROUND CIRCLES

In this project we investigate families of curves, called *hypocycloids* and *epicycloids,* that are generated by the motion of a point on a circle that rolls inside or outside another circle.

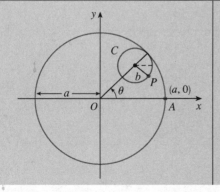

1. A **hypocycloid** is a curve traced out by a fixed point P on a circle C of radius b as C rolls on the inside of a circle with center O and radius a. Show that if the initial position of P is $(a, 0)$ and the parameter θ is chosen as in the figure, then parametric equations of the hypocycloid are

$$x = (a - b) \cos \theta + b \cos\left(\frac{a - b}{b}\theta\right). \qquad y = (a - b) \sin \theta - b \sin\left(\frac{a - b}{b}\theta\right)$$

Graphing calculator or computer required

2. Use a graphing device (or the interactive graphic in TEC Module 10.1B) to draw the graphs of hypocycloids with a a positive integer and $b = 1$. How does the value of a affect the graph? Show that if we take $a = 4$, then the parametric equations of the hypocycloid reduce to

$$x = 4\cos^3\theta \qquad y = 4\sin^3\theta$$

This curve is called a **hypocycloid of four cusps**, or an **astroid**.

3. Now try $b = 1$ and $a = n/d$, a fraction where n and d have no common factor. First let $n = 1$ and try to determine graphically the effect of the denominator d on the shape of the graph. Then let n vary while keeping d constant. What happens when $n = d + 1$?

4. What happens if $b = 1$ and a is irrational? Experiment with an irrational number like $\sqrt{2}$ or $e - 2$. Take larger and larger values for θ and speculate on what would happen if we were to graph the hypocycloid for all real values of θ.

5. If the circle C rolls on the *outside* of the fixed circle, the curve traced out by P is called an **epicycloid**. Find parametric equations for the epicycloid.

6. Investigate the possible shapes for epicycloids. Use methods similar to Problems 2–4.

10.2 Calculus with Parametric Curves

Having seen how to represent curves by parametric equations, we now apply the methods of calculus to these parametric curves. In particular, we solve problems involving tangents, area, arc length, and surface area.

Tangents

Suppose f and g are differentiable functions and we want to find the tangent line at a point on the curve $x = f(t)$, $y = g(t)$ where y is also a differentiable function of x. Then the Chain Rule gives

$$\frac{dy}{dt} = \frac{dy}{dx} \cdot \frac{dx}{dt}$$

If $dx/dt \neq 0$, we can solve for dy/dx:

If we think of the curve as being traced out by a moving particle, then dy/dt and dx/dt are the vertical and horizontal velocities of the particle and Formula 1 says that the slope of the tangent is the ratio of these velocities.

$$\boxed{1} \qquad \frac{dy}{dx} = \frac{\dfrac{dy}{dt}}{\dfrac{dx}{dt}} \qquad \text{if} \quad \frac{dx}{dt} \neq 0$$

Equation 1 (which you can remember by thinking of canceling the dt's) enables us to find the slope dy/dx of the tangent to a parametric curve without having to eliminate the parameter t. We see from $\boxed{1}$ that the curve has a horizontal tangent when $dy/dt = 0$ (provided that $dx/dt \neq 0$) and it has a vertical tangent when $dx/dt = 0$ (provided that $dy/dt \neq 0$). This information is useful for sketching parametric curves.

As we know from Chapter 4, it is also useful to consider d^2y/dx^2. This can be found by replacing y by dy/dx in Equation 1:

$\oslash$ Note that $\dfrac{d^2y}{dx^2} \neq \dfrac{\dfrac{d^2y}{dt^2}}{\dfrac{d^2x}{dt^2}}$

$$\frac{d^2y}{dx^2} = \frac{d}{dx}\left(\frac{dy}{dx}\right) = \frac{\dfrac{d}{dt}\left(\dfrac{dy}{dx}\right)}{\dfrac{dx}{dt}}$$

EXAMPLE 1 A curve C is defined by the parametric equations $x = t^2$, $y = t^3 - 3t$.
(a) Show that C has two tangents at the point $(3, 0)$ and find their equations.
(b) Find the points on C where the tangent is horizontal or vertical.
(c) Determine where the curve is concave upward or downward.
(d) Sketch the curve.

SOLUTION
(a) Notice that $y = t^3 - 3t = t(t^2 - 3) = 0$ when $t = 0$ or $t = \pm\sqrt{3}$. Therefore the point $(3, 0)$ on C arises from two values of the parameter, $t = \sqrt{3}$ and $t = -\sqrt{3}$. This indicates that C crosses itself at $(3, 0)$. Since

$$\frac{dy}{dx} = \frac{dy/dt}{dx/dt} = \frac{3t^2 - 3}{2t} = \frac{3}{2}\left(t - \frac{1}{t}\right)$$

the slope of the tangent when $t = \pm\sqrt{3}$ is $dy/dx = \pm 6/(2\sqrt{3}) = \pm\sqrt{3}$, so the equations of the tangents at $(3, 0)$ are

$$y = \sqrt{3}\,(x - 3) \qquad \text{and} \qquad y = -\sqrt{3}\,(x - 3)$$

(b) C has a horizontal tangent when $dy/dx = 0$, that is, when $dy/dt = 0$ and $dx/dt \neq 0$. Since $dy/dt = 3t^2 - 3$, this happens when $t^2 = 1$, that is, $t = \pm 1$. The corresponding points on C are $(1, -2)$ and $(1, 2)$. C has a vertical tangent when $dx/dt = 2t = 0$, that is, $t = 0$. (Note that $dy/dt \neq 0$ there.) The corresponding point on C is $(0, 0)$.

(c) To determine concavity we calculate the second derivative:

$$\frac{d^2y}{dx^2} = \frac{\dfrac{d}{dt}\left(\dfrac{dy}{dx}\right)}{\dfrac{dx}{dt}} = \frac{\dfrac{3}{2}\left(1 + \dfrac{1}{t^2}\right)}{2t} = \frac{3(t^2 + 1)}{4t^3}$$

Thus the curve is concave upward when $t > 0$ and concave downward when $t < 0$.

(d) Using the information from parts (b) and (c), we sketch C in Figure 1. ▬

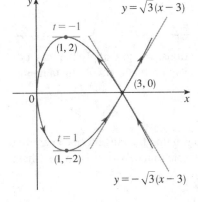

$y = \sqrt{3}(x - 3)$

$t = -1$

$(1, 2)$

$(3, 0)$

$t = 1$

$(1, -2)$

$y = -\sqrt{3}(x - 3)$

FIGURE 1

V **EXAMPLE 2**
(a) Find the tangent to the cycloid $x = r(\theta - \sin\theta)$, $y = r(1 - \cos\theta)$ at the point where $\theta = \pi/3$. (See Example 7 in Section 10.1.)
(b) At what points is the tangent horizontal? When is it vertical?

SOLUTION
(a) The slope of the tangent line is

$$\frac{dy}{dx} = \frac{dy/d\theta}{dx/d\theta} = \frac{r\sin\theta}{r(1 - \cos\theta)} = \frac{\sin\theta}{1 - \cos\theta}$$

When $\theta = \pi/3$, we have

$$x = r\left(\frac{\pi}{3} - \sin\frac{\pi}{3}\right) = r\left(\frac{\pi}{3} - \frac{\sqrt{3}}{2}\right) \qquad y = r\left(1 - \cos\frac{\pi}{3}\right) = \frac{r}{2}$$

and

$$\frac{dy}{dx} = \frac{\sin(\pi/3)}{1 - \cos(\pi/3)} = \frac{\sqrt{3}/2}{1 - \frac{1}{2}} = \sqrt{3}$$

Therefore the slope of the tangent is $\sqrt{3}$ and its equation is

$$y - \frac{r}{2} = \sqrt{3}\left(x - \frac{r\pi}{3} + \frac{r\sqrt{3}}{2}\right) \quad \text{or} \quad \sqrt{3}\,x - y = r\left(\frac{\pi}{\sqrt{3}} - 2\right)$$

The tangent is sketched in Figure 2.

FIGURE 2

(b) The tangent is horizontal when $dy/dx = 0$, which occurs when $\sin \theta = 0$ and $1 - \cos \theta \neq 0$, that is, $\theta = (2n - 1)\pi$, n an integer. The corresponding point on the cycloid is $((2n - 1)\pi r, 2r)$.

When $\theta = 2n\pi$, both $dx/d\theta$ and $dy/d\theta$ are 0. It appears from the graph that there are vertical tangents at those points. We can verify this by using l'Hospital's Rule as follows:

$$\lim_{\theta \to 2n\pi^{+}} \frac{dy}{dx} = \lim_{\theta \to 2n\pi^{+}} \frac{\sin \theta}{1 - \cos \theta} = \lim_{\theta \to 2n\pi^{+}} \frac{\cos \theta}{\sin \theta} = \infty$$

A similar computation shows that $dy/dx \to -\infty$ as $\theta \to 2n\pi^{-}$, so indeed there are vertical tangents when $\theta = 2n\pi$, that is, when $x = 2n\pi r$.

Areas

We know that the area under a curve $y = F(x)$ from a to b is $A = \int_a^b F(x)\,dx$, where $F(x) \geq 0$. If the curve is traced out once by the parametric equations $x = f(t)$ and $y = g(t)$, $\alpha \leq t \leq \beta$, then we can calculate an area formula by using the Substitution Rule for Definite Integrals as follows:

The limits of integration for t are found as usual with the Substitution Rule. When $x = a$, t is either α or β. When $x = b$, t is the remaining value.

$$A = \int_a^b y\,dx = \int_\alpha^\beta g(t)f'(t)\,dt \quad \left[\text{or} \quad \int_\beta^\alpha g(t)f'(t)\,dt\right]$$

V **EXAMPLE 3** Find the area under one arch of the cycloid

$$x = r(\theta - \sin \theta) \qquad y = r(1 - \cos \theta)$$

(See Figure 3.)

SOLUTION One arch of the cycloid is given by $0 \leq \theta \leq 2\pi$. Using the Substitution Rule with $y = r(1 - \cos \theta)$ and $dx = r(1 - \cos \theta)\,d\theta$, we have

$$A = \int_0^{2\pi r} y\,dx = \int_0^{2\pi} r(1 - \cos \theta)\, r(1 - \cos \theta)\,d\theta$$

$$= r^2 \int_0^{2\pi} (1 - \cos \theta)^2\, d\theta = r^2 \int_0^{2\pi} (1 - 2\cos \theta + \cos^2\theta)\, d\theta$$

$$= r^2 \int_0^{2\pi} \left[1 - 2\cos \theta + \tfrac{1}{2}(1 + \cos 2\theta)\right] d\theta$$

$$= r^2 \left[\tfrac{3}{2}\theta - 2\sin \theta + \tfrac{1}{4}\sin 2\theta\right]_0^{2\pi}$$

$$= r^2\left(\tfrac{3}{2} \cdot 2\pi\right) = 3\pi r^2$$

FIGURE 3

The result of Example 3 says that the area under one arch of the cycloid is three times the area of the rolling circle that generates the cycloid (see Example 7 in Section 10.1). Galileo guessed this result but it was first proved by the French mathematician Roberval and the Italian mathematician Torricelli.

▮ Arc Length

We already know how to find the length L of a curve C given in the form $y = F(x)$, $a \leqslant x \leqslant b$. Formula 8.1.3 says that if F' is continuous, then

$$\boxed{1} \qquad L = \int_a^b \sqrt{1 + \left(\frac{dy}{dx}\right)^2}\, dx$$

Suppose that C can also be described by the parametric equations $x = f(t)$ and $y = g(t)$, $\alpha \leqslant t \leqslant \beta$, where $dx/dt = f'(t) > 0$. This means that C is traversed once, from left to right, as t increases from α to β and $f(\alpha) = a$, $f(\beta) = b$. Putting Formula 1 into Formula 2 and using the Substitution Rule, we obtain

$$L = \int_a^b \sqrt{1 + \left(\frac{dy}{dx}\right)^2}\, dx = \int_\alpha^\beta \sqrt{1 + \left(\frac{dy/dt}{dx/dt}\right)^2}\, \frac{dx}{dt}\, dt$$

Since $dx/dt > 0$, we have

$$\boxed{3} \qquad L = \int_\alpha^\beta \sqrt{\left(\frac{dx}{dt}\right)^2 + \left(\frac{dy}{dt}\right)^2}\, dt$$

Even if C can't be expressed in the form $y = F(x)$, Formula 3 is still valid but we obtain it by polygonal approximations. We divide the parameter interval $[\alpha, \beta]$ into n subintervals of equal width Δt. If $t_0, t_1, t_2, \ldots, t_n$ are the endpoints of these subintervals, then $x_i = f(t_i)$ and $y_i = g(t_i)$ are the coordinates of points $P_i(x_i, y_i)$ that lie on C and the polygon with vertices $P_0, P_1, \ldots, P_n$ approximates C. (See Figure 4.)

As in Section 8.1, we define the length L of C to be the limit of the lengths of these approximating polygons as $n \to \infty$:

$$L = \lim_{n \to \infty} \sum_{i=1}^{n} |P_{i-1}P_i|$$

FIGURE 4

The Mean Value Theorem, when applied to f on the interval $[t_{i-1}, t_i]$, gives a number t_i^* in (t_{i-1}, t_i) such that

$$f(t_i) - f(t_{i-1}) = f'(t_i^*)(t_i - t_{i-1})$$

If we let $\Delta x_i = x_i - x_{i-1}$ and $\Delta y_i = y_i - y_{i-1}$, this equation becomes

$$\Delta x_i = f'(t_i^*)\, \Delta t$$

Similarly, when applied to g, the Mean Value Theorem gives a number t_i^{**} in (t_{i-1}, t_i) such that

$$\Delta y_i = g'(t_i^{**})\, \Delta t$$

Therefore

$$|P_{i-1}P_i| = \sqrt{(\Delta x_i)^2 + (\Delta y_i)^2} = \sqrt{[f'(t_i^*)\,\Delta t]^2 + [g'(t_i^{**})\,\Delta t]^2}$$
$$= \sqrt{[f'(t_i^*)]^2 + [g'(t_i^{**})]^2}\, \Delta t$$

and so

$$\boxed{4} \qquad L = \lim_{n \to \infty} \sum_{i=1}^{n} \sqrt{[f'(t_i^*)]^2 + [g'(t_i^{**})]^2}\, \Delta t$$

The sum in $\boxed{4}$ resembles a Riemann sum for the function $\sqrt{[f'(t)]^2 + [g'(t)]^2}$ but it is not exactly a Riemann sum because $t_i^* \neq t_i^{**}$ in general. Nevertheless, if f' and g' are continuous, it can be shown that the limit in $\boxed{4}$ is the same as if t_i^* and t_i^{**} were equal, namely,

$$L = \int_\alpha^\beta \sqrt{[f'(t)]^2 + [g'(t)]^2}\, dt$$

Thus, using Leibniz notation, we have the following result, which has the same form as Formula 3.

$\boxed{5}$ **Theorem** If a curve C is described by the parametric equations $x = f(t)$, $y = g(t)$, $\alpha \leq t \leq \beta$, where f' and g' are continuous on $[\alpha, \beta]$ and C is traversed exactly once as t increases from α to β, then the length of C is

$$L = \int_\alpha^\beta \sqrt{\left(\frac{dx}{dt}\right)^2 + \left(\frac{dy}{dt}\right)^2}\, dt$$

Notice that the formula in Theorem 5 is consistent with the general formulas $L = \int ds$ and $(ds)^2 = (dx)^2 + (dy)^2$ of Section 8.1.

EXAMPLE 4 If we use the representation of the unit circle given in Example 2 in Section 10.1,

$$x = \cos t \qquad y = \sin t \qquad 0 \leq t \leq 2\pi$$

then $dx/dt = -\sin t$ and $dy/dt = \cos t$, so Theorem 5 gives

$$L = \int_0^{2\pi} \sqrt{\left(\frac{dx}{dt}\right)^2 + \left(\frac{dy}{dt}\right)^2}\, dt = \int_0^{2\pi} \sqrt{\sin^2 t + \cos^2 t}\, dt = \int_0^{2\pi} dt = 2\pi$$

as expected. If, on the other hand, we use the representation given in Example 3 in Section 10.1,

$$x = \sin 2t \qquad y = \cos 2t \qquad 0 \leq t \leq 2\pi$$

then $dx/dt = 2\cos 2t$, $dy/dt = -2\sin 2t$, and the integral in Theorem 5 gives

$$\int_0^{2\pi} \sqrt{\left(\frac{dx}{dt}\right)^2 + \left(\frac{dy}{dt}\right)^2}\, dt = \int_0^{2\pi} \sqrt{4\cos^2 2t + 4\sin^2 2t}\, dt = \int_0^{2\pi} 2\, dt = 4\pi$$

⊘ Notice that the integral gives twice the arc length of the circle because as t increases from 0 to 2π, the point $(\sin 2t, \cos 2t)$ traverses the circle twice. In general, when finding the length of a curve C from a parametric representation, we have to be careful to ensure that C is traversed only once as t increases from α to β. ▬

V EXAMPLE 5 Find the length of one arch of the cycloid $x = r(\theta - \sin\theta)$, $y = r(1 - \cos\theta)$.

SOLUTION From Example 3 we see that one arch is described by the parameter interval $0 \leq \theta \leq 2\pi$. Since

$$\frac{dx}{d\theta} = r(1 - \cos\theta) \qquad \text{and} \qquad \frac{dy}{d\theta} = r\sin\theta$$

we have

$$L = \int_0^{2\pi} \sqrt{\left(\frac{dx}{d\theta}\right)^2 + \left(\frac{dy}{d\theta}\right)^2} \, d\theta$$

$$= \int_0^{2\pi} \sqrt{r^2(1 - \cos\theta)^2 + r^2\sin^2\theta} \, d\theta$$

$$= \int_0^{2\pi} \sqrt{r^2(1 - 2\cos\theta + \cos^2\theta + \sin^2\theta)} \, d\theta$$

$$= r\int_0^{2\pi} \sqrt{2(1 - \cos\theta)} \, d\theta$$

The result of Example 5 says that the length of one arch of a cycloid is eight times the radius of the generating circle (see Figure 5). This was first proved in 1658 by Sir Christopher Wren, who later became the architect of St. Paul's Cathedral in London.

FIGURE 5

To evaluate this integral we use the identity $\sin^2 x = \frac{1}{2}(1 - \cos 2x)$ with $\theta = 2x$, which gives $1 - \cos\theta = 2\sin^2(\theta/2)$. Since $0 \le \theta \le 2\pi$, we have $0 \le \theta/2 \le \pi$ and so $\sin(\theta/2) \ge 0$. Therefore

$$\sqrt{2(1 - \cos\theta)} = \sqrt{4\sin^2(\theta/2)} = 2|\sin(\theta/2)| = 2\sin(\theta/2)$$

and so

$$L = 2r\int_0^{2\pi} \sin(\theta/2) \, d\theta = 2r\left[-2\cos(\theta/2)\right]_0^{2\pi}$$

$$= 2r[2 + 2] = 8r$$

Surface Area

In the same way as for arc length, we can adapt Formula 8.2.5 to obtain a formula for surface area. If the curve given by the parametric equations $x = f(t)$, $y = g(t)$, $\alpha \le t \le \beta$, is rotated about the x-axis, where f', g' are continuous and $g(t) \ge 0$, then the area of the resulting surface is given by

6
$$S = \int_\alpha^\beta 2\pi y \sqrt{\left(\frac{dx}{dt}\right)^2 + \left(\frac{dy}{dt}\right)^2} \, dt$$

The general symbolic formulas $S = \int 2\pi y \, ds$ and $S = \int 2\pi x \, ds$ (Formulas 8.2.7 and 8.2.8) are still valid, but for parametric curves we use

EXAMPLE 6 Show that the surface area of a sphere of radius r is $4\pi r^2$.

SOLUTION The sphere is obtained by rotating the semicircle

$$x = r\cos t \qquad y = r\sin t \qquad 0 \le t \le \pi$$

about the x-axis. Therefore, from Formula 6, we get

$$S = \int_0^\pi 2\pi r\sin t \sqrt{(-r\sin t)^2 + (r\cos t)^2} \, dt$$

$$= 2\pi\int_0^\pi r\sin t \sqrt{r^2(\sin^2 t + \cos^2 t)} \, dt = 2\pi\int_0^\pi r\sin t \cdot r \, dt$$

$$= 2\pi r^2\int_0^\pi \sin t \, dt = 2\pi r^2(-\cos t)\Big]_0^\pi = 4\pi r^2$$

10.2 Exercises

1–2 Find dy/dx.

1. $x = t \sin t$, $\quad y = t^2 + t$

2. $x = 1/t$, $\quad y = \sqrt{t}\, e^{-t}$

3–6 Find an equation of the tangent to the curve at the point corresponding to the given value of the parameter.

3. $x = t^4 + 1$, $\quad y = t^3 + t$; $\quad t = -1$

4. $x = t - t^{-1}$, $\quad y = 1 + t^2$; $\quad t = 1$

5. $x = t \cos t$, $\quad y = t \sin t$; $\quad t = \pi$

6. $x = \cos\theta + \sin 2\theta$, $\quad y = \sin\theta + \cos 2\theta$; $\quad \theta = 0$

7–8 Find an equation of the tangent to the curve at the given point by two methods: (a) without eliminating the parameter and (b) by first eliminating the parameter.

7. $x = 1 + \ln t$, $\quad y = t^2 + 2$; $\quad (1, 3)$

8. $x = 1 + \sqrt{t}$, $\quad y = e^{t^2}$; $\quad (2, e)$

 9–10 Find an equation of the tangent(s) to the curve at the given point. Then graph the curve and the tangent(s).

9. $x = 6 \sin t$, $\quad y = t^2 + t$; $\quad (0, 0)$

10. $x = \cos t + \cos 2t$, $\quad y = \sin t + \sin 2t$; $\quad (-1, 1)$

11–16 Find dy/dx and d^2y/dx^2. For which values of t is the curve concave upward?

11. $x = t^2 + 1$, $\quad y = t^2 + t$

12. $x = t^3 - 12t$, $\quad y = t^2 - 1$

13. $x = e^t$, $\quad y = te^{-t}$

14. $x = t^2 + 1$, $\quad y = e^t - 1$

15. $x = 2 \sin t$, $\quad y = 3 \cos t$, $\quad 0 < t < 2\pi$

16. $x = \cos 2t$, $\quad y = \cos t$, $\quad 0 < t < \pi$

17–20 Find the points on the curve where the tangent is horizontal or vertical. If you have a graphing device, graph the curve to check your work.

17. $x = t^3 - 3t$, $\quad y = t^2 - 3$

18. $x = t^3 - 3t$, $\quad y = t^3 - 3t^2$

19. $x = \cos\theta$, $\quad y = \cos 3\theta$

20. $x = e^{\sin\theta}$, $\quad y = e^{\cos\theta}$

---

 21. Use a graph to estimate the coordinates of the rightmost point on the curve $x = t - t^6$, $y = e^t$. Then use calculus to find the exact coordinates.

22. Use a graph to estimate the coordinates of the lowest point and the leftmost point on the curve $x = t^4 - 2t$, $y = t + t^4$. Then find the exact coordinates.

23–24 Graph the curve in a viewing rectangle that displays all the important aspects of the curve.

23. $x = t^4 - 2t^3 - 2t^2$, $\quad y = t^3 - t$

24. $x = t^4 + 4t^3 - 8t^2$, $\quad y = 2t^2 - t$

---

25. Show that the curve $x = \cos t$, $y = \sin t \cos t$ has two tangents at $(0, 0)$ and find their equations. Sketch the curve.

26. Graph the curve $x = \cos t + 2 \cos 2t$, $y = \sin t + 2 \sin 2t$ to discover where it crosses itself. Then find equations of both tangents at that point.

27. (a) Find the slope of the tangent line to the trochoid $x = r\theta - d \sin\theta$, $y = r - d \cos\theta$ in terms of θ. (See Exercise 40 in Section 10.1.)
(b) Show that if $d < r$, then the trochoid does not have a vertical tangent.

28. (a) Find the slope of the tangent to the astroid $x = a \cos^3\theta$, $y = a \sin^3\theta$ in terms of θ. (Astroids are explored in the Laboratory Project on page 644.)
(b) At what points is the tangent horizontal or vertical?
(c) At what points does the tangent have slope 1 or -1?

29. At what points on the curve $x = 2t^3$, $y = 1 + 4t - t^2$ does the tangent line have slope 1?

30. Find equations of the tangents to the curve $x = 3t^2 + 1$, $y = 2t^3 + 1$ that pass through the point $(4, 3)$.

31. Use the parametric equations of an ellipse, $x = a \cos\theta$, $y = b \sin\theta$, $0 \le \theta \le 2\pi$, to find the area that it encloses.

32. Find the area enclosed by the curve $x = t^2 - 2t$, $y = \sqrt{t}$ and the y-axis.

33. Find the area enclosed by the x-axis and the curve $x = 1 + e^t$, $y = t - t^2$.

34. Find the area of the region enclosed by the astroid $x = a \cos^3\theta$, $y = a \sin^3\theta$. (Astroids are explored in the Laboratory Project on page 644.)

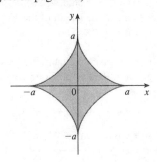

35. Find the area under one arch of the trochoid of Exercise 40 in Section 10.1 for the case $d < r$.

---

36. Let $\mathcal{R}$ be the region enclosed by the loop of the curve in Example 1.
  (a) Find the area of $\mathcal{R}$.
  (b) If $\mathcal{R}$ is rotated about the x-axis, find the volume of the resulting solid.
  (c) Find the centroid of $\mathcal{R}$.

37–40 Set up an integral that represents the length of the curve. Then use your calculator to find the length correct to four decimal places.

37. $x = t + e^{-t}, \quad y = t - e^{-t}, \quad 0 \leqslant t \leqslant 2$

38. $x = t^2 - t, \quad y = t^4, \quad 1 \leqslant t \leqslant 4$

39. $x = t - 2 \sin t, \quad y = 1 - 2 \cos t, \quad 0 \leqslant t \leqslant 4\pi$

40. $x = t + \sqrt{t}, \quad y = t - \sqrt{t}, \quad 0 \leqslant t \leqslant 1$

41–44 Find the exact length of the curve.

41. $x = 1 + 3t^2, \quad y = 4 + 2t^3, \quad 0 \leqslant t \leqslant 1$

42. $x = e^t + e^{-t}, \quad y = 5 - 2t, \quad 0 \leqslant t \leqslant 3$

43. $x = t \sin t, \quad y = t \cos t, \quad 0 \leqslant t \leqslant 1$

44. $x = 3 \cos t - \cos 3t, \quad y = 3 \sin t - \sin 3t, \quad 0 \leqslant t \leqslant \pi$

45–46 Graph the curve and find its length.

45. $x = e^t \cos t, \quad y = e^t \sin t, \quad 0 \leqslant t \leqslant \pi$

46. $x = \cos t + \ln(\tan \frac{1}{2}t), \quad y = \sin t, \quad \pi/4 \leqslant t \leqslant 3\pi/4$

---

47. Graph the curve $x = \sin t + \sin 1.5t$, $y = \cos t$ and find its length correct to four decimal places.

48. Find the length of the loop of the curve $x = 3t - t^3$, $y = 3t^2$.

49. Use Simpson's Rule with $n = 6$ to estimate the length of the curve $x = t - e^t$, $y = t + e^t$, $-6 \leqslant t \leqslant 6$.

50. In Exercise 43 in Section 10.1 you were asked to derive the parametric equations $x = 2a \cot \theta$, $y = 2a \sin^2 \theta$ for the curve called the witch of Maria Agnesi. Use Simpson's Rule with $n = 4$ to estimate the length of the arc of this curve given by $\pi/4 \leqslant \theta \leqslant \pi/2$.

51–52 Find the distance traveled by a particle with position (x, y) as t varies in the given time interval. Compare with the length of the curve.

51. $x = \sin^2 t, \quad y = \cos^2 t, \quad 0 \leqslant t \leqslant 3\pi$

52. $x = \cos^2 t, \quad y = \cos t, \quad 0 \leqslant t \leqslant 4\pi$

---

53. Show that the total length of the ellipse $x = a \sin \theta$, $y = b \cos \theta$, $a > b > 0$, is

$$L = 4a \int_0^{\pi/2} \sqrt{1 - e^2 \sin^2 \theta} \; d\theta$$

where e is the eccentricity of the ellipse ($e = c/a$, where $c = \sqrt{a^2 - b^2}$).

54. Find the total length of the astroid $x = a \cos^3 \theta$, $y = a \sin^3 \theta$, where $a > 0$.

CAS 55. (a) Graph the epitrochoid with equations

$$x = 11 \cos t - 4 \cos(11t/2)$$

$$y = 11 \sin t - 4 \sin(11t/2)$$

  What parameter interval gives the complete curve?
  (b) Use your CAS to find the approximate length of this curve.

CAS 56. A curve called **Cornu's spiral** is defined by the parametric equations

$$x = C(t) = \int_0^t \cos(\pi u^2/2) \; du$$

$$y = S(t) = \int_0^t \sin(\pi u^2/2) \; du$$

where C and S are the Fresnel functions that were introduced in Chapter 5.
  (a) Graph this curve. What happens as $t \to \infty$ and as $t \to -\infty$?
  (b) Find the length of Cornu's spiral from the origin to the point with parameter value t.

57–60 Set up an integral that represents the area of the surface obtained by rotating the given curve about the x-axis. Then use your calculator to find the surface area correct to four decimal places.

57. $x = t \sin t, \quad y = t \cos t, \quad 0 \leqslant t \leqslant \pi/2$

58. $x = \sin t, \quad y = \sin 2t, \quad 0 \leqslant t \leqslant \pi/2$

59. $x = 1 + te^t, \quad y = (t^2 + 1)e^t, \quad 0 \leqslant t \leqslant 1$

60. $x = t^2 - t^3, \quad y = t + t^4, \quad 0 \leqslant t \leqslant 1$

61–63 Find the exact area of the surface obtained by rotating the given curve about the x-axis.

61. $x = t^3, \quad y = t^2, \quad 0 \leqslant t \leqslant 1$

62. $x = 3t - t^3, \quad y = 3t^2, \quad 0 \leqslant t \leqslant 1$

63. $x = a \cos^3 \theta, \quad y = a \sin^3 \theta, \quad 0 \leqslant \theta \leqslant \pi/2$

---

64. Graph the curve

$$x = 2 \cos \theta - \cos 2\theta \qquad y = 2 \sin \theta - \sin 2\theta$$

If this curve is rotated about the x-axis, find the area of the resulting surface. (Use your graph to help find the correct parameter interval.)

65–66 Find the surface area generated by rotating the given curve about the y-axis.

65. $x = 3t^2, \quad y = 2t^3, \quad 0 \leqslant t \leqslant 5$

66. $x = e^t - t, \quad y = 4e^{t/2}, \quad 0 \leqslant t \leqslant 1$

67. If f' is continuous and $f'(t) \neq 0$ for $a \leqslant t \leqslant b$, show that the parametric curve $x = f(t)$, $y = g(t)$, $a \leqslant t \leqslant b$, can be put in the form $y = F(x)$. [*Hint:* Show that f^{-1} exists.]

68. Use Formula 2 to derive Formula 7 from Formula 8.2.5 for the case in which the curve can be represented in the form $y = F(x)$, $a \leqslant x \leqslant b$.

69. The **curvature** at a point P of a curve is defined as

$$\kappa = \left| \frac{d\phi}{ds} \right|$$

where ϕ is the angle of inclination of the tangent line at P, as shown in the figure. Thus the curvature is the absolute value of the rate of change of ϕ with respect to arc length. It can be regarded as a measure of the rate of change of direction of the curve at P and will be studied in greater detail in Chapter 13.

(a) For a parametric curve $x = x(t)$, $y = y(t)$, derive the formula

$$\kappa = \frac{|\dot{x}\ddot{y} - \ddot{x}\dot{y}|}{[\dot{x}^2 + \dot{y}^2]^{3/2}}$$

where the dots indicate derivatives with respect to t, so $\dot{x} = dx/dt$. [*Hint:* Use $\phi = \tan^{-1}(dy/dx)$ and Formula 2 to find $d\phi/dt$. Then use the Chain Rule to find $d\phi/ds$.]

(b) By regarding a curve $y = f(x)$ as the parametric curve $x = x$, $y = f(x)$, with parameter x, show that the formula in part (a) becomes

$$\kappa = \frac{|d^2y/dx^2|}{[1 + (dy/dx)^2]^{3/2}}$$

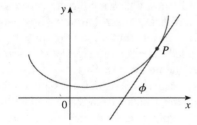

70. (a) Use the formula in Exercise 69(b) to find the curvature of the parabola $y = x^2$ at the point $(1, 1)$.

(b) At what point does this parabola have maximum curvature?

71. Use the formula in Exercise 69(a) to find the curvature of the cycloid $x = \theta - \sin\theta$, $y = 1 - \cos\theta$ at the top of one of its arches.

72. (a) Show that the curvature at each point of a straight line is $\kappa = 0$.

(b) Show that the curvature at each point of a circle of radius r is $\kappa = 1/r$.

73. A string is wound around a circle and then unwound while being held taut. The curve traced by the point P at the end of the string is called the **involute** of the circle. If the circle has radius r and center O and the initial position of P is $(r, 0)$, and if the parameter θ is chosen as in the figure, show that parametric equations of the involute are

$$x = r(\cos\theta + \theta\sin\theta) \qquad y = r(\sin\theta - \theta\cos\theta)$$

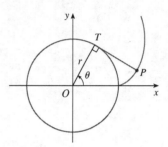

74. A cow is tied to a silo with radius r by a rope just long enough to reach the opposite side of the silo. Find the area available for grazing by the cow.

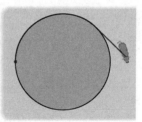

LABORATORY PROJECT BÉZIER CURVES

Bézier curves are used in computer-aided design and are named after the French mathematician Pierre Bézier (1910–1999), who worked in the automotive industry. A cubic Bézier curve is determined by four *control points*, $P_0(x_0, y_0)$, $P_1(x_1, y_1)$, $P_2(x_2, y_2)$, and $P_3(x_3, y_3)$, and is defined by the parametric equations

$$x = x_0(1 - t)^3 + 3x_1t(1 - t)^2 + 3x_2t^2(1 - t) + x_3t^3$$

$$y = y_0(1 - t)^3 + 3y_1t(1 - t)^2 + 3y_2t^2(1 - t) + y_3t^3$$

Graphing calculator or computer required

where $0 \leqslant t \leqslant 1$. Notice that when $t = 0$ we have $(x, y) = (x_0, y_0)$ and when $t = 1$ we have $(x, y) = (x_3, y_3)$, so the curve starts at P_0 and ends at P_3.

1. Graph the Bézier curve with control points $P_0(4, 1)$, $P_1(28, 48)$, $P_2(50, 42)$, and $P_3(40, 5)$. Then, on the same screen, graph the line segments P_0P_1, P_1P_2, and P_2P_3. (Exercise 31 in Section 10.1 shows how to do this.) Notice that the middle control points P_1 and P_2 don't lie on the curve; the curve starts at P_0, heads toward P_1 and P_2 without reaching them, and ends at P_3.

2. From the graph in Problem 1, it appears that the tangent at P_0 passes through P_1 and the tangent at P_3 passes through P_2. Prove it.

3. Try to produce a Bézier curve with a loop by changing the second control point in Problem 1.

4. Some laser printers use Bézier curves to represent letters and other symbols. Experiment with control points until you find a Bézier curve that gives a reasonable representation of the letter C.

5. More complicated shapes can be represented by piecing together two or more Bézier curves. Suppose the first Bézier curve has control points P_0, P_1, P_2, P_3 and the second one has control points P_3, P_4, P_5, P_6. If we want these two pieces to join together smoothly, then the tangents at P_3 should match and so the points P_2, P_3, and P_4 all have to lie on this common tangent line. Using this principle, find control points for a pair of Bézier curves that represent the letter S.

10.3 Polar Coordinates

FIGURE 1

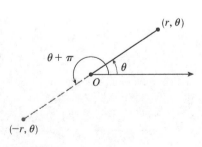

FIGURE 2

A coordinate system represents a point in the plane by an ordered pair of numbers called coordinates. Usually we use Cartesian coordinates, which are directed distances from two perpendicular axes. Here we describe a coordinate system introduced by Newton, called the **polar coordinate system**, which is more convenient for many purposes.

We choose a point in the plane that is called the **pole** (or origin) and is labeled O. Then we draw a ray (half-line) starting at O called the **polar axis**. This axis is usually drawn horizontally to the right and corresponds to the positive x-axis in Cartesian coordinates.

If P is any other point in the plane, let r be the distance from O to P and let θ be the angle (usually measured in radians) between the polar axis and the line OP as in Figure 1. Then the point P is represented by the ordered pair (r, θ) and r, θ are called **polar coordinates** of P. We use the convention that an angle is positive if measured in the counterclockwise direction from the polar axis and negative in the clockwise direction. If $P = O$, then $r = 0$ and we agree that $(0, \theta)$ represents the pole for any value of θ.

We extend the meaning of polar coordinates (r, θ) to the case in which r is negative by agreeing that, as in Figure 2, the points $(-r, \theta)$ and (r, θ) lie on the same line through O and at the same distance $|r|$ from O, but on opposite sides of O. If $r > 0$, the point (r, θ) lies in the same quadrant as θ; if $r < 0$, it lies in the quadrant on the opposite side of the pole. Notice that $(-r, \theta)$ represents the same point as $(r, \theta + \pi)$.

EXAMPLE 1 Plot the points whose polar coordinates are given.

(a) $(1, 5\pi/4)$ (b) $(2, 3\pi)$ (c) $(2, -2\pi/3)$ (d) $(-3, 3\pi/4)$

SOLUTION The points are plotted in Figure 3. In part (d) the point $(-3, 3\pi/4)$ is located three units from the pole in the fourth quadrant because the angle $3\pi/4$ is in the second quadrant and $r = -3$ is negative.

FIGURE 3

In the Cartesian coordinate system every point has only one representation, but in the polar coordinate system each point has many representations. For instance, the point $(1, 5\pi/4)$ in Example 1(a) could be written as $(1, -3\pi/4)$ or $(1, 13\pi/4)$ or $(-1, \pi/4)$. (See Figure 4.)

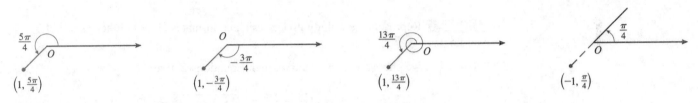

FIGURE 4

In fact, since a complete counterclockwise rotation is given by an angle 2π, the point represented by polar coordinates (r, θ) is also represented by

$$(r, \theta + 2n\pi) \qquad \text{and} \qquad (-r, \theta + (2n + 1)\pi)$$

where n is any integer.

The connection between polar and Cartesian coordinates can be seen from Figure 5, in which the pole corresponds to the origin and the polar axis coincides with the positive x-axis. If the point P has Cartesian coordinates (x, y) and polar coordinates (r, θ), then, from the figure, we have

$$\cos \theta = \frac{x}{r} \qquad \sin \theta = \frac{y}{r}$$

and so

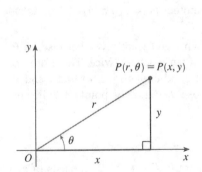

FIGURE 5

$\boxed{1}$
$$\boxed{\quad x = r \cos \theta \qquad y = r \sin \theta \quad}$$

Although Equations 1 were deduced from Figure 5, which illustrates the case where $r > 0$ and $0 < \theta < \pi/2$, these equations are valid for all values of r and θ. (See the general definition of $\sin \theta$ and $\cos \theta$ in Appendix D.)

Equations 1 allow us to find the Cartesian coordinates of a point when the polar coordinates are known. To find r and θ when x and y are known, we use the equations

$$\boxed{2} \qquad r^2 = x^2 + y^2 \qquad \tan\theta = \frac{y}{x}$$

which can be deduced from Equations 1 or simply read from Figure 5.

EXAMPLE 2 Convert the point $(2, \pi/3)$ from polar to Cartesian coordinates.

SOLUTION Since $r = 2$ and $\theta = \pi/3$, Equations 1 give

$$x = r\cos\theta = 2\cos\frac{\pi}{3} = 2 \cdot \frac{1}{2} = 1$$

$$y = r\sin\theta = 2\sin\frac{\pi}{3} = 2 \cdot \frac{\sqrt{3}}{2} = \sqrt{3}$$

Therefore the point is $\left(1, \sqrt{3}\,\right)$ in Cartesian coordinates.

EXAMPLE 3 Represent the point with Cartesian coordinates $(1, -1)$ in terms of polar coordinates.

SOLUTION If we choose r to be positive, then Equations 2 give

$$r = \sqrt{x^2 + y^2} = \sqrt{1^2 + (-1)^2} = \sqrt{2}$$

$$\tan\theta = \frac{y}{x} = -1$$

Since the point $(1, -1)$ lies in the fourth quadrant, we can choose $\theta = -\pi/4$ or $\theta = 7\pi/4$. Thus one possible answer is $\left(\sqrt{2}, -\pi/4\right)$; another is $\left(\sqrt{2}, 7\pi/4\right)$.

NOTE Equations 2 do not uniquely determine θ when x and y are given because, as θ increases through the interval $0 \leqslant \theta < 2\pi$, each value of $\tan\theta$ occurs twice. Therefore, in converting from Cartesian to polar coordinates, it's not good enough just to find r and θ that satisfy Equations 2. As in Example 3, we must choose θ so that the point (r, θ) lies in the correct quadrant.

$r = \frac{1}{2}$

$r = 4$

$r = 2$

$r = 1$

x

FIGURE 6

Polar Curves

The **graph of a polar equation** $r = f(\theta)$, or more generally $F(r, \theta) = 0$, consists of all points P that have at least one polar representation (r, θ) whose coordinates satisfy the equation.

▽ EXAMPLE 4 What curve is represented by the polar equation $r = 2$?

SOLUTION The curve consists of all points (r, θ) with $r = 2$. Since r represents the distance from the point to the pole, the curve $r = 2$ represents the circle with center O and radius 2. In general, the equation $r = a$ represents a circle with center O and radius $|a|$. (See Figure 6.)

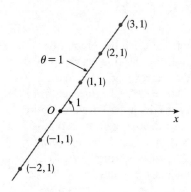

FIGURE 7

EXAMPLE 5 Sketch the polar curve $\theta = 1$.

SOLUTION This curve consists of all points (r, θ) such that the polar angle θ is 1 radian. It is the straight line that passes through O and makes an angle of 1 radian with the polar axis (see Figure 7). Notice that the points $(r, 1)$ on the line with $r > 0$ are in the first quadrant, whereas those with $r < 0$ are in the third quadrant.

EXAMPLE 6

(a) Sketch the curve with polar equation $r = 2 \cos \theta$.
(b) Find a Cartesian equation for this curve.

SOLUTION

(a) In Figure 8 we find the values of r for some convenient values of θ and plot the corresponding points (r, θ). Then we join these points to sketch the curve, which appears to be a circle. We have used only values of θ between 0 and π, since if we let θ increase beyond π, we obtain the same points again.

FIGURE 8
Table of values and graph of $r = 2 \cos \theta$

θ	$r = 2 \cos \theta$
0	2
$\pi/6$	$\sqrt{3}$
$\pi/4$	$\sqrt{2}$
$\pi/3$	1
$\pi/2$	0
$2\pi/3$	-1
$3\pi/4$	$-\sqrt{2}$
$5\pi/6$	$-\sqrt{3}$
π	-2

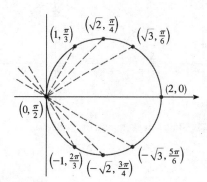

(b) To convert the given equation to a Cartesian equation we use Equations 1 and 2. From $x = r \cos \theta$ we have $\cos \theta = x/r$, so the equation $r = 2 \cos \theta$ becomes $r = 2x/r$, which gives

$$2x = r^2 = x^2 + y^2 \qquad \text{or} \qquad x^2 + y^2 - 2x = 0$$

Completing the square, we obtain

$$(x - 1)^2 + y^2 = 1$$

which is an equation of a circle with center $(1, 0)$ and radius 1.

Figure 9 shows a geometrical illustration that the circle in Example 6 has the equation $r = 2 \cos \theta$. The angle OPQ is a right angle (Why?) and so $r/2 = \cos \theta$.

FIGURE 9

FIGURE 10

$r = 1 + \sin\theta$ in Cartesian coordinates,
$0 \leqslant \theta \leqslant 2\pi$

☑ **EXAMPLE 7** Sketch the curve $r = 1 + \sin\theta$.

SOLUTION Instead of plotting points as in Example 6, we first sketch the graph of
$r = 1 + \sin\theta$ in *Cartesian* coordinates in Figure 10 by shifting the sine curve up one
unit. This enables us to read at a glance the values of r that correspond to increasing
values of θ. For instance, we see that as θ increases from 0 to $\pi/2$, r (the distance from O)
increases from 1 to 2, so we sketch the corresponding part of the polar curve in Figure
11(a). As θ increases from $\pi/2$ to π, Figure 10 shows that r decreases from 2 to 1, so
we sketch the next part of the curve as in Figure 11(b). As θ increases from π to $3\pi/2$,
r decreases from 1 to 0 as shown in part (c). Finally, as θ increases from $3\pi/2$ to 2π,
r increases from 0 to 1 as shown in part (d). If we let θ increase beyond 2π or decrease
beyond 0, we would simply retrace our path. Putting together the parts of the curve
from Figure 11(a)–(d), we sketch the complete curve in part (e). It is called a **cardioid**
because it's shaped like a heart.

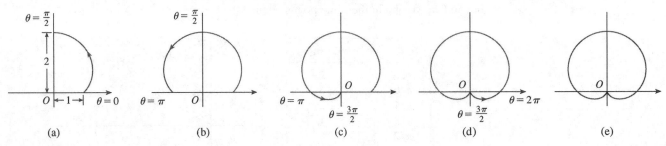

FIGURE 11 Stages in sketching the cardioid $r = 1 + \sin\theta$

EXAMPLE 8 Sketch the curve $r = \cos 2\theta$.

TEC Module 10.3 helps you see how
polar curves are traced out by showing
animations similar to Figures 10–13.

SOLUTION As in Example 7, we first sketch $r = \cos 2\theta$, $0 \leqslant \theta \leqslant 2\pi$, in Cartesian coordinates in Figure 12. As θ increases from 0 to $\pi/4$, Figure 12 shows that r decreases
from 1 to 0 and so we draw the corresponding portion of the polar curve in Figure 13
(indicated by ①). As θ increases from $\pi/4$ to $\pi/2$, r goes from 0 to -1. This means that
the distance from O increases from 0 to 1, but instead of being in the first quadrant this
portion of the polar curve (indicated by ②) lies on the opposite side of the pole in the
third quadrant. The remainder of the curve is drawn in a similar fashion, with the arrows
and numbers indicating the order in which the portions are traced out. The resulting
curve has four loops and is called a **four-leaved rose**.

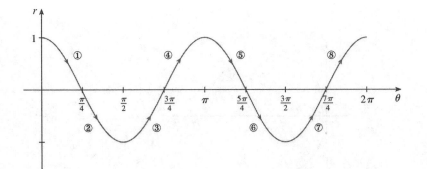

FIGURE 12
$r = \cos 2\theta$ in Cartesian coordinates

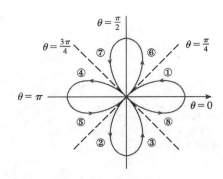

FIGURE 13
Four-leaved rose $r = \cos 2\theta$

Symmetry

When we sketch polar curves it is sometimes helpful to take advantage of symmetry. The following three rules are explained by Figure 14.

(a) If a polar equation is unchanged when θ is replaced by $-\theta$, the curve is symmetric about the polar axis.

(b) If the equation is unchanged when r is replaced by $-r$, or when θ is replaced by $\theta + \pi$, the curve is symmetric about the pole. (This means that the curve remains unchanged if we rotate it through 180° about the origin.)

(c) If the equation is unchanged when θ is replaced by $\pi - \theta$, the curve is symmetric about the vertical line $\theta = \pi/2$.

(a)

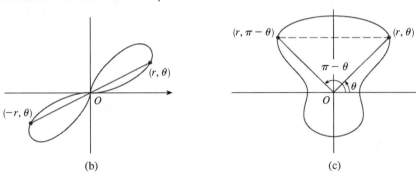

(b)   (c)

FIGURE 14

The curves sketched in Examples 6 and 8 are symmetric about the polar axis, since $\cos(-\theta) = \cos\theta$. The curves in Examples 7 and 8 are symmetric about $\theta = \pi/2$ because $\sin(\pi - \theta) = \sin\theta$ and $\cos 2(\pi - \theta) = \cos 2\theta$. The four-leaved rose is also symmetric about the pole. These symmetry properties could have been used in sketching the curves. For instance, in Example 6 we need only have plotted points for $0 \le \theta \le \pi/2$ and then reflected about the polar axis to obtain the complete circle.

Tangents to Polar Curves

To find a tangent line to a polar curve $r = f(\theta)$, we regard θ as a parameter and write its parametric equations as

$$x = r\cos\theta = f(\theta)\cos\theta \qquad y = r\sin\theta = f(\theta)\sin\theta$$

Then, using the method for finding slopes of parametric curves (Equation 10.2.1) and the Product Rule, we have

$$\boxed{3} \qquad \frac{dy}{dx} = \frac{\dfrac{dy}{d\theta}}{\dfrac{dx}{d\theta}} = \frac{\dfrac{dr}{d\theta}\sin\theta + r\cos\theta}{\dfrac{dr}{d\theta}\cos\theta - r\sin\theta}$$

We locate horizontal tangents by finding the points where $dy/d\theta = 0$ (provided that $dx/d\theta \neq 0$). Likewise, we locate vertical tangents at the points where $dx/d\theta = 0$ (provided that $dy/d\theta \neq 0$).

Notice that if we are looking for tangent lines at the pole, then $r = 0$ and Equation 3 simplifies to

$$\frac{dy}{dx} = \tan\theta \qquad \text{if} \quad \frac{dr}{d\theta} \neq 0$$

For instance, in Example 8 we found that $r = \cos 2\theta = 0$ when $\theta = \pi/4$ or $3\pi/4$. This means that the lines $\theta = \pi/4$ and $\theta = 3\pi/4$ (or $y = x$ and $y = -x$) are tangent lines to $r = \cos 2\theta$ at the origin.

EXAMPLE 9

(a) For the cardioid $r = 1 + \sin \theta$ of Example 7, find the slope of the tangent line when $\theta = \pi/3$.

(b) Find the points on the cardioid where the tangent line is horizontal or vertical.

SOLUTION Using Equation 3 with $r = 1 + \sin \theta$, we have

$$\frac{dy}{dx} = \frac{\dfrac{dr}{d\theta}\sin\theta + r\cos\theta}{\dfrac{dr}{d\theta}\cos\theta - r\sin\theta} = \frac{\cos\theta\sin\theta + (1 + \sin\theta)\cos\theta}{\cos\theta\cos\theta - (1 + \sin\theta)\sin\theta}$$

$$= \frac{\cos\theta\,(1 + 2\sin\theta)}{1 - 2\sin^2\theta - \sin\theta} = \frac{\cos\theta\,(1 + 2\sin\theta)}{(1 + \sin\theta)(1 - 2\sin\theta)}$$

(a) The slope of the tangent at the point where $\theta = \pi/3$ is

$$\left.\frac{dy}{dx}\right|_{\theta=\pi/3} = \frac{\cos(\pi/3)(1 + 2\sin(\pi/3))}{(1 + \sin(\pi/3))(1 - 2\sin(\pi/3))} = \frac{\frac{1}{2}\left(1 + \sqrt{3}\right)}{\left(1 + \sqrt{3}/2\right)\left(1 - \sqrt{3}\right)}$$

$$= \frac{1 + \sqrt{3}}{\left(2 + \sqrt{3}\right)\left(1 - \sqrt{3}\right)} = \frac{1 + \sqrt{3}}{-1 - \sqrt{3}} = -1$$

(b) Observe that

$$\frac{dy}{d\theta} = \cos\theta\,(1 + 2\sin\theta) = 0 \qquad \text{when } \theta = \frac{\pi}{2}, \frac{3\pi}{2}, \frac{7\pi}{6}, \frac{11\pi}{6}$$

$$\frac{dx}{d\theta} = (1 + \sin\theta)(1 - 2\sin\theta) = 0 \qquad \text{when } \theta = \frac{3\pi}{2}, \frac{\pi}{6}, \frac{5\pi}{6}$$

Therefore there are horizontal tangents at the points $(2, \pi/2)$, $\left(\frac{1}{2}, 7\pi/6\right)$, $\left(\frac{1}{2}, 11\pi/6\right)$ and vertical tangents at $\left(\frac{3}{2}, \pi/6\right)$ and $\left(\frac{3}{2}, 5\pi/6\right)$. When $\theta = 3\pi/2$, both $dy/d\theta$ and $dx/d\theta$ are 0, so we must be careful. Using l'Hospital's Rule, we have

$$\lim_{\theta \to (3\pi/2)^-} \frac{dy}{dx} = \left(\lim_{\theta \to (3\pi/2)^-} \frac{1 + 2\sin\theta}{1 - 2\sin\theta}\right)\left(\lim_{\theta \to (3\pi/2)^-} \frac{\cos\theta}{1 + \sin\theta}\right)$$

$$= -\frac{1}{3}\lim_{\theta \to (3\pi/2)^-} \frac{\cos\theta}{1 + \sin\theta} = -\frac{1}{3}\lim_{\theta \to (3\pi/2)^-} \frac{-\sin\theta}{\cos\theta} = \infty$$

By symmetry,

$$\lim_{\theta \to (3\pi/2)^+} \frac{dy}{dx} = -\infty$$

Thus there is a vertical tangent line at the pole (see Figure 15).

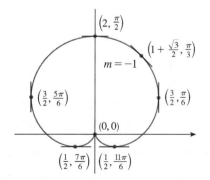

FIGURE 15
Tangent lines for $r = 1 + \sin\theta$

NOTE Instead of having to remember Equation 3, we could employ the method used to derive it. For instance, in Example 9 we could have written

$$x = r \cos \theta = (1 + \sin \theta) \cos \theta = \cos \theta + \tfrac{1}{2} \sin 2\theta$$

$$y = r \sin \theta = (1 + \sin \theta) \sin \theta = \sin \theta + \sin^2 \theta$$

Then we have

$$\frac{dy}{dx} = \frac{dy/d\theta}{dx/d\theta} = \frac{\cos \theta + 2 \sin \theta \cos \theta}{-\sin \theta + \cos 2\theta} = \frac{\cos \theta + \sin 2\theta}{-\sin \theta + \cos 2\theta}$$

which is equivalent to our previous expression.

Graphing Polar Curves with Graphing Devices

Although it's useful to be able to sketch simple polar curves by hand, we need to use a graphing calculator or computer when we are faced with a curve as complicated as the ones shown in Figures 16 and 17.

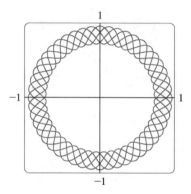

FIGURE 16
$r = \sin^2(2.4\theta) + \cos^4(2.4\theta)$

FIGURE 17
$r = \sin^2(1.2\theta) + \cos^3(6\theta)$

Some graphing devices have commands that enable us to graph polar curves directly. With other machines we need to convert to parametric equations first. In this case we take the polar equation $r = f(\theta)$ and write its parametric equations as

$$x = r \cos \theta = f(\theta) \cos \theta \qquad y = r \sin \theta = f(\theta) \sin \theta$$

Some machines require that the parameter be called t rather than θ.

EXAMPLE 10 Graph the curve $r = \sin(8\theta/5)$.

SOLUTION Let's assume that our graphing device doesn't have a built-in polar graphing command. In this case we need to work with the corresponding parametric equations, which are

$$x = r \cos \theta = \sin(8\theta/5) \cos \theta \qquad y = r \sin \theta = \sin(8\theta/5) \sin \theta$$

In any case we need to determine the domain for θ. So we ask ourselves: How many complete rotations are required until the curve starts to repeat itself? If the answer is n, then

$$\sin \frac{8(\theta + 2n\pi)}{5} = \sin\left(\frac{8\theta}{5} + \frac{16n\pi}{5}\right) = \sin \frac{8\theta}{5}$$

and so we require that $16n\pi/5$ be an even multiple of π. This will first occur when $n = 5$. Therefore we will graph the entire curve if we specify that $0 \leq \theta \leq 10\pi$.

FIGURE 18

$r = \sin(8\theta/5)$

In Exercise 53 you are asked to prove analytically what we have discovered from the graphs in Figure 19.

Switching from θ to t, we have the equations

$$x = \sin(8t/5)\cos t \qquad y = \sin(8t/5)\sin t \qquad 0 \le t \le 10\pi$$

and Figure 18 shows the resulting curve. Notice that this rose has 16 loops.

V   EXAMPLE 11 Investigate the family of polar curves given by $r = 1 + c\sin\theta$. How does the shape change as c changes? (These curves are called **limaçons**, after a French word for snail, because of the shape of the curves for certain values of c.)

SOLUTION Figure 19 shows computer-drawn graphs for various values of c. For $c > 1$ there is a loop that decreases in size as c decreases. When $c = 1$ the loop disappears and the curve becomes the cardioid that we sketched in Example 7. For c between 1 and $\frac{1}{2}$ the cardioid's cusp is smoothed out and becomes a "dimple." When c decreases from $\frac{1}{2}$ to 0, the limaçon is shaped like an oval. This oval becomes more circular as $c \to 0$, and when $c = 0$ the curve is just the circle $r = 1$.

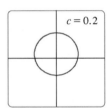

$c = 2.5$ $c = 1.7$ $c = 1$ $c = 0.7$ $c = 0.5$ $c = 0.2$

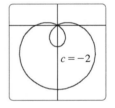

$c = 0$ $c = -0.2$ $c = -0.5$ $c = -0.8$ $c = -1$ $c = -2$

FIGURE 19

Members of the family of limaçons $r = 1 + c\sin\theta$

The remaining parts of Figure 19 show that as c becomes negative, the shapes change in reverse order. In fact, these curves are reflections about the horizontal axis of the corresponding curves with positive c.

Limaçons arise in the study of planetary motion. In particular, the trajectory of Mars, as viewed from the planet Earth, has been modeled by a limaçon with a loop, as in the parts of Figure 19 with $|c| > 1$.

10.3   Exercises

1–2 Plot the point whose polar coordinates are given. Then find two other pairs of polar coordinates of this point, one with $r > 0$ and one with $r < 0$.

1. (a) $(2, \pi/3)$ (b) $(1, -3\pi/4)$ (c) $(-1, \pi/2)$

2. (a) $(1, 7\pi/4)$ (b) $(-3, \pi/6)$ (c) $(1, -1)$

3–4 Plot the point whose polar coordinates are given. Then find the Cartesian coordinates of the point.

3. (a) $(1, \pi)$ (b) $(2, -2\pi/3)$ (c) $(-2, 3\pi/4)$

4. (a) $\left(-\sqrt{2}, 5\pi/4\right)$ (b) $(1, 5\pi/2)$ (c) $(2, -7\pi/6)$

5–6 The Cartesian coordinates of a point are given.
(i) Find polar coordinates (r, θ) of the point, where $r > 0$ and $0 \le \theta < 2\pi$.
(ii) Find polar coordinates (r, θ) of the point, where $r < 0$ and $0 \le \theta < 2\pi$.

5. (a) $(2, -2)$ (b) $\left(-1, \sqrt{3}\right)$

6. (a) $\left(3\sqrt{3}, 3\right)$ (b) $(1, -2)$

⌂ Graphing calculator or computer required   **1.** Homework Hints available at stewartcalculus.com

7–12 Sketch the region in the plane consisting of points whose polar coordinates satisfy the given conditions.

7. $1 \leqslant r \leqslant 2$

8. $0 \leqslant r < 2, \quad \pi \leqslant \theta \leqslant 3\pi/2$

9. $r \geqslant 0, \quad \pi/4 \leqslant \theta \leqslant 3\pi/4$

10. $1 \leqslant r \leqslant 3, \quad \pi/6 < \theta < 5\pi/6$

11. $2 < r < 3, \quad 5\pi/3 \leqslant \theta \leqslant 7\pi/3$

12. $r \geqslant 1, \quad \pi \leqslant \theta \leqslant 2\pi$

---

13. Find the distance between the points with polar coordinates $(2, \pi/3)$ and $(4, 2\pi/3)$.

14. Find a formula for the distance between the points with polar coordinates (r_1, θ_1) and (r_2, θ_2).

15–20 Identify the curve by finding a Cartesian equation for the curve.

15. $r = 2$ **16.** $r \cos \theta = 1$

17. $r = 2 \cos \theta$ **18.** $\theta = \pi/3$

19. $r^2 \cos 2\theta = 1$ **20.** $r = \tan \theta \sec \theta$

21–26 Find a polar equation for the curve represented by the given Cartesian equation.

21. $y = 2$ **22.** $y = x$

23. $y = 1 + 3x$ **24.** $4y^2 = x$

25. $x^2 + y^2 = 2cx$ **26.** $xy = 4$

27–28 For each of the described curves, decide if the curve would be more easily given by a polar equation or a Cartesian equation. Then write an equation for the curve.

27. (a) A line through the origin that makes an angle of $\pi/6$ with the positive x-axis
(b) A vertical line through the point $(3, 3)$

28. (a) A circle with radius 5 and center $(2, 3)$
(b) A circle centered at the origin with radius 4

29–46 Sketch the curve with the given polar equation by first sketching the graph of r as a function of θ in Cartesian coordinates.

29. $r = -2 \sin \theta$ **30.** $r = 1 - \cos \theta$

31. $r = 2(1 + \cos \theta)$ **32.** $r = 1 + 2 \cos \theta$

33. $r = \theta, \ \theta \geqslant 0$ **34.** $r = \ln \theta, \ \theta \geqslant 1$

35. $r = 4 \sin 3\theta$ **36.** $r = \cos 5\theta$

37. $r = 2 \cos 4\theta$ **38.** $r = 3 \cos 6\theta$

39. $r = 1 - 2 \sin \theta$ **40.** $r = 2 + \sin \theta$

41. $r^2 = 9 \sin 2\theta$ **42.** $r^2 = \cos 4\theta$

43. $r = 2 + \sin 3\theta$ **44.** $r^2\theta = 1$

45. $r = 1 + 2 \cos 2\theta$ **46.** $r = 3 + 4 \cos \theta$

47–48 The figure shows a graph of r as a function of θ in Cartesian coordinates. Use it to sketch the corresponding polar curve.

47.

48.

---

49. Show that the polar curve $r = 4 + 2 \sec \theta$ (called a **conchoid**) has the line $x = 2$ as a vertical asymptote by showing that $\lim_{r \to \pm\infty} x = 2$. Use this fact to help sketch the conchoid.

50. Show that the curve $r = 2 - \csc \theta$ (also a conchoid) has the line $y = -1$ as a horizontal asymptote by showing that $\lim_{r \to \pm\infty} y = -1$. Use this fact to help sketch the conchoid.

51. Show that the curve $r = \sin \theta \tan \theta$ (called a **cissoid of Diocles**) has the line $x = 1$ as a vertical asymptote. Show also that the curve lies entirely within the vertical strip $0 \leqslant x < 1$. Use these facts to help sketch the cissoid.

52. Sketch the curve $(x^2 + y^2)^3 = 4x^2y^2$.

53. (a) In Example 11 the graphs suggest that the limaçon $r = 1 + c \sin \theta$ has an inner loop when $|c| > 1$. Prove that this is true, and find the values of θ that correspond to the inner loop.
(b) From Figure 19 it appears that the limaçon loses its dimple when $c = \frac{1}{2}$. Prove this.

54. Match the polar equations with the graphs labeled I–VI. Give reasons for your choices. (Don't use a graphing device.)
(a) $r = \sqrt{\theta}, \quad 0 \leqslant \theta \leqslant 16\pi$ (b) $r = \theta^2, \quad 0 \leqslant \theta \leqslant 16\pi$
(c) $r = \cos(\theta/3)$ (d) $r = 1 + 2\cos \theta$
(e) $r = 2 + \sin 3\theta$ (f) $r = 1 + 2 \sin 3\theta$

I

II

III

IV

V

VI
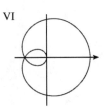

55–60 Find the slope of the tangent line to the given polar curve at the point specified by the value of θ.

55. $r = 2 \sin \theta$, $\quad \theta = \pi/6$

56. $r = 2 - \sin \theta$, $\quad \theta = \pi/3$

57. $r = 1/\theta$, $\quad \theta = \pi$

58. $r = \cos(\theta/3)$, $\quad \theta = \pi$

59. $r = \cos 2\theta$, $\quad \theta = \pi/4$

60. $r = 1 + 2\cos\theta$, $\quad \theta = \pi/3$

61–64 Find the points on the given curve where the tangent line is horizontal or vertical.

61. $r = 3\cos\theta$

62. $r = 1 - \sin\theta$

63. $r = 1 + \cos\theta$

64. $r = e^{\theta}$

65. Show that the polar equation $r = a \sin\theta + b \cos\theta$, where $ab \neq 0$, represents a circle, and find its center and radius.

66. Show that the curves $r = a \sin\theta$ and $r = a \cos\theta$ intersect at right angles.

 67–72 Use a graphing device to graph the polar curve. Choose the parameter interval to make sure that you produce the entire curve.

67. $r = 1 + 2\sin(\theta/2)$ (nephroid of Freeth)

68. $r = \sqrt{1 - 0.8 \sin^2\theta}$ (hippopede)

69. $r = e^{\sin\theta} - 2\cos(4\theta)$ (butterfly curve)

70. $r = |\tan\theta|^{|\cot\theta|}$ (valentine curve)

71. $r = 1 + \cos^{999}\theta$ (PacMan curve)

72. $r = \sin^2(4\theta) + \cos(4\theta)$

 73. How are the graphs of $r = 1 + \sin(\theta - \pi/6)$ and $r = 1 + \sin(\theta - \pi/3)$ related to the graph of $r = 1 + \sin\theta$? In general, how is the graph of $r = f(\theta - \alpha)$ related to the graph of $r = f(\theta)$?

 74. Use a graph to estimate the y-coordinate of the highest points on the curve $r = \sin 2\theta$. Then use calculus to find the exact value.

 75. Investigate the family of curves with polar equations $r = 1 + c \cos\theta$, where c is a real number. How does the shape change as c changes?

76. Investigate the family of polar curves

$$r = 1 + \cos^n\theta$$

where n is a positive integer. How does the shape change as n increases? What happens as n becomes large? Explain the shape for large n by considering the graph of r as a function of θ in Cartesian coordinates.

77. Let P be any point (except the origin) on the curve $r = f(\theta)$. If ψ is the angle between the tangent line at P and the radial line OP, show that

$$\tan\psi = \frac{r}{dr/d\theta}$$

[*Hint:* Observe that $\psi = \phi - \theta$ in the figure.]

78. (a) Use Exercise 77 to show that the angle between the tangent line and the radial line is $\psi = \pi/4$ at every point on the curve $r = e^{\theta}$.
   (b) Illustrate part (a) by graphing the curve and the tangent lines at the points where $\theta = 0$ and $\pi/2$.
   (c) Prove that any polar curve $r = f(\theta)$ with the property that the angle ψ between the radial line and the tangent line is a constant must be of the form $r = Ce^{k\theta}$, where C and k are constants.

LABORATORY PROJECT   FAMILIES OF POLAR CURVES

In this project you will discover the interesting and beautiful shapes that members of families of polar curves can take. You will also see how the shape of the curve changes when you vary the constants.

1. (a) Investigate the family of curves defined by the polar equations $r = \sin n\theta$, where n is a positive integer. How is the number of loops related to n?
   (b) What happens if the equation in part (a) is replaced by $r = |\sin n\theta|$?

2. A family of curves is given by the equations $r = 1 + c \sin n\theta$, where c is a real number and n is a positive integer. How does the graph change as n increases? How does it change as c changes? Illustrate by graphing enough members of the family to support your conclusions.

 Graphing calculator or computer required

3. A family of curves has polar equations

$$r = \frac{1 - a \cos \theta}{1 + a \cos \theta}$$

Investigate how the graph changes as the number a changes. In particular, you should identify the transitional values of a for which the basic shape of the curve changes.

4. The astronomer Giovanni Cassini (1625–1712) studied the family of curves with polar equations

$$r^4 - 2c^2 r^2 \cos 2\theta + c^4 - a^4 = 0$$

where a and c are positive real numbers. These curves are called the **ovals of Cassini** even though they are oval shaped only for certain values of a and c. (Cassini thought that these curves might represent planetary orbits better than Kepler's ellipses.) Investigate the variety of shapes that these curves may have. In particular, how are a and c related to each other when the curve splits into two parts?

10.4 Areas and Lengths in Polar Coordinates

FIGURE 1

In this section we develop the formula for the area of a region whose boundary is given by a polar equation. We need to use the formula for the area of a sector of a circle:

$$\boxed{1} \qquad A = \tfrac{1}{2} r^2 \theta$$

where, as in Figure 1, r is the radius and θ is the radian measure of the central angle. Formula 1 follows from the fact that the area of a sector is proportional to its central angle: $A = (\theta/2\pi)\pi r^2 = \tfrac{1}{2} r^2 \theta$. (See also Exercise 35 in Section 7.3.)

Let $\mathcal{R}$ be the region, illustrated in Figure 2, bounded by the polar curve $r = f(\theta)$ and by the rays $\theta = a$ and $\theta = b$, where f is a positive continuous function and where $0 < b - a \le 2\pi$. We divide the interval $[a, b]$ into subintervals with endpoints θ_0, θ_1, θ_2, ..., θ_n and equal width $\Delta\theta$. The rays $\theta = \theta_i$ then divide $\mathcal{R}$ into n smaller regions with central angle $\Delta\theta = \theta_i - \theta_{i-1}$. If we choose θ_i^* in the ith subinterval $[\theta_{i-1}, \theta_i]$, then the area ΔA_i of the ith region is approximated by the area of the sector of a circle with central angle $\Delta\theta$ and radius $f(\theta_i^*)$. (See Figure 3.)

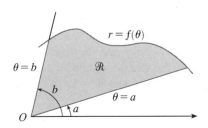

FIGURE 2

Thus from Formula 1 we have

$$\Delta A_i \approx \tfrac{1}{2}[f(\theta_i^*)]^2 \, \Delta\theta$$

and so an approximation to the total area A of $\mathcal{R}$ is

$$\boxed{2} \qquad A \approx \sum_{i=1}^{n} \tfrac{1}{2}[f(\theta_i^*)]^2 \, \Delta\theta$$

It appears from Figure 3 that the approximation in $\boxed{2}$ improves as $n \to \infty$. But the sums in $\boxed{2}$ are Riemann sums for the function $g(\theta) = \tfrac{1}{2}[f(\theta)]^2$, so

$$\lim_{n \to \infty} \sum_{i=1}^{n} \tfrac{1}{2}[f(\theta_i^*)]^2 \, \Delta\theta = \int_a^b \tfrac{1}{2}[f(\theta)]^2 \, d\theta$$

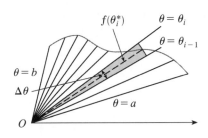

FIGURE 3

It therefore appears plausible (and can in fact be proved) that the formula for the area A of the polar region $\mathcal{R}$ is

$$\boxed{3} \qquad A = \int_a^b \tfrac{1}{2}[f(\theta)]^2 \, d\theta$$

Formula 3 is often written as

$$\boxed{4} \qquad A = \int_a^b \tfrac{1}{2} r^2 \, d\theta$$

with the understanding that $r = f(\theta)$. Note the similarity between Formulas 1 and 4.

When we apply Formula 3 or 4 it is helpful to think of the area as being swept out by a rotating ray through O that starts with angle a and ends with angle b.

V EXAMPLE 1 Find the area enclosed by one loop of the four-leaved rose $r = \cos 2\theta$.

SOLUTION The curve $r = \cos 2\theta$ was sketched in Example 8 in Section 10.3. Notice from Figure 4 that the region enclosed by the right loop is swept out by a ray that rotates from $\theta = -\pi/4$ to $\theta = \pi/4$. Therefore Formula 4 gives

$$A = \int_{-\pi/4}^{\pi/4} \tfrac{1}{2} r^2 \, d\theta = \tfrac{1}{2} \int_{-\pi/4}^{\pi/4} \cos^2 2\theta \, d\theta = \int_0^{\pi/4} \cos^2 2\theta \, d\theta$$

$$A = \int_0^{\pi/4} \tfrac{1}{2}(1 + \cos 4\theta) \, d\theta = \tfrac{1}{2}\left[\theta + \tfrac{1}{4}\sin 4\theta\right]_0^{\pi/4} = \frac{\pi}{8}$$

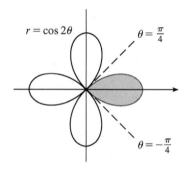

$r = \cos 2\theta$ $\theta = \dfrac{\pi}{4}$

$\theta = -\dfrac{\pi}{4}$

FIGURE 4

V EXAMPLE 2 Find the area of the region that lies inside the circle $r = 3 \sin \theta$ and outside the cardioid $r = 1 + \sin \theta$.

SOLUTION The cardioid (see Example 7 in Section 10.3) and the circle are sketched in Figure 5 and the desired region is shaded. The values of a and b in Formula 4 are determined by finding the points of intersection of the two curves. They intersect when $3 \sin \theta = 1 + \sin \theta$, which gives $\sin \theta = \tfrac{1}{2}$, so $\theta = \pi/6, 5\pi/6$. The desired area can be found by subtracting the area inside the cardioid between $\theta = \pi/6$ and $\theta = 5\pi/6$ from the area inside the circle from $\pi/6$ to $5\pi/6$. Thus

$$A = \tfrac{1}{2} \int_{\pi/6}^{5\pi/6} (3 \sin \theta)^2 \, d\theta - \tfrac{1}{2} \int_{\pi/6}^{5\pi/6} (1 + \sin \theta)^2 \, d\theta$$

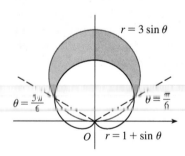

$r = 3 \sin \theta$

$\theta = \dfrac{5\pi}{6}$ $\theta = \dfrac{\pi}{6}$

O $r = 1 + \sin \theta$

FIGURE 5

Since the region is symmetric about the vertical axis $\theta = \pi/2$, we can write

$$A = 2\left[\tfrac{1}{2}\int_{\pi/6}^{\pi/2} 9 \sin^2\theta \, d\theta - \tfrac{1}{2}\int_{\pi/6}^{\pi/2}(1 + 2\sin\theta + \sin^2\theta)\,d\theta\right]$$

$$= \int_{\pi/6}^{\pi/2} (8 \sin^2\theta - 1 - 2 \sin \theta)\,d\theta$$

$$= \int_{\pi/6}^{\pi/2} (3 - 4 \cos 2\theta - 2 \sin \theta)\,d\theta \qquad \left[\text{because } \sin^2\theta = \tfrac{1}{2}(1 - \cos 2\theta)\right]$$

$$= 3\theta - 2 \sin 2\theta + 2 \cos \theta\Big]_{\pi/6}^{\pi/2} = \pi$$

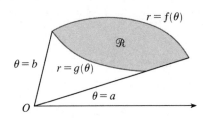

FIGURE 6

Example 2 illustrates the procedure for finding the area of the region bounded by two polar curves. In general, let $\mathcal{R}$ be a region, as illustrated in Figure 6, that is bounded by curves with polar equations $r = f(\theta)$, $r = g(\theta)$, $\theta = a$, and $\theta = b$, where $f(\theta) \geqslant g(\theta) \geqslant 0$ and $0 < b - a \leqslant 2\pi$. The area A of $\mathcal{R}$ is found by subtracting the area inside $r = g(\theta)$ from the area inside $r = f(\theta)$, so using Formula 3 we have

$$A = \int_a^b \tfrac{1}{2}[f(\theta)]^2 \, d\theta - \int_a^b \tfrac{1}{2}[g(\theta)]^2 \, d\theta$$

$$= \tfrac{1}{2} \int_a^b \left([f(\theta)]^2 - [g(\theta)]^2 \right) d\theta$$

⊘ **CAUTION** The fact that a single point has many representations in polar coordinates sometimes makes it difficult to find all the points of intersection of two polar curves. For instance, it is obvious from Figure 5 that the circle and the cardioid have three points of intersection; however, in Example 2 we solved the equations $r = 3 \sin \theta$ and $r = 1 + \sin \theta$ and found only two such points, $\left(\tfrac{3}{2}, \pi/6\right)$ and $\left(\tfrac{3}{2}, 5\pi/6\right)$. The origin is also a point of intersection, but we can't find it by solving the equations of the curves because the origin has no single representation in polar coordinates that satisfies both equations. Notice that, when represented as $(0, 0)$ or $(0, \pi)$, the origin satisfies $r = 3 \sin \theta$ and so it lies on the circle; when represented as $(0, 3\pi/2)$, it satisfies $r = 1 + \sin \theta$ and so it lies on the cardioid. Think of two points moving along the curves as the parameter value θ increases from 0 to 2π. On one curve the origin is reached at $\theta = 0$ and $\theta = \pi$; on the other curve it is reached at $\theta = 3\pi/2$. The points don't collide at the origin because they reach the origin at different times, but the curves intersect there nonetheless.

Thus, to find *all* points of intersection of two polar curves, it is recommended that you draw the graphs of both curves. It is especially convenient to use a graphing calculator or computer to help with this task.

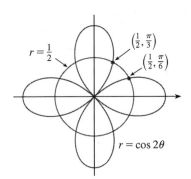

FIGURE 7

EXAMPLE 3 Find all points of intersection of the curves $r = \cos 2\theta$ and $r = \tfrac{1}{2}$.

SOLUTION If we solve the equations $r = \cos 2\theta$ and $r = \tfrac{1}{2}$, we get $\cos 2\theta = \tfrac{1}{2}$ and, therefore, $2\theta = \pi/3, 5\pi/3, 7\pi/3, 11\pi/3$. Thus the values of θ between 0 and 2π that satisfy both equations are $\theta = \pi/6, 5\pi/6, 7\pi/6, 11\pi/6$. We have found four points of intersection: $\left(\tfrac{1}{2}, \pi/6\right)$, $\left(\tfrac{1}{2}, 5\pi/6\right)$, $\left(\tfrac{1}{2}, 7\pi/6\right)$, and $\left(\tfrac{1}{2}, 11\pi/6\right)$.

However, you can see from Figure 7 that the curves have four other points of intersection—namely, $\left(\tfrac{1}{2}, \pi/3\right)$, $\left(\tfrac{1}{2}, 2\pi/3\right)$, $\left(\tfrac{1}{2}, 4\pi/3\right)$, and $\left(\tfrac{1}{2}, 5\pi/3\right)$. These can be found using symmetry or by noticing that another equation of the circle is $r = -\tfrac{1}{2}$ and then solving the equations $r = \cos 2\theta$ and $r = -\tfrac{1}{2}$. ∎

Arc Length

To find the length of a polar curve $r = f(\theta)$, $a \leqslant \theta \leqslant b$, we regard θ as a parameter and write the parametric equations of the curve as

$$x = r \cos \theta = f(\theta) \cos \theta \qquad y = r \sin \theta = f(\theta) \sin \theta$$

Using the Product Rule and differentiating with respect to θ, we obtain

$$\frac{dx}{d\theta} = \frac{dr}{d\theta} \cos \theta - r \sin \theta \qquad \frac{dy}{d\theta} = \frac{dr}{d\theta} \sin \theta + r \cos \theta$$

so, using $\cos^2\theta + \sin^2\theta = 1$, we have

$$\left(\frac{dx}{d\theta}\right)^2 + \left(\frac{dy}{d\theta}\right)^2 = \left(\frac{dr}{d\theta}\right)^2 \cos^2\theta - 2r\frac{dr}{d\theta}\cos\theta\,\sin\theta + r^2\sin^2\theta$$

$$+ \left(\frac{dr}{d\theta}\right)^2 \sin^2\theta + 2r\frac{dr}{d\theta}\sin\theta\,\cos\theta + r^2\cos^2\theta$$

$$= \left(\frac{dr}{d\theta}\right)^2 + r^2$$

Assuming that f' is continuous, we can use Theorem 10.2.5 to write the arc length as

$$L = \int_a^b \sqrt{\left(\frac{dx}{d\theta}\right)^2 + \left(\frac{dy}{d\theta}\right)^2}\, d\theta$$

Therefore the length of a curve with polar equation $r = f(\theta)$, $a \leqslant \theta \leqslant b$, is

$$\boxed{5} \qquad \boxed{L = \int_a^b \sqrt{r^2 + \left(\frac{dr}{d\theta}\right)^2}\, d\theta}$$

V   EXAMPLE 4   Find the length of the cardioid $r = 1 + \sin\theta$.

SOLUTION   The cardioid is shown in Figure 8. (We sketched it in Example 7 in Section 10.3.) Its full length is given by the parameter interval $0 \leqslant \theta \leqslant 2\pi$, so Formula 5 gives

$$L = \int_0^{2\pi} \sqrt{r^2 + \left(\frac{dr}{d\theta}\right)^2}\, d\theta = \int_0^{2\pi} \sqrt{(1 + \sin\theta)^2 + \cos^2\theta}\, d\theta$$

$$= \int_0^{2\pi} \sqrt{2 + 2\sin\theta}\, d\theta$$

We could evaluate this integral by multiplying and dividing the integrand by $\sqrt{2 - 2\sin\theta}$, or we could use a computer algebra system. In any event, we find that the length of the cardioid is $L = 8$.

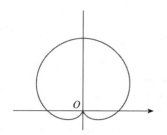

FIGURE 8
$r = 1 + \sin\theta$

10.4   Exercises

1–4 Find the area of the region that is bounded by the given curve and lies in the specified sector.

1. $r = \theta^2$, $0 \leqslant \theta \leqslant \pi/4$

2. $r = e^{\theta/2}$, $\pi \leqslant \theta \leqslant 2\pi$

3. $r^2 = 9\sin 2\theta$, $r \geqslant 0$, $0 \leqslant \theta \leqslant \pi/2$

4. $r = \tan\theta$, $\pi/6 \leqslant \theta \leqslant \pi/3$

5–8 Find the area of the shaded region.

5.

$r = \sqrt{\theta}$

6.

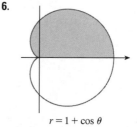

$r = 1 + \cos\theta$

Graphing calculator or computer required   **1.** Homework Hints available at stewartcalculus.com

7.

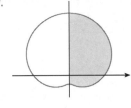

$r = 4 + 3 \sin \theta$

8.

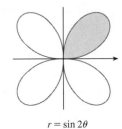

$r = \sin 2\theta$

9–12 Sketch the curve and find the area that it encloses.

9. $r = 2 \sin \theta$ **10.** $r = 1 - \sin \theta$

11. $r = 3 + 2 \cos \theta$ **12.** $r = 4 + 3 \sin \theta$

13–16 Graph the curve and find the area that it encloses.

13. $r = 2 + \sin 4\theta$ **14.** $r = 3 - 2 \cos 4\theta$

15. $r = \sqrt{1 + \cos^2(5\theta)}$ **16.** $r = 1 + 5 \sin 6\theta$

17–21 Find the area of the region enclosed by one loop of the curve.

17. $r = 4 \cos 3\theta$ **18.** $r^2 = \sin 2\theta$

19. $r = \sin 4\theta$ **20.** $r = 2 \sin 5\theta$

21. $r = 1 + 2 \sin \theta$ (inner loop)

22. Find the area enclosed by the loop of the **strophoid** $r = 2 \cos \theta - \sec \theta$.

23–28 Find the area of the region that lies inside the first curve and outside the second curve.

23. $r = 2 \cos \theta$, $r = 1$ **24.** $r = 1 - \sin \theta$, $r = 1$

25. $r^2 = 8 \cos 2\theta$, $r = 2$

26. $r = 2 + \sin \theta$, $r = 3 \sin \theta$

27. $r = 3 \cos \theta$, $r = 1 + \cos \theta$

28. $r = 3 \sin \theta$, $r = 2 - \sin \theta$

29–34 Find the area of the region that lies inside both curves.

29. $r = \sqrt{3} \cos \theta$, $r = \sin \theta$

30. $r = 1 + \cos \theta$, $r = 1 - \cos \theta$

31. $r = \sin 2\theta$, $r = \cos 2\theta$

32. $r = 3 + 2 \cos \theta$, $r = 3 + 2 \sin \theta$

33. $r^2 = \sin 2\theta$, $r^2 = \cos 2\theta$

34. $r = a \sin \theta$, $r = b \cos \theta$, $a > 0$, $b > 0$

35. Find the area inside the larger loop and outside the smaller loop of the limaçon $r = \frac{1}{2} + \cos \theta$.

36. Find the area between a large loop and the enclosed small loop of the curve $r = 1 + 2 \cos 3\theta$.

37–42 Find all points of intersection of the given curves.

37. $r = 1 + \sin \theta$, $r = 3 \sin \theta$

38. $r = 1 - \cos \theta$, $r = 1 + \sin \theta$

39. $r = 2 \sin 2\theta$, $r = 1$

40. $r = \cos 3\theta$, $r = \sin 3\theta$

41. $r = \sin \theta$, $r = \sin 2\theta$

42. $r^2 = \sin 2\theta$, $r^2 = \cos 2\theta$

43. The points of intersection of the cardioid $r = 1 + \sin \theta$ and the spiral loop $r = 2\theta$, $-\pi/2 \le \theta \le \pi/2$, can't be found exactly. Use a graphing device to find the approximate values of θ at which they intersect. Then use these values to estimate the area that lies inside both curves.

44. When recording live performances, sound engineers often use a microphone with a cardioid pickup pattern because it suppresses noise from the audience. Suppose the microphone is placed 4 m from the front of the stage (as in the figure) and the boundary of the optimal pickup region is given by the cardioid $r = 8 + 8 \sin \theta$, where r is measured in meters and the microphone is at the pole. The musicians want to know the area they will have on stage within the optimal pickup range of the microphone. Answer their question.

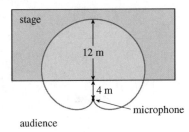

45–48 Find the exact length of the polar curve.

45. $r = 2 \cos \theta$, $0 \le \theta \le \pi$

46. $r = 5^\theta$, $0 \le \theta \le 2\pi$

47. $r = \theta^2$, $0 \le \theta \le 2\pi$

48. $r = 2(1 + \cos \theta)$

49–50 Find the exact length of the curve. Use a graph to determine the parameter interval.

49. $r = \cos^4(\theta/4)$ **50.** $r = \cos^2(\theta/2)$

51–54 Use a calculator to find the length of the curve correct to four decimal places. If necessary, graph the curve to determine the parameter interval.

51. One loop of the curve $r = \cos 2\theta$

52. $r = \tan \theta, \quad \pi/6 \leqslant \theta \leqslant \pi/3$

53. $r = \sin(6 \sin \theta)$

54. $r = \sin(\theta/4)$

55. (a) Use Formula 10.2.6 to show that the area of the surface generated by rotating the polar curve

$$r = f(\theta) \qquad a \leqslant \theta \leqslant b$$

(where f' is continuous and $0 \leqslant a < b \leqslant \pi$) about the polar axis is

$$S = \int_a^b 2\pi r \sin\theta \sqrt{r^2 + \left(\frac{dr}{d\theta}\right)^2}\, d\theta$$

(b) Use the formula in part (a) to find the surface area generated by rotating the lemniscate $r^2 = \cos 2\theta$ about the polar axis.

56. (a) Find a formula for the area of the surface generated by rotating the polar curve $r = f(\theta)$, $a \leqslant \theta \leqslant b$ (where f' is continuous and $0 \leqslant a < b \leqslant \pi$), about the line $\theta = \pi/2$.
(b) Find the surface area generated by rotating the lemniscate $r^2 = \cos 2\theta$ about the line $\theta = \pi/2$.

10.5   Conic Sections

In this section we give geometric definitions of parabolas, ellipses, and hyperbolas and derive their standard equations. They are called **conic sections**, or **conics**, because they result from intersecting a cone with a plane as shown in Figure 1.

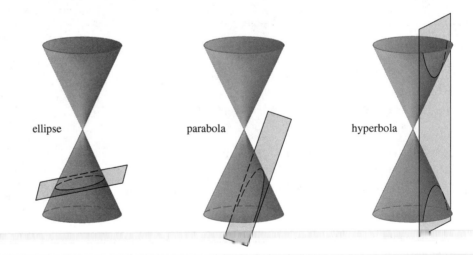

FIGURE 1

Conics

▪ Parabolas

A **parabola** is the set of points in a plane that are equidistant from a fixed point F (called the **focus**) and a fixed line (called the **directrix**). This definition is illustrated by Figure 2. Notice that the point halfway between the focus and the directrix lies on the parabola; it is called the **vertex**. The line through the focus perpendicular to the directrix is called the **axis** of the parabola.

In the 16th century Galileo showed that the path of a projectile that is shot into the air at an angle to the ground is a parabola. Since then, parabolic shapes have been used in designing automobile headlights, reflecting telescopes, and suspension bridges. (See Problem 20 on page 271 for the reflection property of parabolas that makes them so useful.)

We obtain a particularly simple equation for a parabola if we place its vertex at the origin O and its directrix parallel to the x-axis as in Figure 3. If the focus is the point $(0, p)$, then the directrix has the equation $y = -p$. If $P(x, y)$ is any point on the parabola,

FIGURE 2

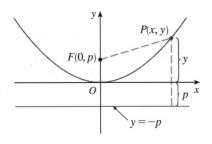

FIGURE 3

then the distance from P to the focus is

$$|PF| = \sqrt{x^2 + (y - p)^2}$$

and the distance from P to the directrix is $|y + p|$. (Figure 3 illustrates the case where $p > 0$.) The defining property of a parabola is that these distances are equal:

$$\sqrt{x^2 + (y - p)^2} = |y + p|$$

We get an equivalent equation by squaring and simplifying:

$$x^2 + (y - p)^2 = |y + p|^2 = (y + p)^2$$
$$x^2 + y^2 - 2py + p^2 = y^2 + 2py + p^2$$
$$x^2 = 4py$$

> **1** An equation of the parabola with focus $(0, p)$ and directrix $y = -p$ is
> $$x^2 = 4py$$

If we write $a = 1/(4p)$, then the standard equation of a parabola **1** becomes $y = ax^2$. It opens upward if $p > 0$ and downward if $p < 0$ [see Figure 4, parts (a) and (b)]. The graph is symmetric with respect to the y-axis because **1** is unchanged when x is replaced by $-x$.

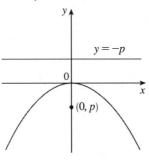

(a) $x^2 = 4py$, $p > 0$

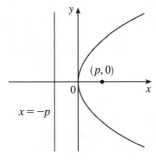

(b) $x^2 = 4py$, $p < 0$ (c) $y^2 = 4px$, $p > 0$

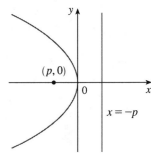

(d) $y^2 = 4px$, $p < 0$

FIGURE 4

If we interchange x and y in **1**, we obtain

> **2** $$y^2 = 4px$$

which is an equation of the parabola with focus $(p, 0)$ and directrix $x = -p$. (Interchanging x and y amounts to reflecting about the diagonal line $y = x$.) The parabola opens to the right if $p > 0$ and to the left if $p < 0$ [see Figure 4, parts (c) and (d)]. In both cases the graph is symmetric with respect to the x-axis, which is the axis of the parabola.

EXAMPLE 1 Find the focus and directrix of the parabola $y^2 + 10x = 0$ and sketch the graph.

SOLUTION If we write the equation as $y^2 = -10x$ and compare it with Equation 2, we see that $4p = -10$, so $p = -\frac{5}{2}$. Thus the focus is $(p, 0) = \left(-\frac{5}{2}, 0\right)$ and the directrix is $x = \frac{5}{2}$. The sketch is shown in Figure 5.

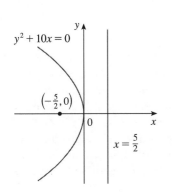

FIGURE 5

Ellipses

An **ellipse** is the set of points in a plane the sum of whose distances from two fixed points F_1 and F_2 is a constant (see Figure 6). These two fixed points are called the **foci** (plural of **focus**). One of Kepler's laws is that the orbits of the planets in the solar system are ellipses with the sun at one focus.

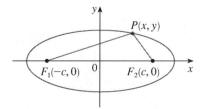

FIGURE 6

FIGURE 7

In order to obtain the simplest equation for an ellipse, we place the foci on the x-axis at the points $(-c, 0)$ and $(c, 0)$ as in Figure 7 so that the origin is halfway between the foci. Let the sum of the distances from a point on the ellipse to the foci be $2a > 0$. Then $P(x, y)$ is a point on the ellipse when

$$|PF_1| + |PF_2| = 2a$$

that is,

$$\sqrt{(x + c)^2 + y^2} + \sqrt{(x - c)^2 + y^2} = 2a$$

or

$$\sqrt{(x - c)^2 + y^2} = 2a - \sqrt{(x + c)^2 + y^2}$$

Squaring both sides, we have

$$x^2 - 2cx + c^2 + y^2 = 4a^2 - 4a\sqrt{(x + c)^2 + y^2} + x^2 + 2cx + c^2 + y^2$$

which simplifies to

$$a\sqrt{(x + c)^2 + y^2} = a^2 + cx$$

We square again:

$$a^2(x^2 + 2cx + c^2 + y^2) = a^4 + 2a^2cx + c^2x^2$$

which becomes

$$(a^2 - c^2)x^2 + a^2y^2 = a^2(a^2 - c^2)$$

From triangle F_1F_2P in Figure 7 we see that $2c < 2a$, so $c < a$ and therefore $a^2 - c^2 > 0$. For convenience, let $b^2 = a^2 - c^2$. Then the equation of the ellipse becomes $b^2x^2 + a^2y^2 = a^2b^2$ or, if both sides are divided by a^2b^2,

$$\boxed{3} \qquad \frac{x^2}{a^2} + \frac{y^2}{b^2} = 1$$

Since $b^2 = a^2 - c^2 < a^2$, it follows that $b < a$. The x-intercepts are found by setting $y = 0$. Then $x^2/a^2 = 1$, or $x^2 = a^2$, so $x = \pm a$. The corresponding points $(a, 0)$ and $(-a, 0)$ are called the **vertices** of the ellipse and the line segment joining the vertices is called the **major axis**. To find the y-intercepts we set $x = 0$ and obtain $y^2 = b^2$, so $y = \pm b$. The line segment joining $(0, b)$ and $(0, -b)$ is the **minor axis**. Equation 3 is unchanged if x is replaced by $-x$ or y is replaced by $-y$, so the ellipse is symmetric about both axes. Notice that if the foci coincide, then $c = 0$, so $a = b$ and the ellipse becomes a circle with radius $r = a = b$.

We summarize this discussion as follows (see also Figure 8).

FIGURE 8

$\dfrac{x^2}{a^2} + \dfrac{y^2}{b^2} = 1, \ a \geqslant b$

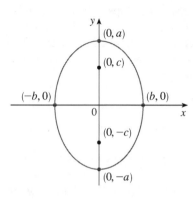

FIGURE 9
$\dfrac{x^2}{b^2} + \dfrac{y^2}{a^2} = 1, \; a \geqslant b$

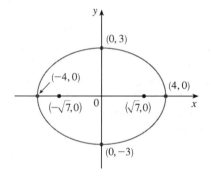

FIGURE 10
$9x^2 + 16y^2 = 144$

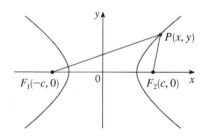

FIGURE 11
P is on the hyperbola when
$|PF_1| - |PF_2| = \pm 2a$.

$\boxed{4}$ The ellipse

$$\frac{x^2}{a^2} + \frac{y^2}{b^2} = 1 \qquad a \geqslant b > 0$$

has foci $(\pm c, 0)$, where $c^2 = a^2 - b^2$, and vertices $(\pm a, 0)$.

If the foci of an ellipse are located on the y-axis at $(0, \pm c)$, then we can find its equation by interchanging x and y in $\boxed{4}$. (See Figure 9.)

$\boxed{5}$ The ellipse

$$\frac{x^2}{b^2} + \frac{y^2}{a^2} = 1 \qquad a \geqslant b > 0$$

has foci $(0, \pm c)$, where $c^2 = a^2 - b^2$, and vertices $(0, \pm a)$.

V **EXAMPLE 2**   Sketch the graph of $9x^2 + 16y^2 = 144$ and locate the foci.

SOLUTION   Divide both sides of the equation by 144:

$$\frac{x^2}{16} + \frac{y^2}{9} = 1$$

The equation is now in the standard form for an ellipse, so we have $a^2 = 16$, $b^2 = 9$, $a = 4$, and $b = 3$. The x-intercepts are ± 4 and the y-intercepts are ± 3. Also, $c^2 = a^2 - b^2 = 7$, so $c = \sqrt{7}$ and the foci are $\left(\pm\sqrt{7}, 0\right)$. The graph is sketched in Figure 10.   ▬

V **EXAMPLE 3**   Find an equation of the ellipse with foci $(0, \pm 2)$ and vertices $(0, \pm 3)$.

SOLUTION   Using the notation of $\boxed{5}$, we have $c = 2$ and $a = 3$. Then we obtain $b^2 = a^2 - c^2 = 9 - 4 = 5$, so an equation of the ellipse is

$$\frac{x^2}{5} + \frac{y^2}{9} = 1$$

Another way of writing the equation is $9x^2 + 5y^2 = 45$.   ▬

Like parabolas, ellipses have an interesting reflection property that has practical consequences. If a source of light or sound is placed at one focus of a surface with elliptical cross-sections, then all the light or sound is reflected off the surface to the other focus (see Exercise 65). This principle is used in *lithotripsy*, a treatment for kidney stones. A reflector with elliptical cross-section is placed in such a way that the kidney stone is at one focus. High-intensity sound waves generated at the other focus are reflected to the stone and destroy it without damaging surrounding tissue. The patient is spared the trauma of surgery and recovers within a few days.

▬ Hyperbolas

A **hyperbola** is the set of all points in a plane the difference of whose distances from two fixed points F_1 and F_2 (the foci) is a constant. This definition is illustrated in Figure 11.

Hyperbolas occur frequently as graphs of equations in chemistry, physics, biology, and economics (Boyle's Law, Ohm's Law, supply and demand curves). A particularly significant application of hyperbolas is found in the navigation systems developed in World Wars I and II (see Exercise 51).

Notice that the definition of a hyperbola is similar to that of an ellipse; the only change is that the sum of distances has become a difference of distances. In fact, the derivation of the equation of a hyperbola is also similar to the one given earlier for an ellipse. It is left as Exercise 52 to show that when the foci are on the x-axis at $(\pm c, 0)$ and the difference of distances is $|PF_1| - |PF_2| = \pm 2a$, then the equation of the hyperbola is

$$\boxed{6} \qquad \frac{x^2}{a^2} - \frac{y^2}{b^2} = 1$$

where $c^2 = a^2 + b^2$. Notice that the x-intercepts are again $\pm a$ and the points $(a, 0)$ and $(-a, 0)$ are the **vertices** of the hyperbola. But if we put $x = 0$ in Equation 6 we get $y^2 = -b^2$, which is impossible, so there is no y-intercept. The hyperbola is symmetric with respect to both axes.

To analyze the hyperbola further, we look at Equation 6 and obtain

$$\frac{x^2}{a^2} = 1 + \frac{y^2}{b^2} \geqslant 1$$

This shows that $x^2 \geqslant a^2$, so $|x| = \sqrt{x^2} \geqslant a$. Therefore we have $x \geqslant a$ or $x \leqslant -a$. This means that the hyperbola consists of two parts, called its *branches*.

When we draw a hyperbola it is useful to first draw its **asymptotes**, which are the dashed lines $y = (b/a)x$ and $y = -(b/a)x$ shown in Figure 12. Both branches of the hyperbola approach the asymptotes; that is, they come arbitrarily close to the asymptotes. [See Exercise 73 in Section 4.5, where these lines are shown to be slant asymptotes.]

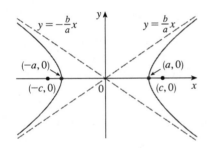

FIGURE 12
$\dfrac{x^2}{a^2} - \dfrac{y^2}{b^2} = 1$

> $\boxed{7}$ The hyperbola
> $$\frac{x^2}{a^2} - \frac{y^2}{b^2} = 1$$
> has foci $(\pm c, 0)$, where $c^2 = a^2 + b^2$, vertices $(\pm a, 0)$, and asymptotes $y = \pm(b/a)x$.

If the foci of a hyperbola are on the y-axis, then by reversing the roles of x and y we obtain the following information, which is illustrated in Figure 13.

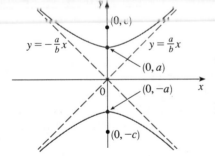

FIGURE 13
$\dfrac{y^2}{a^2} - \dfrac{x^2}{b^2} = 1$

> $\boxed{8}$ The hyperbola
> $$\frac{y^2}{a^2} - \frac{x^2}{b^2} = 1$$
> has foci $(0, \pm c)$, where $c^2 = a^2 + b^2$, vertices $(0, \pm a)$, and asymptotes $y = \pm(a/b)x$.

EXAMPLE 4 Find the foci and asymptotes of the hyperbola $9x^2 - 16y^2 = 144$ and sketch its graph.

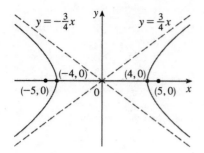

FIGURE 14
$9x^2 - 16y^2 = 144$

SOLUTION If we divide both sides of the equation by 144, it becomes

$$\frac{x^2}{16} - \frac{y^2}{9} = 1$$

which is of the form given in $\boxed{7}$ with $a = 4$ and $b = 3$. Since $c^2 = 16 + 9 = 25$, the foci are $(\pm 5, 0)$. The asymptotes are the lines $y = \frac{3}{4}x$ and $y = -\frac{3}{4}x$. The graph is shown in Figure 14.

EXAMPLE 5 Find the foci and equation of the hyperbola with vertices $(0, \pm 1)$ and asymptote $y = 2x$.

SOLUTION From $\boxed{8}$ and the given information, we see that $a = 1$ and $a/b = 2$. Thus $b = a/2 = \frac{1}{2}$ and $c^2 = a^2 + b^2 = \frac{5}{4}$. The foci are $\left(0, \pm\sqrt{5}/2\right)$ and the equation of the hyperbola is

$$y^2 - 4x^2 = 1$$

▪ Shifted Conics

As discussed in Appendix C, we shift conics by taking the standard equations $\boxed{1}$, $\boxed{2}$, $\boxed{4}$, $\boxed{5}$, $\boxed{7}$, and $\boxed{8}$ and replacing x and y by $x - h$ and $y - k$.

EXAMPLE 6 Find an equation of the ellipse with foci $(2, -2)$, $(4, -2)$ and vertices $(1, -2)$, $(5, -2)$.

SOLUTION The major axis is the line segment that joins the vertices $(1, -2)$, $(5, -2)$ and has length 4, so $a = 2$. The distance between the foci is 2, so $c = 1$. Thus $b^2 = a^2 - c^2 = 3$. Since the center of the ellipse is $(3, -2)$, we replace x and y in $\boxed{4}$ by $x - 3$ and $y + 2$ to obtain

$$\frac{(x - 3)^2}{4} + \frac{(y + 2)^2}{3} = 1$$

as the equation of the ellipse.

V **EXAMPLE 7** Sketch the conic $9x^2 - 4y^2 - 72x + 8y + 176 = 0$ and find its foci.

SOLUTION We complete the squares as follows:

$$4(y^2 - 2y) - 9(x^2 - 8x) = 176$$

$$4(y^2 - 2y + 1) - 9(x^2 - 8x + 16) = 176 + 4 - 144$$

$$4(y - 1)^2 - 9(x - 4)^2 = 36$$

$$\frac{(y - 1)^2}{9} - \frac{(x - 4)^2}{4} = 1$$

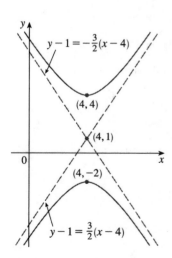

FIGURE 15
$9x^2 - 4y^2 - 72x + 8y + 176 = 0$

This is in the form $\boxed{8}$ except that x and y are replaced by $x - 4$ and $y - 1$. Thus $a^2 = 9$, $b^2 = 4$, and $c^2 = 13$. The hyperbola is shifted four units to the right and one unit upward. The foci are $\left(4, 1 + \sqrt{13}\right)$ and $\left(4, 1 - \sqrt{13}\right)$ and the vertices are $(4, 4)$ and $(4, -2)$. The asymptotes are $y - 1 = \pm\frac{3}{2}(x - 4)$. The hyperbola is sketched in Figure 15.

10.5   **Exercises**

1–8 Find the vertex, focus, and directrix of the parabola and sketch its graph.

1. $x^2 = 6y$

2. $2y^2 = 3x$

3. $2x = -y^2$

4. $3x^2 + 8y = 0$

5. $(x + 2)^2 = 8(y - 3)$

6. $x - 1 = (y + 5)^2$

7. $y^2 + 2y + 12x + 25 = 0$

8. $y + 12x - 2x^2 = 16$

9–10 Find an equation of the parabola. Then find the focus and directrix.

9.

10.

11–16 Find the vertices and foci of the ellipse and sketch its graph.

11. $\dfrac{x^2}{9} + \dfrac{y^2}{5} = 1$

12. $\dfrac{x^2}{64} + \dfrac{y^2}{100} = 1$

13. $4x^2 + y^2 = 16$

14. $4x^2 + 25y^2 = 25$

15. $9x^2 - 18x + 4y^2 = 27$

16. $x^2 + 3y^2 + 2x - 12y + 10 = 0$

17–18 Find an equation of the ellipse. Then find its foci.

17.

18.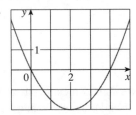

19–24 Find the vertices, foci, and asymptotes of the hyperbola and sketch its graph.

19. $\dfrac{y^2}{25} - \dfrac{x^2}{9} = 1$

20. $\dfrac{x^2}{36} - \dfrac{y^2}{64} = 1$

21. $x^2 - y^2 = 100$

22. $y^2 - 16x^2 = 16$

23. $4x^2 - y^2 - 24x - 4y + 28 = 0$

24. $y^2 - 4x^2 - 2y + 16x = 31$

25–30 Identify the type of conic section whose equation is given and find the vertices and foci.

25. $x^2 = y + 1$

26. $x^2 = y^2 + 1$

27. $x^2 = 4y - 2y^2$

28. $y^2 - 8y = 6x - 16$

29. $y^2 + 2y = 4x^2 + 3$

30. $4x^2 + 4x + y^2 = 0$

31–48 Find an equation for the conic that satisfies the given conditions.

31. Parabola,   vertex $(0, 0)$,   focus $(1, 0)$

32. Parabola,   focus $(0, 0)$,   directrix $y = 6$

33. Parabola,   focus $(-4, 0)$,   directrix $x = 2$

34. Parabola,   focus $(3, 6)$,   vertex $(3, 2)$

35. Parabola,   vertex $(2, 3)$,   vertical axis, passing through $(1, 5)$

36. Parabola,   horizontal axis, passing through $(-1, 0)$, $(1, -1)$, and $(3, 1)$

37. Ellipse,   foci $(\pm 2, 0)$,   vertices $(\pm 5, 0)$

38. Ellipse,   foci $(0, \pm 5)$,   vertices $(0, \pm 13)$

39. Ellipse,   foci $(0, 2)$, $(0, 6)$,   vertices $(0, 0)$, $(0, 8)$

40. Ellipse,   foci $(0, -1)$, $(8, -1)$,   vertex $(9, -1)$

41. Ellipse,   center $(-1, 4)$,   vertex $(-1, 0)$,   focus $(-1, 6)$

42. Ellipse,   foci $(\pm 4, 0)$,   passing through $(-4, 1.8)$

43. Hyperbola,   vertices $(\pm 3, 0)$,   foci $(\pm 5, 0)$

44. Hyperbola,   vertices $(0, \pm 2)$,   foci $(0, \pm 5)$

45. Hyperbola,   vertices $(-3, -4)$, $(-3, 6)$, foci $(-3, -7)$, $(-3, 9)$

46. Hyperbola,   vertices $(-1, 2)$, $(7, 2)$, foci $(-2, 2)$, $(8, 2)$

47. Hyperbola,   vertices $(\pm 3, 0)$,   asymptotes $y = \pm 2x$

48. Hyperbola,   foci $(2, 0)$, $(2, 8)$, asymptotes $y = 3 + \frac{1}{2}x$ and $y = 5 - \frac{1}{2}x$

49. The point in a lunar orbit nearest the surface of the moon is called *perilune* and the point farthest from the surface is called *apolune*. The *Apollo 11* spacecraft was placed in an elliptical lunar orbit with perilune altitude 110 km and apolune altitude 314 km (above the moon). Find an equation of this ellipse if the radius of the moon is 1728 km and the center of the moon is at one focus.

50. A cross-section of a parabolic reflector is shown in the figure. The bulb is located at the focus and the opening at the focus is 10 cm.
(a) Find an equation of the parabola.
(b) Find the diameter of the opening $|CD|$, 11 cm from the vertex.

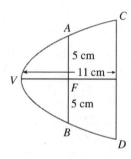

51. In the LORAN (LOng RAnge Navigation) radio navigation system, two radio stations located at A and B transmit simultaneous signals to a ship or an aircraft located at P. The onboard computer converts the time difference in receiving these signals into a distance difference $|PA| - |PB|$, and this, according to the definition of a hyperbola, locates the ship or aircraft on one branch of a hyperbola (see the figure). Suppose that station B is located 400 mi due east of station A on a coastline. A ship received the signal from B 1200 microseconds (μs) before it received the signal from A.
(a) Assuming that radio signals travel at a speed of 980 ft/μs, find an equation of the hyperbola on which the ship lies.
(b) If the ship is due north of B, how far off the coastline is the ship?

52. Use the definition of a hyperbola to derive Equation 6 for a hyperbola with foci $(\pm c, 0)$ and vertices $(\pm a, 0)$.

53. Show that the function defined by the upper branch of the hyperbola $y^2/a^2 - x^2/b^2 = 1$ is concave upward.

54. Find an equation for the ellipse with foci $(1, 1)$ and $(-1, -1)$ and major axis of length 4.

55. Determine the type of curve represented by the equation

$$\frac{x^2}{k} + \frac{y^2}{k - 16} = 1$$

in each of the following cases: (a) $k > 16$, (b) $0 < k < 16$, and (c) $k < 0$.
(d) Show that all the curves in parts (a) and (b) have the same foci, no matter what the value of k is.

56. (a) Show that the equation of the tangent line to the parabola $y^2 = 4px$ at the point (x_0, y_0) can be written as

$$y_0 y = 2p(x + x_0)$$

(b) What is the x-intercept of this tangent line? Use this fact to draw the tangent line.

57. Show that the tangent lines to the parabola $x^2 = 4py$ drawn from any point on the directrix are perpendicular.

58. Show that if an ellipse and a hyperbola have the same foci, then their tangent lines at each point of intersection are perpendicular.

59. Use parametric equations and Simpson's Rule with $n = 8$ to estimate the circumference of the ellipse $9x^2 + 4y^2 = 36$.

60. The planet Pluto travels in an elliptical orbit around the sun (at one focus). The length of the major axis is 1.18×10^{10} km and the length of the minor axis is 1.14×10^{10} km. Use Simpson's Rule with $n = 10$ to estimate the distance traveled by the planet during one complete orbit around the sun.

61. Find the area of the region enclosed by the hyperbola $x^2/a^2 - y^2/b^2 = 1$ and the vertical line through a focus.

62. (a) If an ellipse is rotated about its major axis, find the volume of the resulting solid.
(b) If it is rotated about its minor axis, find the resulting volume.

63. Find the centroid of the region enclosed by the x-axis and the top half of the ellipse $9x^2 + 4y^2 = 36$.

64. (a) Calculate the surface area of the ellipsoid that is generated by rotating an ellipse about its major axis.
(b) What is the surface area if the ellipse is rotated about its minor axis?

65. Let $P(x_1, y_1)$ be a point on the ellipse $x^2/a^2 + y^2/b^2 = 1$ with foci F_1 and F_2 and let α and β be the angles between the lines

PF_1, PF_2 and the ellipse as shown in the figure. Prove that $\alpha = \beta$. This explains how whispering galleries and lithotripsy work. Sound coming from one focus is reflected and passes through the other focus. [*Hint:* Use the formula in Problem 19 on page 271 to show that $\tan \alpha = \tan \beta$.]

hyperbola. It shows that light aimed at a focus F_2 of a hyperbolic mirror is reflected toward the other focus F_1.)

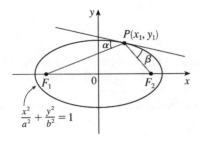

$$\frac{x^2}{a^2} + \frac{y^2}{b^2} = 1$$

66. Let $P(x_1, y_1)$ be a point on the hyperbola $x^2/a^2 - y^2/b^2 = 1$ with foci F_1 and F_2 and let α and β be the angles between the lines PF_1, PF_2 and the hyperbola as shown in the figure. Prove that $\alpha = \beta$. (This is the reflection property of the

10.6   Conic Sections in Polar Coordinates

In the preceding section we defined the parabola in terms of a focus and directrix, but we defined the ellipse and hyperbola in terms of two foci. In this section we give a more unified treatment of all three types of conic sections in terms of a focus and directrix. Furthermore, if we place the focus at the origin, then a conic section has a simple polar equation, which provides a convenient description of the motion of planets, satellites, and comets.

---

1   Theorem   Let F be a fixed point (called the **focus**) and l be a fixed line (called the **directrix**) in a plane. Let e be a fixed positive number (called the **eccentricity**). The set of all points P in the plane such that

$$\frac{|PF|}{|Pl|} = e$$

(that is, the ratio of the distance from F to the distance from l is the constant e) is a conic section. The conic is

(a)   an ellipse if $e < 1$

(b)   a parabola if $e = 1$

(c)   a hyperbola if $e > 1$

PROOF   Notice that if the eccentricity is $e = 1$, then $|PF| = |Pl|$ and so the given condition simply becomes the definition of a parabola as given in Section 10.5.

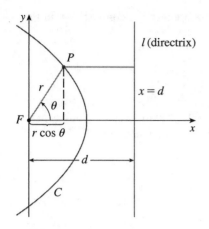

FIGURE 1

Let us place the focus F at the origin and the directrix parallel to the y-axis and d units to the right. Thus the directrix has equation $x = d$ and is perpendicular to the polar axis. If the point P has polar coordinates (r, θ), we see from Figure 1 that

$$|PF| = r \qquad |Pl| = d - r\cos\theta$$

Thus the condition $|PF|/|Pl| = e$, or $|PF| = e|Pl|$, becomes

$$\boxed{2} \qquad r = e(d - r\cos\theta)$$

If we square both sides of this polar equation and convert to rectangular coordinates, we get

$$x^2 + y^2 = e^2(d - x)^2 = e^2(d^2 - 2dx + x^2)$$

or

$$(1 - e^2)x^2 + 2de^2x + y^2 = e^2d^2$$

After completing the square, we have

$$\boxed{3} \qquad \left(x + \frac{e^2d}{1 - e^2}\right)^2 + \frac{y^2}{1 - e^2} = \frac{e^2d^2}{(1 - e^2)^2}$$

If $e < 1$, we recognize Equation 3 as the equation of an ellipse. In fact, it is of the form

$$\frac{(x - h)^2}{a^2} + \frac{y^2}{b^2} = 1$$

where

$$\boxed{4} \qquad h = -\frac{e^2d}{1 - e^2} \qquad a^2 = \frac{e^2d^2}{(1 - e^2)^2} \qquad b^2 = \frac{e^2d^2}{1 - e^2}$$

In Section 10.5 we found that the foci of an ellipse are at a distance c from the center, where

$$\boxed{5} \qquad c^2 = a^2 - b^2 = \frac{e^4d^2}{(1 - e^2)^2}$$

This shows that

$$c = \frac{e^2d}{1 - e^2} = -h$$

and confirms that the focus as defined in Theorem 1 means the same as the focus defined in Section 10.5. It also follows from Equations 4 and 5 that the eccentricity is given by

$$e = \frac{c}{a}$$

If $e > 1$, then $1 - e^2 < 0$ and we see that Equation 3 represents a hyperbola. Just as we did before, we could rewrite Equation 3 in the form

$$\frac{(x - h)^2}{a^2} - \frac{y^2}{b^2} = 1$$

and see that

$$e = \frac{c}{a} \qquad \text{where} \quad c^2 = a^2 + b^2$$

By solving Equation 2 for r, we see that the polar equation of the conic shown in Figure 1 can be written as

$$r = \frac{ed}{1 + e \cos \theta}$$

If the directrix is chosen to be to the left of the focus as $x = -d$, or if the directrix is chosen to be parallel to the polar axis as $y = \pm d$, then the polar equation of the conic is given by the following theorem, which is illustrated by Figure 2. (See Exercises 21–23.)

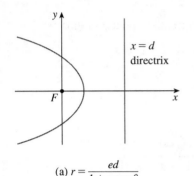

(a) $r = \dfrac{ed}{1 + e \cos \theta}$

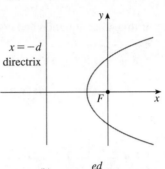

(b) $r = \dfrac{ed}{1 - e \cos \theta}$

(c) $r = \dfrac{ed}{1 + e \sin \theta}$

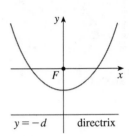

(d) $r = \dfrac{ed}{1 - e \sin \theta}$

FIGURE 2
Polar equations of conics

---

6 **Theorem** A polar equation of the form

$$r = \frac{ed}{1 \pm e \cos \theta} \qquad \text{or} \qquad r = \frac{ed}{1 \pm e \sin \theta}$$

represents a conic section with eccentricity e. The conic is an ellipse if $e < 1$, a parabola if $e = 1$, or a hyperbola if $e > 1$.

V **EXAMPLE 1** Find a polar equation for a parabola that has its focus at the origin and whose directrix is the line $y = -6$.

SOLUTION Using Theorem 6 with $e = 1$ and $d = 6$, and using part (d) of Figure 2, we see that the equation of the parabola is

$$r = \frac{6}{1 - \sin \theta}$$

V **EXAMPLE 2** A conic is given by the polar equation

$$r = \frac{10}{3 - 2 \cos \theta}$$

Find the eccentricity, identify the conic, locate the directrix, and sketch the conic.

SOLUTION Dividing numerator and denominator by 3, we write the equation as

$$r = \frac{\frac{10}{3}}{1 - \frac{2}{3} \cos \theta}$$

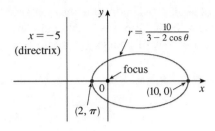

FIGURE 3

From Theorem 6 we see that this represents an ellipse with $e = \frac{2}{3}$. Since $ed = \frac{10}{3}$, we have

$$d = \frac{\frac{10}{3}}{e} = \frac{\frac{10}{3}}{\frac{2}{3}} = 5$$

so the directrix has Cartesian equation $x = -5$. When $\theta = 0$, $r = 10$; when $\theta = \pi$, $r = 2$. So the vertices have polar coordinates $(10, 0)$ and $(2, \pi)$. The ellipse is sketched in Figure 3.

EXAMPLE 3 Sketch the conic $r = \dfrac{12}{2 + 4 \sin \theta}$.

SOLUTION Writing the equation in the form

$$r = \frac{6}{1 + 2 \sin \theta}$$

we see that the eccentricity is $e = 2$ and the equation therefore represents a hyperbola. Since $ed = 6$, $d = 3$ and the directrix has equation $y = 3$. The vertices occur when $\theta = \pi/2$ and $3\pi/2$, so they are $(2, \pi/2)$ and $(-6, 3\pi/2) = (6, \pi/2)$. It is also useful to plot the x-intercepts. These occur when $\theta = 0$, π; in both cases $r = 6$. For additional accuracy we could draw the asymptotes. Note that $r \rightarrow \pm\infty$ when $1 + 2 \sin \theta \rightarrow 0^+$ or 0^- and $1 + 2 \sin \theta = 0$ when $\sin \theta = -\frac{1}{2}$. Thus the asymptotes are parallel to the rays $\theta = 7\pi/6$ and $\theta = 11\pi/6$. The hyperbola is sketched in Figure 4.

FIGURE 4

$$r = \frac{12}{2 + 4 \sin \theta}$$

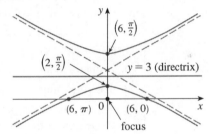

When rotating conic sections, we find it much more convenient to use polar equations than Cartesian equations. We just use the fact (see Exercise 73 in Section 10.3) that the graph of $r = f(\theta - \alpha)$ is the graph of $r = f(\theta)$ rotated counterclockwise about the origin through an angle α.

V EXAMPLE 4 If the ellipse of Example 2 is rotated through an angle $\pi/4$ about the origin, find a polar equation and graph the resulting ellipse.

SOLUTION We get the equation of the rotated ellipse by replacing θ with $\theta - \pi/4$ in the equation given in Example 2. So the new equation is

$$r = \frac{10}{3 - 2 \cos(\theta - \pi/4)}$$

FIGURE 5

We use this equation to graph the rotated ellipse in Figure 5. Notice that the ellipse has been rotated about its left focus.

In Figure 6 we use a computer to sketch a number of conics to demonstrate the effect of varying the eccentricity e. Notice that when e is close to 0 the ellipse is nearly circular, whereas it becomes more elongated as $e \rightarrow 1^-$. When $e = 1$, of course, the conic is a parabola.

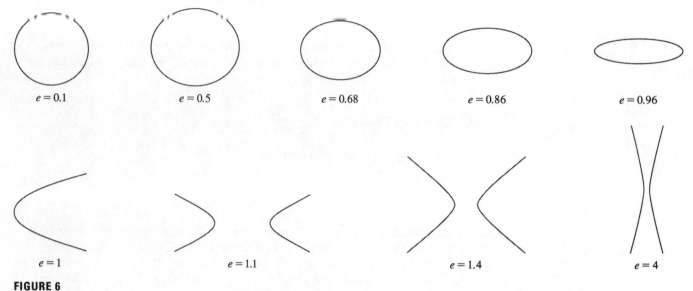

FIGURE 6

▮ Kepler's Laws

In 1609 the German mathematician and astronomer Johannes Kepler, on the basis of huge amounts of astronomical data, published the following three laws of planetary motion.

> **Kepler's Laws**
> 1. A planet revolves around the sun in an elliptical orbit with the sun at one focus.
> 2. The line joining the sun to a planet sweeps out equal areas in equal times.
> 3. The square of the period of revolution of a planet is proportional to the cube of the length of the major axis of its orbit.

Although Kepler formulated his laws in terms of the motion of planets around the sun, they apply equally well to the motion of moons, comets, satellites, and other bodies that orbit subject to a single gravitational force. In Section 13.4 we will show how to deduce Kepler's Laws from Newton's Laws. Here we use Kepler's First Law, together with the polar equation of an ellipse, to calculate quantities of interest in astronomy.

For purposes of astronomical calculations, it's useful to express the equation of an ellipse in terms of its eccentricity e and its semimajor axis a. We can write the distance d from the focus to the directrix in terms of a if we use $\boxed{4}$:

$$a^2 = \frac{e^2 d^2}{(1 - e^2)^2} \quad \Rightarrow \quad d^2 = \frac{a^2(1 - e^2)^2}{e^2} \quad \Rightarrow \quad d = \frac{a(1 - e^2)}{e}$$

So $ed = a(1 - e^2)$. If the directrix is $x = d$, then the polar equation is

$$r = \frac{ed}{1 + e \cos \theta} = \frac{a(1 - e^2)}{1 + e \cos \theta}$$

> **7** The polar equation of an ellipse with focus at the origin, semimajor axis a, eccentricity e, and directrix $x = d$ can be written in the form
>
> $$r = \frac{a(1 - e^2)}{1 + e \cos \theta}$$

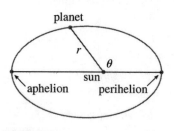

planet

r

θ

sun

aphelion   perihelion

FIGURE 7

The positions of a planet that are closest to and farthest from the sun are called its **perihelion** and **aphelion**, respectively, and correspond to the vertices of the ellipse. (See Figure 7.) The distances from the sun to the perihelion and aphelion are called the **perihelion distance** and **aphelion distance**, respectively. In Figure 1 the sun is at the focus F, so at perihelion we have $\theta = 0$ and, from Equation 7,

$$r = \frac{a(1 - e^2)}{1 + e \cos 0} = \frac{a(1 - e)(1 + e)}{1 + e} = a(1 - e)$$

Similarly, at aphelion $\theta = \pi$ and $r = a(1 + e)$.

> **8** The perihelion distance from a planet to the sun is $a(1 - e)$ and the aphelion distance is $a(1 + e)$.

EXAMPLE 5

(a) Find an approximate polar equation for the elliptical orbit of the earth around the sun (at one focus) given that the eccentricity is about 0.017 and the length of the major axis is about 2.99×10^8 km.
(b) Find the distance from the earth to the sun at perihelion and at aphelion.

SOLUTION

(a) The length of the major axis is $2a = 2.99 \times 10^8$, so $a = 1.495 \times 10^8$. We are given that $e = 0.017$ and so, from Equation 7, an equation of the earth's orbit around the sun is

$$r = \frac{a(1 - e^2)}{1 + e \cos \theta} = \frac{(1.495 \times 10^8)[1 - (0.017)^2]}{1 + 0.017 \cos \theta}$$

or, approximately,

$$r = \frac{1.49 \times 10^8}{1 + 0.017 \cos \theta}$$

(b) From **8**, the perihelion distance from the earth to the sun is

$$a(1 - e) \approx (1.495 \times 10^8)(1 - 0.017) \approx 1.47 \times 10^8 \text{ km}$$

and the aphelion distance is

$$a(1 + e) \approx (1.495 \times 10^8)(1 + 0.017) \approx 1.52 \times 10^8 \text{ km}$$

10.6 Exercises

1–8 Write a polar equation of a conic with the focus at the origin and the given data.

1. Ellipse, eccentricity $\frac{1}{2}$, directrix $x = 4$

2. Parabola, directrix $x = -3$

3. Hyperbola, eccentricity 1.5, directrix $y = 2$

4. Hyperbola, eccentricity 3, directrix $x = 3$

5. Parabola, vertex $(4, 3\pi/2)$

6. Ellipse, eccentricity 0.8, vertex $(1, \pi/2)$

7. Ellipse, eccentricity $\frac{1}{2}$, directrix $r = 4 \sec \theta$

8. Hyperbola, eccentricity 3, directrix $r = -6 \csc \theta$

9–16 (a) Find the eccentricity, (b) identify the conic, (c) give an equation of the directrix, and (d) sketch the conic.

9. $r = \dfrac{4}{5 - 4 \sin \theta}$

10. $r = \dfrac{12}{3 - 10 \cos \theta}$

11. $r = \dfrac{1}{1 + \sin \theta}$

12. $r = \dfrac{3}{2 + 2 \cos \theta}$

13. $r = \dfrac{9}{6 + 2 \cos \theta}$

14. $r = \dfrac{8}{4 + 5 \sin \theta}$

15. $r = \dfrac{3}{4 - 8 \cos \theta}$

16. $r = \dfrac{10}{5 - 6 \sin \theta}$

17. (a) Find the eccentricity and directrix of the conic $r = 1/(1 - 2 \sin \theta)$ and graph the conic and its directrix.
    (b) If this conic is rotated counterclockwise about the origin through an angle $3\pi/4$, write the resulting equation and graph its curve.

18. Graph the conic $r = 4/(5 + 6 \cos \theta)$ and its directrix. Also graph the conic obtained by rotating this curve about the origin through an angle $\pi/3$.

19. Graph the conics $r = e/(1 - e \cos \theta)$ with $e = 0.4, 0.6,$ 0.8, and 1.0 on a common screen. How does the value of e affect the shape of the curve?

20. (a) Graph the conics $r = ed/(1 + e \sin \theta)$ for $e = 1$ and various values of d. How does the value of d affect the shape of the conic?
    (b) Graph these conics for $d = 1$ and various values of e. How does the value of e affect the shape of the conic?

21. Show that a conic with focus at the origin, eccentricity e, and directrix $x = -d$ has polar equation
$$r = \frac{ed}{1 - e \cos \theta}$$

22. Show that a conic with focus at the origin, eccentricity e, and directrix $y = d$ has polar equation
$$r = \frac{ed}{1 + e \sin \theta}$$

23. Show that a conic with focus at the origin, eccentricity e, and directrix $y = -d$ has polar equation
$$r = \frac{ed}{1 - e \sin \theta}$$

24. Show that the parabolas $r = c/(1 + \cos \theta)$ and $r = d/(1 - \cos \theta)$ intersect at right angles.

25. The orbit of Mars around the sun is an ellipse with eccentricity 0.093 and semimajor axis 2.28×10^8 km. Find a polar equation for the orbit.

26. Jupiter's orbit has eccentricity 0.048 and the length of the major axis is 1.56×10^9 km. Find a polar equation for the orbit.

27. The orbit of Halley's comet, last seen in 1986 and due to return in 2062, is an ellipse with eccentricity 0.97 and one focus at the sun. The length of its major axis is 36.18 AU. [An astronomical unit (AU) is the mean distance between the earth and the sun, about 93 million miles.] Find a polar equation for the orbit of Halley's comet. What is the maximum distance from the comet to the sun?

28. The Hale-Bopp comet, discovered in 1995, has an elliptical orbit with eccentricity 0.9951 and the length of the major axis is 356.5 AU. Find a polar equation for the orbit of this comet. How close to the sun does it come?

© Dean Ketelsen

29. The planet Mercury travels in an elliptical orbit with eccentricity 0.206. Its minimum distance from the sun is 4.6×10^7 km. Find its maximum distance from the sun.

30. The distance from the planet Pluto to the sun is 4.43×10^9 km at perihelion and 7.37×10^9 km at aphelion. Find the eccentricity of Pluto's orbit.

31. Using the data from Exercise 29, find the distance traveled by the planet Mercury during one complete orbit around the sun. (If your calculator or computer algebra system evaluates definite integrals, use it. Otherwise, use Simpson's Rule.)

⊞ Graphing calculator or computer required   **1.** Homework Hints available at stewartcalculus.com

10 Review

Concept Check

1. (a) What is a parametric curve?
(b) How do you sketch a parametric curve?

2. (a) How do you find the slope of a tangent to a parametric curve?
(b) How do you find the area under a parametric curve?

3. Write an expression for each of the following:
(a) The length of a parametric curve
(b) The area of the surface obtained by rotating a parametric curve about the x-axis

4. (a) Use a diagram to explain the meaning of the polar coordinates (r, θ) of a point.
(b) Write equations that express the Cartesian coordinates (x, y) of a point in terms of the polar coordinates.
(c) What equations would you use to find the polar coordinates of a point if you knew the Cartesian coordinates?

5. (a) How do you find the slope of a tangent line to a polar curve?
(b) How do you find the area of a region bounded by a polar curve?
(c) How do you find the length of a polar curve?

6. (a) Give a geometric definition of a parabola.
(b) Write an equation of a parabola with focus $(0, p)$ and directrix $y = -p$. What if the focus is $(p, 0)$ and the directrix is $x = -p$?

7. (a) Give a definition of an ellipse in terms of foci.
(b) Write an equation for the ellipse with foci $(\pm c, 0)$ and vertices $(\pm a, 0)$.

8. (a) Give a definition of a hyperbola in terms of foci.
(b) Write an equation for the hyperbola with foci $(\pm c, 0)$ and vertices $(\pm a, 0)$.
(c) Write equations for the asymptotes of the hyperbola in part (b).

9. (a) What is the eccentricity of a conic section?
(b) What can you say about the eccentricity if the conic section is an ellipse? A hyperbola? A parabola?
(c) Write a polar equation for a conic section with eccentricity e and directrix $x = d$. What if the directrix is $x = -d$? $y = d$? $y = -d$?

True-False Quiz

Determine whether the statement is true or false. If it is true, explain why. If it is false, explain why or give an example that disproves the statement.

1. If the parametric curve $x = f(t)$, $y = g(t)$ satisfies $g'(1) = 0$, then it has a horizontal tangent when $t = 1$.

2. If $x = f(t)$ and $y = g(t)$ are twice differentiable, then
$$\frac{d^2y}{dx^2} = \frac{d^2y/dt^2}{d^2x/dt^2}$$

3. The length of the curve $x = f(t)$, $y = g(t)$, $a \le t \le b$, is $\int_a^b \sqrt{[f'(t)]^2 + [g'(t)]^2}\, dt$.

4. If a point is represented by (x, y) in Cartesian coordinates (where $x \ne 0$) and (r, θ) in polar coordinates, then $\theta = \tan^{-1}(y/x)$.

5. The polar curves $r = 1 - \sin 2\theta$ and $r = \sin 2\theta - 1$ have the same graph.

6. The equations $r = 2$, $x^2 + y^2 = 4$, and $x = 2 \sin 3t$, $y = 2 \cos 3t$ $(0 \le t \le 2\pi)$ all have the same graph.

7. The parametric equations $x = t^2$, $y = t^4$ have the same graph as $x = t^3$, $y = t^6$.

8. The graph of $y^2 = 2y + 3x$ is a parabola.

9. A tangent line to a parabola intersects the parabola only once.

10. A hyperbola never intersects its directrix.

Exercises

1–4 Sketch the parametric curve and eliminate the parameter to find the Cartesian equation of the curve.

1. $x = t^2 + 4t$, $y = 2 - t$, $-4 \le t \le 1$

2. $x = 1 + e^{2t}$, $y = e^t$

3. $x = \cos\theta$, $y = \sec\theta$, $0 \le \theta < \pi/2$

4. $x = 2\cos\theta$, $y = 1 + \sin\theta$

5. Write three different sets of parametric equations for the curve $y = \sqrt{x}$.

6. Use the graphs of $x = f(t)$ and $y = g(t)$ to sketch the parametric curve $x = f(t)$, $y = g(t)$. Indicate with arrows the direction in which the curve is traced as t increases.

7. (a) Plot the point with polar coordinates $(4, 2\pi/3)$. Then find its Cartesian coordinates.

   (b) The Cartesian coordinates of a point are $(-3, 3)$. Find two sets of polar coordinates for the point.

8. Sketch the region consisting of points whose polar coordinates satisfy $1 \le r < 2$ and $\pi/6 \le \theta \le 5\pi/6$.

9–16 Sketch the polar curve.

9. $r = 1 - \cos\theta$

10. $r = \sin 4\theta$

11. $r = \cos 3\theta$

12. $r = 3 + \cos 3\theta$

13. $r = 1 + \cos 2\theta$

14. $r = 2\cos(\theta/2)$

15. $r = \dfrac{3}{1 + 2\sin\theta}$

16. $r = \dfrac{3}{2 - 2\cos\theta}$

17–18 Find a polar equation for the curve represented by the given Cartesian equation.

17. $x + y = 2$

18. $x^2 + y^2 = 2$

19. The curve with polar equation $r = (\sin\theta)/\theta$ is called a **cochleoid**. Use a graph of r as a function of θ in Cartesian coordinates to sketch the cochleoid by hand. Then graph it with a machine to check your sketch.

20. Graph the ellipse $r = 2/(4 - 3\cos\theta)$ and its directrix. Also graph the ellipse obtained by rotation about the origin through an angle $2\pi/3$.

21–24 Find the slope of the tangent line to the given curve at the point corresponding to the specified value of the parameter.

21. $x = \ln t$, $y = 1 + t^2$; $t = 1$

22. $x = t^3 + 6t + 1$, $y = 2t - t^2$; $t = -1$

23. $r = e^{-\theta}$; $\theta = \pi$

24. $r = 3 + \cos 3\theta$; $\theta = \pi/2$

25–26 Find dy/dx and d^2y/dx^2.

25. $x = t + \sin t$, $y = t - \cos t$

26. $x = 1 + t^2$, $y = t - t^3$

27. Use a graph to estimate the coordinates of the lowest point on the curve $x = t^3 - 3t$, $y = t^2 + t + 1$. Then use calculus to find the exact coordinates.

28. Find the area enclosed by the loop of the curve in Exercise 27.

29. At what points does the curve

$$x = 2a\cos t - a\cos 2t \qquad y = 2a\sin t - a\sin 2t$$

have vertical or horizontal tangents? Use this information to help sketch the curve.

30. Find the area enclosed by the curve in Exercise 29.

31. Find the area enclosed by the curve $r^2 = 9\cos 5\theta$.

32. Find the area enclosed by the inner loop of the curve $r = 1 - 3\sin\theta$.

33. Find the points of intersection of the curves $r = 2$ and $r = 4\cos\theta$.

34. Find the points of intersection of the curves $r = \cot\theta$ and $r = 2\cos\theta$.

35. Find the area of the region that lies inside both of the circles $r = 2\sin\theta$ and $r = \sin\theta + \cos\theta$.

36. Find the area of the region that lies inside the curve $r = 2 + \cos 2\theta$ but outside the curve $r = 2 + \sin\theta$.

37–40 Find the length of the curve.

37. $x = 3t^2$, $y = 2t^3$, $0 \le t \le 2$

38. $x = 2 + 3t$, $y = \cosh 3t$, $0 \le t \le 1$

39. $r = 1/\theta$, $\pi \le \theta \le 2\pi$

40. $r = \sin^3(\theta/3)$, $0 \le \theta \le \pi$

Graphing calculator or computer required   CAS   Computer algebra system required

41–42 Find the area of the surface obtained by rotating the given curve about the *x*-axis.

41. $x = 4\sqrt{t}$, $y = \dfrac{t^3}{3} + \dfrac{1}{2t^2}$, $1 \leqslant t \leqslant 4$

42. $x = 2 + 3t$, $y = \cosh 3t$, $0 \leqslant t \leqslant 1$

---

43. The curves defined by the parametric equations

$$x = \frac{t^2 - c}{t^2 + 1} \qquad y = \frac{t(t^2 - c)}{t^2 + 1}$$

are called **strophoids** (from a Greek word meaning "to turn or twist"). Investigate how these curves vary as *c* varies.

44. A family of curves has polar equations $r^a = |\sin 2\theta|$ where *a* is a positive number. Investigate how the curves change as *a* changes.

45–48 Find the foci and vertices and sketch the graph.

45. $\dfrac{x^2}{9} + \dfrac{y^2}{8} = 1$ **46.** $4x^2 - y^2 = 16$

47. $6y^2 + x - 36y + 55 = 0$

48. $25x^2 + 4y^2 + 50x - 16y = 59$

---

49. Find an equation of the ellipse with foci $(\pm 4, 0)$ and vertices $(\pm 5, 0)$.

50. Find an equation of the parabola with focus $(2, 1)$ and directrix $x = -4$.

51. Find an equation of the hyperbola with foci $(0, \pm 4)$ and asymptotes $y = \pm 3x$.

52. Find an equation of the ellipse with foci $(3, \pm 2)$ and major axis with length 8.

53. Find an equation for the ellipse that shares a vertex and a focus with the parabola $x^2 + y = 100$ and that has its other focus at the origin.

54. Show that if *m* is any real number, then there are exactly two lines of slope *m* that are tangent to the ellipse $x^2/a^2 + y^2/b^2 = 1$ and their equations are $y = mx \pm \sqrt{a^2 m^2 + b^2}$.

55. Find a polar equation for the ellipse with focus at the origin, eccentricity $\frac{1}{3}$, and directrix with equation $r = 4 \sec \theta$.

56. Show that the angles between the polar axis and the asymptotes of the hyperbola $r = ed/(1 - e \cos \theta)$, $e > 1$, are given by $\cos^{-1}(\pm 1/e)$.

57. A curve called the **folium of Descartes** is defined by the parametric equations

$$x = \frac{3t}{1 + t^3} \qquad y = \frac{3t^2}{1 + t^3}$$

(a) Show that if (a, b) lies on the curve, then so does (b, a); that is, the curve is symmetric with respect to the line $y = x$. Where does the curve intersect this line?

(b) Find the points on the curve where the tangent lines are horizontal or vertical.

(c) Show that the line $y = -x - 1$ is a slant asymptote.

(d) Sketch the curve.

(e) Show that a Cartesian equation of this curve is $x^3 + y^3 = 3xy$.

(f) Show that the polar equation can be written in the form

$$r = \frac{3 \sec \theta \tan \theta}{1 + \tan^3 \theta}$$

(g) Find the area enclosed by the loop of this curve.

(h) Show that the area of the loop is the same as the area that lies between the asymptote and the infinite branches of the curve. (Use a computer algebra system to evaluate the integral.)

CAS

1. A curve is defined by the parametric equations

$$x = \int_1^t \frac{\cos u}{u}\, du \qquad y = \int_1^t \frac{\sin u}{u}\, du$$

Find the length of the arc of the curve from the origin to the nearest point where there is a vertical tangent line

2. (a) Find the highest and lowest points on the curve $x^4 + y^4 = x^2 + y^2$.
   (b) Sketch the curve. (Notice that it is symmetric with respect to both axes and both of the lines $y = \pm x$, so it suffices to consider $y \geqslant x \geqslant 0$ initially.)
   [CAS] (c) Use polar coordinates and a computer algebra system to find the area enclosed by the curve.

3. What is the smallest viewing rectangle that contains every member of the family of polar curves $r = 1 + c \sin \theta$, where $0 \leqslant c \leqslant 1$? Illustrate your answer by graphing several members of the family in this viewing rectangle.

4. Four bugs are placed at the four corners of a square with side length a. The bugs crawl counterclockwise at the same speed and each bug crawls directly toward the next bug at all times. They approach the center of the square along spiral paths.
   (a) Find the polar equation of a bug's path assuming the pole is at the center of the square. (Use the fact that the line joining one bug to the next is tangent to the bug's path.)
   (b) Find the distance traveled by a bug by the time it meets the other bugs at the center.

FIGURE FOR PROBLEM 4

5. Show that any tangent line to a hyperbola touches the hyperbola halfway between the points of intersection of the tangent and the asymptotes.

6. A circle C of radius $2r$ has its center at the origin. A circle of radius r rolls without slipping in the counterclockwise direction around C. A point P is located on a fixed radius of the rolling circle at a distance b from its center, $0 < b < r$. [See parts (i) and (ii) of the figure.] Let L be the line from the center of C to the center of the rolling circle and let θ be the angle that L makes with the positive x-axis.
   (a) Using θ as a parameter, show that parametric equations of the path traced out by P are

$$x = b \cos 3\theta + 3r \cos \theta \qquad y = b \sin 3\theta + 3r \sin \theta$$

   Note: If $b = 0$, the path is a circle of radius $3r$; if $b = r$, the path is an *epicycloid*. The path traced out by P for $0 < b < r$ is called an *epitrochoid*.
   (b) Graph the curve for various values of b between 0 and r.
   (c) Show that an equilateral triangle can be inscribed in the epitrochoid and that its centroid is on the circle of radius b centered at the origin.
   Note: This is the principle of the Wankel rotary engine. When the equilateral triangle rotates with its vertices on the epitrochoid, its centroid sweeps out a circle whose center is at the center of the curve.
   (d) In most rotary engines the sides of the equilateral triangles are replaced by arcs of circles centered at the opposite vertices as in part (iii) of the figure. (Then the diameter of the rotor is constant.) Show that the rotor will fit in the epitrochoid if $b \leqslant \frac{3}{2}(2 - \sqrt{3})r$.

(i)

(ii)

(iii)

SPECIAL FUNCTIONS

Power Functions $f(x) = x^a$

(i) $f(x) = x^n$, n a positive integer

n even

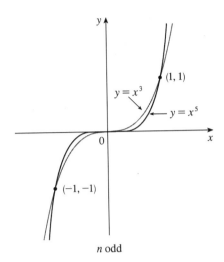

n odd

(ii) $f(x) = x^{1/n} = \sqrt[n]{x}$, n a positive integer

$$f(x) = \sqrt{x}$$

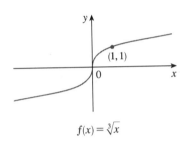

$$f(x) = \sqrt[3]{x}$$

(iii) $f(x) = x^{-1} = \dfrac{1}{x}$

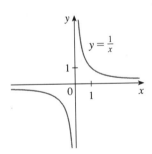

Inverse Trigonometric Functions

$\arcsin x = \sin^{-1}x = y \iff \sin y = x$ and $-\dfrac{\pi}{2} \leqslant y \leqslant \dfrac{\pi}{2}$

$\arccos x = \cos^{-1}x = y \iff \cos y = x$ and $0 \leqslant y \leqslant \pi$

$\arctan x = \tan^{-1}x = y \iff \tan y = x$ and $-\dfrac{\pi}{2} < y < \dfrac{\pi}{2}$

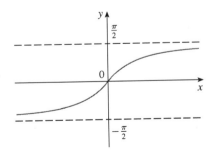

$$y = \tan^{-1}x = \arctan x$$

$$\lim_{x \to -\infty} \tan^{-1}x = -\dfrac{\pi}{2}$$

$$\lim_{x \to \infty} \tan^{-1}x = \dfrac{\pi}{2}$$

SPECIAL FUNCTIONS

Exponential and Logarithmic Functions

$$\log_a x = y \iff a^y = x$$

$$\ln x = \log_e x, \quad \text{where} \quad \ln e = 1$$

$$\ln x = y \iff e^y = x$$

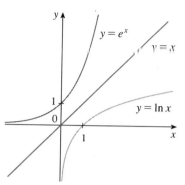

Cancellation Equations	Laws of Logarithms

$$\log_a(a^x) = x \qquad a^{\log_a x} = x$$

$$\ln(e^x) = x \qquad e^{\ln x} = x$$

1. $\log_a(xy) = \log_a x + \log_a y$

2. $\log_a\!\left(\dfrac{x}{y}\right) = \log_a x - \log_a y$

3. $\log_a(x^r) = r \log_a x$

$$\lim_{x \to -\infty} e^x = 0 \qquad \lim_{x \to \infty} e^x = \infty$$

$$\lim_{x \to 0^+} \ln x = -\infty \qquad \lim_{x \to \infty} \ln x = \infty$$

Exponential functions

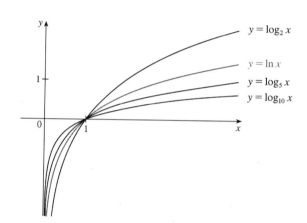

Logarithmic functions

Hyperbolic Functions

$$\sinh x = \frac{e^x - e^{-x}}{2} \qquad\qquad \operatorname{csch} x = \frac{1}{\sinh x}$$

$$\cosh x = \frac{e^x + e^{-x}}{2} \qquad\qquad \operatorname{sech} x = \frac{1}{\cosh x}$$

$$\tanh x = \frac{\sinh x}{\cosh x} \qquad\qquad \coth x = \frac{\cosh x}{\sinh x}$$

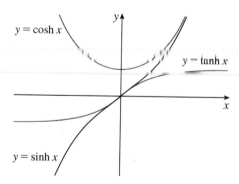

Inverse Hyperbolic Functions

$$y = \sinh^{-1}x \iff \sinh y = x$$

$$y = \cosh^{-1}x \iff \cosh y = x \quad \text{and} \quad y \geq 0$$

$$y = \tanh^{-1}x \iff \tanh y = x$$

$$\sinh^{-1}x = \ln\!\left(x + \sqrt{x^2 + 1}\right)$$

$$\cosh^{-1}x = \ln\!\left(x + \sqrt{x^2 - 1}\right)$$

$$\tanh^{-1}x = \tfrac{1}{2}\ln\!\left(\frac{1 + x}{1 - x}\right)$$

DIFFERENTIATION RULES

General Formulas

1. $\dfrac{d}{dx}(c) = 0$

2. $\dfrac{d}{dx}[cf(x)] = cf'(x)$

3. $\dfrac{d}{dx}[f(x) + g(x)] = f'(x) + g'(x)$

4. $\dfrac{d}{dx}[f(x) - g(x)] = f'(x) - g'(x)$

5. $\dfrac{d}{dx}[f(x)g(x)] = f(x)g'(x) + g(x)f'(x)$ (Product Rule)

6. $\dfrac{d}{dx}\left[\dfrac{f(x)}{g(x)}\right] = \dfrac{g(x)f'(x) - f(x)g'(x)}{[g(x)]^2}$ (Quotient Rule)

7. $\dfrac{d}{dx}f(g(x)) = f'(g(x))g'(x)$ (Chain Rule)

8. $\dfrac{d}{dx}(x^n) = nx^{n-1}$ (Power Rule)

Exponential and Logarithmic Functions

9. $\dfrac{d}{dx}(e^x) = e^x$

10. $\dfrac{d}{dx}(a^x) = a^x \ln a$

11. $\dfrac{d}{dx}\ln|x| = \dfrac{1}{x}$

12. $\dfrac{d}{dx}(\log_a x) = \dfrac{1}{x \ln a}$

Trigonometric Functions

13. $\dfrac{d}{dx}(\sin x) = \cos x$

14. $\dfrac{d}{dx}(\cos x) = -\sin x$

15. $\dfrac{d}{dx}(\tan x) = \sec^2 x$

16. $\dfrac{d}{dx}(\csc x) = -\csc x \cot x$

17. $\dfrac{d}{dx}(\sec x) = \sec x \tan x$

18. $\dfrac{d}{dx}(\cot x) = -\csc^2 x$

Inverse Trigonometric Functions

19. $\dfrac{d}{dx}(\sin^{-1}x) = \dfrac{1}{\sqrt{1 - x^2}}$

20. $\dfrac{d}{dx}(\cos^{-1}x) = -\dfrac{1}{\sqrt{1 - x^2}}$

21. $\dfrac{d}{dx}(\tan^{-1}x) = \dfrac{1}{1 + x^2}$

22. $\dfrac{d}{dx}(\csc^{-1}x) = -\dfrac{1}{x\sqrt{x^2 - 1}}$

23. $\dfrac{d}{dx}(\sec^{-1}x) = \dfrac{1}{x\sqrt{x^2 - 1}}$

24. $\dfrac{d}{dx}(\cot^{-1}x) = -\dfrac{1}{1 + x^2}$

Hyperbolic Functions

25. $\dfrac{d}{dx}(\sinh x) = \cosh x$

26. $\dfrac{d}{dx}(\cosh x) = \sinh x$

27. $\dfrac{d}{dx}(\tanh x) = \operatorname{sech}^2 x$

28. $\dfrac{d}{dx}(\operatorname{csch} x) = -\operatorname{csch} x \coth x$

29. $\dfrac{d}{dx}(\operatorname{sech} x) = -\operatorname{sech} x \tanh x$

30. $\dfrac{d}{dx}(\coth x) = -\operatorname{csch}^2 x$

Inverse Hyperbolic Functions

31. $\dfrac{d}{dx}(\sinh^{-1}x) = \dfrac{1}{\sqrt{1 + x^2}}$

32. $\dfrac{d}{dx}(\cosh^{-1}x) = \dfrac{1}{\sqrt{x^2 - 1}}$

33. $\dfrac{d}{dx}(\tanh^{-1}x) = \dfrac{1}{1 - x^2}$

34. $\dfrac{d}{dx}(\operatorname{csch}^{-1}x) = -\dfrac{1}{|x|\sqrt{x^2 + 1}}$

35. $\dfrac{d}{dx}(\operatorname{sech}^{-1}x) = -\dfrac{1}{x\sqrt{1 - x^2}}$

36. $\dfrac{d}{dx}(\coth^{-1}x) = \dfrac{1}{1 - x^2}$

TABLE OF INTEGRALS

Basic Forms

1. $\int u\,dv = uv - \int v\,du$

2. $\int u^n\,du = \dfrac{u^{n+1}}{n+1} + C, \quad n \neq -1$

3. $\int \dfrac{du}{u} = \ln|u| + C$

4. $\int e^u\,du = e^u + C$

5. $\int a^u\,du = \dfrac{a^u}{\ln a} + C$

6. $\int \sin u\,du = -\cos u + C$

7. $\int \cos u\,du = \sin u + C$

8. $\int \sec^2 u\,du = \tan u + C$

9. $\int \csc^2 u\,du = -\cot u + C$

10. $\int \sec u \tan u\,du = \sec u + C$

11. $\int \csc u \cot u\,du = -\csc u + C$

12. $\int \tan u\,du = \ln|\sec u| + C$

13. $\int \cot u\,du = \ln|\sin u| + C$

14. $\int \sec u\,du = \ln|\sec u + \tan u| + C$

15. $\int \csc u\,du = \ln|\csc u - \cot u| + C$

16. $\int \dfrac{du}{\sqrt{a^2 - u^2}} = \sin^{-1}\dfrac{u}{a} + C, \quad a > 0$

17. $\int \dfrac{du}{a^2 + u^2} = \dfrac{1}{a}\tan^{-1}\dfrac{u}{a} + C$

18. $\int \dfrac{du}{u\sqrt{u^2 - a^2}} = \dfrac{1}{a}\sec^{-1}\dfrac{u}{a} + C$

19. $\int \dfrac{du}{a^2 - u^2} = \dfrac{1}{2a}\ln\left|\dfrac{u+a}{u-a}\right| + C$

20. $\int \dfrac{du}{u^2 - a^2} = \dfrac{1}{2a}\ln\left|\dfrac{u-a}{u+a}\right| + C$

Forms Involving $\sqrt{a^2 + u^2}$, $a > 0$

21. $\int \sqrt{a^2 + u^2}\,du = \dfrac{u}{2}\sqrt{a^2 + u^2} + \dfrac{a^2}{2}\ln\left(u + \sqrt{a^2 + u^2}\right) + C$

22. $\int u^2 \sqrt{a^2 + u^2}\,du = \dfrac{u}{8}(a^2 + 2u^2)\sqrt{a^2 + u^2} - \dfrac{a^4}{8}\ln\left(u + \sqrt{a^2 + u^2}\right) + C$

23. $\int \dfrac{\sqrt{a^2 + u^2}}{u}\,du = \sqrt{a^2 + u^2} - a\ln\left|\dfrac{a + \sqrt{a^2 + u^2}}{u}\right| + C$

24. $\int \dfrac{\sqrt{a^2 + u^2}}{u^2}\,du = -\dfrac{\sqrt{a^2 + u^2}}{u} + \ln\left(u + \sqrt{a^2 + u^2}\right) + C$

25. $\int \dfrac{du}{\sqrt{a^2 + u^2}} = \ln\left(u + \sqrt{a^2 + u^2}\right) + C$

26. $\int \dfrac{u^2\,du}{\sqrt{a^2 + u^2}} = \dfrac{u}{2}\sqrt{a^2 + u^2} - \dfrac{a^2}{2}\ln\left(u + \sqrt{a^2 + u^2}\right) + C$

27. $\int \dfrac{du}{u\sqrt{a^2 + u^2}} = -\dfrac{1}{a}\ln\left|\dfrac{\sqrt{a^2 + u^2} + a}{u}\right| + C$

28. $\int \dfrac{du}{u^2\sqrt{a^2 + u^2}} = -\dfrac{\sqrt{a^2 + u^2}}{a^2 u} + C$

29. $\int \dfrac{du}{(a^2 + u^2)^{3/2}} = \dfrac{u}{a^2\sqrt{a^2 + u^2}} + C$

TABLE OF INTEGRALS

Forms Involving $\sqrt{a^2 - u^2}$, $a > 0$

30. $\displaystyle \int \sqrt{a^2 - u^2}\, du = \frac{u}{2}\sqrt{a^2 - u^2} + \frac{a^2}{2}\sin^{-1}\frac{u}{a} + C$

31. $\displaystyle \int u^2\sqrt{a^2 - u^2}\, du = \frac{u}{8}(2u^2 - a^2)\sqrt{a^2 - u^2} + \frac{a^4}{8}\sin^{-1}\frac{u}{a} + C$

32. $\displaystyle \int \frac{\sqrt{a^2 - u^2}}{u}\, du = \sqrt{a^2 - u^2} - a\ln\left|\frac{a + \sqrt{a^2 - u^2}}{u}\right| + C$

33. $\displaystyle \int \frac{\sqrt{a^2 - u^2}}{u^2}\, du = -\frac{1}{u}\sqrt{a^2 - u^2} - \sin^{-1}\frac{u}{a} + C$

34. $\displaystyle \int \frac{u^2\, du}{\sqrt{a^2 - u^2}} = -\frac{u}{2}\sqrt{a^2 - u^2} + \frac{a^2}{2}\sin^{-1}\frac{u}{a} + C$

35. $\displaystyle \int \frac{du}{u\sqrt{a^2 - u^2}} = -\frac{1}{a}\ln\left|\frac{a + \sqrt{a^2 - u^2}}{u}\right| + C$

36. $\displaystyle \int \frac{du}{u^2\sqrt{a^2 - u^2}} = -\frac{1}{a^2 u}\sqrt{a^2 - u^2} + C$

37. $\displaystyle \int (a^2 - u^2)^{3/2}\, du = -\frac{u}{8}(2u^2 - 5a^2)\sqrt{a^2 - u^2} + \frac{3a^4}{8}\sin^{-1}\frac{u}{a} + C$

38. $\displaystyle \int \frac{du}{(a^2 - u^2)^{3/2}} = \frac{u}{a^2\sqrt{a^2 - u^2}} + C$

Forms Involving $\sqrt{u^2 - a^2}$, $a > 0$

39. $\displaystyle \int \sqrt{u^2 - a^2}\, du = \frac{u}{2}\sqrt{u^2 - a^2} - \frac{a^2}{2}\ln\left|u + \sqrt{u^2 - a^2}\right| + C$

40. $\displaystyle \int u^2\sqrt{u^2 - a^2}\, du = \frac{u}{8}(2u^2 - a^2)\sqrt{u^2 - a^2} - \frac{a^4}{8}\ln\left|u + \sqrt{u^2 - a^2}\right| + C$

41. $\displaystyle \int \frac{\sqrt{u^2 - a^2}}{u}\, du = \sqrt{u^2 - a^2} - a\cos^{-1}\frac{a}{|u|} + C$

42. $\displaystyle \int \frac{\sqrt{u^2 - a^2}}{u^2}\, du = -\frac{\sqrt{u^2 - a^2}}{u} + \ln\left|u + \sqrt{u^2 - a^2}\right| + C$

43. $\displaystyle \int \frac{du}{\sqrt{u^2 - a^2}} = \ln\left|u + \sqrt{u^2 - a^2}\right| + C$

44. $\displaystyle \int \frac{u^2\, du}{\sqrt{u^2 - a^2}} = \frac{u}{2}\sqrt{u^2 - a^2} + \frac{a^2}{2}\ln\left|u + \sqrt{u^2 - a^2}\right| + C$

45. $\displaystyle \int \frac{du}{u^2\sqrt{u^2 - a^2}} = \frac{\sqrt{u^2 - a^2}}{a^2 u} + C$

46. $\displaystyle \int \frac{du}{(u^2 - a^2)^{3/2}} = -\frac{u}{a^2\sqrt{u^2 - a^2}} + C$

TABLE OF INTEGRALS

Forms Involving $a + bu$

47. $\displaystyle\int \frac{u\,du}{a + bu} = \frac{1}{b^2}\left(a + bu - a\ln|a + bu|\right) + C$

48. $\displaystyle\int \frac{u^2\,du}{a + bu} = \frac{1}{2b^3}\left[(a + bu)^2 - 4a(a + bu) + 2a^2\ln|a + bu|\right] + C$

49. $\displaystyle\int \frac{du}{u(a + bu)} = \frac{1}{a}\ln\left|\frac{u}{a + bu}\right| + C$

50. $\displaystyle\int \frac{du}{u^2(a + bu)} = -\frac{1}{au} + \frac{b}{a^2}\ln\left|\frac{a + bu}{u}\right| + C$

51. $\displaystyle\int \frac{u\,du}{(a + bu)^2} = \frac{a}{b^2(a + bu)} + \frac{1}{b^2}\ln|a + bu| + C$

52. $\displaystyle\int \frac{du}{u(a + bu)^2} = \frac{1}{a(a + bu)} - \frac{1}{a^2}\ln\left|\frac{a + bu}{u}\right| + C$

53. $\displaystyle\int \frac{u^2\,du}{(a + bu)^2} = \frac{1}{b^3}\left(a + bu - \frac{a^2}{a + bu} - 2a\ln|a + bu|\right) + C$

54. $\displaystyle\int u\sqrt{a + bu}\,du = \frac{2}{15b^2}(3bu - 2a)(a + bu)^{3/2} + C$

55. $\displaystyle\int \frac{u\,du}{\sqrt{a + bu}} = \frac{2}{3b^2}(bu - 2a)\sqrt{a + bu} + C$

56. $\displaystyle\int \frac{u^2\,du}{\sqrt{a + bu}} = \frac{2}{15b^3}(8a^2 + 3b^2u^2 - 4abu)\sqrt{a + bu} + C$

57. $\displaystyle\int \frac{du}{u\sqrt{a + bu}} = \frac{1}{\sqrt{a}}\ln\left|\frac{\sqrt{a + bu} - \sqrt{a}}{\sqrt{a + bu} + \sqrt{a}}\right| + C,\quad \text{if } a > 0$

$\displaystyle\qquad\qquad\quad = \frac{2}{\sqrt{-a}}\tan^{-1}\sqrt{\frac{a + bu}{-a}} + C,\qquad \text{if } a < 0$

58. $\displaystyle\int \frac{\sqrt{a + bu}}{u}\,du = 2\sqrt{a + bu} + a\int \frac{du}{u\sqrt{a + bu}}$

59. $\displaystyle\int \frac{\sqrt{a + bu}}{u^2}\,du = -\frac{\sqrt{a + bu}}{u} + \frac{b}{2}\int \frac{du}{u\sqrt{a + bu}}$

60. $\displaystyle\int u^n\sqrt{a + bu}\,du = \frac{2}{b(2n + 3)}\left[u^n(a + bu)^{3/2} - na\int u^{n-1}\sqrt{a + bu}\,du\right]$

61. $\displaystyle\int \frac{u^n\,du}{\sqrt{a + bu}} = \frac{2u^n\sqrt{a + bu}}{b(2n + 1)} - \frac{2na}{b(2n + 1)}\int \frac{u^{n-1}\,du}{\sqrt{a + bu}}$

62. $\displaystyle\int \frac{du}{u^n\sqrt{a + bu}} = -\frac{\sqrt{a + bu}}{a(n - 1)u^{n-1}} - \frac{b(2n - 3)}{2a(n - 1)}\int \frac{du}{u^{n-1}\sqrt{a + bu}}$

TABLE OF INTEGRALS

Trigonometric Forms

63. $\int \sin^2 u\, du = \frac{1}{2}u - \frac{1}{4}\sin 2u + C$

64. $\int \cos^2 u\, du = \frac{1}{2}u + \frac{1}{4}\sin 2u + C$

65. $\int \tan^2 u\, du = \tan u - u + C$

66. $\int \cot^2 u\, du = -\cot u - u + C$

67. $\int \sin^3 u\, du = -\frac{1}{3}(2 + \sin^2 u)\cos u + C$

68. $\int \cos^3 u\, du = \frac{1}{3}(2 + \cos^2 u)\sin u + C$

69. $\int \tan^3 u\, du = \frac{1}{2}\tan^2 u + \ln|\cos u| + C$

70. $\int \cot^3 u\, du = -\frac{1}{2}\cot^2 u - \ln|\sin u| + C$

71. $\int \sec^3 u\, du = \frac{1}{2}\sec u \tan u + \frac{1}{2}\ln|\sec u + \tan u| + C$

72. $\int \csc^3 u\, du = -\frac{1}{2}\csc u \cot u + \frac{1}{2}\ln|\csc u - \cot u| + C$

73. $\int \sin^n u\, du = -\frac{1}{n}\sin^{n-1}u \cos u + \frac{n-1}{n}\int \sin^{n-2}u\, du$

74. $\int \cos^n u\, du = \frac{1}{n}\cos^{n-1}u \sin u + \frac{n-1}{n}\int \cos^{n-2}u\, du$

75. $\int \tan^n u\, du = \frac{1}{n-1}\tan^{n-1}u - \int \tan^{n-2}u\, du$

76. $\int \cot^n u\, du = \frac{-1}{n-1}\cot^{n-1}u - \int \cot^{n-2}u\, du$

77. $\int \sec^n u\, du = \frac{1}{n-1}\tan u \sec^{n-2}u + \frac{n-2}{n-1}\int \sec^{n-2}u\, du$

78. $\int \csc^n u\, du = \frac{-1}{n-1}\cot u \csc^{n-2}u + \frac{n-2}{n-1}\int \csc^{n-2}u\, du$

79. $\int \sin au \sin bu\, du = \frac{\sin(a-b)u}{2(a-b)} - \frac{\sin(a+b)u}{2(a+b)} + C$

80. $\int \cos au \cos bu\, du = \frac{\sin(a-b)u}{2(a-b)} + \frac{\sin(a+b)u}{2(a+b)} + C$

81. $\int \sin au \cos bu\, du = -\frac{\cos(a-b)u}{2(a-b)} - \frac{\cos(a+b)u}{2(a+b)} + C$

82. $\int u \sin u\, du = \sin u - u \cos u + C$

83. $\int u \cos u\, du = \cos u + u \sin u + C$

84. $\int u^n \sin u\, du = -u^n \cos u + n \int u^{n-1} \cos u\, du$

85. $\int u^n \cos u\, du = u^n \sin u - n \int u^{n-1} \sin u\, du$

86. $\int \sin^n u \cos^m u\, du = -\frac{\sin^{n-1}u \cos^{m+1}u}{n+m} + \frac{n-1}{n+m}\int \sin^{n-2}u \cos^m u\, du$

$\qquad = \frac{\sin^{n+1}u \cos^{m-1}u}{n+m} + \frac{m-1}{n+m}\int \sin^n u \cos^{m-2}u\, du$

Inverse Trigonometric Forms

87. $\int \sin^{-1}u\, du = u \sin^{-1}u + \sqrt{1-u^2} + C$

88. $\int \cos^{-1}u\, du = u \cos^{-1}u - \sqrt{1-u^2} + C$

89. $\int \tan^{-1}u\, du = u \tan^{-1}u - \frac{1}{2}\ln(1+u^2) + C$

90. $\int u \sin^{-1}u\, du = \frac{2u^2-1}{4}\sin^{-1}u + \frac{u\sqrt{1-u^2}}{4} + C$

91. $\int u \cos^{-1}u\, du = \frac{2u^2-1}{4}\cos^{-1}u - \frac{u\sqrt{1-u^2}}{4} + C$

92. $\int u \tan^{-1}u\, du = \frac{u^2+1}{2}\tan^{-1}u - \frac{u}{2} + C$

93. $\int u^n \sin^{-1}u\, du = \frac{1}{n+1}\left[u^{n+1}\sin^{-1}u - \int \frac{u^{n+1}\, du}{\sqrt{1-u^2}}\right], \quad n \neq -1$

94. $\int u^n \cos^{-1}u\, du = \frac{1}{n+1}\left[u^{n+1}\cos^{-1}u + \int \frac{u^{n+1}\, du}{\sqrt{1-u^2}}\right], \quad n \neq -1$

95. $\int u^n \tan^{-1}u\, du = \frac{1}{n+1}\left[u^{n+1}\tan^{-1}u - \int \frac{u^{n+1}\, du}{1+u^2}\right], \quad n \neq -1$

TABLE OF INTEGRALS

Exponential and Logarithmic Forms

96. $\int u e^{au}\, du = \dfrac{1}{a^2}(au - 1)e^{au} + C$

97. $\int u^n e^{au}\, du = \dfrac{1}{a} u^n e^{au} - \dfrac{n}{a}\int u^{n-1}e^{au}\, du$

98. $\int e^{au}\sin bu\, du = \dfrac{e^{au}}{a^2 + b^2}(a\sin bu - b\cos bu) + C$

99. $\int e^{au}\cos bu\, du = \dfrac{e^{au}}{a^2 + b^2}(a\cos bu + b\sin bu) + C$

100. $\int \ln u\, du = u\ln u - u + C$

101. $\int u^n \ln u\, du = \dfrac{u^{n+1}}{(n+1)^2}[(n+1)\ln u - 1] + C$

102. $\int \dfrac{1}{u\ln u}\, du = \ln|\ln u| + C$

Hyperbolic Forms

103. $\int \sinh u\, du = \cosh u + C$

104. $\int \cosh u\, du = \sinh u + C$

105. $\int \tanh u\, du = \ln\cosh u + C$

106. $\int \coth u\, du = \ln|\sinh u| + C$

107. $\int \operatorname{sech} u\, du = \tan^{-1}|\sinh u| + C$

108. $\int \operatorname{csch} u\, du = \ln\left|\tanh\tfrac{1}{2}u\right| + C$

109. $\int \operatorname{sech}^2 u\, du = \tanh u + C$

110. $\int \operatorname{csch}^2 u\, du = -\coth u + C$

111. $\int \operatorname{sech} u \tanh u\, du = -\operatorname{sech} u + C$

112. $\int \operatorname{csch} u \coth u\, du = -\operatorname{csch} u + C$

Forms Involving $\sqrt{2au - u^2}$, $a > 0$

113. $\int \sqrt{2au - u^2}\, du = \dfrac{u - a}{2}\sqrt{2au - u^2} + \dfrac{a^2}{2}\cos^{-1}\left(\dfrac{a - u}{a}\right) + C$

114. $\int u\sqrt{2au - u^2}\, du = \dfrac{2u^2 - au - 3a^2}{6}\sqrt{2au - u^2} + \dfrac{a^3}{2}\cos^{-1}\left(\dfrac{a - u}{a}\right) + C$

115. $\int \dfrac{\sqrt{2au - u^2}}{u}\, du = \sqrt{2au - u^2} + a\cos^{-1}\left(\dfrac{a - u}{a}\right) + C$

116. $\int \dfrac{\sqrt{2au - u^2}}{u^2}\, du = -\dfrac{2\sqrt{2au - u^2}}{u} - \cos^{-1}\left(\dfrac{a - u}{a}\right) + C$

117. $\int \dfrac{du}{\sqrt{2au - u^2}} = \cos^{-1}\left(\dfrac{a - u}{a}\right) + C$

118. $\int \dfrac{u\, du}{\sqrt{2au - u^2}} = -\sqrt{2au - u^2} + a\cos^{-1}\left(\dfrac{a - u}{a}\right) + C$

119. $\int \dfrac{u^2\, du}{\sqrt{2au - u^2}} = -\dfrac{(u + 3a)}{2}\sqrt{2au - u^2} + \dfrac{3a^2}{2}\cos^{-1}\left(\dfrac{a - u}{a}\right) + C$

120. $\int \dfrac{du}{u\sqrt{2au - u^2}} = -\dfrac{\sqrt{2au - u^2}}{au} + C$